$139.95 per copy (in United States)
Price is subject to change without prior notice.

0174

The 2014 *Residential Cost Data*, 33rd annual edition, and all of the RSMeans annual cost data books for 2014, are dedicated to the memory of our respected colleague and friend, Paula Reale-Camelio.

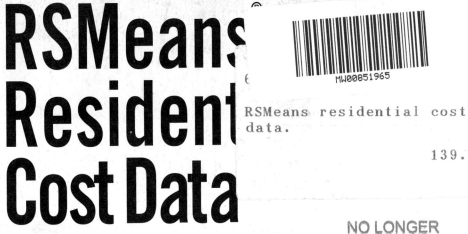

RSMeans Residential Cost Data

33RD ANNUAL EDITION

2014

RSMeans
A division of Reed Construction Data, LLC
Construction Publishers & Consultants
700 Longwater Drive
Norwell, MA 02061
USA
1-800-334-3509
www.rsmeans.com

Copyright 2013 by RSMeans
A division of Reed Construction Data, LLC
All rights reserved.

Printed in the United States of America
ISSN 0896-8624
ISBN 978-1-940238-16-6

The authors, editors, and engineers of RSMeans apply diligence and judgment in locating and using reliable sources for the information published. However, RSMeans makes no express or implied warranty or guarantee in connection with the content of the information contained herein, including the accuracy, correctness, value, sufficiency, or completeness of the data, methods, and other information contained herein. RSMeans makes no express or implied warranty of merchantability or fitness for a particular purpose. RSMeans shall have no liability to any customer or third party for any loss, expense, or damage, including consequential, incidental, special, or punitive damage, including lost profits or lost revenue, caused directly or indirectly by any error or omission, or arising out of, or in connection with, the information contained herein.

Senior Editor
Bob Mewis, CCC *(4, 6, 7, 14, 41, 44)**

Contributing Editors
Christopher Babbitt
Adrian C. Charest, PE *(26, 27, 28, 48)*
Gary W. Christensen
David G. Drain, PE *(33)*
Cheryl Elsmore
David Fiske
Robert Fortier, PE *(2, 31, 32, 34, 35, 46)*
Robert J. Kuchta *(8)*
Thomas Lane
Robert C. McNichols
Genevieve Medeiros
Melville J. Mossman, PE *(21, 22, 23)**
Jeannene D. Murphy
Marilyn Phelan, AIA *(9, 10, 11, 12)*
Stephen C. Plotner *(3, 5)*
Siobhan Soucie
Phillip R. Waier, PE *(1,13)*

Cover Design
Wendy McBay
Paul Robertson
Wayne Engebretson

Chief Operating Officer
Richard Remington

**Vice President,
Business Development**
Steven Ritchie

**Vice President,
Finance & Operations**
Renée Pinczes

Senior Director, Inside Sales
Derek F. Dean

Sales Manager
Reid Clanton

Director, Engineering
Bob Mewis, CCC

**Senior Director, Product
Management**
Jennifer Johnson

**Senior Product
Marketing Manager**
Andrea Sillah

**Senior Director,
Operations**
Rodney L. Sharples

Production Manager
Michael Kokernak

Production
Jill Goodman
Jonathan Forgit
Debbie Panarelli
Sara Rutan
Mary Lou Geary

Technical Support
Christopher Anderson
Gary L. Hoitt
Kathryn S. Rodriguez

* Numbers in italics are the divisional responsibilities for each editor. Please contact the designated editor directly with any questions.

This book is printed on 90% recycled paper using soy-based ink and is entirely recyclable.

PRINTED WITH
SOY INK

Related RSMeans Products and Services

This book is aimed primarily at single family and small multi-family housing projects costing up to $1,000,000.

The engineers at RSMeans suggest the following products and services as companion information resources to *RSMeans Residential Cost Data*:

Construction Cost Data Books

Square Foot Costs 2014
Residential Repair and Remodeling Costs 2014

Reference Books

Estimating Building Costs
RSMeans Estimating Handbook
Green Building: Project Planning & Estimating
How to Estimate with RSMeans Data
Plan Reading & Material Takeoff
Project Scheduling & Management for Construction
Universal Design Ideas for Style, Comfort & Safety

Seminars and In-House Training

Unit Price Estimating
RSMeans Online® Training
RSMeans Data for Job Order Contracting (JOC)
Practical Project Management for Construction Professionals
Scheduling with MSProject for Construction Professionals
Mechanical & Electrical Estimating

RSMeans Online Bookstore

Visit RSMeans at **www.rsmeans.com** for a one-stop portal for the most reliable and current resources available on the market. Here you can learn about our more than 20 annual cost data books, also available on CD and online versions, as well as our libary of reference books and RSMeans seminars.

RSMeans Electronic Data

Get the information found in RSMeans cost books electronically at **RSMeansOnline.com**.

RSMeans Business Solutions

Cost engineers and analysts conduct facility life cycle and benchmark research studies and predictive cost modeling, as well as offer consultation services for conceptual estimating, real property management, and job order contracting. Research studies are designed with the application of proprietary cost and project data from Reed Construction Data and RSMeans' extensive North American databases. Analysts offer building product manufacturers qualitative and quantitative market research, as well as time/motion studies for new products, and Web-based dashboards for market opportunity analysis. Clients are from both the public and private sectors, including federal, state, and municipal agencies; corporations; institutions; construction management firms; hospitals; and associations.

RSMeans for Job Order Contracting (JOC)

Best practice job order contracting (JOC) services support the owner in the development of their program. RSMeans develops all required contracting documents, works with stakeholders, and develops qualified and experienced contractor lists. RSMeans JOCWorks® software is the best of class in the functional tools that meet JOC specific requirements. RSMeans data is organized to meet JOC cost estimating requirements.

Construction Costs for Software Applications

More than 25 unit price and assemblies cost databases are available through a number of leading estimating and facilities management software providers (listed below). For more information see the "Other RSMeans Products" pages at the back of this publication.

RSMeansData™ is also available to federal, state, and local government agencies as multi-year, multi-seat licenses.

- 4Clicks-Solutions, LLC
- Assetworks
- Beck Technology
- BSD – Building Systems Design, Inc.
- CMS – Construction Management Software
- Corecon Technologies, Inc.
- CorVet Systems
- Hard Dollar Corporation
- Maxwell Systems
- MC^2
- MOCA Systems
- Parsons Corporation
- ProEst
- Refined Data
- Sage Timberline Office
- UDA Technologies, Inc.
- US Cost, Inc.
- VFA – Vanderweil Facility Advisers
- WinEstimator, Inc.
- R & K Solutions
- Tririga

Table of Contents

Foreword

Our Mission

Since 1942, RSMeans has been actively engaged in construction cost publishing and consulting throughout North America.

Today, more than 70 years after RSMeans began, our primary objective remains the same: to provide you, the construction and facilities professional, with the most current and comprehensive construction cost data possible.

Whether you are a contractor, owner, architect, engineer, facilities manager, or anyone else who needs a reliable construction cost estimate, you'll find this publication to be a highly useful and necessary tool.

With the constant flow of new construction methods and materials today, it's difficult to find the time to look at and evaluate all the different construction cost possibilities. In addition, because labor and material costs keep changing, last year's cost information is not a reliable basis for today's estimate or budget.

That's why so many construction professionals turn to RSMeans. We keep track of the costs for you, along with a wide range of other key information, from city cost indexes . . . to productivity rates . . . to crew composition . . . to contractor's overhead and profit rates.

RSMeans performs these functions by collecting data from all facets of the industry and organizing it in a format that is instantly accessible to you. From the preliminary budget to the detailed unit price estimate, you'll find the data in this book useful for all phases of construction cost determination.

The Staff, the Organization, and Our Services

When you purchase one of RSMeans' publications, you are, in effect, hiring the services of a full-time staff of construction and engineering professionals.

Our thoroughly experienced and highly qualified staff works daily at collecting, analyzing, and disseminating comprehensive cost information for your needs. These staff members have years of practical construction experience and engineering training prior to joining the firm. As a result, you can count on them not only for accurate cost figures, but also for additional background reference information that will help you create a realistic estimate.

The RSMeans organization is always prepared to help you solve construction problems through its variety of data solutions, including online, CD, and print book formats, as well as cost estimating expertise available via our business solutions, training, and seminars.

Besides a full array of construction cost estimating books, RSMeans also publishes a number of other reference works for the construction industry. Subjects include construction estimating and project and business management, special topics such as green building and job order contracting, and a library of facility management references.

In addition, you can access all of our construction cost data electronically in convenient CD format or on the web. Visit **RSMeansOnline.com** for more information on our 24/7 online cost data.

What's more, you can increase your knowledge and improve your construction estimating and management performance with an RSMeans construction seminar or in-house training program. These two-day seminar programs offer unparalleled opportunities for everyone in your organization to become updated on a wide variety of construction-related issues.

RSMeans is also a worldwide provider of construction cost management and analysis services for commercial and government owners.

In short, RSMeans can provide you with the tools and expertise for constructing accurate and dependable construction estimates and budgets in a variety of ways.

Robert Snow Means Established a Tradition of Quality That Continues Today

Robert Snow Means spent years building RSMeans, making certain he always delivered a quality product.

Today, at RSMeans, we do more than talk about the quality of our data and the usefulness of our books. We stand behind all of our data, from historical cost indexes to construction materials and techniques to current costs.

If you have any questions about our products or services, please call us toll-free at 1-800-334-3509. Our customer service representatives will be happy to assist you. You can also visit our website at **www.rsmeans.com**

How the Book is Built: an Overview

The Construction Specifications Institute (CSI) and Construction Specifications Canada (CSC) have produced the 2012 edition of MasterFormat®, a system of titles and numbers used extensively to organize construction information.

All unit price data in the RSMeans cost data books is now arranged in the 50-division MasterFormat® 2012 system.

A Powerful Construction Tool

You have in your hands one of the most powerful construction tools available today. A successful project is built on the foundation of an accurate and dependable estimate. This book will enable you to construct just such an estimate.

For the casual user the book is designed to be:

- quickly and easily understood so you can get right to your estimate.
- filled with valuable information so you can understand the necessary factors that go into the cost estimate.

For the regular user, the book is designed to be:

- a handy desk reference that can be quickly referred to for key costs.
- a comprehensive, fully reliable source of current construction costs and productivity rates so you'll be prepared to estimate any project.
- a source book for preliminary project cost, product selections, and alternate materials and methods.

To meet all of these requirements, we have organized the book into the following clearly defined sections.

Quick Start

See our "Quick Start" instructions on the following page to get started right away.

Estimating with RSMeans Unit Price Cost Data

Please refer to these steps for guidance on completing an estimate using RSMeans unit price cost data.

Square Foot Cost Section

This section lists Square Foot costs for typical residential construction projects. The organizational format used divides the projects into basic building classes. These classes are defined at the beginning of the section. The individual projects are further divided into ten common components of construction.

The Table of Contents, an explanation of square foot prices, and an outline of a typical page layout are located at the beginning of this section.

Assemblies Cost Section

This section uses an "Assemblies" (sometimes referred to as "systems") format grouping all the functional elements of a building into nine construction divisions.

At the top of each "Assembly" cost table is an illustration, a brief description, and the design criteria used to develop the cost. Each of the components and its contributing cost to the system is shown.

Material: These cost figures include a standard 10% markup for "handling." They are national average material costs as of January of the current year and include delivery to the job site.

Installation: The installation costs include labor and equipment, plus a markup for the installing contractor's overhead and profit.

For a complete breakdown and explanation of a typical "Assemblies" page, see "How to Use the Assemblies Cost Tables" at the beginning of the Assemblies Section.

Unit Price Section

All cost data has been divided into the 50 divisions according to the MasterFormat system of classification and numbering. For a listing of these divisions and an outline of their subdivisions, see the Unit Price Section Table of Contents.

Estimating tips are included at the beginning of each division.

Reference Section

This section includes information on Equipment Rental Costs, Crew Listings, Location Factors, Reference Tables, and a listing of Abbreviations.

Equipment Rental Costs: This section contains the average costs to rent and operate hundreds of pieces of construction equipment.

Crew Listings: This section lists all the crews referenced in the book. For the purposes of this book, a crew is composed of more than one trade classification and/or the addition of power equipment to any trade classification.

Power equipment is included in the cost of the crew. Costs are shown both with the bare labor rates and with the installing contractor's overhead and profit added. For each, the total crew cost per eight-hour day and the composite cost per labor-hour are listed.

Location Factors: You can adjust total project costs to over 900 locations throughout the U.S. and Canada by using the data in this section.

Reference Tables: At the beginning of selected major classifications in the Unit Price Section are "reference numbers" shown in a shaded box. These numbers refer you to related information in the Reference Section. In this section, you'll find reference tables, explanations, and estimating information that support how we develop the unit price data, technical data, and estimating procedures.

Abbreviations: A listing of abbreviations used throughout this book, along with the terms they represent, is included in this section.

Index

A comprehensive listing of all terms and subjects in this book will help you quickly find what you need when you are not sure where it falls in MasterFormat.

The Scope of This Book

This book is designed to be as comprehensive and as easy to use as possible. To that end we have made certain assumptions and limited its scope in two key ways:

1. We have established material prices based on a national average.
2. We have computed labor costs based on a seven major region average of residential wage rates.

Project Size/Type

The material prices in RSMeans cost data books are "contractor's prices." They are the prices that contractors can expect to pay at the lumberyards, suppliers/distributers warehouses, etc. Small orders of speciality items would be higher than the costs shown, while very large orders, such as truckload lots, would be less. The variation would depend on the size, timing, and negotiating power of the contractor. The labor costs are primarily for new construction or major renovations rather than repairs or minor alterations. **With reasonable exercise of judgment, the figures can be used for any building work.**

Absolute Essentials for a Quick Start

If you feel you are ready to use this book and don't think you will need the detailed instructions that begin on the following page, this Absolute Essentials for a Quick Start page is for you. These steps will allow you to get started estimating in a matter of minutes.

1 Scope

Think through the project that you will be estimating, and identify the many individual work tasks that will need to be covered in your estimate.

2 Quantify

Determine the number of units that will be required for each work task that you identified.

3 Pricing

Locate individual Unit Price line items that match the work tasks you identified. The Unit Price Section Table of Contents that begins on page 1 and the Index in the back of the book will help you find these line items.

4 Multiply

Multiply the Total Incl O&P cost for a Unit Price line item in the book by your quantity for that item. The price you calculate will be an estimate for a completed item of work performed by a subcontractor. Keep adding line items in this manner to build your estimate.

5 Project Overhead

Include project overhead items in your estimate. These items are needed to make the job run and are typically, but not always, provided by the General Contractor. They can be found in Division 1. An alternate method of estimating project overhead costs is to apply a percentage of the total project cost.

Include rented tools not included in crews, waste, rubbish handling, and cleanup.

6 Estimate Summary

Include General Contractor's markup on subcontractors, General Contractor's office overhead and profit, and sales tax on materials and equipment.

Adjust your estimate to the project's location by using the City Cost Indexes or Location Factors found in the Reference Section.

Editors' Note: We urge you to spend time reading and understanding the supporting material in the front of this book. An accurate estimate requires experience, knowledge, and careful calculation. The more you know about how we at RSMeans developed the data, the more accurate your estimate will be. In addition, it is important to take into consideration the reference material in the back of the book such as Equipment Listings, Crew Listings, City Cost Indexes, Location Factors, and Reference Tables.

Estimating with RSMeans Unit Price Cost Data

Following these steps will allow you to complete an accurate estimate using RSMeans Unit Price cost data.

1 Scope Out the Project

- Identify the individual work tasks that will need to be covered in your estimate.
- The Unit Price data in this book has been divided into 50 Divisions according to the CSI MasterFormat 2010—their titles are listed on the back cover of your book.
- Think through the project and identify those CSI Divisions needed in your estimate.
- The Unit Price Section Table of Contents on page 1 may also be helpful when scoping out your project.
- Experienced estimators find it helpful to begin with Division 2 and continue through completion. Division 1 can be estimated after the full project scope is known.

2 Quantify

- Determine the number of units required for each work task that you identified.
- Experienced estimators include an allowance for waste in their quantities. (Waste is not included in RSMeans Unit Price line items unless so stated.)

3 Price the Quantities

- Use the Unit Price Table of Contents, and the Index, to locate individual Unit Price line items for your estimate.
- Reference Numbers indicated within a Unit Price section refer to additional information that you may find useful.
- The crew indicates who is performing the work for that task. Crew codes are expanded in the Crew Listings in the Reference Section to include all trades and equipment that comprise the crew.

- The Daily Output is the amount of work the crew is expected to do in one day.
- The Labor-Hours value is the amount of time it will take for the crew to install one unit of work.
- The abbreviated Unit designation indicates the unit of measure upon which the crew, productivity, and prices are based.
- Bare Costs are shown for materials, labor, and equipment needed to complete the Unit Price line item. Bare costs do not include waste, project overhead, payroll insurance, payroll taxes, main office overhead, or profit.
- The Total Incl O&P cost is the billing rate or invoice amount of the installing contractor or subcontractor who performs the work for the Unit Price line item.

4 Multiply

- Multiply the total number of units needed for your project by the Total Incl O&P cost for each Unit Price line item.
- Be careful that your take off unit of measure matches the unit of measure in the Unit column.
- The price you calculate is an estimate for a completed item of work.
- Keep scoping individual tasks, determining the number of units required for those tasks, matching each task with individual Unit Price line items in the book, and multiply quantities by Total Incl O&P costs.
- An estimate completed in this manner is priced as if a subcontractor, or set of subcontractors, is performing the work. The estimate does not yet include Project Overhead or Estimate Summary components such as General Contractor markups on subcontracted work, General Contractor office overhead and profit, contingency, and location factor.

5 Project Overhead

- Include project overhead items from Division 1 – General Requirements.
- These items are needed to make the job run. They are typically, but not always, provided by the General Contractor. Items include, but are not limited to, field personnel, insurance, performance bond, permits, testing, temporary utilities, field office and storage facilities, temporary scaffolding and platforms, equipment mobilization and demobilization, temporary roads and sidewalks, winter protection, temporary barricades and fencing, temporary security, temporary signs, field engineering and layout, final cleaning and commissioning.
- Each item should be quantified, and matched to individual Unit Price line items in Division 1, and then priced and added to your estimate.
- An alternate method of estimating project overhead costs is to apply a percentage of the total project cost, usually 5% to 15% with an average of 10% (see General Conditions, page ix).
- Include other project related expenses in your estimate such as:
  - Rented equipment not itemized in the Crew Listings
  - Rubbish handling throughout the project (see 02 41 19.19)

6 Estimate Summary

- Include sales tax as required by laws of your state or county.
- Include the General Contractor's markup on self-performed work, usually 5% to 15% with an average of 10%.
- Include the General Contractor's markup on subcontracted work, usually 5% to 15% with an average of 10%.
- Include General Contractor's main office overhead and profit:
  - RSMeans gives general guidelines on the General Contractor's main office overhead (see section 01 31 13.50 and Reference Number R013113-50).
  - RSMeans gives no guidance on the General Contractor's profit.
  - Markups will depend on the size of the General Contractor's operations, his projected annual revenue, the level of risk he is taking on, and on the level of competition in the local area and for this project in particular.
- Include a contingency, usually 3% to 5%, if appropriate.
- Adjust your estimate to the project's location by using the City Cost Indexes or the Location Factors in the Reference Section:
  - Look at the rules on the pages for How to Use the City Cost Indexes to see how to apply the Indexes for your location.
  - When the proper Index or Factor has been identified for the project's location, convert it to a multiplier by dividing it by 100, and then multiply that multiplier by your estimated total cost. The original estimated total cost will now be adjusted up or down from the national average to a total that is appropriate for your location.

Editors' Notes:

1) We urge you to spend time reading and understanding the supporting material in the front of this book. An accurate estimate requires experience, knowledge, and careful calculation. The more you know about how we at RSMeans developed the data, the more accurate your estimate will be. In addition, it is important to take into consideration the reference material in the back of the book such as Equipment Listings, Crew Listings, City Cost Indexes, Location Factors, and Reference Tables.

2) Contractors who are bidding or are involved in JOC, DOC, SABER, or IDIQ type contracts are cautioned that workers' compensation insurance, federal and state payroll taxes, waste, project supervision, project overhead, main office overhead, and profit are not included in bare costs. The coefficient or multiplier must cover these costs.

How to Use the Book: The Details

What's Behind the Numbers? The Development of Cost Data

The staff at RSMeans continually monitors developments in the construction industry in order to ensure reliable, thorough, and up-to-date cost information. While overall construction costs may vary relative to general economic conditions, price fluctuations within the industry are dependent upon many factors. Individual price variations may, in fact, be opposite to overall economic trends. Therefore, costs are constantly tracked and complete updates are published yearly. Also, new items are frequently added in response to changes in materials and methods.

Costs—$ (U.S.)

All costs represent U.S. national averages and are given in U.S. dollars. The RSMeans City Cost Indexes can be used to adjust costs to a particular location. The City Cost Indexes for Canada can be used to adjust U.S. national averages to local costs in Canadian dollars. No exchange rate conversion is necessary.

G The processes or products identified by the green symbol in our publications have been determined to be environmentally responsible and/or resource-efficient solely by the RSMeans engineering staff. The inclusion of the green symbol does not represent compliance with any specific industry association or standard.

Material Costs

The RSMeans staff contacts manufacturers, dealers, distributors, and contractors all across the U.S. and Canada to determine national average material costs. If you have access to current material costs for your specific location, you may wish to make adjustments to reflect differences from the national average. Included within material costs are fasteners for a normal installation. RSMeans engineers use manufacturers' recommendations, written specifications, and/or standard construction practice for size and spacing of fasteners. Adjustments to material costs may be required for your specific application or location. The manufacturer's warranty is assumed. Extended warranties are not included in the material costs. Material costs do not include sales tax.

Labor Costs

Labor costs are based on the average of wage rates from 30 major U.S. cities. Rates are determined from labor union agreements or prevailing wages for construction trades for the current year. Rates, along with overhead and profit markups, are listed on the inside back cover of this book.

- If wage rates in your area vary from those used in this book, or if rate increases are expected within a given year, labor costs should be adjusted accordingly.

Labor costs reflect productivity based on actual working conditions. In addition to actual installation, these figures include time spent during a normal weekday on tasks such as, material receiving and handling, mobilization at site, site movement, breaks, and cleanup. Productivity data is developed over an extended period so as not to be influenced by abnormal variations and reflects a typical average.

Equipment Costs

Equipment costs include not only rental, but also operating costs for equipment under normal use. The operating costs include parts and labor for routine servicing such as repair and replacement of pumps, filters, and worn lines. Normal operating expendables, such as fuel, lubricants, tires, and electricity (where applicable), are also included. Extaordinary operating expendables with highly variable wear patterns, such as diamond bits and blades, are excluded. These costs are included under materials. Equipment rental rates are obtained from industry sources throughout North America—contractors, suppliers, dealers, manufacturers, and distributors.

Equipment costs do not include operators' wages; nor do they include the cost to move equipment to a job site (mobilization) or from a job site (demobilization).

Equipment Cost/Day——The cost of power equipment required for each crew is included in the Crew Listings in the Reference Section (small tools that are considered as essential everyday tools are not listed out separately). The Crew Listings itemize specialized tools and heavy equipment along with labor trades. The daily cost of itemized equipment included in a crew is based on dividing the weekly bare rental rate by 5 (number of working days per week) and then adding the hourly operating cost times 8 (the number of hours per day). This Equipment Cost/Day is shown in the last column of the Equipment Rental Cost pages in the Reference Section.

Mobilization/Demobilization——The cost to move construction equipment from an equipment yard or rental company to the job site and back again is not included in equipment costs. Mobilization (to the site) and demobilization (from the site) costs can be found in the Unit Price Section. If a piece of equipment is already at the job site, it is not appropriate to utilize mobil./demob. costs again in an estimate.

Factors Affecting Costs

Costs can vary depending upon a number of variables. Here's how we have handled the main factors affecting costs.

Quality——The prices for materials and the workmanship upon which productivity is based represent sound construction work. They are also in line with U.S. government specifications.

Overtime——We have made no allowance for overtime. If you anticipate premium time or work beyond normal working hours, be sure to make an appropriate adjustment to your labor costs.

Productivity—— The productivity, daily output, and labor-hour figures for each line item are based on working an eight-hour day in daylight hours in moderate temperatures. For work that extends beyond normal work hours or is performed under adverse conditions, productivity may decrease. (See "How RSMeans Data Works" for more on productivity.)

Size of Project—— The size, scope of work, and type of construction project will have a significant impact on cost. Economies of scale can reduce costs for large projects. Unit costs can often run higher for small projects. Costs in this book are intended for the size and type of project as previously described in "How the Book Is Built: An Overview." Costs for projects of a significantly different size or type should be adjusted accordingly.

Location——Material prices in this book are for metropolitan areas. However, in dense urban areas, traffic and site storage limitations may increase costs. Beyond a 20-mile radius of large cities, extra trucking or transportation charges may also increase the material costs slightly. On the other hand, lower wage rates may be in effect. Be sure to consider both of these factors when preparing an estimate, particularly if the job site is located in a central city or remote rural location.

In addition, highly specialized subcontract items may require travel and per-diem expenses for mechanics.

Other Factors——

- season of year
- contractor management
- weather conditions
- local union restrictions
- building code requirements
- availability of:
  - adequate energy
  - skilled labor
  - building materials
- owner's special requirements/restrictions
- safety requirements
- environmental considerations

General Conditions——The "Square Foot" and "Assemblies" sections of this book use costs that include the installing contractor's overhead and profit (O&P). The Unit Price Section presents cost data in two ways: Bare Costs and Total Cost including O&P (Overhead and Profit). General Conditions, when applicable, should also be added to the Total Cost including O&P. The costs for General Conditions are listed in Division 1 of the Unit Price Section and the Reference Section of this book. General Conditions for the Installing Contractor may range from 0% to 10% of the Total Cost including O&P. For the General or Prime Contractor, costs for General Conditions may range from 5% to 15% of the Total Cost including O&P, with a figure of 10% as the most typical allowance.

Overhead & Profit——Total Cost, including O&P, for the Installing Contractor is shown in the last column on both the Unit Price and the Assemblies pages of this book. This figure is the sum of the bare material cost plus 10% for profit, the bare labor cost plus overhead and profit, and the bare equipment cost plus 10% for profit. Details for the calculation of Overhead and Profit on labor are shown on the inside back cover and in the Reference Section of this book. (See "How RSMeans Data Works" for an example of this calculation.)

Unpredictable Factors——General business conditions influence "in-place" costs of all items. Substitute materials and construction methods may have to be employed. These may affect the installed cost and/or life cycle costs. Such factors may be difficult to evaluate and cannot necessarily be predicted on the basis of the job's location in a particular section of the country. Thus, where these factors apply, you may find significant, but unavoidable cost variations for which you will have to apply a measure of judgment to your estimate.

Rounding of Costs

In general, all unit prices in excess of $5.00 have been rounded to make them easier to use and still maintain adequate precision of the results. The rounding rules we have chosen are in the following table.

Prices from . . .	Rounded to the nearest . . .
$.01 to $5.00	$.01
$5.01 to $20.00	$.05
$20.01 to $100.00	$.50
$100.01 to $300.00	$1.00
$300.01 to $1,000.00	$5.00
$1,000.01 to $10,000.00	$25.00
$10,000.01 to $50,000.00	$100.00
$50,000.01 and above	$500.00

Final Checklist

Estimating can be a straightforward process provided you remember the basics. Here's a checklist of some of the steps you should remember to complete before finalizing your estimate.

Did you remember to . . .

- factor in the Location Factor for your locale?
- take into consideration which items have been marked up and by how much?
- mark up the entire estimate sufficiently for your purposes?
- read the background information on techniques and technical matters that could impact your project time span and cost?
- include all components of your project in the final estimate?
- double check your figures for accuracy?
- call RSMeans if you have any questions about your estimate or the data you've found in our publications?

Remember, RSMeans stands behind its publications. If you have any questions about your estimate . . . about the costs you've used from our books . . . or even about the technical aspects of the job that may affect your estimate, feel free to call the RSMeans editors at 1-800-334-3509.

Free Quarterly Updates

Stay up-to-date throughout 2014 with RSMeans' free cost data updates four times a year. Sign up online to make sure you have access to the newest data. Every quarter we provide the city cost adjustment factors for hundreds of cities and key materials. Register at: **www.rsmeans2014updates.com**

Square Foot Cost Section

Table of Contents

Introduction to the Square Foot Cost Section

The Square Foot Cost Section of this manual contains costs per square foot for four classes of construction in seven building types. Costs are listed for various exterior wall materials which are typical of the class and building type. There are cost tables for Wings and Ells with modification tables to adjust the base cost of each class of building. Non-standard items can easily be added to the standard structures.

Cost estimating for a residence is a three-step process:

(1) Identification
(2) Listing dimensions
(3) Calculations

Guidelines and a sample cost estimating procedure are shown on the following pages.

Identification

To properly identify a residential building, the class of construction, type, and exterior wall material must be determined. Page 8 has drawings and guidelines for determining the class of construction. There are also detailed specifications and additional drawings at the beginning of each set of tables to further aid in proper building class and type identification.

Sketches for eight types of residential buildings and their configurations are shown on pages 10 and 11. Definitions of living area are next to each sketch. Sketches and definitions of garage types are on page 12.

Living Area

Base cost tables are prepared as costs per square foot of living area. The living area of a residence is that area which is suitable and normally designed for full time living. It does not include basement recreation rooms or finished attics, although these areas are often considered full time living areas by the owners.

Living area is calculated from the exterior dimensions without the need to adjust for exterior wall thickness. When calculating the living area of a 1-1/2 story, two story, three story or tri-level residence, overhangs and other differences in size and shape between floors must be considered.

Only the floor area with a ceiling height of six feet or more in a 1-1/2 story residence is considered living area. In bi-levels and tri-levels, the areas that are below grade are considered living area, even when these areas may not be completely finished.

Base Tables and Modifications

Base cost tables show the base cost per square foot without a basement, with one full bath and one full kitchen for economy and average homes, and an additional half bath for custom and luxury models. Adjustments for finished and unfinished basements are part of the base cost tables. Adjustments for multi-family residences, additional bathrooms, townhouses, alternative roofs, and air conditioning and heating systems are listed in Modifications, Adjustments and Alternatives tables below the base cost tables.

Costs for other modifications, adjustments and alternatives, including garages, breezeways and site improvements, are on pages 93 to 96.

Listing of Dimensions

To use this section of the manual, only the dimensions used to calculate the horizontal area of the building and additions, modifications, adjustments and alternatives are needed. The dimensions, normally the length and width, can come from drawings or field measurements. For ease in calculation, consider measuring in tenths of feet, i.e., 9 ft. 6 in. = 9.5 ft., 9 ft. 4 in. = 9.3 ft.

In all cases, make a sketch of the building. Any protrusions or other variations in shape should be noted on the sketch with dimensions.

Calculations

The calculations portion of the estimate is a two-step activity:

(1) The selection of appropriate costs from the tables

(2) Computations

Selection of Appropriate Costs

To select the appropriate cost from the base tables, the following information is needed:

(1) Class of construction
   (a) Economy
   (b) Average
   (c) Custom
   (d) Luxury
(2) Type of residence
   (a) 1 story
   (b) 1-1/2 story
   (c) 2 story
   (d) 3 story
   (e) Bi-level
   (f) Tri-level
(3) Occupancy
   (a) One family
   (b) Two family
   (c) Three family
(4) Building configuration
   (a) Detached
   (b) Town/Row house
   (c) Semi-detached
(5) Exterior wall construction
   (a) Wood frame
   (b) Brick veneer
   (c) Solid masonry
(6) Living areas

Modifications are classified by class, type, and size.

Computations

The computation process should take the following sequence:

(1) Multiply the base cost by the area.

(2) Add or subtract the modifications, adjustments, and alternatives.

(3) Apply the location modifier.

When selecting costs, interpolate or use the cost that most nearly matches the structure under study. This applies to size, exterior wall construction, and class.

How to Use the Residential Square Foot Cost Pages

The following is a detailed explanation of a sample entry in the Residential Square Foot Cost Section. Each bold number below corresponds to the item being described on the facing page with the appropriate component of the sample entry following in parenthesis.

Prices listed are costs that include overhead and profit of the installing contractor. Total model costs include an additional markup for General Contractors' overhead and profit, and fees specific to class of construction.

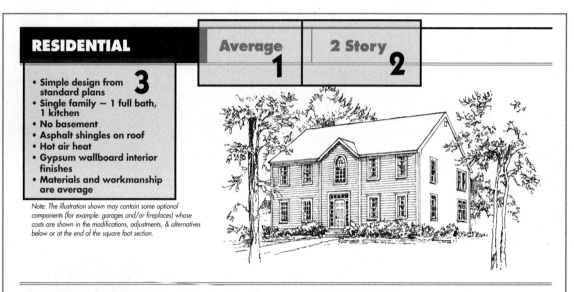

RESIDENTIAL | **Average** **1** | **2 Story** **2**

3
- Simple design from standard plans
- Single family — 1 full bath, 1 kitchen
- No basement
- Asphalt shingles on roof
- Hot air heat
- Gypsum wallboard interior finishes
- Materials and workmanship are average

Note: The illustration shown may contain some optional components (for example: garages and/or fireplaces) whose costs are shown in the modifications, adjustments, & alternatives below or at the end of the square foot section.

Base cost per square foot of living area

Exterior Wall **4**	1000	1200	1400	1600	1800	Living Area **5** 2000	2200	2600	3000	3400	3800
Wood Siding - Wood Frame	133.80	121.10	115.25	111.15	106.95	102.40 **6**	99.45	93.75	88.30	85.85	83.50
Brick Veneer - Wood Frame	141.30	128.15	121.75	117.35	112.80	108.10	104.85	98.65	92.75	90.10	87.55
Stucco on Wood Frame	130.10	117.70	112.00	108.05	104.05	99.70	96.85	91.35	86.05	83.70	81.50
Solid Masonry	158.05	143.65	136.20	131.20	125.80	120.65	116.75	109.45	102.75	99.60	96.60
Finished Basement, Add **7**	21.80	21.50	20.80	20.35	19.75	19.45 **8**	19.00	18.35	17.85	17.50	17.25
Unfinished Basement, Add	8.55	8.00	7.50	7.20	6.90	6.70	6.45	6.00	5.70	5.50	5.35

Modifications

Add to the total cost
Upgrade Kitchen Cabinets	$ + 4320
Solid Surface Countertops (Included) **9**	
Full Bath - including plumbing, wall and floor finishes	+ 7120
Half Bath - including plumbing, wall and floor finishes	+ 4097
One Car Attached Garage	+ 13,653
One Car Detached Garage	+ 17,986
Fireplace & Chimney	+ 6660

Adjustments

For multi family - add to total cost
Additional Kitchen	$ + 8159
Additional Bath	+ 7120
Additional Entry & Exit	+ 1620
Separate Heating	+ 1392
Separate Electric	+ 1986

For Townhouse/Rowhouse -
Multiply cost per square foot by **10**
Inner Unit	.90
End Unit	.95

Alternatives

Add to or deduct from the cost per square foot of living area
Cedar Shake Roof	+ 1.55
Clay Tile Roof	+ 3.80
Slate Roof	+ 3.30
Upgrade Walls to Skim Coat Plaster	+ .50
Upgrade Ceilings to Textured Finish	+ .50
Air Conditioning, in Heating Ductwork **11**	+ 2.86
In Separate Ductwork	+ 5.52
Heating Systems, Hot Water	+ 2
Heat Pump	+ 2.97
Electric Heat	– .37
Not Heated	– 2.93

Additional upgrades or components

Kitchen Cabinets & Countertops	Page 93
Bathroom Vanities	94
Fireplaces & Chimneys	94
Windows, Skylights & Dormers	94
Appliances	95
Breezeways & Porches	95
Finished Attic **12**	95
Garages	96
Site Improvements	96
Wings & Ells	56

1 Class of Construction (Average)
The class of construction depends upon the design and specifications of the plan. The four classes are economy, average, custom, and luxury.

2 Type of Residence (2 Story)
The building type describes the number of stories or levels in the model. The seven building types are 1 story, 1-1/2 story, 2 story, 2-1/2 story, 3 story, bi-level, and tri-level.

3 Specification Highlights (Hot Air Heat)
These specifications include information concerning the components of the model, including the number of baths, roofing types, HVAC systems, and materials and workmanship. If the components listed are not appropriate, modifications can be made by consulting the information shown lower on the page or the Assemblies Section.

4 Exterior Wall System (Wood Siding -Wood Frame)
This section includes the types of exterior wall systems and the structural frame used. The exterior wall systems shown are typical of the class of construction and the building type shown.

5 Living Areas (2000 SF)
The living area is that area of the residence which is suitable and normally designed for full time living. It does not include basement recreation rooms or finished attics. Living area is calculated from the exterior dimensions without the need to adjust for exterior wall thickness. When calculating the living area of a 1-1/2 story, 2 story, 3 story or tri-level residence, overhangs and other differences in size and shape between floors must be considered. Only the floor area with a ceiling height of seven feet or more in a 1-1/2 story residence is considered living area. In bi-levels and tri-levels, the areas that are below grade are considered living area, even when these areas may not be completely finished. A range of various living areas for the residential model are shown to aid in selection of values from the matrix.

6 Base Costs per Square Foot of Living Area ($102.40)
Base cost tables show the cost per square foot of living area without a basement, with one full bath and one full kitchen for economy and average homes, and an additional half bath for custom and luxury models. When selecting costs, interpolate or use the cost that most nearly matches the residence under consideration for size, exterior wall system, and class of construction. Prices listed are costs that include overhead and profit of the installing contractor, a general contractor markup, and an allowance for plans that vary by class of construction. For additional information on contractor overhead and architectural fees, see the Reference Section.

7 Basement Types (Finished)
The two types of basements are finished and unfinished. The specifications and components for both are shown on the Building Classes page in the Introduction to this section.

8 Additional Costs for Basements ($19.45 or $6.70)
These values indicate the additional cost per square foot of living area for either a finished or an unfinished basement.

9 Modifications and Adjustments (Upgrade Kitchen Cabinets $4320)
Modifications and Adjustments are costs added to or subtracted from the total cost of the residence. The total cost of the residence is equal to the cost per square foot of living area times the living area. Typical modifications and adjustments include kitchens, baths, garages and fireplaces.

10 Multiplier for Townhouse/ Rowhouse (Inner Unit .90)
The multipliers shown adjust the base costs per square foot of living area for the common wall condition encountered in townhouses or rowhouses.

11 Alternatives (Skim Coat Plaster $.50)
Alternatives are costs added to or subtracted from the base cost per square foot of living area. Typical alternatives include variations in kitchens, baths, roofing, and air conditioning and heating systems.

12 Additional Upgrades or Components (Wings & Ells page 56)
Costs for additional upgrades or components, including wings or ells, breezeways, porches, finished attics, and site improvements, are shown in other locations in the Residential Square Foot Cost Section.

2

		Cost Per Square Foot Of Living Area			% of Total
		Mat.	Inst.	Total	(rounded)
1 Site Work	Site preparation for slab; 4' deep trench excavation for foundation wall.		.81	.81	0.8%
2 Foundation	Continuous reinforced concrete footing 8" deep x 18" wide; dampproofed and insulated reinforced concrete foundation wall, 8" thick, 4' deep, 4" concrete slab on 4" crushed stone base and polyethylene vapor barrier, trowel finish.	3.11	4.13	7.24	7.1%
3 Framing	Exterior walls - 2" x 4" wood studs, 16" O.C.; 1/2" plywood sheathing; 2" x 6" rafters 16" O.C. with 1/2" plywood sheathing, 4 in 12 pitch; 2" x 6" ceiling joists 16" O.C.; 2" x 8" floor joists 16" O.C. with 5/8" plywood subfloor; 1/2" plywood subfloor on 1" x 2" wood sleepers 16" O.C.	7.06	9.12	16.18	15.8%
4 Exterior Walls	Beveled wood siding and building paper on insulated wood frame walls; 6" attic insulation; double hung windows; 3 flush solid core wood exterior doors with storms.	13.63	5.80	19.43	19.0%
5 Roofing	25 year asphalt shingles; #15 felt building paper; aluminum gutters, downspouts, drip edge and flashings.	1.08	1.23	2.31	2.3%
6 Interiors	Walls and ceilings, 1/2" taped and finished gypsum wallboard, primed and painted with 2 coats; painted baseboard and trim, finished hardwood floor 40%, carpet with 1/2" underlayment 40%, vinyl tile with 1/2" underlayment 15%, ceramic tile with 1/2" underlayment 5%; hollow core and louvered doors.	14.19	14.69	28.88	28.2%
7 Specialties	Average grade kitchen cabinets - 14 L.F. wall and base with solid surface counter top and kitchen sink; 40 gallon electric water heater.	2.74	.93	3.67	3.6%
8 Mechanical	1 lavatory, white, wall hung; 1 water closet, white; 1 bathtub with shower; enameled steel, white; gas fired warm air heat.	3.17	3.03	6.20	6.1%
9 Electrical	200 Amp. service; Romex wiring; incandescent lighting fixtures, switches, receptacles.	1.15	1.69	2.84	2.8%
10 Overhead	Contractor's overhead and profit and plans.	7.82	7.02	14.84	14.5%
	Total	53.95	48.45	102.40	

4 **5** **6** **7** **3** **8** **9**

1 Specifications

The parameters for an example dwelling from the previous pages are listed here. Included are the square foot dimensions of the proposed building. Living Area takes into account the number of floors and other factors needed to define a building's total square footage. Perimeter dimensions are defined in terms of linear feet.

2 Building Type

This is a sketch of a cross section view through the dwelling. It is shown to help define the living area for the building type. For more information, see the Building Types pages in the Introduction.

3 Components (3 Framing)

This page contains the ten components needed to develop the complete square foot cost of the typical dwelling specified. All components are defined with a description of the materials and/or task involved. Use cost figures from each component to estimate the cost per square foot of that section of the project. The components listed on this page are typical of all sizes of residences from the facing page. Specific quantities of components required would vary with the size of the dwelling and the exterior wall system.

4 Materials (7.06)

This column gives the amount needed to develop the cost of materials. The figures given here are not bare costs. Ten percent has been added to bare material cost for profit.

5 Installation (9.12)

Installation includes labor and equipment costs. The labor rates included here incorporate the total overhead and profit costs for the installing contractor. The average mark-up used to create these figures is 72.0% over and above bare labor costs. The equipment rates include 10% for profit.

6 Total (16.18)

This column lists the sum of two figures. Use this total to determine the sum of material cost plus installation cost. The result is a convenient total cost for each of the ten components.

7 % of Total (rounded) (15.8%)

This column represents the percent of the total cost for this component group.

8 Overhead

The costs in components 1 through 9 include overhead and profit for the installing contractor. Item 10 is overhead and profit for the general contractor. This is typically a percentage mark-up of all other costs. The amount depends on size and type of dwelling, building class, and economic conditions. An allowance for plans or design has been included where appropriate.

9 Bottom Line Total (102.40)

This figure is the complete square foot cost for the construction project and equals the sum of total material and total labor costs. To determine total project cost, multiply the bottom line total by the living area.

Building Classes

Economy Class

An economy class residence is usually built from stock plans. The materials and workmanship are sufficient to satisfy building codes. Low construction cost is more important than distinctive features. The overall shape of the foundation and structure is seldom other than square or rectangular.

An unfinished basement includes 7' high 8" thick foundation wall composed of either concrete block or cast-in-place concrete.

Included in the finished basement cost are inexpensive paneling or drywall as the interior finish on the foundation walls, a low cost sponge backed carpeting adhered to the concrete floor, a drywall ceiling, and overhead lighting.

Custom Class

A custom class residence is usually built from plans and specifications with enough features to give the building a distinction of design. Materials and workmanship are generally above average with obvious attention given to construction details. Construction normally exceeds building code requirements.

An unfinished basement includes a 7'-6" high 10" thick cast-in-place concrete foundation wall or a 7'-6" high 12" thick concrete block foundation wall.

A finished basement includes painted drywall on insulated 2" x4" wood furring as the interior finish to the concrete walls, a suspended ceiling, carpeting adhered to the concrete floor, overhead lighting and heating.

Class

An average class residence is a simple design and built from standard plans. Materials and workmanship are average, but often exceed minimum building codes. There are frequently special features that give the residence some distinctive characteristics.

An unfinished basement includes 7'-6" high 8" thick foundation wall composed of either cast-in-place concrete or concrete block.

Included in the finished basement are plywood paneling or drywall on furring that is fastened to the foundation walls, sponge backed carpeting adhered to the concrete floor, a suspended ceiling, overhead lighting and heating.

Luxury Class

A luxury class residence is built from an architect's plan for a specific owner. It is unique both in design and workmanship. There are many special features, and construction usually exceeds all building codes. It is obvious that primary attention is placed on the owner's comfort and pleasure. Construction is supervised by an architect.

An unfinished basement includes 8' high 12" thick foundation wall that is composed of cast-in-place concrete or concrete block.

A finished basement includes painted drywall on 2" x4" wood furring as the interior finish, suspended ceiling, tackless carpet on wood subfloor with sleepers, overhead lighting and heating.

Configurations

Detached House

This category of residence is a free-standing separate building with or without an attached garage. It has four complete walls.

Semi-Detached House

This category of residence has two living units side-by-side. The common wall is a fireproof wall. Semi-detached residences can be treated as a row house with two end units. Semi-detached residences can be any of the building types.

Town/Row House

This category of residence has a number of attached units made up of inner units and end units. The units are joined by common walls. The inner units have only two exterior walls. The common walls are fireproof. The end units have three walls and a common wall. Town houses/row houses can be any of the building types.

Building Types

One Story

This is an example of a one-story dwelling. The living area of this type of residence is confined to the ground floor. The headroom in the attic is usually too low for use as a living area.

One-and-a-half Story

The living area in the upper level of this type of residence is 50% to 90% of the ground floor. This is made possible by a combination of this design's high-peaked roof and/or dormers. Only the upper level area with a ceiling height of 7 feet or more is considered living area. The living area of this residence is the sum of the ground floor area plus the area on the second level with a ceiling height of 7 feet or more.

One Story with Finished Attic

The main living area in this type of residence is the ground floor. The upper level or attic area has sufficient headroom for use as a living area. This is made possible by a high peaked roof. The living area in the attic is less than 50% of the ground floor. The living area of this type of residence is the ground floor area only. The finished attic is considered an adjustment.

Two Story

This type of residence has a second floor or upper level area which is equal or nearly equal to the ground floor area. The upper level of this type of residence can range from 90% to 110% of the ground floor area, depending on setbacks or overhangs. The living area is the sum of the ground floor area and the upper level floor area.

Two-and-one-half Story

This type of residence has two levels of equal or nearly equal area and a third level which has a living area that is 50% to 90% of the ground floor. This is made possible by a high peaked roof, extended wall heights and/or dormers. Only the upper level area with a ceiling height of 7 feet or more is considered living area. The living area of this residence is the sum of the ground floor area, the second floor area and the area on the third level with a ceiling height of 7 feet or more.

Bi-level

This type of residence has two living areas, one above the other. One area is about 4 feet below grade and the second is about 4 feet above grade. Both areas are equal in size. The lower level in this type of residence is originally designed and built to serve as a living area and not as a basement. Both levels have full ceiling heights. The living area is the sum of the lower level area and the upper level area.

Three Story

This type of residence has three levels which are equal or nearly equal. As in the 2 story residence, the second and third floor areas may vary slightly depending on setbacks or overhangs. The living area is the sum of the ground floor area and the two upper level floor areas.

Tri-level

This type of residence has three levels of living area: one at grade level, one about 4 feet below grade, and one about 4 feet above grade. All levels are originally designed to serve as living areas. All levels have full ceiling heights. The living area is a sum of the areas of each of the three levels.

Garage Types

Attached Garage

Shares a common wall with the dwelling. Access is typically through a door between dwelling and garage.

Basement Garage

Constructed under the roof of the dwelling but below the living area.

Built-In Garage

Constructed under the second floor living space and above basement level of dwelling. Reduces gross square feet of living area.

Detached Garage

Constructed apart from the main dwelling. Shares no common area or wall with the dwelling.

Building Components

1. Excavation	11. Collar Ties	21. Fascia	31. Backfill	41. Sub-floor
2. Sill Plate	12. Ridge Rafter	22. Downspout	32. Drainage Stone	42. Finish Floor
3. Basement Window	13. Roof Sheathing	23. Shutter	33. Drainage Tile	43. Attic Insulation
4. Floor Joist	14. Roof Felt	24. Window	34. Wall Footing	44. Soffit
5. Shoe Plate	15. Roof Shingles	25. Wall Shingles	35. Gravel	45. Ceiling Strapping
6. Studs	16. Flashing	26. Weather Barrier	36. Concrete Slab	46. Wall Insulation
7. Drywall	17. Flue Lining	27. Wall Sheathing	37. Column Footing	47. Cross Bridging
8. Plate	18. Chimney	28. Fire Stop	38. Pipe Column	48. Bulkhead Stairs
9. CeiHng Joists	19. Roof Shingles	29. Dampproofing	39. Expansion Joint	
10. Rafters	20. Gutter	30. Foundation Wall	40. Girder	

Exterior Wall Construction

Typical Frame Construction

Typical wood frame construction consists of wood studs with insulation between them. A typical exterior surface is made up of sheathing, building paper and exterior siding consisting of wood, vinyl, aluminum or stucco over the wood sheathing.

Brick Veneer

Typical brick veneer construction consists of wood studs with insulation between them. A typical exterior surface is sheathing, building paper and an exterior of brick tied to the sheathing, with metal strips.

Stone

Typical solid masonry construction consists of a stone or block wall covered on the exterior with brick, stone or other masonry.

Residential Cost Estimate Worksheet

Worksheet Instructions

The residential cost estimate worksheet can be used as an outline for developing a residential construction or replacement cost. It is also useful for insurance appraisals. The design of the worksheet helps eliminate errors and omissions. To use the worksheet, follow the example below.

1. Fill out the owner's name, residence address, the estimator or appraiser's name, some type of project identifying number or code, and the date.

2. Determine from the plans, specifications, owner's description, photographs or any other means possible the class of construction. The models in this book use economy, average, custom and luxury as classes. Fill in the appropriate box.

3. Fill in the appropriate box for the residence type, configuration, occupancy, and exterior wall. If you require clarification, the pages preceding this worksheet describe each of these.

4. Next, the living area of the residence must be established. The heated or air conditioned space of the residence, not including the basement, should be measured. It is easiest to break the structure up into separate components as shown in the example. The main house (A), a one-and-one-half story wing (B), and a one story wing (C). The breezeway (D), garage (E), and open covered porch (F) will be treated differently. Data entry blocks for the living area are included on the worksheet for your use. Keep each level of each component separate, and fill out the blocks as shown.

5. By using the information on the worksheet, find the model, wing or ell in the following square foot cost pages that best matches the class, type, exterior finish and size of the residence being estimated. Use the Modifications, Adjustments, and Alternatives to determine the adjusted cost per square foot of living area for each component.

6. For each component, multiply the cost per square foot by the living area square footage. If the residence is a townhouse/rowhouse, a multiplier should be applied based upon the configuration.

7. The second page of the residential cost estimate worksheet has space for the additional components of a house. The cost for additional bathrooms, finished attic space, breezeways, porches, fireplaces, appliance or cabinet upgrades, and garages should be added on this page. The information for each of these components is found with the model being used, or in the Modifications, Adjustments, and Alternatives pages.

8. Add the total from page one of the estimate worksheet and the items listed on page two. The sum is the adjusted total building cost.

9. Depending on the use of the final estimated cost, one of the remaining two boxes should be filled out. Any additional items or exclusions should be added or subtracted at this time. The data contained in this book is a national average. Construction costs are different throughout the country. To allow for this difference, a location factor based upon the first three digits of the residence's zip code must be applied. The location factor is a multiplier that increases or decreases the adjusted total building cost. Find the appropriate location factor and calculate the local cost. If depreciation is a concern, a dollar figure should be subtracted at this point.

10. No residence will match a model exactly. Many differences will be found. At this level of estimating, a variation of plus or minus 10% should be expected.

Adjustments Instructions

No residence matches a model exactly in shape, material, or specifications. The common differences are:

1. Two or more exterior wall systems:
   a. Partial basement
   b. Partly finished basement
2. Specifications or features that are between two classes
3. Crawl space instead of a basement

EXAMPLES

Below are quick examples. See pages 17–19 for complete examples of cost adjustments for these differences:

1. Residence "A" is an average one-story structure with 1,600 S.F. of living area and no basement. Three walls are wood siding on wood frame, and the fourth wall is brick veneer on wood frame. The brick veneer wall is 35% of the exterior wall area.

   Use page 38 to calculate the Base Cost per S.F. of Living Area. Wood Siding for 1,600 S.F. = $104.95 per S.F. Brick Veneer for 1,600 S.F. = $121.25 per S.F.

   .65 ($104.95) + .35 ($121.25) = $110.65 per S.F. of Living Area.

2. a. Residence "B" is the same as Residence "A"; However, it has an unfinished basement under 50% of the building. To adjust the $110.65 per S.F. of living area for this partial basement, use page 38.

   $110.65 + .50 ($10.85) = $116.08 per S.F. of Living Area.

   b. Residence "C" is the same as Residence "A"; However, it has a full basement under the entire building. 640 S.F. or 40% of the basement area is finished.

   Using Page 38:

   $110.65 + .40 ($31.30) + .60 ($10.85) = $129.68 per S.F. of Living Area.

3. When specifications or features of a building are between classes, estimate the percent deviation, and use two tables to calculate the cost per S.F.

   A two-story residence with wood siding and 1,800 S.F. of living area has features 30% better than Average, but 70% less than Custom.

   From pages 42 and 64:

Custom 1,800 S.F. Base Cost	**=**	**$130.75 per S.F.**
Average 1,800 S.F. Base Cost	**=**	**$106.95 per S.F.**
DIFFERENCE	**=**	**$23.80 per S.F.**
Cost is $106.95 + .30 ($23.80)	**=**	**$114.09 per S.F. of Living Area.**

4. To add the cost of a crawl space, use the cost of an unfinished basement as a maximum. For specific costs of components to be added or deducted, such as vapor barrier, underdrain, and floor, see the "Assemblies" section, pages 97 to 281.

Model Residence Example

First Floor Plan

Second Floor Plan

A = Main House
B = 1-1/2 Story Wing
C = 1 Story Wing
D = Breezeway
E = Garage
F = Open Covered Porch

RESIDENTIAL
COST ESTIMATE

OWNERS NAME:	**Albert Westenberg**	APPRAISER:	**Nicole Wojtowicz**
RESIDENCE ADDRESS:	**300 Sygiel Road**	PROJECT:	**# 55**
CITY, STATE, ZIP CODE:	**Three Rivers, MA 01080**	DATE:	**Jan. 1, 2014**

CLASS OF CONSTRUCTION	RESIDENCE TYPE	CONFIGURATION	EXTERIOR WALL SYSTEM
☐ ECONOMY	☐ 1 STORY	☑ DETACHED	☑ WOOD SIDING - WOOD FRAME
☑ AVERAGE	☐ 11/2 STORY	☐ TOWN/ROW HOUSE	☐ BRICK VENEER - WOOD FRAME
☐ CUSTOM	☑ 2 STORY	☐ SEMI-DETACHED	☐ STUCCO ON WOOD FRAME
☐ LUXURY	☐ 2 1/2 STORY		☐ PAINTED CONCRETE BLOCK
	☐ 3 STORY	OCCUPANCY	☐ SOLID MASONRY (AVERAGE & CUSTOM)
	☐ BI-LEVEL	☑ ONE FAMILY	☐ STONE VENEER - WOOD FRAME
	☐ TRI-LEVEL	☐ TWO FAMILY	☐ SOLID BRICK (LUXURY)
		☐ THREE FAMILY	☐ SOLID STONE (LUXURY)
		☐ OTHER	

* LIVING AREA (Main Building)

First Level	1288	S.F.
Second level	1288	S.F.
Third Level		S.F.
Total	2576	S.F.

* LIVING AREA (Wing or Ell)   (B)

First Level	360	S.F.
Second level	310	S.F.
Third Level		S.F.
Total	670	S.F.

* LIVING AREA (Wing or Ell)   (C)

First Level	192	S.F.
Second level		S.F.
Third Level		S.F.
Total	192	S.F.

asement Area is not part of living area.

MAIN BUILDING				COSTS PER S.F. LIVING AREA	
Cost per Square Foot of Living Area, from Page	42			$	93.75
Basement Addition:		% Finished,	100	% Unfinished	+	6.00
Roof Cover Adjustment:	Cedar Shake	Type, Page	42	(Add or Deduct)	( )	1.55
Central Air Conditioning:	☐ Separate Ducts	☑ Heating Ducts, Page	42		+	2.86
Heating System Adjustment:		Type, Page		(Add or Deduct)	( )	
Main Building: Adjusted Cost per S.F. of Living Area				$ # 104.16	

MAIN BUILDING TOTAL COST	$ 104.16 /S.F.	x	2,576 S.F.	x		=	$ 268,316
	Cost per S.F. Living Area		Living Area		Town/Row House Multiplier (Use 1 for Detached)		TOTAL COST

WING OR ELL (B)	1 - 1/2	STORY	COSTS PER S.F. LIVING AREA	
Cost per Square Foot of Living Area, from Page	56		$	90.65
Basement Addition:	100 % Finished,	% Unfinished	+	28.25
Roof Cover Adjustment:	Type, Page	(Add or Deduct)	( )	—
Central Air Conditioning: ☐ Separate Ducts	☑ Heating Ducts, Page	42	+	2.86
Heating System Adjustment:	Type, Page	(Add or Deduct)	( )	—
Wing or Ell (B): Adjusted Cost per S.F. of Living Area			$ # 121.76	

WING OR ELL (B) TOTAL COST	$ 121.76 /S.F.	x	670 S.F.	=	$ 81,579
	Cost per S.F. Living Area		Living Area		TOTAL COST

WING OR ELL (C)	1	STORY	COSTS PER S.F. LIVING AREA	
Cost per Square Foot of Living Area, from Page	# 56	(WOOD SIDING)	$	153.15
Basement Addition:	% Finished,	% Unfinished	+	—
Roof Cover Adjustment:	Type, Page	(Add or Deduct)	( )	—
Central Air Conditioning: ☐ Separate Ducts	☐ Heating Ducts, Page		+	—
Heating System Adjustment:	Type, Page	(Add or Deduct)	( )	—
Wing or Ell (C) Adjusted Cost per S.F. of Living Area			$ 153.15	

WING OR ELL (C) TOTAL COST	$ 153.15 /S.F.	x	192 S.F.	=	$ 29,405
	Cost per S.F. Living Area		Living Area		TOTAL COST

	TOTAL THIS PAGE	379,300

RESIDENTIAL
COST ESTIMATE

				QUANTITY		UNIT COST		
Total Page 1							$	379,300
Additional Bathrooms:	2	Full,	1	Half	2 @ 7120	1 @ 4097				+	18,337
Finished Attic:	N/A	Ft. x		Ft.		S.F.			
Breezeway: ☑ Open ☐ closed	12	Ft. x	12	Ft.	144	S.F.	33.89	+	4,880
Covered Porch: ☑ Open ☐ Enclosed	18	Ft. x	12	Ft.	216	S.F.	35.51	+	7,670
Fireplace: ☑ Interior Chimney ☐ Exterior Chimney								
☑ No. of Flues (2) ☑ Additional Fireplaces	1 - 2nd Story						+	11,167
Appliances:							+	—
Kitchen Cabinets Adjustments:			(±)					—
☑ Garage ☐ Carport: 2 Car(s) Description Wood, Attached	(±)						23,160
Miscellaneous:							+	

ADJUSTED TOTAL BUILDING COST	$	444,514

REPLACEMENT COST		
ADJUSTED TOTAL BUILDING COST	$	444,514
Site Improvements		
(A) Paving & Sidewalks	$	
(B) Landscaping	$	
(C) Fences	$	
(D) Swimming Pools	$	
(E) Miscellaneous	$	
TOTAL	$	444,514
Location Factor	x	1.050
Location Replacement Cost	$	466,739
Depreciation	-$	46,674
LOCAL DEPRECIATED COST	$	420,065

INSURANCE COST		
ADJUSTED TOTAL BUILDING COST	$	
Insurance Exclusions		
(A) Footings, sitework, Underground Piping	-$	
(B) Architects Fees	-$	
Total Building Cost Less Exclusion	$	
Location Factor	x	
LOCAL INSURABLE REPLACEMENT COST	$	

SKETCH AND ADDITIONAL CALCULATIONS

Economy Class

1 Story

© Home Planners, Inc.

1-1/2 Story

2 Story

Bi-Level

Tri-Level

©Design Basics, Inc.

- **Mass produced from stock plans**
- **Single family — 1 full bath, 1 kitchen**
- **No basement**
- **Asphalt shingles on roof**
- **Hot air heat**
- **Gypsum wallboard interior finishes**
- **Materials and workmanship are sufficient to meet codes**

Note: The illustration shown may contain some optional components (for example: garages and/or fireplaces) whose costs are shown in the modifications, adjustments, & alternatives below or at the end of the square foot section.

©Home Planners, Inc.

Base cost per square foot of living area

Exterior Wall	Living Area										
	600	800	1000	1200	1400	1600	1800	2000	2400	2800	3200
Wood Siding - Wood Frame	124.80	112.85	103.70	96.45	90.00	85.95	83.90	81.20	75.60	71.60	68.90
Brick Veneer - Wood Frame	131.55	118.85	109.20	101.35	94.50	90.10	87.95	85.00	79.10	74.80	71.90
Stucco on Wood Frame	118.20	106.95	98.30	91.60	85.65	81.80	79.90	77.45	72.20	68.45	66.00
Painted Concrete Block	125.55	113.50	104.30	97.00	90.50	86.40	84.35	81.65	76.00	71.95	69.20
Finished Basement, Add	31.25	29.40	28.15	26.95	26.00	25.45	25.05	24.55	23.85	23.35	22.85
Unfinished Basement, Add	13.75	12.25	11.25	10.30	9.55	9.10	8.80	8.45	7.85	7.45	7.05

Modifications

Add to the total cost

Upgrade Kitchen Cabinets	$ + 920
Solid Surface Countertops	+ 661
Full Bath - including plumbing, wall and floor finishes	+ 5695
Half Bath - including plumbing, wall and floor finishes	+ 3277
One Car Attached Garage	+ 12,308
One Car Detached Garage	+ 15,837
Fireplace & Chimney	+ 5692

Adjustments

For multi family - add to total cost

Additional Kitchen	$ + 4618
Additional Bath	+ 5695
Additional Entry & Exit	+ 1620
Separate Heating	+ 1392
Separate Electric	+ 1115

For Townhouse/Rowhouse - Multiply cost per square foot by

Inner Unit	.95
End Unit	.97

Alternatives

Add to or deduct from the cost per square foot of living area

Composition Roll Roofing	– 1.10
Cedar Shake Roof	+ 3.65
Upgrade Walls and Ceilings to Skim Coat Plaster	+ .68
Upgrade Ceilings to Textured Finish	+ .50
Air Conditioning, in Heating Ductwork	+ 4.57
In Separate Ductwork	+ 6.69
Heating Systems, Hot Water	+ 2.10
Heat Pump	+ 2.45
Electric Heat	– .85
Not Heated	– 3.76

Additional upgrades or components

Kitchen Cabinets & Countertops	Page 93
Bathroom Vanities	94
Fireplaces & Chimneys	94
Windows, Skylights & Dormers	94
Appliances	95
Breezeways & Porches	95
Finished Attic	95
Garages	96
Site Improvements	96
Wings & Ells	34

			Cost Per Square Foot Of Living Area			% of Total
			Mat.	Inst.	Total	(rounded)
1	**Site Work**	Site preparation for slab; 4' deep trench excavation for foundation wall.		1.31	1.31	1.4%
2	**Foundation**	Continuous reinforced concrete footing, 8" deep x 18" wide; dampproofed and insulated 8" thick reinforced concrete block foundation wall, 4' deep; 4" concrete slab on 4" crushed stone base and polyethylene vapor barrier, trowel finish.	5.63	7.41	13.04	14.2%
3	**Framing**	Exterior walls - 2" x 4" wood studs, 16" O.C.; 1/2" insulation board sheathing; wood truss roof frame, 24" O.C. with 1/2" plywood sheathing, 4 in 12 pitch.	4.82	6.33	11.15	12.2%
4	**Exterior Walls**	Metal lath reinforced stucco exterior on insulated wood frame walls; 6" attic insulation; sliding sash wood windows; 2 flush solid core wood exterior doors with storms.	6.97	6.78	13.75	15.0%
5	**Roofing**	20 year asphalt shingles; #15 felt building paper; aluminum gutters, downspouts, drip edge and flashings.	2.09	2.40	4.49	4.9%
6	**Interiors**	Walls and ceilings, 1/2" taped and finished gypsum wallboard, primed and painted with 2 coats; painted baseboard and trim; rubber backed carpeting 80%, asphalt tile 20%; hollow core wood interior doors.	9.90	12.25	22.15	24.2%
7	**Specialties**	Economy grade kitchen cabinets - 6 L.F. wall and base with plastic laminate counter top and kitchen sink; 30 gallon electric water heater.	2.65	.98	3.63	4.0%
8	**Mechanical**	1 lavatory, white, wall hung; 1 water closet, white; 1 bathtub, enameled steel, white; gas fired warm air heat.	4.15	3.56	7.71	8.4%
9	**Electrical**	100 Amp. service; Romex wiring; incandescent lighting fixtures, switches, receptacles.	.91	1.50	2.41	2.6%
10	**Overhead**	Contractor's overhead and profit.	5.58	6.38	11.96	13.1%
	Total		42.70	48.90	**91.60**	

- **Mass produced from stock plans**
- **Single family — 1 full bath, 1 kitchen**
- **No basement**
- **Asphalt shingles on roof**
- **Hot air heat**
- **Gypsum wallboard interior finishes**
- **Materials and workmanship are sufficient to meet codes**

Note: The illustration shown may contain some optional components (for example: garages and/or fireplaces) whose costs are shown in the modifications, adjustments, & alternatives below or at the end of the square foot section.

Base cost per square foot of living area

Exterior Wall	Living Area										
	600	800	1000	1200	1400	1600	1800	2000	2400	2800	3200
Wood Siding - Wood Frame	142.95	118.65	106.00	100.10	95.90	89.25	86.15	82.90	75.95	73.35	70.55
Brick Veneer - Wood Frame	152.40	125.50	112.30	106.05	101.50	94.40	91.00	87.45	80.05	77.25	74.15
Stucco on Wood Frame	133.75	111.95	99.80	94.25	90.35	84.25	81.40	78.35	72.00	69.60	67.05
Painted Concrete Block	144.00	119.40	106.70	100.75	96.55	89.85	86.70	83.35	76.40	73.80	70.95
Finished Basement, Add	23.95	20.35	19.45	18.75	18.30	17.60	17.20	16.85	16.05	15.75	15.35
Unfinished Basement, Add	12.10	9.30	8.55	7.95	7.55	7.00	6.70	6.45	5.85	5.55	5.25

Modifications

Add to the total cost

Upgrade Kitchen Cabinets	$ + 920
Solid Surface Countertops	+ 661
Full Bath - including plumbing, wall and floor finishes	+ 5695
Half Bath - including plumbing, wall and floor finishes	+ 3277
One Car Attached Garage	+ 12,308
One Car Detached Garage	+ 15,837
Fireplace & Chimney	+ 5692

Adjustments

For multi family - add to total cost

Additional Kitchen	$ + 4618
Additional Bath	+ 5695
Additional Entry & Exit	+ 1620
Separate Heating	+ 1392
Separate Electric	+ 1115

For Townhouse/Rowhouse - Multiply cost per square foot by

Inner Unit	.95
End Unit	.97

Alternatives

Add to or deduct from the cost per square foot of living area

Composition Roll Roofing	– .75
Cedar Shake Roof	+ 2.60
Upgrade Walls and Ceilings to Skim Coat Plaster	+ .68
Upgrade Ceilings to Textured Finish	+ .50
Air Conditioning, in Heating Ductwork	+ 3.41
In Separate Ductwork	+ 5.88
Heating Systems, Hot Water	+ 2.00
Heat Pump	+ 2.70
Electric Heat	– .68
Not Heated	– 3.46

Additional upgrades or components

Kitchen Cabinets & Countertops	Page 93
Bathroom Vanities	94
Fireplaces & Chimneys	94
Windows, Skylights & Dormers	94
Appliances	95
Breezeways & Porches	95
Finished Attic	95
Garages	96
Site Improvements	96
Wings & Ells	34

Important: See the Reference Section for Location Factors (to adjust for your city) and Estimating Forms.

Economy 1-1/2 Story

Living Area - 1600 S.F.
Perimeter - 135 L.F.

		Cost Per Square Foot Of Living Area			% of Total
		Mat.	Inst.	Total	(rounded)
1 Site Work	Site preparation for slab; 4' deep trench excavation for foundation wall.		.98	.98	1.1%
2 Foundation	Continuous reinforced concrete footing, 8" deep x 18" wide; dampproofed and insulated 8" thick reinforced concrete block foundation wall, 4' deep; 4" concrete slab on 4" crushed stone base and polyethylene vapor barrier, trowel finish.	3.77	5.03	8.80	9.9%
3 Framing	Exterior walls - 2" x 4" wood studs, 16" O.C.; 1/2" insulation board sheathing; 2" x 6" rafters, 16" O.C. with 1/2" plywood sheathing, 8 in 12 pitch; 2" x 8" floor joists 16" O.C. with bridging and 5/8" plywood subfloor.	5.01	7.11	12.12	13.6%
4 Exterior Walls	Beveled wood siding and building paper on insulated wood frame walls; 6" attic insulation; double hung windows; 2 flush solid core wood exterior doors with storms.	12.22	5.35	17.57	19.7%
5 Roofing	20 year asphalt shingles; #15 felt building paper; aluminum gutters, downspouts, drip edge and flashings.	1.31	1.50	2.81	3.1%
6 Interiors	Walls and ceilings, 1/2" taped and finished gypsum wallboard, primed and painted with 2 coats; painted baseboard and trim; rubber backed carpeting 80%, asphalt tile 20%; hollow core wood interior doors.	10.88	13.00	23.88	26.8%
7 Specialties	Economy grade kitchen cabinets - 6 L.F. wall and base with plastic laminate counter top and kitchen sink; 30 gallon electric water heater.	1.99	.73	2.72	3.0%
8 Mechanical	1 lavatory, white, wall hung; 1 water closet, white; 1 bathtub, enameled steel, white; gas fired warm air heat.	3.37	3.18	6.55	7.3%
9 Electrical	100 Amp. service; Romex wiring; incandescent lighting fixtures, switches, receptacles.	.83	1.35	2.18	2.4%
10 Overhead	Contractor's overhead and profit.	5.92	5.72	11.64	13.0%
Total		45.30	43.95	**89.25**	

- **Mass produced from stock plans**
- **Single family — 1 full bath, 1 kitchen**
- **No basement**
- **Asphalt shingles on roof**
- **Hot air heat**
- **Gypsum wallboard interior finishes**
- **Materials and workmanship are sufficient to meet codes**

Note: The illustration shown may contain some optional components (for example: garages and/or fireplaces) whose costs are shown in the modifications, adjustments, & alternatives below or at the end of the square foot section.

Base cost per square foot of living area

Exterior Wall	Living Area										
	1000	1200	1400	1600	1800	2000	2200	2600	3000	3400	3800
Wood Siding - Wood Frame	112.85	101.90	96.95	93.45	89.95	85.90	83.30	78.40	73.50	71.35	69.35
Brick Veneer - Wood Frame	120.15	108.65	103.25	99.50	95.60	91.40	88.50	83.10	77.85	75.45	73.30
Stucco on Wood Frame	105.65	95.30	90.75	87.55	84.35	80.55	78.25	73.75	69.20	67.30	65.55
Painted Concrete Block	113.65	102.65	97.65	94.10	90.55	86.50	83.85	78.90	73.95	71.75	69.75
Finished Basement, Add	16.35	15.65	15.10	14.75	14.35	14.10	13.80	13.25	12.90	12.65	12.45
Unfinished Basement, Add	7.45	6.90	6.45	6.15	5.80	5.60	5.40	4.95	4.70	4.50	4.30

Modifications

Add to the total cost

Upgrade Kitchen Cabinets	$ + 920
Solid Surface Countertops	+ 661
Full Bath - including plumbing, wall and floor finishes	+ 5695
Half Bath - including plumbing, wall and floor finishes	+ 3277
One Car Attached Garage	+ 12,308
One Car Detached Garage	+ 15,837
Fireplace & Chimney	+ 6290

Adjustments

For multi family - add to total cost

Additional Kitchen	$ + 4618
Additional Bath	+ 5695
Additional Entry & Exit	+ 1620
Separate Heating	+ 1392
Separate Electric	+ 1115

For Townhouse/Rowhouse - Multiply cost per square foot by

Inner Unit	.93
End Unit	.96

Alternatives

Add to or deduct from the cost per square foot of living area

Composition Roll Roofing	– .55
Cedar Shake Roof	+ 1.80
Upgrade Walls and Ceilings to Skim Coat Plaster	+ .69
Upgrade Ceilings to Textured Finish	+ .50
Air Conditioning, in Heating Ductwork	+ 2.77
In Separate Ductwork	+ 5.39
Heating Systems, Hot Water	+ 1.95
Heat Pump	+ 2.87
Electric Heat	– .59
Not Heated	– 3.27

Additional upgrades or components

Kitchen Cabinets & Countertops	Page 93
Bathroom Vanities	94
Fireplaces & Chimneys	94
Windows, Skylights & Dormers	94
Appliances	95
Breezeways & Porches	95
Finished Attic	95
Garages	96
Site Improvements	96
Wings & Ells	34

Important: See the Reference Section for Location Factors (to adjust for your city) and Estimating Forms.

			Cost Per Square Foot Of Living Area			% of Total
			Mat.	Inst.	Total	(rounded)
1	**Site Work**	Site preparation for slab; 4' deep trench excavation for foundation wall.		.79	.79	0.9%
2	**Foundation**	Continuous reinforced concrete footing, 8" deep x 18" wide; dampproofed and insulated 8" thick reinforced concrete block foundation wall, 4' deep; 4" concrete slab on 4" crushed stone base and polyethylene vapor barrier, trowel finish.	3.02	4.02	7.04	8.2%
3	**Framing**	Exterior walls - 2" x 4" wood studs, 16" O.C.; 1/2" insulation board sheathing; wood truss roof frame, 24" O.C. with 1/2" plywood sheathing, 4 in 12 pitch; 2" x 8" floor joists 16" O.C. with bridging and 5/8" plywood subfloor.	5.15	7.48	12.63	14.7%
4	**Exterior Walls**	Beveled wood siding and building paper on insulated wood frame walls; 6" attic insulation; double hung windows; 2 flush solid core wood exterior doors with storms.	12.62	5.44	18.06	21.0%
5	**Roofing**	20 year asphalt shingles; #15 felt building paper; aluminum gutters, downspouts, drip edge and flashings.	1.05	1.20	2.25	2.6%
6	**Interiors**	Walls and ceilings, 1/2" taped and finished gypsum wallboard, primed and painted with 2 coats; painted baseboard and trim; rubber backed carpeting 80%, asphalt tile 20%; hollow core wood interior doors.	10.81	13.01	23.82	27.7%
7	**Specialties**	Economy grade kitchen cabinets - 6 L.F. wall and base with plastic laminate counter top and kitchen sink; 30 gallon electric water heater.	1.59	.59	2.18	2.5%
8	**Mechanical**	1 lavatory, white, wall hung; 1 water closet, white; 1 bathtub, enameled steel, white; gas fired warm air heat.	2.93	2.96	5.89	6.9%
9	**Electrical**	100 Amp. service; Romex wiring; incandescent lighting fixtures; switches, receptacles.	.78	1.26	2.04	2.4%
10	**Overhead**	Contractor's overhead and profit.	5.70	5.50	11.20	13.0%
		Total	43.65	42.25	**85.90**	

- **Mass produced from stock plans**
- **Single family — 1 full bath, 1 kitchen**
- **No basement**
- **Asphalt shingles on roof**
- **Hot air heat**
- **Gypsum wallboard interior finishes**
- **Materials and workmanship are sufficient to meet codes**

Note: The illustration shown may contain some optional components (for example: garages and/or fireplaces) whose costs are shown in the modifications, adjustments, & alternatives below or at the end of the square foot section.

Base cost per square foot of living area

Exterior Wall	Living Area										
	1000	1200	1400	1600	1800	2000	2200	2600	3000	3400	3800
Wood Siding - Wood Frame	104.50	94.20	89.65	86.60	83.40	79.65	77.40	73.00	68.55	66.60	64.80
Brick Veneer - Wood Frame	109.95	99.25	94.40	91.10	87.70	83.75	81.25	76.50	71.75	69.70	67.80
Stucco on Wood Frame	99.15	89.20	85.00	82.15	79.30	75.60	73.55	69.55	65.30	63.55	61.95
Painted Concrete Block	105.10	94.75	90.20	87.10	83.95	80.10	77.75	73.40	68.90	66.95	65.15
Finished Basement, Add	16.35	15.65	15.10	14.75	14.35	14.10	13.80	13.25	12.90	12.65	12.45
Unfinished Basement, Add	7.45	6.90	6.45	6.15	5.80	5.60	5.40	4.95	4.70	4.50	4.30

Modifications

Add to the total cost

Upgrade Kitchen Cabinets	$ + 920
Solid Surface Countertops	+ 661
Full Bath - including plumbing, wall and floor finishes	+ 5695
Half Bath - including plumbing, wall and floor finishes	+ 3277
One Car Attached Garage	+ 12,308
One Car Detached Garage	+ 15,837
Fireplace & Chimney	+ 5692

Adjustments

For multi family - add to total cost

Additional Kitchen	$ + 4618
Additional Bath	+ 5695
Additional Entry & Exit	+ 1620
Separate Heating	+ 1392
Separate Electric	+ 1115

For Townhouse/Rowhouse -
Multiply cost per square foot by

Inner Unit	.94
End Unit	.97

Alternatives

Add to or deduct from the cost per square foot of living area

Composition Roll Roofing	– .55
Cedar Shake Roof	+ 1.80
Upgrade Walls and Ceilings to Skim Coat Plaster	+ .65
Upgrade Ceilings to Textured Finish	+ .50
Air Conditioning, in Heating Ductwork	+ 2.77
In Separate Ductwork	+ 5.39
Heating Systems, Hot Water	+ 1.95
Heat Pump	+ 2.87
Electric Heat	– .59
Not Heated	– 3.27

Additional upgrades or components

Kitchen Cabinets & Countertops	Page 93
Bathroom Vanities	94
Fireplaces & Chimneys	94
Windows, Skylights & Dormers	94
Appliances	95
Breezeways & Porches	95
Finished Attic	95
Garages	96
Site Improvements	96
Wings & Ells	34

Important: See the Reference Section for Location Factors (to adjust for your city) and Estimating Forms.

			Cost Per Square Foot Of Living Area			% of Total
			Mat.	Inst.	Total	(rounded)
1	**Site Work**	Excavation for lower level, 4' deep. Site preparation for slab.		.79	.79	1.0%
2	**Foundation**	Continuous reinforced concrete footing, 8" deep x 18" wide; dampproofed and insulated 8" thick reinforced concrete block foundation wall, 4' deep; 4" concrete slab on 4" crushed stone base and polyethylene vapor barrier, trowel finish.	3.02	4.02	7.04	8.8%
3	**Framing**	Exterior walls - 2" x 4" wood studs, 16" O.C.; 1/2" insulation board sheathing; wood truss roof frame, 24" O.C. with 1/2" plywood sheathing, 4 in 12 pitch; 2" x 8" floor joists 16" O.C. with bridging and 5/8" plywood subfloor.	4.85	7.03	11.88	14.9%
4	**Exterior Walls**	Beveled wood siding and building paper on insulated wood frame walls; 6" attic insulation; double hung windows; 2 flush solid core wood exterior doors with storms.	9.78	4.27	14.05	17.6%
5	**Roofing**	20 year asphalt shingles; #15 felt building paper; aluminum gutters, downspouts, drip edge and flashings.	1.05	1.20	2.25	2.8%
6	**Interiors**	Walls and ceilings, 1/2" taped and finished gypsum wallboard, primed and painted with 2 coats; painted baseboard and trim, rubber backed carpeting 80%, asphalt tile 20%; hollow core wood interior doors.	10.54	12.60	23.14	29.1%
7	**Specialties**	Economy grade kitchen cabinets - 6 L.F. wall and base with plastic laminate counter top and kitchen sink; 30 gallon electric water heater.	1.59	.59	2.18	2.7%
8	**Mechanical**	1 lavatory, white, wall hung; 1 water closet, white; 1 bathtub, enameled steel, white; gas fired warm air heat.	2.93	2.96	5.89	7.4%
9	**Electrical**	100 Amp. service; Romex wiring; incandescent lighting fixtures; switches, receptacles.	.78	1.26	2.04	2.6%
10	**Overhead**	Contractor's overhead and profit.	5.16	5.23	10.39	13.0%
	Total		39.70	39.95	**79.65**	

- **Mass produced from stock plans**
- **Single family — 1 full bath, 1 kitchen**
- **No basement**
- **Asphalt shingles on roof**
- **Hot air heat**
- **Gypsum wallboard interior finishes**
- **Materials and workmanship are sufficient to meet codes**

Note: The illustration shown may contain some optional components (for example: garages and/or fireplaces) whose costs are shown in the modifications, adjustments, & alternatives below or at the end of the square foot section.

©Design Basics, Inc.

Base cost per square foot of living area

Exterior Wall	Living Area										
	1200	1500	1800	2000	2200	2400	2800	3200	3600	4000	4400
Wood Siding - Wood Frame	96.35	88.30	82.40	80.05	76.50	73.70	71.50	68.55	65.00	63.80	61.05
Brick Veneer - Wood Frame	101.40	92.85	86.55	83.95	80.20	77.25	74.90	71.65	67.90	66.65	63.70
Stucco on Wood Frame	91.40	83.80	78.35	76.20	72.80	70.25	68.20	65.50	62.20	61.05	58.50
Solid Masonry	96.90	88.75	82.85	80.45	76.90	74.10	71.85	68.90	65.35	64.10	61.35
Finished Basement, Add*	19.65	18.70	17.95	17.65	17.30	16.95	16.65	16.25	15.90	15.75	15.45
Unfinished Basement, Add*	8.20	7.45	6.90	6.60	6.35	6.05	5.85	5.55	5.25	5.10	4.90

*Basement under middle level only.

Modifications

Add to the total cost

Upgrade Kitchen Cabinets	$ + 920
Solid Surface Countertops	+ 661
Full Bath - including plumbing, wall and floor finishes	+ 5695
Half Bath - including plumbing, wall and floor finishes	+ 3277
One Car Attached Garage	+ 12,308
One Car Detached Garage	+ 15,837
Fireplace & Chimney	+ 5692

Adjustments

For multi family - add to total cost

Additional Kitchen	$ + 4618
Additional Bath	+ 5695
Additional Entry & Exit	+ 1620
Separate Heating	+ 1392
Separate Electric	+ 1115

For Townhouse/Rowhouse - Multiply cost per square foot by

Inner Unit	.93
End Unit	.96

Alternatives

Add to or deduct from the cost per square foot of living area

Composition Roll Roofing	– .75
Cedar Shake Roof	+ 2.60
Upgrade Walls and Ceilings to Skim Coat Plaster	+ .59
Upgrade Ceilings to Textured Finish	+ .50
Air Conditioning, in Heating Ductwork	+ 2.37
In Separate Ductwork	+ 5.01
Heating Systems, Hot Water	+ 1.87
Heat Pump	+ 2.97
Electric Heat	– .51
Not Heated	– 3.17

Additional upgrades or components

Kitchen Cabinets & Countertops	Page 93
Bathroom Vanities	94
Fireplaces & Chimneys	94
Windows, Skylights & Dormers	94
Appliances	95
Breezeways & Porches	95
Finished Attic	95
Garages	96
Site Improvements	96
Wings & Ells	34

Important: See the Reference Section for Location Factors (to adjust for your city) and Estimating Forms.

Economy Tri-Level

Living Area - 2400 S.F.
Perimeter - 163 L.F.

		Cost Per Square Foot Of Living Area			% of Total
		Mat.	Inst.	Total	(rounded)
1 **Site Work**	Site preparation for slab; 4' deep trench excavation for foundation wall, excavation for lower level, 4' deep.		.66	.66	0.9%
2 **Foundation**	Continuous reinforced concrete footing, 8" deep x 18" wide; dampproofed and insulated 8" thick reinforced concrete block foundation wall, 4' deep; 4" concrete slab on 4" crushed stone base and polyethylene vapor barrier, trowel finish.	3.39	4.37	7.76	10.5%
3 **Framing**	Exterior walls - 2" x 4" wood studs, 16" O.C.; 1/2" insulation board sheathing; wood truss roof frame, 24" O.C. with 1/2" plywood sheathing, 4 in 12 pitch; 2" x 8" floor joists 16" O.C. with bridging and 5/8" plywood subfloor.	4.55	6.31	10.86	14.7%
4 **Exterior Walls**	Beveled wood siding and building paper on insulated wood frame walls; 6" attic insulation; double hung windows; 2 flush solid core wood exterior doors with storms.	8.45	3.74	12.19	16.5%
5 **Roofing**	20 year asphalt shingles; #15 felt building paper; aluminum gutters, downspouts, drip edge and flashings.	1.39	1.60	2.99	4.1%
6 **Interiors**	Walls and ceilings, 1/2" taped and finished gypsum wallboard, primed and painted with 2 coats; painted baseboard and trim, rubber backed carpeting 80%, asphalt tile 20%; hollow core wood interior doors.	9.29	11.18	20.47	27.8%
7 **Specialties**	Economy grade kitchen cabinets - 6 L.F. wall and base with plastic laminate counter top and kitchen sink; 30 gallon electric water heater.	1.32	.50	1.82	2.5%
8 **Mechanical**	1 lavatory, white, wall hung; 1 water closet, white; 1 bathtub, enameled steel, white; gas fired warm air heat.	2.61	2.80	5.41	7.3%
9 **Electrical**	100 Amp. service; Romex wiring; incandescent lighting fixtures, switches, receptacles.	.74	1.20	1.94	2.6%
10 **Overhead**	Contractor's overhead and profit.	4.76	4.84	9.60	13.0%
	Total	36.50	37.20	**73.70**	

1 Story — Base cost per square foot of living area

Exterior Wall	Living Area							
	50	100	200	300	400	500	600	700
Wood Siding - Wood Frame	174.10	132.30	114.25	94.70	88.75	85.20	82.75	83.40
Brick Veneer - Wood Frame	191.10	144.50	124.40	101.40	94.80	90.85	88.20	88.60
Stucco on Wood Frame	157.35	120.40	104.30	88.00	82.75	79.60	77.50	78.30
Painted Concrete Block	175.90	133.65	115.35	95.40	89.40	85.80	83.40	84.00
Finished Basement, Add	47.45	38.75	35.20	29.20	27.95	27.25	26.80	26.40
Unfinished Basement, Add	26.15	19.40	16.60	11.90	11.00	10.45	10.10	9.85

1-1/2 Story — Base cost per square foot of living area

Exterior Wall	Living Area							
	100	200	300	400	500	600	700	800
Wood Siding - Wood Frame	137.50	110.45	93.80	83.65	78.65	76.20	73.10	72.20
Brick Veneer - Wood Frame	152.75	122.55	103.95	91.55	85.95	83.10	79.60	78.70
Stucco on Wood Frame	122.60	98.50	83.85	75.90	71.45	69.45	66.70	65.90
Painted Concrete Block	139.20	111.75	94.90	84.50	79.45	76.95	73.85	72.95
Finished Basement, Add	31.75	28.15	25.75	23.10	22.40	21.90	21.45	21.40
Unfinished Basement, Add	16.10	13.30	11.40	9.35	8.80	8.45	8.05	8.05

2 Story — Base cost per square foot of living area

Exterior Wall	Living Area							
	100	200	400	600	800	1000	1200	1400
Wood Siding - Wood Frame	140.70	104.30	88.50	72.60	67.45	64.35	62.25	63.10
Brick Veneer - Wood Frame	157.70	116.50	98.65	79.35	73.55	70.00	67.65	68.30
Stucco on Wood Frame	124.00	92.40	78.55	66.00	61.50	58.75	56.95	57.95
Painted Concrete Block	142.55	105.65	89.55	73.35	68.10	64.95	62.85	63.65
Finished Basement, Add	23.75	19.45	17.65	14.65	14.05	13.65	13.40	13.25
Unfinished Basement, Add	13.10	9.70	8.35	5.95	5.55	5.25	5.05	4.90

Base costs do not include bathroom or kitchen facilities. Use Modifications/Adjustments/Alternatives on pages 93–96 where appropriate.

1 Story

1-1/2 Story

2 Story

2-1/2 Story

Bi-Level

Tri-Level

- **Simple design from standard plans**
- **Single family — 1 full bath, 1 kitchen**
- **No basement**
- **Asphalt shingles on roof**
- **Hot air heat**
- **Gypsum wallboard interior finishes**
- **Materials and workmanship are average**

Note: The illustration shown may contain some optional components (for example: garages and/or fireplaces) whose costs are shown in the modifications, adjustments, & alternatives below or at the end of the square foot section.

eHome Planners, Inc.

Base cost per square foot of living area

Exterior Wall	Living Area										
	600	800	1000	1200	1400	1600	1800	2000	2400	2800	3200
Wood Siding - Wood Frame	151.30	136.60	125.70	117.05	109.70	104.95	102.30	99.25	92.80	88.25	85.15
Brick Veneer - Wood Frame	170.30	154.80	143.30	134.10	126.25	121.25	118.50	115.15	108.35	103.50	100.15
Stucco on Wood Frame	159.85	145.50	134.90	126.50	119.35	114.75	112.20	109.25	103.05	98.55	95.60
Solid Masonry	185.80	168.70	155.90	145.40	136.60	130.90	127.80	123.90	116.40	110.90	107.00
Finished Basement, Add	37.90	36.65	34.95	33.40	32.15	31.30	30.80	30.15	29.25	28.55	27.85
Unfinished Basement, Add	15.60	14.15	13.10	12.10	11.30	10.85	10.55	10.15	9.55	9.15	8.75

Modifications

Add to the total cost

Upgrade Kitchen Cabinets	$ + 4320
Solid Surface Countertops (Included)	
Full Bath - including plumbing, wall and floor finishes	+ 7120
Half Bath - including plumbing, wall and floor finishes	+ 4097
One Car Attached Garage	+ 13,653
One Car Detached Garage	+ 17,986
Fireplace & Chimney	+ 6030

Adjustments

For multi family - add to total cost

Additional Kitchen	$ + 8159
Additional Bath	+ 7120
Additional Entry & Exit	+ 1620
Separate Heating	+ 1392
Separate Electric	+ 1986

For Townhouse/Rowhouse - Multiply cost per square foot by

Inner Unit	.92
End Unit	.96

Alternatives

Add to or deduct from the cost per square foot of living area

Cedar Shake Roof	+ 3.10
Clay Tile Roof	+ 7.55
Slate Roof	+ 6.60
Upgrade Walls to Skim Coat Plaster	+ .42
Upgrade Ceilings to Textured Finish	+ .50
Air Conditioning, in Heating Ductwork	+ 4.73
In Separate Ductwork	+ 6.95
Heating Systems, Hot Water	+ 2.14
Heat Pump	+ 2.55
Electric Heat	– .47
Not Heated	– 3.14

Additional upgrades or components

Kitchen Cabinets & Countertops	Page 93
Bathroom Vanities	94
Fireplaces & Chimneys	94
Windows, Skylights & Dormers	94
Appliances	95
Breezeways & Porches	95
Finished Attic	95
Garages	96
Site Improvements	96
Wings & Ells	56

			Cost Per Square Foot Of Living Area			% of Total
			Mat.	Inst.	Total	(rounded)
1	**Site Work**	Site preparation for slab; 4' deep trench excavation for foundation wall.		1.01	1.01	1.0%
2	**Foundation**	Continuous reinforced concrete footing 8" deep x 18" wide; dampproofed and insulated reinforced concrete foundation wall, 8" thick, 4' deep; 4" concrete slab on 4" crushed stone base and polyethylene vapor barrier, trowel finish.	5.22	6.75	11.97	11.4%
3	**Framing**	Exterior walls - 2" x 4" wood studs, 16" O.C.; 1/2" plywood sheathing; 2" x 6" rafters 16" O.C. with 1/2" plywood sheathing, 4 in 12 pitch; 2" x 6" ceiling joists 16" O.C.; 1/2" plywood subfloor on 1" x 2" wood sleepers 16" O.C.	6.25	9.47	15.72	15.0%
4	**Exterior Walls**	Beveled wood siding and building paper on insulated wood frame walls; 6" attic insulation; double hung windows; 3 flush solid core wood exterior doors with storms.	11.24	5.00	16.24	15.5%
5	**Roofing**	25 year asphalt shingles; #15 felt building paper; aluminum gutters, downspouts, drip edge and flashings.	2.15	2.47	4.62	4.4%
6	**Interiors**	Walls and ceilings, 1/2" taped and finished gypsum wallboard, primed and painted with 2 coats; painted baseboard and trim, finished hardwood floor 40%, carpet with 1/2" underlayment 40%, vinyl tile with 1/2" underlayment 15%, ceramic tile with 1/2" underlayment 5%; hollow core and louvered doors.	12.43	13.10	25.53	24.3%
7	**Specialties**	Average grade kitchen cabinets - 14 L.F. wall and base with solid surface counter top and kitchen sink; 40 gallon electric water heater.	3.43	1.16	4.59	4.4%
8	**Mechanical**	1 lavatory, white, wall hung; 1 water closet, white; 1 bathtub with shower, enameled steel, white; gas fired warm air heat.	3.67	3.25	6.92	6.6%
9	**Electrical**	200 Amp. service; Romex wiring; incandescent lighting fixtures, switches, receptacles.	1.25	1.83	3.08	2.9%
10	**Overhead**	Contractor's overhead and profit and plans.	7.76	7.51	15.27	14.5%
	Total		53.40	51.55	**104.95**	

- **Simple design from standard plans**
- **Single family — 1 full bath, 1 kitchen**
- **No basement**
- **Asphalt shingles on roof**
- **Hot air heat**
- **Gypsum wallboard interior finishes**
- **Materials and workmanship are average**

Note: The illustration shown may contain some optional components (for example: garages and/or fireplaces) whose costs are shown in the modifications, adjustments, & alternatives below or at the end of the square foot section.

©By Designer

Base cost per square foot of living area

Exterior Wall	Living Area										
	600	800	1000	1200	1400	1600	1800	2000	2400	2800	3200
Wood Siding - Wood Frame	169.45	141.55	126.60	119.60	114.60	107.05	103.45	99.60	91.80	88.75	85.50
Brick Veneer - Wood Frame	179.20	148.65	133.15	125.75	120.45	112.35	108.45	104.35	96.05	92.75	89.15
Stucco on Wood Frame	164.70	138.10	123.45	116.60	111.75	104.45	100.95	97.25	89.70	86.75	83.65
Solid Masonry	200.85	164.35	147.70	139.40	133.45	124.15	119.60	114.95	105.40	101.65	97.40
Finished Basement, Add	30.90	26.95	25.75	24.90	24.25	23.35	22.75	22.30	21.35	20.85	20.35
Unfinished Basement, Add	13.50	10.60	9.80	9.25	8.85	8.25	7.95	7.65	7.05	6.75	6.50

Modifications

Add to the total cost

Upgrade Kitchen Cabinets	$ + 4320
Solid Surface Countertops (Included)	
Full Bath - including plumbing, wall and floor finishes	+ 7120
Half Bath - including plumbing, wall and floor finishes	+ 4097
One Car Attached Garage	+ 13,653
One Car Detached Garage	+ 17,986
Fireplace & Chimney	+ 6030

Adjustments

For multi family - add to total cost

Additional Kitchen	$ + 8159
Additional Bath	+ 7120
Additional Entry & Exit	+ 1620
Separate Heating	+ 1392
Separate Electric	+ 1986

For Townhouse/Rowhouse - Multiply cost per square foot by

Inner Unit	.92
End Unit	.96

Alternatives

Add to or deduct from the cost per square foot of living area

Cedar Shake Roof	+ 2.25
Clay Tile Roof	+ 5.45
Slate Roof	+ 4.80
Upgrade Walls to Skim Coat Plaster	+ .48
Upgrade Ceilings to Textured Finish	+ .50
Air Conditioning, in Heating Ductwork	+ 3.59
In Separate Ductwork	+ 6.08
Heating Systems, Hot Water	+ 2.04
Heat Pump	+ 2.82
Electric Heat	– .43
Not Heated	– 3.02

Additional upgrades or components

Kitchen Cabinets & Countertops	Page 93
Bathroom Vanities	94
Fireplaces & Chimneys	94
Windows, Skylights & Dormers	94
Appliances	95
Breezeways & Porches	95
Finished Attic	95
Garages	96
Site Improvements	96
Wings & Ells	56

Living Area - 1800 S.F.
Perimeter - 144 L.F.

		Cost Per Square Foot Of Living Area			% of Total
		Mat.	Inst.	Total	(rounded)
1 Site Work	Site preparation for slab; 4' deep trench excavation for foundation wall.		.90	.90	0.9%
2 Foundation	Continuous reinforced concrete footing 8" deep x 18" wide; dampproofed and insulated reinforced concrete foundation wall, 8" thick, 4' deep; 4" concrete slab on 4" crushed stone base and polyethylene vapor barrier, trowel finish.	3.72	4.97	8.69	8.4%
3 Framing	Exterior walls - 2" x 4" wood studs, 16" O.C.; 1/2" plywood sheathing; 2" x 6" rafters 16" O.C. with 1/2" plywood sheathing, 8 in 12 pitch; 2" x 8" floor joists 16" O.C. with 5/8" plywood subfloor; 1/2" plywood subfloor on 1" x 2" wood sleepers 16" O.C.	6.71	8.82	15.53	15.0%
4 Exterior Walls	Beveled wood siding and building paper on insulated wood frame walls; 6" attic insulation; double hung windows; 3 flush solid core wood exterior doors with storms.	12.44	5.37	17.81	17.2%
5 Roofing	25 year asphalt shingles; #15 felt building paper; aluminum gutters, downspouts, drip edge and flashings.	1.35	1.54	2.89	2.8%
6 Interiors	Walls and ceilings, 1/2" taped and finished gypsum wallboard, primed and painted with 2 coats; painted baseboard and trim, finished hardwood floor 40%, carpet with 1/2" underlayment 40%, vinyl tile with 1/2" underlayment 15%, ceramic tile with 1/2" underlayment 5%; hollow core and louvered doors.	14.35	14.69	29.04	28.1%
7 Specialties	Average grade kitchen cabinets - 14 L.F. wall and base with solid surface counter top and kitchen sink; 40 gallon electric water heater.	3.04	1.03	4.07	3.9%
8 Mechanical	1 lavatory, white, wall hung; 1 water closet, white; 1 bathtub with shower, enameled steel, white; gas fired warm air heat.	3.39	3.13	6.52	6.3%
9 Electrical	200 Amp. service; Romex wiring; incandescent lighting fixtures, switches, receptacles.	1.19	1.76	2.95	2.9%
10 Overhead	Contractor's overhead and profit and plans.	7.86	7.19	15.05	14.5%
Total		54.05	49.40	**103.45**	

- **Simple design from standard plans**
- **Single family — 1 full bath, 1 kitchen**
- **No basement**
- **Asphalt shingles on roof**
- **Hot air heat**
- **Gypsum wallboard interior finishes**
- **Materials and workmanship are average**

Note: The illustration shown may contain some optional components (for example: garages and/or fireplaces) whose costs are shown in the modifications, adjustments, & alternatives below or at the end of the square foot section.

Base cost per square foot of living area

Exterior Wall	Living Area										
	1000	1200	1400	1600	1800	2000	2200	2600	3000	3400	3800
Wood Siding - Wood Frame	133.80	121.10	115.25	111.15	106.95	102.40	99.45	93.75	88.30	85.85	83.50
Brick Veneer - Wood Frame	141.30	128.15	121.75	117.35	112.80	108.10	104.85	98.65	92.75	90.10	87.55
Stucco on Wood Frame	130.10	117.70	112.00	108.05	104.05	99.70	96.85	91.35	86.05	83.70	81.50
Solid Masonry	158.05	143.65	136.20	131.20	125.80	120.65	116.75	109.45	102.75	99.60	96.60
Finished Basement, Add	21.80	21.50	20.80	20.35	19.75	19.45	19.00	18.35	17.85	17.50	17.25
Unfinished Basement, Add	8.55	8.00	7.50	7.20	6.90	6.70	6.45	6.00	5.70	5.50	5.35

Modifications

Add to the total cost

Upgrade Kitchen Cabinets	$ + 4320
Solid Surface Countertops (Included)	
Full Bath - including plumbing, wall and floor finishes	+ 7120
Half Bath - including plumbing, wall and floor finishes	+ 4097
One Car Attached Garage	+ 13,653
One Car Detached Garage	+ 17,986
Fireplace & Chimney	+ 6660

Adjustments

For multi family - add to total cost

Additional Kitchen	$ + 8159
Additional Bath	+ 7120
Additional Entry & Exit	+ 1620
Separate Heating	+ 1392
Separate Electric	+ 1986

For Townhouse/Rowhouse - Multiply cost per square foot by

Inner Unit	.90
End Unit	.95

Alternatives

Add to or deduct from the cost per square foot of living area

Cedar Shake Roof	+ 1.55
Clay Tile Roof	+ 3.80
Slate Roof	+ 3.30
Upgrade Walls to Skim Coat Plaster	+ .50
Upgrade Ceilings to Textured Finish	+ .50
Air Conditioning, in Heating Ductwork	+ 2.86
In Separate Ductwork	+ 5.52
Heating Systems, Hot Water	+ 2.00
Heat Pump	+ 2.97
Electric Heat	– .37
Not Heated	– 2.93

Additional upgrades or components

Kitchen Cabinets & Countertops	Page 93
Bathroom Vanities	94
Fireplaces & Chimneys	94
Windows, Skylights & Dormers	94
Appliances	95
Breezeways & Porches	95
Finished Attic	95
Garages	96
Site Improvements	96
Wings & Ells	56

Important: See the Reference Section for Location Factors (to adjust for your city) and Estimating Forms.

		Cost Per Square Foot Of Living Area			% of Total
		Mat.	Inst.	Total	(rounded)
1 Site Work	Site preparation for slab; 4' deep trench excavation for foundation wall.		.81	.81	0.8%
2 Foundation	Continuous reinforced concrete footing 8" deep x 18" wide; dampproofed and insulated reinforced concrete foundation wall, 8" thick, 4' deep, 4" concrete slab on 4" crushed stone base and polyethylene vapor barrier, trowel finish.	3.11	4.13	7.24	7.1%
3 Framing	Exterior walls - 2" x 4" wood studs, 16" O.C.; 1/2" plywood sheathing; 2" x 6" rafters 16" O.C. with 1/2" plywood sheathing, 4 in 12 pitch; 2" x 6" ceiling joists 16" O.C.; 2" x 8" floor joists 16" O.C. with 5/8" plywood subfloor; 1/2" plywood subfloor on 1" x 2" wood sleepers 16" O.C.	7.06	9.12	16.18	15.8%
4 Exterior Walls	Beveled wood siding and building paper on insulated wood frame walls; 6" attic insulation; double hung windows; 3 flush solid core wood exterior doors with storms.	13.63	5.80	19.43	19.0%
5 Roofing	25 year asphalt shingles; #15 felt building paper; aluminum gutters, downspouts, drip edge and flashings.	1.08	1.23	2.31	2.3%
6 Interiors	Walls and ceilings, 1/2" taped and finished gypsum wallboard, primed and painted with 2 coats; painted baseboard and trim, finished hardwood floor 40%, carpet with 1/2" underlayment 40%, vinyl tile with 1/2" underlayment 15%, ceramic tile with 1/2" underlayment 5%; hollow core and louvered doors.	14.19	14.69	28.88	28.2%
7 Specialties	Average grade kitchen cabinets - 14 L.F. wall and base with solid surface counter top and kitchen sink; 40 gallon electric water heater.	2.74	.93	3.67	3.6%
8 Mechanical	1 lavatory, white, wall hung; 1 water closet, white; 1 bathtub with shower; enameled steel, white; gas fired warm air heat.	3.17	3.03	6.20	6.1%
9 Electrical	200 Amp. service; Romex wiring; incandescent lighting fixtures, switches, receptacles.	1.15	1.69	2.84	2.8%
10 Overhead	Contractor's overhead and profit and plans.	7.82	7.02	14.84	14.5%
Total		53.95	48.45	**102.40**	

- Simple design from standard plans
- Single family — 1 full bath, 1 kitchen
- No basement
- Asphalt shingles on roof
- Hot air heat
- Gypsum wallboard interior finishes
- Materials and workmanship are average

Note: The illustration shown may contain some optional components (for example: garages and/or fireplaces) whose costs are shown in the modifications, adjustments, & alternatives below or at the end of the square foot section.

Base cost per square foot of living area

Exterior Wall	Living Area										
	1200	1400	1600	1800	2000	2400	2800	3200	3600	4000	4400
Wood Siding - Wood Frame	132.65	124.60	113.60	111.60	107.60	101.20	96.10	91.00	88.35	83.70	82.20
Brick Veneer - Wood Frame	140.65	131.80	120.25	118.30	113.85	106.85	101.50	95.90	93.05	88.00	86.40
Stucco on Wood Frame	128.65	121.00	110.30	108.30	104.50	98.40	93.45	88.60	86.10	81.55	80.15
Solid Masonry	158.55	148.00	135.10	133.15	127.80	119.45	113.55	106.85	103.40	97.60	95.75
Finished Basement, Add	18.35	18.00	17.30	17.25	16.80	16.10	15.80	15.30	14.95	14.60	14.45
Unfinished Basement, Add	7.15	6.55	6.15	6.05	5.80	5.40	5.20	4.85	4.65	4.45	4.35

Modifications

Add to the total cost

Upgrade Kitchen Cabinets	$ + 4320
Solid Surface Countertops (Included)	
Full Bath - including plumbing, wall and floor finishes	+ 7120
Half Bath - including plumbing, wall and floor finishes	+ 4097
One Car Attached Garage	+ 13,653
One Car Detached Garage	+ 17,986
Fireplace & Chimney	+ 7307

Adjustments

For multi family - add to total cost

Additional Kitchen	$ + 8159
Additional Bath	+ 7120
Additional Entry & Exit	+ 1620
Separate Heating	+ 1392
Separate Electric	+ 1986

For Townhouse/Rowhouse - Multiply cost per square foot by

Inner Unit	.90
End Unit	.95

Alternatives

Add to or deduct from the cost per square foot of living area

Cedar Shake Roof	+ 1.35
Clay Tile Roof	+ 3.25
Slate Roof	+ 2.85
Upgrade Walls to Skim Coat Plaster	+ .48
Upgrade Ceilings to Textured Finish	+ .50
Air Conditioning, in Heating Ductwork	+ 2.60
In Separate Ductwork	+ 5.33
Heating Systems, Hot Water	+ 1.80
Heat Pump	+ 3.06
Electric Heat	− .66
Not Heated	− 3.42

Additional upgrades or components

Kitchen Cabinets & Countertops	Page 93
Bathroom Vanities	94
Fireplaces & Chimneys	94
Windows, Skylights & Dormers	94
Appliances	95
Breezeways & Porches	95
Finished Attic	95
Garages	96
Site Improvements	96
Wings & Ells	56

Important: See the Reference Section for Location Factors (to adjust for your city) and Estimating Forms.

		Cost Per Square Foot Of Living Area			% of Total
		Mat.	Inst.	Total	(rounded)
1 Site Work	Site preparation for slab; 4' deep trench excavation for foundation wall.		.50	.50	0.5%
2 Foundation	Continuous reinforced concrete footing 8" deep x 18" wide, dampproofed and insulated reinforced concrete foundation wall, 8" thick, 4' deep; 4" concrete slab on 4" crushed stone base and polyethylene vapor barrier, trowel finish.	2.23	2.93	5.16	5.7%
3 Framing	Exterior walls - 2" x 4" wood studs, 16" O.C.; 1/2" plywood sheathing; 2" x 6" rafters 16" O.C. with 1/2" plywood sheathing, 4 in 12 pitch; 2" x 6" ceiling joists 16" O.C.; 2" x 8" floor joists 16" O.C. with 5/8" plywood subfloor; 1/2" plywood subfloor on 1" x 2" wood sleepers 16" O.C.	7.08	8.93	16.01	17.6%
4 Exterior Walls	Beveled wood siding and building paper on insulated wood frame walls; 6" attic insulation; double hung windows; 3 flush solid core wood exterior doors with storms.	11.55	4.87	16.42	18.0%
5 Roofing	25 year asphalt shingles; #15 felt building paper; aluminum gutters, downspouts, drip edge and flashings.	.82	.95	1.77	1.9%
6 Interiors	Walls and ceilings, 1/2" taped and finished gypsum wallboard, primed and painted with 2 coats; painted baseboard and trim, finished hardwood floor 40%, carpet with 1/2" underlayment 40%, vinyl tile with 1/2" underlayment 15%, ceramic tile with 1/2" underlayment 5%; hollow core and louvered doors.	13.88	14.19	28.07	30.8%
7 Specialties	Average grade kitchen cabinets - 14 L.F. wall and base with solid surface counter top and kitchen sink; 40 gallon electric water heater.	1.72	.58	2.30	2.5%
8 Mechanical	1 lavatory, white, wall hung; 1 water closet, white; 1 bathtub with shower, enameled steel, white; gas fired warm air heat.	2.41	2.68	5.09	5.6%
9 Electrical	200 Amp. service; Romex wiring; incandescent lighting fixtures, switches, receptacles.	.99	1.47	2.46	2.7%
10 Overhead	Contractor's overhead and profit and plans.	6.92	6.30	13.22	14.5%
Total		47.60	43.40	**91.00**	

- **Simple design from standard plans**
- **Single family — 1 full bath, 1 kitchen**
- **No basement**
- **Asphalt shingles on roof**
- **Hot air heat**
- **Gypsum wallboard interior finishes**
- **Materials and workmanship are average**

Note: The illustration shown may contain some optional components (for example: garages and/or fireplaces) whose costs are shown in the modifications, adjustments, & alternatives below or at the end of the square foot section.

Base cost per square foot of living area

Exterior Wall	Living Area										
	1500	1800	2100	2500	3000	3500	4000	4500	5000	5500	6000
Wood Siding - Wood Frame	123.05	111.65	106.65	102.70	95.30	92.05	87.50	82.60	81.10	79.20	77.45
Brick Veneer - Wood Frame	130.65	118.65	113.15	108.95	100.95	97.40	92.30	87.10	85.50	83.40	81.40
Stucco on Wood Frame	119.40	108.25	103.40	99.65	92.50	89.40	85.05	80.40	78.95	77.20	75.50
Solid Masonry	147.40	134.20	127.65	122.80	113.55	109.30	103.15	97.10	95.15	92.75	90.15
Finished Basement, Add	15.75	15.60	15.15	14.80	14.30	13.95	13.55	13.20	13.05	12.90	12.65
Unfinished Basement, Add	5.80	5.40	5.10	4.90	4.55	4.40	4.15	3.95	3.80	3.70	3.60

Modifications

Add to the total cost

Upgrade Kitchen Cabinets	$ + 4320
Solid Surface Countertops (Included)	
Full Bath - including plumbing, wall and floor finishes	+ 7120
Half Bath - including plumbing, wall and floor finishes	+ 4097
One Car Attached Garage	+ 13,653
One Car Detached Garage	+ 17,986
Fireplace & Chimney	+ 7307

Adjustments

For multi family - add to total cost

Additional Kitchen	$ + 8159
Additional Bath	+ 7120
Additional Entry & Exit	+ 1620
Separate Heating	+ 1392
Separate Electric	+ 1986

For Townhouse/Rowhouse - Multiply cost per square foot by

Inner Unit	.88
End Unit	.94

Alternatives

Add to or deduct from the cost per square foot of living area

Cedar Shake Roof	+ 1.05
Clay Tile Roof	+ 2.50
Slate Roof	+ 2.20
Upgrade Walls to Skim Coat Plaster	+ .50
Upgrade Ceilings to Textured Finish	+ .50
Air Conditioning, in Heating Ductwork	+ 2.60
In Separate Ductwork	+ 5.33
Heating Systems, Hot Water	+ 1.80
Heat Pump	+ 3.06
Electric Heat	- .51
Not Heated	- 3.18

Additional upgrades or components

Kitchen Cabinets & Countertops	Page 93
Bathroom Vanities	94
Fireplaces & Chimneys	94
Windows, Skylights & Dormers	94
Appliances	95
Breezeways & Porches	95
Finished Attic	95
Garages	96
Site Improvements	96
Wings & Ells	56

Living Area - 3000 S.F.
Perimeter - 135 L.F.

		Cost Per Square Foot Of Living Area			% of Total
		Mat.	Inst.	Total	(rounded)
1 Site Work	Site preparation for slab; 4' deep trench excavation for foundation wall.		.54	.54	0.6%
2 Foundation	Continuous reinforced concrete footing 8" deep x 18" wide, dampproofed and insulated reinforced concrete foundation wall, 8" thick, 4' deep; 4" concrete slab on 4" crushed stone base and polyethylene vapor barrier, trowel finish.	2.07	2.77	4.84	5.1%
3 Framing	Exterior walls - 2" x 4" wood studs, 16" O.C.; 1/2" plywood sheathing; 2" x 6" rafters 16" O.C. with 1/2" plywood sheathing, 4 in 12 pitch; 2" x 6" ceiling joists 16" O.C.; 2" x 8" floor joists 16" O.C. with 5/8" plywood subfloor; 1/2" plywood subfloor on 1" x 2" wood sleepers 16" O.C.	7.34	9.20	16.54	17.4%
4 Exterior Walls	Horizontal beveled wood siding; building paper; 3-1/2" batt insulation; wood double hung windows; 3 flush solid core wood exterior doors; storms and screens.	13.20	5.54	18.74	19.7%
5 Roofing	25 year asphalt shingles; #15 felt building paper; aluminum gutters, downspouts, drip edge and flashings.	.72	.82	1.54	1.6%
6 Interiors	Walls and ceilings, 1/2" taped and finished gypsum wallboard, primed and painted with 2 coats; painted baseboard and trim, finished hardwood floor 40%, carpet with 1/2" underlayment 40%, vinyl tile with 1/2" underlayment 15%, ceramic tile with 1/2" underlayment 5%; hollow core and louvered doors.	14.38	14.71	29.09	30.5%
7 Specialties	Average grade kitchen cabinets - 14 L.F. wall and base with solid surface counter top and kitchen sink; 40 gallon electric water heater.	1.82	.61	2.43	2.5%
8 Mechanical	1 lavatory, white, wall hung; 1 water closet, white; 1 bathtub with shower, enameled steel, white; gas fired warm air heat.	2.49	2.72	5.21	5.5%
9 Electrical	200 Amp. service; Romex wiring; incandescent lighting fixtures, switches, receptacles.	1.00	1.50	2.50	2.6%
10 Overhead	Contractor's overhead and profit and plans.	7.33	6.54	13.87	14.6%
	Total	50.35	44.95	**95.30**	

- **Simple design from standard plans**
- **Single family — 1 full bath, 1 kitchen**
- **No basement**
- **Asphalt shingles on roof**
- **Hot air heat**
- **Gypsum wallboard interior finishes**
- **Materials and workmanship are average**

Note: The illustration shown may contain some optional components (for example: garages and/or fireplaces) whose costs are shown in the modifications, adjustments, & alternatives below or at the end of the square foot section.

Base cost per square foot of living area

Exterior Wall	Living Area										
	1000	1200	1400	1600	1800	2000	2200	2600	3000	3400	3800
Wood Siding - Wood Frame	124.75	112.70	107.40	103.60	99.90	95.60	93.00	87.90	82.85	80.70	78.65
Brick Veneer - Wood Frame	130.40	118.00	112.25	108.30	104.30	99.85	97.00	91.60	86.30	83.90	81.70
Stucco on Wood Frame	121.95	110.15	104.95	101.30	97.75	93.55	91.00	86.10	81.25	79.10	77.15
Solid Masonry	143.00	129.60	123.20	118.70	114.10	109.30	105.95	99.70	93.80	91.00	88.45
Finished Basement, Add	21.80	21.50	20.80	20.35	19.75	19.45	19.00	18.35	17.85	17.50	17.25
Unfinished Basement, Add	8.55	8.00	7.50	7.20	6.90	6.70	6.45	6.00	5.70	5.50	5.35

Modifications

Add to the total cost

Upgrade Kitchen Cabinets	$ + 4320
Solid Surface Countertops (Included)	
Full Bath - including plumbing, wall and floor finishes	+ 7120
Half Bath - including plumbing, wall and floor finishes	+ 4097
One Car Attached Garage	+ 13,653
One Car Detached Garage	+ 17,986
Fireplace & Chimney	+ 6030

Adjustments

For multi family - add to total cost

Additional Kitchen	$ + 8159
Additional Bath	+ 7120
Additional Entry & Exit	+ 1620
Separate Heating	+ 1392
Separate Electric	+ 1986

For Townhouse/Rowhouse - Multiply cost per square foot by

Inner Unit	.91
End Unit	.96

Alternatives

Add to or deduct from the cost per square foot of living area

Cedar Shake Roof	+ 1.55
Clay Tile Roof	+ 3.80
Slate Roof	+ 3.30
Upgrade Walls to Skim Coat Plaster	+ .46
Upgrade Ceilings to Textured Finish	+ .50
Air Conditioning, in Heating Ductwork	+ 2.86
In Separate Ductwork	+ 5.52
Heating Systems, Hot Water	+ 2.00
Heat Pump	+ 2.97
Electric Heat	– .37
Not Heated	– 2.93

Additional upgrades or components

Kitchen Cabinets & Countertops	Page 93
Bathroom Vanities	94
Fireplaces & Chimneys	94
Windows, Skylights & Dormers	94
Appliances	95
Breezeways & Porches	95
Finished Attic	95
Garages	96
Site Improvements	96
Wings & Ells	56

			Cost Per Square Foot Of Living Area			% of Total
			Mat.	Inst.	Total	(rounded)
1	**Site Work**	Excavation for lower level, 4' deep. Site preparation for slab.		.81	.81	0.8%
2	**Foundation**	Continuous reinforced concrete footing 8" deep x 18" wide, dampproofed and insulated reinforced concrete foundation wall, 8" thick, 4' deep; 4" concrete slab on 4" crushed stone base and polyethylene vapor barrier, trowel finish.	3.11	4.13	7.24	7.6%
3	**Framing**	Exterior walls - 2" x 4" wood studs, 16" O.C.; 1/2" plywood sheathing; 2" x 6" rafters 16" O.C. with 1/2" plywood sheathing, 4 in 12 pitch; 2" x 6" ceiling joists 16" O.C.; 2" x 8" floor joists 16" O.C. with 5/8" plywood subfloor; 1/2" plywood subfloor on 1" x 2" wood sleepers 16" O.C.	6.76	8.66	15.42	16.1%
4	**Exterior Walls**	Horizontal beveled wood siding; building paper; 3-1/2" batt insulation; wood double hung windows; 3 flush solid core wood exterior doors; storms and screens.	10.53	4.54	15.07	15.8%
5	**Roofing**	25 year asphalt shingles; #15 felt building paper; aluminum gutters, downspouts, drip edge and flashings.	1.08	1.23	2.31	2.4%
6	**Interiors**	Walls and ceilings, 1/2" taped and finished gypsum wallboard, primed and painted with 2 coats; painted baseboard and trim, finished hardwood floor 40%, carpet with 1/2" underlayment 40%, vinyl tile with 1/2" underlayment 15%, ceramic tile with 1/2" underlayment 5%; hollow core and louvered doors.	13.91	14.26	28.17	29.5%
7	**Specialties**	Average grade kitchen cabinets - 14 L.F. wall and base with solid surface counter top and kitchen sink; 40 gallon electric water heater.	2.74	.93	3.67	3.8%
8	**Mechanical**	1 lavatory, white, wall hung; 1 water closet, white; 1 bathtub with shower, enameled steel, white; gas fired warm air heat.	3.17	3.03	6.20	6.5%
9	**Electrical**	200 Amp. service; Romex wiring; incandescent lighting fixtures, switches, receptacles.	1.15	1.69	2.84	3.0%
10	**Overhead**	Contractor's overhead and profit and plans.	7.20	6.67	13.87	14.5%
	Total		49.65	45.95	**95.60**	

- **Simple design from standard plans**
- **Single family — 1 full bath, 1 kitchen**
- **No basement**
- **Asphalt shingles on roof**
- **Hot air heat**
- **Gypsum wallboard interior finishes**
- **Materials and workmanship are average**

Note: The illustration shown may contain some optional components (for example: garages and/or fireplaces) whose costs are shown in the modifications, adjustments, & alternatives below or at the end of the square foot section.

eDesign Basics, Inc.

Base cost per square foot of living area

| Exterior Wall | Living Area | | | | | | | | | | |
	1200	1500	1800	2100	2400	2700	3000	3400	3800	4200	4600
Wood Siding - Wood Frame	118.40	109.05	102.15	96.10	92.30	90.00	87.60	85.35	81.50	78.40	76.85
Brick Veneer - Wood Frame	123.60	113.75	106.40	100.00	95.90	93.50	90.85	88.50	84.45	81.20	79.50
Stucco on Wood Frame	115.85	106.70	100.05	94.25	90.50	88.35	86.00	83.80	80.05	77.05	75.55
Solid Masonry	135.15	124.25	115.85	108.65	103.95	101.30	98.20	95.55	91.05	87.30	85.45
Finished Basement, Add*	25.05	24.60	23.55	22.75	22.15	21.85	21.45	21.15	20.70	20.30	20.10
Unfinished Basement, Add*	9.50	8.80	8.20	7.65	7.35	7.15	6.85	6.70	6.45	6.20	6.10

*Basement under middle level only.

Modifications

Add to the total cost

Upgrade Kitchen Cabinets	$ + 4320
Solid Surface Countertops (Included)	
Full Bath - including plumbing, wall and floor finishes	+ 7120
Half Bath - including plumbing, wall and floor finishes	+ 4097
One Car Attached Garage	+ 13,653
One Car Detached Garage	+ 17,986
Fireplace & Chimney	+ 6030

Adjustments

For multi family - add to total cost

Additional Kitchen	$ + 8159
Additional Bath	+ 7120
Additional Entry & Exit	+ 1620
Separate Heating	+ 1392
Separate Electric	+ 1986

For Townhouse/Rowhouse - Multiply cost per square foot by

Inner Unit	.90
End Unit	.95

Alternatives

Add to or deduct from the cost per square foot of living area

Cedar Shake Roof	+ 2.25
Clay Tile Roof	+ 5.45
Slate Roof	+ 4.80
Upgrade Walls to Skim Coat Plaster	+ .40
Upgrade Ceilings to Textured Finish	+ .50
Air Conditioning, in Heating Ductwork	+ 2.41
In Separate Ductwork	+ 5.20
Heating Systems, Hot Water	+ 1.93
Heat Pump	+ 3.10
Electric Heat	– .31
Not Heated	– 2.82

Additional upgrades or components

Kitchen Cabinets & Countertops	Page 93
Bathroom Vanities	94
Fireplaces & Chimneys	94
Windows, Skylights & Dormers	94
Appliances	95
Breezeways & Porches	95
Finished Attic	95
Garages	96
Site Improvements	96
Wings & Ells	56

		Cost Per Square Foot Of Living Area			% of Total
		Mat.	Inst.	Total	(rounded)
1 Site Work	Site preparation for slab; 4' deep trench excavation for foundation wall, excavation for lower level, 4' deep.		.68	.68	0.7%
2 Foundation	Continuous reinforced concrete footing 8" deep x 18" wide; dampproofed and insulated reinforced concrete foundation wall, 8" thick, 4' deep; 4" concrete slab on 4" crushed stone base and polyethylene vapor barrier, trowel finish.	3.49	4.49	7.98	8.6%
3 Framing	Exterior walls - 2" x 4" wood studs, 16" O.C.; 1/2" plywood sheathing; 2" x 6" rafters 16" O.C. with 1/2" plywood sheathing, 4 in 12 pitch; 2" x 6" ceiling joists 16" O.C.; 2" x 8" floor joists 16" O.C. with 5/8" plywood subfloor; 1/2" plywood subfloor on 1" x 2" wood sleepers 16" O.C.	6.22	8.14	14.36	15.6%
4 Exterior Walls	Horizontal beveled wood siding: building paper; 3-1/2" batt insulation; wood double hung windows; 3 flush solid core wood exterior doors; storms and screens.	9.09	3.96	13.05	14.1%
5 Roofing	25 year asphalt shingles; #15 felt building paper; aluminum gutters, downspouts, drip edge and flashings.	1.43	1.64	3.07	3.3%
6 Interiors	Walls and ceilings, 1/2" taped and finished gypsum wallboard, primed and painted with 2 coats; painted baseboard and trim, finished hardwood floor 40%, carpet with 1/2" underlayment 40%, vinyl tile with 1/2" underlayment 15%, ceramic tile with 1/2" underlayment 5%; hollow core and louvered doors.	14.46	13.93	28.39	30.8%
7 Specialties	Average grade kitchen cabinets - 14 L.F. wall and base with solid surface counter top and kitchen sink; 40 gallon electric water heater.	2.28	.77	3.05	3.3%
8 Mechanical	1 lavatory, white, wall hung; 1 water closet, white; 1 bathtub with shower, enameled steel, white; gas fired warm air heat.	2.76	2.87	5.63	6.1%
9 Electrical	200 Amp. service; Romex wiring; incandescent lighting fixtures, switches, receptacles.	1.07	1.59	2.66	2.9%
10 Overhead	Contractor's overhead and profit and plans.	6.95	6.48	13.43	14.6%
	Total	47.75	44.55	**92.30**	

- **Post and beam frame**
- **Log exterior walls**
- **Simple design from standard plans**
- **Single family — 1 full bath, 1 kitchen**
- **No basement**
- **Asphalt shingles on roof**
- **Hot air heat**
- **Gypsum wallboard interior finishes**
- **Materials and workmanship are average**

Note: The illustration shown may contain some optional components (for example: garages and/or fireplaces) whose costs are shown in the modifications, adjustments, & alternatives below or at the end of the square foot section.

Base cost per square foot of living area

Exterior Wall	Living Area										
	600	800	1000	1200	1400	1600	1800	2000	2400	2800	3200
6" Log - Solid Wall	168.40	152.75	140.95	131.55	123.60	118.40	115.60	112.15	105.30	100.30	96.85
8" Log - Solid Wall	158.15	143.50	132.60	124.00	116.75	112.00	109.45	106.35	99.95	95.45	92.35
Finished Basement, Add	37.90	36.65	34.95	33.40	32.15	31.30	30.80	30.15	29.25	28.55	27.85
Unfinished Basement, Add	15.60	14.15	13.10	12.10	11.30	10.85	10.55	10.15	9.55	9.15	8.75

Modifications

Add to the total cost

Upgrade Kitchen Cabinets	$ + 4320
Solid Surface Countertops (Included)	
Full Bath - including plumbing, wall and floor finishes	+ 7120
Half Bath - including plumbing, wall and floor finishes	+ 4097
One Car Attached Garage	+ 13,653
One Car Detached Garage	+ 17,986
Fireplace & Chimney	+ 6030

Adjustments

For multi family - add to total cost

Additional Kitchen	$ + 8159
Additional Bath	+ 7120
Additional Entry & Exit	+ 1620
Separate Heating	+ 1392
Separate Electric	+ 1986

For Townhouse/Rowhouse - Multiply cost per square foot by

Inner Unit	.92
End Unit	.96

Alternatives

Add to or deduct from the cost per square foot of living area

Cedar Shake Roof	+ 3.10
Air Conditioning, in Heating Ductwork	+ 4.73
In Separate Ductwork	+ 6.94
Heating Systems, Hot Water	+ 2.14
Heat Pump	+ 2.54
Electric Heat	– .49
Not Heated	– 3.14

Additional upgrades or components

Kitchen Cabinets & Countertops	Page 93
Bathroom Vanities	94
Fireplaces & Chimneys	94
Windows, Skylights & Dormers	94
Appliances	95
Breezeways & Porches	95
Finished Attic	95
Garages	96
Site Improvements	96
Wings & Ells	56

		Cost Per Square Foot Of Living Area			% of Total
		Mat.	Inst.	Total	(rounded)
1 Site Work	Site preparation for slab; 4' deep trench excavation for foundation wall.		1.01	1.01	0.9%
2 Foundation	Continuous reinforced concrete footing 8" deep x 18" wide; dampproofed and insulated reinforced concrete foundation wall, 8" thick, 4' deep; 4" concrete slab on 4" crushed stone base and polyethylene vapor barrier, trowel finish.	5.22	6.75	11.97	10.1%
3 Framing	Exterior walls - Precut traditional log home. Handcrafted white cedar or pine logs. Delivery included.	22.58	14.65	37.23	31.4%
4 Exterior Walls	Wood double hung windows, solid wood exterior doors.	5.46	2.92	8.38	7.1%
5 Roofing	25 year asphalt shingles; #15 felt building paper; aluminum gutters, downspouts, drip edge and flashings.	2.15	2.47	4.62	3.9%
6 Interiors	Walls and ceilings, 1/2" taped and finished gypsum wallboard, primed and painted with 2 coats; painted baseboard and trim, finished hardwood floor 40%, carpet with 1/2" underlayment 40%, vinyl tile with 1/2" underlayment 15%, ceramic tile with 1/2" underlayment 5%; hollow core and louvered doors.	11.61	11.79	23.40	19.8%
7 Specialties	Average grade kitchen cabinets - 14 L.F. wall and base with solid surface counter top and kitchen sink; 40 gallon electric water heater.	3.43	1.16	4.59	3.9%
8 Mechanical	1 lavatory, white, wall hung; 1 water closet, white; 1 bathtub with shower, enameled steel, white; gas fired warm air heat.	3.67	3.25	6.92	5.8%
9 Electrical	200 Amp. service; Romex wiring; incandescent lighting fixtures, switches, receptacles.	1.25	1.83	3.08	2.6%
10 Overhead	Contractor's overhead and profit and plans.	9.43	7.77	17.20	14.5%
Total		64.80	53.60	**118.40**	

- **Post and beam frame**
- **Log exterior walls**
- **Simple design from standard plans**
- **Single family — 1 full bath, 1 kitchen**
- **No basement**
- **Asphalt shingles on roof**
- **Hot air heat**
- **Gypsum wallboard interior finishes**
- **Materials and workmanship are average**

Note: The illustration shown may contain some optional components (for example: garages and/or fireplaces) whose costs are shown in the modifications, adjustments, & alternatives below or at the end of the square foot section.

Base cost per square foot of living area

Exterior Wall	Living Area										
	1000	1200	1400	1600	1800	2000	2200	2600	3000	3400	3800
6" Log - Solid Wall	149.25	135.90	129.30	124.80	120.15	115.35	112.00	105.60	99.60	96.85	94.20
8" Log - Solid Wall	138.15	125.60	119.70	115.60	111.50	107.00	104.05	98.45	92.95	90.50	88.25
Finished Basement, Add	21.80	21.50	20.80	20.35	19.75	19.45	19.00	18.35	17.85	17.50	17.25
Unfinished Basement, Add	8.55	8.00	7.50	7.20	6.90	6.70	6.45	6.00	5.70	5.50	5.35

Modifications

Add to the total cost

Upgrade Kitchen Cabinets	$ + 4320
Solid Surface Countertops (Included)	
Full Bath - including plumbing, wall and floor finishes	+ 7120
Half Bath - including plumbing, wall and floor finishes	+ 4097
One Car Attached Garage	+ 13,653
One Car Detached Garage	+ 17,986
Fireplace & Chimney	+ 6660

Adjustments

For multi family - add to total cost

Additional Kitchen	$ + 8159
Additional Bath	+ 7120
Additional Entry & Exit	+ 1620
Separate Heating	+ 1392
Separate Electric	+ 1986

For Townhouse/Rowhouse - Multiply cost per square foot by

Inner Unit	.92
End Unit	.96

Alternatives

Add to or deduct from the cost per square foot of living area

Cedar Shake Roof	+ 1.55
Air Conditioning, in Heating Ductwork	+ 2.86
In Separate Ductwork	+ 5.52
Heating Systems, Hot Water	+ 2.00
Heat Pump	+ 2.97
Electric Heat	– .37
Not Heated	– 2.93

Additional upgrades or components

Kitchen Cabinets & Countertops	Page 93
Bathroom Vanities	94
Fireplaces & Chimneys	94
Windows, Skylights & Dormers	94
Appliances	95
Breezeways & Porches	95
Finished Attic	95
Garages	96
Site Improvements	96
Wings & Ells	56

Solid Wall 2 Story

Living Area - 2000 S.F.
Perimeter - 135 L.F.

		Cost Per Square Foot Of Living Area			% of Total
		Mat.	Inst.	Total	(rounded)
1 Site Work	Site preparation for slab; 4' deep trench excavation for foundation wall.		.81	.81	0.7%
2 Foundation	Continuous reinforced concrete footing 8" deep x 18" wide; dampproofed and insulated reinforced concrete foundation wall, 8" thick, 4' deep, 4" concrete slab on 4" crushed stone base and polyethylene vapor barrier, trowel finish.	3.11	4.13	7.24	6.3%
3 Framing	Exterior walls - Precut traditional log home. Handcrafted white cedar or pine logs. Delivery included.	25.06	15.16	40.22	34.9%
4 Exterior Walls	Wood double hung windows, solid wood exterior doors.	6.09	3.09	9.18	8.0%
5 Roofing	25 year asphalt shingles; #15 felt building paper; aluminum gutters, downspouts, drip edge and flashings.	1.08	1.23	2.31	2.0%
6 Interiors	Walls and ceilings, 1/2" taped and finished gypsum wallboard, primed and painted with 2 coats; painted baseboard and trim, finished hardwood floor 40%, carpet with 1/2" underlayment 40%, vinyl tile with 1/2" underlayment 15%, ceramic tile with 1/2" underlayment 5%; hollow core and louvered doors.	13.11	12.99	26.10	22.6%
7 Specialties	Average grade kitchen cabinets - 14 L.F. wall and base with solid surface counter top and kitchen sink; 40 gallon electric water heater.	2.74	.93	3.67	3.2%
8 Mechanical	1 lavatory, white, wall hung; 1 water closet, white; 1 bathtub with shower; enameled steel, white; gas fired warm air heat.	3.17	3.03	6.20	5.4%
9 Electrical	200 Amp. service; Romex wiring; incandescent lighting fixtures, switches, receptacles.	1.15	1.69	2.84	2.5%
10 Overhead	Contractor's overhead and profit and plans.	9.44	7.34	16.78	14.5%
	Total	64.95	50.40	**115.35**	

1 Story — Base cost per square foot of living area

Exterior Wall	Living Area							
	50	100	200	300	400	500	600	700
Wood Siding - Wood Frame	198.95	153.15	133.20	112.40	105.85	101.90	99.35	100.20
Brick Veneer - Wood Frame	204.55	153.75	131.75	107.40	100.20	95.85	92.95	93.65
Stucco on Wood Frame	190.05	146.70	127.80	108.70	102.55	98.80	96.30	97.35
Solid Masonry	255.65	193.65	167.00	134.90	126.10	120.80	118.95	119.00
Finished Basement, Add	60.60	50.20	45.25	36.80	35.20	34.15	33.50	33.05
Unfinished Basement, Add	28.35	21.45	18.60	13.80	12.85	12.25	11.90	11.60

1-1/2 Story — Base cost per square foot of living area

Exterior Wall	Living Area							
	100	200	300	400	500	600	700	800
Wood Siding - Wood Frame	159.85	128.70	110.00	99.05	93.35	90.65	87.25	86.15
Brick Veneer - Wood Frame	215.90	161.50	133.90	117.30	108.95	104.50	99.70	97.85
Stucco on Wood Frame	192.45	142.70	118.30	105.10	97.75	93.95	89.65	87.95
Solid Masonry	250.85	189.45	157.25	135.50	125.70	120.40	114.65	112.70
Finished Basement, Add	40.85	37.00	33.60	29.95	28.90	28.25	27.70	27.55
Unfinished Basement, Add	17.80	14.95	13.00	10.90	10.30	9.95	9.60	9.50

2 Story — Base cost per square foot of living area

Exterior Wall	Living Area							
	100	200	400	600	800	1000	1200	1400
Wood Siding - Wood Frame	160.05	119.95	102.35	85.35	79.60	76.15	73.90	74.95
Brick Veneer - Wood Frame	220.10	153.70	123.40	99.45	91.20	86.25	83.00	83.45
Stucco on Wood Frame	193.80	134.95	107.80	89.00	81.85	77.50	74.70	75.40
Solid Masonry	259.20	181.70	146.75	115.00	105.20	99.30	95.45	95.40
Finished Basement, Add	32.30	27.15	24.60	20.45	19.60	19.10	18.75	18.45
Unfinished Basement, Add	14.35	10.90	9.45	7.05	6.55	6.25	6.10	5.95

Base costs do not include bathroom or kitchen facilities. Use Modifications/Adjustments/Alternatives on pages 93–96 where appropriate.

1 Story

1-1/2 Story

2 Story

2-1/2 Story

Bi-Level

Tri-Level

- A distinct residence from designer's plans
- Single family — 1 full bath, 1 half bath, 1 kitchen
- No basement
- Asphalt shingles on roof
- Forced hot air heat/air conditioning
- Gypsum wallboard interior finishes
- Materials and workmanship are above average

Note: The illustration shown may contain some optional components (for example: garages and/or fireplaces) whose costs are shown in the modifications, adjustments, & alternatives below or at the end of the square foot section.

©Design Basics, Inc.

Base cost per square foot of living area

Exterior Wall	Living Area										
	800	1000	1200	1400	1600	1800	2000	2400	2800	3200	3600
Wood Siding - Wood Frame	181.05	163.25	149.50	138.40	130.80	126.55	121.55	112.35	105.65	101.05	96.15
Brick Veneer - Wood Frame	202.25	183.65	169.10	157.40	149.35	144.85	139.50	129.80	122.75	117.85	112.60
Stone Veneer - Wood Frame	209.85	190.55	175.30	163.05	154.65	150.00	144.30	134.25	126.80	121.55	116.15
Solid Masonry	214.05	194.45	178.80	166.20	157.65	152.80	147.05	136.65	129.10	123.65	118.10
Finished Basement, Add	56.80	56.70	54.30	52.35	51.10	50.40	49.35	47.95	46.85	45.85	44.95
Unfinished Basement, Add	24.05	22.75	21.50	20.45	19.85	19.50	18.95	18.20	17.60	17.15	16.65

Modifications

Add to the total cost

Upgrade Kitchen Cabinets	$ + 1315
Solid Surface Countertops (Included)	
Full Bath - including plumbing, wall and floor finishes	+ 8543
Half Bath - including plumbing, wall and floor finishes	+ 4916
Two Car Attached Garage	+ 26,684
Two Car Detached Garage	+ 30,391
Fireplace & Chimney	+ 6305

Adjustments

For multi family - add to total cost

Additional Kitchen	$ + 16,589
Additional Full Bath & Half Bath	+ 13,459
Additional Entry & Exit	+ 1620
Separate Heating & Air Conditioning	+ 6803
Separate Electric	+ 1986

For Townhouse/Rowhouse - Multiply cost per square foot by

Inner Unit	.90
End Unit	.95

Alternatives

Add to or deduct from the cost per square foot of living area

Cedar Shake Roof	+ 2.05
Clay Tile Roof	+ 6.50
Slate Roof	+ 5.50
Upgrade Ceilings to Textured Finish	+ .50
Air Conditioning, in Heating Ductwork	Base System
Heating Systems, Hot Water	+ 2.20
Heat Pump	+ 2.53
Electric Heat	– 1.38
Not Heated	– 3.94

Additional upgrades or components

Kitchen Cabinets & Countertops	Page 93
Bathroom Vanities	94
Fireplaces & Chimneys	94
Windows, Skylights & Dormers	94
Appliances	95
Breezeways & Porches	95
Finished Attic	95
Garages	96
Site Improvements	96
Wings & Ells	74

Important: See the Reference Section for Location Factors (to adjust for your city) and Estimating Forms.

			Cost Per Square Foot Of Living Area			% of Total
			Mat.	Inst.	Total	(rounded)
1	**Site Work**	Site preparation for slab; 4' deep trench excavation for foundation wall.		.79	.79	0.7%
2	**Foundation**	Continuous reinforced concrete footing 8" deep x 18" wide; dampproofed and insulated concrete block foundation wall, 12" thick, 4' deep, with grout and reinforcing; 4" concrete slab on 4" crushed stone base and polyethylene vapor barrier, trowel finish.	5.88	7.41	13.29	11.8%
3	**Framing**	Exterior walls - 2" x 6" wood studs, 16" O.C.; 1/2" plywood sheathing; 2" x 8" rafters 16" O.C. with 1/2" plywood sheathing, 4 in 12 pitch; 2" x 6" ceiling joists 16" O.C.; 5/8" plywood subfloor on 1" x 3" wood sleepers 16" O.C.	4.16	6.85	11.01	9.8%
4	**Exterior Walls**	Horizontal beveled wood siding; building paper; 6" batt insulation; wood double hung windows; 3 solid core wood exterior doors; storms and screens.	9.88	3.48	13.36	11.9%
5	**Roofing**	30 year asphalt shingles; #15 felt building paper; aluminum gutters, downspouts and drip edge; copper flashings.	4.31	3.58	7.89	7.0%
6	**Interiors**	Walls and ceilings - 5/8" gypsum wallboard, skim coat plaster, painted with primer and 2 coats; hardwood baseboard and trim, sanded and finished; hardwood floor 70%, ceramic tile with underlayment 20%, vinyl tile with underlayment 10%; wood panel interior doors, primed and painted with 2 coats.	13.86	12.89	26.75	23.8%
7	**Specialties**	Custom grade kitchen cabinets - 20 L.F. wall and base with solid surface counter top and kitchen sink; 4 L.F. bathroom vanity; 75 gallon electric water heater, medicine cabinet.	6.03	1.30	7.33	6.5%
8	**Mechanical**	Gas fired warm air heat/air conditioning; one full bath including: bathtub, corner shower, built in lavatory and water closet; one 1/2 bath including: built in lavatory and water closet.	6.82	3.35	10.17	9.1%
9	**Electrical**	200 Amp. service; Romex wiring; fluorescent and incandescent lighting fixtures, switches, receptacles.	1.22	1.81	3.03	2.7%
10	**Overhead**	Contractor's overhead and profit and design.	10.44	8.29	18.73	16.7%
	Total		62.60	49.75	**112.35**	

- **A distinct residence from designer's plans**
- **Single family — 1 full bath, 1 half bath, 1 kitchen**
- **No basement**
- **Asphalt shingles on roof**
- **Forced hot air heat/air conditioning**
- **Gypsum wallboard interior finishes**
- **Materials and workmanship are above average**

Note: The illustration shown may contain some optional components (for example: garages and/or fireplaces) whose costs are shown in the modifications, adjustments, & alternatives below or at the end of the square foot section.

©Donald A. Gardner Architects, Inc.

Base cost per square foot of living area

Exterior Wall	Living Area										
	1000	1200	1400	1600	1800	2000	2400	2800	3200	3600	4000
Wood Siding - Wood Frame	163.10	151.45	143.10	133.10	127.40	121.80	111.30	106.45	102.00	98.60	93.75
Brick Veneer - Wood Frame	172.30	160.05	151.30	140.55	134.45	128.45	117.20	112.05	107.15	103.55	98.45
Stone Veneer - Wood Frame	180.30	167.55	158.45	147.05	140.60	134.35	122.40	116.95	111.70	107.95	102.50
Solid Masonry	184.75	171.70	162.45	150.70	144.05	137.55	125.30	119.65	114.20	110.35	104.70
Finished Basement, Add	37.60	37.90	36.90	35.40	34.60	33.85	32.30	31.65	30.85	30.40	29.75
Unfinished Basement, Add	16.20	15.50	14.95	14.20	13.75	13.40	12.60	12.25	11.85	11.65	11.30

Modifications

Add to the total cost

Upgrade Kitchen Cabinets	$ + 1315
Solid Surface Countertops (Included)	
Full Bath - including plumbing, wall and floor finishes	+ 8543
Half Bath - including plumbing, wall and floor finishes	+ 4916
Two Car Attached Garage	+ 26,684
Two Car Detached Garage	+ 30,391
Fireplace & Chimney	+ 6305

Adjustments

For multi family - add to total cost

Additional Kitchen	$ + 16,589
Additional Full Bath & Half Bath	+ 13,459
Additional Entry & Exit	+ 1620
Separate Heating & Air Conditioning	+ 6803
Separate Electric	+ 1986

*For Townhouse/Rowhouse -
Multiply cost per square foot by*

Inner Unit	.90
End Unit	.95

Alternatives

Add to or deduct from the cost per square foot of living area

Cedar Shake Roof	+ 1.45
Clay Tile Roof	+ 4.65
Slate Roof	+ 4.00
Upgrade Ceilings to Textured Finish	+ .50
Air Conditioning, in Heating Ductwork	Base System
Heating Systems, Hot Water	+ 2.10
Heat Pump	+ 2.64
Electric Heat	– 1.22
Not Heated	– 3.63

Additional upgrades or components

Kitchen Cabinets & Countertops	Page 93
Bathroom Vanities	94
Fireplaces & Chimneys	94
Windows, Skylights & Dormers	94
Appliances	95
Breezeways & Porches	95
Finished Attic	95
Garages	96
Site Improvements	96
Wings & Ells	74

Important: See the Reference Section for Location Factors (to adjust for your city) and Estimating Forms.

Custom 1-1/2 Story

Living Area - 2800 S.F.
Perimeter - 175 L.F.

			Cost Per Square Foot Of Living Area			% of Total
			Mat.	Inst.	Total	(rounded)
1	**Site Work**	Site preparation for slab; 4' deep trench excavation for foundation wall.		.68	.68	0.6%
2	**Foundation**	Continuous reinforced concrete footing 8" deep x 18" wide; dampproofed and insulated concrete block foundation wall, 12" thick, 4' deep, with grout and reinforcing; 4" concrete slab on 4" crushed stone base and polyethylene vapor barrier, trowel finish.	4.12	5.29	9.41	8.8%
3	**Framing**	Exterior walls - 2" x 6" wood studs, 16" O.C.; 1/2" plywood sheathing; 2" x 8" rafters 16" O.C. with 1/2" plywood sheathing, 8 in 12 pitch; 2" x 10" floor joists 16" O.C. with 5/8" plywood subfloor; 5/8" plywood subfloor on 1" x 3" wood sleepers 16" O.C.	5.41	7.21	12.62	11.9%
4	**Exterior Walls**	Horizontal beveled wood siding; building paper; 6" batt insulation; wood double hung windows; 3 solid core wood exterior doors; storms and screens.	10.00	3.55	13.55	12.7%
5	**Roofing**	30 year asphalt shingles; #15 felt building paper; aluminum gutters, downspouts and drip edge; copper flashings.	2.70	2.24	4.94	4.6%
6	**Interiors**	Walls and ceilings - 5/8" gypsum wallboard, skim coat plaster, painted with primer and 2 coats; hardwood baseboard and trim, sanded and finished; hardwood floor 70%, ceramic tile with underlayment 20%, vinyl tile with underlayment 10%; wood panel interior doors, primed and painted with 2 coats.	15.28	14.07	29.35	27.6%
7	**Specialties**	Custom grade kitchen cabinets - 20 L.F. wall and base with solid surface counter top and kitchen sink; 4 L.F. bathroom vanity; 75 gallon electric water heater, medicine cabinet.	5.13	1.12	6.25	5.9%
8	**Mechanical**	Gas fired warm air heat/air conditioning; one full bath including: bathtub, corner shower, built in lavatory and water closet; one 1/2 bath including: built in lavatory and water closet.	5.89	3.11	9.00	8.5%
9	**Electrical**	200 Amp. service; Romex wiring; fluorescent and incandescent lighting fixtures, switches, receptacles.	1.16	1.74	2.90	2.7%
10	**Overhead**	Contractor's overhead and profit and design.	9.96	7.79	17.75	16.7%
		Total	59.65	46.80	**106.45**	

- **A distinct residence from designer's plans**
- **Single family — 1 full bath, 1 half bath, 1 kitchen**
- **No basement**
- **Asphalt shingles on roof**
- **Forced hot air heat/air conditioning**
- **Gypsum wallboard interior finishes**
- **Materials and workmanship are above average**

Note: The illustration shown may contain some optional components (for example: garages and/or fireplaces) whose costs are shown in the modifications, adjustments, & alternatives below or at the end of the square foot section.

Base cost per square foot of living area

Exterior Wall	Living Area										
	1200	1400	1600	1800	2000	2400	2800	3200	3600	4000	4400
Wood Siding - Wood Frame	152.65	143.35	136.65	130.75	124.45	115.40	107.75	102.80	99.75	96.55	93.90
Brick Veneer - Wood Frame	162.45	152.50	145.40	138.95	132.40	122.60	114.30	108.90	105.70	102.10	99.25
Stone Veneer - Wood Frame	170.95	160.45	153.00	146.10	139.30	128.80	119.95	114.20	110.80	106.95	103.90
Solid Masonry	175.70	164.90	157.20	150.15	143.15	132.30	123.10	117.20	113.65	109.60	106.55
Finished Basement, Add	30.25	30.50	29.75	28.95	28.40	27.15	26.25	25.60	25.25	24.70	24.45
Unfinished Basement, Add	13.00	12.45	12.05	11.65	11.40	10.75	10.25	9.95	9.75	9.50	9.35

Modifications

Add to the total cost

Upgrade Kitchen Cabinets	$ + 1315
Solid Surface Countertops (Included)	
Full Bath - including plumbing, wall and floor finishes	+ 8543
Half Bath - including plumbing, wall and floor finishes	+ 4916
Two Car Attached Garage	+ 26,684
Two Car Detached Garage	+ 30,391
Fireplace & Chimney	+ 7116

Adjustments

For multi family - add to total cost

Additional Kitchen	$ + 16,589
Additional Full Bath & Half Bath	+ 13,459
Additional Entry & Exit	+ 1620
Separate Heating & Air Conditioning	+ 6803
Separate Electric	+ 1986

For Townhouse/Rowhouse - Multiply cost per square foot by

Inner Unit	.87
End Unit	.93

Alternatives

Add to or deduct from the cost per square foot of living area

Cedar Shake Roof	+ 1.00
Clay Tile Roof	+ 3.25
Slate Roof	+ 2.75
Upgrade Ceilings to Textured Finish	+ .50
Air Conditioning, in Heating Ductwork	Base System
Heating Systems, Hot Water	+ 2.04
Heat Pump	+ 2.95
Electric Heat	− 1.22
Not Heated	− 3.43

Additional upgrades or components

Kitchen Cabinets & Countertops	Page 93
Bathroom Vanities	94
Fireplaces & Chimneys	94
Windows, Skylights & Dormers	94
Appliances	95
Breezeways & Porches	95
Finished Attic	95
Garages	96
Site Improvements	96
Wings & Ells	74

Custom 2 Story

Living Area - 2800 S.F.
Perimeter - 156 L.F.

		Cost Per Square Foot Of Living Area			% of Total
		Mat.	Inst.	Total	(rounded)
1 **Site Work**	Site preparation for slab; 4' deep trench excavation for foundation wall.		.68	.68	0.6%
2 **Foundation**	Continuous reinforced concrete footing 8" deep x 18" wide; dampproofed and insulated concrete block foundation wall, 12" thick, 4' deep, with grout and reinforcing; 4" concrete slab on 4" crushed stone base and polyethylene vapor barrier, trowel finish.	3.49	4.54	8.03	7.5%
3 **Framing**	Exterior walls - 2" x 6" wood studs, 16" O.C.; 1/2" plywood sheathing; 2" x 8" rafters 16" O.C. with 1/2" plywood sheathing, 6 in 12 pitch; 2" x 8" ceiling joists 16" O.C.; 2" x 10" floor joists 16" O.C. with 5/8" plywood subfloor; 5/8" plywood subfloor on 1" x 3" wood sleepers 16" O.C.	5.95	7.44	13.39	12.4%
4 **Exterior Walls**	Horizontal beveled wood siding; building paper; 6" batt insulation; wood double hung windows; 3 solid core wood exterior doors; storms and screens.	11.41	4.06	15.47	14.4%
5 **Roofing**	30 year asphalt shingles; #15 felt building paper; aluminum gutters, downspouts and drip edge; copper flashings.	2.15	1.79	3.94	3.7%
6 **Interiors**	Walls and ceilings - 5/8" gypsum wallboard, skim coat plaster, painted with primer and 2 coats; hardwood baseboard and trim, sanded and finished; hardwood floor 70%, ceramic tile with underlayment 20%, vinyl tile with underlayment 10%; wood panel interior doors, primed and painted with 2 coats.	15.56	14.38	29.94	27.8%
7 **Specialties**	Custom grade kitchen cabinets - 20 L.F. wall and base with solid surface counter top and kitchen sink; 4 L.F. bathroom vanity; 75 gallon electric water heater, medicine cabinet.	5.13	1.12	6.25	5.8%
8 **Mechanical**	Gas fired warm air heat/air conditioning; one full bath including: bathtub, corner shower; built in lavatory and water closet; one 1/2 bath including: built in lavatory and water closet.	6.04	3.16	9.20	8.5%
9 **Electrical**	200 Amp. service; Romex wiring; fluorescent and incandescent lighting fixtures, switches, receptacles.	1.16	1.74	2.90	2.7%
10 **Overhead**	Contractor's overhead and profit and design.	10.16	7.79	17.95	16.7%
Total		61.05	46.70	**107.75**	

- **A distinct residence from designer's plans**
- **Single family — 1 full bath, 1 half bath, 1 kitchen**
- **No basement**
- **Asphalt shingles on roof**
- **Forced hot air heat/air conditioning**
- **Gypsum wallboard interior finishes**
- **Materials and workmanship are above average**

Note: The illustration shown may contain some optional components (for example: garages and/or fireplaces) whose costs are shown in the modifications, adjustments, & alternatives below or at the end of the square foot section.

Base cost per square foot of living area

Exterior Wall	Living Area										
	1500	1800	2100	2400	2800	3200	3600	4000	4500	5000	5500
Wood Siding - Wood Frame	149.95	134.75	125.80	120.40	113.40	106.70	103.15	97.40	94.30	91.60	88.90
Brick Veneer - Wood Frame	160.15	144.15	134.20	128.40	121.00	113.65	109.65	103.45	100.10	97.05	94.10
Stone Veneer - Wood Frame	169.05	152.30	141.55	135.30	127.65	119.60	115.40	108.75	105.10	101.85	98.60
Solid Masonry	174.05	156.90	145.60	139.20	131.35	123.00	118.55	111.65	107.90	104.55	101.10
Finished Basement, Add	24.00	24.00	22.80	22.20	21.70	20.85	20.35	19.85	19.45	19.10	18.80
Unfinished Basement, Add	10.40	9.85	9.20	8.95	8.70	8.25	8.00	7.75	7.55	7.40	7.20

Modifications

Add to the total cost

Upgrade Kitchen Cabinets	$ + 1315
Solid Surface Countertops (Included)	
Full Bath - including plumbing, wall and floor finishes	+ 8543
Half Bath - including plumbing, wall and floor finishes	+ 4916
Two Car Attached Garage	+ 26,684
Two Car Detached Garage	+ 30,391
Fireplace & Chimney	+ 8036

Adjustments

For multi family - add to total cost

Additional Kitchen	$ + 16,589
Additional Full Bath & Half Bath	+ 13,459
Additional Entry & Exit	+ 1620
Separate Heating & Air Conditioning	+ 6803
Separate Electric	+ 1986

For Townhouse/Rowhouse -
Multiply cost per square foot by

Inner Unit	.87
End Unit	.94

Alternatives

Add to or deduct from the cost per square foot of living area

Cedar Shake Roof	+ .90
Clay Tile Roof	+ 2.80
Slate Roof	+ 2.40
Upgrade Ceilings to Textured Finish	+ .50
Air Conditioning, in Heating Ductwork	Base System
Heating Systems, Hot Water	+ 1.84
Heat Pump	+ 3.06
Electric Heat	– 2.14
Not Heated	– 3.43

Additional upgrades or components

Important: See the Reference Section for Location Factors (to adjust for your city) and Estimating Forms.

Living Area - 3200 S.F.
Perimeter - 150 L.F.

		Cost Per Square Foot Of Living Area			% of Total
		Mat.	Inst.	Total	(rounded)
1 Site Work	Site preparation for slab; 4' deep trench excavation for foundation wall.		.60	.60	0.6%
2 Foundation	Continuous reinforced concrete footing 8" deep x 18" wide; dampproofed and insulated concrete block foundation wall, 12" thick, 4' deep, with grout and reinforcing; 4" concrete slab on 4" crushed stone base and polyethylene vapor barrier, trowel finish.	2.88	3.76	6.64	6.2%
3 Framing	Exterior walls - 2" x 6" wood studs, 16" O.C.; 1/2" plywood sheathing; 2" x 8" rafters 16" O.C. with 1/2" plywood sheathing, 6 in 12 pitch; 2" x 8" ceiling joists 16" O.C.; 2" x 10" floor joists 16" O.C. with 5/8" plywood subfloor; 5/8" plywood subfloor on 1" x 3" wood sleepers 16" O.C.	6.43	7.76	14.19	13.3%
4 Exterior Walls	Horizontal beveled wood siding; building paper; 6" batt insulation; wood double hung windows; 3 solid core wood exterior doors; storms and screens.	11.82	4.18	16.00	15.0%
5 Roofing	30 year asphalt shingles; #15 felt building paper; aluminum gutters, downspouts and drip edge; copper flashings.	1.65	1.37	3.02	2.8%
6 Interiors	Walls and ceilings - 5/8" gypsum wallboard, skim coat plaster, painted with primer and 2 coats; hardwood baseboard and trim, sanded and finished; hardwood floor 70%, ceramic tile with underlayment 20%, vinyl tile with underlayment 10%; wood panel interior doors, primed and painted with 2 coats.	16.45	15.23	31.68	29.7%
7 Specialties	Custom grade kitchen cabinets - 20 L.F. wall and base with solid surface counter top and kitchen sink; 4 L.F. bathroom vanity; 75 gallon electric water heater, medicine cabinet.	4.51	.97	5.48	5.1%
8 Mechanical	Gas fired warm air heat/air conditioning; one full bath including: bathtub, corner shower; built in lavatory and water closet; one 1/2 bath including: built in lavatory and water closet.	5.47	3.04	8.51	8.0%
9 Electrical	200 Amp. service; Romex wiring; fluorescent and incandescent lighting fixtures, switches, receptacles.	1.13	1.69	2.82	2.6%
10 Overhead	Contractor's overhead and profit and design.	10.06	7.70	17.76	16.6%
Total		60.40	46.30	**106.70**	

- **A distinct residence from designer's plans**
- **Single family — 1 full bath, 1 half bath, 1 kitchen**
- **No basement**
- **Asphalt shingles on roof**
- **Forced hot air heat/air conditioning**
- **Gypsum wallboard interior finishes**
- **Materials and workmanship are above average**

Note: The illustration shown may contain some optional components (for example: garages and/or fireplaces) whose costs are shown in the modifications, adjustments, & alternatives below or at the end of the square foot section.

Base cost per square foot of living area

Exterior Wall	Living Area										
	1500	1800	2100	2500	3000	3500	4000	4500	5000	5500	6000
Wood Siding - Wood Frame	149.45	134.40	127.05	120.95	111.45	106.80	101.10	95.20	93.00	90.65	88.30
Brick Veneer - Wood Frame	160.05	144.25	136.20	129.70	119.40	114.35	107.90	101.50	99.15	96.50	93.85
Stone Veneer - Wood Frame	169.25	152.70	144.15	137.35	126.30	120.85	113.85	107.00	104.45	101.60	98.65
Solid Masonry	174.35	157.50	148.60	141.55	130.15	124.50	117.25	110.05	107.40	104.50	101.35
Finished Basement, Add	21.05	21.05	20.30	19.70	18.90	18.40	17.70	17.25	17.00	16.75	16.40
Unfinished Basement, Add	9.15	8.65	8.25	8.00	7.55	7.30	6.95	6.75	6.60	6.50	6.30

Modifications

Add to the total cost

Upgrade Kitchen Cabinets	$ + 1315
Solid Surface Countertops (Included)	
Full Bath - including plumbing, wall and floor finishes	+ 8543
Half Bath - including plumbing, wall and floor finishes	+ 4916
Two Car Attached Garage	+ 26,684
Two Car Detached Garage	+ 30,391
Fireplace & Chimney	+ 8036

Adjustments

For multi family - add to total cost

Additional Kitchen	$ + 16,589
Additional Full Bath & Half Bath	+ 13,459
Additional Entry & Exit	+ 1620
Separate Heating & Air Conditioning	+ 6803
Separate Electric	+ 1986

For Townhouse/Rowhouse - Multiply cost per square foot by

Inner Unit	.85
End Unit	.93

Alternatives

Add to or deduct from the cost per square foot of living area

Cedar Shake Roof	+ .70
Clay Tile Roof	+ 2.15
Slate Roof	+ 1.85
Upgrade Ceilings to Textured Finish	+ .50
Air Conditioning, in Heating Ductwork	Base System
Heating Systems, Hot Water	+ 1.84
Heat Pump	+ 3.06
Electric Heat	– 2.14
Not Heated	– 3.32

Additional upgrades or components

Kitchen Cabinets & Countertops	Page 93
Bathroom Vanities	94
Fireplaces & Chimneys	94
Windows, Skylights & Dormers	94
Appliances	95
Breezeways & Porches	95
Finished Attic	95
Garages	96
Site Improvements	96
Wings & Ells	74

Important: See the Reference Section for Location Factors (to adjust for your city) and Estimating Forms.

Custom 3 Story

Living Area - 3000 S.F.
Perimeter - 135 L.F.

			Cost Per Square Foot Of Living Area			% of Total
			Mat.	Inst.	Total	(rounded)
1	**Site Work**	Site preparation for slab; 4' deep trench excavation for foundation wall.		.64	.64	0.6%
2	**Foundation**	Continuous reinforced concrete footing 8" deep x 18" wide; dampproofed and insulated concrete block foundation wall, 12" thick, 4' deep, with grout and reinforcing; 4" concrete slab on 4" crushed stone base and polyethylene vapor barrier, trowel finish.	2.70	3.55	6.25	5.6%
3	**Framing**	Exterior walls - 2" x 6" wood studs, 16" O.C.; 1/2" plywood sheathing; 2" x 8" rafters 16" O.C. with 1/2" plywood sheathing, 6 in 12 pitch; 2" x 8" ceiling joists 16" O.C.; 2" x 10" floor joists 16" O.C. with 5/8" plywood subfloor; 5/8" plywood subfloor on 1" x 3" wood sleepers 16" O.C.	6.78	8.00	14.78	13.3%
4	**Exterior Walls**	Horizontal beveled wood siding; building paper; 6" batt insulation; wood double hung windows; 3 solid core wood exterior doors; storms and screens.	13.52	4.80	18.32	16.4%
5	**Roofing**	30 year asphalt shingles; #15 felt building paper; aluminum gutters, downspouts and drip edge; copper flashings.	1.43	1.19	2.62	2.4%
6	**Interiors**	Walls and ceilings - 5/8" gypsum wallboard, skim coat plaster, painted with primer and 2 coats; hardwood baseboard and trim, sanded and finished; hardwood floor 70%, ceramic tile with underlayment 20%, vinyl tile with underlayment 10%; wood panel interior doors, primed and painted with 2 coats.	17.00	15.76	32.76	29.4%
7	**Specialties**	Custon grade kitchen cabinets - 20 L.F. wall and base with solid surface counter top and kitchen sink; 4 L.F. bathroom vanity; 75 gallon electric water heater, medicine cabinet.	4.79	1.03	5.82	5.2%
8	**Mechanical**	Gas fired warm air heat/air conditioning; one full bath including: bathtub, corner shower; built in lavatory and water closet; one 1/2 bath including: built in lavatory and water closet.	5.74	3.10	8.84	7.9%
9	**Electrical**	200 Amp. service; Romex wiring; fluorescent and incandescent lighting fixtures, switches, receptacles.	1.14	1.72	2.86	2.6%
10	**Overhead**	Contractor's overhead and profit and design.	10.60	7.96	18.56	16.7%
	Total		63.70	47.75	**111.45**	

- **A distinct residence from designer's plans**
- **Single family — 1 full bath, 1 half bath, 1 kitchen**
- **No basement**
- **Asphalt shingles on roof**
- **Forced hot air heat/air conditioning**
- **Gypsum wallboard interior finishes**
- **Materials and workmanship are above average**

Note: The illustration shown may contain some optional components (for example: garages and/or fireplaces) whose costs are shown in the modifications, adjustments, & alternatives below or at the end of the square foot section.

Base cost per square foot of living area

Exterior Wall	Living Area										
	1200	1400	1600	1800	2000	2400	2800	3200	3600	4000	4400
Wood Siding - Wood Frame	144.20	135.45	129.10	123.70	117.65	109.25	102.15	97.55	94.70	91.85	89.30
Brick Veneer - Wood Frame	151.55	142.30	135.70	129.90	123.55	114.65	107.00	102.10	99.15	96.00	93.30
Stone Veneer - Wood Frame	157.95	148.35	141.45	135.25	128.75	119.35	111.30	106.10	102.95	99.60	96.75
Solid Masonry	161.50	151.70	144.60	138.25	131.65	121.95	113.65	108.30	105.10	101.60	98.75
Finished Basement, Add	30.25	30.50	29.75	28.95	28.40	27.15	26.25	25.60	25.25	24.70	24.45
Unfinished Basement, Add	13.00	12.45	12.05	11.65	11.40	10.75	10.25	9.95	9.75	9.50	9.35

Modifications

Add to the total cost

Upgrade Kitchen Cabinets	$ + 1315
Solid Surface Countertops (Included)	
Full Bath - including plumbing, wall and floor finishes	+ 8543
Half Bath - including plumbing, wall and floor finishes	+ 4916
Two Car Attached Garage	+ 26,684
Two Car Detached Garage	+ 30,391
Fireplace & Chimney	+ 6305

Adjustments

For multi family - add to total cost

Additional Kitchen	$ + 16,589
Additional Full Bath & Half Bath	+ 13,459
Additional Entry & Exit	+ 1620
Separate Heating & Air Conditioning	+ 6803
Separate Electric	+ 1986

For Townhouse/Rowhouse -
Multiply cost per square foot by

Inner Unit	.89
End Unit	.95

Alternatives

Add to or deduct from the cost per square foot of living area

Cedar Shake Roof	+ 1.00
Clay Tile Roof	+ 3.25
Slate Roof	+ 2.75
Upgrade Ceilings to Textured Finish	+ .50
Air Conditioning, in Heating Ductwork	Base System
Heating Systems, Hot Water	+ 2.04
Heat Pump	+ 2.95
Electric Heat	− 1.22
Not Heated	− 3.32

Additional upgrades or components

Kitchen Cabinets & Countertops	Page 93
Bathroom Vanities	94
Fireplaces & Chimneys	94
Windows, Skylights & Dormers	94
Appliances	95
Breezeways & Porches	95
Finished Attic	95
Garages	96
Site Improvements	96
Wings & Ells	74

Important: See the Reference Section for Location Factors (to adjust for your city) and Estimating Forms.

		Cost Per Square Foot Of Living Area			% of Total
		Mat.	Inst.	Total	(rounded)
1 Site Work	Excavation for lower level, 4' deep. Site preparation for slab.		.68	.68	0.7%
2 Foundation	Continuous reinforced concrete footing 8" deep x 18" wide; dampproofed and insulated concrete block foundation wall, 12" thick, 4' deep, with grout and reinforcing; 4" concrete slab on 4" crushed stone base and polyethylene vapor barrier, trowel finish.	3.49	4.54	8.03	7.9%
3 Framing	Exterior walls - 2" x 6" wood studs, 16" O.C.; 1/2" plywood sheathing; 2" x 8" rafters 16" O.C. with 1/2" plywood sheathing, 6 in 12 pitch; 2" x 8" ceiling joists 16" O.C.; 2" x 10" floor joists 16" O.C. with 5/8" plywood subfloor; 5/8" plywood subfloor on 1" x 3" wood sleepers 16" O.C.	5.66	7.10	12.76	12.5%
4 Exterior Walls	Horizontal beveled wood siding; building paper; 6" batt insulation; wood double hung windows; 3 solid core wood exterior doors; storms and screens.	8.89	3.15	12.04	11.8%
5 Roofing	30 year asphalt shingles; #15 felt building paper; aluminum gutters, downspouts and drip edge; copper flashings.	2.15	1.79	3.94	3.9%
6 Interiors	Walls and ceilings - 5/8" gypsum wallboard, skim coat plaster, painted with primer and 2 coats; hardwood baseboard and trim, sanded and finished; hardwood floor 70%, ceramic tile with underlayment 20%, vinyl tile with underlayment 10%; wood panel interior doors, primed and painted with 2 coats.	15.33	14.00	29.33	28.7%
7 Specialties	Custom grade kitchen cabinets - 20 L.F. wall and base with solid surface counter top and kitchen sink; 4 L.F. bathroom vanity; 75 gallon electric water heater, medicine cabinet.	5.13	1.12	6.25	6.1%
8 Mechanical	Gas fired warm air heat/air conditioning; one full bath including: bathtub, corner shower, built in lavatory and water closet; one 1/2 bath including: built in lavatory and water closet.	6.04	3.16	9.20	9.0%
9 Electrical	200 Amp. service; Romex wiring; fluorescent and incandescent lighting fixtures, switches, receptacles.	1.16	1.74	2.90	2.8%
10 Overhead	Contractor's overhead and profit and design.	9.55	7.47	17.02	16.7%
Total		57.40	44.75	**102.15**	

- A distinct residence from designer's plans
- Single family — 1 full bath, 1 half bath, 1 kitchen
- No basement
- Asphalt shingles on roof
- Forced hot air heat/air conditioning
- Gypsum wallboard interior finishes
- Materials and workmanship are above average

Note: The illustration shown may contain some optional components (for example: garages and/or fireplaces) whose costs are shown in the modifications, adjustments, & alternatives below or at the end of the square foot section.

©Design Basics, Inc.

Base cost per square foot of living area

Exterior Wall	Living Area										
	1200	1500	1800	2100	2400	2800	3200	3600	4000	4500	5000
Wood Siding - Wood Frame	148.25	134.30	123.90	115.20	109.45	105.20	100.30	95.05	92.85	87.85	85.25
Brick Veneer - Wood Frame	155.55	140.85	129.85	120.60	114.55	110.05	104.85	99.25	96.90	91.60	88.75
Stone Veneer - Wood Frame	161.90	146.65	135.05	125.35	119.00	114.35	108.80	102.95	100.45	94.90	91.85
Solid Masonry	165.45	149.85	137.90	128.00	121.45	116.70	110.95	105.00	102.40	96.70	93.60
Finished Basement, Add*	37.90	37.85	36.20	34.95	34.10	33.50	32.75	31.95	31.60	30.95	30.45
Unfinished Basement, Add*	16.05	15.20	14.35	13.65	13.20	12.95	12.50	12.15	11.95	11.60	11.35

*Basement under middle level only.

Modifications

Add to the total cost

Upgrade Kitchen Cabinets	$ + 1315
Solid Surface Countertops (Included)	
Full Bath - including plumbing, wall and floor finishes	+ 8543
Half Bath - including plumbing, wall and floor finishes	+ 4916
Two Car Attached Garage	+ 26,684
Two Car Detached Garage	+ 30,391
Fireplace & Chimney	+ 6305

Adjustments

For multi family - add to total cost

Additional Kitchen	$ + 16,589
Additional Full Bath & Half Bath	+ 13,459
Additional Entry & Exit	+ 1620
Separate Heating & Air Conditioning	+ 6803
Separate Electric	+ 1986

For Townhouse/Rowhouse - Multiply cost per square foot by

Inner Unit	.87
End Unit	.94

Alternatives

Add to or deduct from the cost per square foot of living area

Cedar Shake Roof	+ 1.45
Clay Tile Roof	+ 4.65
Slate Roof	+ 4.00
Upgrade Ceilings to Textured Finish	+ .50
Air Conditioning, in Heating Ductwork	Base System
Heating Systems, Hot Water	+ 1.97
Heat Pump	+ 3.08
Electric Heat	− 1.08
Not Heated	− 3.32

Additional upgrades or components

Kitchen Cabinets & Countertops	Page 93
Bathroom Vanities	94
Fireplaces & Chimneys	94
Windows, Skylights & Dormers	94
Appliances	95
Breezeways & Porches	95
Finished Attic	95
Garages	96
Site Improvements	96
Wings & Ells	74

Important: See the Reference Section for Location Factors (to adjust for your city) and Estimating Forms.

		Cost Per Square Foot Of Living Area			% of Total
		Mat.	Inst.	Total	(rounded)
1 Site Work	Site preparation for slab; 4' deep trench excavation for foundation wall, excavation for lower level, 4' deep.		.60	.60	0.6%
2 Foundation	Continuous reinforced concrete footing 8" deep x 18" wide; dampproofed and insulated concrete block foundation wall, 12" thick, 4' deep, with grout and reinforcing; 4" concrete slab on 4" crushed stone base and polyethylene vapor barrier, trowel finish.	4.11	5.23	9.34	9.3%
3 Framing	Exterior walls - 2" x 6" wood studs, 16" O.C.; 1/2" plywood sheathing; 2" x 8" rafters 16" O.C. with 1/2" plywood sheathing, 6 in 12 pitch; 2" x 8" ceiling joists 16" O.C.; 2" x 10" floor joists 16" O.C. with 5/8" plywood subfloor; 5/8" plywood subfloor on 1" x 3" wood sleepers 16" O.C.	5.09	6.97	12.06	12.0%
4 Exterior Walls	Horizontal beveled wood siding; building paper; 6" batt insulation; wood double hung windows; 3 solid core wood exterior doors; storms and screens.	8.55	3.02	11.57	11.5%
5 Roofing	30 year asphalt shingles; #15 felt building paper; aluminum gutters, downspouts and drip edge; copper flashings.	2.87	2.38	5.25	5.2%
6 Interiors	Walls and ceilings - 5/8" gypsum wallboard, skim coat plaster, painted with primer and 2 coats; hardwood baseboard and trim, sanded and finished; hardwood floor 70%, ceramic tile with underlayment 20%, vinyl tile with underlayment 10%; wood panel interior doors, primed and painted with 2 coats.	14.56	13.41	27.97	27.9%
7 Specialties	Custom grade kitchen cabinets - 20 L.F. wall and base with solid surface counter top and kitchen sink; 4 L.F. bathroom vanity; 75 gallon electric water heater, medicine cabinet.	4.51	.97	5.48	5.5%
8 Mechanical	Gas fired warm air heat/air conditioning; one full bath including: bathtub, corner shower, built in lavatory and water closet; one 1/2 bath including: built in lavatory and water closet.	5.47	3.04	8.51	8.5%
9 Electrical	200 Amp. service; Romex wiring; fluorescent and incandescent lighting fixtures, switches, receptacles.	1.13	1.69	2.82	2.8%
10 Overhead	Contractor's overhead and profit and design.	9.26	7.44	16.70	16.7%
Total		55.55	44.75	100.30	

1 Story — Base cost per square foot of living area

Exterior Wall	Living Area							
	50	100	200	300	400	500	600	700
Wood Siding - Wood Frame	235.80	184.10	161.65	137.75	130.40	125.90	123.00	123.95
Brick Veneer - Wood Frame	260.50	201.80	176.35	147.60	139.20	134.20	130.85	131.55
Stone Veneer - Wood Frame	282.05	217.15	189.20	156.05	146.90	141.30	137.70	138.15
Solid Masonry	294.00	225.75	196.30	160.85	151.20	145.35	141.50	141.80
Finished Basement, Add	90.60	77.55	70.35	58.35	55.95	54.50	53.55	52.85
Unfinished Basement, Add	66.25	45.70	36.20	27.80	25.60	24.25	23.35	22.70

1-1/2 Story — Base cost per square foot of living area

Exterior Wall	Living Area							
	100	200	300	400	500	600	700	800
Wood Siding - Wood Frame	189.00	155.70	135.45	123.40	117.35	114.40	110.65	109.60
Brick Veneer - Wood Frame	211.05	173.35	150.15	134.85	127.95	124.40	120.10	118.95
Stone Veneer - Wood Frame	230.20	188.70	162.95	144.85	137.15	133.10	128.35	127.15
Solid Masonry	240.95	197.30	170.15	150.45	142.30	137.95	132.90	131.70
Finished Basement, Add	60.75	56.30	51.50	46.15	44.75	43.80	42.90	42.80
Unfinished Basement, Add	39.55	30.05	25.60	21.75	20.45	19.55	18.80	18.55

2 Story — Base cost per square foot of living area

Exterior Wall	Living Area							
	100	200	400	600	800	1000	1200	1400
Wood Siding - Wood Frame	188.85	145.15	126.00	107.60	101.40	97.55	95.05	96.40
Brick Veneer - Wood Frame	213.50	162.75	140.65	117.45	110.15	105.80	102.95	103.95
Stone Veneer - Wood Frame	235.00	178.15	153.50	125.95	117.85	112.95	109.80	110.50
Solid Masonry	247.05	186.75	160.65	130.70	122.15	116.95	113.60	114.20
Finished Basement, Add	45.40	38.80	35.15	29.25	28.00	27.30	26.80	26.45
Unfinished Basement, Add	33.15	22.85	18.15	13.95	12.80	12.15	11.65	11.40

Base costs do not include bathroom or kitchen facilities. Use Modifications/Adjustments/Alternatives on pages 93–96 where appropriate.

Important: See the Reference Section for Location Factors (to adjust for your city) and Estimating Forms.

1 Story

1-1/2 Story

2 Story

2-1/2 Story

Bi-Level

Tri-Level

- Unique residence built from an architect's plan
- Single family — 1 full bath, 1 half bath, 1 kitchen
- No basement
- Cedar shakes on roof
- Forced hot air heat/air conditioning
- Gypsum wallboard interior finishes
- Many special features
- Extraordinary materials and workmanship

Note: The illustration shown may contain some optional components (for example: garages and/or fireplaces) whose costs are shown in the modifications, adjustments, & alternatives below or at the end of the square foot section.

©Home Planners, Inc.

Base cost per square foot of living area

Exterior Wall	Living Area										
	1000	1200	1400	1600	1800	2000	2400	2800	3200	3600	4000
Wood Siding - Wood Frame	208.10	191.70	178.60	169.60	164.40	158.60	147.90	140.10	134.75	129.00	124.40
Brick Veneer - Wood Frame	217.20	199.90	186.05	176.60	171.20	164.90	153.65	145.45	139.65	133.60	128.75
Solid Brick	232.35	213.55	198.55	188.20	182.40	175.45	163.35	154.35	147.95	141.30	135.95
Solid Stone	236.15	217.05	201.65	191.20	185.25	178.15	165.80	156.60	150.05	143.25	137.75
Finished Basement, Add	54.90	59.00	56.65	55.10	54.25	52.85	51.15	49.75	48.55	47.45	46.55
Unfinished Basement, Add	24.45	22.95	21.75	21.00	20.55	19.85	19.00	18.25	17.65	17.10	16.65

Modifications

Add to the total cost

Upgrade Kitchen Cabinets	$ + 1735
Solid Surface Countertops (Included)	
Full Bath - including plumbing, wall and floor finishes	+ 10,251
Half Bath - including plumbing, wall and floor finishes	+ 5900
Two Car Attached Garage	+ 30,537
Two Car Detached Garage	+ 34,570
Fireplace & Chimney	+ 9032

Adjustments

For multi family - add to total cost

Additional Kitchen	$ + 21,242
Additional Full Bath & Half Bath	+ 16,151
Additional Entry & Exit	+ 2306
Separate Heating & Air Conditioning	+ 6803
Separate Electric	+ 1986

*For Townhouse/Rowhouse -
Multiply cost per square foot by*

Inner Unit	.90
End Unit	.95

Alternatives

Add to or deduct from the cost per square foot of living area

Heavyweight Asphalt Shingles	– 2.05
Clay Tile Roof	+ 4.45
Slate Roof	+ 3.50
Upgrade Ceilings to Textured Finish	+ .50
Air Conditioning, in Heating Ductwork	Base System
Heating Systems, Hot Water	+ 2.37
Heat Pump	+ 2.73
Electric Heat	– 1.22
Not Heated	– 4.29

Additional upgrades or components

Kitchen Cabinets & Countertops	Page 93
Bathroom Vanities	94
Fireplaces & Chimneys	94
Windows, Skylights & Dormers	94
Appliances	95
Breezeways & Porches	95
Finished Attic	95
Garages	96
Site Improvements	96
Wings & Ells	92

Important: See the Reference Section for Location Factors (to adjust for your city) and Estimating Forms.

Living Area - 2800 S.F.
Perimeter - 219 L.F.

		Cost Per Square Foot Of Living Area			% of Total
		Mat.	Inst.	Total	(rounded)
1 Site Work	Site preparation for slab; 4' deep trench excavation for foundation wall.		.73	.73	0.5%
2 Foundation	Continuous reinforced concrete footing 12" deep x 24" wide; dampproofed and insulated concrete block foundation wall, 12" thick, 4' deep, grouted and reinforced; 4" concrete slab on 4" crushed stone base and polyethylene vapor barrier, trowel finish.	6.88	7.69	14.57	10.4%
3 Framing	Exterior walls - 2" x 6" wood studs, 16" O.C.; 5/8" plywood sheathing; 2" x 10" rafters 16" O.C. with 5/8" plywood sheathing, 6 in 12 pitch; 2" x 8" ceiling joists 16" O.C.; 5/8" plywood subfloor on 1" x 3" wood sleepers 16" O.C.	11.43	14.07	25.50	18.2%
4 Exterior Walls	Horizontal beveled wood siding; building paper; 6" batt insulation; wood double hung windows; 3 solid core wood exterior doors; storms and screens.	9.34	3.40	12.74	9.1%
5 Roofing	Red cedar shingles; #15 felt building paper; aluminum gutters, downspouts and drip edge; copper flashings.	5.03	4.17	9.20	6.6%
6 Interiors	Walls and ceilings - 5/8" gypsum wallboard, skim coat plaster, painted with primer and 2 coats; hardwood baseboard and trim, sanded and finished; hardwood floor 70%, ceramic tile with underlayment 20%, vinyl tile with underlayment 10%; wood panel interior doors, primed and painted with 2 coats.	14.22	14.20	28.42	20.3%
7 Specialties	Luxury grade kitchen cabinets - 25 L.F. wall and base with solid surface counter top and kitchen sink; 6 L.F. bathroom vanity; 75 gallon electric water heater; medicine cabinet.	6.69	1.42	8.11	5.8%
8 Mechanical	Gas fired warm air heat/air conditioning; one full bath including: bathtub, corner shower; built in lavatory and water closet; one 1/2 bath including: built in lavatory and water closet.	6.77	3.48	10.25	7.3%
9 Electrical	200 Amp. service; Romex wiring; fluorescent and incandescent lighting fixtures; intercom, switches, receptacles.	1.38	2.08	3.46	2.5%
10 Overhead	Contractor's overhead and profit and architect's fees.	14.81	12.31	27.12	19.4%
Total		76.55	63.55	**140.10**	

- **Unique residence built from an architect's plan**
- **Single family — 1 full bath, 1 half bath, 1 kitchen**
- **No basement**
- **Cedar shakes on roof**
- **Forced hot air heat/air conditioning**
- **Gypsum wallboard interior finishes**
- **Many special features**
- **Extraordinary materials and workmanship**

Note: The illustration shown may contain some optional components (for example: garages and/or fireplaces) whose costs are shown in the modifications, adjustments, & alternatives below or at the end of the square foot section.

©Larry E. Belk Designs

Base cost per square foot of living area

Exterior Wall	Living Area										
	1000	1200	1400	1600	1800	2000	2400	2800	3200	3600	4000
Wood Siding - Wood Frame	193.45	179.35	169.20	157.45	150.60	144.05	131.85	126.00	120.80	116.70	111.20
Brick Veneer - Wood Frame	203.95	189.15	178.60	166.00	158.75	151.75	138.60	132.45	126.70	122.45	116.50
Solid Brick	221.45	205.60	194.20	180.20	172.30	164.60	149.90	143.15	136.65	131.95	125.40
Solid Stone	225.90	209.75	198.20	183.80	175.65	167.75	152.75	145.85	139.20	134.35	127.65
Finished Basement, Add	38.55	41.85	40.60	38.75	37.75	36.85	34.95	34.10	33.10	32.55	31.80
Unfinished Basement, Add	17.65	16.80	16.20	15.30	14.80	14.35	13.40	12.95	12.45	12.15	11.80

Modifications

Add to the total cost

Upgrade Kitchen Cabinets	$ + 1735
Solid Surface Countertops (Included)	
Full Bath - including plumbing, wall and floor finishes	+ 10,251
Half Bath - including plumbing, wall and floor finishes	+ 5900
Two Car Attached Garage	+ 30,537
Two Car Detached Garage	+ 34,570
Fireplace & Chimney	+ 9032

Adjustments

For multi family - add to total cost

Additional Kitchen	$ + 21,242
Additional Full Bath & Half Bath	+ 16,151
Additional Entry & Exit	+ 2306
Separate Heating & Air Conditioning	+ 6803
Separate Electric	+ 1986

*For Townhouse/Rowhouse -
Multiply cost per square foot by*

Inner Unit	.90
End Unit	.95

Alternatives

Add to or deduct from the cost per square foot of living area

Heavyweight Asphalt Shingles	– 1.45
Clay Tile Roof	+ 3.20
Slate Roof	+ 2.55
Upgrade Ceilings to Textured Finish	+ .50
Air Conditioning, in Heating Ductwork	Base System
Heating Systems, Hot Water	+ 2.27
Heat Pump	+ 3.04
Electric Heat	– 1.22
Not Heated	– 3.96

Additional upgrades or components

Kitchen Cabinets & Countertops	Page 93
Bathroom Vanities	94
Fireplaces & Chimneys	94
Windows, Skylights & Dormers	94
Appliances	95
Breezeways & Porches	95
Finished Attic	95
Garages	96
Site Improvements	96
Wings & Ells	92

Luxury 1-1/2 Story

Living Area - 2800 S.F.
Perimeter - 175 L.F.

		Cost Per Square Foot Of Living Area			% of Total
		Mat.	Inst.	Total	(rounded)
1 Site Work	Site preparation for slab; 4' deep trench excavation for foundation wall.		.73	.73	0.6%
2 Foundation	Continuous reinforced concrete footing 12" deep x 24" wide; dampproofed and insulated concrete block foundation wall, 12" thick, 4' deep, grouted and reinforced; 4" concrete slab on 4" crushed stone base and polyethylene vapor barrier, trowel finish.	4.98	5.80	10.78	8.6%
3 Framing	Exterior walls - 2" x 6" wood studs, 16" O.C.; 5/8" plywood sheathing; 2" x 10" rafters 16" O.C. with 5/8" plywood sheathing, 8 in 12 pitch; 2" x 8" ceiling joists 16" O.C.; 2" x 12" floor joists 16" O.C. with 5/8" plywood subfloor; 5/8" plywood subfloor on 1" x 3" wood sleepers 16" O.C.	6.92	9.14	16.06	12.7%
4 Exterior Walls	Horizontal beveled wood siding; building paper; 6" batt insulation; wood double hung windows; 3 solid core wood exterior doors; storms and screens.	10.36	3.83	14.19	11.3%
5 Roofing	Red cedar shingles; #15 felt building paper; aluminum gutters, downspouts and drip edge; copper flashings.	3.14	2.61	5.75	4.6%
6 Interiors	Walls and ceilings - 5/8" gypsum wallboard, skim coat plaster, painted with primer and 2 coats; hardwood baseboard and trim, sanded and finished; hardwood floor 70%, ceramic tile with underlayment 20%, vinyl tile with underlayment 10%; wood panel interior doors, primed and painted with 2 coats.	16.23	16.08	32.31	25.6%
7 Specialties	Luxury grade kitchen cabinets - 25 L.F. wall and base with solid surface counter top and kitchen sink; 6 L.F. bathroom vanity; 75 gallon electric water heater; medicine cabinet.	6.69	1.42	8.11	6.4%
8 Mechanical	Gas fired warm air heat/air conditioning; one full bath including: bathtub, corner shower; built in lavatory and water closet; one 1/2 bath including: built in lavatory and water closet.	6.77	3.48	10.25	8.1%
9 Electrical	200 Amp. service; Romex wiring; fluorescent and incandescent lighting fixtures; intercom, switches, receptacles.	1.38	2.08	3.46	2.7%
10 Overhead	Contractor's overhead and profit and architect's fees.	13.53	10.83	24.36	19.3%
	Total	70.00	56.00	**126.00**	

- Unique residence built from an architect's plan
- Single family — 1 full bath, 1 half bath, 1 kitchen
- No basement
- Cedar shakes on roof
- Forced hot air heat/air conditioning
- Gypsum wallboard interior finishes
- Many special features
- Extraordinary materials and workmanship

Note: The illustration shown may contain some optional components (for example: garages and/or fireplaces) whose costs are shown in the modifications, adjustments, & alternatives below or at the end of the square foot section.

Base cost per square foot of living area

Exterior Wall	Living Area										
	1200	1400	1600	1800	2000	2400	2800	3200	3600	4000	4400
Wood Siding - Wood Frame	178.85	167.80	159.80	152.85	145.55	134.95	126.10	120.30	116.70	113.05	109.95
Brick Veneer - Wood Frame	190.10	178.30	169.85	162.30	154.60	143.15	133.55	127.30	123.40	119.40	116.05
Solid Brick	208.85	195.75	186.60	178.05	169.80	156.85	146.00	138.90	134.65	129.95	126.30
Solid Stone	213.50	200.20	190.75	182.00	173.65	160.30	149.15	141.90	137.45	132.60	128.90
Finished Basement, Add	31.00	33.60	32.75	31.75	31.05	29.55	28.40	27.60	27.15	26.50	26.15
Unfinished Basement, Add	14.15	13.50	13.10	12.55	12.20	11.50	10.85	10.50	10.25	9.95	9.75

Modifications

Add to the total cost

Upgrade Kitchen Cabinets	$ + 1735
Solid Surface Countertops (Included)	
Full Bath - including plumbing, wall and floor finishes	+ 10,251
Half Bath - including plumbing, wall and floor finishes	+ 5900
Two Car Attached Garage	+ 30,537
Two Car Detached Garage	+ 34,570
Fireplace & Chimney	+ 9900

Adjustments

For multi family - add to total cost

Additional Kitchen	$ + 21,242
Additional Full Bath & Half Bath	+ 16,151
Additional Entry & Exit	+ 2306
Separate Heating & Air Conditioning	+ 6803
Separate Electric	+ 1986

For Townhouse/Rowhouse - Multiply cost per square foot by

Inner Unit	.86
End Unit	.93

Alternatives

Add to or deduct from the cost per square foot of living area

Heavyweight Asphalt Shingles	– 1.00
Clay Tile Roof	+ 2.25
Slate Roof	+ 1.75
Upgrade Ceilings to Textured Finish	+ .50
Air Conditioning, in Heating Ductwork	Base System
Heating Systems, Hot Water	+ 2.20
Heat Pump	+ 3.20
Electric Heat	– 1.10
Not Heated	– 3.74

Additional upgrades or components

Kitchen Cabinets & Countertops	Page 93
Bathroom Vanities	94
Fireplaces & Chimneys	94
Windows, Skylights & Dormers	94
Appliances	95
Breezeways & Porches	95
Finished Attic	95
Garages	96
Site Improvements	96
Wings & Ells	92

Important: See the Reference Section for Location Factors (to adjust for your city) and Estimating Forms.

		Cost Per Square Foot Of Living Area			% of Total
		Mat.	Inst.	Total	(rounded)
1 Site Work	Site preparation for slab; 4' deep trench excavation for foundation wall.		.64	.64	0.5%
2 Foundation	Continuous reinforced concrete footing 12" deep x 24" wide; dampproofed and insulated concrete block foundation wall, 12" thick, 4' deep, grouted and reinforced; 4" concrete slab on 4" crushed stone base and polyethylene vapor barrier, trowel finish.	4.05	4.73	8.78	7.3%
3 Framing	Exterior walls - 2" x 6" wood studs, 16" O.C.; 5/8" plywood sheathing; 2" x 10" rafters 16" O.C. with 5/8" plywood sheathing, 6 in 12 pitch; 2" x 8" ceiling joists 16" O.C.; 2" x 12" floor joists 16" O.C. with 5/8" plywood subfloor; 5/8" plywood subfloor on 1" x 3" wood sleepers 16" O.C.	6.97	9.06	16.03	13.3%
4 Exterior Walls	Horizontal beveled wood siding, building paper; 6" batt insulation; wood double hung windows; 3 solid core wood exterior doors; storms and screens.	10.95	4.06	15.01	12.5%
5 Roofing	Red cedar shingles; #15 felt building paper; aluminum gutters, downspouts and drip edge; copper flashings.	2.51	2.09	4.60	3.8%
6 Interiors	Walls and ceilings - 5/8" gypsum wallboard, skim coat plaster, painted with primer and 2 coats; hardwood baseboard and trim, sanded and finished; hardwood floor 70%, ceramic tile with underlayment 20%, vinyl tile with underlayment 10%; wood panel interior doors, primed and painted with 2 coats.	16.00	15.99	31.99	26.6%
7 Specialties	Luxury grade kitchen cabinets - 25 L.F. wall and base with solid surface counter top and kitchen sink; 6 L.F. bathroom vanity; 75 gallon electric water heater; medicine cabinet.	5.87	1.22	7.09	5.9%
8 Mechanical	Gas fired warm air heat/air conditioning; one full bath including: bathtub, corner shower; built in lavatory and water closet; one 1/2 bath including: built in lavatory and water closet.	6.14	3.35	9.49	7.9%
9 Electrical	200 Amp. service; Romex wiring; fluorescent and incandescent lighting fixtures; intercom, switches, receptacles.	1.35	2.03	3.38	2.8%
10 Overhead	Contractor's overhead and profit and architect's fee.	12.91	10.38	23.29	19.4%
Total		66.75	53.55	**120.30**	

- **Unique residence built from an architect's plan**
- **Single family — 1 full bath, 1 half bath, 1 kitchen**
- **No basement**
- **Cedar shakes on roof**
- **Forced hot air heat/air conditioning**
- **Gypsum wallboard interior finishes**
- **Many special features**
- **Extraordinary materials and workmanship**

Note: The illustration shown may contain some optional components (for example: garages and/or fireplaces) whose costs are shown in the modifications, adjustments, & alternatives below or at the end of the square foot section.

©Larry W. Garnett & Associates, Inc

Base cost per square foot of living area

Exterior Wall	Living Area										
	1500	1800	2100	2500	3000	3500	4000	4500	5000	5500	6000
Wood Siding - Wood Frame	173.75	156.15	145.70	137.95	127.50	119.95	112.70	109.15	106.00	102.85	99.35
Brick Veneer - Wood Frame	185.45	166.90	155.40	147.05	135.80	127.45	119.65	115.70	112.25	108.85	105.05
Solid Brick	204.90	184.80	171.40	162.20	149.55	140.05	131.25	126.70	122.75	118.80	114.60
Solid Stone	209.90	189.35	175.45	166.00	153.05	143.20	134.15	129.40	125.40	121.30	117.00
Finished Basement, Add	24.70	26.55	25.10	24.25	23.15	22.15	21.50	21.00	20.50	20.15	19.90
Unfinished Basement, Add	11.40	10.75	10.00	9.65	9.05	8.55	8.20	7.95	7.75	7.60	7.40

Modifications

Add to the total cost

Upgrade Kitchen Cabinets	$ + 1735
Solid Surface Countertops (Included)	
Full Bath - including plumbing, wall and floor finishes	+ 10,251
Half Bath - including plumbing, wall and floor finishes	+ 5900
Two Car Attached Garage	+ 30,537
Two Car Detached Garage	+ 34,570
Fireplace & Chimney	+ 10,835

Adjustments

For multi family - add to total cost

Additional Kitchen	$ + 21,242
Additional Full Bath & Half Bath	+ 16,151
Additional Entry & Exit	+ 2306
Separate Heating & Air Conditioning	+ 6803
Separate Electric	+ 1986

For Townhouse/Rowhouse - Multiply cost per square foot by

Inner Unit	.86
End Unit	.93

Alternatives

Add to or deduct from the cost per square foot of living area

Heavyweight Asphalt Shingles	– .90
Clay Tile Roof	+ 1.90
Slate Roof	+ 1.50
Upgrade Ceilings to Textured Finish	+ .50
Air Conditioning, in Heating Ductwork	Base System
Heating Systems, Hot Water	+ 1.99
Heat Pump	+ 3.29
Electric Heat	– 2.16
Not Heated	– 3.74

Additional upgrades or components

Kitchen Cabinets & Countertops	Page 93
Bathroom Vanities	94
Fireplaces & Chimneys	94
Windows, Skylights & Dormers	94
Appliances	95
Breezeways & Porches	95
Finished Attic	95
Garages	96
Site Improvements	96
Wings & Ells	92

Luxury 2-1/2 Story

Living Area - 3000 S.F.
Perimeter - 148 L.F.

		Cost Per Square Foot Of Living Area			% of Total
		Mat.	Inst.	Total	(rounded)
1 Site Work	Site preparation for slab; 4' deep trench excavation for foundation wall.		.69	.69	0.5%
2 Foundation	Continuous reinforced concrete footing 12" deep x 24" wide; dampproofed and insulated concrete block foundation wall, 12" thick, 4' deep, grouted and reinforced; 4" concrete slab on 4" crushed stone base and polyethylene vapor barrier, trowel finish.	3.56	4.29	7.85	6.2%
3 Framing	Exterior walls - 2" x 6" wood studs, 16" O.C.; 5/8" plywood sheathing; 2" x 10" rafters 16" O.C. with 5/8" plywood sheathing, 8 in 12 pitch; 2" x 8" ceiling joists 16" O.C.; 2" x 12" floor joists 16" O.C. with 5/8" plywood subfloor; 5/8" plywood subfloor on 1" x 3" wood sleepers 16" O.C.	7.22	9.33	16.55	13.0%
4 Exterior Walls	Horizontal beveled wood siding; building paper; 6" batt insulation; wood double hung windows; 3 solid core wood exterior doors; storms and screens.	12.79	4.74	17.53	13.7%
5 Roofing	Red cedar shingles; #15 felt building paper; aluminum gutters, downspouts and drip edge; copper flashings.	1.93	1.61	3.54	2.8%
6 Interiors	Walls and ceilings - 5/8" gypsum wallboard, skim coat plaster, painted with primer and 2 coats; hardwood baseboard and trim, sanded and finished; hardwood floor 70%, ceramic tile with underlayment 20%, vinyl tile with underlayment 10%; wood panel interior doors, primed and painted with 2 coats.	18.05	17.79	35.84	28.1%
7 Specialties	Luxury grade kitchen cabinets - 25 L.F. wall and base with solid surface counter top and kitchen sink; 6 L.F. bathroom vanity; 75 gallon electric water heater; medicine cabinet.	6.24	1.31	7.55	5.9%
8 Mechanical	Gas fired warm air heat/air conditioning; one full bath including: bathtub, corner shower; built in lavatory and water closet; one 1/2 bath including: built in lavatory and water closet.	6.45	3.43	9.88	7.7%
9 Electrical	200 Amp. service; Romex wiring; fluorescent and incandescent lighting fixtures; intercom, switches, receptacles.	1.36	2.06	3.42	2.7%
10 Overhead	Contractor's overhead and profit and architect's fee.	13.80	10.85	24.65	19.3%
Total		71.40	56.10	**127.50**	

- Unique residence built from an architect's plan
- Single family — 1 full bath, 1 half bath, 1 kitchen
- No basement
- Cedar shakes on roof
- Forced hot air heat/air conditioning
- Gypsum wallboard interior finishes
- Many special features
- Extraordinary materials and workmanship

Note: The illustration shown may contain some optional components (for example: garages and/or fireplaces) whose costs are shown in the modifications, adjustments, & alternatives below or at the end of the square foot section.

Base cost per square foot of living area

Exterior Wall	Living Area										
	1500	1800	2100	2500	3000	3500	4000	4500	5000	5500	6000
Wood Siding - Wood Frame	172.65	155.25	146.65	139.40	128.50	122.95	116.40	109.55	107.05	104.30	101.55
Brick Veneer - Wood Frame	184.80	166.50	157.10	149.40	137.55	131.60	124.25	116.80	114.10	111.05	107.85
Solid Brick	205.10	185.20	174.60	166.15	152.75	146.00	137.30	128.80	125.70	122.25	118.40
Solid Stone	210.15	189.90	179.05	170.35	156.60	149.55	140.60	131.90	128.70	125.05	121.10
Finished Basement, Add	21.70	23.40	22.35	21.70	20.70	20.05	19.25	18.65	18.35	18.05	17.65
Unfinished Basement, Add	10.00	9.45	8.95	8.65	8.15	7.85	7.40	7.15	7.00	6.85	6.60

Modifications

Add to the total cost

Upgrade Kitchen Cabinets	$ + 1735
Solid Surface Countertops (Included)	
Full Bath - including plumbing, wall and floor finishes	+ 10,251
Half Bath - including plumbing, wall and floor finishes	+ 5900
Two Car Attached Garage	+ 30,537
Two Car Detached Garage	+ 34,570
Fireplace & Chimney	+ 10,835

Adjustments

For multi family - add to total cost

Additional Kitchen	$ + 21,242
Additional Full Bath & Half Bath	+ 16,151
Additional Entry & Exit	+ 2306
Separate Heating & Air Conditioning	+ 6803
Separate Electric	+ 1986

*For Townhouse/Rowhouse -
Multiply cost per square foot by*

Inner Unit	.84
End Unit	.92

Alternatives

Add to or deduct from the cost per square foot of living area

Heavyweight Asphalt Shingles	– .70
Clay Tile Roof	+ 1.50
Slate Roof	+ 1.15
Upgrade Ceilings to Textured Finish	+ .50
Air Conditioning, in Heating Ductwork	Base System
Heating Systems, Hot Water	+ 1.99
Heat Pump	+ 3.29
Electric Heat	– 2.16
Not Heated	– 3.63

Additional upgrades or components

Kitchen Cabinets & Countertops	Page 93
Bathroom Vanities	94
Fireplaces & Chimneys	94
Windows, Skylights & Dormers	94
Appliances	95
Breezeways & Porches	95
Finished Attic	95
Garages	96
Site Improvements	96
Wings & Ells	92

Important: See the Reference Section for Location Factors (to adjust for your city) and Estimating Forms.

Luxury 3 Story

Living Area - 3000 S.F.
Perimeter - 135 L.F.

			Cost Per Square Foot Of Living Area			% of Total
			Mat.	Inst.	Total	(rounded)
1	**Site Work**	Site preparation for slab; 4' deep trench excavation for foundation wall.		.69	.69	0.5%
2	**Foundation**	Continuous reinforced concrete footing 12" deep x 24" wide; dampproofed and insulated concrete block foundation wall, 12" thick, 4' deep, grouted and reinforced; 4" concrete slab on 4" crushed stone base and polyethylene vapor barrier, trowel finish.	3.20	3.89	7.09	5.5%
3	**Framing**	Exterior walls - 2" x 6" wood studs, 16" O.C.; 5/8" plywood sheathing; 2" x 10" rafters 16" O.C. with 5/8" plywood sheathing, 6 in 12 pitch; 2" x 8" ceiling joists 16" O.C.; 2" x 12" floor joists 16" O.C. with 5/8" plywood subfloor; 5/8" plywood subfloor on 1" x 3" wood sleepers 16" O.C.	7.36	9.44	16.80	13.1%
4	**Exterior Walls**	Horizontal beveled wood siding; building paper; 6" batt insulation; wood double hung windows; 3 solid core wood exterior doors; storms and screens.	13.96	5.17	19.13	14.9%
5	**Roofing**	Red cedar shingles; #15 felt building paper; aluminum gutters, downspouts and drip edge; copper flashings.	1.67	1.39	3.06	2.4%
6	**Interiors**	Walls and ceilings - 5/8" gypsum wallboard, skim coat plaster, painted with primer and 2 coats; hardwood baseboard and trim, sanded and finished; hardwood floor 70%, ceramic tile with underlayment 20%, vinyl tile with underlayment 10%; wood panel interior doors, primed and painted with 2 coats.	18.09	17.91	36.00	28.0%
7	**Specialties**	Luxury grade kitchen cabinets - 25 L.F. wall and base with solid surface counter top and kitchen sink; 6 L.F. bathroom vanity; 75 gallon electric water heater; medicine cabinet.	6.24	1.31	7.55	5.9%
8	**Mechanical**	Gas fired warm air heat/air conditioning; one full bath including: bathtub, corner shower; built in lavatory and water closet; one 1/2 bath including: built in lavatory and water closet.	6.45	3.43	9.88	7.7%
9	**Electrical**	200 Amp. service; Romex wiring; fluorescent and incandescent lighting fixtures; intercom, switches, receptacles.	1.36	2.06	3.42	2.7%
10	**Overhead**	Contractor's overhead and profit and architect's fees.	14.02	10.86	24.88	19.4%
	Total		72.35	56.15	**128.50**	

- **Unique residence built from an architect's plan**
- **Single family — 1 full bath, 1 half bath, 1 kitchen**
- **No basement**
- **Cedar shakes on roof**
- **Forced hot air heat/air conditioning**
- **Gypsum wallboard interior finishes**
- **Many special features**
- **Extraordinary materials and workmanship**

Note: The illustration shown may contain some optional components (for example: garages and/or fireplaces) whose costs are shown in the modifications, adjustments, & alternatives below or at the end of the square foot section.

Base cost per square foot of living area

Exterior Wall	Living Area										
	1200	1400	1600	1800	2000	2400	2800	3200	3600	4000	4400
Wood Siding - Wood Frame	169.40	159.00	151.45	144.95	137.95	128.15	119.85	114.40	111.00	107.75	104.75
Brick Veneer - Wood Frame	177.80	166.90	159.00	152.00	144.75	134.25	125.45	119.65	116.10	112.50	109.35
Solid Brick	191.95	180.00	171.55	163.85	156.15	144.55	134.75	128.40	124.55	120.40	117.05
Solid Stone	195.45	183.30	174.75	166.85	159.00	147.15	137.15	130.65	126.65	122.40	118.95
Finished Basement, Add	31.00	33.60	32.75	31.75	31.05	29.55	28.40	27.60	27.15	26.50	26.15
Unfinished Basement, Add	14.15	13.50	13.10	12.55	12.20	11.50	10.85	10.50	10.25	9.95	9.75

Modifications

Add to the total cost

Upgrade Kitchen Cabinets	$ + 1735
Solid Surface Countertops (Included)	
Full Bath - including plumbing, wall and floor finishes	+ 10,251
Half Bath - including plumbing, wall and floor finishes	+ 5900
Two Car Attached Garage	+ 30,537
Two Car Detached Garage	+ 34,570
Fireplace & Chimney	+ 9032

Adjustments

For multi family - add to total cost

Additional Kitchen	$ + 21,242
Additional Full Bath & Half Bath	+ 16,151
Additional Entry & Exit	+ 2306
Separate Heating & Air Conditioning	+ 6803
Separate Electric	+ 1986

For Townhouse/Rowhouse - Multiply cost per square foot by

Inner Unit	.89
End Unit	.94

Alternatives

Add to or deduct from the cost per square foot of living area

Heavyweight Asphalt Shingles	– 1.00
Clay Tile Roof	+ 2.25
Slate Roof	+ 1.75
Upgrade Ceilings to Textured Finish	+ .50
Air Conditioning, in Heating Ductwork	Base System
Heating Systems, Hot Water	+ 2.20
Heat Pump	+ 3.20
Electric Heat	– 1.10
Not Heated	– 3.74

Additional upgrades or components

Kitchen Cabinets & Countertops	Page 93
Bathroom Vanities	94
Fireplaces & Chimneys	94
Windows, Skylights & Dormers	94
Appliances	95
Breezeways & Porches	95
Finished Attic	95
Garages	96
Site Improvements	96
Wings & Ells	92

Luxury Bi-Level

Living Area - 3200 S.F.
Perimeter - 163 L.F.

			Cost Per Square Foot Of Living Area			% of Total
			Mat.	Inst.	Total	(rounded)
1	**Site Work**	Excavation for lower level, 4' deep. Site preparation for slab.		.64	.64	0.6%
2	**Foundation**	Continuous reinforced concrete footing 12" deep x 24" wide; dampproofed and insulated concrete block foundation wall, 12" thick, 4' deep, grouted and reinforced; 4" concrete slab on 4" crushed stone base and polyethylene vapor barrier, trowel finish.	4.05	4.73	8.78	7.7%
3	**Framing**	Exterior walls - 2" x 6" wood studs, 16" O.C.; 5/8" plywood sheathing; 2" x 10" rafters 16" O.C. with 5/8" plywood sheathing, 6 in 12 pitch; 2" x 8" ceiling joists 16" O.C.; 2" x 12" floor joists 16" O.C. with 5/8" plywood subfloor; 5/8" plywood subfloor on 1" x 3" wood sleepers 16" O.C.	6.65	8.62	15.27	13.3%
4	**Exterior Walls**	Horizontal beveled wood siding; building paper; 6" batt insulation; wood double hung windows; 3 solid core wood exterior doors; storms and screens.	8.52	3.14	11.66	10.2%
5	**Roofing**	Red cedar shingles: #15 felt building paper; aluminum gutters, downspouts and drip edge; copper flashings.	2.51	2.09	4.60	4.0%
6	**Interiors**	Walls and ceilings - 5/8" gypsum wallboard, skim coat plaster, painted with primer and 2 coats; hardwood baseboard and trim, sanded and finished; hardwood floor 70%, ceramic tile with underlayment 20%; vinyl tile with underlayment 10%; wood panel interior doors, primed and painted with 2 coats.	15.76	15.60	31.36	27.4%
7	**Specialties**	Luxury grade kitchen cabinets - 25 L.F. wall and base with solid surface counter top and kitchen sink; 6 L.F. bathroom vanity; 75 gallon electric water heater; medicine cabinet.	5.87	1.22	7.09	6.2%
8	**Mechanical**	Gas fired warm air heat/air conditioning; one full bath including: bathtub, corner shower; built in lavatory and water closet; one 1/2 bath including: built in lavatory and water closet.	6.14	3.35	9.49	8.3%
9	**Electrical**	200 Amp. service; Romex wiring; fluorescent and incandescent lighting fixtures; intercom, switches, receptacles.	1.35	2.03	3.38	3.0%
10	**Overhead**	Contractor's overhead and profit and architect's fees.	12.20	9.93	22.13	19.3%
	Total		63.05	51.35	**114.40**	

89

- **Unique residence built from an architect's plan**
- **Single family — 1 full bath, 1 half bath, 1 kitchen**
- **No basement**
- **Cedar shakes on roof**
- **Forced hot air heat/air conditioning**
- **Gypsum wallboard interior finishes**
- **Many special features**
- **Extraordinary materials and workmanship**

Note: The illustration shown may contain some optional components (for example: garages and/or fireplaces) whose costs are shown in the modifications, adjustments, & alternatives below or at the end of the square foot section.

©Home Planners, Inc.

Base cost per square foot of living area

Exterior Wall	Living Area										
	1500	1800	2100	2400	2800	3200	3600	4000	4500	5000	5500
Wood Siding - Wood Frame	158.95	146.85	136.70	129.90	124.85	119.10	113.00	110.40	104.80	101.65	98.10
Brick Veneer - Wood Frame	166.60	153.60	142.90	135.75	130.45	124.30	117.80	115.10	109.10	105.70	101.95
Solid Brick	179.20	165.00	153.30	145.45	139.75	132.90	125.85	122.90	116.25	112.50	108.40
Solid Stone	182.40	167.90	155.90	147.95	142.10	135.10	127.90	124.85	118.05	114.20	110.05
Finished Basement, Add*	36.55	39.35	37.75	36.70	35.95	34.95	34.05	33.65	32.75	32.15	31.65
Unfinished Basement, Add*	16.25	15.25	14.45	13.95	13.65	13.15	12.65	12.45	12.00	11.65	11.40

*Basement under middle level only.

Modifications

Add to the total cost

Upgrade Kitchen Cabinets	$ + 1735
Solid Surface Countertops (Included)	
Full Bath - including plumbing, wall and floor finishes	+ 10,251
Half Bath - including plumbing, wall and floor finishes	+ 5900
Two Car Attached Garage	+ 30,537
Two Car Detached Garage	+ 34,570
Fireplace & Chimney	+ 9032

Adjustments

For multi family - add to total cost

Additional Kitchen	$ + 21,242
Additional Full Bath & Half Bath	+ 16,151
Additional Entry & Exit	+ 2306
Separate Heating & Air Conditioning	+ 6803
Separate Electric	+ 1986

For Townhouse/Rowhouse - Multiply cost per square foot by

Inner Unit	.86
End Unit	.93

Alternatives

Add to or deduct from the cost per square foot of living area

Heavyweight Asphalt Shingles	– 1.45
Clay Tile Roof	+ 3.20
Slate Roof	+ 2.55
Upgrade Ceilings to Textured Finish	+ .50
Air Conditioning, in Heating Ductwork	Base System
Heating Systems, Hot Water	+ 2.13
Heat Pump	+ 3.32
Electric Heat	– .97
Not Heated	– 3.63

Additional upgrades or components

Kitchen Cabinets & Countertops	Page 93
Bathroom Vanities	94
Fireplaces & Chimneys	94
Windows, Skylights & Dormers	94
Appliances	95
Breezeways & Porches	95
Finished Attic	95
Garages	96
Site Improvements	96
Wings & Ells	92

Important: See the Reference Section for Location Factors (to adjust for your city) and Estimating Forms.

		Cost Per Square Foot Of Living Area			% of Total
		Mat.	Inst.	Total	(rounded)
1 Site Work	Site preparation for slab; 4' deep trench excavation for foundation wall, excavation for lower level, 4' deep.		.58	.58	0.5%
2 Foundation	Continuous reinforced concrete footing 12" deep x 24" wide; dampproofed and insulated concrete block foundation wall, 12" thick, 4' deep, grouted and reinforced; 4" concrete slab on 4" crushed stone base and polyethylene vapor barrier, trowel finish.	4.82	5.44	10.26	9.1%
3 Framing	Exterior walls - 2" x 6" wood studs, 16" O.C.; 5/8" plywood sheathing; 2" x 10" rafters 16" O.C. with 5/8" plywood sheathing, 6 in 12 pitch; 2" x 8" ceiling joists 16" O.C.; 2" x 12" floor joists 16" O.C. with 5/8" plywood subfloor; 5/8" plywood subfloor on 1" x 3" wood sleepers 16" O.C.	6.56	8.64	15.20	13.5%
4 Exterior Walls	Horizontal beveled wood siding; building paper; 6" batt insulation; wood double hung windows; 3 solid core wood exterior doors; storms and screens.	8.15	3.00	11.15	9.9%
5 Roofing	Red cedar shingles; #15 felt building paper; aluminum gutters, downspouts and drip edge; copper flashings.	3.36	2.78	6.14	5.4%
6 Interiors	Walls and ceilings - 5/8" gypsum wallboard, skim coat plaster, painted with primer and 2 coats; hardwood baseboard and trim, sanded and finished; hardwood floor 70%, ceramic tile with underlayment 20%, vinyl tile with underlayment 10%; wood panel interior doors, primed and painted with 2 coats.	14.80	14.59	29.39	26.0%
7 Specialties	Luxury grade kitchen cabinets - 25 L.F. wall and base with solid surface counter top and kitchen sink; 6 L.F. bathroom vanity; 75 gallon electric water heater; medicine cabinet.	5.19	1.09	6.28	5.6%
8 Mechanical	Gas fired warm air heat/air conditioning; one full bath including: bathtub, corner shower; built in lavatory and water closet; one 1/2 bath including: built in lavatory and water closet.	5.61	3.22	8.83	7.8%
9 Electrical	200 Amp. service; Romex wiring; fluorescent and incandescent lighting fixtures; intercom, switches, receptacles.	1.31	1.98	3.29	2.9%
10 Overhead	Contractor's overhead and profit and architect's fees.	11.95	9.93	21.88	19.4%
Total		61.75	51.25	**113.00**	

1 Story — Base cost per square foot of living area

Exterior Wall	Living Area							
	50	100	200	300	400	500	600	700
Wood Siding - Wood Frame	252.90	195.25	170.10	143.40	135.25	130.20	127.00	128.00
Brick Veneer - Wood Frame	281.20	215.50	186.95	154.65	145.35	139.65	136.00	136.70
Solid Brick	328.40	249.15	215.05	173.35	162.20	155.40	150.95	151.15
Solid Stone	340.30	257.65	222.15	178.05	166.45	159.35	154.70	154.75
Finished Basement, Add	98.10	88.90	79.80	64.60	61.50	59.65	58.45	57.65
Unfinished Basement, Add	50.90	39.20	34.35	26.30	24.70	23.70	23.10	22.60

1-1/2 Story — Base cost per square foot of living area

Exterior Wall	Living Area							
	100	200	300	400	500	600	700	800
Wood Siding - Wood Frame	200.85	163.80	141.15	127.70	120.90	117.70	113.45	112.25
Brick Veneer - Wood Frame	226.10	184.00	158.05	140.85	133.05	129.15	124.30	123.00
Solid Brick	268.30	217.70	186.15	162.80	153.30	148.25	142.35	140.90
Solid Stone	278.95	226.25	193.15	168.30	158.35	153.10	146.90	145.45
Finished Basement, Add	64.60	63.85	57.80	51.05	49.20	48.00	46.85	46.75
Unfinished Basement, Add	32.35	27.55	24.30	20.70	19.75	19.10	18.50	18.40

2 Story — Base cost per square foot of living area

Exterior Wall	Living Area							
	100	200	400	600	800	1000	1200	1400
Wood Siding - Wood Frame	198.00	149.20	127.85	107.30	100.40	96.10	93.40	94.75
Brick Veneer - Wood Frame	226.25	169.45	144.75	118.55	110.50	105.55	102.40	103.45
Solid Brick	273.50	203.15	172.80	137.30	127.35	121.30	117.35	117.85
Solid Stone	285.35	211.65	179.85	141.95	131.65	125.20	121.10	121.50
Finished Basement, Add	49.10	44.50	39.95	32.30	30.80	29.90	29.25	28.85
Unfinished Basement, Add	25.45	19.60	17.20	13.15	12.35	11.85	11.55	11.30

Base costs do not include bathroom or kitchen facilities. Use Modifications/Adjustments/Alternatives on pages 93–96 where appropriate.

Important: See the Reference Section for Location Factors (to adjust for your city) and Estimating Forms.

Kitchen cabinets - Base units, hardwood *(Cost per Unit)*

	Economy	Average	Custom	Luxury
24" deep, 35" high,				
One top drawer,				
One door below				
12" wide	$ 236	$ 315	$ 419	$ 551
15" wide	244	325	432	569
18" wide	263	350	466	613
21" wide	274	365	485	639
24" wide	319	425	565	744
Four drawers				
12" wide	248	330	439	578
15" wide	251	335	446	586
18" wide	274	365	485	639
24" wide	300	400	532	700
Two top drawers,				
Two doors below				
27" wide	341	455	605	796
30" wide	368	490	652	858
33" wide	379	505	672	884
36" wide	394	525	698	919
42" wide	416	555	738	971
48" wide	443	590	785	1033
Range or sink base				
(Cost per unit)				
Two doors below				
30" wide	308	410	545	718
33" wide	330	440	585	770
36" wide	345	460	612	805
42" wide	364	485	645	849
48" wide	379	505	672	884
Corner Base Cabinet				
(Cost per unit)				
36" wide	533	710	944	1243
Lazy Susan *(Cost per unit)*				
With revolving door	705	940	1250	1645

Kitchen cabinets - Wall cabinets, hardwood *(Cost per Unit)*

	Economy	Average	Custom	Luxury
12" deep, 2 doors				
12" high				
30" wide	$ 214	$ 285	$ 379	$ 499
36" wide	251	335	446	586
15" high				
30" wide	218	290	386	508
33" wide	263	350	466	613
36" wide	266	355	472	621
24" high				
30" wide	281	375	499	656
36" wide	311	415	552	726
42" wide	353	470	625	823
30" high, 1 door				
12" wide	200	267	355	467
15" wide	221	295	392	516
18" wide	240	320	426	560
24" wide	278	370	492	648
30" high, 2 doors				
27" wide	300	400	532	700
30" wide	319	425	565	744
36" wide	356	475	632	831
42" wide	383	510	678	893
48" wide	431	575	765	1006
Corner wall, 30" high				
24" wide	319	425	565	744
30" wide	338	450	599	788
36" wide	379	505	672	884
Broom closet				
84" high, 24" deep				
18" wide	578	770	1024	1348
Oven Cabinet				
84" high, 24" deep				
27" wide	863	1150	1530	2013

Kitchen countertops *(Cost per L.F.)*

	Economy	Average	Custom	Luxury
Solid Surface				
24" wide, no backsplash	108	144	192	252
with backsplash	117	156	207	273
Stock plastic laminate, 24" wide				
with backsplash	25	33	44	58
Custom plastic laminate, no splash				
7/8" thick, alum. molding	35	47	63	82
1-1/4" thick, no splash	40	53	71	94
Marble				
1/2" - 3/4" thick w/splash	53	70	93	123
Maple, laminated				
1-1/2" thick w/splash	84	112	149	196
Stainless steel				
(per S.F.)	137	183	243	320
Cutting blocks, recessed				
16" x 20" x 1" (each)	115	153	203	268

Vanity bases *(Cost per Unit)*

2 door, 30" high, 21" deep	Economy	Average	Custom	Luxury
24" wide	278	370	492	648
30" wide	334	445	592	779
36" wide	334	445	592	779
48" wide	428	570	758	998

Solid surface vanity tops *(Cost Each)*

Center bowl	Economy	Average	Custom	Luxury
22" x 25"	$ 420	$ 454	$ 490	$ 529
22" x 31"	480	518	559	604
22" x 37"	555	599	647	699
22" x 49"	685	740	799	863

Fireplaces & Chimneys *(Cost per Unit)*

	1-1/2 Story	2 Story	3 Story
Economy (prefab metal)			
Exterior chimney & 1 fireplace	$ 5691	$ 6288	$ 6898
Interior chimney & 1 fireplace	5453	6063	6343
Average (masonry)			
Exterior chimney & 1 fireplace	6029	6661	7307
Interior chimney & 1 fireplace	5777	6422	6719
For more than 1 flue, add	410	698	1170
For more than 1 fireplace, add	4045	4045	4045
Custom (masonry)			
Exterior chimney & 1 fireplace	6304	7115	8035
Interior chimney & 1 fireplace	5910	6690	7211
For more than 1 flue, add	494	856	1432
For more than 1 fireplace, add	4528	4528	4528
Luxury (masonry)			
Exterior chimney & 1 fireplace	9032	9900	10834
Interior chimney & 1 fireplace	8617	9421	9972
For more than 1 flue, add	745	1244	1737
For more than 1 fireplace, add	7119	7119	7119

Windows and Skylights *(Cost Each)*

	Economy	Average	Custom	Luxury
Fixed Picture Windows				
3'-6" x 4'-0"	$ 347	$ 462	$ 615	$ 809
4'-0" x 6'-0"	620	827	1100	1447
5'-0" x 6'-0"	691	921	1225	1612
6'-0" x 6'-0"	691	921	1225	1612
Bay/Bow Windows				
8'-0" x 5'-0"	860	1146	1525	2007
10'-0" x 5'-0"	930	1240	1650	2171
10'-0" x 6'-0"	1466	1954	2600	3421
12'-0" x 6'-0"	1903	2537	3375	4441
Palladian Windows				
3'-2" x 6'-4"		1466	1950	2566
4'-0" x 6'-0"		1729	2300	3026
5'-5" x 6'-10"		2255	3000	3947
8'-0" x 6'-0"		2650	3525	4638
Skylights				
46" x 21-1/2"	592	910	1115	1227
46" x 28"	614	945	1170	1287
57" x 44"	673	1035	1150	1265

Dormers *(Cost/S.F. of plan area)*

	Economy	Average	Custom	Luxury
Framing and Roofing Only				
Gable dormer, 2" x 6" roof frame	$ 29	$ 33	$ 35	$ 58
2" x 8" roof frame	30	34	36	61
Shed dormer, 2" x 6" roof frame	18	21	24	37
2" x 8" roof frame	20	22	25	38
2" x 10" roof frame	21	24	26	39

Appliances *(Cost per Unit)*

	Economy	Average	Custom	Luxury
Range				
30" free standing, 1 oven	$ 545	$ 1448	$ 1899	$ 2350
2 oven	1400	2125	2488	2850
30" built-in, 1 oven	820	1360	1630	1900
2 oven	1650	1898	2022	2145
21" free standing				
1 oven	560	605	628	650
Counter Top Ranges				
4 burner standard	400	988	1282	1575
As above with griddle	1425	2800	3488	4175
Microwave Oven	248	494	617	740
Compactor				
4 to 1 compaction	790	1020	1135	1250
Deep Freeze				
15 to 23 C.F.	730	878	952	1025
30 C.F.	845	1023	1112	1200
Dehumidifier, portable, auto.				
15 pint	282	325	346	367
30 pint	228	262	279	296
Washing Machine, automatic	690	1420	1785	2150
Water Heater				
Electric, glass lined				
30 gal.	595	728	794	860
80 gal.	1650	2063	2269	2475
Water Heater, Gas, glass lined				
30 gal.	1075	1313	1432	1550
50 gal.	1325	1638	1794	1950
Dishwasher, built-in				
2 cycles	415	598	689	780
4 or more cycles	565	700	1100	1500
Dryer, automatic	670	1560	2005	2450
Garage Door Opener	525	628	679	730
Garbage Disposal	157	229	265	300
Heater, Electric, built-in				
1250 watt ceiling type	233	289	317	345
1250 watt wall type	305	330	343	355
Wall type w/blower				
1500 watt	305	351	374	397
3000 watt	540	621	662	702
Hood For Range, 2 speed				
30" wide	187	606	816	1025
42" wide	293	1334	1855	2375
Humidifier, portable				
7 gal. per day	144	166	177	187
15 gal. per day	229	264	281	298
Ice Maker, automatic				
13 lb. per day	1050	1208	1287	1365
51 lb. per day	1975	2272	2420	2568
Refrigerator, no frost				
10-12 C.F.	525	558	574	590
14-16 C.F.	620	713	759	805
18-20 C.F.	765	1233	1467	1700
21-29 C.F.	1150	2525	3213	3900
Sump Pump, 1/3 H.P.	315	443	507	570

Breezeway *(Cost per S.F.)*

Class	Type	Area (S.F.)			
		50	100	150	200
Economy	Open	$ 43.99	$ 36.73	$ 32.38	$ 30.20
	Enclosed	160.11	113.89	93.91	80.85
Average	Open	52.20	42.61	37.48	34.91
	Enclosed	164.65	119.19	99.02	88.70
Custom	Open	62.68	51.55	45.49	42.47
	Enclosed	220.43	159.28	131.86	117.90
Luxury	Open	70.40	58.09	51.64	48.41
	Enclosed	259.21	184.60	151.41	134.58

Porches *(Cost per S.F.)*

Class	Type	Area (S.F.)				
		25	50	100	200	300
Economy	Open	$ 78.79	$ 59.29	$ 44.68	$ 34.33	$ 30.99
	Enclosed	168.38	133.94	88.07	66.76	58.38
Average	Open	83.11	63.99	47.03	35.51	31.77
	Enclosed	182.81	145.86	93.44	68.86	59.38
Custom	Open	133.43	97.43	74.77	56.21	54.91
	Enclosed	224.21	181.21	119.18	90.17	96.76
Luxury	Open	150.96	110.24	83.50	61.07	55.40
	Enclosed	262.68	237.45	152.55	111.21	92.19

Finished attic *(Cost per S.F.)*

Class	Area (S.F.)				
	400	500	600	800	1000
Economy	$ 19.93	$ 19.27	$ 18.46	$ 18.15	$ 17.48
Average	31.05	30.37	29.63	29.26	28.44
Custom	39.69	38.81	37.92	37.34	36.58
Luxury	50.65	49.43	48.27	47.12	46.35

Alarm system *(Cost per System)*

	Burglar Alarm	Smoke Detector
Economy	$ 415	$ 71
Average	475	86
Custom	820	196
Luxury	1200	255

Sauna, prefabricated
(Cost per unit, including heater and controls—7' high)

Size	Cost
6' x 4'	$ 5975
6' x 5'	6250
6' x 6'	6975
6' x 9'	8450
8' x 10'	11,200
8' x 12'	12,600
10' x 12'	13,200

Garages *

(Costs include exterior wall systems comparable with the quality of the residence. Included in the cost is an allowance for one personnel door, manual overhead door(s) and electrical fixture.)

Class	Type									
	Detached			Attached			Built-in		Basement	
	One Car	Two Car	Three Car	One Car	Two Car	Three Car	One Car	Two Car	One Car	Two Car
Economy										
Wood	$15,837	$24,288	$32,739	$12,308	$21,275	$29,726	$-1583	$-3166	$1720	$2384
Masonry	21,936	31,921	41,906	16,125	26,625	36,610	-2332	-4664		
Average										
Wood	17,986	26,978	35,969	13,653	23,160	32,152	-1847	-3694	1947	2839
Masonry	21,977	31,972	41,968	16,150	26,661	36,656	-2337	-3828		
Custom										
Wood	19,740	30,391	41,041	15,360	26,684	37,335	-3104	-2848	2923	4789
Masonry	24,116	35,867	47,618	18,098	30,523	42,274	-3642	-3923		
Luxury										
Wood	22,156	34,570	46,983	17,449	30,537	42,950	-3212	-3062	3864	6229
Masonry	28,630	42,672	56,713	21,500	36,216	50,257	-4007	-4652		

*See the Introduction to this section for definitions of garage types.

Swimming pools *(Cost per S.F.)*

Residential		
In-ground		$ 34.00 - 83.50
Deck equipment		1.30
Paint pool, preparation & 3 coats (epoxy)		5.25
Rubber base paint		4.62
Pool Cover		.92
Swimming Pool Heaters		
(not including wiring, external piping, base or pad)		
Gas		
155 MBH		$ 2975.00
190 MBH		3550.00
500 MBH		12,600.
Electric		
15 KW	7200 gallon pool	2825.00
24 KW	9600 gallon pool	3250.00
54 KW	24,000 gallon pool	5075.00

Wood and coal stoves

Wood Only		
Free Standing (minimum)		$ 1750
Fireplace Insert (minimum)		1961
Coal Only		
Free Standing		$ 2216
Fireplace Insert		2426
Wood and Coal		
Free Standing		$ 4559
Fireplace Insert		4672

Sidewalks *(Cost per S.F.)*

Concrete, 3000 psi with wire mesh	4" thick	$ 3.74
	5" thick	4.53
	6" thick	5.08
Precast concrete patio blocks (natural)	2" thick	6.50
Precast concrete patio blocks (colors)	2" thick	6.90
Flagstone, bluestone	1" thick	16.50
Flagstone, bluestone	1-1/2" thick	21.75
Slate (natural, irregular)	3/4" thick	18.40
Slate (random rectangular)	1/2" thick	29.35
Seeding		
Fine grading & seeding includes lime, fertilizer & seed per S.Y.		2.94
Lawn Sprinkler System	per S.F.	1.09

Fencing *(Cost per L.F.)*

Chain Link, 4' high, galvanized		$ 15.85
Gate, 4' high (each)		198.00
Cedar Picket, 3' high, 2 rail		14.50
Gate (each)		228.00
3 Rail, 4' high		17.90
Gate (each)		248.00
Cedar Stockade, 3 Rail, 6' high		17.75
Gate (each)		249.00
Board & Battens, 2 sides 6' high, pine		26.00
6' high, cedar		35.00
No. 1 Cedar, basketweave, 6' high		36.00
Gate, 6' high (each)		255.00

Carport *(Cost per S.F.)*

Economy	$ 9.12
Average	13.72
Custom	20.09
Luxury	23.36

Assemblies Section

Table of Contents

How to Use the Assemblies Cost Tables

The following is a detailed explanation of a sample Assemblies Cost Table. Included are an illustration and accompanying system descriptions. Additionally, related systems and price sheets may be included. Next to each bold number below is the item being described with the appropriate component of the sample entry following in parenthesis. General contractors should add an additional markup to the figures shown in the Assemblies section. Note: Throughout this section, the words assembly and system are used interchangeably.

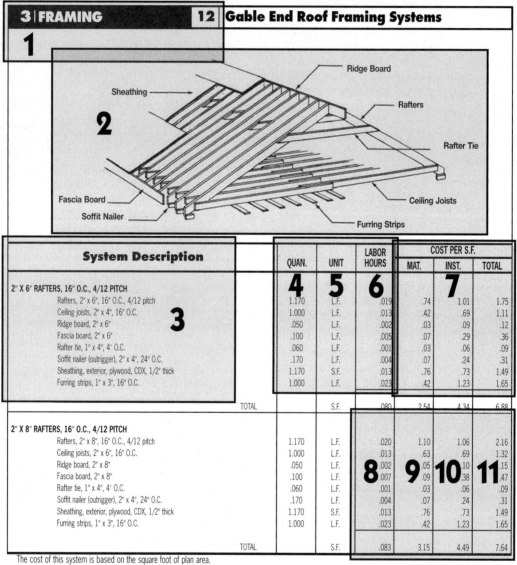

3 | FRAMING   **12**   **Gable End Roof Framing Systems**

1

2

Sheathing
Ridge Board
Rafters
Rafter Tie
Fascia Board
Soffit Nailer
Ceiling Joists
Furring Strips

System Description	QUAN.	UNIT	LABOR HOURS	COST PER S.F. MAT.	INST.	TOTAL
	4	**5**	**6**	**7**		
2″ X 6″ RAFTERS, 16″ O.C., 4/12 PITCH						
Rafters, 2″ x 6″, 16″ O.C., 4/12 pitch	1.170	L.F.	.019	.74	1.01	1.75
Ceiling joists, 2″ x 4″, 16″ O.C.	1.000	L.F.	.013	.42	.69	1.11
Ridge board, 2″ x 6″	.050	L.F.	.002	.03	.09	.12
Fascia board, 2″ x 6″	.100	L.F.	.005	.07	.29	.36
Rafter tie, 1″ x 4″, 4′ O.C.	.060	L.F.	.001	.03	.06	.09
Soffit nailer (outrigger), 2″ x 4″, 24″ O.C.	.170	L.F.	.004	.07	.24	.31
Sheathing, exterior, plywood, CDX, 1/2″ thick	1.170	S.F.	.013	.76	.73	1.49
Furring strips, 1″ x 3″, 16″ O.C.	1.000	L.F.	.023	.42	1.23	1.65
3						
TOTAL		S.F.	.080	2.54	4.34	6.88
2″ X 8″ RAFTERS, 16″ O.C., 4/12 PITCH						
Rafters, 2″ x 8″, 16″ O.C., 4/12 pitch	1.170	L.F.	.020	1.10	1.06	2.16
Ceiling joists, 2″ x 6″, 16″ O.C.	1.000	L.F.	.013	.63	.69	1.32
Ridge board, 2″ x 8″	.050	L.F.	.002	.05	.10	.15
Fascia board, 2″ x 8″	.100	L.F.	.007	.09	.38	.47
Rafter tie, 1″ x 4″, 4′ O.C.	.060	L.F.	.001	.03	.06	.09
Soffit nailer (outrigger), 2″ x 4″, 24″ O.C.	.170	L.F.	.004	.07	.24	.31
Sheathing, exterior, plywood, CDX, 1/2″ thick	1.170	S.F.	.013	.76	.73	1.49
Furring strips, 1″ x 3″, 16″ O.C.	1.000	L.F.	.023	.42	1.23	1.65
	8	**9**	**10**	**11**		
TOTAL		S.F.	.083	3.15	4.49	7.64

The cost of this system is based on the square foot of plan area.
All quantities have been adjusted accordingly.

Description	QUAN.	UNIT	LABOR HOURS	COST PER S.F. MAT.	INST.	TOTAL
12						

1 System Identification (3 Framing 12)

Each Assemblies section has been assigned a unique identification number, component category, system number and system description.

2 Illustration

At the top of most assembly pages is an illustration with individual components labeled. Elements involved in the total system function are shown.

3 System Description (2 " x6 " Rafters, 16 " O.C., 4/12 Pitch)

The components of a typical system are listed separately to show what has been included in the development of the total system price. Each page includes a brief outline of any special conditions to be used when pricing a system. Alternative components can be found on the opposite page. Simply insert any chosen new element into the chart to develop a custom system.

4 Quantities for Each Component

Each material in a system is shown with the quantity required for the system unit. For example, there are 1.170 L.F. of rafter per S.F. of plan area.

5 Unit of Measure for Each Component

The abbreviated designation indicates the unit of measure, as defined by industry standards, upon which the individual component has been priced. In this example, items are priced by the linear foot (L.F.) or the square foot (S.F.).

6 Labor Hours

This is the amount of time it takes to install the quantity of the individual component.

7 Unit of Measure (Cost per S.F.)

In the three right-hand columns, each cost figure is adjusted to agree with the unit of measure for the entire system. In this case, cost per S.F. is the common unit of measure.

8 Labor Hours (.083)

The labor hours column shows the amount of time necessary to install the system per the unit of measure. For example, it takes .083 labor hours to install one square foot (plan area) of this roof framing system.

9 Materials (3.15)

This column contains the material cost of each element. These cost figures include 10% for profit.

10 Installation (4.49)

This column contains labor and equipment costs. Labor rates include bare cost and the installing contractor's overhead and profit. On the average, the labor cost will be 69.5% over the bare labor cost. Equipment costs include 10% for profit.

11 Totals (7.64)

The figure in this column is the sum of the material and installation costs.

12 Work Sheet

Using the selective price sheet on the page opposite each system, it is possible to create estimates with alternative items for any number of systems.

Backfill

Excavate

System Description	QUAN.	UNIT	LABOR HOURS	COST EACH		
				MAT.	INST.	TOTAL
BUILDING, 24′ X 38′, 4′ DEEP						
Cut & chip light trees to 6″ diam.	.190	Acre	9.120		745.75	745.75
Excavator, hydraulic, crawler mtd., 1 C.Y. cap. = 100 C.Y./hr.	174.000	C.Y.	3.480		363.66	363.66
Backfill, dozer, 4″ lifts, no compaction	87.000	C.Y.	.580		138.33	138.33
Rough grade, dozer, 30′ from building	87.000	C.Y.	.580		138.33	138.33
TOTAL		Ea.	13.760		1,386.07	1,386.07
BUILDING, 26′ X 46′, 4′ DEEP						
Cut & chip light trees to 6″ diam.	.210	Acre	10.080		824.25	824.25
Excavator, hydraulic, crawler mtd., 1 C.Y. cap. = 100 C.Y./hr.	201.000	C.Y.	4.020		420.09	420.09
Backfill, dozer, 4″ lifts, no compaction	100.000	C.Y.	.667		159	159
Rough grade, dozer, 30′ from building	100.000	C.Y.	.667		159	159
TOTAL		Ea.	15.434		1,562.34	1,562.34
BUILDING, 26′ X 60′, 4′ DEEP						
Cut & chip light trees to 6″ diam.	.240	Acre	11.520		942	942
Excavator, hydraulic, crawler mtd., 1 C.Y. cap. = 100 C.Y./hr.	240.000	C.Y.	4.800		501.60	501.60
Backfill, dozer, 4″ lifts, no compaction	120.000	C.Y.	.800		190.80	190.80
Rough grade, dozer, 30′ from building	120.000	C.Y.	.800		190.80	190.80
TOTAL		Ea.	17.920		1,825.20	1,825.20
BUILDING, 30′ X 66′, 4′ DEEP						
Cut & chip light trees to 6″ diam.	.260	Acre	12.480		1,020.50	1,020.50
Excavator, hydraulic, crawler mtd., 1 C.Y. cap. = 100 C.Y./hr.	268.000	C.Y.	5.360		560.12	560.12
Backfill, dozer, 4″ lifts, no compaction	134.000	C.Y.	.894		213.06	213.06
Rough grade, dozer, 30′ from building	134.000	C.Y.	.894		213.06	213.06
TOTAL		Ea.	19.628		2,006.74	2,006.74

The costs in this system are on a cost each basis.
Quantities are based on 1′-0″ clearance on each side of footing.

Description	QUAN.	UNIT	LABOR HOURS	COST EACH		
				MAT.	INST.	TOTAL

Footing Excavation Price Sheet	QUAN.	UNIT	LABOR HOURS	COST EACH MAT.	COST EACH INST.	COST EACH TOTAL
Clear and grub, medium brush, 30' from building, 24' x 38'	.190	Acre	9.120		745	745
26' x 46'	.210	Acre	10.080		825	825
26' x 60'	.240	Acre	11.520		945	945
30' x 66'	.260	Acre	12.480		1,025	1,025
Light trees, to 6" dia. cut & chip, 24' x 38'	.190	Acre	9.120		745	745
26' x 46'	.210	Acre	10.080		825	825
26' x 60'	.240	Acre	11.520		945	945
30' x 66'	.260	Acre	12.480		1,025	1,025
Medium trees, to 10" dia. cut & chip, 24' x 38'	.190	Acre	13.029		1,075	1,075
26' x 46'	.210	Acre	14.400		1,175	1,175
26' x 60'	.240	Acre	16.457		1,350	1,350
30' x 66'	.260	Acre	17.829		1,450	1,450
Excavation, footing, 24' x 38', 2' deep	68.000	C.Y.	.906		142	142
4' deep	174.000	C.Y.	2.319		365	365
8' deep	384.000	C.Y.	5.119		800	800
26' x 46', 2' deep	79.000	C.Y.	1.053		165	165
4' deep	201.000	C.Y.	2.679		420	420
8' deep	404.000	C.Y.	5.385		840	840
26' x 60', 2' deep	94.000	C.Y.	1.253		196	196
4' deep	240.000	C.Y.	3.199		500	500
8' deep	483.000	C.Y.	6.438		1,000	1,000
30' x 66', 2' deep	105.000	C.Y.	1.400		220	220
4' deep	268.000	C.Y.	3.572		560	560
8' deep	539.000	C.Y.	7.185		1,125	1,125
Backfill, 24' x 38', 2" lifts, no compaction	34.000	C.Y.	.227		54	54
Compaction, air tamped, add	34.000	C.Y.	2.267		460	460
4" lifts, no compaction	87.000	C.Y.	.580		138	138
Compaction, air tamped, add	87.000	C.Y.	5.800		1,175	1,175
8" lifts, no compaction	192.000	C.Y.	1.281		305	305
Compaction, air tamped, add	192.000	C.Y.	12.801		2,600	2,600
26' x 46', 2" lifts, no compaction	40.000	C.Y.	.267		64	64
Compaction, air tamped, add	40.000	C.Y.	2.667		540	540
4" lifts, no compaction	100.000	C.Y.	.667		159	159
Compaction, air tamped, add	100.000	C.Y.	6.667		1,350	1,350
8" lifts, no compaction	202.000	C.Y.	1.347		320	320
Compaction, air tamped, add	202.000	C.Y.	13.467		2,750	2,750
26' x 60', 2" lifts, no compaction	47.000	C.Y.	.313		75	75
Compaction, air tamped, add	47.000	C.Y.	3.133		635	635
4" lifts, no compaction	120.000	C.Y.	.800		191	191
Compaction, air tamped, add	120.000	C.Y.	8.000		1,625	1,625
8" lifts, no compaction	242.000	C.Y.	1.614		385	385
Compaction, air tamped, add	242.000	C.Y.	16.134		3,275	3,275
30' x 66', 2" lifts, no compaction	53.000	C.Y.	.354		84	84
Compaction, air tamped, add	53.000	C.Y.	3.534		720	720
4" lifts, no compaction	134.000	C.Y.	.894		213	213
Compaction, air tamped, add	134.000	C.Y.	8.934		1,800	1,800
8" lifts, no compaction	269.000	C.Y.	1.794		430	430
Compaction, air tamped, add	269.000	C.Y.	17.934		3,650	3,650
Rough grade, 30' from building, 24' x 38'	87.000	C.Y.	.580		138	138
26' x 46'	100.000	C.Y.	.667		159	159
26' x 60'	120.000	C.Y.	.800		191	191
30' x 66'	134.000	C.Y.	.894		213	213

Backfill

Excavate

System Description	QUAN.	UNIT	LABOR HOURS	COST EACH		
				MAT.	INST.	TOTAL
BUILDING, 24′ X 38′, 8′ DEEP						
Medium clearing	.190	Acre	2.027		281.20	281.20
Excavate, track loader, 1-1/2 C.Y. bucket	550.000	C.Y.	7.860		1,006.50	1,006.50
Backfill, dozer, 8″ lifts, no compaction	180.000	C.Y.	1.201		286.20	286.20
Rough grade, dozer, 30′ from building	280.000	C.Y.	1.868		445.20	445.20
TOTAL		Ea.	12.956		2,019.10	2,019.10
BUILDING, 26′ X 46′, 8′ DEEP						
Medium clearing	.210	Acre	2.240		310.80	310.80
Excavate, track loader, 1-1/2 C.Y. bucket	672.000	C.Y.	9.603		1,229.76	1,229.76
Backfill, dozer, 8″ lifts, no compaction	220.000	C.Y.	1.467		349.80	349.80
Rough grade, dozer, 30′ from building	340.000	C.Y.	2.268		540.60	540.60
TOTAL		Ea.	15.578		2,430.96	2,430.96
BUILDING, 26′ X 60′, 8′ DEEP						
Medium clearing	.240	Acre	2.560		355.20	355.20
Excavate, track loader, 1-1/2 C.Y. bucket	829.000	C.Y.	11.846		1,517.07	1,517.07
Backfill, dozer, 8″ lifts, no compaction	270.000	C.Y.	1.801		429.30	429.30
Rough grade, dozer, 30′ from building	420.000	C.Y.	2.801		667.80	667.80
TOTAL		Ea.	19.008		2,969.37	2,969.37
BUILDING, 30′ X 66′, 8′ DEEP						
Medium clearing	.260	Acre	2.773		384.80	384.80
Excavate, track loader, 1-1/2 C.Y. bucket	990.000	C.Y.	14.147		1,811.70	1,811.70
Backfill dozer, 8″ lifts, no compaction	320.000	C.Y.	2.134		508.80	508.80
Rough grade, dozer, 30′ from building	500.000	C.Y.	3.335		795	795
TOTAL		Ea.	22.389		3,500.30	3,500.30

The costs in this system are on a cost each basis.
Quantities are based on 1′-0″ clearance beyond footing projection.

Description	QUAN.	UNIT	LABOR HOURS	COST EACH		
				MAT.	INST.	TOTAL

Foundation Excavation Price Sheet	QUAN.	UNIT	LABOR HOURS	COST EACH		
				MAT.	INST.	TOTAL
Clear & grub, medium brush, 30' from building, 24' x 38'	.190	Acre	2.027		281	281
26' x 46'	.210	Acre	2.240		310	310
26' x 60'	.240	Acre	2.560		355	355
30' x 66'	.260	Acre	2.773		385	385
Light trees, to 6" dia. cut & chip, 24' x 38'	.190	Acre	9.120		745	745
26' x 46'	.210	Acre	10.080		825	825
26' x 60'	.240	Acre	11.520		945	945
30' x 66'	.260	Acre	12.480		1,025	1,025
Medium trees, to 10" dia. cut & chip, 24' x 38'	.190	Acre	13.029		1,075	1,075
26' x 46'	.210	Acre	14.400		1,175	1,175
26' x 60'	.240	Acre	16.457		1,350	1,350
30' x 66'	.260	Acre	17.829		1,450	1,450
Excavation, basement, 24' x 38', 2' deep	98.000	C.Y.	1.400		180	180
4' deep	220.000	C.Y.	3.144		405	405
8' deep	550.000	C.Y.	7.860		1,000	1,000
26' x 46', 2' deep	123.000	C.Y.	1.758		226	226
4' deep	274.000	C.Y.	3.915		500	500
8' deep	672.000	C.Y.	9.603		1,225	1,225
26' x 60', 2' deep	157.000	C.Y.	2.244		288	288
4' deep	345.000	C.Y.	4.930		630	630
8' deep	829.000	C.Y.	11.846		1,525	1,525
30' x 66', 2' deep	192.000	C.Y.	2.744		350	350
4' deep	419.000	C.Y.	5.988		765	765
8' deep	990.000	C.Y.	14.147		1,825	1,825
Backfill, 24' x 38', 2" lifts, no compaction	32.000	C.Y.	.213		51	51
Compaction, air tamped, add	32.000	C.Y.	2.133		435	435
4" lifts, no compaction	72.000	C.Y.	.480		115	115
Compaction, air tamped, add	72.000	C.Y.	4.800		975	975
8" lifts, no compaction	180.000	C.Y.	1.201		287	287
Compaction, air tamped, add	180.000	C.Y.	12.001		2,450	2,450
26' x 46', 2" lifts, no compaction	40.000	C.Y.	.267		64	64
Compaction, air tamped, add	40.000	C.Y.	2.667		540	540
4" lifts, no compaction	90.000	C.Y.	.600		144	144
Compaction, air tamped, add	90.000	C.Y.	6.000		1,225	1,225
8" lifts, no compaction	220.000	C.Y.	1.467		350	350
Compacton, air tamped, add	220.000	C.Y.	14.667		3,000	3,000
26' x 60', 2" lifts, no compaction	50.000	C.Y.	.334		79.50	79.50
Compaction, air tamped, add	50.000	C.Y.	3.334		680	680
4" lifts, no compaction	110.000	C.Y.	.734		175	175
Compaction, air tamped, add	110.000	C.Y.	7.334		1,475	1,475
8" lifts, no compaction	270.000	C.Y.	1.801		430	430
Compaction, air tamped, add	270.000	C.Y.	18.001		3,675	3,675
30' x 66', 2" lifts, no compaction	60.000	C.Y.	.400		95	95
Compaction, air tamped, add	60.000	C.Y.	4.000		815	815
4" lifts, no compaction	130.000	C.Y.	.867		207	207
Compaction, air tamped, add	130.000	C.Y.	8.667		1,775	1,775
8" lifts, no compaction	320.000	C.Y.	2.134		510	510
Compaction, air tamped, add	320.000	C.Y.	21.334		4,325	4,325
Rough grade, 30' from building, 24' x 38'	280.000	C.Y.	1.868		445	445
26' x 46'	340.000	C.Y.	2.268		540	540
26' x 60'	420.000	C.Y.	2.801		665	665
30' x 66'	500.000	C.Y.	3.335		795	795

System Description	QUAN.	UNIT	LABOR HOURS	COST PER L.F.		
				MAT.	INST.	TOTAL
2' DEEP						
Excavation, backhoe	.296	C.Y.	.032		2.30	2.30
Alternate pricing method, 4" deep	.111	C.Y.	.044	3.89	2.06	5.95
Utility, sewer, 6" cast iron	1.000	L.F.	.283	27.52	15.35	42.87
Compaction in 12" layers, hand tamp, add to above	.185	C.Y.	.044		1.74	1.74
TOTAL		L.F.	.403	31.41	21.45	52.86
4' DEEP						
Excavation, backhoe	.889	C.Y.	.095		6.91	6.91
Alternate pricing method, 4" deep	.111	C.Y.	.044	3.89	2.06	5.95
Utility, sewer, 6" cast iron	1.000	L.F.	.283	27.52	15.35	42.87
Compaction in 12" layers, hand tamp, add to above	.778	C.Y.	.183		7.31	7.31
TOTAL		L.F.	.605	31.41	31.63	63.04
6' DEEP						
Excavation, backhoe	1.770	C.Y.	.189		13.77	13.77
Alternate pricing method, 4" deep	.111	C.Y.	.044	3.89	2.06	5.95
Utility, sewer, 6" cast iron	1.000	L.F.	.283	27.52	15.35	42.87
Compaction in 12" layers, hand tamp, add to above	1.660	C.Y.	.391		15.60	15.60
TOTAL		L.F.	.907	31.41	46.78	78.19
8' DEEP						
Excavation, backhoe	2.960	C.Y.	.316		23.03	23.03
Alternate pricing method, 4" deep	.111	C.Y.	.044	3.89	2.06	5.95
Utility, sewer, 6" cast iron	1.000	L.F.	.283	27.52	15.35	42.87
Compaction in 12" layers, hand tamp, add to above	2.850	C.Y.	.671		26.79	26.79
TOTAL		L.F.	1.314	31.41	67.23	98.64

The costs in this system are based on a cost per linear foot of trench,
and based on 2' wide at bottom of trench up to 6' deep.

Description	QUAN.	UNIT	LABOR HOURS	COST PER L.F.		
				MAT.	INST.	TOTAL

Utility Trenching Price Sheet	QUAN.	UNIT	LABOR HOURS	COST PER UNIT		
				MAT.	INST.	TOTAL
Excavation, bottom of trench 2' wide, 2' deep	.296	C.Y.	.032		2.30	2.30
4' deep	.889	C.Y.	.095		6.90	6.90
6' deep	1.770	C.Y.	.142		10.70	10.70
8' deep	2.960	C.Y.	.105		19.85	19.85
Bedding, sand, bottom of trench 2' wide, no compaction, pipe, 2" diameter	.070	C.Y.	.028	2.45	1.30	3.75
4" diameter	.084	C.Y.	.034	2.94	1.56	4.50
6" diameter	.105	C.Y.	.042	3.68	1.95	5.63
8" diameter	.122	C.Y.	.049	4.27	2.27	6.54
Compacted, pipe, 2" diameter	.074	C.Y.	.030	2.59	1.38	3.97
4" diameter	.092	C.Y.	.037	3.22	1.71	4.93
6" diameter	.111	C.Y.	.044	3.89	2.06	5.95
8" diameter	.129	C.Y.	.052	4.52	2.40	6.92
3/4" stone, bottom of trench 2' wide, pipe, 4" diameter	.082	C.Y.	.033	2.87	1.53	4.40
6" diameter	.099	C.Y.	.040	3.47	1.84	5.31
3/8" stone, bottom of trench 2' wide, pipe, 4" diameter	.084	C.Y.	.034	2.94	1.56	4.50
6" diameter	.102	C.Y.	.041	3.57	1.90	5.47
Utilities, drainage & sewerage, corrugated plastic, 6" diameter	1.000	L.F.	.069	3.62	2.82	6.44
8" diameter	1.000	L.F.	.072	7.60	2.95	10.55
Bituminous fiber, 4" diameter	1.000	L.F.	.064	1.61	2.63	4.24
6" diameter	1.000	L.F.	.069	3.62	2.82	6.44
8" diameter	1.000	L.F.	.072	7.60	2.95	10.55
Concrete, non-reinforced, 6" diameter	1.000	L.F.	.181	6.15	9.25	15.40
8" diameter	1.000	L.F.	.214	6.80	11	17.80
PVC, SDR 35, 4" diameter	1.000	L.F.	.064	1.61	2.63	4.24
6" diameter	1.000	L.F.	.069	3.62	2.82	6.44
8" diameter	1.000	L.F.	.072	7.60	2.95	10.55
Gas & service, polyethylene, 1-1/4" diameter	1.000	L.F.	.059	1.93	2.89	4.82
Steel sched.40, 1" diameter	1.000	L.F.	.107	5.80	6.55	12.35
2" diameter	1.000	L.F.	.114	9.05	7	16.05
Sub-drainage, PVC, perforated, 3" diameter	1.000	L.F.	.064	1.61	2.63	4.24
4" diameter	1.000	L.F.	.064	1.61	2.63	4.24
5" diameter	1.000	L.F.	.069	3.62	2.82	6.44
6" diameter	1.000	L.F.	.069	3.62	2.82	6.44
Water service, copper, type K, 3/4"	1.000	L.F.	.083	6.60	5.25	11.85
1" diameter	1.000	L.F.	.093	8.95	5.85	14.80
PVC, 3/4"	1.000	L.F.	.121	2.83	7.60	10.43
1" diameter	1.000	L.F.	.134	3.35	8.40	11.75
Backfill, bottom of trench 2' wide no compact, 2' deep, pipe, 2" diameter	.226	L.F.	.053		2.12	2.12
4" diameter	.212	L.F.	.050		1.99	1.99
6" diameter	.185	L.F.	.044		1.74	1.74
4' deep, pipe, 2" diameter	.819	C.Y.	.193		7.70	7.70
4" diameter	.805	C.Y.	.189		7.55	7.55
6" diameter	.778	C.Y.	.183		7.30	7.30
6' deep, pipe, 2" diameter	1.700	C.Y.	.400		16	16
4" diameter	1.690	C.Y.	.398		15.90	15.90
6" diameter	1.660	C.Y.	.391		15.60	15.60
8' deep, pipe, 2" diameter	2.890	C.Y.	.680		27	27
4" diameter	2.870	C.Y.	.675		27	27
6" diameter	2.850	C.Y.	.671		27	27

Asphalt · Brick Edge · Gravel Fill

System Description	QUAN.	UNIT	LABOR HOURS	COST PER S.F.		
				MAT.	INST.	TOTAL
ASPHALT SIDEWALK SYSTEM, 3′ WIDE WALK						
Gravel fill, 4″ deep	1.000	S.F.	.001	.35	.05	.40
Compact fill	.012	C.Y.			.02	.02
Handgrade	1.000	S.F.	.004		.17	.17
Walking surface, bituminous paving, 2″ thick	1.000	S.F.	.007	.88	.35	1.23
Edging, brick, laid on edge	.670	L.F.	.079	2.04	3.82	5.86
TOTAL		S.F.	.091	3.27	4.41	7.68
CONCRETE SIDEWALK SYSTEM, 3′ WIDE WALK						
Gravel fill, 4″ deep	1.000	S.F.	.001	.35	.05	.40
Compact fill	.012	C.Y.			.02	.02
Handgrade	1.000	S.F.	.004		.17	.17
Walking surface, concrete, 4″ thick	1.000	S.F.	.040	1.82	1.92	3.74
Edging, brick, laid on edge	.670	L.F.	.079	2.04	3.82	5.86
TOTAL		S.F.	.124	4.21	5.98	10.19
PAVERS, BRICK SIDEWALK SYSTEM, 3′ WIDE WALK						
Sand base fill, 4″ deep	1.000	S.F.	.001	.55	.09	.64
Compact fill	.012	C.Y.			.02	.02
Handgrade	1.000	S.F.	.004		.17	.17
Walking surface, brick pavers	1.000	S.F.	.160	3.43	7.70	11.13
Edging, redwood, untreated, 1″ x 4″	.670	L.F.	.032	1.66	1.74	3.40
TOTAL		S.F.	.197	5.64	9.72	15.36

The costs in this system are based on a cost per square foot of sidewalk area. Concrete used is 3000 p.s.i.

Description	QUAN.	UNIT	LABOR HOURS	COST PER S.F.		
				MAT.	INST.	TOTAL

Sidewalk Price Sheet	QUAN.	UNIT	LABOR HOURS	COST PER S.F.		
				MAT.	INST.	TOTAL
Base, crushed stone, 3″ deep	1.000	S.F.	.001	.34	.10	.44
6″ deep	1.000	S.F.	.001	.67	.10	.77
9″ deep	1.000	S.F.	.002	.98	.14	1.12
12″ deep	1.000	S.F.	.002	1.39	.17	1.56
Bank run gravel, 6″ deep	1.000	S.F.	.001	.52	.08	.60
9″ deep	1.000	S.F.	.001	.76	.10	.86
12″ deep	1.000	S.F.	.001	1.04	.13	1.17
Compact base, 3″ deep	.009	C.Y.	.001		.01	.01
6″ deep	.019	C.Y.	.001		.03	.03
9″ deep	.028	C.Y.	.001		.05	.05
Handgrade	1.000	S.F.	.004		.17	.17
Surface, brick, pavers dry joints, laid flat, running bond	1.000	S.F.	.160	3.43	7.70	11.13
Basket weave	1.000	S.F.	.168	3.92	8.10	12.02
Herringbone	1.000	S.F.	.174	3.92	8.35	12.27
Laid on edge, running bond	1.000	S.F.	.229	4.21	11	15.21
Mortar jts. laid flat, running bond	1.000	S.F.	.192	4.12	9.25	13.37
Basket weave	1.000	S.F.	.202	4./0	9.70	14.40
Herringbone	1.000	S.F.	.209	4.70	10	14.70
Laid on edge, running bond	1.000	S.F.	.274	5.05	13.20	18.25
Bituminous paving, 1-1/2″ thick	1.000	S.F.	.006	.66	.26	.92
2″ thick	1.000	S.F.	.007	.88	.35	1.23
2-1/2″ thick	1.000	S.F.	.008	1.12	.38	1.50
Sand finish, 3/4″ thick	1.000	S.F.	.001	.35	.11	.46
1″ thick	1.000	S.F.	.001	.43	.14	.57
Concrete, reinforced, broom finish, 4″ thick	1.000	S.F.	.040	1.82	1.92	3.74
5″ thick	1.000	S.F.	.044	2.42	2.11	4.53
6″ thick	1.000	S.F.	.047	2.82	2.26	5.08
Crushed stone, white marble, 3″ thick	1.000	S.F.	.009	.44	.38	.82
Bluestone, 3″ thick	1.000	S.F.	.009	.24	.38	.62
Flagging, bluestone, 1″	1.000	S.F.	.198	7	9.50	16.50
1-1/2″	1.000	S.F.	.188	12.70	9.05	21.75
Slate, natural cleft, 3/4″	1.000	S.F.	.174	10.05	8.35	18.40
Random rect., 1/2″	1.000	S.F.	.152	22	7.35	29.35
Granite blocks	1.000	S.F.	.174	12.75	8.35	21.10
Edging, corrugated aluminum, 4″, 3′ wide walk	.666	L.F.	.008	1.43	.44	1.87
4′ wide walk	.500	L.F.	.006	1.08	.33	1.41
6″, 3′ wide walk	.666	L.F.	.010	1.78	.53	2.31
4′ wide walk	.500	L.F.	.007	1.34	.40	1.74
Redwood-cedar-cypress, 1″ x 4″, 3′ wide walk	.666	L.F.	.021	.85	1.15	2
4′ wide walk	.500	L.F.	.016	.64	.87	1.51
2″ x 4″, 3′ wide walk	.666	L.F.	.032	1.66	1.74	3.40
4′ wide walk	.500	L.F.	.024	1.25	1.31	2.56
Brick, dry joints, 3′ wide walk	.666	L.F.	.079	2.04	3.82	5.86
4′ wide walk	.500	L.F.	.059	1.53	2.85	4.38
Mortar joints, 3′ wide walk	.666	L.F.	.095	2.45	4.58	7.03
4′ wide walk	.500	L.F.	.071	1.83	3.42	5.25

Asphalt Topping — Asphalt Binder — Brick Edging — Excavation — Base

System Description	QUAN.	UNIT	LABOR HOURS	COST PER S.F.		
				MAT.	INST.	TOTAL
ASPHALT DRIVEWAY TO 10' WIDE						
Excavation, driveway to 10' wide, 6" deep	.019	C.Y.			.04	.04
Base, 6" crushed stone	1.000	S.F.	.001	.67	.10	.77
Handgrade base	1.000	S.F.	.004		.17	.17
2" thick base	1.000	S.F.	.002	.88	.20	1.08
1" topping	1.000	S.F.	.001	.43	.14	.57
Edging, brick pavers	.200	L.F.	.024	.61	1.14	1.75
TOTAL		S.F.	.032	2.59	1.79	4.38
CONCRETE DRIVEWAY TO 10' WIDE						
Excavation, driveway to 10' wide, 6" deep	.019	C.Y.			.04	.04
Base, 6" crushed stone	1.000	S.F.	.001	.67	.10	.77
Handgrade base	1.000	S.F.	.004		.17	.17
Surface, concrete, 4" thick	1.000	S.F.	.040	1.82	1.92	3.74
Edging, brick pavers	.200	L.F.	.024	.61	1.14	1.75
TOTAL		S.F.	.069	3.10	3.37	6.47
PAVERS, BRICK DRIVEWAY TO 10' WIDE						
Excavation, driveway to 10' wide, 6" deep	.019	C.Y.			.04	.04
Base, 6" sand	1.000	S.F.	.001	.87	.13	1
Handgrade base	1.000	S.F.	.004		.17	.17
Surface, pavers, brick laid flat, running bond	1.000	S.F.	.160	3.43	7.70	11.13
Edging, redwood, untreated, 2" x 4"	.200	L.F.	.010	.50	.52	1.02
TOTAL		S.F.	.175	4.80	8.56	13.36

Description	QUAN.	UNIT	LABOR HOURS	COST PER S.F.		
				MAT.	INST.	TOTAL

Driveway Price Sheet	QUAN.	UNIT	LABOR HOURS	COST PER S.F.		
				MAT.	INST.	TOTAL
Excavation, by machine, 10' wide, 6" deep	.019	C.Y.	.001		.04	.04
12" deep	.037	C.Y.	.001		.08	.08
18" deep	.055	C.Y.	.001		.12	.12
20' wide, 6" deep	.019	C.Y.	.001		.04	.04
12" deep	.037	C.Y.	.001		.08	.08
18" deep	.055	C.Y.	.001		.12	.12
Base, crushed stone, 10' wide, 3" deep	1.000	S.F.	.001	.34	.06	.40
6" deep	1.000	S.F.	.001	.67	.10	.77
9" deep	1.000	S.F.	.002	.98	.14	1.12
20' wide, 3" deep	1.000	S.F.	.001	.34	.06	.40
6" deep	1.000	S.F.	.001	.67	.10	.77
9" deep	1.000	S.F.	.002	.98	.14	1.12
Bank run gravel, 10' wide, 3" deep	1.000	S.F.	.001	.26	.05	.31
6" deep	1.000	S.F.	.001	.52	.08	.60
9" deep	1.000	S.F.	.001	.76	.10	.86
20' wide, 3" deep	1.000	S.F.	.001	.26	.05	.31
6" deep	1.000	S.F.	.001	.52	.08	.60
9" deep	1.000	S.F.	.001	.76	.10	.86
Handgrade, 10' wide	1.000	S.F.	.004		.17	.17
20' wide	1.000	S.F.	.004		.17	.17
Surface, asphalt, 10' wide, 3/4" topping, 1" base	1.000	S.F.	.002	1.03	.25	1.28
2" base	1.000	S.F.	.003	1.23	.31	1.54
1" topping, 1" base	1.000	S.F.	.002	1.11	.28	1.39
2" base	1.000	S.F.	.003	1.31	.34	1.65
20' wide, 3/4" topping, 1" base	1.000	S.F.	.002	1.03	.25	1.28
2" base	1.000	S.F.	.003	1.23	.31	1.54
1" topping, 1" base	1.000	S.F.	.002	1.11	.28	1.39
2" base	1.000	S.F.	.003	1.31	.34	1.65
Concrete, 10' wide, 4" thick	1.000	S.F.	.040	1.82	1.92	3.74
6" thick	1.000	S.F.	.047	2.82	2.26	5.08
20' wide, 4" thick	1.000	S.F.	.040	1.82	1.92	3.74
6" thick	1.000	S.F.	.047	2.82	2.26	5.08
Paver, brick 10' wide dry joints, running bond, laid flat	1.000	S.F.	.160	3.43	7.70	11.13
Laid on edge	1.000	S.F.	.229	4.21	11	15.21
Mortar joints, laid flat	1.000	S.F.	.192	4.12	9.25	13.37
Laid on edge	1.000	S.F.	.274	5.05	13.20	18.25
20' wide, running bond, dry jts., laid flat	1.000	S.F.	.160	3.43	7.70	11.13
Laid on edge	1.000	S.F.	.229	4.21	11	15.21
Mortar joints, laid flat	1.000	S.F.	.192	4.12	9.25	13.37
Laid on edge	1.000	S.F.	.274	5.05	13.20	18.25
Crushed stone, 10' wide, white marble, 3"	1.000	S.F.	.009	.44	.38	.82
Bluestone, 3"	1.000	S.F.	.009	.24	.38	.62
20' wide, white marble, 3"	1.000	S.F.	.009	.44	.38	.82
Bluestone, 3"	1.000	S.F.	.009	.24	.38	.62
Soil cement, 10' wide	1.000	S.F.	.007	.44	1.04	1.48
20' wide	1.000	S.F.	.007	.44	1.04	1.48
Granite blocks, 10' wide	1.000	S.F.	.174	12.75	8.35	21.10
20' wide	1.000	S.F.	.174	12.75	8.35	21.10
Asphalt block, solid 1-1/4" thick	1.000	S.F.	.119	10.10	5.70	15.80
Solid 3" thick	1.000	S.F.	.123	14.15	5.90	20.05
Edging, brick, 10' wide	.200	L.F.	.024	.61	1.14	1.75
20' wide	.100	L.F.	.012	.31	.57	.88
Redwood, untreated 2" x 4", 10' wide	.200	L.F.	.010	.50	.52	1.02
20' wide	.100	L.F.	.005	.25	.26	.51
Granite, 4 1/2" x 12" straight, 10' wide	.200	L.F.	.032	1.35	1.98	3.33
20' wide	.100	L.F.	.016	.68	1	1.68
Finishes, asphalt sealer, 10' wide	1.000	S.F.	.023	1.42	.94	2.36
20' wide	1.000	S.F.	.023	1.42	.94	2.36
Concrete, exposed aggregate 10' wide	1.000	S.F.	.013	.47	.64	1.11
20' wide	1.000	S.F.	.013	.47	.64	1.11

Backfill

4″ Bituminous Solid Fiber Pipe

Building Paper

Crushed Stone Backfill

Septic Tank

Distribution Box

4″ Bituminous Perforated Fiber Pipe

Excavation

System Description	QUAN.	UNIT	LABOR HOURS	COST EACH		
				MAT.	INST.	TOTAL
SEPTIC SYSTEM WITH 1000 S.F. LEACHING FIELD, 1000 GALLON TANK						
Tank, 1000 gallon, concrete	1.000	Ea.	3.500	1,200	171.25	1,371.25
Distribution box, concrete	1.000	Ea.	1.000	86	40	126
4″ PVC pipe	25.000	L.F.	1.600	40.25	65.75	106
Tank and field excavation	119.000	C.Y.	13.130		1,237.60	1,237.60
Crushed stone backfill	76.000	C.Y.	12.160	2,850	747.08	3,597.08
Backfill with excavated material	36.000	C.Y.	.240		57.24	57.24
Building paper	125.000	S.Y.	2.430	67.50	135	202.50
4″ PVC perforated pipe	145.000	L.F.	9.280	233.45	381.35	614.80
4″ pipe fittings	2.000	Ea.	1.939	69	109	178
TOTAL		Ea.	45.279	4,546.20	2,944.27	7,490.47
SEPTIC SYSTEM WITH 1000 S.F. LEACHING FIELD, 1500 GALLON TANK						
Tank, 1500 gallon, concrete	1.000	Ea.	4.000	1,650	196	1,846
Distribution box, concrete	1.000	Ea.	1.000	86	40	126
4″ PVC pipe	25.000	L.F.	1.600	40.25	65.75	106
Tank and field excavation	119.000	C.Y.	13.130		1,237.60	1,237.60
Crushed stone backfill	76.000	C.Y.	12.160	2,850	747.08	3,597.08
Backfill with excavated material	36.000	C.Y.	.240		57.24	57.24
Building paper	125.000	S.Y.	2.430	67.50	135	202.50
4″ PVC perforated pipe	145.000	L.F.	9.280	233.45	381.35	614.80
4″ pipe fittings	2.000	Ea.	1.939	69	109	178
TOTAL		Ea.	45.779	4,996.20	2,969.02	7,965.22
SEPTIC SYSTEM WITH 2 LEACHING PITS, 1000 GALLON TANK						
Tank, 1000 gallon, concrete	1.000	Ea.	3.500	1,200	171.25	1,371.25
Distribution box, concrete	1.000	Ea.	1.000	86	40	126
4″ PVC pipe	75.000	L.F.	4.800	120.75	197.25	318
Excavation for tank only	20.000	C.Y.	2.207		208	208
Crushed stone backfill	10.000	C.Y.	1.600	375	98.30	473.30
Backfill with excavated material	55.000	C.Y.	.367		87.45	87.45
Pits, 6′ diameter, including excavation and stone backfill	2.000	Ea.	11.915	1,950	584	2,534
TOTAL		Ea.	25.389	3,731.75	1,386.25	5,118

The costs in this system include all necessary piping and excavation.

Septic Systems Price Sheet	QUAN.	UNIT	LABOR HOURS	COST EACH		
				MAT.	INST.	TOTAL
Tank, precast concrete, 1000 gallon	1.000	Ea.	3.500	1,200	171	1,371
2000 gallon	1.000	Ea.	5.600	2,150	275	2,425
Distribution box, concrete, 5 outlets	1.000	Ea.	1.000	86	40	126
12 outlets	1.000	Ea.	2.000	525	80	605
4" pipe, PVC, solid	25.000	L.F.	1.600	40.50	66	106.50
Tank and field excavation, 1000 S.F. field	119.000	C.Y.	6.565		1,250	1,250
2000 S.F. field	190.000	C.Y.	10.482		1,975	1,975
Tank excavation only, 1000 gallon tank	20.000	C.Y.	1.103		208	208
2000 gallon tank	32.000	C.Y.	1.765		335	335
Backfill, crushed stone 1000 S.F. field	76.000	C.Y.	12.160	2,850	750	3,600
2000 S.F. field	140.000	C.Y.	22.400	5,250	1,375	6,625
Backfill with excavated material, 1000 S.F. field	36.000	C.Y.	.240		57.50	57.50
2000 S.F. field	60.000	C.Y.	.400		95	95
6' diameter pits	55.000	C.Y.	.367		87.50	87.50
3' diameter pits	42.000	C.Y.	.280		66.50	66.50
Building paper, 1000 S.F. field	125.000	S.Y.	2.376	66	132	198
2000 S.F. field	250.000	S.Y.	4.860	135	270	405
4" pipe, PVC, perforated, 1000 S.F. field	145.000	L.F.	9.280	233	380	613
2000 S.F. field	265.000	L.F.	16.960	425	695	1,120
Pipe fittings, bituminous fiber, 1000 S.F. field	2.000	Ea.	1.939	69	109	178
2000 S.F. field	4.000	Ea.	3.879	138	218	356
Leaching pit, including excavation and stone backfill, 3' diameter	1.000	Ea.		730	219	949
6' diameter	1.000	Ea.		975	292	1,267

System Description	QUAN.	UNIT	LABOR HOURS	COST PER UNIT		
				MAT.	INST.	TOTAL
Chain link fence						
Galv.9ga. wire, 1-5/8"post 10'O.C., 1-3/8"top rail, 2"corner post, 3'hi	1.000	L.F.	.130	10	5.35	15.35
4' high	1.000	L.F.	.141	10.05	5.80	15.85
6' high	1.000	L.F.	.209	11.95	8.60	20.55
Add for gate 3' wide 1-3/8" frame 3' high	1.000	Ea.	2.000	91	82.50	173.50
4' high	1.000	Ea.	2.400	98.50	99	197.50
6' high	1.000	Ea.	2.400	123	99	222
Add for gate 4' wide 1-3/8" frame 3' high	1.000	Ea.	2.667	95.50	110	205.50
4' high	1.000	Ea.	2.667	104	110	214
6' high	1.000	Ea.	3.000	131	124	255
Alum.9ga. wire, 1-5/8"post, 10'O.C., 1-3/8"top rail, 2"corner post,3'hi	1.000	L.F.	.130	8.20	5.35	13.55
4' high	1.000	L.F.	.141	7.85	5.80	13.65
6' high	1.000	L.F.	.209	10.25	8.60	18.85
Add for gate 3' wide 1-3/8" frame 3' high	1.000	Ea.	2.000	131	82.50	213.50
4' high	1.000	Ea.	2.400	142	99	241
6' high	1.000	Ea.	2.400	182	99	281
Add for gate 4' wide 1-3/8" frame 3' high	1.000	Ea.	2.400	139	99	238
4' high	1.000	Ea.	2.667	149	110	259
6' high	1.000	Ea.	3.000	193	124	317
Vinyl 9ga. wire, 1-5/8"post 10'O.C., 1-3/8"top rail, 2"corner post,3'hi	1.000	L.F.	.130	8.15	5.35	13.50
4' high	1.000	L.F.	.141	8	5.80	13.80
6' high	1.000	L.F.	.209	10.45	8.60	19.05
Add for gate 3' wide 1-3/8" frame 3' high	1.000	Ea.	2.000	103	82.50	185.50
4' high	1.000	Ea.	2.400	109	99	208
6' high	1.000	Ea.	2.400	133	99	232
Add for gate 4' wide 1-3/8" frame 3' high	1.000	Ea.	2.400	110	99	209
4' high	1.000	Ea.	2.667	113	110	223
6' high	1.000	Ea.	3.000	145	124	269
Tennis court, chain link fence, 10' high						
Galv.11ga.wire, 2"post 10'O.C., 1-3/8"top rail, 2-1/2"corner post	1.000	L.F.	.253	8.30	10.40	18.70
Add for gate 3' wide 1-3/8" frame	1.000	Ea.	2.400	244	99	343
Alum.11ga.wire, 2"post 10'O.C., 1-3/8"top rail, 2-1/2"corner post	1.000	L.F.	.253	9.50	10.40	19.90
Add for gate 3' wide 1-3/8" frame	1.000	Ea.	2.400	142	99	241
Vinyl 11ga.wire,2"post 10' O.C.,1-3/8"top rail,2-1/2"corner post	1.000	L.F.	.253	8	10.40	18.40
Add for gate 3' wide 1-3/8" frame	1.000	Ea.	2.400	185	99	284
Railings, commercial						
Aluminum balcony rail, 1-1/2" posts with pickets	1.000	L.F.	.164	67.50	11.65	79.15
With expanded metal panels	1.000	L.F.	.164	88	11.65	99.65
With porcelain enamel panel inserts	1.000	L.F.	.164	82.50	11.65	94.15
Mild steel, ornamental rounded top rail	1.000	L.F.	.164	76.50	11.65	88.15
As above, but pitch down stairs	1.000	L.F.	.183	82.50	13	95.50
Steel pipe, welded, 1-1/2" round, painted	1.000	L.F.	.160	30	11.40	41.40
Galvanized	1.000	L.F.	.160	42	11.40	53.40
Residential, stock units, mild steel, deluxe	1.000	L.F.	.102	17.25	7.25	24.50
Economy	1.000	L.F.	.102	12.85	7.25	20.10

System Description	QUAN.	UNIT	LABOR HOURS	COST PER UNIT		
				MAT.	INST.	TOTAL
Basketweave, 3/8"x4" boards, 2"x4" stringers on spreaders, 4"x4" posts						
No. 1 cedar, 6' high	1.000	L.F.	.150	28	8.05	36.05
Treated pine, 6' high	1.000	L.F.	.160	37.50	8.60	46.10
Board fence, 1"x4" boards, 2"x4" rails, 4"x4" posts						
Preservative treated, 2 rail, 3' high	1.000	L.F.	.166	9.95	8.90	18.85
4' high	1.000	L.F.	.178	11.50	9.55	21.05
3 rail, 5' high	1.000	L.F.	.185	12.70	9.95	22.65
6' high	1.000	L.F.	.192	14.55	10.35	24.90
Western cedar, No. 1, 2 rail, 3' high	1.000	L.F.	.166	10.80	8.90	19.70
3 rail, 4' high	1.000	L.F.	.178	11.90	9.55	21.45
5' high	1.000	L.F.	.185	13.50	9.95	23.45
6' high	1.000	L.F.	.192	14.45	10.35	24.80
No. 1 cedar, 2 rail, 3' high	1.000	L.F.	.166	13.05	8.90	21.95
4' high	1.000	L.F.	.178	15.15	9.55	24.70
3 rail, 5' high	1.000	L.F.	.185	18.65	9.95	28.60
6' high	1.000	L.F.	.192	20.50	10.35	30.85
Shadow box, 1"x6" boards, 2"x4" rails, 4"x4" posts						
Fir, pine or spruce, treated, 3 rail, 6' high	1.000	L.F.	.160	17.50	8.60	26.10
No. 1 cedar, 3 rail, 4' high	1.000	L.F.	.185	19.35	9.95	29.30
6' high	1.000	L.F.	.192	24.50	10.35	34.85
Open rail, split rails, No. 1 cedar, 2 rail, 3' high	1.000	L.F.	.150	12.85	8.05	20.90
3 rail, 4' high	1.000	L.F.	.160	13.30	8.60	21.90
No. 2 cedar, 2 rail, 3' high	1.000	L.F.	.150	12	8.05	20.05
3 rail, 4' high	1.000	L.F.	.160	9.55	8.60	18.15
Open rail, rustic rails, No. 1 cedar, 2 rail, 3' high	1.000	L.F.	.150	10.30	8.05	18.35
3 rail, 4' high	1.000	L.F.	.160	9.90	8.60	18.50
No. 2 cedar, 2 rail, 3' high	1.000	L.F.	.150	9.60	8.05	17.65
3 rail, 4' high	1.000	L.F.	.160	8	8.60	16.60
Rustic picket, molded pine pickets, 2 rail, 3' high	1.000	L.F.	.171	8.40	9.25	17.65
3 rail, 4' high	1.000	L.F.	.197	9.65	10.60	20.25
No. 1 cedar, 2 rail, 3' high	1.000	L.F.	.171	9.80	9.25	19.05
3 rail, 4' high	1.000	L.F.	.197	11.25	10.60	21.85
Picket fence, fir, pine or spruce, preserved, treated						
2 rail, 3' high	1.000	L.F.	.171	7.45	9.25	16.70
3 rail, 4' high	1.000	L.F.	.185	8.40	9.95	18.35
Western cedar, 2 rail, 3' high	1.000	L.F.	.171	8.15	9.25	17.40
3 rail, 4' high	1.000	L.F.	.185	8.25	9.95	18.20
No. 1 cedar, 2 rail, 3' high	1.000	L.F.	.171	13.70	9.25	22.95
3 rail, 4' high	1.000	L.F.	.185	17.60	9.95	27.55
Stockade, No. 1 cedar, 3-1/4" rails, 6' high	1.000	L.F.	.150	13.10	8.05	21.15
8' high	1.000	L.F.	.155	18.15	8.30	26.45
No. 2 cedar, treated rails, 6' high	1.000	L.F.	.150	13.50	8.05	21.55
Treated pine, treated rails, 6' high	1.000	L.F.	.150	14.05	8.05	22.10
Gates, No. 2 cedar, picket, 3'-6" wide 4' high	1.000	Ea.	2.667	71.50	144	215.50
No. 2 cedar, rustic round, 3' wide, 3' high	1.000	Ea.	2.667	110	144	254
No. 2 cedar, stockade screen, 3'-6" wide, 6' high	1.000	Ea.	3.000	88	162	250
General, wood, 3'-6" wide, 4' high	1.000	Ea.	2.400	75	130	205
6' high	1.000	Ea.	3.000	93.50	162	255.50

System Description	QUAN.	UNIT	LABOR HOURS	COST PER L.F.		
				MAT.	INST.	TOTAL
8″ THICK BY 18″ WIDE FOOTING						
Concrete, 3000 psi	.040	C.Y.		4.36		4.36
Place concrete, direct chute	.040	C.Y.	.016		.70	.70
Forms, footing, 4 uses	1.330	SFCA	.103	.94	4.84	5.78
Reinforcing, 1/2″ diameter bars, 2 each	1.380	Lb.	.011	.76	.61	1.37
Keyway, 2″ x 4″, beveled, 4 uses	1.000	L.F.	.015	.22	.81	1.03
Dowels, 1/2″ diameter bars, 2′ long, 6′ O.C.	.166	Ea.	.006	.13	.32	.45
TOTAL		L.F.	.151	6.41	7.28	13.69
12″ THICK BY 24″ WIDE FOOTING						
Concrete, 3000 psi	.070	C.Y.		7.63		7.63
Place concrete, direct chute	.070	C.Y.	.028		1.22	1.22
Forms, footing, 4 uses	2.000	SFCA	.155	1.42	7.28	8.70
Reinforcing, 1/2″ diameter bars, 2 each	1.380	Lb.	.011	.76	.61	1.37
Keyway, 2″ x 4″, beveled, 4 uses	1.000	L.F.	.015	.22	.81	1.03
Dowels, 1/2″ diameter bars, 2′ long, 6′ O.C.	.166	Ea.	.006	.13	.32	.45
TOTAL		L.F.	.215	10.16	10.24	20.40
12″ THICK BY 36″ WIDE FOOTING						
Concrete, 3000 psi	.110	C.Y.		11.99		11.99
Place concrete, direct chute	.110	C.Y.	.044		1.93	1.93
Forms, footing, 4 uses	2.000	SFCA	.155	1.42	7.28	8.70
Reinforcing, 1/2″ diameter bars, 2 each	1.380	Lb.	.011	.76	.61	1.37
Keyway, 2″ x 4″, beveled, 4 uses	1.000	L.F.	.015	.22	.81	1.03
Dowels, 1/2″ diameter bars, 2′ long, 6′ O.C.	.166	Ea.	.006	.13	.32	.45
TOTAL		L.F.	.231	14.52	10.95	25.47

The footing costs in this system are on a cost per linear foot basis.

Description	QUAN.	UNIT	LABOR HOURS	COST PER S.F.		
				MAT.	INST.	TOTAL

Footing Price Sheet	QUAN.	UNIT	LABOR HOURS	COST PER L.F.		
				MAT.	INST.	TOTAL
Concrete, 8″ thick by 18″ wide footing						
2000 psi concrete	.040	C.Y.		4.08		4.08
2500 psi concrete	.040	C.Y.		4.20		4.20
3000 psi concrete	.040	C.Y.		4.36		4.36
3500 psi concrete	.040	C.Y.		4.44		4.44
4000 psi concrete	.040	C.Y.		4.56		4.56
12″ thick by 24″ wide footing						
2000 psi concrete	.070	C.Y.		7.15		7.15
2500 psi concrete	.070	C.Y.		7.35		7.35
3000 psi concrete	.070	C.Y.		7.65		7.65
3500 psi concrete	.070	C.Y.		7.75		7.75
4000 psi concrete	.070	C.Y.		8		8
12″ thick by 36″ wide footing						
2000 psi concrete	.110	C.Y.		11.20		11.20
2500 psi concrete	.110	C.Y.		11.55		11.55
3000 psi concrete	.110	C.Y.		12		12
3500 psi concrete	.110	C.Y.		12.20		12.20
4000 psi concrete	.110	C.Y.		12.55		12.55
Place concrete, 8″ thick by 18″ wide footing, direct chute	.040	C.Y.	.016		.70	.70
Pumped concrete	.040	C.Y.	.017		.98	.98
Crane & bucket	.040	C.Y.	.032		2.02	2.02
12″ thick by 24″ wide footing, direct chute	.070	C.Y.	.028		1.22	1.22
Pumped concrete	.070	C.Y.	.030		1.71	1.71
Crane & bucket	.070	C.Y.	.056		3.54	3.54
12″ thick by 36″ wide footing, direct chute	.110	C.Y.	.044		1.93	1.93
Pumped concrete	.110	C.Y.	.047		2.68	2.68
Crane & bucket	.110	C.Y.	.088		5.55	5.55
Forms, 8″ thick footing, 1 use	1.330	SFCA	.140	2.93	6.55	9.48
4 uses	1.330	SFCA	.103	.94	4.84	5.78
12″ thick footing, 1 use	2.000	SFCA	.211	4.40	9.90	14.30
4 uses	2.000	SFCA	.155	1.42	7.30	8.72
Reinforcing, 3/8″ diameter bar, 1 each	.400	Lb.	.003	.22	.18	.40
2 each	.800	Lb.	.006	.44	.35	.79
3 each	1.200	Lb.	.009	.66	.53	1.19
1/2″ diameter bar, 1 each	.700	Lb.	.005	.39	.31	.70
2 each	1.380	Lb.	.011	.76	.61	1.37
3 each	2.100	Lb.	.016	1.16	.92	2.08
5/8″ diameter bar, 1 each	1.040	Lb.	.008	.57	.46	1.03
2 each	2.080	Lb.	.016	1.14	.92	2.06
Keyway, beveled, 2″ x 4″, 1 use	1.000	L.F.	.030	.44	1.62	2.06
2 uses	1.000	L.F.	.023	.33	1.22	1.55
2″ x 6″, 1 use	1.000	L.F.	.032	.62	1.72	2.34
2 uses	1.000	L.F.	.024	.47	1.29	1.76
Dowels, 2 feet long, 6′ O.C., 3/8″ bar	.166	Ea.	.005	.07	.30	.37
1/2″ bar	.166	Ea.	.006	.13	.32	.45
5/8″ bar	.166	Ea.	.006	.21	.36	.57
3/4″ bar	.166	Ea.	.006	.21	.36	.57

Sill Plate — Anchor Bolts
Parging
Dampproofing — Masonry Reinforcing
Insulation — Concrete Blocks
— Grout

System Description	QUAN.	UNIT	LABOR HOURS	COST PER S.F.		
				MAT.	INST.	TOTAL
8″ WALL, GROUTED, FULL HEIGHT						
Concrete block, 8″ x 16″ x 8″	1.000	S.F.	.094	3.23	4.62	7.85
Masonry reinforcing, every second course	.750	L.F.	.002	.19	.11	.30
Parging, plastering with portland cement plaster, 1 coat	1.000	S.F.	.014	.25	.72	.97
Dampproofing, bituminous coating, 1 coat	1.000	S.F.	.012	.25	.60	.85
Insulation, 1″ rigid polystyrene	1.000	S.F.	.010	.57	.54	1.11
Grout, solid, pumped	1.000	S.F.	.059	1.24	2.84	4.08
Anchor bolts, 1/2″ diameter, 8″ long, 4′ O.C.	.060	Ea.	.004	.10	.19	.29
Sill plate, 2″ x 4″, treated	.250	L.F.	.007	.13	.39	.52
TOTAL		S.F.	.202	5.96	10.01	15.97
12″ WALL, GROUTED, FULL HEIGHT						
Concrete block, 8″ x 16″ x 12″	1.000	S.F.	.160	4.68	7.70	12.38
Masonry reinforcing, every second course	.750	L.F.	.003	.13	.16	.29
Parging, plastering with portland cement plaster, 1 coat	1.000	S.F.	.014	.25	.72	.97
Dampproofing, bituminous coating, 1 coat	1.000	S.F.	.012	.25	.60	.85
Insulation, 1″ rigid polystyrene	1.000	S.F.	.010	.57	.54	1.11
Grout, solid, pumped	1.000	S.F.	.063	2.03	3.01	5.04
Anchor bolts, 1/2″ diameter, 8″ long, 4′ O.C.	.060	Ea.	.004	.10	.19	.29
Sill plate, 2″ x 4″, treated	.250	L.F.	.007	.13	.39	.52
TOTAL		S.F.	.273	8.14	13.31	21.45

The costs in this system are based on a square foot of wall. Do not subtract for window or door openings.

Description	QUAN.	UNIT	LABOR HOURS	COST PER S.F.		
				MAT.	INST.	TOTAL

Block Wall Systems	QUAN.	UNIT	LABOR HOURS	COST PER S.F.		
				MAT.	INST.	TOTAL
Concrete, block, 8" x 16" x, 6" thick	1.000	S.F.	.089	2.91	4.32	7.23
8" thick	1.000	S.F.	.093	3.23	4.62	7.85
10" thick	1.000	S.F.	.095	3.77	5.60	9.37
12" thick	1.000	S.F.	.122	4.68	7.70	12.38
Solid block, 8" x 16" x, 6" thick	1.000	S.F.	.091	3.10	4.46	7.56
8" thick	1.000	S.F.	.096	4.53	4.73	9.26
10" thick	1.000	S.F.	.096	4.53	4.73	9.26
12" thick	1.000	S.F.	.126	6.55	6.60	13.15
Masonry reinforcing, wire strips, to 8" wide, every course	1.500	L.F.	.004	.38	.21	.59
Every 2nd course	.750	L.F.	.002	.19	.11	.30
Every 3rd course	.500	L.F.	.001	.13	.07	.20
Every 4th course	.400	L.F.	.001	.10	.06	.16
Wire strips to 12" wide, every course	1.500	L.F.	.006	.26	.32	.58
Every 2nd course	.750	L.F.	.003	.13	.16	.29
Every 3rd course	.500	L.F.	.002	.09	.11	.20
Every 4th course	.400	L.F.	.002	.07	.08	.15
Parging, plastering with portland cement plaster, 1 coat	1.000	S.F.	.014	.25	.72	.97
2 coats	1.000	S.F.	.022	.39	1.11	1.50
Dampproofing, bituminous, brushed on, 1 coat	1.000	S.F.	.012	.25	.60	.85
2 coats	1.000	S.F.	.016	.50	.80	1.30
Sprayed on, 1 coat	1.000	S.F.	.010	.25	.48	.73
2 coats	1.000	S.F.	.016	.49	.80	1.29
Troweled on, 1/16" thick	1.000	S.F.	.016	.37	.80	1.17
1/8" thick	1.000	S.F.	.020	.65	1	1.65
1/2" thick	1.000	S.F.	.023	2.10	1.14	3.24
Insulation, rigid, fiberglass, 1.5#/C.F., unfaced						
1-1/2" thick R 6.2	1.000	S.F.	.008	.44	.43	.87
2" thick R 8.5	1.000	S.F.	.008	.50	.43	.93
3" thick R 13	1.000	S.F.	.010	.62	.54	1.16
Perlite, 1" thick R 2.77	1.000	S.F.	.010	.40	.54	.94
2" thick R 5.55	1.000	S.F.	.011	.79	.59	1.38
Polystyrene, extruded, 1" thick R 5.4	1.000	S.F.	.010	.57	.54	1.11
2" thick R 10.8	1.000	S.F.	.011	1.64	.59	2.23
Molded 1" thick R 3.85	1.000	S.F.	.010	.26	.54	.80
2" thick R 7.7	1.000	S.F.	.011	.79	.59	1.38
Grout, concrete block cores, 6" thick	1.000	S.F.	.044	.93	2.14	3.07
8" thick	1.000	S.F.	.059	1.24	2.84	4.08
10" thick	1.000	S.F.	.061	1.63	2.92	4.55
12" thick	1.000	S.F.	.063	2.03	3.01	5.04
Anchor bolts, 2' on center, 1/2" diameter, 8" long	.120	Ea.	.005	.20	.39	.59
12" long	.120	Ea.	.005	.22	.39	.61
3/4" diameter, 8" long	.120	Ea.	.006	.53	.40	.93
12" long	.120	Ea.	.006	.66	.41	1.07
4' on center, 1/2" diameter, 8" long	.060	Ea.	.002	.10	.19	.29
12" long	.060	Ea.	.003	.11	.19	.30
3/4" diameter, 8" long	.060	Ea.	.003	.26	.20	.46
12" long	.060	Ea.	.003	.33	.20	.53
Sill plates, treated, 2" x 4"	.250	L.F.	.007	.13	.39	.52
4" x 4"	.250	L.F.	.007	.33	.37	.70

System Description	QUAN.	UNIT	LABOR HOURS	COST PER S.F.		
				MAT.	INST.	TOTAL
8″ THICK, POURED CONCRETE WALL						
Concrete, 8″ thick , 3000 psi	.025	C.Y.		2.73		2.73
Forms, prefabricated plywood, up to 8′ high	2.000	SFCA	.120	1.88	5.72	7.60
Reinforcing, light	.670	Lb.	.004	.37	.21	.58
Placing concrete, direct chute	.025	C.Y.	.013		.58	.58
Dampproofing, brushed on, 2 coats	1.000	S.F.	.016	.50	.80	1.30
Rigid insulation, 1″ polystyrene	1.000	S.F.	.010	.57	.54	1.11
Anchor bolts, 1/2″ diameter, 12″ long, 4′ O.C.	.060	Ea.	.004	.11	.19	.30
Sill plates, 2″ x 4″, treated	.250	L.F.	.007	.13	.39	.52
TOTAL		S.F.	.174	6.29	8.43	14.72
12″ THICK, POURED CONCRETE WALL						
Concrete, 12″ thick, 3000 psi	.040	C.Y.		4.36		4.36
Forms, prefabricated plywood, up to 8′ high	2.000	SFCA	.120	1.88	5.72	7.60
Reinforcing, light	1.000	Lb.	.005	.55	.31	.86
Placing concrete, direct chute	.040	C.Y.	.019		.85	.85
Dampproofing, brushed on, 2 coats	1.000	S.F.	.016	.50	.80	1.30
Rigid insulation, 1″ polystyrene	1.000	S.F.	.010	.57	.54	1.11
Anchor bolts, 1/2″ diameter, 12″ long, 4′ O.C.	.060	Ea.	.004	.11	.19	.30
Sill plates, 2″ x 4″ treated	.250	L.F.	.007	.13	.39	.52
TOTAL		S.F.	.181	8.10	8.80	16.90

The costs in this system are based on sq. ft. of wall. Do not subtract for window and door openings. The costs assume a 4′ high wall.

Description	QUAN.	UNIT	LABOR HOURS	COST PER S.F.		
				MAT.	INST.	TOTAL

Concrete Wall Price Sheet	QUAN.	UNIT	LABOR HOURS	COST PER S.F.		
				MAT.	INST.	TOTAL
Formwork, prefabricated plywood, up to 8' high	2.000	SFCA	.081	1.88	5.70	7.58
Over 8' to 16' high	2.000	SFCA	.076	1.98	7.60	9.58
Job built forms, 1 use per month	2.000	SFCA	.320	5.80	12.40	18.20
4 uses per month	2.000	SFCA	.221	2.18	9.05	11.23
Reinforcing, 8" wall, light reinforcing	.670	Lb.	.004	.37	.21	.58
Heavy reinforcing	1.500	Lb.	.008	.83	.47	1.30
10" wall, light reinforcing	.850	Lb.	.005	.47	.26	.73
Heavy reinforcing	2.000	Lb.	.011	1.10	.62	1.72
12" wall light reinforcing	1.000	Lb.	.005	.55	.31	.86
Heavy reinforcing	2.250	Lb.	.012	1.24	.70	1.94
Placing concrete, 8" wall, direct chute	.025	C.Y.	.013		.58	.58
Pumped concrete	.025	C.Y.	.016		.91	.91
Crane & bucket	.025	C.Y.	.023		1.42	1.42
10" wall, direct chute	.030	C.Y.	.016		.70	.70
Pumped concrete	.030	C.Y.	.019		1.10	1.10
Crane & bucket	.030	C.Y.	.027		1.71	1.71
12" wall, direct chute	.040	C.Y.	.019		.85	.85
Pumped concrete	.040	C.Y.	.023		1.33	1.33
Crane & bucket	.040	C.Y.	.032		2.02	2.02
Dampproofing, bituminous, brushed on, 1 coat	1.000	S.F.	.012	.25	.60	.85
2 coats	1.000	S.F.	.016	.50	.80	1.30
Sprayed on, 1 coat	1.000	S.F.	.010	.25	.48	.73
2 coats	1.000	S.F.	.016	.49	.80	1.29
Troweled on, 1/16" thick	1.000	S.F.	.016	.37	.80	1.17
1/8" thick	1.000	S.F.	.020	.65	1	1.65
1/2" thick	1.000	S.F.	.023	2.10	1.14	3.24
Insulation rigid, fiberglass, 1.5#/C.F., unfaced						
1-1/2" thick, R 6.2	1.000	S.F.	.008	.44	.43	.87
2" thick, R 8.3	1.000	S.F.	.008	.50	.43	.93
3" thick, R 12.4	1.000	S.F.	.010	.62	.54	1.16
Perlite, 1" thick R 2.77	1.000	S.F.	.010	.40	.54	.94
2" thick R 5.55	1.000	S.F.	.011	.79	.59	1.38
Polystyrene, extruded, 1" thick R 5.40	1.000	S.F.	.010	.57	.54	1.11
2" thick R 10.8	1.000	S.F.	.011	1.64	.59	2.23
Molded, 1" thick R 3.85	1.000	S.F.	.010	.26	.54	.80
2" thick R 7.70	1.000	S.F.	.011	.79	.59	1.38
Anchor bolts, 2' on center, 1/2" diameter, 8" long	.120	Ea.	.005	.20	.39	.59
12" long	.120	Ea.	.005	.22	.39	.61
3/4" diameter, 8" long	.120	Ea.	.006	.53	.40	.93
12" long	.120	Ea.	.006	.66	.41	1.07
Sill plates, treated lumber, 2" x 4"	.250	L.F.	.007	.13	.39	.52
4" x 4"	.250	L.F.	.007	.33	.37	.70

Top Plates

Sheathing

Studs

Asphalt Paper

Insulation

Vapor Barrier

Bottom Plate

System Description	QUAN.	UNIT	LABOR HOURS	COST PER S.F.		
				MAT.	INST.	TOTAL
2" X 4" STUDS, 16" O.C., WALL						
Studs, 2" x 4", 16" O.C., treated	1.000	L.F.	.015	.54	.79	1.33
Plates, double top plate, single bottom plate, treated, 2" x 4"	.750	L.F.	.011	.41	.59	1
Sheathing, 1/2", exterior grade, CDX, treated	1.000	S.F.	.014	.90	.77	1.67
Asphalt paper, 15# roll	1.100	S.F.	.002	.07	.13	.20
Vapor barrier, 4 mil polyethylene	1.000	S.F.	.002	.04	.12	.16
Fiberglass insulation, 3-1/2" thick	1.000	S.F.	.007	.34	.38	.72
TOTAL		S.F.	.051	2.30	2.78	5.08
2" X 6" STUDS, 16" O.C., WALL						
Studs, 2" x 6", 16" O.C., treated	1.000	L.F.	.016	.83	.86	1.69
Plates, double top plate, single bottom plate, treated, 2" x 6"	.750	L.F.	.012	.62	.65	1.27
Sheathing, 5/8" exterior grade, CDX, treated	1.000	S.F.	.015	1.39	.82	2.21
Asphalt paper, 15# roll	1.100	S.F.	.002	.07	.13	.20
Vapor barrier, 4 mil polyethylene	1.000	S.F.	.002	.04	.12	.16
Fiberglass insulation, 6" thick	1.000	S.F.	.007	.46	.38	.84
TOTAL		S.F.	.054	3.41	2.96	6.37
2" X 8" STUDS, 16" O.C., WALL						
Studs, 2" x 8", 16" O.C. treated	1.000	L.F.	.018	1.11	.96	2.07
Plates, double top plate, single bottom plate, treated, 2" x 8"	.750	L.F.	.013	.83	.72	1.55
Sheathing, 3/4" exterior grade, CDX, treated	1.000	S.F.	.016	1.44	.89	2.33
Asphalt paper, 15# roll	1.100	S.F.	.002	.07	.13	.20
Vapor barrier, 4 mil polyethylene	1.000	S.F.	.002	.04	.12	.16
Fiberglass insulation, 9" thick	1.000	S.F.	.006	.77	.32	1.09
TOTAL		S.F.	.057	4.26	3.14	7.40

The costs in this system are based on a sq. ft. of wall area. Do not subtract for window or door openings. The costs assume a 4' high wall.

Description	QUAN.	UNIT	LABOR HOURS	COST PER S.F.		
				MAT.	INST.	TOTAL

Wood Wall Foundation Price Sheet	QUAN.	UNIT	LABOR HOURS	COST PER S.F.		
				MAT.	INST.	TOTAL
Studs, treated, 2" x 4", 12" O.C.	1.250	L.F.	.018	.68	.99	1.67
16" O.C.	1.000	L.F.	.015	.54	.79	1.33
2" x 6", 12" O.C.	1.250	L.F.	.020	1.04	1.08	2.12
16" O.C.	1.000	L.F.	.016	.83	.86	1.69
2" x 8", 12" O.C.	1.250	L.F.	.022	1.39	1.20	2.59
16" O.C.	1.000	L.F.	.018	1.11	.96	2.07
Plates, treated double top single bottom, 2" x 4"	.750	L.F.	.011	.41	.59	1
2" x 6"	.750	L.F.	.012	.62	.65	1.27
2" x 8"	.750	L.F.	.013	.83	.72	1.55
Sheathing, treated exterior grade CDX, 1/2" thick	1.000	S.F.	.014	.90	.77	1.67
5/8" thick	1.000	S.F.	.015	1.39	.82	2.21
3/4" thick	1.000	S.F.	.016	1.44	.89	2.33
Asphalt paper, 15# roll	1.100	S.F.	.002	.07	.13	.20
Vapor barrier, polyethylene, 4 mil	1.000	S.F.	.002	.03	.12	.15
10 mil	1.000	S.F.	.002	.10	.12	.22
Insulation, rigid, fiberglass, 1.5#/C.F., unfaced	1.000	S.F.	.008	.30	.43	.73
1-1/2" thick, R 6.2	1.000	S.F.	.008	.44	.43	.87
2" thick, R 8.3	1.000	S.F.	.008	.50	.43	.93
3" thick, R 12.4	1.000	S.F.	.010	.63	.55	1.18
Perlite 1" thick, R 2.77	1.000	S.F.	.010	.40	.54	.94
2" thick, R 5.55	1.000	S.F.	.011	.79	.59	1.38
Polystyrene, extruded, 1" thick, R 5.40	1.000	S.F.	.010	.57	.54	1.11
2" thick, R 10.8	1.000	S.F.	.011	1.64	.59	2.23
Molded 1" thick, R 3.85	1.000	S.F.	.010	.26	.54	.80
2" thick, R 7.7	1.000	S.F.	.011	.79	.59	1.38
Non rigid, batts, fiberglass, paper backed, 3-1/2" thick roll, R 11	1.000	S.F.	.005	.34	.38	.72
6", R 19	1.000	S.F.	.006	.46	.38	.84
9", R 30	1.000	S.F.	.006	.77	.32	1.09
12", R 38	1.000	S.F.	.006	.98	.32	1.30
Mineral fiber, paper backed, 3-1/2", R 13	1.000	S.F.	.005	.66	.27	.93
6", R 19	1.000	S.F.	.005	1.04	.27	1.31
10", R 30	1.000	S.F.	.006	1.37	.32	1.69

Concrete Slab — Expansion Material

Bank Run Gravel

Welded Wire Fabric

Vapor Barrier

System Description	QUAN.	UNIT	LABOR HOURS	COST PER S.F.		
				MAT.	INST.	TOTAL
4″ THICK SLAB						
Concrete, 4″ thick, 3000 psi concrete	.012	C.Y.		1.31		1.31
Place concrete, direct chute	.012	C.Y.	.005		.23	.23
Bank run gravel, 4″ deep	1.000	S.F.	.001	.39	.06	.45
Polyethylene vapor barrier, .006″ thick	1.000	S.F.	.002	.04	.12	.16
Edge forms, expansion material	.100	L.F.	.005	.03	.25	.28
Welded wire fabric, 6 x 6, 10/10 (W1.4/W1.4)	1.100	S.F.	.005	.18	.30	.48
Steel trowel finish	1.000	S.F.	.014		.68	.68
TOTAL		S.F.	.032	1.95	1.64	3.59
6″ THICK SLAB						
Concrete, 6″ thick, 3000 psi concrete	.019	C.Y.		2.07		2.07
Place concrete, direct chute	.019	C.Y.	.008		.36	.36
Bank run gravel, 4″ deep	1.000	S.F.	.001	.39	.06	.45
Polyethylene vapor barrier, .006″ thick	1.000	S.F.	.002	.04	.12	.16
Edge forms, expansion material	.100	L.F.	.005	.03	.25	.28
Welded wire fabric, 6 x 6, 10/10 (W1.4/W1.4)	1.100	S.F.	.005	.18	.30	.48
Steel trowel finish	1.000	S.F.	.014		.68	.68
TOTAL		S.F.	.035	2.71	1.77	4.48

The slab costs in this section are based on a cost per square foot of floor area.

Description	QUAN.	UNIT	LABOR HOURS	COST PER S.F.		
				MAT.	INST.	TOTAL

Floor Slab Price Sheet	QUAN.	UNIT	LABOR HOURS	COST PER S.F.		
				MAT.	INST.	TOTAL
Concrete, 4" thick slab, 2000 psi concrete	.012	C.Y.		1.22		1.22
2500 psi concrete	.012	C.Y.		1.26		1.26
3000 psi concrete	.012	C.Y.		1.31		1.31
3500 psi concrete	.012	C.Y.		1.33		1.33
4000 psi concrete	.012	C.Y.		1.37		1.37
4500 psi concrete	.012	C.Y.		1.40		1.40
5" thick slab, 2000 psi concrete	.015	C.Y.		1.53		1.53
2500 psi concrete	.015	C.Y.		1.58		1.58
3000 psi concrete	.015	C.Y.		1.64		1.64
3500 psi concrete	.015	C.Y.		1.67		1.67
4000 psi concrete	.015	C.Y.		1.71		1.71
4500 psi concrete	.015	C.Y.		1.76		1.76
6" thick slab, 2000 psi concrete	.019	C.Y.		1.94		1.94
2500 psi concrete	.019	C.Y.		2		2
3000 psi concrete	.019	C.Y.		2.07		2.07
3500 psi concrete	.019	C.Y.		2.11		2.11
4000 psi concrete	.019	C.Y.		2.17		2.17
4500 psi concrete	.019	C.Y.		2.22		2.22
Place concrete, 4" slab, direct chute	.012	C.Y.	.005		.23	.23
Pumped concrete	.012	C.Y.	.006		.34	.34
Crane & bucket	.012	C.Y.	.008		.50	.50
5" slab, direct chute	.015	C.Y.	.007		.29	.29
Pumped concrete	.015	C.Y.	.007		.42	.42
Crane & bucket	.015	C.Y.	.010		.62	.62
6" slab, direct chute	.019	C.Y.	.008		.36	.36
Pumped concrete	.019	C.Y.	.009		.53	.53
Crane & bucket	.019	C.Y.	.012		.78	.78
Gravel, bank run, 4" deep	1.000	S.F.	.001	.39	.06	.45
6" deep	1.000	S.F.	.001	.52	.08	.60
9" deep	1.000	S.F.	.001	.76	.10	.86
12" deep	1.000	S.F.	.001	1.04	.13	1.17
3/4" crushed stone, 3" deep	1.000	S.F.	.001	.34	.06	.40
6" deep	1.000	S.F.	.001	.67	.10	.77
9" deep	1.000	S.F.	.002	.98	.14	1.12
12" deep	1.000	S.F.	.002	1.39	.17	1.56
Vapor barrier polyethylene, .004" thick	1.000	S.F.	.002	.03	.12	.15
.006" thick	1.000	S.F.	.002	.04	.12	.16
Edge forms, expansion material, 4" thick slab	.100	L.F.	.004	.02	.17	.19
6" thick slab	.100	L.F.	.005	.03	.25	.28
Welded wire fabric 6 x 6, 10/10 (W1.4/W1.4)	1.100	S.F.	.005	.18	.30	.48
6 x 6, 6/6 (W2.9/W2.9)	1.100	S.F.	.006	.28	.35	.63
4 x 4, 10/10 (W1.4/W1.4)	1.100	S.F.	.006	.24	.33	.57
Finish concrete, screed finish	1.000	S.F.	.009		.28	.28
Float finish	1.000	S.F.	.011		.28	.28
Steel trowel, for resilient floor	1.000	S.F.	.013		.88	.88
For finished floor	1.000	S.F.	.015		.68	.68

System Description	QUAN.	UNIT	LABOR HOURS	COST PER S.F.		
				MAT.	INST.	TOTAL
2″ X 8″, 16″ O.C.						
Wood joists, 2″ x 8″, 16″ O.C.	1.000	L.F.	.015	.94	.79	1.73
Bridging, 1″ x 3″, 6′ O.C.	.080	Pr.	.005	.05	.27	.32
Box sills, 2″ x 8″	.150	L.F.	.002	.14	.12	.26
Concrete filled steel column, 4″ diameter	.125	L.F.	.002	.27	.13	.40
Girder, built up from three 2″ x 8″	.125	L.F.	.013	.35	.72	1.07
Sheathing, plywood, subfloor, 5/8″ CDX	1.000	S.F.	.012	.82	.64	1.46
Furring, 1″ x 3″, 16″ O.C.	1.000	L.F.	.023	.42	1.23	1.65
TOTAL		S.F.	.072	2.99	3.90	6.89
2″ X 10″, 16″ O.C.						
Wood joists, 2″ x 10″, 16″ OC	1.000	L.F.	.018	1.25	.96	2.21
Bridging, 1″ x 3″, 6′ OC	.080	Pr.	.005	.05	.27	.32
Box sills, 2″ x 10″	.150	L.F.	.003	.19	.14	.33
Concrete filled steel column, 4″ diameter	.125	L.F.	.002	.27	.13	.40
Girder, built up from three 2″ x 10″	.125	L.F.	.014	.47	.77	1.24
Sheathing, plywood, subfloor, 5/8″ CDX	1.000	S.F.	.012	.82	.64	1.46
Furring, 1″ x 3″,16″ OC	1.000	L.F.	.023	.42	1.23	1.65
TOTAL		S.F.	.077	3.47	4.14	7.61
2″ X 12″, 16″ O.C.						
Wood joists, 2″ x 12″, 16″ O.C.	1.000	L.F.	.018	1.70	.99	2.69
Bridging, 1″ x 3″, 6′ O.C.	.080	Pr.	.005	.05	.27	.32
Box sills, 2″ x 12″	.150	L.F.	.003	.26	.15	.41
Concrete filled steel column, 4″ diameter	.125	L.F.	.002	.27	.13	.40
Girder, built up from three 2″ x 12″	.125	L.F.	.015	.64	.81	1.45
Sheathing, plywood, subfloor, 5/8″ CDX	1.000	S.F.	.012	.82	.64	1.46
Furring, 1″ x 3″, 16″ O.C.	1.000	L.F.	.023	.42	1.23	1.65
TOTAL		S.F.	.078	4.16	4.22	8.38

Floor costs on this page are given on a cost per square foot basis.

Description	QUAN.	UNIT	LABOR HOURS	COST PER S.F.		
				MAT.	INST.	TOTAL

Floor Framing Price Sheet (Wood)	QUAN.	UNIT	LABOR HOURS	COST PER S.F.		
				MAT.	INST.	TOTAL
Joists, #2 or better, pine, 2" x 4", 12" O.C.	1.250	L.F.	.016	.53	.86	1.39
16" O.C.	1.000	L.F.	.013	.42	.69	1.11
2" x 6", 12" O.C.	1.250	L.F.	.016	.79	.86	1.65
16" O.C.	1.000	L.F.	.013	.63	.69	1.32
2" x 8", 12" O.C.	1.250	L.F.	.018	1.18	.99	2.17
16" O.C.	1.000	L.F.	.015	.94	.79	1.73
2" x 10", 12" O.C.	1.250	L.F.	.022	1.56	1.20	2.76
16" O.C.	1.000	L.F.	.018	1.25	.96	2.21
2" x 12", 12" O.C.	1.250	L.F.	.023	2.13	1.24	3.37
16" O.C.	1.000	L.F.	.018	1.70	.99	2.69
Bridging, wood 1" x 3", joists 12" O.C.	.100	Pr.	.006	.07	.33	.40
16" O.C.	.080	Pr.	.005	.05	.27	.32
Metal, galvanized, joists 12" O.C.	.100	Pr.	.006	.10	.33	.43
16" O.C.	.080	Pr.	.005	.08	.27	.35
Compression type, joists 12" O.C.	.100	Pr.	.004	.10	.22	.32
16" O.C.	.080	Pr.	.003	.08	.17	.25
Box sills, #2 or better pine, 2" x 4"	.150	L.F.	.002	.06	.10	.16
2" x 6"	.150	L.F.	.002	.09	.10	.19
2" x 8"	.150	L.F.	.002	.14	.12	.26
2" x 10"	.150	L.F.	.003	.19	.14	.33
2" x 12"	.150	L.F.	.003	.26	.15	.41
Girders, including lally columns, 3 pieces spiked together, 2" x 8"	.125	L.F.	.015	.62	.85	1.47
2" x 10"	.125	L.F.	.016	.74	.90	1.64
2" x 12"	.125	L.F.	.017	.91	.94	1.85
Solid girders, 3" x 8"	.040	L.F.	.004	.39	.22	.61
3" x 10"	.040	L.F.	.004	.42	.23	.65
3" x 12"	.040	L.F.	.004	.45	.24	.69
4" x 8"	.040	L.F.	.004	.43	.24	.67
4" x 10"	.040	L.F.	.004	.46	.25	.71
4" x 12"	.040	L.F.	.004	.50	.26	.76
Steel girders, bolted & including fabrication, wide flange shapes						
12" deep, 14#/l.f.	.040	L.F.	.003	1.04	.26	1.30
10" deep, 15#/l.f.	.040	L.F.	.003	1.04	.26	1.30
8" deep, 10#/l.f.	.040	L.F.	.003	.70	.26	.96
6" deep, 9#/l.f.	.040	L.F.	.003	.63	.26	.89
5" deep, 16#/l.f.	.040	L.F.	.003	1.04	.26	1.30
Sheathing, plywood exterior grade CDX, 1/2" thick	1.000	S.F.	.011	.65	.62	1.27
5/8" thick	1.000	S.F.	.012	.82	.64	1.46
3/4" thick	1.000	S.F.	.013	.97	.69	1.66
Boards, 1" x 8" laid regular	1.000	S.F.	.016	2.09	.86	2.95
Laid diagonal	1.000	S.F.	.019	2.09	1.02	3.11
1" x 10" laid regular	1.000	S.F.	.015	2.14	.79	2.93
Laid diagonal	1.000	S.F.	.018	2.14	.96	3.10
Furring, 1" x 3", 12" O.C.	1.250	L.F.	.029	.53	1.54	2.07
16" O.C.	1.000	L.F.	.023	.42	1.23	1.65
24" O.C.	.750	L.F.	.017	.32	.92	1.24

System Description	QUAN.	UNIT	LABOR HOURS	COST PER S.F.		
				MAT.	INST.	TOTAL
9-1/2″ COMPOSITE WOOD JOISTS, 16″ O.C.						
CWJ, 9-1/2″, 16″ O.C., 15′ span	1.000	L.F.	.018	1.90	.96	2.86
Temp. strut line, 1″ x 4″, 8′ O.C.	.160	L.F.	.003	.08	.17	.25
CWJ rim joist, 9-1/2″	.150	L.F.	.003	.29	.14	.43
Concrete filled steel column, 4″ diameter	.125	L.F.	.002	.27	.13	.40
Girder, built up from three 2″ x 8″	.125	L.F.	.013	.35	.72	1.07
Sheathing, plywood, subfloor, 5/8″ CDX	1.000	S.F.	.012	.82	.64	1.46
TOTAL		S.F.	.051	3.71	2.76	6.47
11-1/2″ COMPOSITE WOOD JOISTS, 16″ O.C.						
CWJ, 11-1/2″, 16″ O.C., 18′ span	1.000	L.F.	.018	2.15	.98	3.13
Temp. strut line, 1″ x 4″, 8′ O.C.	.160	L.F.	.003	.08	.17	.25
CWJ rim joist, 11-1/2″	.150	L.F.	.003	.32	.15	.47
Concrete filled steel column, 4″ diameter	.125	L.F.	.002	.27	.13	.40
Girder, built up from three 2″ x 10″	.125	L.F.	.014	.47	.77	1.24
Sheathing, plywood, subfloor, 5/8″ CDX	1.000	S.F.	.012	.82	.64	1.46
TOTAL		S.F.	.052	4.11	2.84	6.95
14″ COMPOSITE WOOD JOISTS, 16″ O.C.						
CWJ, 14″, 16″ O.C., 22′ span	1.000	L.F.	.020	2.55	1.05	3.60
Temp. strut line, 1″ x 4″, 8′ O.C.	.160	L.F.	.003	.08	.17	.25
CWJ rim joist, 14″	.150	L.F.	.003	.38	.16	.54
Concrete filled steel column, 4″ diameter	.600	L.F.	.002	.27	.13	.40
Girder, built up from three 2″ x 12″	.600	L.F.	.015	.64	.81	1.45
Sheathing, plywood, subfloor, 5/8″ CDX	1.000	S.F.	.012	.82	.64	1.46
TOTAL		S.F.	.055	4.74	2.96	7.70

Floor costs on this page are given on a cost per square foot basis.

Description	QUAN.	UNIT	LABOR HOURS	COST PER S.F.		
				MAT.	INST.	TOTAL

Floor Framing Price Sheet (Wood)	QUAN.	UNIT	LABOR HOURS	COST PER S.F.		
				MAT.	INST.	TOTAL
Composite wood joist 9-1/2″ deep, 12″ O.C.	1.250	L.F.	.022	2.38	1.20	3.58
16″ O.C.	1.000	L.F.	.018	1.90	.96	2.86
11-1/2″ deep, 12″ O.C.	1.250	L.F.	.023	2.69	1.23	3.92
16″ O.C.	1.000	L.F.	.018	2.15	.98	3.13
14″ deep, 12″ O.C.	1.250	L.F.	.024	3.19	1.31	4.50
16″ O.C.	1.000	L.F.	.020	2.55	1.05	3.60
16″ deep, 12″ O.C.	1.250	L.F.	.026	4.72	1.38	6.10
16″ O.C.	1.000	L.F.	.021	3.78	1.10	4.88
CWJ rim joist, 9-1/2″	.150	L.F.	.003	.29	.14	.43
11-1/2″	.150	L.F.	.003	.32	.15	.47
14″	.150	L.F.	.003	.38	.16	.54
16″	.150	L.F.	.003	.57	.17	.74
Girders, including lally columns, 3 pieces spiked together, 2″ x 8″	.125	L.F.	.015	.62	.85	1.47
2″ x 10″	.125	L.F.	.016	.74	.90	1.64
2″ x 12″	.125	L.F.	.017	.91	.94	1.85
Solid girders, 3″ x 8″	.040	L.F.	.004	.39	.22	.61
3″ x 10″	.040	L.F.	.004	.42	.23	.65
3″ x 12″	.040	L.F.	.004	.45	.24	.69
4″ x 8″	.040	L.F.	.004	.43	.24	.67
4″ x 10″	.040	L.F.	.004	.46	.25	.71
4″ x 12″	.040	L.F.	.004	.50	.26	.76
Steel girders, bolted & including fabrication, wide flange shapes						
12″ deep, 14#/l.f.	.040	L.F.	.061	24	6.10	30.10
10″ deep, 15#/l.f.	.040	L.F.	.067	26	6.65	32.65
8″ deep, 10#/l.f.	.040	L.F.	.067	17.50	6.65	24.15
6″ deep, 9#/l.f.	.040	L.F.	.067	15.75	6.65	22.40
5″ deep, 16#/l.f.	.040	L.F.	.064	25	6.45	31.45
Sheathing, plywood exterior grade CDX, 1/2″ thick	1.000	S.F.	.011	.65	.62	1.27
5/8″ thick	1.000	S.F.	.012	.82	.64	1.46
3/4″ thick	1.000	S.F.	.013	.97	.69	1.66
Boards, 1″ x 8″ laid regular	1.000	S.F.	.016	2.09	.86	2.95
Laid diagonal	1.000	S.F.	.019	2.09	1.02	3.11
1″ x 10″ laid regular	1.000	S.F.	.015	2.14	.79	2.93
Laid diagonal	1.000	S.F.	.018	2.14	.96	3.10
Furring, 1″ x 3″, 12″ O.C.	1.250	L.F.	.029	.53	1.54	2.07
16″ O.C.	1.000	L.F.	.023	.42	1.23	1.65
24″ O.C.	.750	L.F.	.017	.32	.92	1.24

Cont. 2" x 4" Ribbon

Plywood Sheathing

Girder

Wood Floor Trusses

System Description	QUAN.	UNIT	LABOR HOURS	COST PER S.F.		
				MAT.	INST.	TOTAL
12" OPEN WEB JOISTS, 16" O.C.						
OWJ 12", 16" O.C., 21' span	1.000	L.F.	.018	3.40	.98	4.38
Continuous ribbing, 2" x 4"	.150	L.F.	.002	.06	.10	.16
Concrete filled steel column, 4" diameter	.125	L.F.	.002	.27	.13	.40
Girder, built up from three 2" x 8"	.125	L.F.	.013	.35	.72	1.07
Sheathing, plywood, subfloor, 5/8" CDX	1.000	S.F.	.012	.82	.64	1.46
Furring, 1" x 3", 16" O.C.	1.000	L.F.	.023	.42	1.23	1.65
TOTAL		S.F.	.070	5.32	3.80	9.12
14" OPEN WEB WOOD JOISTS, 16" O.C.						
OWJ 14", 16" O.C., 22' span	1.000	L.F.	.020	3.60	1.05	4.65
Continuous ribbing, 2" x 4"	.150	L.F.	.002	.06	.10	.16
Concrete filled steel column, 4" diameter	.125	L.F.	.002	.27	.13	.40
Girder, built up from three 2" x 10"	.125	L.F.	.014	.47	.77	1.24
Sheathing, plywood, subfloor, 5/8" CDX	1.000	S.F.	.012	.82	.64	1.46
Furring, 1" x 3",16" O.C.	1.000	L.F.	.023	.42	1.23	1.65
TOTAL		S.F.	.073	5.64	3.92	9.56
16" OPEN WEB WOOD JOISTS, 16" O.C.						
OWJ 16", 16" O.C., 24' span	1.000	L.F.	.021	4.03	1.10	5.13
Continuous ribbing, 2" x 4"	.150	L.F.	.002	.06	.10	.16
Concrete filled steel column, 4" diameter	.125	L.F.	.002	.27	.13	.40
Girder, built up from three 2" x 12"	.125	L.F.	.015	.64	.81	1.45
Sheathing, plywood, subfloor, 5/8" CDX	1.000	S.F.	.012	.82	.64	1.46
Furring, 1" x 3", 16" O.C.	1.000	L.F.	.023	.42	1.23	1.65
TOTAL		S.F.	.075	6.24	4.01	10.25

Floor costs on this page are given on a cost per square foot basis.

Description	QUAN.	UNIT	LABOR HOURS	COST PER S.F.		
				MAT.	INST.	TOTAL

Floor Framing Price Sheet (Wood)

Floor Framing Price Sheet (Wood)	QUAN.	UNIT	LABOR HOURS	COST PER S.F.		
				MAT.	INST.	TOTAL
Open web joists, 12″ deep, 12″ O.C.	1.250	L.F.	.023	4.25	1.23	5.48
16″ O.C.	1.000	L.F.	.018	3.40	.98	4.38
14″ deep, 12″ O.C.	1.250	L.F.	.024	4.50	1.31	5.81
16″ O.C.	1.000	L.F.	.020	3.60	1.05	4.65
16 ″ deep, 12″ O.C.	1.250	L.F.	.026	5.05	1.38	6.43
16″ O.C.	1.000	L.F.	.021	4.03	1.10	5.13
18″ deep, 12″ O.C.	1.250	L.F.	.027	5.50	1.47	6.97
16″ O.C.	1.000	L.F.	.022	4.40	1.18	5.58
Continuous ribbing, 2″ x 4″	.150	L.F.	.002	.06	.10	.16
2″ x 6″	.150	L.F.	.002	.09	.10	.19
2″ x 8″	.150	L.F.	.002	.14	.12	.26
2″ x 10″	.150	L.F.	.003	.19	.14	.33
2″ x 12″	.150	L.F.	.003	.26	.15	.41
Girders, including lally columns, 3 pieces spiked together, 2″ x 8″	.125	L.F.	.015	.62	.85	1.47
2″ x 10″	.125	L.F.	.016	.74	.90	1.64
2″ x 12″	.125	L.F.	.017	.91	.94	1.85
Solid girders, 3″ x 8″	.040	L.F.	.004	.39	.22	.61
3″ x 10″	.040	L.F.	.004	.42	.23	.65
3″ x 12″	.040	L.F.	.004	.45	.24	.69
4″ x 8″	.040	L.F.	.004	.43	.24	.67
4″ x 10″	.040	L.F.	.004	.46	.25	.71
4″ x 12″	.040	L.F.	.004	.50	.26	.76
Steel girders, bolted & including fabrication, wide flange shapes						
12″ deep, 14#/l.f.	.040	L.F.	.061	24	6.10	30.10
10″ deep, 15#/l.f.	.040	L.F.	.067	26	6.65	32.65
8″ deep, 10#/l.f.	.040	L.F.	.067	17.50	6.65	24.15
6″ deep, 9#/l.f.	.040	L.F.	.067	15.75	6.65	22.40
5″ deep, 16#/l.f.	.040	L.F.	.064	25	6.45	31.45
Sheathing, plywood exterior grade CDX, 1/2″ thick	1.000	S.F.	.011	.65	.62	1.27
5/8″ thick	1.000	S.F.	.012	.82	.64	1.46
3/4″ thick	1.000	S.F.	.013	.97	.69	1.66
Boards, 1″ x 8″ laid regular					.86	2.95
Laid diagonal					1.02	3.11
1″ x 10″ laid regular					.79	2.93
Laid diagonal					.96	3.10
Furring, 1″ x 3″, 12″ O.C.					1.54	2.07
16″ O.C.					1.23	1.65
24″ O.C.					.92	1.24

System Description	QUAN.	UNIT	LABOR HOURS	COST PER S.F.		
				MAT.	INST.	TOTAL
2" X 4", 16" O.C.						
2" x 4" studs, 16" O.C.	1.000	L.F.	.015	.41	.79	1.20
Plates, 2" x 4", double top, single bottom	.375	L.F.	.005	.15	.30	.45
Corner bracing, let-in, 1" x 6"	.063	L.F.	.003	.06	.18	.24
Sheathing, 1/2" plywood, CDX	1.000	S.F.	.011	.65	.62	1.27
TOTAL		S.F.	.034	1.27	1.89	3.16
2" X 4", 24" O.C.						
2" x 4" studs, 24" O.C.	.750	L.F.	.011	.31	.59	.90
Plates, 2" x 4", double top, single bottom	.375	L.F.	.005	.15	.30	.45
Corner bracing, let-in, 1" x 6"	.063	L.F.	.002	.06	.12	.18
Sheathing, 1/2" plywood, CDX	1.000	S.F.	.011	.65	.62	1.27
TOTAL		S.F.	.029	1.17	1.63	2.80
2" X 6", 16" O.C.						
2" x 6" studs, 16" O.C.	1.000	L.F.	.016	.63	.86	1.49
Plates, 2" x 6", double top, single bottom	.375	L.F.	.006	.24	.32	.56
Corner bracing, let-in, 1" x 6"	.063	L.F.	.003	.06	.18	.24
Sheathing, 1/2" plywood, CDX	1.000	S.F.	.014	.65	.77	1.42
TOTAL		S.F.	.039	1.58	2.13	3.71
2" X 6", 24" O.C.						
2" x 6" studs, 24" O.C.	.750	L.F.	.012	.47	.65	1.12
Plates, 2" x 6", double top, single bottom	.375	L.F.	.006	.24	.32	.56
Corner bracing, let-in, 1" x 6"	.063	L.F.	.002	.06	.12	.18
Sheathing, 1/2" plywood, CDX	1.000	S.F.	.011	.65	.62	1.27
TOTAL		S.F.	.031	1.42	1.71	3.13

The wall costs on this page are given in cost per square foot of wall.
For window and door openings see below.

Description	QUAN.	UNIT	LABOR HOURS	COST PER S.F.		
				MAT.	INST.	TOTAL

Exterior Wall Framing Price Sheet	QUAN.	UNIT	LABOR HOURS	COST PER S.F.		
				MAT.	INST.	TOTAL
Studs, #2 or better, 2" x 4", 12" O.C.	1.250	L.F.	.018	.51	.99	1.50
16" O.C.	1.000	L.F.	.015	.41	.79	1.20
24" O.C.	.750	L.F.	.011	.31	.59	.90
32" O.C.	.600	L.F.	.009	.25	.47	.72
2" x 6", 12" O.C.	1.250	L.F.	.020	.79	1.08	1.87
16" O.C.	1.000	L.F.	.016	.63	.86	1.49
24" O.C.	.750	L.F.	.012	.47	.65	1.12
32" O.C.	.600	L.F.	.010	.38	.52	.90
2" x 8", 12" O.C.	1.250	L.F.	.025	1.48	1.35	2.83
16" O.C.	1.000	L.F.	.020	1.18	1.08	2.26
24" O.C.	.750	L.F.	.015	.89	.81	1.70
32" O.C.	.600	L.F.	.012	.71	.65	1.36
Plates, #2 or better, double top, single bottom, 2" x 4"	.375	L.F.	.005	.15	.30	.45
2" x 6"	.375	L.F.	.006	.24	.32	.56
2" x 8"	.375	L.F.	.008	.44	.41	.85
Corner bracing, let-in 1" x 6" boards, studs, 12" O.C.	.070	L.F.	.004	.06	.20	.26
16" O.C.	.063	L.F.	.003	.06	.18	.24
24" O.C.	.063	L.F.	.002	.06	.12	.18
32" O.C.	.057	L.F.	.002	.05	.11	.16
Let-in steel ("T" shape), studs, 12" O.C.	.070	L.F.	.001	.06	.05	.11
16" O.C.	.063	L.F.	.001	.06	.05	.11
24" O.C.	.063	L.F.	.001	.06	.05	.11
32" O.C.	.057	L.F.	.001	.05	.04	.09
Sheathing, plywood CDX, 3/8" thick	1.000	S.F.	.010	.55	.57	1.12
1/2" thick	1.000	S.F.	.011	.65	.62	1.27
5/8" thick	1.000	S.F.	.012	.82	.66	1.48
3/4" thick	1.000	S.F.	.013	.97	.72	1.69
Boards, 1" x 6", laid regular	1.000	S.F.	.025	1.92	1.33	3.25
Laid diagonal	1.000	S.F.	.027	1.92	1.48	3.40
1" x 8", laid regular	1.000	S.F.	.021	2.09	1.13	3.22
Laid diagonal	1.000	S.F.	.025	2.09	1.33	3.42
Wood fiber, regular, no vapor barrier, 1/2" thick	1.000	S.F.	.013	.66	.72	1.38
5/8" thick	1.000	S.F.	.013	.84	.72	1.56
Asphalt impregnated 25/32" thick	1.000	S.F.	.013	.35	.72	1.07
1/2" thick	1.000	S.F.	.013	.26	.72	.98
Polystyrene, regular, 3/4" thick	1.000	S.F.	.010	.57	.54	1.11
2" thick	1.000	S.F.	.011	1.64	.59	2.23
Fiberglass, foil faced, 1" thick	1.000	S.F.	.008	.99	.43	1.42
2" thick	1.000	S.F.	.009	1.86	.49	2.35

Window & Door Openings	QUAN.	UNIT	LABOR HOURS	COST EACH		
				MAT.	INST.	TOTAL
The following costs are to be added to the total costs of the wall for each opening. Do not subtract the area of the openings.						
Headers, 2" x 6" double, 2' long	4.000	L.F.	.178	2.52	9.60	12.12
3' long	6.000	L.F.	.267	3.78	14.40	18.18
4' long	8.000	L.F.	.356	5.05	19.20	24.25
5' long	10.000	L.F.	.444	6.30	24	30.30
2" x 8" double, 4' long	8.000	L.F.	.376	7.50	20.50	28
5' long	10.000	L.F.	.471	9.40	25.50	34.90
6' long	12.000	L.F.	.565	11.30	30.50	41.80
8' long	16.000	L.F.	.753	15.05	40.50	55.55
2" x 10" double, 4' long	8.000	L.F.	.400	10	21.50	31.50
6' long	12.000	L.F.	.600	15	32.50	47.50
8' long	16.000	L.F.	.800	20	43	63
10' long	20.000	L.F.	1.000	25	54	79
2" x 12" double, 8' long	16.000	L.F.	.853	27	46	73
12' long	24.000	L.F.	1.280	41	69	110

137

System Description	QUAN.	UNIT	LABOR HOURS	COST PER S.F.		
				MAT.	INST.	TOTAL
2″ X 6″ RAFTERS, 16″ O.C., 4/12 PITCH						
Rafters, 2″ x 6″, 16″ O.C., 4/12 pitch	1.170	L.F.	.019	.74	1.01	1.75
Ceiling joists, 2″ x 4″, 16″ O.C.	1.000	L.F.	.013	.42	.69	1.11
Ridge board, 2″ x 6″	.050	L.F.	.002	.03	.09	.12
Fascia board, 2″ x 6″	.100	L.F.	.005	.07	.29	.36
Rafter tie, 1″ x 4″, 4′ O.C.	.060	L.F.	.001	.03	.06	.09
Soffit nailer (outrigger), 2″ x 4″, 24″ O.C.	.170	L.F.	.004	.07	.24	.31
Sheathing, exterior, plywood, CDX, 1/2″ thick	1.170	S.F.	.013	.76	.73	1.49
Furring strips, 1″ x 3″, 16″ O.C.	1.000	L.F.	.023	.42	1.23	1.65
TOTAL		S.F.	.080	2.54	4.34	6.88
2″ X 8″ RAFTERS, 16″ O.C., 4/12 PITCH						
Rafters, 2″ x 8″, 16″ O.C., 4/12 pitch	1.170	L.F.	.020	1.10	1.06	2.16
Ceiling joists, 2″ x 6″, 16″ O.C.	1.000	L.F.	.013	.63	.69	1.32
Ridge board, 2″ x 8″	.050	L.F.	.002	.05	.10	.15
Fascia board, 2″ x 8″	.100	L.F.	.007	.09	.38	.47
Rafter tie, 1″ x 4″, 4′ O.C.	.060	L.F.	.001	.03	.06	.09
Soffit nailer (outrigger), 2″ x 4″, 24″ O.C.	.170	L.F.	.004	.07	.24	.31
Sheathing, exterior, plywood, CDX, 1/2″ thick	1.170	S.F.	.013	.76	.73	1.49
Furring strips, 1″ x 3″, 16″ O.C.	1.000	L.F.	.023	.42	1.23	1.65
TOTAL		S.F.	.083	3.15	4.49	7.64

The cost of this system is based on the square foot of plan area.
All quantities have been adjusted accordingly.

Description	QUAN.	UNIT	LABOR HOURS	COST PER S.F.		
				MAT.	INST.	TOTAL

Gable End Roof Framing Price Sheet	QUAN.	UNIT	LABOR HOURS	COST PER S.F.		
				MAT.	INST.	TOTAL
Rafters, #2 or better, 16″ O.C., 2″ x 6″, 4/12 pitch	1.170	L.F.	.019	.74	1.01	1.75
8/12 pitch	1.330	L.F.	.027	.84	1.44	2.28
2″ x 8″, 4/12 pitch	1.170	L.F.	.020	1.10	1.06	2.16
8/12 pitch	1.330	L.F.	.028	1.25	1.53	2.78
2″ x 10″, 4/12 pitch	1.170	L.F.	.030	1.46	1.60	3.06
8/12 pitch	1.330	L.F.	.043	1.66	2.33	3.99
24″ O.C., 2″ x 6″, 4/12 pitch	.940	L.F.	.015	.59	.81	1.40
8/12 pitch	1.060	L.F.	.021	.67	1.14	1.81
2″ x 8″, 4/12 pitch	.940	L.F.	.016	.88	.86	1.74
8/12 pitch	1.060	L.F.	.023	1	1.22	2.22
2″ x 10″, 4/12 pitch	.940	L.F.	.024	1.18	1.29	2.47
8/12 pitch	1.060	L.F.	.034	1.33	1.86	3.19
Ceiling joist, #2 or better, 2″ x 4″, 16″ O.C.	1.000	L.F.	.013	.42	.69	1.11
24″ O.C.	.750	L.F.	.010	.32	.52	.84
2″ x 6″, 16″ O.C.	1.000	L.F.	.013	.63	.69	1.32
24″ O.C.	.750	L.F.	.010	.47	.52	.99
2″ x 8″, 16″ O.C.	1.000	L.F.	.015	.94	.79	1.73
24″ O.C.	.750	L.F.	.011	.71	.59	1.30
2″ x 10″, 16″ O.C.	1.000	L.F.	.018	1.25	.96	2.21
24″ O.C.	.750	L.F.	.013	.94	.72	1.66
Ridge board, #2 or better, 1″ x 6″	.050	L.F.	.001	.04	.07	.11
1″ x 8″	.050	L.F.	.001	.07	.08	.15
1″ x 10″	.050	L.F.	.002	.09	.09	.18
2″ x 6″	.050	L.F.	.002	.03	.09	.12
2″ x 8″	.050	L.F.	.002	.05	.10	.15
2″ x 10″	.050	L.F.	.002	.06	.11	.17
Fascia board, #2 or better, 1″ x 6″	.100	L.F.	.004	.05	.21	.26
1″ x 8″	.100	L.F.	.005	.06	.25	.31
1″ x 10″	.100	L.F.	.005	.07	.28	.35
2″ x 6″	.100	L.F.	.006	.08	.31	.39
2″ x 8″	.100	L.F.	.007	.09	.38	.47
2″ x 10″	.100	L.F.	.004	.25	.19	.44
Rafter tie, #2 or better, 4′ O.C., 1″ x 4″	.060	L.F.	.001	.03	.06	.09
1″ x 6″	.060	L.F.	.001	.03	.07	.10
2″ x 4″	.060	L.F.	.002	.04	.09	.13
2″ x 6″	.060	L.F.	.002	.05	.11	.16
Soffit nailer (outrigger), 2″ x 4″, 16″ O.C.	.220	L.F.	.006	.09	.31	.40
24″ O.C.	.170	L.F.	.004	.07	.24	.31
2″ x 6″, 16″ O.C.	.220	L.F.	.006	.11	.35	.46
24″ O.C.	.170	L.F.	.005	.08	.28	.36
Sheathing, plywood CDX, 4/12 pitch, 3/8″ thick.	1.170	S.F.	.012	.64	.67	1.31
1/2″ thick	1.170	S.F.	.013	.76	.73	1.49
5/8″ thick	1.170	S.F.	.014	.96	.77	1.73
8/12 pitch, 3/8″	1.330	S.F.	.014	.73	.76	1.49
1/2″ thick	1.330	S.F.	.015	.86	.82	1.68
5/8″ thick	1.330	S.F.	.016	1.09	.88	1.97
Boards, 4/12 pitch roof, 1″ x 6″	1.170	S.F.	.026	2.25	1.39	3.64
1″ x 8″	1.170	S.F.	.021	2.45	1.16	3.61
8/12 pitch roof, 1″ x 6″	1.330	S.F.	.029	2.55	1.58	4.13
1″ x 8″	1.330	S.F.	.024	2.78	1.32	4.10
Furring, 1″ x 3″, 12″ O.C.	1.200	L.F.	.027	.50	1.48	1.98
16″ O.C.	1.000	L.F.	.023	.42	1.23	1.65
24″ O.C.	.800	L.F.	.018	.34	.98	1.32

Sheathing · Trusses · Fascia Board · Furring

System Description	QUAN.	UNIT	LABOR HOURS	COST PER S.F.		
				MAT.	INST.	TOTAL
TRUSS, 16″ O.C., 4/12 PITCH, 1′ OVERHANG, 26′ SPAN						
Truss, 40# loading, 16″ O.C., 4/12 pitch, 26′ span	.030	Ea.	.021	2.64	1.42	4.06
Fascia board, 2″ x 6″	.100	L.F.	.005	.07	.29	.36
Sheathing, exterior, plywood, CDX, 1/2″ thick	1.170	S.F.	.013	.76	.73	1.49
Furring, 1″ x 3″, 16″ O.C.	1.000	L.F.	.023	.42	1.23	1.65
TOTAL		S.F.	.062	3.89	3.67	7.56
TRUSS, 16″ O.C., 8/12 PITCH, 1′ OVERHANG, 26′ SPAN						
Truss, 40# loading, 16″ O.C., 8/12 pitch, 26′ span	.030	Ea.	.023	3.33	1.56	4.89
Fascia board, 2″ x 6″	.100	L.F.	.005	.07	.29	.36
Sheathing, exterior, plywood, CDX, 1/2″ thick	1.330	S.F.	.015	.86	.82	1.68
Furring, 1″ x 3″, 16″ O.C.	1.000	L.F.	.023	.42	1.23	1.65
TOTAL		S.F.	.066	4.68	3.90	8.58
TRUSS, 24″ O.C., 4/12 PITCH, 1′ OVERHANG, 26′ SPAN						
Truss, 40# loading, 24″ O.C., 4/12 pitch, 26′ span	.020	Ea.	.014	1.76	.95	2.71
Fascia board, 2″ x 6″	.100	L.F.	.005	.07	.29	.36
Sheathing, exterior, plywood, CDX, 1/2″ thick	1.170	S.F.	.013	.76	.73	1.49
Furring, 1″ x 3″, 16″ O.C.	1.000	L.F.	.023	.42	1.23	1.65
TOTAL		S.F.	.055	3.01	3.20	6.21
TRUSS, 24″ O.C., 8/12 PITCH, 1′ OVERHANG, 26′ SPAN						
Truss, 40# loading, 24″ O.C., 8/12 pitch, 26′ span	.020	Ea.	.015	2.22	1.04	3.26
Fascia board, 2″ x 6″	.100	L.F.	.005	.07	.29	.36
Sheathing, exterior, plywood, CDX, 1/2″ thick	1.330	S.F.	.015	.86	.82	1.68
Furring, 1″ x 3″, 16″ O.C.	1.000	L.F.	.023	.42	1.23	1.65
TOTAL		S.F.	.058	3.57	3.38	6.95

The cost of this system is based on the square foot of plan area.
A one foot overhang is included.

Description	QUAN.	UNIT	LABOR HOURS	COST PER S.F.		
				MAT.	INST.	TOTAL

Truss Roof Framing Price Sheet	QUAN.	UNIT	LABOR HOURS	COST PER S.F.		
				MAT.	INST.	TOTAL
Truss, 40# loading, including 1' overhang, 4/12 pitch, 24' span, 16" O.C.	.033	Ea.	.022	2.79	1.47	4.26
24" O.C.	.022	Ea.	.015	1.86	.99	2.85
26' span, 16" O.C.	.030	Ea.	.021	2.64	1.42	4.06
24" O.C.	.020	Ea.	.014	1.76	.95	2.71
28' span, 16" O.C.	.027	Ea.	.020	2.75	1.37	4.12
24" O.C.	.019	Ea.	.014	1.94	.96	2.90
32' span, 16" O.C.	.024	Ea.	.019	2.86	1.30	4.16
24" O.C.	.016	Ea.	.013	1.90	.86	2.76
36' span, 16" O.C.	.022	Ea.	.019	3.23	1.29	4.52
24" O.C.	.015	Ea.	.013	2.21	.88	3.09
8/12 pitch, 24' span, 16" O.C.	.033	Ea.	.024	3.53	1.61	5.14
24" O.C.	.022	Ea.	.016	2.35	1.07	3.42
26' span, 16" O.C.	.030	Ea.	.023	3.33	1.56	4.89
24" O.C.	.020	Ea.	.015	2.22	1.04	3.26
28' span, 16" O.C.	.027	Ea.	.022	3.32	1.48	4.80
24" O.C.	.019	Ea.	.016	2.34	1.04	3.38
32' span, 16" O.C.	.024	Ea.	.021	3.53	1.43	4.96
24" O.C.	.016	Ea.	.014	2.35	.96	3.31
36' span, 16" O.C.	.022	Ea.	.021	4.03	1.45	5.48
24" O.C.	.015	Ea.	.015	2.75	.99	3.74
Fascia board, #2 or better, 1" x 6"	.100	L.F.	.004	.05	.21	.26
1" x 8"	.100	L.F.	.005	.06	.25	.31
1" x 10"	.100	L.F.	.005	.07	.28	.35
2" x 6"	.100	L.F.	.006	.08	.31	.39
2" x 8"	.100	L.F.	.007	.09	.38	.47
2" x 10"	.100	L.F.	.009	.13	.48	.61
Sheathing, plywood CDX, 4/12 pitch, 3/8" thick	1.170	S.F.	.012	.64	.67	1.31
1/2" thick	1.170	S.F.	.013	.76	.73	1.49
5/8" thick	1.170	S.F.	.014	.96	.77	1.73
8/12 pitch, 3/8" thick	1.330	S.F.	.014	.73	.76	1.49
1/2" thick	1.330	S.F.	.015	.86	.82	1.68
5/8" thick	1.330	S.F.	.016	1.09	.88	1.97
Boards, 4/12 pitch, 1" x 6"	1.170	S.F.	.026	2.25	1.39	3.64
1" x 8"	1.170	S.F.	.021	2.45	1.16	3.61
8/12 pitch, 1" x 6"	1.330	S.F.	.029	2.55	1.58	4.13
1" x 8"	1.330	S.F.	.024	2.78	1.32	4.10
Furring, 1" x 3", 12" O.C.	1.200	L.F.	.027	.50	1.48	1.98
16" O.C.	1.000	L.F.	.023	.42	1.23	1.65
24" O.C.	.800	L.F.	.018	.34	.98	1.32
Truss, 40# loading, including 1' overhang, 4/12 pitch, 24' span, 16" O.C.						

System Description	QUAN.	UNIT	LABOR HOURS	COST PER S.F.		
				MAT.	INST.	TOTAL
2″ X 6″, 16″ O.C., 4/12 PITCH						
Hip rafters, 2″ x 8″, 4/12 pitch	.160	L.F.	.004	.15	.19	.34
Jack rafters, 2″ x 6″, 16″ O.C., 4/12 pitch	1.430	L.F.	.038	.90	2.06	2.96
Ceiling joists, 2″ x 6″, 16″ O.C.	1.000	L.F.	.013	.63	.69	1.32
Fascia board, 2″ x 8″	.220	L.F.	.016	.21	.84	1.05
Soffit nailer (outrigger), 2″ x 4″, 24″ O.C.	.220	L.F.	.006	.09	.31	.40
Sheathing, 1/2″ exterior plywood, CDX	1.570	S.F.	.018	1.02	.97	1.99
Furring strips, 1″ x 3″, 16″ O.C.	1.000	L.F.	.023	.42	1.23	1.65
TOTAL		S.F.	.118	3.42	6.29	9.71
2″ X 8″, 16″ O.C., 4/12 PITCH						
Hip rafters, 2″ x 10″, 4/12 pitch	.160	L.F.	.004	.20	.24	.44
Jack rafters, 2″ x 8″, 16″ O.C., 4/12 pitch	1.430	L.F.	.047	1.34	2.52	3.86
Ceiling joists, 2″ x 6″, 16″ O.C.	1.000	L.F.	.013	.63	.69	1.32
Fascia board, 2″ x 8″	.220	L.F.	.012	.16	.65	.81
Soffit nailer (outrigger), 2″ x 4″, 24″ O.C.	.220	L.F.	.006	.09	.31	.40
Sheathing, 1/2″ exterior plywood, CDX	1.570	S.F.	.018	1.02	.97	1.99
Furring strips, 1″ x 3″, 16″ O.C.	1.000	L.F.	.023	.42	1.23	1.65
TOTAL		S.F.	.123	3.86	6.61	10.47

The cost of this system is based on S.F. of plan area. Measurement is area under the hip roof only. See gable roof system for added costs.

Description	QUAN.	UNIT	LABOR HOURS	COST PER S.F.		
				MAT.	INST.	TOTAL

Hip Roof Framing Price Sheet	QUAN.	UNIT	LABOR HOURS	COST PER S.F.		
				MAT.	INST.	TOTAL
Hip rafters, #2 or better, 2" x 6", 4/12 pitch	.160	L.F.	.003	.10	.18	.28
8/12 pitch	.210	L.F.	.006	.13	.31	.44
2" x 8", 4/12 pitch	.160	L.F.	.004	.15	.19	.34
8/12 pitch	.210	L.F.	.006	.20	.33	.53
2" x 10", 4/12 pitch	.160	L.F.	.004	.20	.24	.44
8/12 pitch roof	.210	L.F.	.008	.26	.41	.67
Jack rafters, #2 or better, 16" O.C., 2" x 6", 4/12 pitch	1.430	L.F.	.038	.90	2.06	2.96
8/12 pitch	1.800	L.F.	.061	1.13	3.28	4.41
2" x 8", 4/12 pitch	1.430	L.F.	.047	1.34	2.52	3.86
8/12 pitch	1.800	L.F.	.075	1.69	4.03	5.72
2" x 10", 4/12 pitch	1.430	L.F.	.051	1.79	2.75	4.54
8/12 pitch	1.800	L.F.	.082	2.25	4.45	6.70
24" O.C., 2" x 6", 4/12 pitch	1.150	L.F.	.031	.72	1.66	2.38
8/12 pitch	1.440	L.F.	.048	.91	2.62	3.53
2" x 8", 4/12 pitch	1.150	L.F.	.038	1.08	2.02	3.10
8/12 pitch	1.440	L.F.	.060	1.35	3.23	4.58
2" x 10", 4/12 pitch	1.150	L.F.	.041	1.44	2.21	3.65
8/12 pitch	1.440	L.F.	.066	1.80	3.56	5.36
Ceiling joists, #2 or better, 2" x 4", 16" O.C.	1.000	L.F.	.013	.42	.69	1.11
24" O.C.	.750	L.F.	.010	.32	.52	.84
2" x 6", 16" O.C.	1.000	L.F.	.013	.63	.69	1.32
24" O.C.	.750	L.F.	.010	.47	.52	.99
2" x 8", 16" O.C.	1.000	L.F.	.015	.94	.79	1.73
24" O.C.	.750	L.F.	.011	.71	.59	1.30
2" x 10", 16" O.C.	1.000	L.F.	.018	1.25	.96	2.21
24" O.C.	.750	L.F.	.013	.94	.72	1.66
Fascia board, #2 or better, 1" x 6"	.220	L.F.	.009	.11	.46	.57
1" x 8"	.220	L.F.	.010	.13	.54	.67
1" x 10"	.220	L.F.	.011	.15	.61	.76
2" x 6"	.220	L.F.	.013	.17	.68	.85
2" x 8"	.220	L.F.	.016	.21	.84	1.05
2" x 10"	.220	L.F.	.020	.28	1.06	1.34
Soffit nailer (outrigger), 2" x 4", 16" O.C.	.280	L.F.	.007	.12	.39	.51
24" O.C.	.220	L.F.	.006	.09	.31	.40
2" x 8", 16" O.C.	.280	L.F.	.007	.20	.36	.56
24" O.C.	.220	L.F.	.005	.16	.29	.45
Sheathing, plywood CDX, 4/12 pitch, 3/8" thick	1.570	S.F.	.016	.86	.89	1.75
1/2" thick	1.570	S.F.	.018	1.02	.97	1.99
5/8" thick	1.570	S.F.	.019	1.29	1.04	2.33
8/12 pitch, 3/8" thick	1.900	S.F.	.020	1.05	1.08	2.13
1/2" thick	1.900	S.F.	.022	1.24	1.18	2.42
5/8" thick	1.900	S.F.	.023	1.56	1.25	2.81
Boards, 4/12 pitch, 1" x 6" boards	1.450	S.F.	.032	2.78	1.73	4.51
1" x 8" boards	1.450	S.F.	.027	3.03	1.44	4.47
8/12 pitch, 1" x 6" boards	1.750	S.F.	.039	3.36	2.08	5.44
1" x 8" boards	1.750	S.F.	.032	3.66	1.73	5.39
Furring, 1" x 3", 12" O.C.	1.200	L.F.	.027	.50	1.48	1.98
16" O.C.	1.000	L.F.	.023	.42	1.23	1.65
24" O.C.	.800	L.F.	.018	.34	.98	1.32

System Description	QUAN.	UNIT	LABOR HOURS	COST PER S.F.		
				MAT.	INST.	TOTAL
2″ X 6″ RAFTERS, 16″ O.C.						
Roof rafters, 2″ x 6″, 16″ O.C.	1.430	L.F.	.029	.90	1.54	2.44
Ceiling joists, 2″ x 6″, 16″ O.C.	.710	L.F.	.009	.45	.49	.94
Stud wall, 2″ x 4″, 16″ O.C., including plates	.790	L.F.	.012	.33	.67	1
Furring strips, 1″ x 3″, 16″ O.C.	.710	L.F.	.016	.30	.87	1.17
Ridge board, 2″ x 8″	.050	L.F.	.002	.05	.10	.15
Fascia board, 2″ x 6″	.100	L.F.	.006	.08	.31	.39
Sheathing, exterior grade plywood, 1/2″ thick	1.450	S.F.	.017	.94	.90	1.84
TOTAL		S.F.	.091	3.05	4.88	7.93
2″ X 8″ RAFTERS, 16″ O.C.						
Roof rafters, 2″ x 8″, 16″ O.C.	1.430	L.F.	.031	1.34	1.64	2.98
Ceiling joists, 2″ x 6″, 16″ O.C.	.710	L.F.	.009	.45	.49	.94
Stud wall, 2″ x 4″, 16″ O.C., including plates	.790	L.F.	.012	.33	.67	1
Furring strips, 1″ x 3″, 16″ O.C.	.710	L.F.	.016	.30	.87	1.17
Ridge board, 2″ x 8″	.050	L.F.	.002	.05	.10	.15
Fascia board, 2″ x 8″	.100	L.F.	.007	.09	.38	.47
Sheathing, exterior grade plywood, 1/2″ thick	1.450	S.F.	.017	.94	.90	1.84
TOTAL		S.F.	.094	3.50	5.05	8.55

The cost of this system is based on the square foot of plan area on the first floor.

Description	QUAN.	UNIT	LABOR HOURS	COST PER S.F.		
				MAT.	INST.	TOTAL

Gambrel Roof Framing Price Sheet	QUAN.	UNIT	LABOR HOURS	COST PER S.F.		
				MAT.	INST.	TOTAL
Roof rafters, #2 or better, 2″ x 6″, 16″ O.C.	1.430	L.F.	.029	.90	1.54	2.44
24″ O.C.	1.140	L.F.	.023	.72	1.23	1.95
2″ x 8″, 16″ O.C.	1.430	L.F.	.031	1.34	1.64	2.98
24″ O.C.	1.140	L.F.	.024	1.07	1.31	2.38
2″ x 10″, 16″ O.C.	1.430	L.F.	.046	1.79	2.50	4.29
24″ O.C.	1.140	L.F.	.037	1.43	2	3.43
Ceiling joist, #2 or better, 2″ x 4″, 16″ O.C.	.710	L.F.	.009	.30	.49	.79
24″ O.C.	.570	L.F.	.007	.24	.39	.63
2″ x 6″, 16″ O.C.	.710	L.F.	.009	.45	.49	.94
24″ O.C.	.570	L.F.	.007	.36	.39	.75
2″ x 8″, 16″ O.C.	.710	L.F.	.010	.67	.56	1.23
24″ O.C.	.570	L.F.	.008	.54	.45	.99
Stud wall, #2 or better, 2″ x 4″, 16″ O.C.	.790	L.F.	.012	.33	.67	1
24″ O.C.	.630	L.F.	.010	.26	.54	.80
2″ x 6″, 16″ O.C.	.790	L.F.	.014	.50	.77	1.27
24″ O.C.	.630	L.F.	.011	.40	.61	1.01
Furring, 1″ x 3″, 16″ O.C.	.710	L.F.	.016	.30	.87	1.17
24″ O.C.	.590	L.F.	.013	.25	.73	.98
Ridge board, #2 or better, 1″ x 6″	.050	L.F.	.001	.04	.07	.11
1″ x 8″	.050	L.F.	.001	.07	.08	.15
1″ x 10″	.050	L.F.	.002	.09	.09	.18
2″ x 6″	.050	L.F.	.002	.03	.09	.12
2″ x 8″	.050	L.F.	.002	.05	.10	.15
2″ x 10″	.050	L.F.	.002	.06	.11	.17
Fascia board, #2 or better, 1″ x 6″	.100	L.F.	.004	.05	.21	.26
1″ x 8″	.100	L.F.	.005	.06	.25	.31
1″ x 10″	.100	L.F.	.005	.07	.28	.35
2″ x 6″	.100	L.F.	.006	.08	.31	.39
2″ x 8″	.100	L.F.	.007	.09	.38	.47
2″ x 10″	.100	L.F.	.009	.13	.48	.61
Sheathing, plywood, exterior grade CDX, 3/8″ thick	1.450	S.F.	.015	.80	.83	1.63
1/2″ thick	1.450	S.F.	.017	.94	.90	1.84
5/8″ thick	1.450	S.F.	.018	1.19	.96	2.15
3/4″ thick	1.450	S.F.	.019	1.41	1.04	2.45
Boards, 1″ x 6″, laid regular	1.450	S.F.	.032	2.78	1.73	4.51
Laid diagonal	1.450	S.F.	.036	2.78	1.93	4.71
1″ x 8″, laid regular	1.450	S.F.	.027	3.03	1.44	4.47
Laid diagonal	1.450	S.F.	.032	3.03	1.73	4.76

System Description	QUAN.	UNIT	LABOR HOURS	COST PER S.F.		
				MAT.	INST.	TOTAL
2″ X 6″ RAFTERS, 16″ O.C.						
Roof rafters, 2″ x 6″, 16″ O.C.	1.210	L.F.	.033	.76	1.77	2.53
Rafter plates, 2″ x 6″, double top, single bottom	.364	L.F.	.010	.23	.53	.76
Ceiling joists, 2″ x 4″, 16″ O.C.	.920	L.F.	.012	.39	.63	1.02
Hip rafter, 2″ x 6″	.070	L.F.	.002	.04	.12	.16
Jack rafter, 2″ x 6″, 16″ O.C.	1.000	L.F.	.039	.63	2.11	2.74
Ridge board, 2″ x 6″	.018	L.F.	.001	.01	.03	.04
Sheathing, exterior grade plywood, 1/2″ thick	2.210	S.F.	.025	1.44	1.37	2.81
Furring strips, 1″ x 3″, 16″ O.C.	.920	L.F.	.021	.39	1.13	1.52
TOTAL		S.F.	.143	3.89	7.69	11.58
2″ X 8″ RAFTERS, 16″ O.C.						
Roof rafters, 2″ x 8″, 16″ O.C.	1.210	L.F.	.036	1.14	1.94	3.08
Rafter plates, 2″ x 8″, double top, single bottom	.364	L.F.	.011	.34	.58	.92
Ceiling joists, 2″ x 6″, 16″ O.C.	.920	L.F.	.012	.58	.63	1.21
Hip rafter, 2″ x 8″	.070	L.F.	.002	.07	.13	.20
Jack rafter, 2″ x 8″, 16″ O.C.	1.000	L.F.	.048	.94	2.58	3.52
Ridge board, 2″ x 8″	.018	L.F.	.001	.02	.03	.05
Sheathing, exterior grade plywood, 1/2″ thick	2.210	S.F.	.025	1.44	1.37	2.81
Furring strips, 1″ x 3″, 16″ O.C.	.920	L.F.	.021	.39	1.13	1.52
TOTAL		S.F.	.156	4.92	8.39	13.31

The cost of this system is based on the square foot of plan area.

Description	QUAN.	UNIT	LABOR HOURS	COST PER S.F.		
				MAT.	INST.	TOTAL

Mansard Roof Framing Price Sheet	QUAN.	UNIT	LABOR HOURS	COST PER S.F.		
				MAT.	INST.	TOTAL
Roof rafters, #2 or better, 2″ x 6″, 16″ O.C.	1.210	L.F.	.033	.76	1.77	2.53
24″ O.C.	.970	L.F.	.026	.61	1.42	2.03
2″ x 8″, 16″ O.C.	1.210	L.F.	.036	1.14	1.94	3.08
24″ O.C.	.970	L.F.	.029	.91	1.55	2.46
2″ x 10″, 16″ O.C.	1.210	L.F.	.046	1.51	2.46	3.97
24″ O.C.	.970	L.F.	.037	1.21	1.97	3.18
Rafter plates, #2 or better double top single bottom, 2″ x 6″	.364	L.F.	.010	.23	.53	.76
2″ x 8″	.364	L.F.	.011	.34	.58	.92
2″ x 10″	.364	L.F.	.014	.46	.74	1.20
Ceiling joist, #2 or better, 2″ x 4″, 16″ O.C.	.920	L.F.	.012	.39	.63	1.02
24″ O.C.	.740	L.F.	.009	.31	.51	.82
2″ x 6″, 16″ O.C.	.920	L.F.	.012	.58	.63	1.21
24″ O.C.	.740	L.F.	.009	.47	.51	.98
2″ x 8″, 16″ O.C.	.920	L.F.	.013	.86	.73	1.59
24″ O.C.	.740	L.F.	.011	.70	.58	1.28
Hip rafter, #2 or better, 2″ x 6″	.070	L.F.	.002	.04	.12	.16
2″ x 8″	.070	L.F.	.002	.07	.13	.20
2″ x 10″	.070	L.F.	.003	.09	.16	.25
Jack rafter, #2 or better, 2″ x 6″, 16″ O.C.	1.000	L.F.	.039	.63	2.11	2.74
24″ O.C.	.800	L.F.	.031	.50	1.69	2.19
2″ x 8″, 16″ O.C.	1.000	L.F.	.048	.94	2.58	3.52
24″ O.C.	.800	L.F.	.038	.75	2.06	2.81
Ridge board, #2 or better, 1″ x 6″	.018	L.F.	.001	.02	.03	.05
1″ x 8″	.018	L.F.	.001	.02	.03	.05
1″ x 10″	.018	L.F.	.001	.03	.03	.06
2″ x 6″	.018	L.F.	.001	.01	.03	.04
2″ x 8″	.018	L.F.	.001	.02	.03	.05
2″ x 10″	.018	L.F.	.001	.02	.04	.06
Sheathing, plywood exterior grade CDX, 3/8″ thick	2.210	S.F.	.023	1.22	1.26	2.48
1/2″ thick	2.210	S.F.	.025	1.44	1.37	2.81
5/8″ thick	2.210	S.F.	.027	1.81	1.46	3.27
3/4″ thick	2.210	S.F.	.029	2.14	1.59	3.73
Boards, 1″ x 6″, laid regular	2.210	S.F.	.049	4.24	2.63	6.87
Laid diagonal	2.210	S.F.	.054	4.24	2.94	7.18
1″ x 8″, laid regular	2.210	S.F.	.040	4.62	2.19	6.81
Laid diagonal	2.210	S.F.	.049	4.62	2.63	7.25
Furring, 1″ x 3″, 12″ O.C.	1.150	L.F.	.026	.48	1.41	1.89
24″ O.C.	.740	L.F.	.017	.31	.91	1.22

Sheathing · Fascia · Fascia · Rafters

System Description	QUAN.	UNIT	LABOR HOURS	COST PER S.F.		
				MAT.	INST.	TOTAL
2″ X 6″,16″ O.C., 4/12 PITCH						
Rafters, 2″ x 6″, 16″ O.C., 4/12 pitch	1.170	L.F.	.019	.74	1.01	1.75
Fascia, 2″ x 6″	.100	L.F.	.006	.08	.31	.39
Bridging, 1″ x 3″, 6′ O.C.	.080	Pr.	.005	.05	.27	.32
Sheathing, exterior grade plywood, 1/2″ thick	1.230	S.F.	.014	.80	.76	1.56
TOTAL		S.F.	.044	1.67	2.35	4.02
2″ X 6″, 24″ O.C., 4/12 PITCH						
Rafters, 2″ x 6″, 24″ O.C., 4/12 pitch	.940	L.F.	.015	.59	.81	1.40
Fascia, 2″ x 6″	.100	L.F.	.006	.08	.31	.39
Bridging, 1″ x 3″, 6′ O.C.	.060	Pr.	.004	.04	.20	.24
Sheathing, exterior grade plywood, 1/2″ thick	1.230	S.F.	.014	.80	.76	1.56
TOTAL		S.F.	.039	1.51	2.08	3.59
2″ X 8″, 16″ O.C., 4/12 PITCH						
Rafters, 2″ x 8″, 16″ O.C., 4/12 pitch	1.170	L.F.	.020	1.10	1.06	2.16
Fascia, 2″ x 8″	.100	L.F.	.007	.09	.38	.47
Bridging, 1″ x 3″, 6′ O.C.	.080	Pr.	.005	.05	.27	.32
Sheathing, exterior grade plywood, 1/2″ thick	1.230	S.F.	.014	.80	.76	1.56
TOTAL		S.F.	.046	2.04	2.47	4.51
2″ X 8″, 24″ O.C., 4/12 PITCH						
Rafters, 2″ x 8″, 24″ O.C., 4/12 pitch	.940	L.F.	.016	.88	.86	1.74
Fascia, 2″ x 8″	.100	L.F.	.007	.09	.38	.47
Bridging, 1″ x 3″, 6′ O.C.	.060	Pr.	.004	.04	.20	.24
Sheathing, exterior grade plywood, 1/2″ thick	1.230	S.F.	.014	.80	.76	1.56
TOTAL		S.F.	.041	1.81	2.20	4.01

The cost of this system is based on the square foot of plan area.
A 1′ overhang is assumed. No ceiling joists or furring are included.

Description	QUAN.	UNIT	LABOR HOURS	COST PER S.F.		
				MAT.	INST.	TOTAL

Shed/Flat Roof Framing Price Sheet

	QUAN.	UNIT	LABOR HOURS	COST PER S.F. MAT.	COST PER S.F. INST.	COST PER S.F. TOTAL
Rafters, #2 or better, 16" O.C., 2" x 4", 0 - 4/12 pitch	1.170	L.F.	.014	.55	.75	1.30
5/12 - 8/12 pitch	1.330	L.F.	.020	.63	1.08	1.71
2" x 6", 0 - 4/12 pitch	1.170	L.F.	.019	.74	1.01	1.75
5/12 - 8/12 pitch	1.330	L.F.	.027	.84	1.44	2.28
2" x 8", 0 - 4/12 pitch	1.170	L.F.	.020	1.10	1.06	2.16
5/12 - 8/12 pitch	1.330	L.F.	.028	1.25	1.53	2.78
2" x 10", 0 - 4/12 pitch	1.170	L.F.	.030	1.46	1.60	3.06
5/12 - 8/12 pitch	1.330	L.F.	.043	1.66	2.33	3.99
24" O.C., 2" x 4", 0 - 4/12 pitch	.940	L.F.	.011	.45	.61	1.06
5/12 - 8/12 pitch	1.060	L.F.	.021	.67	1.14	1.81
2" x 6", 0 - 4/12 pitch	.940	L.F.	.015	.59	.81	1.40
5/12 - 8/12 pitch	1.060	L.F.	.021	.67	1.14	1.81
2" x 8", 0 - 4/12 pitch	.940	L.F.	.016	.88	.86	1.74
5/12 - 8/12 pitch	1.060	L.F.	.023	1	1.22	2.22
2" x 10", 0 - 4/12 pitch	.940	L.F.	.024	1.18	1.29	2.47
5/12 - 8/12 pitch	1.060	L.F.	.034	1.33	1.86	3.19
Fascia, #2 or better,, 1" x 4"	.100	L.F.	.003	.04	.15	.19
1" x 6"	.100	L.F.	.004	.05	.21	.26
1" x 8"	.100	L.F.	.005	.06	.25	.31
1" x 10"	.100	L.F.	.005	.07	.28	.35
2" x 4"	.100	L.F.	.005	.06	.26	.32
2" x 6"	.100	L.F.	.006	.08	.31	.39
2" x 8"	.100	L.F.	.007	.09	.38	.47
2" x 10"	.100	L.F.	.009	.13	.48	.61
Bridging, wood 6' O.C., 1" x 3", rafters, 16" O.C.	.080	Pr.	.005	.05	.27	.32
24" O.C.	.060	Pr.	.004	.04	.20	.24
Metal, galvanized, rafters, 16" O.C.	.080	Pr.	.005	.08	.27	.35
24" O.C.	.060	Pr.	.003	.13	.19	.32
Compression type, rafters, 16" O.C.	.080	Pr.	.003	.08	.17	.25
24" O.C.	.060	Pr.	.002	.06	.13	.19
Sheathing, plywood, exterior grade, 3/8" thick, flat 0 - 4/12 pitch	1.230	S.F.	.013	.68	.70	1.38
5/12 - 8/12 pitch	1.330	S.F.	.014	.73	.76	1.49
1/2" thick, flat 0 - 4/12 pitch	1.230	S.F.	.014	.80	.76	1.56
5/12 - 8/12 pitch	1.330	S.F.	.015	.86	.82	1.68
5/8" thick, flat 0 - 4/12 pitch	1.230	S.F.	.015	1.01	.81	1.82
5/12 - 8/12 pitch	1.330	S.F.	.016	1.09	.88	1.97
3/4" thick, flat 0 - 4/12 pitch	1.230	S.F.	.016	1.19	.89	2.08
5/12 - 8/12 pitch	1.330	S.F.	.018	1.29	.96	2.25
Boards, 1" x 6", laid regular, flat 0 - 4/12 pitch	1.230	S.F.	.027	2.36	1.46	3.82
5/12 - 8/12 pitch	1.330	S.F.	.041	2.55	2.21	4.76
Laid diagonal, flat 0 - 4/12 pitch	1.230	S.F.	.030	2.36	1.64	4
5/12 - 8/12 pitch	1.330	S.F.	.044	2.55	2.39	4.94
1" x 8", laid regular, flat 0 - 4/12 pitch	1.230	S.F.	.022	2.57	1.22	3.79
5/12 - 8/12 pitch	1.330	S.F.	.034	2.78	1.81	4.59
Laid diagonal, flat 0 - 4/12 pitch	1.230	S.F.	.027	2.57	1.46	4.03
5/12 - 8/12 pitch	1.330	S.F.	.044	2.55	2.39	4.94

Valley Rafter
Sheathing
Fascia Board
Headers
Ridge Board
Rafters
Studs & Plates
Trimmer Rafters

System Description	QUAN.	UNIT	LABOR HOURS	COST PER S.F.		
				MAT.	INST.	TOTAL
2″ X 6″, 16″ O.C.						
Dormer rafter, 2″ x 6″, 16″ O.C.	1.330	L.F.	.036	.84	1.94	2.78
Ridge board, 2″ x 6″	.280	L.F.	.009	.18	.48	.66
Trimmer rafters, 2″ x 6″	.880	L.F.	.014	.55	.76	1.31
Wall studs & plates, 2″ x 4″, 16″ O.C.	3.160	L.F.	.056	1.33	3	4.33
Fascia, 2″ x 6″	.220	L.F.	.012	.16	.65	.81
Valley rafter, 2″ x 6″, 16″ O.C.	.280	L.F.	.009	.18	.47	.65
Cripple rafter, 2″ x 6″, 16″ O.C.	.560	L.F.	.022	.35	1.18	1.53
Headers, 2″ x 6″, doubled	.670	L.F.	.030	.42	1.61	2.03
Ceiling joist, 2″ x 4″, 16″ O.C.	1.000	L.F.	.013	.42	.69	1.11
Sheathing, exterior grade plywood, 1/2″ thick	3.610	S.F.	.041	2.35	2.24	4.59
TOTAL		S.F.	.242	6.78	13.02	19.80
2″ X 8″, 16″ O.C.						
Dormer rafter, 2″ x 8″, 16″ O.C.	1.330	L.F.	.039	1.25	2.13	3.38
Ridge board, 2″ x 8″	.280	L.F.	.010	.26	.54	.80
Trimmer rafter, 2″ x 8″	.880	L.F.	.015	.83	.80	1.63
Wall studs & plates, 2″ x 4″, 16″ O.C.	3.160	L.F.	.056	1.33	3	4.33
Fascia, 2″ x 8″	.220	L.F.	.016	.21	.84	1.05
Valley rafter, 2″ x 8″, 16″ O.C.	.280	L.F.	.010	.26	.52	.78
Cripple rafter, 2″ x 8″, 16″ O.C.	.560	L.F.	.027	.53	1.44	1.97
Headers, 2″ x 8″, doubled	.670	L.F.	.032	.63	1.70	2.33
Ceiling joist, 2″ x 4″, 16″ O.C.	1.000	L.F.	.013	.42	.69	1.11
Sheathing,, exterior grade plywood, 1/2″ thick	3.610	S.F.	.041	2.35	2.24	4.59
TOTAL		S.F.	.259	8.07	13.90	21.97

The cost in this system is based on the square foot of plan area.
The measurement being the plan area of the dormer only.

Description	QUAN.	UNIT	LABOR HOURS	COST PER S.F.		
				MAT.	INST.	TOTAL

Gable Dormer Framing Price Sheet	QUAN.	UNIT	LABOR HOURS	COST PER S.F.		
				MAT.	INST.	TOTAL
Dormer rafters, #2 or better, 2″ x 4″, 16″ O.C.	1.330	L.F.	.029	.67	1.55	2.22
24″ O.C.	1.060	L.F.	.023	.54	1.24	1.78
2″ x 6″, 16″ O.C.	1.330	L.F.	.036	.84	1.94	2.78
24″ O.C.	1.060	L.F.	.029	.67	1.55	2.22
2″ x 8″, 16″ O.C.	1.330	L.F.	.039	1.25	2.13	3.38
24″ O.C.	1.060	L.F.	.031	1	1.70	2.70
Ridge board, #2 or better, 1″ x 4″	.280	L.F.	.006	.20	.32	.52
1″ x 6″	.280	L.F.	.007	.25	.40	.65
1″ x 8″	.280	L.F.	.008	.37	.44	.81
2″ x 4″	.280	L.F.	.007	.14	.39	.53
2″ x 6″	.280	L.F.	.009	.18	.48	.66
2″ x 8″	.280	L.F.	.010	.26	.54	.80
Trimmer rafters, #2 or better, 2″ x 4″	.880	L.F.	.011	.44	.61	1.05
2″ x 6″	.880	L.F.	.014	.55	.76	1.31
2″ x 8″	.880	L.F.	.015	.83	.80	1.63
2″ x 10″	.880	L.F.	.022	1.10	1.21	2.31
Wall studs & plates, #2 or better, 2″ x 4″ studs, 16″ O.C.	3.160	L.F.	.056	1.33	3	4.33
24″ O.C.	2.800	L.F.	.050	1.18	2.66	3.84
2″ x 6″ studs, 16″ O.C.	3.160	L.F.	.063	1.99	3.41	5.40
24″ O.C.	2.800	L.F.	.056	1.76	3.02	4.78
Fascia, #2 or better, 1″ x 4″	.220	L.F.	.006	.08	.35	.43
1″ x 6″	.220	L.F.	.008	.10	.42	.52
1″ x 8″	.220	L.F.	.009	.12	.49	.61
2″ x 4″	.220	L.F.	.011	.14	.58	.72
2″ x 6″	.220	L.F.	.014	.18	.73	.91
2″ x 8″	.220	L.F.	.016	.21	.84	1.05
Valley rafter, #2 or better, 2″ x 4″	.280	L.F.	.007	.14	.38	.52
2″ x 6″	.280	L.F.	.009	.18	.47	.65
2″ x 8″	.280	L.F.	.010	.26	.52	.78
2″ x 10″	.280	L.F.	.012	.35	.64	.99
Cripple rafter, #2 or better, 2″ x 4″, 16″ O.C.	.560	L.F.	.018	.28	.95	1.23
24″ O.C.	.450	L.F.	.014	.23	.76	.99
2″ x 6″, 16″ O.C.	.560	L.F.	.022	.35	1.18	1.53
24″ O.C.	.450	L.F.	.018	.28	.95	1.23
2″ x 8″, 16″ O.C.	.560	L.F.	.027	.53	1.44	1.97
24″ O.C.	.450	L.F.	.021	.42	1.16	1.58
Headers, #2 or better double header, 2″ x 4″	.670	L.F.	.024	.34	1.30	1.64
2″ x 6″	.670	L.F.	.030	.42	1.61	2.03
2″ x 8″	.670	L.F.	.032	.63	1.70	2.33
2″ x 10″	.670	L.F.	.034	.84	1.81	2.65
Ceiling joist, #2 or better, 2″ x 4″, 16″ O.C.	1.000	L.F.	.013	.42	.69	1.11
24″ O.C.	.800	L.F.	.010	.34	.55	.89
2″ x 6″, 16″ O.C.	1.000	L.F.	.013	.63	.69	1.32
24″ O.C.	.800	L.F.	.010	.50	.55	1.05
Sheathing, plywood exterior grade, 3/8″ thick	3.610	S.F.	.038	1.99	2.06	4.05
1/2″ thick	3.610	S.F.	.041	2.35	2.24	4.59
5/8″ thick	3.610	S.F.	.044	2.96	2.38	5.34
3/4″ thick	3.610	S.F.	.048	3.50	2.60	6.10
Boards, 1″ x 6″, laid regular	3.610	S.F.	.089	6.95	4.80	11.75
Laid diagonal	3.610	S.F.	.099	6.95	5.35	12.30
1″ x 8″, laid regular	3.610	S.F.	.076	7.55	4.08	11.63
Laid diagonal	3.610	S.F.	.089	7.55	4.80	12.35

Sheathing
Ceiling Joists
Rafters
Fascia Board
Studs & Plates
Trimmer Rafters

System Description	QUAN.	UNIT	LABOR HOURS	COST PER S.F.		
				MAT.	INST.	TOTAL
2″ X 6″ RAFTERS, 16″ O.C.						
Dormer rafter, 2″ x 6″, 16″ O.C.	1.080	L.F.	.029	.68	1.58	2.26
Trimmer rafter, 2″ x 6″	.400	L.F.	.006	.25	.34	.59
Studs & plates, 2″ x 4″, 16″ O.C.	2.750	L.F.	.049	1.16	2.61	3.77
Fascia, 2″ x 6″	.250	L.F.	.014	.18	.73	.91
Ceiling joist, 2″ x 4″, 16″ O.C.	1.000	L.F.	.013	.42	.69	1.11
Sheathing, exterior grade plywood, CDX, 1/2″ thick	2.940	S.F.	.034	1.91	1.82	3.73
TOTAL		S.F.	.145	4.60	7.77	12.37
2″ X 8″ RAFTERS, 16″ O.C.						
Dormer rafter, 2″ x 8″, 16″ O.C.	1.080	L.F.	.032	1.02	1.73	2.75
Trimmer rafter, 2″ x 8″	.400	L.F.	.007	.38	.36	.74
Studs & plates, 2″ x 4″, 16″ O.C.	2.750	L.F.	.049	1.16	2.61	3.77
Fascia, 2″ x 8″	.250	L.F.	.018	.24	.96	1.20
Ceiling joist, 2″ x 6″, 16″ O.C.	1.000	L.F.	.013	.63	.69	1.32
Sheathing, exterior grade plywood, CDX, 1/2″ thick	2.940	S.F.	.034	1.91	1.82	3.73
TOTAL		S.F.	.153	5.34	8.17	13.51
2″ X 10″ RAFTERS, 16″ O.C.						
Dormer rafter, 2″ x 10″, 16″ O.C.	1.080	L.F.	.041	1.35	2.19	3.54
Trimmer rafter, 2″ x 10″	.400	L.F.	.010	.50	.55	1.05
Studs & plates, 2″ x 4″, 16″ O.C.	2.750	L.F.	.049	1.16	2.61	3.77
Fascia, 2″ x 10″	.250	L.F.	.022	.31	1.20	1.51
Ceiling joist, 2″ x 6″, 16″ O.C.	1.000	L.F.	.013	.63	.69	1.32
Sheathing, exterior grade plywood, CDX, 1/2″ thick	2.940	S.F.	.034	1.91	1.82	3.73
TOTAL		S.F.	.169	5.86	9.06	14.92

The cost in this system is based on the square foot of plan area.
The measurement is the plan area of the dormer only.

Description	QUAN.	UNIT	LABOR HOURS	COST PER S.F.		
				MAT.	INST.	TOTAL

Shed Dormer Framing Price Sheet	QUAN.	UNIT	LABOR HOURS	COST PER S.F. MAT.	INST.	TOTAL
Dormer rafters, #2 or better, 2" x 4", 16" O.C.	1.080	L.F.	.023	.54	1.26	1.80
24" O.C.	.860	L.F.	.019	.43	1	1.43
2" x 6", 16" O.C.	1.080	L.F.	.029	.68	1.58	2.26
24" O.C.	.860	L.F.	.023	.54	1.26	1.80
2" x 8", 16" O.C.	1.080	L.F.	.032	1.02	1.73	2.75
24" O.C.	.860	L.F.	.025	.81	1.38	2.19
2" x 10", 16" O.C.	1.080	L.F.	.041	1.35	2.19	3.54
24" O.C.	.860	L.F.	.032	1.08	1.75	2.83
Trimmer rafter, #2 or better, 2" x 4"	.400	L.F.	.005	.20	.28	.48
2" x 6"	.400	L.F.	.006	.25	.34	.59
2" x 8"	.400	L.F.	.007	.38	.36	.74
2" x 10"	.400	L.F.	.010	.50	.55	1.05
Studs & plates, #2 or better, 2" x 4", 16" O.C.	2.750	L.F.	.049	1.16	2.61	3.77
24" O.C.	2.200	L.F.	.039	.92	2.09	3.01
2" x 6", 16" O.C.	2.750	L.F.	.055	1.73	2.97	4.70
24" O.C.	2.200	L.F.	.044	1.39	2.38	3.77
Fascia, #2 or better, 1" x 4"	.250	L.F.	.006	.08	.35	.43
1" x 6"	.250	L.F.	.008	.10	.42	.52
1" x 8"	.250	L.F.	.009	.12	.49	.61
2" x 4"	.250	L.F.	.011	.14	.58	.72
2" x 6"	.250	L.F.	.014	.18	.73	.91
2" x 8"	.250	L.F.	.018	.24	.96	1.20
Ceiling joist, #2 or better, 2" x 4", 16" O.C.	1.000	L.F.	.013	.42	.69	1.11
24" O.C.	.800	L.F.	.010	.34	.55	.89
2" x 6", 16" O.C.	1.000	L.F.	.013	.63	.69	1.32
24" O.C.	.800	L.F.	.010	.50	.55	1.05
2" x 8", 16" O.C.	1.000	L.F.	.015	.94	.79	1.73
24" O.C.	.800	L.F.	.012	.75	.63	1.38
Sheathing, plywood exterior grade, 3/8" thick	2.940	S.F.	.031	1.62	1.68	3.30
1/2" thick	2.940	S.F.	.034	1.91	1.82	3.73
5/8" thick	2.940	S.F.	.036	2.41	1.94	4.35
3/4" thick	2.940	S.F.	.039	2.85	2.12	4.97
Boards, 1" x 6", laid regular	2.940	S.F.	.072	5.65	3.91	9.56
Laid diagonal	2.940	S.F.	.080	5.65	4.35	10
1" x 8", laid regular	2.940	S.F.	.062	6.15	3.32	9.47
Laid diagonal	2.940	S.F.	.072	6.15	3.91	10.06

Window Openings	QUAN.	UNIT	LABOR HOURS	COST EACH MAT.	INST.	TOTAL
The following are to be added to the total cost of the dormers for window openings. Do not subtract window area from the stud wall quantities.						
Headers, 2" x 6" doubled, 2' long	4.000	L.F.	.178	2.52	9.60	12.12
3' long	6.000	L.F.	.267	3.78	14.40	18.18
4' long	8.000	L.F.	.356	5.05	19.20	24.25
5' long	10.000	L.F.	.444	6.30	24	30.30
2" x 8" doubled, 4' long	8.000	L.F.	.376	7.50	20.50	28
5' long	10.000	L.F.	.471	9.40	25.50	34.90
6' long	12.000	L.F.	.565	11.30	30.50	41.80
8' long	16.000	L.F.	.753	15.05	40.50	55.55
2" x 10" doubled, 4' long	8.000	L.F.	.400	10	21.50	31.50
6' long	12.000	L.F.	.600	15	32.50	47.50
8' long	16.000	L.F.	.800	20	43	63
10' long	20.000	L.F.	1.000	25	54	79

Bracing — Top Plates

Studs — Bottom Plate

System Description	QUAN.	UNIT	LABOR HOURS	COST PER S.F.		
				MAT.	INST.	TOTAL
2″ X 4″, 16″ O.C.						
2″ x 4″ studs, #2 or better, 16″ O.C.	1.000	L.F.	.015	.41	.79	1.20
Plates, double top, single bottom	.375	L.F.	.005	.15	.30	.45
Cross bracing, let-in, 1″ x 6″	.080	L.F.	.004	.07	.23	.30
TOTAL		S.F.	.024	.63	1.32	1.95
2″ X 4″, 24″ O.C.						
2″ x 4″ studs, #2 or better, 24″ O.C.	.800	L.F.	.012	.33	.63	.96
Plates, double top, single bottom	.375	L.F.	.005	.15	.30	.45
Cross bracing, let-in, 1″ x 6″	.080	L.F.	.003	.07	.15	.22
TOTAL		S.F.	.020	.55	1.08	1.63
2″ X 6″, 16″ O.C.						
2″ x 6″ studs, #2 or better, 16″ O.C.	1.000	L.F.	.016	.63	.86	1.49
Plates, double top, single bottom	.375	L.F.	.006	.24	.32	.56
Cross bracing, let-in, 1″ x 6″	.080	L.F.	.004	.07	.23	.30
TOTAL		S.F.	.026	.94	1.41	2.35
2″ X 6″, 24″ O.C.						
2″ x 6″ studs, #2 or better, 24″ O.C.	.800	L.F.	.013	.50	.69	1.19
Plates, double top, single bottom	.375	L.F.	.006	.24	.32	.56
Cross bracing, let-in, 1″ x 6″	.080	L.F.	.003	.07	.15	.22
TOTAL		S.F.	.022	.81	1.16	1.97

The costs in this system are based on a square foot of wall area. Do not subtract for door or window openings.

Description	QUAN.	UNIT	LABOR HOURS	COST PER S.F.		
				MAT.	INST.	TOTAL

Partition Framing Price Sheet	QUAN.	UNIT	LABOR HOURS	COST PER S.F.		
				MAT.	INST.	TOTAL
Wood studs, #2 or better, 2" x 4", 12" O.C.	1.250	L.F.	.018	.51	.99	1.50
16" O.C.	1.000	L.F.	.015	.41	.79	1.20
24" O.C.	.800	L.F.	.012	.33	.63	.96
32" O.C.	.650	L.F.	.009	.27	.51	.78
2" x 6", 12" O.C.	1.250	L.F.	.020	.79	1.08	1.87
16" O.C.	1.000	L.F.	.016	.63	.86	1.49
24" O.C.	.800	L.F.	.013	.50	.69	1.19
32" O.C.	.650	L.F.	.010	.41	.56	.97
Plates, #2 or better double top single bottom, 2" x 4"	.375	L.F.	.005	.15	.30	.45
2" x 6"	.375	L.F.	.006	.24	.32	.56
2" x 8"	.375	L.F.	.005	.35	.30	.65
Cross bracing, let-in, 1" x 6" boards studs, 12" O.C.	.080	L.F.	.005	.09	.29	.38
16" O.C.	.080	L.F.	.004	.07	.23	.30
24" O.C.	.080	L.F.	.003	.07	.15	.22
32" O.C.	.080	L.F.	.002	.06	.12	.18
Let-in steel (T shaped) studs, 12" O.C.	.080	L.F.	.001	.09	.07	.16
16" O.C.	.080	L.F.	.001	.07	.06	.13
24" O.C.	.080	L.F.	.001	.07	.06	.13
32" O.C.	.080	L.F.	.001	.06	.05	.11
Steel straps studs, 12" O.C.	.080	L.F.	.001	.10	.06	.16
16" O.C.	.080	L.F.	.001	.09	.06	.15
24" O.C.	.080	L.F.	.001	.09	.06	.15
32" O.C.	.080	L.F.	.001	.09	.05	.14
Metal studs, load bearing 24" O.C., 20 ga. galv., 2-1/2" wide	1.000	S.F.	.015	.66	.81	1.47
3-5/8" wide	1.000	S.F.	.015	.78	.83	1.61
4" wide	1.000	S.F.	.016	.82	.84	1.66
6" wide	1.000	S.F.	.016	1.04	.86	1.90
16 ga., 2-1/2" wide	1.000	S.F.	.017	.77	.92	1.69
3-5/8" wide	1.000	S.F.	.017	.91	.94	1.85
4" wide	1.000	S.F.	.018	.96	.96	1.92
6" wide	1.000	S.F.	.018	1.20	.98	2.18
Non-load bearing 24" O.C., 25 ga. galv., 1-5/8" wide	1.000	S.F.	.011	.21	.57	.78
2-1/2" wide	1.000	S.F.	.011	.25	.58	.83
3-5/8" wide	1.000	S.F.	.011	.30	.58	.88
4" wide	1.000	S.F.	.011	.32	.58	.90
6" wide	1.000	S.F.	.011	.41	.60	1.01
20 ga., 2-1/2" wide	1.000	S.F.	.013	.35	.72	1.07
3-5/8" wide	1.000	S.F.	.014	.38	.73	1.11
4" wide	1.000	S.F.	.014	.46	.73	1.19
6" wide	1.000	S.F.	.014	.58	.74	1.32

Window & Door Openings	QUAN.	UNIT	LABOR HOURS	COST EACH		
				MAT.	INST.	TOTAL
The following costs are to be added to the total costs of the walls.						
Do not subtract openings from total wall area.						
Headers, 2" x 6" double, 2' long	4.000	L.F.	.178	2.52	9.60	12.12
3' long	6.000	L.F.	.267	3.78	14.40	18.18
4' long	8.000	L.F.	.356	5.05	19.20	24.25
5' long	10.000	L.F.	.444	6.30	24	30.30
2" x 8" double, 4' long	8.000	L.F.	.376	7.50	20.50	28
5' long	10.000	L.F.	.471	9.40	25.50	34.90
6' long	12.000	L.F.	.565	11.30	30.50	41.80
8' long	16.000	L.F.	.753	15.05	40.50	55.55
2" x 10" double, 4' long	8.000	L.F.	.400	10	21.50	31.50
6' long	12.000	L.F.	.600	15	32.50	47.50
8' long	16.000	L.F.	.800	20	43	63
10' long	20.000	L.F.	1.000	25	54	79
2" x 12" double, 8' long	16.000	L.F.	.853	27	46	73
12' long	24.000	L.F.	1.280	41	69	110

System Description	QUAN.	UNIT	LABOR HOURS	COST PER S.F.		
				MAT.	INST.	TOTAL
6″ THICK CONCRETE BLOCK WALL						
6″ thick concrete block, 6″ x 8″ x 16″	1.000	S.F.	.100	2.30	4.91	7.21
Masonry reinforcing, truss strips every other course	.625	L.F.	.002	.16	.09	.25
Furring, 1″ x 3″, 16″ O.C.	1.000	L.F.	.016	.46	.87	1.33
Masonry insulation, poured perlite	1.000	S.F.	.013	1.98	.72	2.70
Stucco, 2 coats	1.000	S.F.	.069	.24	3.44	3.68
Masonry paint, 2 coats	1.000	S.F.	.016	.22	.74	.96
TOTAL		S.F.	.216	5.36	10.77	16.13
8″ THICK CONCRETE BLOCK WALL						
8″ thick concrete block, 8″ x 8″ x 16″	1.000	S.F.	.107	2.61	5.25	7.86
Masonry reinforcing, truss strips every other course	.625	L.F.	.002	.16	.09	.25
Furring, 1″ x 3″, 16″ O.C.	1.000	L.F.	.016	.46	.87	1.33
Masonry insulation, poured perlite	1.000	S.F.	.018	2.62	.95	3.57
Stucco, 2 coats	1.000	S.F.	.069	.24	3.44	3.68
Masonry paint, 2 coats	1.000	S.F.	.016	.22	.74	.96
TOTAL		S.F.	.228	6.31	11.34	17.65
12″ THICK CONCRETE BLOCK WALL						
12″ thick concrete block, 12″ x 8″ x 16″	1.000	S.F.	.141	4.04	6.80	10.84
Masonry reinforcing, truss strips every other course	.625	L.F.	.003	.11	.13	.24
Furring, 1″ x 3″, 16″ O.C.	1.000	L.F.	.016	.46	.87	1.33
Masonry insulation, poured perlite	1.000	S.F.	.026	3.87	1.40	5.27
Stucco, 2 coats	1.000	S.F.	.069	.24	3.44	3.68
Masonry paint, 2 coats	1.000	S.F.	.016	.22	.74	.96
TOTAL		S.F.	.271	8.94	13.38	22.32

Costs for this system are based on a square foot of wall area. Do not subtract for window openings.

Description	QUAN.	UNIT	LABOR HOURS	COST PER S.F.		
				MAT.	INST.	TOTAL

Masonry Block Price Sheet	QUAN.	UNIT	LABOR HOURS	COST PER S.F.		
				MAT.	INST.	TOTAL
Block concrete, 8" x 16" regular, 4" thick	1.000	S.F.	.093	1.74	4.57	6.31
6" thick	1.000	S.F.	.100	2.30	4.91	7.21
8" thick	1.000	S.F.	.107	2.61	5.25	7.86
10" thick	1.000	S.F.	.111	3.15	5.45	8.60
12" thick	1.000	S.F.	.141	4.04	6.80	10.84
Solid block, 4" thick	1.000	S.F.	.096	2.10	4.73	6.83
6" thick	1.000	S.F.	.104	2.49	5.10	7.59
8" thick	1.000	S.F.	.111	3.91	5.45	9.36
10" thick	1.000	S.F.	.133	5.30	6.40	11.70
12" thick	1.000	S.F.	.148	5.90	7.10	13
Lightweight, 4" thick	1.000	S.F.	.093	1.74	4.57	6.31
6" thick	1.000	S.F.	.100	2.30	4.91	7.21
8" thick	1.000	S.F.	.107	2.61	5.25	7.86
10" thick	1.000	S.F.	.111	3.15	5.45	8.60
12" thick	1.000	S.F.	.141	4.04	6.80	10.84
Split rib profile, 4" thick	1.000	S.F.	.116	3.98	5.70	9.68
6" thick	1.000	S.F.	.123	4.59	6.05	10.64
8" thick	1.000	S.F.	.131	5.30	6.55	11.85
10" thick	1.000	S.F.	.157	5.60	7.55	13.15
12" thick	1.000	S.F.	.175	6.20	8.40	14.60
Masonry reinforcing, wire truss strips, every course, 8" block	1.375	L.F.	.004	.34	.19	.53
12" block	1.375	L.F.	.006	.23	.29	.52
Every other course, 8" block	.625	L.F.	.002	.16	.09	.25
12" block	.625	L.F.	.003	.11	.13	.24
Furring, wood, 1" x 3", 12" O.C.	1.250	L.F.	.020	.58	1.09	1.67
16" O.C.	1.000	L.F.	.016	.46	.87	1.33
24" O.C.	.800	L.F.	.013	.37	.70	1.07
32" O.C.	.640	L.F.	.010	.29	.56	.85
Steel, 3/4" channels, 12" O.C.	1.250	L.F.	.034	.37	1.56	1.93
16" O.C.	1.000	L.F.	.030	.34	1.38	1.72
24" O.C.	.800	L.F.	.023	.22	1.04	1.26
32" O.C.	.640	L.F.	.018	.18	.83	1.01
Masonry insulation, vermiculite or perlite poured 4" thick	1.000	S.F.	.009	1.28	.46	1.74
6" thick	1.000	S.F.	.013	1.96	.71	2.67
8" thick	1.000	S.F.	.018	2.62	.95	3.57
10" thick	1.000	S.F.	.021	3.17	1.15	4.32
12" thick	1.000	S.F.	.026	3.87	1.40	5.27
Block inserts polystyrene, 6" thick	1.000	S.F.		1.32		1.32
8" thick	1.000	S.F.		1.49		1.49
10" thick	1.000	S.F.		1.65		1.65
12" thick	1.000	S.F.		1.82		1.82
Stucco, 1 coat	1.000	S.F.	.057	.20	2.83	3.03
2 coats	1.000	S.F.	.069	.24	3.44	3.68
3 coats	1.000	S.F.	.081	.28	4.05	4.33
Painting, 1 coat	1.000	S.F.	.011	.14	.51	.65
2 coats	1.000	S.F.	.016	.22	.74	.96
Primer & 1 coat	1.000	S.F.	.013	.21	.60	.81
2 coats	1.000	S.F.	.018	.28	.84	1.12
Lath, metal lath expanded 2.5 lb/S.Y., painted	1.000	S.F.	.010	.47	.48	.95
Galvanized	1.000	S.F.	.012	.52	.53	1.05

Brick

Building Paper

Wall Ties

System Description	QUAN.	UNIT	LABOR HOURS	COST PER S.F.		
				MAT.	INST.	TOTAL
SELECT COMMON BRICK						
Brick, select common, running bond	1.000	S.F.	.174	4.88	8.55	13.43
Wall ties, 7/8" x 7", 22 gauge	1.000	Ea.	.008	.15	.41	.56
Building paper, spunbonded polypropylene	1.100	S.F.	.002	.17	.12	.29
Trim, pine, painted	.125	L.F.	.004	.07	.22	.29
TOTAL		S.F.	.188	5.27	9.30	14.57
RED FACED COMMON BRICK						
Brick, common, red faced, running bond	1.000	S.F.	.182	4.40	8.95	13.35
Wall ties, 7/8" x 7", 22 gauge	1.000	Ea.	.008	.15	.41	.56
Building paper, spundbonded polypropylene	1.100	S.F.	.002	.17	.12	.29
Trim, pine, painted	.125	L.F.	.004	.07	.22	.29
TOTAL		S.F.	.196	4.79	9.70	14.49
BUFF OR GREY FACE BRICK						
Brick, buff or grey	1.000	S.F.	.182	4.65	8.95	13.60
Wall ties, 7/8" x 7", 22 gauge	1.000	Ea.	.008	.15	.41	.56
Building paper, spundbonded polypropylene	1.100	S.F.	.002	.17	.12	.29
Trim, pine, painted	.125	L.F.	.004	.07	.22	.29
TOTAL		S.F.	.196	5.04	9.70	14.74
STONE WORK, ROUGH STONE, AVERAGE						
Field stone veneer	1.000	S.F.	.223	8.44	10.95	19.39
Wall ties, 7/8" x 7", 22 gauge	1.000	Ea.	.008	.15	.41	.56
Building paper, spundbonded polypropylene	1.000	S.F.	.002	.17	.12	.29
Trim, pine, painted	.125	L.F.	.004	.07	.22	.29
TOTAL		S.F.	.237	8.83	11.70	20.53

The costs in this system are based on a square foot of wall area. Do not subtract area for window & door openings.

Description	QUAN.	UNIT	LABOR HOURS	COST PER S.F.		
				MAT.	INST.	TOTAL

Brick/Stone Veneer Price Sheet	QUAN.	UNIT	LABOR HOURS	COST PER S.F.		
				MAT.	INST.	TOTAL
Brick						
Select common, running bond	1.000	S.F.	.174	4.88	8.55	13.43
Red faced, running bond	1.000	S.F.	.182	4.40	8.95	13.35
Buff or grey faced, running bond	1.000	S.F.	.182	4.65	8.95	13.60
Header every 6th course	1.000	S.F.	.216	5.10	10.60	15.70
English bond	1.000	S.F.	.286	6.55	14.05	20.60
Flemish bond	1.000	S.F.	.195	4.64	9.60	14.24
Common bond	1.000	S.F.	.267	5.85	13.10	18.95
Stack bond	1.000	S.F.	.182	4.65	8.95	13.60
Jumbo, running bond	1.000	S.F.	.092	4.96	4.51	9.47
Norman, running bond	1.000	S.F.	.125	6.40	6.15	12.55
Norwegian, running bond	1.000	S.F.	.107	5.10	5.25	10.35
Economy, running bond	1.000	S.F.	.129	4.35	6.35	10.70
Engineer, running bond	1.000	S.F.	.154	3.83	7.55	11.38
Roman, running bond	1.000	S.F.	.160	8.50	7.85	16.35
Utility, running bond	1.000	S.F.	.089	5	5.45	10.45
Glazed, running bond	1.000	S.F.	.190	12.55	9.35	21.90
Stone work, rough stone, average	1.000	S.F.	.179	8.45	10.95	19.40
Maximum	1.000	S.F.	.267	12.60	16.35	28.95
Wall ties, galvanized, corrugated 7/8" x 7", 22 gauge	1.000	Ea.	.008	.15	.41	.56
16 gauge	1.000	Ea.	.008	.29	.41	.70
Cavity wall, every 3rd course 6" long Z type, 1/4" diameter	1.330	L.F.	.010	.58	.53	1.11
3/16" diameter	1.330	L.F.	.010	.38	.53	.91
8" long, Z type, 1/4" diameter	1.330	L.F.	.010	.70	.53	1.23
3/16" diameter	1.330	L.F.	.010	.36	.53	.89
Building paper, aluminum and kraft laminated foil, 1 side	1.000	S.F.	.002	.12	.12	.24
2 sides	1.000	S.F.	.002	.14	.12	.26
#15 asphalt paper	1.100	S.F.	.002	.07	.13	.20
Polyethylene, .002" thick	1.000	S.F.	.002	.02	.12	.14
.004" thick	1.000	S.F.	.002	.03	.12	.15
.006" thick	1.000	S.F.	.002	.04	.12	.16
.010" thick	1.000	S.F.	.002	.10	.12	.22
Trim, 1" x 4", cedar	.125	L.F.	.005	.16	.27	.43
Fir	.125	L.F.	.005	.11	.27	.38
Redwood	.125	L.F.	.005	.16	.27	.43
White pine	.125	L.F.	.005	.11	.27	.38

Trim

Building Paper

Beveled Cedar Siding

System Description	QUAN.	UNIT	LABOR HOURS	COST PER S.F.		
				MAT.	INST.	TOTAL
1/2" X 6" BEVELED CEDAR SIDING, "A" GRADE						
1/2" x 6" beveled cedar siding	1.000	S.F.	.027	4.55	1.46	6.01
Building wrap, spundbonded polypropylene	1.100	S.F.	.002	.17	.12	.29
Trim, cedar	.125	L.F.	.005	.16	.27	.43
Paint, primer & 2 coats	1.000	S.F.	.017	.21	.79	1
TOTAL		S.F.	.051	5.09	2.64	7.73
1/2" X 8" BEVELED CEDAR SIDING, "A" GRADE						
1/2" x 8" beveled cedar siding	1.000	S.F.	.024	6.50	1.31	7.81
Building wrap, spundbonded polypropylene	1.100	S.F.	.002	.17	.12	.29
Trim, cedar	.125	L.F.	.005	.16	.27	.43
Paint, primer & 2 coats	1.000	S.F.	.017	.21	.79	1
TOTAL		S.F.	.048	7.04	2.49	9.53
1" X 4" TONGUE & GROOVE, REDWOOD, VERTICAL GRAIN						
Redwood, clear, vertical grain, 1" x 10"	1.000	S.F.	.020	5.37	1.06	6.43
Building wrap, spunbonded polypropylene	1.100	S.F.	.002	.17	.12	.29
Trim, redwood	.125	L.F.	.005	.16	.27	.43
Sealer, 1 coat, stain, 1 coat	1.000	S.F.	.013	.14	.62	.76
TOTAL		S.F.	.040	5.84	2.07	7.91
1" X 6" TONGUE & GROOVE, REDWOOD, VERTICAL GRAIN						
Redwood, clear, vertical grain, 1" x 10"	1.000	S.F.	.020	5.52	1.08	6.60
Building wrap, spunbonded polypropylene	1.100	S.F.	.002	.17	.12	.29
Trim, redwood	.125	L.F.	.005	.16	.27	.43
Sealer, 1 coat, stain, 1 coat	1.000	S.F.	.013	.14	.62	.76
TOTAL		S.F.	.040	5.99	2.09	8.08

The costs in this system are based on a square foot of wall area.
Do not subtract area for door or window openings.

Description	QUAN.	UNIT	LABOR HOURS	COST PER S.F.		
				MAT.	INST.	TOTAL

Wood Siding Price Sheet	QUAN.	UNIT	LABOR HOURS	COST PER S.F.		
				MAT.	INST.	TOTAL
Siding, beveled cedar, "A" grade, 1/2" x 6"	1.000	S.F.	.028	4.55	1.46	6.01
1/2" x 8"	1.000	S.F.	.023	6.50	1.31	7.81
"B" grade, 1/2" x 6"	1.000	S.F.	.032	5.05	1.62	6.67
1/2" x 8"	1.000	S.F.	.029	7.20	1.46	8.66
Clear grade, 1/2" x 6"	1.000	S.F.	.028	5.70	1.83	7.53
1/2" x 8"	1.000	S.F.	.023	8.15	1.64	9.79
Redwood, clear vertical grain, 1/2" x 6"	1.000	S.F.	.036	4.94	1.46	6.40
1/2" x 8"	1.000	S.F.	.032	5.40	1.31	6.71
Clear all heart vertical grain, 1/2" x 6"	1.000	S.F.	.028	5.50	1.62	7.12
1/2" x 8"	1.000	S.F.	.023	6	1.46	7.46
Siding board & batten, cedar, "B" grade, 1" x 10"	1.000	S.F.	.031	4.79	1.03	5.82
1" x 12"	1.000	S.F.	.031	4.79	1.03	5.82
Redwood, clear vertical grain, 1" x 6"	1.000	S.F.	.043	4.94	1.46	6.40
1" x 8"	1.000	S.F.	.018	4.51	1.31	5.82
White pine, #2 & better, 1" x 10"	1.000	S.F.	.029	2.41	1.31	3.72
1" x 12"	1.000	S.F.	.029	2.41	1.31	3.72
Siding vertical, tongue & groove, cedar "B" grade, 1" x 4"	1.000	S.F.	.033	5.15	1.06	6.21
1" x 6"	1.000	S.F.	.024	5.30	1.08	6.38
1" x 8"	1.000	S.F.	.024	5.45	1.12	6.57
1" x 10"	1.000	S.F.	.021	5.60	1.15	6.75
"A" grade, 1" x 4"	1.000	S.F.	.033	4.71	.97	5.68
1" x 6"	1.000	S.F.	.024	4.83	.99	5.82
1" x 8"	1.000	S.F.	.024	4.96	1.02	5.98
1" x 10"	1.000	S.F.	.021	5.10	1.05	6.15
Clear vertical grain, 1" x 4"	1.000	S.F.	.033	4.34	.89	5.23
1" x 6"	1.000	S.F.	.024	4.44	.91	5.35
1" x 8"	1.000	S.F.	.024	4.55	.93	5.48
1" x 10"	1.000	S.F.	.021	4.67	.96	5.63
Redwood, clear vertical grain, 1" x 4"	1.000	S.F.	.033	5.35	1.06	6.41
1" x 6"	1.000	S.F.	.024	5.50	1.08	6.58
1" x 8"	1.000	S.F.	.024	5.70	1.12	6.82
1" x 10"	1.000	S.F.	.021	5.85	1.15	7
Clear all heart vertical grain, 1" x 4"	1.000	S.F.	.033	4.92	.97	5.89
1" x 6"	1.000	S.F.	.024	5.05	.99	6.04
1" x 8"	1.000	S.F.	.024	5.20	1.02	6.22
1" x 10"	1.000	S.F.	.021	5.30	1.05	6.35
White pine, 1" x 10"	1.000	S.F.	.024	3.50	1.15	4.65
Siding plywood, texture 1-11 cedar, 3/8" thick	1.000	S.F.	.024	1.32	1.28	2.60
5/8" thick	1.000	S.F.	.024	2.67	1.28	3.95
Redwood, 3/8" thick	1.000	S.F.	.024	1.32	1.28	2.60
5/8" thick	1.000	S.F.	.024	2.11	1.28	3.39
Fir, 3/8" thick	1.000	S.F.	.024	.90	1.28	2.18
5/8" thick	1.000	S.F.	.024	1.73	1.28	3.01
Southern yellow pine, 3/8" thick	1.000	S.F.	.024	.90	1.28	2.18
5/8" thick	1.000	S.F.	.024	1.31	1.28	2.59
Paper, #15 asphalt felt	1.100	S.F.	.002	.07	.13	.20
Trim, cedar	.125	L.F.	.005	.16	.27	.43
Fir	.125	L.F.	.005	.11	.27	.38
Redwood	.125	L.F.	.005	.16	.27	.43
White pine	.125	L.F.	.005	.11	.27	.38
Painting, primer, & 1 coat	1.000	S.F.	.013	.14	.62	.76
2 coats	1.000	S.F.	.017	.21	.79	1
Stain, sealer, & 1 coat	1.000	S.F.	.017	.15	.80	.95
2 coats	1.000	S.F.	.019	.25	.87	1.12

Trim → ← Building Paper

← White Cedar Shingles

System Description	QUAN.	UNIT	LABOR HOURS	COST PER S.F.		
				MAT.	INST.	TOTAL
WHITE CEDAR SHINGLES, 5″ EXPOSURE						
White cedar shingles, 16″ long, grade "A", 5″ exposure	1.000	S.F.	.033	1.90	1.80	3.70
Building wrap, spunbonded polypropylene	1.100	S.F.	.002	.17	.12	.29
Trim, cedar	.125	S.F.	.005	.16	.27	.43
Paint, primer & 1 coat	1.000	S.F.	.017	.15	.80	.95
TOTAL		S.F.	.057	2.38	2.99	5.37
RESQUARED & REBUTTED PERFECTIONS, 5-1/2″ EXPOSURE						
Resquared & rebutted perfections, 5-1/2″ exposure	1.000	S.F.	.027	3.10	1.44	4.54
Building wrap, spunbonded polypropylene	1.100	S.F.	.002	.17	.12	.29
Trim, cedar	.125	S.F.	.005	.16	.27	.43
Stain, sealer & 1 coat	1.000	S.F.	.017	.15	.80	.95
TOTAL		S.F.	.051	3.58	2.63	6.21
HAND-SPLIT SHAKES, 8-1/2″ EXPOSURE						
Hand-split red cedar shakes, 18″ long, 8-1/2″ exposure	1.000	S.F.	.040	1.97	2.16	4.13
Building wrap, spunbonded polypropylene	1.100	S.F.	.002	.17	.12	.29
Trim, cedar	.125	S.F.	.005	.16	.27	.43
Stain, sealer & 1 coat	1.000	S.F.	.017	.15	.80	.95
TOTAL		S.F.	.064	2.45	3.35	5.80

The costs in this system are based on a square foot of wall area.
Do not subtract area for door or window openings.

Description	QUAN.	UNIT	LABOR HOURS	COST PER S.F.		
				MAT.	INST.	TOTAL

Shingle Siding Price Sheet	QUAN.	UNIT	LABOR HOURS	MAT.	INST.	TOTAL
				COST PER S.F.		
Shingles wood, white cedar 16" long, "A" grade, 5" exposure	1.000	S.F.	.033	1.90	1.80	3.70
7" exposure	1.000	S.F.	.030	1.71	1.62	3.33
8-1/2" exposure	1.000	S.F.	.032	1.09	1.73	2.82
10" exposure	1.000	S.F.	.028	.95	1.51	2.46
"B" grade, 5" exposure	1.000	S.F.	.040	1.65	2.16	3.81
7" exposure	1.000	S.F.	.028	1.16	1.51	2.67
8-1/2" exposure	1.000	S.F.	.024	.99	1.30	2.29
10" exposure	1.000	S.F.	.020	.83	1.08	1.91
Fire retardant, "A" grade, 5" exposure	1.000	S.F.	.033	2.51	1.80	4.31
7" exposure	1.000	S.F.	.028	1.58	1.51	3.09
8-1/2" exposure	1.000	S.F.	.032	1.66	1.73	3.39
10" exposure	1.000	S.F.	.025	1.29	1.34	2.63
Fire retardant, 5" exposure	1.000	S.F.	.029	3.11	1.57	4.68
7" exposure	1.000	S.F.	.036	2.45	1.92	4.37
8-1/2" exposure	1.000	S.F.	.032	2.20	1.73	3.93
10" exposure	1.000	S.F.	.025	1.71	1.34	3.05
Resquared & rebutted, 5-1/2" exposure	1.000	S.F.	.027	3.10	1.44	4.54
7" exposure	1.000	S.F.	.024	2.79	1.30	4.09
8-1/2" exposure	1.000	S.F.	.021	2.48	1.15	3.63
10" exposure	1.000	S.F.	.019	2.17	1.01	3.18
Fire retardant, 5" exposure	1.000	S.F.	.027	3.71	1.44	5.15
7" exposure	1.000	S.F.	.024	3.33	1.30	4.63
8-1/2" exposure	1.000	S.F.	.021	2.96	1.15	4.11
10" exposure	1.000	S.F.	.023	2.01	1.23	3.24
Hand-split, red cedar, 24" long, 7" exposure	1.000	S.F.	.045	3.89	2.42	6.31
8-1/2" exposure	1.000	S.F.	.038	3.34	2.08	5.42
10" exposure	1.000	S.F.	.032	2.78	1.73	4.51
12" exposure	1.000	S.F.	.026	2.22	1.38	3.60
Fire retardant, 7" exposure	1.000	S.F.	.045	4.74	2.42	7.16
8-1/2" exposure	1.000	S.F.	.038	4.07	2.08	6.15
10" exposure	1.000	S.F.	.032	3.39	1.73	5.12
12" exposure	1.000	S.F.	.026	2.70	1.38	4.08
18" long, 5" exposure	1.000	S.F.	.068	3.35	3.67	7.02
7" exposure	1.000	S.F.	.048	2.36	2.59	4.95
8-1/2" exposure	1.000	S.F.	.040	1.97	2.16	4.13
10" exposure	1.000	S.F.	.036	1.77	1.94	3.71
Fire retardant, 5" exposure	1.000	S.F.	.068	4.38	3.67	8.05
7" exposure	1.000	S.F.	.048	3.09	2.59	5.68
8-1/2" exposure	1.000	S.F.	.040	2.58	2.16	4.74
10" exposure	1.000	S.F.	.036	2.31	1.94	4.25
Paper, #15 asphalt felt	1.100	S.F.	.002	.06	.12	.18
Trim, cedar	.125	S.F.	.005	.16	.27	.43
Fir	.125	S.F.	.005	.11	.27	.38
Redwood	.125	S.F.	.005	.16	.27	.43
White pine	.125	S.F.	.005	.11	.27	.38
Painting, primer, & 1 coat	1.000	S.F.	.013	.14	.62	.76
2 coats	1.000	S.F.	.017	.21	.79	1
Staining, sealer, & 1 coat	1.000	S.F.	.017	.15	.80	.95
2 coats	1.000	S.F.	.019	.25	.87	1.12

Aluminum Trim

Building Paper

Alum. Horizontal Siding

Backer Insulation Board

System Description	QUAN.	UNIT	LABOR HOURS	COST PER S.F.		
				MAT.	INST.	TOTAL
ALUMINUM CLAPBOARD SIDING, 8″ WIDE, WHITE						
Aluminum horizontal siding, 8″ clapboard	1.000	S.F.	.031	2.68	1.68	4.36
Backer, insulation board	1.000	S.F.	.008	.44	.43	.87
Trim, aluminum	.600	L.F.	.016	1.01	.85	1.86
Building wrap, spunbonded polypropylene	1.100	S.F.	.002	.17	.12	.29
TOTAL		S.F.	.057	4.30	3.08	7.38
ALUMINUM VERTICAL BOARD & BATTEN, WHITE						
Aluminum vertical board & batten	1.000	S.F.	.027	2.31	1.46	3.77
Backer insulation board	1.000	S.F.	.008	.44	.43	.87
Trim, aluminum	.600	L.F.	.016	1.01	.85	1.86
Building wrap, spunbonded polypropylene	1.100	S.F.	.002	.17	.12	.29
TOTAL		S.F.	.053	3.93	2.86	6.79
VINYL CLAPBOARD SIDING, 8″ WIDE, WHITE						
Vinyl siding, clabboard profile, smooth texture, .042 thick, single 8	1.000	S.F.	.032	.80	1.75	2.55
Backer, insulation board	1.000	S.F.	.008	.44	.43	.87
Vinyl siding, access., outside corner, woodgrain, 4″ face, 3/4″ pocket	.600	L.F.	.014	1.21	.74	1.95
Building wrap, spunbonded polypropylene	1.100	S.F.	.002	.17	.12	.29
TOTAL		S.F.	.056	2.62	3.04	5.66
VINYL VERTICAL BOARD & BATTEN, WHITE						
Vinyl siding, vertical pattern, .046 thick, double 5	1.000	S.F.	.029	1.42	1.57	2.99
Backer, insulation board	1.000	S.F.	.008	.44	.43	.87
Vinyl siding, access., outside corner, woodgrain, 4″ face, 3/4″ pocket	.600	L.F.	.014	1.21	.74	1.95
Building wrap, spunbonded polypropylene	1.100	S.F.	.002	.17	.12	.29
TOTAL		S.F.	.053	3.24	2.86	6.10

The costs in this system are on a square foot of wall basis.
Subtract openings from wall area.

Description	QUAN.	UNIT	LABOR HOURS	COST PER S.F.		
				MAT.	INST.	TOTAL

Metal & Plastic Siding Price Sheet	QUAN.	UNIT	LABOR HOURS	COST PER S.F. MAT.	INST.	TOTAL
Siding, aluminum, .024" thick, smooth, 8" wide, white	1.000	S.F.	.031	2.68	1.68	4.36
Color	1.000	S.F.	.031	2.82	1.68	4.50
Double 4" pattern, 8" wide, white	1.000	S.F.	.031	2.76	1.68	4.44
Color	1.000	S.F.	.031	2.90	1.68	4.58
Double 5" pattern, 10" wide, white	1.000	S.F.	.029	2.70	1.57	4.27
Color	1.000	S.F.	.029	2.84	1.57	4.41
Embossed, single, 8" wide, white	1.000	S.F.	.031	2.68	1.68	4.36
Color	1.000	S.F.	.031	2.82	1.68	4.50
Double 4" pattern, 8" wide, white	1.000	S.F.	.031	2.76	1.68	4.44
Color	1.000	S.F.	.031	2.90	1.68	4.58
Double 5" pattern, 10" wide, white	1.000	S.F.	.029	2.74	1.57	4.31
Color	1.000	S.F.	.029	2.88	1.57	4.45
Alum siding with insulation board, smooth, 8" wide, white	1.000	S.F.	.031	2.42	1.68	4.10
Color	1.000	S.F.	.031	2.56	1.68	4.24
Double 4" pattern, 8" wide, white	1.000	S.F.	.031	2.40	1.68	4.08
Color	1.000	S.F.	.031	2.54	1.68	4.22
Double 5" pattern, 10" wide, white	1.000	S.F.	.029	2.40	1.57	3.97
Color	1.000	S.F.	.029	2.54	1.57	4.11
Embossed, single, 8" wide, white	1.000	S.F.	.031	2.79	1.68	4.47
Color	1.000	S.F.	.031	2.93	1.68	4.61
Double 4" pattern, 8" wide, white	1.000	S.F.	.031	2.83	1.68	4.51
Color	1.000	S.F.	.031	2.97	1.68	4.65
Double 5" pattern, 10" wide, white	1.000	S.F.	.029	2.83	1.57	4.40
Color	1.000	S.F.	.029	2.97	1.57	4.54
Aluminum, shake finish, 10" wide, white	1.000	S.F.	.029	3.03	1.57	4.60
Color	1.000	S.F.	.029	3.17	1.57	4.74
Aluminum, vertical, 12" wide, white	1.000	S.F.	.027	2.31	1.46	3.77
Color	1.000	S.F.	.027	2.45	1.46	3.91
Vinyl siding, 8" wide, smooth, white	1.000	S.F.	.032	.80	1.75	2.55
Color	1.000	S.F.	.032	.95	1.75	2.70
10" wide, Dutch lap, smooth, white	1.000	S.F.	.029	1.07	1.57	2.64
Color	1.000	S.F.	.029	1.22	1.57	2.79
Double 4" pattern, 8" wide, white	1.000	S.F.	.032	.80	1.75	2.55
Color	1.000	S.F.	.032	.95	1.75	2.70
Double 5" pattern, 10" wide, white	1.000	S.F.	.029	.80	1.57	2.37
Color	1.000	S.F.	.029	.95	1.57	2.52
Embossed, single, 8" wide, white	1.000	S.F.	.032	1.19	1.75	2.94
Color	1.000	S.F.	.032	1.34	1.75	3.09
10" wide, white	1.000	S.F.	.029	1.43	1.57	3
Color	1.000	S.F.	.029	1.58	1.57	3.15
Double 4" pattern, 8" wide, white	1.000	S.F.	.032	1.07	1.75	2.82
Color	1.000	S.F.	.032	1.22	1.75	2.97
Double 5" pattern, 10" wide, white	1.000	S.F.	.029	1.07	1.57	2.64
Color	1.000	S.F.	.029	1.22	1.57	2.79
Vinyl, shake finish, 10" wide, white	1.000	S.F.	.029	3.59	2.16	5.75
Color	1.000	S.F.	.029	3.74	2.16	5.90
Vinyl, vertical, double 5" pattern, 10" wide, white	1.000	S.F.	.029	1.42	1.57	2.99
Color	1.000	S.F.	.029	1.57	1.57	3.14
Backer board, installed in siding panels 8" or 10" wide	1.000	S.F.	.008	.44	.43	.87
4' x 8' sheets, polystyrene, 3/4" thick	1.000	S.F.	.010	.57	.54	1.11
4' x 8' fiberboard, plain	1.000	S.F.	.008	.44	.43	.87
Trim, aluminum, white	.600	L.F.	.016	1.01	.85	1.86
Color	.600	L.F.	.016	1.09	.85	1.94
Vinyl, white	.600	L.F.	.014	1.21	.74	1.95
Color	.600	L.F.	.014	1.40	.74	2.14
Paper, #15 asphalt felt	1.100	S.F.	.002	.07	.13	.20
Kraft paper, plain	1.100	S.F.	.002	.13	.13	.26
Foil backed	1.100	S.F.	.002	.15	.13	.28

Description	QUAN.	UNIT	LABOR HOURS	COST PER S.F.		
				MAT.	INST.	TOTAL
Poured insulation, cellulose fiber, R3.8 per inch (1″ thick)	1.000	S.F.	.003	.06	.18	.24
Fiberglass , R4.0 per inch (1″ thick)	1.000	S.F.	.003	.05	.18	.23
Mineral wool, R3.0 per inch (1″ thick)	1.000	S.F.	.003	.04	.18	.22
Polystyrene, R4.0 per inch (1″ thick)	1.000	S.F.	.003	.23	.18	.41
Vermiculite, R2.7 per inch (1″ thick)	1.000	S.F.	.003	.49	.18	.67
Perlite, R2.7 per inch (1″ thick)	1.000	S.F.	.003	.49	.18	.67
Reflective insulation, aluminum foil reinforced with scrim	1.000	S.F.	.004	.16	.23	.39
Reinforced with woven polyolefin	1.000	S.F.	.004	.24	.23	.47
With single bubble air space, R8.8	1.000	S.F.	.005	.29	.29	.58
With double bubble air space, R9.8	1.000	S.F.	.005	.32	.29	.61
Rigid insulation, fiberglass, unfaced,						
1-1/2″ thick, R6.2	1.000	S.F.	.008	.44	.43	.87
2″ thick, R8.3	1.000	S.F.	.008	.50	.43	.93
2-1/2″ thick, R10.3	1.000	S.F.	.010	.62	.54	1.16
3″ thick, R12.4	1.000	S.F.	.010	.62	.54	1.16
Foil faced, 1″ thick, R4.3	1.000	S.F.	.008	.99	.43	1.42
1-1/2″ thick, R6.2	1.000	S.F.	.008	1.49	.43	1.92
2″ thick, R8.7	1.000	S.F.	.009	1.86	.49	2.35
2-1/2″ thick, R10.9	1.000	S.F.	.010	2.18	.54	2.72
3″ thick, R13.0	1.000	S.F.	.010	2.40	.54	2.94
Perlite, 1″ thick R2.77	1.000	S.F.	.010	.40	.54	.94
2″ thick R5.55	1.000	S.F.	.011	.79	.59	1.38
Polystyrene, extruded, blue, 2.2#/C.F., 3/4″ thick R4	1.000	S.F.	.010	.57	.54	1.11
1-1/2″ thick R8.1	1.000	S.F.	.011	1.16	.59	1.75
2″ thick R10.8	1.000	S.F.	.011	1.64	.59	2.23
Molded bead board, white, 1″ thick R3.85	1.000	S.F.	.010	.26	.54	.80
1-1/2″ thick, R5.6	1.000	S.F.	.011	.53	.59	1.12
2″ thick, R7.7	1.000	S.F.	.011	.79	.59	1.38
Non-rigid insulation, batts						
Fiberglass, kraft faced, 3-1/2″ thick, R13, 11″ wide	1.000	S.F.	.005	.34	.38	.72
15″ wide	1.000	S.F.	.005	.34	.38	.72
23″ wide	1.000	S.F.	.005	.34	.38	.72
6″ thick, R19, 11″ wide	1.000	S.F.	.006	.46	.38	.84
15″ wide	1.000	S.F.	.006	.46	.38	.84
23″ wide	1.000	S.F.	.006	.46	.38	.84
9″ thick, R30, 15″ wide	1.000	S.F.	.006	.77	.32	1.09
23″ wide	1.000	S.F.	.006	.77	.32	1.09
12″ thick, R38, 15″ wide	1.000	S.F.	.006	.98	.32	1.30
23″ wide	1.000	S.F.	.006	.98	.32	1.30
Fiberglass, foil faced, 3-1/2″ thick, R13, 15″ wide	1.000	S.F.	.005	.48	.32	.80
23″ wide	1.000	S.F.	.005	.48	.32	.80
6″ thick, R19, 15″ thick	1.000	S.F.	.005	.63	.27	.90
23″ wide	1.000	S.F.	.005	.63	.27	.90
9″ thick, R30, 15″ wide	1.000	S.F.	.006	.98	.32	1.30
23″ wide	1.000	S.F.	.006	.98	.32	1.30

Insulation Systems	QUAN.	UNIT	LABOR HOURS	COST PER S.F.		
				MAT.	INST.	TOTAL
Non-rigid insulation batts						
Fiberglass unfaced, 3-1/2" thick, R13, 15" wide	1.000	S.F.	.005	.35	.27	.62
23" wide	1.000	S.F.	.005	.35	.27	.62
6" thick, R19, 15" wide	1.000	S.F.	.006	.41	.32	.73
23" wide	1.000	S.F.	.006	.41	.32	.73
9" thick, R19, 15" wide	1.000	S.F.	.007	.66	.38	1.04
23" wide	1.000	S.F.	.007	.66	.38	1.04
12" thick, R38, 15" wide	1.000	S.F.	.007	.83	.38	1.21
23" wide	1.000	S.F.	.007	.83	.38	1.21
Mineral fiber batts, 3" thick, R11	1.000	S.F.	.005	.66	.27	.93
3-1/2" thick, R13	1.000	S.F.	.005	.66	.27	.93
6" thick, R19	1.000	S.F.	.005	1.04	.27	1.31
6-1/2" thick, R22	1.000	S.F.	.005	1.04	.27	1.31
10" thick, R30	1.000	S.F.	.006	1.37	.32	1.69

Drip Cap — Snap-in Grille

Caulking

Interior Trim

Window

System Description	QUAN.	UNIT	LABOR HOURS	COST EACH		
				MAT.	INST.	TOTAL
BUILDER'S QUALITY WOOD WINDOW 2′ X 3′, DOUBLE HUNG						
Window, primed, builder's quality, 2′ x 3′, insulating glass	1.000	Ea.	.800	256	43	299
Trim, interior casing	11.000	L.F.	.352	18.37	19.03	37.40
Paint, interior & exterior, primer & 2 coats	2.000	Face	1.778	2.46	82	84.46
Caulking	10.000	L.F.	.278	2	14.80	16.80
Snap-in grille	1.000	Set	.333	56.50	18	74.50
Drip cap, metal	2.000	L.F.	.040	.88	2.16	3.04
TOTAL		Ea.	3.581	336.21	178.99	515.20
PLASTIC CLAD WOOD WINDOW 3′ X 4′, DOUBLE HUNG						
Window, plastic clad, premium, 3′ x 4′, insulating glass	1.000	Ea.	.889	435	48	483
Trim, interior casing	15.000	L.F.	.480	25.05	25.95	51
Paint, interior, primer & 2 coats	1.000	Face	.889	1.23	41	42.23
Caulking	14.000	L.F.	.389	2.80	20.72	23.52
Snap-in grille	1.000	Set	.333	56.50	18	74.50
TOTAL		Ea.	2.980	520.58	153.67	674.25
METAL CLAD WOOD WINDOW, 3′ X 5′, DOUBLE HUNG						
Window, metal clad, deluxe, 3′ x 5′, insulating glass	1.000	Ea.	1.000	410	54	464
Trim, interior casing	17.000	L.F.	.544	28.39	29.41	57.80
Paint, interior, primer & 2 coats	1.000	Face	.889	1.23	41	42.23
Caulking	16.000	L.F.	.444	3.20	23.68	26.88
Snap-in grille	1.000	Set	.235	144	12.70	156.70
Drip cap, metal	3.000	L.F.	.060	1.32	3.24	4.56
TOTAL		Ea.	3.172	588.14	164.03	752.17

The cost of this system is on a cost per each window basis.

Description	QUAN.	UNIT	LABOR HOURS	COST EACH		
				MAT.	INST.	TOTAL

Double Hung Window Price Sheet	QUAN.	UNIT	LABOR HOURS	COST EACH		
				MAT.	INST.	TOTAL
Windows, double-hung, builder's quality, 2' x 3', single glass	1.000	Ea.	.800	231	43	274
Insulating glass	1.000	Ea.	.800	256	43	299
3' x 4', single glass	1.000	Ea.	.889	305	48	353
Insulating glass	1.000	Ea.	.889	320	48	368
4' x 4'-6", single glass	1.000	Ea.	1.000	355	54	409
Insulating glass	1.000	Ea.	1.000	380	54	434
Plastic clad premium insulating glass, 2'-6" x 3'	1.000	Ea.	.800	340	43	383
3' x 3'-6"	1.000	Ea.	.800	370	43	413
3' x 4'	1.000	Ea.	.889	435	48	483
3' x 4'-6"	1.000	Ea.	.889	450	48	498
3' x 5'	1.000	Ea.	1.000	485	54	539
3'-6" x 6'	1.000	Ea.	1.000	540	54	594
Metal clad deluxe insulating glass, 2'-6" x 3'	1.000	Ea.	.800	299	43	342
3' x 3'-6"	1.000	Ea.	.800	345	43	388
3' x 4'	1.000	Ea.	.889	360	48	408
3' x 4'-6"	1.000	Ea.	.889	380	48	428
3' x 5'	1.000	Ea.	1.000	410	54	464
3'-6" x 6'	1.000	Ea.	1.000	495	54	549
Trim, interior casing, window 2' x 3'	11.000	L.F.	.367	18.35	19.05	37.40
2'-6" x 3'	12.000	L.F.	.400	20	21	41
3' x 3'-6"	14.000	L.F.	.467	23.50	24	47.50
3' x 4'	15.000	L.F.	.500	25	26	51
3' x 4'-6"	16.000	L.F.	.533	26.50	27.50	54
3' x 5'	17.000	L.F.	.567	28.50	29.50	58
3'-6" x 6'	20.000	L.F.	.667	33.50	34.50	68
4' x 4'-6"	18.000	L.F.	.600	30	31	61
Paint or stain, interior or exterior, 2' x 3' window, 1 coat	1.000	Face	.444	.51	20.50	21.01
2 coats	1.000	Face	.727	1.01	33.50	34.51
Primer & 1 coat	1.000	Face	.727	.83	33.50	34.33
Primer & 2 coats	1.000	Face	.889	1.23	41	42.23
3' x 4' window, 1 coat	1.000	Face	.667	1.06	31	32.06
2 coats	1.000	Face	.667	1.79	31	32.79
Primer & 1 coat	1.000	Face	.727	1.26	33.50	34.76
Primer & 2 coats	1.000	Face	.889	1.23	41	42.23
4' x 4'-6" window, 1 coat	1.000	Face	.667	1.06	31	32.06
2 coats	1.000	Face	.667	1.79	31	32.79
Primer & 1 coat	1.000	Face	.727	1.26	33.50	34.76
Primer & 2 coats	1.000	Face	.889	1.23	41	42.23
Caulking, window, 2' x 3'	10.000	L.F.	.323	2	14.80	16.80
2'-6" x 3'	11.000	L.F.	.355	2.20	16.30	18.50
3' x 3'-6"	13.000	L.F.	.419	2.60	19.25	21.85
3' x 4'	14.000	L.F.	.452	2.80	20.50	23.30
3' x 4'-6"	15.000	L.F.	.484	3	22	25
3' x 5'	16.000	L.F.	.516	3.20	23.50	26.70
3'-6" x 6'	19.000	L.F.	.613	3.80	28	31.80
4' x 4'-6"	17.000	L.F.	.548	3.40	25	28.40
Grilles, glass size to, 16" x 24" per sash	1.000	Set	.333	56.50	18	74.50
32" x 32" per sash	1.000	Set	.235	144	12.70	156.70
Drip cap, aluminum, 2' long	2.000	L.F.	.040	.88	2.16	3.04
3' long	3.000	L.F.	.060	1.32	3.24	4.56
4' long	4.000	L.F.	.080	1.76	4.32	6.08
Wood, 2' long	2.000	L.F.	.067	3.34	3.46	6.80
3' long	3.000	L.F.	.100	5	5.20	10.20
4' long	4.000	L.F.	.133	6.70	6.90	13.60

Drip Cap — Snap-in Grille — Interior Trim — Caulking — Window

System Description	QUAN.	UNIT	LABOR HOURS	COST EACH		
				MAT.	INST.	TOTAL
BUILDER'S QUALITY WINDOW, WOOD, 2′ BY 3′, CASEMENT						
Window, primed, builder's quality, 2′ x 3′, insulating glass	1.000	Ea.	.800	285	43	328
Trim, interior casing	11.000	L.F.	.352	18.37	19.03	37.40
Paint, interior & exterior, primer & 2 coats	2.000	Face	1.778	2.46	82	84.46
Caulking	10.000	L.F.	.278	2	14.80	16.80
Snap-in grille	1.000	Ea.	.267	35	14.40	49.40
Drip cap, metal	2.000	L.F.	.040	.88	2.16	3.04
TOTAL		Ea.	3.515	343.71	175.39	519.10
PLASTIC CLAD WOOD WINDOW, 2′ X 4′, CASEMENT						
Window, plastic clad, premium, 2′ x 4′, insulating glass	1.000	Ea.	.889	350	48	398
Trim, interior casing	13.000	L.F.	.416	21.71	22.49	44.20
Paint, interior, primer & 2 coats	1.000	Ea.	.889	1.23	41	42.23
Caulking	12.000	L.F.	.333	2.40	17.76	20.16
Snap-in grille	1.000	Ea.	.267	35	14.40	49.40
TOTAL		Ea.	2.794	410.34	143.65	553.99
METAL CLAD WOOD WINDOW, 2′ X 5′, CASEMENT						
Window, metal clad, deluxe, 2′ x 5′, insulating glass	1.000	Ea.	1.000	360	54	414
Trim, interior casing	15.000	L.F.	.480	25.05	25.95	51
Paint, interior, primer & 2 coats	1.000	Ea.	.889	1.23	41	42.23
Caulking	14.000	L.F.	.389	2.80	20.72	23.52
Snap-in grille	1.000	Ea.	.250	47.50	13.50	61
Drip cap, metal	12.000	L.F.	.040	.88	2.16	3.04
TOTAL		Ea.	3.048	437.46	157.33	594.79

The cost of this system is on a cost per each window basis.

Description	QUAN.	UNIT	LABOR HOURS	COST EACH		
				MAT.	INST.	TOTAL

Casement Window Price Sheet	QUAN.	UNIT	LABOR HOURS	COST EACH		
				MAT.	INST.	TOTAL
Window, casement, builders quality, 2′ x 3′, double insulated glass	1.000	Ea.	.800	295	43	338
Insulating glass	1.000	Ea.	.800	285	43	328
2′ x 4′-6″, double insulated glass	1.000	Ea.	.727	960	39.50	999.50
Insulating glass	1.000	Ea.	.727	590	39.50	629.50
2′ x 6′, double insulated glass	1.000	Ea.	.889	475	54	529
Insulating glass	1.000	Ea.	.889	525	54	579
Plastic clad premium insulating glass, 2′ x 3′	1.000	Ea.	.800	289	43	332
2′ x 4′	1.000	Ea.	.889	440	48	488
2′ x 5′	1.000	Ea.	1.000	595	54	649
2′ x 6′	1.000	Ea.	1.000	420	54	474
Metal clad deluxe insulating glass, 2′ x 3′	1.000	Ea.	.800	305	43	348
2′ x 4′	1.000	Ea.	.889	305	48	353
2′ x 5′	1.000	Ea.	1.000	350	54	404
2′ x 6′	1.000	Ea.	1.000	400	54	454
Trim, interior casing, window 2′ x 3′	11.000	L.F.	.367	18.35	19.05	37.40
2′ x 4′	13.000	L.F.	.433	21.50	22.50	44
2′ x 4′-6″	14.000	L.F.	.467	23.50	24	47.50
2′ x 5′	15.000	L.F.	.500	25	26	51
2′ x 6′	17.000	L.F.	.567	28.50	29.50	58
Paint or stain, interior or exterior, 2′ x 3′ window, 1 coat	1.000	Face	.444	.51	20.50	21.01
2 coats	1.000	Face	.727	1.01	33.50	34.51
Primer & 1 coat	1.000	Face	.727	.83	33.50	34.33
Primer & 2 coats	1.000	Face	.889	1.23	41	42.23
2′ x 4′ window, 1 coat	1.000	Face	.444	.51	20.50	21.01
2 coats	1.000	Face	.727	1.01	33.50	34.51
Primer & 1 coat	1.000	Face	.727	.83	33.50	34.33
Primer & 2 coats	1.000	Face	.889	1.23	41	42.23
2′ x 6′ window, 1 coat	1.000	Face	.667	1.06	31	32.06
2 coats	1.000	Face	.667	1.79	31	32.79
Primer & 1 coat	1.000	Face	.727	1.26	33.50	34.76
Primer & 2 coats	1.000	Face	.889	1.23	41	42.23
Caulking, window, 2′ x 3′	10.000	L.F.	.323	2	14.80	16.80
2′ x 4′	12.000	L.F.	.387	2.40	17.75	20.15
2′ x 4′-6″	13.000	L.F.	.419	2.60	19.25	21.85
2′ x 5′	14.000	L.F.	.452	2.80	20.50	23.30
2′ x 6′	16.000	L.F.	.516	3.20	23.50	26.70
Grilles, glass size, to 20″ x 36″	1.000	Ea.	.267	35	14.40	49.40
To 20″ x 56″	1.000	Ea.	.250	47.50	13.50	61
Drip cap, metal, 2′ long	2.000	L.F.	.040	.88	2.16	3.04
Wood, 2′ long	2.000	L.F.	.067	3.34	3.46	6.80

Drip Cap — Interior Trim

Snap-in Grille

Caulking

Window

System Description	QUAN.	UNIT	LABOR HOURS	COST EACH		
				MAT.	INST.	TOTAL
BUILDER'S QUALITY WINDOW, WOOD, 34" X 22", AWNING						
Window, 34" x 22", insulating glass	1.000	Ea.	.800	298	43	341
Trim, interior casing	10.500	L.F.	.336	17.54	18.17	35.71
Paint, interior & exterior, primer & 2 coats	2.000	Face	1.778	2.46	82	84.46
Caulking	9.500	L.F.	.264	1.90	14.06	15.96
Snap-in grille	1.000	Ea.	.267	31	14.40	45.40
Drip cap, metal	3.000	L.F.	.060	1.32	3.24	4.56
TOTAL		Ea.	3.505	352.22	174.87	527.09
PLASTIC CLAD WOOD WINDOW, 40" X 28", AWNING						
Window, plastic clad, premium, 40" x 28", insulating glass	1.000	Ea.	.889	375	48	423
Trim interior casing	13.500	L.F.	.432	22.55	23.36	45.91
Paint, interior, primer & 2 coats	1.000	Face	.889	1.23	41	42.23
Caulking	12.500	L.F.	.347	2.50	18.50	21
Snap-in grille	1.000	Ea.	.267	31	14.40	45.40
TOTAL		Ea.	2.824	432.28	145.26	577.54
METAL CLAD WOOD WINDOW, 48" X 36", AWNING						
Window, metal clad, deluxe, 48" x 36", insulating glass	1.000	Ea.	1.000	410	54	464
Trim, interior casing	15.000	L.F.	.480	25.05	25.95	51
Paint, interior, primer & 2 coats	1.000	Face	.889	1.23	41	42.23
Caulking	14.000	L.F.	.389	2.80	20.72	23.52
Snap-in grille	1.000	Ea.	.250	44	13.50	57.50
Drip cap, metal	4.000	L.F.	.080	1.76	4.32	6.08
TOTAL		Ea.	3.088	484.84	159.49	644.33

The cost of this system is on a cost per each window basis.

Description	QUAN.	UNIT	LABOR HOURS	COST EACH		
				MAT.	INST.	TOTAL

Awning Window Price Sheet	QUAN.	UNIT	LABOR HOURS	COST EACH		
				MAT.	INST.	TOTAL
Windows, awning, builder's quality, 34" x 22", insulated glass	1.000	Ea.	.800	297	43	340
Low E glass	1.000	Ea.	.800	298	43	341
40" x 28", insulated glass	1.000	Ea.	.889	345	48	393
Low E glass	1.000	Ea.	.889	375	48	423
48" x 36", insulated glass	1.000	Ea.	1.000	515	54	569
Low E glass	1.000	Ea.	1.000	540	54	594
Plastic clad premium insulating glass, 34" x 22"	1.000	Ea.	.800	290	43	333
40" x 22"	1.000	Ea.	.800	315	43	358
36" x 28"	1.000	Ea.	.889	335	48	383
36" x 36"	1.000	Ea.	.889	375	48	423
48" x 28"	1.000	Ea.	1.000	405	54	459
60" x 36"	1.000	Ea.	1.000	550	54	604
Metal clad deluxe insulating glass, 34" x 22"	1.000	Ea.	.800	271	48	319
40" x 22"	1.000	Ea.	.800	320	48	368
36" x 25"	1.000	Ea.	.889	299	48	347
40" x 30"	1.000	Ea.	.889	375	48	423
48" x 28"	1.000	Ea.	1.000	380	54	434
60" x 36"	1.000	Ea.	1.000	410	54	464
Trim, interior casing window, 34" x 22"	10.500	L.F.	.350	17.55	18.15	35.70
40" x 22"	11.500	L.F.	.383	19.20	19.90	39.10
36" x 28"	12.500	L.F.	.417	21	21.50	42.50
40" x 28"	13.500	L.F.	.450	22.50	23.50	46
48" x 28"	14.500	L.F.	.483	24	25	49
48" x 36"	15.000	L.F.	.500	25	26	51
Paint or stain, interior or exterior, 34" x 22", 1 coat	1.000	Face	.444	.51	20.50	21.01
2 coats	1.000	Face	.727	1.01	33.50	34.51
Primer & 1 coat	1.000	Face	.727	.83	33.50	34.33
Primer & 2 coats	1.000	Face	.889	1.23	41	42.23
36" x 28", 1 coat	1.000	Face	.444	.51	20.50	21.01
2 coats	1.000	Face	.727	1.01	33.50	34.51
Primer & 1 coat	1.000	Face	.727	.83	33.50	34.33
Primer & 2 coats	1.000	Face	.889	1.23	41	42.23
48" x 36", 1 coat	1.000	Face	.667	1.06	31	32.06
2 coats	1.000	Face	.667	1.79	31	32.79
Primer & 1 coat	1.000	Face	.727	1.26	33.50	34.76
Primer & 2 coats	1.000	Face	.889	1.23	41	42.23
Caulking, window, 34" x 22"	9.500	L.F.	.306	1.90	14.05	15.95
40" x 22"	10.500	L.F.	.339	2.10	15.55	17.65
36" x 28"	11.500	L.F.	.371	2.30	17	19.30
40" x 28"	12.500	L.F.	.403	2.50	18.50	21
48" x 28"	13.500	L.F.	.436	2.70	20	22.70
48" x 36"	14.000	L.F.	.452	2.80	20.50	23.30
Grilles, glass size, to 28" by 16"	1.000	Ea.	.267	31	14.40	45.40
To 44" by 24"	1.000	Ea.	.250	44	13.50	57.50
Drip cap, aluminum, 3' long	3.000	L.F.	.060	1.32	3.24	4.56
3'-6" long	3.500	L.F.	.070	1.54	3.78	5.32
4' long	4.000	L.F.	.080	1.76	4.32	6.08
Wood, 3' long	3.000	L.F.	.100	5	5.20	10.20
3'-6" long	3.500	L.F.	.117	5.85	6.05	11.90
4' long	4.000	L.F.	.133	6.70	6.90	13.60

Drip Cap

Snap-in Grille

Caulking

Interior Trim

Window

System Description	QUAN.	UNIT	LABOR HOURS	COST EACH		
				MAT.	INST.	TOTAL
BUILDER'S QUALITY WOOD WINDOW, 3' X 2', SLIDING						
Window, primed, builder's quality, 3' x 3', insul. glass	1.000	Ea.	.800	340	43	383
Trim, interior casing	11.000	L.F.	.352	18.37	19.03	37.40
Paint, interior & exterior, primer & 2 coats	2.000	Face	1.778	2.46	82	84.46
Caulking	10.000	L.F.	.278	2	14.80	16.80
Snap-in grille	1.000	Set	.333	39	18	57
Drip cap, metal	3.000	L.F.	.060	1.32	3.24	4.56
TOTAL		Ea.	3.601	403.15	180.07	583.22
PLASTIC CLAD WOOD WINDOW, 4' X 3'-6", SLIDING						
Window, plastic clad, premium, 4' x 3'-6", insulating glass	1.000	Ea.	.889	755	48	803
Trim, interior casing	16.000	L.F.	.512	26.72	27.68	54.40
Paint, interior, primer & 2 coats	1.000	Face	.889	1.23	41	42.23
Caulking	17.000	L.F.	.472	3.40	25.16	28.56
Snap-in grille	1.000	Set	.333	39	18	57
TOTAL		Ea.	3.095	825.35	159.84	985.19
METAL CLAD WOOD WINDOW, 6' X 5', SLIDING						
Window, metal clad, deluxe, 6' x 5', insulating glass	1.000	Ea.	1.000	795	54	849
Trim, interior casing	23.000	L.F.	.736	38.41	39.79	78.20
Paint, interior, primer & 2 coats	1.000	Face	.889	1.23	41	42.23
Caulking	22.000	L.F.	.611	4.40	32.56	36.96
Snap-in grille	1.000	Set	.364	47.50	19.65	67.15
Drip cap, metal	6.000	L.F.	.120	2.64	6.48	9.12
TOTAL		Ea.	3.720	889.18	193.48	1,082.66

The cost of this system is on a cost per each window basis.

Description	QUAN.	UNIT	LABOR HOURS	COST EACH		
				MAT.	INST.	TOTAL

Sliding Window Price Sheet	QUAN.	UNIT	LABOR HOURS	COST EACH MAT.	COST EACH INST.	COST EACH TOTAL
Windows, sliding, builder's quality, 3' x 3', single glass	1.000	Ea.	.800	310	43	353
Insulating glass	1.000	Ea.	.800	340	43	383
4' x 3'-6", single glass	1.000	Ea.	.889	390	48	438
Insulating glass	1.000	Ea.	.889	400	48	448
6' x 5', single glass	1.000	Ea.	1.000	535	54	589
Insulating glass	1.000	Ea.	1.000	580	54	634
Plastic clad premium insulating glass, 3' x 3'	1.000	Ea.	.800	665	43	708
4' x 3'-6"	1.000	Ea.	.889	755	48	803
5' x 4'	1.000	Ea.	.889	990	48	1,038
6' x 5'	1.000	Ea.	1.000	1,250	54	1,304
Metal clad deluxe insulating glass, 3' x 3'	1.000	Ea.	.800	360	43	403
4' x 3'-6"	1.000	Ea.	.889	440	48	488
5' x 4'	1.000	Ea.	.889	525	48	573
6' x 5'	1.000	Ea.	1.000	795	54	849
Trim, interior casing, window 3' x 2'	11.000	L.F.	.367	18.35	19.05	37.40
3' x 3'	13.000	L.F.	.433	21.50	22.50	44
4' x 3'-6"	16.000	L.F.	.533	26.50	27.50	54
5' x 4'	19.000	L.F.	.633	31.50	33	64.50
6' x 5'	23.000	L.F.	.767	38.50	40	78.50
Paint or stain, interior or exterior, 3' x 2' window, 1 coat	1.000	Face	.444	.51	20.50	21.01
2 coats	1.000	Face	.727	1.01	33.50	34.51
Primer & 1 coat	1.000	Face	.727	.83	33.50	34.33
Primer & 2 coats	1.000	Face	.889	1.23	41	42.23
4' x 3'-6" window, 1 coat	1.000	Face	.667	1.06	31	32.06
2 coats	1.000	Face	.667	1.79	31	32.79
Primer & 1 coat	1.000	Face	.727	1.26	33.50	34.76
Primer & 2 coats	1.000	Face	.889	1.23	41	42.23
6' x 5' window, 1 coat	1.000	Face	.889	2.87	41	43.87
2 coats	1.000	Face	1.333	5.25	61.50	66.75
Primer & 1 coat	1.000	Face	1.333	4.45	61.50	65.95
Primer & 2 coats	1.000	Face	1.600	6.55	74	80.55
Caulking, window, 3' x 2'	10.000	L.F.	.323	2	14.80	16.80
3' x 3'	12.000	L.F.	.387	2.40	17.75	20.15
4' x 3'-6"	15.000	L.F.	.484	3	22	25
5' x 4'	18.000	L.F.	.581	3.60	26.50	30.10
6' x 5'	22.000	L.F.	.710	4.40	32.50	36.90
Grilles, glass size, to 14" x 36"	1.000	Set	.333	39	18	57
To 36" x 36"	1.000	Set	.364	47.50	19.65	67.15
Drip cap, aluminum, 3' long	3.000	L.F.	.060	1.32	3.24	4.56
4' long	4.000	L.F.	.080	1.76	4.32	6.08
5' long	5.000	L.F.	.100	2.20	5.40	7.60
6' long	6.000	L.F.	.120	2.64	6.50	9.14
Wood, 3' long	3.000	L.F.	.100	5	5.20	10.20
4' long	4.000	L.F.	.133	6.70	6.90	13.60
5' long	5.000	L.F.	.167	8.35	8.65	17
6' long	6.000	L.F.	.200	10	10.40	20.40

Drip Cap

Caulking

Snap-in Grille

Window

System Description	QUAN.	UNIT	LABOR HOURS	COST EACH		
				MAT.	INST.	TOTAL
AWNING TYPE BOW WINDOW, BUILDER'S QUALITY, 8′ X 5′						
Window, primed, builder's quality, 8′ x 5′, insulating glass	1.000	Ea.	1.600	1,450	86.50	1,536.50
Trim, interior casing	27.000	L.F.	.864	45.09	46.71	91.80
Paint, interior & exterior, primer & 1 coat	2.000	Face	3.200	13.10	148	161.10
Caulking	26.000	L.F.	.722	5.20	38.48	43.68
Snap-in grilles	1.000	Set	1.067	140	57.60	197.60
TOTAL		Ea.	7.453	1,653.39	377.29	2,030.68
CASEMENT TYPE BOW WINDOW, PLASTIC CLAD, 10′ X 6′						
Window, plastic clad, premium, 10′ x 6′, insulating glass	1.000	Ea.	2.286	2,875	123	2,998
Trim, interior casing	33.000	L.F.	1.056	55.11	57.09	112.20
Paint, interior, primer & 1 coat	1.000	Face	1.778	2.46	82	84.46
Caulking	32.000	L.F.	.889	6.40	47.36	53.76
Snap-in grilles	1.000	Set	1.333	175	72	247
TOTAL		Ea.	7.342	3,113.97	381.45	3,495.42
DOUBLE HUNG TYPE, METAL CLAD, 9′ X 5′						
Window, metal clad, deluxe, 9′ x 5′, insulating glass	1.000	Ea.	2.667	1,575	144	1,719
Trim, interior casing	29.000	L.F.	.928	48.43	50.17	98.60
Paint, interior, primer & 1 coat	1.000	Face	1.778	2.46	82	84.46
Caulking	28.000	L.F.	.778	5.60	41.44	47.04
Snap-in grilles	1.000	Set	1.067	140	57.60	197.60
TOTAL		Ea.	7.218	1,771.49	375.21	2,146.70

The cost of this system is on a cost per each window basis.

Description	QUAN.	UNIT	LABOR HOURS	COST EACH		
				MAT.	INST.	TOTAL

Bow/Bay Window Price Sheet	QUAN.	UNIT	LABOR HOURS	COST EACH		
				MAT.	INST.	TOTAL
Windows, bow awning type, builder's quality, 8' x 5', insulating glass	1.000	Ea.	1.600	1,650	86.50	1,736.50
Low E glass	1.000	Ea.	1.600	1,450	86.50	1,536.50
12' x 6', insulating glass	1.000	Ea.	2.667	1,500	144	1,644
Low E glass	1.000	Ea.	2.667	1,600	144	1,744
Plastic clad premium insulating glass, 6' x 4'	1.000	Ea.	1.600	1,125	86.50	1,211.50
9' x 4'	1.000	Ea.	2.000	1,500	108	1,608
10' x 5'	1.000	Ea.	2.286	2,475	123	2,598
12' x 6'	1.000	Ea.	2.667	3,225	144	3,369
Metal clad deluxe insulating glass, 6' x 4'	1.000	Ea.	1.600	1,325	86.50	1,411.50
9' x 4'	1.000	Ea.	2.000	1,700	108	1,808
10' x 5'	1.000	Ea.	2.286	2,325	123	2,448
12' x 6'	1.000	Ea.	2.667	2,950	144	3,094
Bow casement type, builder's quality, 8' x 5', single glass	1.000	Ea.	1.600	2,075	86.50	2,161.50
Insulating glass	1.000	Ea.	1.600	2,500	86.50	2,586.50
12' x 6', single glass	1.000	Ea.	2.667	2,575	144	2,719
Insulating glass	1.000	Ea.	2.667	2,625	144	2,769
Plastic clad premium insulating glass, 8' x 5'	1.000	Ea.	1.600	1,925	86.50	2,011.50
10' x 5'	1.000	Ea.	2.000	2,525	108	2,633
10' x 6'	1.000	Ea.	2.286	2,875	123	2,998
12' x 6'	1.000	Ea.	2.667	3,525	144	3,669
Metal clad deluxe insulating glass, 8' x 5'	1.000	Ea.	1.600	1,825	86.50	1,911.50
10' x 5'	1.000	Ea.	2.000	1,975	108	2,083
10' x 6'	1.000	Ea.	2.286	2,325	123	2,448
12' x 6'	1.000	Ea.	2.667	3,225	144	3,369
Bow, double hung type, builder's quality, 8' x 4', single glass	1.000	Ea.	1.600	1,450	86.50	1,536.50
Insulating glass	1.000	Ea.	1.600	1,575	86.50	1,661.50
9' x 5', single glass	1.000	Ea.	2.667	1,575	144	1,719
Insulating glass	1.000	Ea.	2.667	1,650	144	1,794
Plastic clad premium insulating glass, 7' x 4'	1.000	Ea.	1.600	1,500	86.50	1,586.50
8' x 4'	1.000	Ea.	2.000	1,525	108	1,633
8' x 5'	1.000	Ea.	2.286	1,600	123	1,723
9' x 5'	1.000	Ea.	2.667	1,650	144	1,794
Metal clad deluxe insulating glass, 7' x 4'	1.000	Ea.	1.600	1,400	86.50	1,486.50
8' x 4'	1.000	Ea.	2.000	1,450	108	1,558
8' x 5'	1.000	Ea.	2.286	1,500	123	1,623
9' x 5'	1.000	Ea.	2.667	1,575	144	1,719
Trim, interior casing, window 7' x 4'	1.000	Ea.	.767	38.50	40	78.50
8' x 5'	1.000	Ea.	.900	45	46.50	91.50
10' x 6'	1.000	Ea.	1.100	55	57	112
12' x 6'	1.000	Ea.	1.233	62	64	126
Paint or stain, interior, or exterior, 7' x 4' window, 1 coat	1.000	Face	.889	2.87	41	43.87
Primer & 1 coat	1.000	Face	1.333	4.45	61.50	65.95
8' x 5' window, 1 coat	1.000	Face	.889	2.87	41	43.87
Primer & 1 coat	1.000	Face	1.333	4.45	61.50	65.95
10' x 6' window, 1 coat	1.000	Face	1.333	2.12	62	64.12
Primer & 1 coat	1.000	Face	1.778	2.46	82	84.46
12' x 6' window, 1 coat	1.000	Face	1.778	5.75	82	87.75
Primer & 1 coat	1.000	Face	2.667	8.90	123	131.90
Drip cap, vinyl moulded window, 7' long	1.000	Ea.	.533	125	24.50	149.50
8' long	1.000	Ea.	.533	143	28	171
Caulking, window, 7' x 4'	1.000	Ea.	.710	4.40	32.50	36.90
8' x 5'	1.000	Ea.	.839	5.20	38.50	43.70
10' x 6'	1.000	Ea.	1.032	6.40	47.50	53.90
12' x 6'	1.000	Ea.	1.161	7.20	53.50	60.70
Grilles, window, 7' x 4'	1.000	Set	.800	105	43	148
8' x 5'	1.000	Set	1.067	140	57.50	197.50
10' x 6'	1.000	Set	1.333	175	72	247
12' x 6'	1.000	Set	1.600	210	86.50	296.50

System Description	QUAN.	UNIT	LABOR HOURS	COST EACH		
				MAT.	INST.	TOTAL
BUILDER'S QUALITY PICTURE WINDOW, 4' X 4'						
Window, primed, builder's quality, 3'-0" x 4', insulating glass	1.000	Ea.	1.333	475	72	547
Trim, interior casing	17.000	L.F.	.544	28.39	29.41	57.80
Paint, interior & exterior, primer & 2 coats	2.000	Face	1.778	2.46	82	84.46
Caulking	16.000	L.F.	.444	3.20	23.68	26.88
Snap-in grille	1.000	Ea.	.267	132	14.40	146.40
Drip cap, metal	4.000	L.F.	.080	1.76	4.32	6.08
TOTAL		Ea.	4.446	642.81	225.81	868.62
PLASTIC CLAD WOOD WINDOW, 4'-6" X 6'-6"						
Window, plastic clad, prem., 4'-6" x 6'-6", insul. glass	1.000	Ea.	1.455	1,025	78.50	1,103.50
Trim, interior casing	23.000	L.F.	.736	38.41	39.79	78.20
Paint, interior, primer & 2 coats	1.000	Face	.889	1.23	41	42.23
Caulking	22.000	L.F.	.611	4.40	32.56	36.96
Snap-in grille	1.000	Ea.	.267	132	14.40	146.40
TOTAL		Ea.	3.958	1,201.04	206.25	1,407.29
METAL CLAD WOOD WINDOW, 6'-6" X 6'-6"						
Window, metal clad, deluxe, 6'-0" x 6'-0", insulating glass	1.000	Ea.	1.600	765	86.50	851.50
Trim interior casing	27.000	L.F.	.864	45.09	46.71	91.80
Paint, interior, primer & 2 coats	1.000	Face	1.600	6.55	74	80.55
Caulking	26.000	L.F.	.722	5.20	38.48	43.68
Snap-in grille	1.000	Ea.	.267	132	14.40	146.40
Drip cap, metal	6.500	L.F.	.130	2.86	7.02	9.88
TOTAL		Ea.	5.183	956.70	267.11	1,223.81

The cost of this system is on a cost per each window basis.

Description	QUAN.	UNIT	LABOR HOURS	COST EACH		
				MAT.	INST.	TOTAL

Fixed Window Price Sheet	QUAN.	UNIT	LABOR HOURS	COST EACH		
				MAT.	INST.	TOTAL
Window-picture, builder's quality, 4' x 4', single glass	1.000	Ea.	1.333	465	72	537
Insulating glass	1.000	Ea.	1.333	475	72	547
4' x 4'-6", single glass	1.000	Ea.	1.455	605	78.50	683.50
Insulating glass	1.000	Ea.	1.455	585	78.50	663.50
5' x 4', single glass	1.000	Ea.	1.455	640	78.50	718.50
Insulating glass	1.000	Ea.	1.455	665	78.50	743.50
6' x 4'-6", single glass	1.000	Ea.	1.600	690	86.50	776.50
Insulating glass	1.000	Ea.	1.600	700	86.50	786.50
Plastic clad premium insulating glass, 4' x 4'	1.000	Ea.	1.333	545	72	617
4'-6" x 6'-6"	1.000	Ea.	1.455	1,025	78.50	1,103.50
5'-6" x 6'-6"	1.000	Ea.	1.600	1,150	86.50	1,236.50
6'-6" x 6'-6"	1.000	Ea.	1.600	1,150	86.50	1,236.50
Metal clad deluxe insulating glass, 4' x 4'	1.000	Ea.	1.333	410	72	482
4'-6" x 6'-6"	1.000	Ea.	1.455	600	78.50	678.50
5'-6" x 6'-6"	1.000	Ea.	1.600	670	86.50	756.50
6'-6" x 6'-6"	1.000	Ea.	1.600	765	86.50	851.50
Trim, interior casing, window 4' x 4'	17.000	L.F.	.567	28.50	29.50	58
4'-6" x 4'-6"	19.000	L.F.	.633	31.50	33	64.50
5'-0" x 4'-0"	19.000	L.F.	.633	31.50	33	64.50
4'-6" x 6'-6"	23.000	L.F.	.767	38.50	40	78.50
5'-6" x 6'-6"	25.000	L.F.	.833	42	43.50	85.50
6'-6" x 6'-6"	27.000	L.F.	.900	45	46.50	91.50
Paint or stain, interior or exterior, 4' x 4' window, 1 coat	1.000	Face	.667	1.06	31	32.06
2 coats	1.000	Face	.667	1.79	31	32.79
Primer & 1 coat	1.000	Face	.727	1.26	33.50	34.76
Primer & 2 coats	1.000	Face	.889	1.23	41	42.23
4'-6" x 6'-6" window, 1 coat	1.000	Face	.667	1.06	31	32.06
2 coats	1.000	Face	.667	1.79	31	32.79
Primer & 1 coat	1.000	Face	.727	1.26	33.50	34.76
Primer & 2 coats	1.000	Face	.889	1.23	41	42.23
6'-6" x 6'-6" window, 1 coat	1.000	Face	.889	2.87	41	43.87
2 coats	1.000	Face	1.333	5.25	61.50	66.75
Primer & 1 coat	1.000	Face	1.333	4.45	61.50	65.95
Primer & 2 coats	1.000	Face	1.600	6.55	74	80.55
Caulking, window, 4' x 4'	1.000	Ea.	.516	3.20	23.50	26.70
4'-6" x 4'-6"	1.000	Ea.	.581	3.60	26.50	30.10
5'-0" x 4'-0"	1.000	Ea.	.581	3.60	26.50	30.10
4'-6" x 6'-6"	1.000	Ea.	.710	4.40	32.50	36.90
5'-6" x 6'-6"	1.000	Ea.	.774	4.80	35.50	40.30
6'-6" x 6'-6"	1.000	Ea.	.839	5.20	38.50	43.70
Grilles, glass size, to 48" x 48"	1.000	Ea.	.267	132	14.40	146.40
To 60" x 68"	1.000	Ea.	.286	202	15.45	217.45
Drip cap, aluminum, 4' long	4.000	L.F.	.080	1.76	4.32	6.08
4'-6" long	4.500	L.F.	.090	1.98	4.86	6.84
5' long	5.000	L.F.	.100	2.20	5.40	7.60
6' long	6.000	L.F.	.120	2.64	6.50	9.14
Wood, 4' long	4.000	L.F.	.133	6.70	6.90	13.60
4'-6" long	4.500	L.F.	.150	7.50	7.80	15.30
5' long	5.000	L.F.	.167	8.35	8.65	17
6' long	6.000	L.F.	.200	10	10.40	20.40

Drip Cap — Door — Frame & Exterior Casing — Interior Casing — Sill

System Description	QUAN.	UNIT	LABOR HOURS	COST EACH		
				MAT.	INST.	TOTAL
COLONIAL, 6 PANEL, 3′ X 6′-8″, WOOD						
Door, 3′ x 6′-8″ x 1-3/4″ thick, pine, 6 panel colonial	1.000	Ea.	1.067	490	57.50	547.50
Frame, 5-13/16″ deep, incl. exterior casing & drip cap	17.000	L.F.	.725	146.20	39.10	185.30
Interior casing, 2-1/2″ wide	18.000	L.F.	.576	30.06	31.14	61.20
Sill, 8/4 x 8″ deep	3.000	L.F.	.480	56.40	25.95	82.35
Butt hinges, brass, 4-1/2″ x 4-1/2″	1.500	Pr.		31.50		31.50
Lockset	1.000	Ea.	.571	55	31	86
Weatherstripping, metal, spring type, bronze	1.000	Set	1.053	25.50	57	82.50
Paint, interior & exterior, primer & 2 coats	2.000	Face	1.778	13	82	95
TOTAL		Ea.	6.250	847.66	323.69	1,171.35
SOLID CORE BIRCH, FLUSH, 3′ X 6′-8″						
Door, 3′ x 6′-8″, 1-3/4″ thick, birch, flush solid core	1.000	Ea.	1.067	130	57.50	187.50
Frame, 5-13/16″ deep, incl. exterior casing & drip cap	17.000	L.F.	.725	146.20	39.10	185.30
Interior casing, 2-1/2″ wide	18.000	L.F.	.576	30.06	31.14	61.20
Sill, 8/4 x 8″ deep	3.000	L.F.	.480	56.40	25.95	82.35
Butt hinges, brass, 4-1/2″ x 4-1/2″	1.500	Pr.		31.50		31.50
Lockset	1.000	Ea.	.571	55	31	86
Weatherstripping, metal, spring type, bronze	1.000	Set	1.053	25.50	57	82.50
Paint, Interior & exterior, primer & 2 coats	2.000	Face	1.778	12.10	82	94.10
TOTAL		Ea.	6.250	486.76	323.69	810.45

These systems are on a cost per each door basis.

Description	QUAN.	UNIT	LABOR HOURS	COST EACH		
				MAT.	INST.	TOTAL

Entrance Door Price Sheet	QUAN.	UNIT	LABOR HOURS	COST EACH		
				MAT.	INST.	TOTAL
Door exterior wood 1-3/4" thick, pine, dutch door, 2'-8" x 6'-8" minimum	1.000	Ea.	1.333	865	72	937
Maximum	1.000	Ea.	1.600	990	86.50	1,076.50
3'-0" x 6'-8", minimum	1.000	Ea.	1.333	865	72	937
Maximum	1.000	Ea.	1.600	990	86.50	1,076.50
Colonial, 6 panel, 2'-8" x 6'-8"	1.000	Ea.	1.000	545	54	599
3'-0" x 6'-8"	1.000	Ea.	1.067	490	57.50	547.50
8 panel, 2'-6" x 6'-8"	1.000	Ea.	1.000	635	54	689
3'-0" x 6'-8"	1.000	Ea.	1.067	625	57.50	682.50
Flush, birch, solid core, 2'-8" x 6'-8"	1.000	Ea.	1.000	125	54	179
3'-0" x 6'-8"	1.000	Ea.	1.067	130	57.50	187.50
Porch door, 2'-8" x 6'-8"	1.000	Ea.	1.000	630	54	684
3'-0" x 6'-8"	1.000	Ea.	1.067	655	54	712.50
Hand carved mahogany, 2'-8" x 6'-8"	1.000	Ea.	1.067	1,550	57.50	1,607.50
3'-0" x 6'-8"	1.000	Ea.	1.067	1,525	57.50	1,582.50
Rosewood, 2'-8" x 6'-8"	1.000	Ea.	1.067	825	57.50	882.50
3'-0" x 6-8"	1.000	Ea.	1.067	825	57.50	882.50
Door, metal clad wood 1-3/8" thick raised panel, 2'-8" x 6'-8"	1.000	Ea.	1.067	335	51	386
3'-0" x 6'-8"	1.000	Ea.	1.067	271	57.50	328.50
Deluxe metal door, 3'-0" x 6'-8"	1.000	Ea.	1.231	271	57.50	328.50
3'-0" x 6'-8"	1.000	Ea.	1.231	271	57.50	328.50
Frame, pine, including exterior trim & drip cap, 5/4, x 4-9/16" deep	17.000	L.F.	.725	124	39	163
5-13/16" deep	17.000	L.F	.725	146	39	185
6-9/16" deep	17.000	L.F.	.725	148	39	187
Safety glass lites, add	1.000	Ea.		84.50		84.50
Interior casing, 2'-8" x 6'-8" door	18.000	L.F.	.600	30	31	61
3'-0" x 6'-8" door	19.000	L.F.	.633	31.50	33	64.50
Sill, oak, 8/4 x 8" deep	3.000	L.F.	.480	56.50	26	82.50
8/4 x 10" deep	3.000	L.F.	.533	73.50	29	102.50
Butt hinges, steel plated, 4-1/2" x 4-1/2", plain	1.500	Pr.		31.50		31.50
Ball bearing	1.500	Pr.		55.50		55.50
Bronze, 4-1/2" x 4-1/2", plain	1.500	Pr.		44.50		44.50
Ball bearing	1.500	Pr.		57		57
Lockset, minimum	1.000	Ea.	.571	55	31	86
Maximum	1.000	Ea.	1.000	242	54	296
Weatherstripping, metal, interlocking, zinc	1.000	Set	2.667	48.50	144	192.50
Bronze	1.000	Set	2.667	61.50	144	205.50
Spring type, bronze	1.000	Set	1.053	25.50	57	82.50
Rubber, minimum	1.000	Set	1.053	10	57	67
Maximum	1.000	Set	1.143	12.20	61.50	73.70
Felt minimum	1.000	Set	.571	4.07	31	35.07
Maximum	1.000	Set	.615	4.76	33	37.76
Paint or stain, flush door, interior or exterior, 1 coat	2.000	Face	.941	4.34	43	47.34
2 coats	2.000	Face	1.455	8.70	67	75.70
Primer & 1 coat	2.000	Face	1.455	8.05	67	75.05
Primer & 2 coats	2.000	Face	1.778	12.10	82	94.10
Paneled door, interior & exterior, 1 coat	2.000	Face	1.143	4.64	53	57.64
2 coats	2.000	Face	2.000	9.30	92	101.30
Primer & 1 coat	2.000	Face	1.455	8.60	67	75.60
Primer & 2 coats	2.000	Face	1.778	13	82	95

System Description	QUAN.	UNIT	LABOR HOURS	COST EACH		
				MAT.	INST.	TOTAL
WOOD SLIDING DOOR, 8' WIDE, PREMIUM						
Wood, 5/8" thick tempered insul. glass, 8' wide, premium	1.000	Ea.	5.333	2,000	288	2,288
Interior casing	22.000	L.F.	.704	36.74	38.06	74.80
Exterior casing	22.000	L.F.	.704	36.74	38.06	74.80
Sill, oak, 8/4 x 8" deep	8.000	L.F.	1.280	150.40	69.20	219.60
Drip cap	8.000	L.F.	.160	3.52	8.64	12.16
Paint, interior & exterior, primer & 2 coats	2.000	Face	2.816	18.48	130.24	148.72
TOTAL		Ea.	10.997	2,245.88	572.20	2,818.08
ALUMINUM SLIDING DOOR, 8' WIDE, PREMIUM						
Aluminum, 5/8" tempered insul. glass, 8' wide, premium	1.000	Ea.	5.333	1,825	288	2,113
Interior casing	22.000	L.F.	.704	36.74	38.06	74.80
Exterior casing	22.000	L.F.	.704	36.74	38.06	74.80
Sill, oak, 8/4 x 8" deep	8.000	L.F.	1.280	150.40	69.20	219.60
Drip cap	8.000	L.F.	.160	3.52	8.64	12.16
Paint, interior & exterior, primer & 2 coats	2.000	Face	2.816	18.48	130.24	148.72
TOTAL		Ea.	10.997	2,070.88	572.20	2,643.08

The cost of this system is on a cost per each door basis.

Description	QUAN.	UNIT	LABOR HOURS	COST EACH		
				MAT.	INST.	TOTAL

Sliding Door Price Sheet	QUAN.	UNIT	LABOR HOURS	COST PER UNIT		
				MAT.	INST.	TOTAL
Sliding door, wood, 5/8" thick, tempered insul. glass, 6' wide, premium	1.000	Ea.	4.000	1,575	216	1,791
Economy	1.000	Ea.	4.000	1,275	216	1,491
8'wide, wood premium	1.000	Ea.	5.333	2,000	288	2,288
Economy	1.000	Ea.	5.333	1,650	288	1,938
12' wide, wood premium	1.000	Ea.	6.400	3,300	345	3,645
Economy	1.000	Ea.	6.400	2,700	345	3,045
Aluminum, 5/8" thick, tempered insul. glass, 6'wide, premium	1.000	Ea.	4.000	1,725	216	1,941
Economy	1.000	Ea.	4.000	995	216	1,211
8'wide, premium	1.000	Ea.	5.333	1,825	288	2,113
Economy	1.000	Ea.	5.333	1,550	288	1,838
12' wide, premium	1.000	Ea.	6.400	3,275	345	3,620
Economy	1.000	Ea.	6.400	1,675	345	2,020
Interior casing, 6' wide door	20.000	L.F.	.667	33.50	34.50	68
8' wide door	22.000	L.F.	.733	36.50	38	74.50
12' wide door	26.000	L.F.	.867	43.50	45	88.50
Exterior casing, 6' wide door	20.000	L.F.	.667	33.50	34.50	68
8' wide door	22.000	L.F.	.733	36.50	38	74.50
12' wide door	26.000	L.F.	.867	43.50	45	88.50
Sill, oak, 8/4 x 8" deep, 6' wide door	6.000	L.F.	.960	113	52	165
8' wide door	8.000	L.F.	1.280	150	69	219
12' wide door	12.000	L.F.	1.920	226	104	330
8/4 x 10" deep, 6' wide door	6.000	L.F.	1.067	147	57.50	204.50
8' wide door	8.000	L.F.	1.422	196	77	273
12' wide door	12.000	L.F.	2.133	294	115	409
Drip cap, 6' wide door	6.000	L.F.	.120	2.64	6.50	9.14
8' wide door	8.000	L.F.	.160	3.52	8.65	12.17
12' wide door	12.000	L.F.	.240	5.30	12.95	18.25
Paint or stain, interior & exterior, 6' wide door, 1 coat	2.000	Face	1.600	5.60	73.50	79.10
2 coats	2.000	Face	1.600	5.60	73.50	79.10
Primer & 1 coat	2.000	Face	1.778	11.20	82.50	93.70
Primer & 2 coats	2.000	Face	2.560	16.80	118	134.80
8' wide door, 1 coat	2.000	Face	1.760	6.15	81	87.15
2 coats	2.000	Face	1.760	6.15	81	87.15
Primer & 1 coat	2.000	Face	1.955	12.30	90.50	102.80
Primer & 2 coats	2.000	Face	2.816	18.50	130	148.50
12' wide door, 1 coat	2.000	Face	2.080	7.30	95.50	102.80
2 coats	2.000	Face	2.080	7.30	95.50	102.80
Primer & 1 coat	2.000	Face	2.311	14.55	107	121.55
Primer & 2 coats	2.000	Face	3.328	22	154	176
Aluminum door, trim only, interior & exterior, 6' door, 1 coat	2.000	Face	.800	2.80	37	39.80
2 coats	2.000	Face	.800	2.80	37	39.80
Primer & 1 coat	2.000	Face	.889	5.60	41	46.60
Primer & 2 coats	2.000	Face	1.280	8.40	59	67.40
8' wide door, 1 coat	2.000	Face	.880	3.08	40.50	43.58
2 coats	2.000	Face	.880	3.08	40.50	43.58
Primer & 1 coat	2.000	Face	.978	6.15	45.50	51.65
Primer & 2 coats	2.000	Face	1.408	9.25	65	74.25
12' wide door, 1 coat	2.000	Face	1.040	3.64	48	51.64
2 coats	2.000	Face	1.040	3.64	48	51.64
Primer & 1 coat	2.000	Face	1.155	7.30	53.50	60.80
Primer & 2 coats	2.000	Face	1.664	10.90	77	87.90

Exterior Trim — Drip Cap — Door — Weatherstripping — Jamb

System Description	QUAN.	UNIT	LABOR HOURS	COST EACH		
				MAT.	INST.	TOTAL
OVERHEAD, SECTIONAL GARAGE DOOR, 9' X 7'						
Wood, overhead sectional door, std., incl. hardware, 9' x 7'	1.000	Ea.	2.000	1,000	108	1,108
Jamb & header blocking, 2" x 6"	25.000	L.F.	.901	15.75	48.75	64.50
Exterior trim	25.000	L.F.	.800	41.75	43.25	85
Paint, interior & exterior, primer & 2 coats	2.000	Face	3.556	26	164	190
Weatherstripping, molding type	1.000	Set	.736	38.41	39.79	78.20
Drip cap	9.000	L.F.	.180	3.96	9.72	13.68
TOTAL		Ea.	8.173	1,125.87	413.51	1,539.38
OVERHEAD, SECTIONAL GARAGE DOOR, 16' X 7'						
Wood, overhead sectional, std., incl. hardware, 16' x 7'	1.000	Ea.	2.667	1,800	144	1,944
Jamb & header blocking, 2" x 6"	30.000	L.F.	1.081	18.90	58.50	77.40
Exterior trim	30.000	L.F.	.960	50.10	51.90	102
Paint, interior & exterior, primer & 2 coats	2.000	Face	5.333	39	246	285
Weatherstripping, molding type	1.000	Set	.960	50.10	51.90	102
Drip cap	16.000	L.F.	.320	7.04	17.28	24.32
TOTAL		Ea.	11.321	1,965.14	569.58	2,534.72
OVERHEAD, SWING-UP TYPE, GARAGE DOOR, 16' X 7'						
Wood, overhead, swing-up, std., incl. hardware, 16' x 7'	1.000	Ea.	2.667	990	144	1,134
Jamb & header blocking, 2" x 6"	30.000	L.F.	1.081	18.90	58.50	77.40
Exterior trim	30.000	L.F.	.960	50.10	51.90	102
Paint, interior & exterior, primer & 2 coats	2.000	Face	5.333	39	246	285
Weatherstripping, molding type	1.000	Set	.960	50.10	51.90	102
Drip cap	16.000	L.F.	.320	7.04	17.28	24.32
TOTAL		Ea.	11.321	1,155.14	569.58	1,724.72

This system is on a cost per each door basis.

Description	QUAN.	UNIT	LABOR HOURS	COST EACH		
				MAT.	INST.	TOTAL

Resi Garage Door Price Sheet	QUAN.	UNIT	LABOR HOURS	COST EACH MAT.	INST.	TOTAL
Overhead, sectional, including hardware, fiberglass, 9' x 7', standard	1.000	Ea.	3.030	1,025	164	1,189
Deluxe	1.000	Ea.	3.030	1,250	164	1,414
16' x 7', standard	1.000	Ea.	2.667	1,725	144	1,869
Deluxe	1.000	Ea.	2.667	2,350	144	2,494
Hardboard, 9' x 7', standard	1.000	Ea.	2.000	650	108	758
Deluxe	1.000	Ea.	2.000	900	108	1,008
16' x 7', standard	1.000	Ea.	2.667	1,350	144	1,494
Deluxe	1.000	Ea.	2.667	1,575	144	1,719
Metal, 9' x 7', standard	1.000	Ea.	3.030	755	164	919
Deluxe	1.000	Ea.	2.000	1,000	108	1,108
16' x 7', standard	1.000	Ea.	5.333	955	288	1,243
Deluxe	1.000	Ea.	2.667	1,550	144	1,694
Wood, 9' x 7', standard	1.000	Ea.	2.000	1,000	108	1,108
Deluxe	1.000	Ea.	2.000	2,350	108	2,458
16' x 7', standard	1.000	Ea.	2.667	1,800	144	1,944
Deluxe	1.000	Ea.	2.667	3,325	144	3,469
Overhead swing-up type including hardware, fiberglass, 9' x 7', standard	1.000	Ea.	2.000	1,100	108	1,208
Deluxe	1.000	Ea.	2.000	1,200	108	1,308
16' x 7', standard	1.000	Ea.	2.667	1,375	144	1,519
Deluxe	1.000	Ea.	2.667	1,750	144	1,894
Hardboard, 9' x 7', standard	1.000	Ea.	2.000	605	108	713
Deluxe	1.000	Ea.	2.000	715	108	823
16' x 7', standard	1.000	Ea.	2.667	735	144	879
Deluxe	1.000	Ea.	2.667	935	144	1,079
Metal, 9' x 7', standard	1.000	Ea.	2.000	660	108	768
Deluxe	1.000	Ea.	2.000	1,050	108	1,158
16' x 7', standard	1.000	Ea.	2.667	880	144	1,024
Deluxe	1.000	Ea.	2.667	1,200	144	1,344
Wood, 9' x 7', standard	1.000	Ea.	2.000	770	108	878
Deluxe	1.000	Ea.	2.000	1,225	108	1,333
16' x 7', standard	1.000	Ea.	2.667	990	144	1,134
Deluxe	1.000	Ea.	2.667	2,300	144	2,444
Jamb & header blocking, 2" x 6", 9' x 7' door	25.000	L.F.	.901	15.75	49	64.75
16' x 7' door	30.000	L.F.	1.081	18.90	58.50	77.40
2" x 8", 9' x 7' door	25.000	L.F.	1.000	23.50	54	77.50
16' x 7' door	30.000	L.F.	1.200	28	65	93
Exterior trim, 9' x 7' door	25.000	L.F.	.833	42	43.50	85.50
16' x 7' door	30.000	L.F.	1.000	50	52	102
Paint or stain, interior & exterior, 9' x 7' door, 1 coat	1.000	Face	2.286	9.30	106	115.30
2 coats	1.000	Face	4.000	18.55	184	202.55
Primer & 1 coat	1.000	Face	2.909	17.25	134	151.25
Primer & 2 coats	1.000	Face	3.556	26	164	190
16' x 7' door, 1 coat	1.000	Face	3.429	13.90	159	172.90
2 coats	1.000	Face	6.000	28	276	304
Primer & 1 coat	1.000	Face	4.364	26	201	227
Primer & 2 coats	1.000	Face	5.333	39	246	285
Weatherstripping, molding type, 9' x 7' door	1.000	Set	.767	38.50	40	78.50
16' x 7' door	1.000	Set	1.000	50	52	102
Drip cap, 9' door	9.000	L.F.	.180	3.96	9.70	13.66
16' door	16.000	L.F.	.320	7.05	17.30	24.35
Garage door opener, economy	1.000	Ea.	1.000	470	54	524
Deluxe, including remote control	1.000	Ea.	1.000	675	54	729

Drywall ⟶   ⟵ Finish Drywall

⟵ Window

Corner Bead ⟶

⟶ Sill

System Description	QUAN.	UNIT	LABOR HOURS	COST EACH		
				MAT.	INST.	TOTAL
SINGLE HUNG, 2′ X 3′ OPENING						
Window, 2′ x 3′ opening, enameled, insulating glass	1.000	Ea.	1.600	274	104	378
Blocking, 1″ x 3″ furring strip nailers	10.000	L.F.	.146	4.20	7.90	12.10
Drywall, 1/2″ thick, standard	5.000	S.F.	.040	1.65	2.15	3.80
Corner bead, 1″ x 1″, galvanized steel	8.000	L.F.	.160	1.36	8.64	10
Finish drywall, tape and finish corners inside and outside	16.000	L.F.	.269	1.92	14.56	16.48
Sill, slate	2.000	L.F.	.400	25.30	19.20	44.50
TOTAL		Ea.	2.615	308.43	156.45	464.88
SLIDING, 3′ X 2′ OPENING						
Window, 3′ x 2′ opening, enameled, insulating glass	1.000	Ea.	1.600	255	104	359
Blocking, 1″ x 3″ furring strip nailers	10.000	L.F.	.146	4.20	7.90	12.10
Drywall, 1/2″ thick, standard	5.000	S.F.	.040	1.65	2.15	3.80
Corner bead, 1″ x 1″, galvanized steel	7.000	L.F.	.140	1.19	7.56	8.75
Finish drywall, tape and finish corners inside and outside	14.000	L.F.	.236	1.68	12.74	14.42
Sill, slate	3.000	L.F.	.600	37.95	28.80	66.75
TOTAL		Ea.	2.762	301.67	163.15	464.82
AWNING, 3′-1″ X 3′-2″						
Window, 3′-1″ x 3′-2″ opening, enameled, insul. glass	1.000	Ea.	1.600	390	104	494
Blocking, 1″ x 3″ furring strip, nailers	12.500	L.F.	.182	5.25	9.88	15.13
Drywall, 1/2″ thick, standard	4.500	S.F.	.036	1.49	1.94	3.43
Corner bead, 1″ x 1″, galvanized steel	9.250	L.F.	.185	1.57	9.99	11.56
Finish drywall, tape and finish corners, inside and outside	18.500	L.F.	.312	2.22	16.84	19.06
Sill, slate	3.250	L.F.	.650	41.11	31.20	72.31
TOTAL		Ea.	2.965	441.64	173.85	615.49

Description	QUAN.	UNIT	LABOR HOURS	COST PER S.F.		
				MAT.	INST.	TOTAL

Aluminum Window Price Sheet	QUAN.	UNIT	LABOR HOURS	COST EACH		
				MAT.	INST.	TOTAL
Window, aluminum, awning, 3'-1" x 3'-2", standard glass	1.000	Ea.	1.600	385	104	489
Insulating glass	1.000	Ea.	1.600	390	104	494
4'-5" x 5'-3", standard glass	1.000	Ea.	2.000	435	131	566
Insulating glass	1.000	Ea.	2.000	505	131	636
Casement, 3'-1" x 3'-2", standard glass	1.000	Ea.	1.600	405	104	509
Insulating glass	1.000	Ea.	1.600	555	104	659
Single hung, 2' x 3', standard glass	1.000	Ea.	1.600	226	104	330
Insulating glass	1.000	Ea.	1.600	274	104	378
2'-8" x 6'-8", standard glass	1.000	Ea.	2.000	400	131	531
Insulating glass	1.000	Ea.	2.000	515	131	646
3'-4" x 5'-0", standard glass	1.000	Ea.	1.778	325	116	441
Insulating glass	1.000	Ea.	1.778	360	116	476
Sliding, 3' x 2', standard glass	1.000	Ea.	1.600	239	104	343
Insulating glass	1.000	Ea.	1.600	255	104	359
5' x 3', standard glass	1.000	Ea.	1.778	365	116	481
Insulating glass	1.000	Ea.	1.778	425	116	541
8' x 4', standard glass	1.000	Ea.	2.667	385	174	559
Insulating glass	1.000	Ea.	2.667	620	174	794
Blocking, 1" x 3" furring, opening 3' x 2'	10.000	L.F.	.146	4.20	7.90	12.10
3' x 3'	12.500	L.F.	.182	5.25	9.90	15.15
3' x 5'	16.000	L.F.	.233	6.70	12.65	19.35
4' x 4'	16.000	L.F.	.233	6.70	12.65	19.35
4' x 5'	18.000	L.F.	.262	7.55	14.20	21.75
4' x 6'	20.000	L.F.	.291	8.40	15.80	24.20
4' x 8'	24.000	L.F.	.349	10.10	18.95	29.05
6'-8" x 2'-8"	19.000	L.F.	.276	8	15	23
Drywall, 1/2" thick, standard, opening 3' x 2'	5.000	S.F.	.040	1.65	2.15	3.80
3' x 3'	6.000	S.F.	.048	1.98	2.58	4.56
3' x 5'	8.000	S.F.	.064	2.64	3.44	6.08
4' x 4'	8.000	S.F.	.064	2.64	3.44	6.08
4' x 5'	9.000	S.F.	.072	2.97	3.87	6.84
4' x 6'	10.000	S.F.	.080	3.30	4.30	7.60
4' x 8'	12.000	S.F.	.096	3.96	5.15	9.11
6'-8" x 2'	9.500	S.F.	.076	3.14	4.09	7.23
Corner bead, 1" x 1", galvanized steel, opening 3' x 2'	7.000	L.F.	.140	1.19	7.55	8.74
3' x 3'	9.000	L.F.	.180	1.53	9.70	11.23
3' x 5'	11.000	L.F.	.220	1.87	11.90	13.77
4' x 4'	12.000	L.F.	.240	2.04	12.95	14.99
4' x 5'	13.000	L.F.	.260	2.21	14.05	16.26
4' x 6'	14.000	L.F.	.280	2.38	15.10	17.48
4' x 8'	16.000	L.F.	.320	2.72	17.30	20.02
6'-8" x 2'	15.000	L.F.	.300	2.55	16.20	18.75
Tape and finish corners, inside and outside, opening 3' x 2'	14.000	L.F.	.204	1.68	12.75	14.43
3' x 3'	18.000	L.F.	.262	2.16	16.40	18.56
3' x 5'	22.000	L.F.	.320	2.64	20	22.64
4' x 4'	24.000	L.F.	.349	2.88	22	24.88
4' x 5'	26.000	L.F.	.378	3.12	23.50	26.62
4' x 6'	28.000	L.F.	.407	3.36	25.50	28.86
4' x 8'	32.000	L.F.	.466	3.84	29	32.84
6'-8" x 2'	30.000	L.F.	.437	3.60	27.50	31.10
Sill, slate, 2' long	2.000	L.F.	.400	25.50	19.20	44.70
3' long	3.000	L.F.	.600	38	29	67
4' long	4.000	L.F.	.800	50.50	38.50	89
Wood, 1-5/8" x 6-1/4", 2' long	2.000	L.F.	.128	10.50	6.90	17.40
3' long	3.000	L.F.	.192	15.75	10.40	26.15
4' long	4.000	L.F.	.256	21	13.85	34.85

Aluminum Window → ← Aluminum Door

System Description	QUAN.	UNIT	LABOR HOURS	COST EACH		
				MAT.	INST.	TOTAL
Storm door, aluminum, combination, storm & screen, anodized, 2'-6" x 6'-8"	1.000	Ea.	1.067	198	57.50	255.50
2'-8" x 6'-8"	1.000	Ea.	1.143	182	61.50	243.50
3'-0" x 6'-8"	1.000	Ea.	1.143	179	61.50	240.50
Mill finish, 2'-6" x 6'-8"	1.000	Ea.	1.067	259	57.50	316.50
2'-8" x 6'-8"	1.000	Ea.	1.143	259	61.50	320.50
3'-0" x 6'-8"	1.000	Ea.	1.143	284	61.50	345.50
Painted, 2'-6" x 6'-8"	1.000	Ea.	1.067	325	57.50	382.50
2'-8" x 6'-8"	1.000	Ea.	1.143	315	61.50	376.50
3'-0" x 6'-8"	1.000	Ea.	1.143	335	61.50	396.50
Wood, combination, storm & screen, crossbuck, 2'-6" x 6'-9"	1.000	Ea.	1.455	375	78.50	453.50
2'-8" x 6'-9"	1.000	Ea.	1.600	330	86.50	416.50
3'-0" x 6'-9"	1.000	Ea.	1.778	340	96	436
Full lite, 2'-6" x 6'-9"	1.000	Ea.	1.455	350	78.50	428.50
2'-8" x 6'-9"	1.000	Ea.	1.600	350	86.50	436.50
3'-0" x 6'-9"	1.000	Ea.	1.778	355	96	451
Windows, aluminum, combination storm & screen, basement, 1'-10" x 1'-0"	1.000	Ea.	.533	38.50	29	67.50
2'-9" x 1'-6"	1.000	Ea.	.533	42	29	71
3'-4" x 2'-0"	1.000	Ea.	.533	48.50	29	77.50
Double hung, anodized, 2'-0" x 3'-5"	1.000	Ea.	.533	99	29	128
2'-6" x 5'-0"	1.000	Ea.	.571	121	31	152
4'-0" x 6'-0"	1.000	Ea.	.640	249	34.50	283.50
Painted, 2'-0" x 3'-5"	1.000	Ea.	.533	110	29	139
2'-6" x 5'-0"	1.000	Ea.	.571	176	31	207
4'-0" x 6'-0"	1.000	Ea.	.640	300	34.50	334.50
Fixed window, anodized, 4'-6" x 4'-6"	1.000	Ea.	.640	132	34.50	166.50
5'-8" x 4'-6"	1.000	Ea.	.800	158	43	201
Painted, 4'-6" x 4'-6"	1.000	Ea.	.640	139	34.50	173.50
5'-8" x 4'-6"	1.000	Ea.	.800	158	43	201

Aluminum Louvered →

← Raised Panel

Wood Louvered

System Description	QUAN.	UNIT	LABOR HOURS	COST PER PAIR		
				MAT.	INST.	TOTAL
Shutters, exterior blinds, aluminum, louvered, 1'-4" wide, 3"-0" long	1.000	Set	.800	82.50	43	125.50
4'-0" long	1.000	Set	.800	98.50	43	141.50
5'-4" long	1.000	Set	.800	130	43	173
6'-8" long	1.000	Set	.889	166	48	214
Wood, louvered, 1'-2" wide, 3'-3" long	1.000	Set	.800	237	43	280
4'-7" long	1.000	Set	.800	310	43	353
5'-3" long	1.000	Set	.800	390	43	433
1'-6" wide, 3'-3" long	1.000	Set	.800	288	43	331
4'-7" long	1.000	Set	.800	385	43	428
Polystyrene, louvered, 1'-2" wide, 3'-3" long	1.000	Set	.800	71.50	43	114.50
4'-7" long	1.000	Set	.800	97	43	140
5'-3" long	1.000	Set	.800	112	43	155
6'-8" long	1.000	Set	.889	139	48	187
Vinyl, louvered, 1'-2" wide, 4'-7" long	1.000	Set	.720	87.50	38.50	126
1'-4" x 6'-8" long	1.000	Set	.889	139	48	187

System Description	QUAN.	UNIT	LABOR HOURS	COST PER S.F.		
				MAT.	INST.	TOTAL
ASPHALT, ROOF SHINGLES, CLASS A						
Shingles, inorganic class A, 210-235 lb./sq., 4/12 pitch	1.160	S.F.	.017	1.07	.87	1.94
Drip edge, metal, 5" wide	.150	L.F.	.003	.09	.16	.25
Building paper, #15 felt	1.300	S.F.	.002	.08	.09	.17
Ridge shingles, asphalt	.042	L.F.	.001	.09	.05	.14
Soffit & fascia, white painted aluminum, 1' overhang	.083	L.F.	.012	.38	.65	1.03
Rake trim, 1" x 6"	.040	L.F.	.002	.05	.09	.14
Rake trim, prime and paint	.040	L.F.	.002	.01	.08	.09
Gutter, seamless, aluminum painted	.083	L.F.	.005	.24	.32	.56
Downspouts, aluminum painted	.035	L.F.	.002	.08	.09	.17
TOTAL		S.F.	.046	2.09	2.40	4.49
WOOD, CEDAR SHINGLES NO. 1 PERFECTIONS, 18" LONG						
Shingles, wood, cedar, No. 1 perfections, 4/12 pitch	1.160	S.F.	.035	3	1.88	4.88
Drip edge, metal, 5" wide	.150	L.F.	.003	.09	.16	.25
Building paper, #15 felt	1.300	S.F.	.002	.08	.09	.17
Ridge shingles, cedar	.042	L.F.	.001	.19	.06	.25
Soffit & fascia, white painted aluminum, 1' overhang	.083	L.F.	.012	.38	.65	1.03
Rake trim, 1" x 6"	.040	L.F.	.002	.05	.09	.14
Rake trim, prime and paint	.040	L.F.	.002	.01	.08	.09
Gutter, seamless, aluminum, painted	.083	L.F.	.005	.24	.32	.56
Downspouts, aluminum, painted	.035	L.F.	.002	.08	.09	.17
TOTAL		S.F.	.064	4.12	3.42	7.54

The prices in these systems are based on a square foot of plan area.
All quantities have been adjusted accordingly.

Description	QUAN.	UNIT	LABOR HOURS	COST PER S.F.		
				MAT.	INST.	TOTAL

Gable End Roofing Price Sheet	QUAN.	UNIT	LABOR HOURS	COST PER S.F.		
				MAT.	INST.	TOTAL
Shingles, asphalt, inorganic, class A, 210-235 lb./sq., 4/12 pitch	1.160	S.F.	.017	1.07	.87	1.94
8/12 pitch	1.330	S.F.	.019	1.16	.94	2.10
Laminated, multi-layered, 240-260 lb./sq., 4/12 pitch	1.160	S.F.	.021	1.39	1.06	2.45
8/12 pitch	1.330	S.F.	.023	1.51	1.15	2.66
Premium laminated, multi-layered, 260-300 lb./sq., 4/12 pitch	1.160	S.F.	.027	2.17	1.37	3.54
8/12 pitch	1.330	S.F.	.030	2.35	1.48	3.83
Clay tile, Spanish tile, red, 4/12 pitch	1.160	S.F.	.053	7.40	2.62	10.02
8/12 pitch	1.330	S.F.	.058	8	2.83	10.83
Mission tile, red, 4/12 pitch	1.160	S.F.	.083	5.35	2.62	7.97
8/12 pitch	1.330	S.F.	.090	5.80	2.83	8.63
French tile, red, 4/12 pitch	1.160	S.F.	.071	15	2.40	17.40
8/12 pitch	1.330	S.F.	.077	16.25	2.60	18.85
Slate, Buckingham, Virginia, black, 4/12 pitch	1.160	S.F.	.055	6.30	2.75	9.05
8/12 pitch	1.330	S.F.	.059	6.85	2.98	9.83
Vermont, black or grey, 4/12 pitch	1.160	S.F.	.055	6.05	2.75	8.80
8/12 pitch	1.330	S.F.	.059	6.55	2.98	9.53
Wood, No. 1 red cedar, 5X, 16" long, 5" exposure, 4/12 pitch	1.160	S.F.	.038	3.49	2.08	5.57
8/12 pitch	1.330	S.F.	.042	3.78	2.25	6.03
Fire retardant, 4/12 pitch	1.160	S.F.	.038	4.22	2.08	6.30
8/12 pitch	1.330	S.F.	.042	4.57	2.25	6.82
18" long, No.1 perfections, 5" exposure, 4/12 pitch	1.160	S.F.	.035	3	1.88	4.88
8/12 pitch	1.330	S.F.	.038	3.25	2.04	5.29
Fire retardant, 4/12 pitch	1.160	S.F.	.035	3.73	1.88	5.61
8/12 pitch	1.330	S.F.	.038	4.04	2.04	6.08
Resquared & rebutted, 18" long, 6" exposure, 4/12 pitch	1.160	S.F.	.032	3.72	1.73	5.45
8/12 pitch	1.330	S.F.	.035	4.03	1.87	5.90
Fire retardant, 4/12 pitch	1.160	S.F.	.032	4.45	1.73	6.18
8/12 pitch	1.330	S.F.	.035	4.82	1.87	6.69
Wood shakes hand split, 24" long, 10" exposure, 4/12 pitch	1.160	S.F.	.038	3.34	2.08	5.42
8/12 pitch	1.330	S.F.	.042	3.61	2.25	5.86
Fire retardant, 4/12 pitch	1.160	S.F.	.038	4.07	2.08	6.15
8/12 pitch	1.330	S.F.	.042	4.40	2.25	6.65
18" long, 8" exposure, 4/12 pitch	1.160	S.F.	.048	2.36	2.59	4.95
8/12 pitch	1.330	S.F.	.052	2.56	2.81	5.37
Fire retardant, 4/12 pitch	1.160	S.F.	.048	3.09	2.59	5.68
8/12 pitch	1.330	S.F.	.052	3.35	2.81	6.16
Drip edge, metal, 5" wide	.150	L.F.	.003	.09	.16	.25
8" wide	.150	L.F.	.003	.11	.16	.27
Building paper, #15 asphalt felt	1.300	S.F.	.002	.08	.09	.17
Ridge shingles, asphalt	.042	L.F.	.001	.09	.05	.14
Clay	.042	L.F.	.002	.25	.25	.50
Slate	.042	L.F.	.002	.43	.08	.51
Wood, shingles	.042	L.F.	.001	.19	.06	.25
Shakes	.042	L.F.	.001	.19	.06	.25
Soffit & fascia, aluminum, vented, 1' overhang	.083	L.F.	.012	.38	.65	1.03
2' overhang	.083	L.F.	.013	.56	.72	1.28
Vinyl, vented, 1' overhang	.083	L.F.	.011	.37	.60	.97
2' overhang	.083	L.F.	.012	.48	.72	1.20
Wood, board fascia, plywood soffit, 1' overhang	.083	L.F.	.004	.02	.17	.19
2' overhang	.083	L.F.	.006	.03	.26	.29
Rake trim, painted, 1" x 6"	.040	L.F.	.004	.06	.17	.23
1" x 8"	.040	L.F.	.004	.24	.15	.39
Gutter, 5" box, aluminum, seamless, painted	.083	L.F.	.006	.24	.32	.56
Vinyl	.083	L.F.	.006	.14	.31	.45
Downspout, 2" x 3", aluminum, one story house	.035	L.F.	.001	.05	.09	.14
Two story house	.060	L.F.	.003	.09	.15	.24
Vinyl, one story house	.035	L.F.	.002	.08	.09	.17
Two story house	.060	L.F.	.003	.09	.15	.24

Ridge Shingles

Shingles

Building Paper

Drip Edge

Gutter

Soffit & Fascia

Downspouts

System Description	QUAN.	UNIT	LABOR HOURS	COST PER S.F.		
				MAT.	INST.	TOTAL
ASPHALT, ROOF SHINGLES, CLASS A						
Shingles, inorganic, class A, 210-235 lb./sq. 4/12 pitch	1.570	S.F.	.023	1.42	1.16	2.58
Drip edge, metal, 5" wide	.122	L.F.	.002	.07	.13	.20
Building paper, #15 asphalt felt	1.800	S.F.	.002	.11	.12	.23
Ridge shingles, asphalt	.075	L.F.	.002	.17	.09	.26
Soffit & fascia, white painted aluminum, 1' overhang	.120	L.F.	.017	.55	.94	1.49
Gutter, seamless, aluminum, painted	.120	L.F.	.008	.34	.46	.80
Downspouts, aluminum, painted	.035	L.F.	.002	.08	.09	.17
TOTAL		S.F.	.056	2.74	2.99	5.73
WOOD, CEDAR SHINGLES, NO. 1 PERFECTIONS, 18" LONG						
Shingles, red cedar, No. 1 perfections, 5" exp., 4/12 pitch	1.570	S.F.	.047	4	2.51	6.51
Drip edge, metal, 5" wide	.122	L.F.	.002	.07	.13	.20
Building paper, #15 asphalt felt	1.800	S.F.	.002	.11	.12	.23
Ridge shingles, wood, cedar	.075	L.F.	.002	.33	.12	.45
Soffit & fascia, white painted aluminum, 1' overhang	.120	L.F.	.017	.55	.94	1.49
Gutter, seamless, aluminum, painted	.120	L.F.	.008	.34	.46	.80
Downspouts, aluminum, painted	.035	L.F.	.002	.08	.09	.17
TOTAL		S.F.	.080	5.48	4.37	9.85

The prices in these systems are based on a square foot of plan area.
All quantities have been adjusted accordingly.

Description	QUAN.	UNIT	LABOR HOURS	COST PER S.F.		
				MAT.	INST.	TOTAL

Hip Roof - Roofing Price Sheet	QUAN.	UNIT	LABOR HOURS	COST PER S.F.		
				MAT.	INST.	TOTAL
Shingles, asphalt, inorganic, class A, 210-235 lb./sq., 4/12 pitch	1.570	S.F.	.023	1.42	1.16	2.58
8/12 pitch	1.850	S.F.	.028	1.69	1.38	3.07
Laminated, multi-layered, 240-260 lb./sq., 4/12 pitch	1.570	S.F.	.028	1.86	1.42	3.28
8/12 pitch	1.850	S.F.	.034	2.20	1.68	3.88
Prem. laminated, multi-layered, 260-300 lb./sq., 4/12 pitch	1.570	S.F.	.037	2.90	1.82	4.72
8/12 pitch	1.850	S.F.	.043	3.44	2.17	5.61
Clay tile, Spanish tile, red, 4/12 pitch	1.570	S.F.	.071	9.85	3.49	13.34
8/12 pitch	1.850	S.F.	.084	11.70	4.14	15.84
Mission tile, red, 4/12 pitch	1.570	S.F.	.111	7.10	3.49	10.59
8/12 pitch	1.850	S.F.	.132	8.45	4.14	12.59
French tile, red, 4/12 pitch	1.570	S.F.	.095	20	3.20	23.20
8/12 pitch	1.850	S.F.	.113	24	3.80	27.80
Slate, Buckingham, Virginia, black, 4/12 pitch	1.570	S.F.	.073	8.40	3.66	12.06
8/12 pitch	1.850	S.F.	.087	10	4.35	14.35
Vermont, black or grey, 4/12 pitch	1.570	S.F.	.073	8.10	3.66	11.76
8/12 pitch	1.850	S.F.	.087	9.60	4.35	13.95
Wood, red cedar, No.1 5X, 16" long, 5" exposure, 4/12 pitch	1.570	S.F.	.051	4.66	2.77	7.43
8/12 pitch	1.850	S.F.	.061	5.55	3.29	8.84
Fire retardant, 4/12 pitch	1.570	S.F.	.051	5.65	2.77	8.42
8/12 pitch	1.850	S.F.	.061	6.70	3.29	9.99
18" long, No.1 perfections, 5" exposure, 4/12 pitch	1.570	S.F.	.047	4	2.51	6.51
8/12 pitch	1.850	S.F.	.055	4.75	2.98	7.73
Fire retardant, 4/12 pitch	1.570	S.F.	.047	4.97	2.51	7.48
8/12 pitch	1.850	S.F.	.055	5.90	2.98	8.88
Resquared & rebutted, 18" long, 6" exposure, 4/12 pitch	1.570	S.F.	.043	4.96	2.30	7.26
8/12 pitch	1.850	S.F.	.051	5.90	2.74	8.64
Fire retardant, 4/12 pitch	1.570	S.F.	.043	5.95	2.30	8.25
8/12 pitch	1.850	S.F.	.051	7.05	2.74	9.79
Wood shakes hand split, 24" long, 10" exposure, 4/12 pitch	1.570	S.F.	.051	4.45	2.77	7.22
8/12 pitch	1.850	S.F.	.061	5.30	3.29	8.59
Fire retardant, 4/12 pitch	1.570	S.F.	.051	5.40	2.77	8.17
8/12 pitch	1.850	S.F.	.061	6.45	3.29	9.74
18" long, 8" exposure, 4/12 pitch	1.570	S.F.	.064	3.15	3.46	6.61
8/12 pitch	1.850	S.F.	.076	3.74	4.10	7.84
Fire retardant, 4/12 pitch	1.570	S.F.	.064	4.12	3.46	7.58
8/12 pitch	1.850	S.F.	.076	4.89	4.10	8.99
Drip edge, metal, 5" wide	.122	L.F.	.002	.07	.13	.20
8" wide	.122	L.F.	.002	.09	.13	.22
Building paper, #15 asphalt felt	1.800	S.F.	.002	.11	.12	.23
Ridge shingles, asphalt	.075	L.F.	.002	.17	.09	.26
Clay	.075	L.F.	.003	.45	.45	.90
Slate	.075	L.F.	.003	.77	.15	.92
Wood, shingles	.075	L.F.	.002	.33	.12	.45
Shakes	.075	L.F.	.002	.33	.12	.45
Soffit & fascia, aluminum, vented, 1' overhang	.120	L.F.	.017	.55	.94	1.49
2' overhang	.120	L.F.	.019	.82	1.04	1.86
Vinyl, vented, 1' overhang	.120	L.F.	.016	.53	.86	1.39
2' overhang	.120	L.F.	.017	.70	1.04	1.74
Wood, board fascia, plywood soffit, 1' overhang	.120	L.F.	.004	.02	.17	.19
2' overhang	.120	L.F.	.006	.03	.26	.29
Gutter, 5" box, aluminum, seamless, painted	.120	L.F.	.008	.34	.46	.80
Vinyl	.120	L.F.	.009	.21	.45	.66
Downspout, 2" x 3", aluminum, one story house	.035	L.F.	.002	.08	.09	.17
Two story house	.060	L.F.	.003	.09	.15	.24
Vinyl, one story house	.035	L.F.	.001	.05	.09	.14
Two story house	.060	L.F.	.003	.09	.15	.24

System Description	QUAN.	UNIT	LABOR HOURS	COST PER S.F.		
				MAT.	INST.	TOTAL
ASPHALT, ROOF SHINGLES, CLASS A						
Shingles, asphalt, inorganic, class A, 210-235 lb./sq.	1.450	S.F.	.022	1.34	1.09	2.43
Drip edge, metal, 5" wide	.146	L.F.	.003	.08	.16	.24
Building paper, #15 asphalt felt	1.500	S.F.	.002	.09	.10	.19
Ridge shingles, asphalt	.042	L.F.	.001	.09	.05	.14
Soffit & fascia, painted aluminum, 1' overhang	.083	L.F.	.012	.38	.65	1.03
Rake trim, 1" x 6"	.063	L.F.	.003	.08	.14	.22
Rake trim, prime and paint	.063	L.F.	.003	.02	.13	.15
Gutter, seamless, alumunum, painted	.083	L.F.	.005	.24	.32	.56
Downspouts, aluminum, painted	.042	L.F.	.002	.09	.11	.20
TOTAL		S.F.	.053	2.41	2.75	5.16
WOOD, CEDAR SHINGLES, NO. 1 PERFECTIONS, 18" LONG						
Shingles, wood, red cedar, No. 1 perfections, 5" exposure	1.450	S.F.	.044	3.75	2.36	6.11
Drip edge, metal, 5" wide	.146	L.F.	.003	.08	.16	.24
Building paper, #15 asphalt felt	1.500	S.F.	.002	.09	.10	.19
Ridge shingles, wood	.042	L.F.	.001	.19	.06	.25
Soffit & fascia, white painted aluminum, 1' overhang	.083	L.F.	.012	.38	.65	1.03
Rake trim, 1" x 6"	.063	L.F.	.003	.08	.14	.22
Rake trim, prime and paint	.063	L.F.	.001	.02	.06	.08
Gutter, seamless, aluminum, painted	.083	L.F.	.005	.24	.32	.56
Downspouts, aluminum, painted	.042	L.F.	.002	.09	.11	.20
TOTAL		S.F.	.073	4.92	3.96	8.88

The prices in this system are based on a square foot of plan area.
All quantities have been adjusted accordingly.

Description	QUAN.	UNIT	LABOR HOURS	COST PER S.F.		
				MAT.	INST.	TOTAL

Gambrel Roofing Price Sheet	QUAN.	UNIT	LABOR HOURS	COST PER S.F.		
				MAT.	INST.	TOTAL
Shingles, asphalt, standard, inorganic, class A, 210-235 lb./sq.	1.450	S.F.	.022	1.34	1.09	2.43
Laminated, multi-layered, 240-260 lb./sq.	1.450	S.F.	.027	1.74	1.33	3.07
Premium laminated, multi-layered, 260-300 lb./sq.	1.450	S.F.	.034	2.72	1.71	4.43
Slate, Buckingham, Virginia, black	1.450	S.F.	.069	7.90	3.44	11.34
Vermont, black or grey	1.450	S.F.	.069	7.60	3.44	11.04
Wood, red cedar, No.1 5X, 16" long, 5" exposure, plain	1.450	S.F.	.048	4.37	2.60	6.97
Fire retardant	1.450	S.F.	.048	5.30	2.60	7.90
18" long, No.1 perfections, 6" exposure, plain	1.450	S.F.	.044	3.75	2.36	6.11
Fire retardant	1.450	S.F.	.044	4.66	2.36	7.02
Resquared & rebutted, 18" long, 6" exposure, plain	1.450	S.F.	.040	4.65	2.16	6.81
Fire retardant	1.450	S.F.	.040	5.55	2.16	7.71
Shakes, hand split, 24" long, 10" exposure, plain	1.450	S.F.	.048	4.17	2.60	6.77
Fire retardant	1.450	S.F.	.048	5.10	2.60	7.70
18" long, 8" exposure, plain	1.450	S.F.	.060	2.96	3.24	6.20
Fire retardant	1.450	S.F.	.060	3.87	3.24	7.11
Drip edge, metal, 5" wide	.146	L.F.	.003	.08	.16	.24
8" wide	.146	L.F.	.003	.11	.16	.27
Building paper, #15 asphalt felt	1.500	S.F.	.002	.09	.10	.19
Ridge shingles, asphalt	.042	L.F.	.001	.09	.05	.14
Slate	.042	L.F.	.002	.43	.08	.51
Wood, shingles	.042	L.F.	.001	.19	.06	.25
Shakes	.042	L.F.	.001	.19	.06	.25
Soffit & fascia, aluminum, vented, 1' overhang	.083	L.F.	.012	.38	.65	1.03
2' overhang	.083	L.F.	.013	.56	.72	1.28
Vinyl vented, 1' overhang	.083	L.F.	.011	.37	.60	.97
2' overhang	.083	L.F.	.012	.48	.72	1.20
Wood board fascia, plywood soffit, 1' overhang	.083	L.F.	.004	.02	.17	.19
2' overhang	.083	L.F.	.006	.03	.26	.29
Rake trim, painted, 1" x 6"	.063	L.F.	.006	.10	.27	.37
1" x 8"	.063	L.F.	.007	.12	.35	.47
Gutter, 5" box, aluminum, seamless, painted	.083	L.F.	.006	.24	.32	.56
Vinyl	.083	L.F.	.006	.14	.31	.45
Downspout 2" x 3", aluminum, one story house	.042	L.F.	.002	.06	.11	.17
Two story house	.070	L.F.	.003	.10	.18	.28
Vinyl, one story house	.042	L.F.	.002	.06	.11	.17
Two story house	.070	L.F.	.003	.10	.18	.28

System Description	QUAN.	UNIT	LABOR HOURS	COST PER S.F.		
				MAT.	INST.	TOTAL
ASPHALT, ROOF SHINGLES, CLASS A						
Shingles, standard inorganic class A 210-235 lb./sq.	2.210	S.F.	.032	1.96	1.60	3.56
Drip edge, metal, 5" wide	.122	L.F.	.002	.07	.13	.20
Building paper, #15 asphalt felt	2.300	S.F.	.003	.14	.16	.30
Ridge shingles, asphalt	.090	L.F.	.002	.20	.11	.31
Soffit & fascia, white painted aluminum, 1' overhang	.122	L.F.	.018	.56	.96	1.52
Gutter, seamless, aluminum, painted	.122	L.F.	.008	.35	.47	.82
Downspouts, aluminum, painted	.042	L.F.	.002	.09	.11	.20
TOTAL		S.F.	.067	3.37	3.54	6.91
WOOD, CEDAR SHINGLES, NO. 1 PERFECTIONS, 18" LONG						
Shingles, wood, red cedar, No. 1 perfections, 5" exposure	2.210	S.F.	.064	5.50	3.45	8.95
Drip edge, metal, 5" wide	.122	L.F.	.002	.07	.13	.20
Building paper, #15 asphalt felt	2.300	S.F.	.003	.14	.16	.30
Ridge shingles, wood	.090	L.F.	.003	.40	.14	.54
Soffit & fascia, white painted aluminum, 1' overhang	.122	L.F.	.018	.56	.96	1.52
Gutter, seamless, aluminum, painted	.122	L.F.	.008	.35	.47	.82
Downspouts, aluminum, painted	.042	L.F.	.002	.09	.11	.20
TOTAL		S.F.	.100	7.11	5.42	12.53

The prices in these systems are based on a square foot of plan area.
All quantities have been adjusted accordingly.

Description	QUAN.	UNIT	LABOR HOURS	COST PER S.F.		
				MAT.	INST.	TOTAL

Mansard Roofing Price Sheet	QUAN.	UNIT	LABOR HOURS	COST PER S.F. MAT.	INST.	TOTAL
Shingles, asphalt, standard, inorganic, class A, 210-235 lb./sq.	2.210	S.F.	.032	1.96	1.60	3.56
Laminated, multi-layered, 240-260 lb./sq.	2.210	S.F.	.039	2.55	1.95	4.50
Premium laminated, multi-layered, 260-300 lb./sq.	2.210	S.F.	.050	3.98	2.51	6.49
Slate Buckingham, Virginia, black	2.210	S.F.	.101	11.55	5.05	16.60
Vermont, black or grey	2.210	S.F.	.101	11.10	5.05	16.15
Wood, red cedar, No.1 5X, 16" long, 5" exposure, plain	2.210	S.F.	.070	6.40	3.81	10.21
Fire retardant	2.210	S.F.	.070	7.75	3.81	11.56
18" long, No.1 perfections 6" exposure, plain	2.210	S.F.	.064	5.50	3.45	8.95
Fire retardant	2.210	S.F.	.064	6.85	3.45	10.30
Fire retardant	2.210	S.F.	.059	8.15	3.17	11.32
Shakes, hand split, 24" long 10" exposure, plain	2.210	S.F.	.070	6.10	3.81	9.91
Fire retardant	2.210	S.F.	.070	7.45	3.81	11.26
18" long, 8" exposure, plain	2.210	S.F.	.088	4.33	4.75	9.08
Fire retardant	2.210	S.F.	.088	5.65	4.75	10.40
Drip edge, metal, 5" wide	.122	S.F.	.002	.07	.13	.20
8" wide	.122	S.F.	.002	.09	.13	.22
Building paper, #15 asphalt felt	2.300	S.F.	.003	.14	.16	.30
Ridge shingles, asphalt	.090	L.F.	.002	.20	.11	.31
Slate	.090	L.F.	.004	.92	.18	1.10
Wood, shingles	.090	L.F.	.003	.40	.14	.54
Shakes	.090	L.F.	.003	.40	.14	.54
Soffit & fascia, aluminum vented, 1' overhang	.122	L.F.	.018	.56	.96	1.52
2' overhang	.122	L.F.	.020	.83	1.06	1.89
Vinyl vented, 1' overhang	.122	L.F.	.016	.54	.88	1.42
2' overhang	.122	L.F.	.018	.71	1.06	1.77
Wood board fascia, plywood soffit, 1' overhang	.122	L.F.	.013	.32	.66	.98
2' overhang	.122	L.F.	.019	.42	1.02	1.44
Gutter, 5" box, aluminum, seamless, painted	.122	L.F.	.008	.35	.47	.82
Vinyl	.122	L.F.	.009	.21	.46	.67
Downspout 2" x 3", aluminum, one story house	.042	L.F.	.002	.06	.11	.17
Two story house	.070	L.F.	.003	.10	.18	.28
Vinyl, one story house	.042	L.F.	.002	.06	.11	.17
Two story house	.070	L.F.	.003	.10	.18	.28

System Description	QUAN.	UNIT	LABOR HOURS	COST PER S.F.		
				MAT.	INST.	TOTAL
ASPHALT, ROOF SHINGLES, CLASS A						
Shingles, inorganic class A 210-235 lb./sq. 4/12 pitch	1.230	S.F.	.019	1.16	.94	2.10
Drip edge, metal, 5" wide	.100	L.F.	.002	.06	.11	.17
Building paper, #15 asphalt felt	1.300	S.F.	.002	.08	.09	.17
Soffit & fascia, white painted aluminum, 1' overhang	.080	L.F.	.012	.37	.63	1
Rake trim, 1" x 6"	.043	L.F.	.002	.05	.09	.14
Rake trim, prime and paint	.043	L.F.	.002	.01	.09	.10
Gutter, seamless, aluminum, painted	.040	L.F.	.003	.11	.15	.26
Downspouts, painted aluminum	.020	L.F.	.001	.05	.05	.10
TOTAL		S.F.	.043	1.89	2.15	4.04
WOOD, CEDAR SHINGLES, NO. 1 PERFECTIONS, 18" LONG						
Shingles, red cedar, No. 1 perfections, 5" exp., 4/12 pitch	1.230	S.F.	.035	3	1.88	4.88
Drip edge, metal, 5" wide	.100	L.F.	.002	.06	.11	.17
Building paper, #15 asphalt felt	1.300	S.F.	.002	.08	.09	.17
Soffit & fascia, white painted aluminum, 1' overhang	.080	L.F.	.012	.37	.63	1
Rake trim, 1" x 6"	.043	L.F.	.002	.05	.09	.14
Rake trim, prime and paint	.043	L.F.	.001	.01	.04	.05
Gutter, seamless, aluminum, painted	.040	L.F.	.003	.11	.15	.26
Downspouts, painted aluminum	.020	L.F.	.001	.05	.05	.10
TOTAL		S.F.	.058	3.73	3.04	6.77

The prices in these systems are based on a square foot of plan area.
All quantities have been adjusted accordingly.

Description	QUAN.	UNIT	LABOR HOURS	COST PER S.F.		
				MAT.	INST.	TOTAL

Shed Roofing Price Sheet	QUAN.	UNIT	LABOR HOURS	COST PER S.F.		
				MAT.	INST.	TOTAL
Shingles, asphalt, inorganic, class A, 210-235 lb./sq., 4/12 pitch	1.230	S.F.	.017	1.07	.87	1.94
8/12 pitch	1.330	S.F.	.019	1.16	.94	2.10
Laminated, multi-layered, 240-260 lb./sq. 4/12 pitch	1.230	S.F.	.021	1.39	1.06	2.45
8/12 pitch	1.330	S.F.	.023	1.51	1.15	2.66
Premium laminated, multi-layered, 260-300 lb./sq. 4/12 pitch	1.230	S.F.	.027	2.17	1.37	3.54
8/12 pitch	1.330	S.F.	.030	2.35	1.48	3.83
Clay tile, Spanish tile, red, 4/12 pitch	1.230	S.F.	.053	7.40	2.62	10.02
8/12 pitch	1.330	S.F.	.058	8	2.83	10.83
Mission tile, red, 4/12 pitch	1.230	S.F.	.083	5.35	2.62	7.97
8/12 pitch	1.330	S.F.	.090	5.80	2.83	8.63
French tile, red, 4/12 pitch	1.230	S.F.	.071	15	2.40	17.40
8/12 pitch	1.330	S.F.	.077	16.25	2.60	18.85
Slate, Buckingham, Virginia, black, 4/12 pitch	1.230	S.F.	.055	6.30	2.75	9.05
8/12 pitch	1.330	S.F.	.059	6.85	2.98	9.83
Vermont, black or grey, 4/12 pitch	1.230	S.F.	.055	6.05	2.75	8.80
8/12 pitch	1.330	S.F.	.059	6.55	2.98	9.53
Wood, red cedar, No.1 5X, 16" long, 5" exposure, 4/12 pitch	1.230	S.F.	.038	3.49	2.08	5.57
8/12 pitch	1.330	S.F.	.042	3.78	2.25	6.03
Fire retardant, 4/12 pitch	1.230	S.F.	.038	4.22	2.08	6.30
8/12 pitch	1.330	S.F.	.042	4.57	2.25	6.82
18" long, 6" exposure, 4/12 pitch	1.230	S.F.	.035	3	1.88	4.88
8/12 pitch	1.330	S.F.	.038	3.25	2.04	5.29
Fire retardant, 4/12 pitch	1.230	S.F.	.035	3.73	1.88	5.61
8/12 pitch	1.330	S.F.	.038	4.04	2.04	6.08
Resquared & rebutted, 18" long, 6" exposure, 4/12 pitch	1.230	S.F.	.032	3.72	1.73	5.45
8/12 pitch	1.330	S.F.	.035	4.03	1.87	5.90
Fire retardant, 4/12 pitch	1.230	S.F.	.032	4.45	1.73	6.18
8/12 pitch	1.330	S.F.	.035	4.82	1.87	6.69
Wood shakes, hand split, 24" long, 10" exposure, 4/12 pitch	1.230	S.F.	.038	3.34	2.08	5.42
8/12 pitch	1.330	S.F.	.042	3.61	2.25	5.86
Fire retardant, 4/12 pitch	1.230	S.F.	.038	4.07	2.08	6.15
8/12 pitch	1.330	S.F.	.042	4.40	2.25	6.65
18" long, 8" exposure, 4/12 pitch	1.230	S.F.	.048	2.36	2.59	4.95
8/12 pitch	1.330	S.F.	.052	2.56	2.81	5.37
Fire retardant, 4/12 pitch	1.230	S.F.	.048	3.09	2.59	5.68
8/12 pitch	1.330	S.F.	.052	3.35	2.81	6.16
Drip edge, metal, 5" wide	.100	L.F.	.002	.06	.11	.17
8" wide	.100	L.F.	.002	.08	.11	.19
Building paper, #15 asphalt felt	1.300	S.F.	.002	.08	.09	.17
Soffit & fascia, aluminum vented, 1' overhang	.080	L.F.	.012	.37	.63	1
2' overhang	.080	L.F.	.013	.54	.69	1.23
Vinyl vented, 1' overhang	.080	L.F.	.011	.35	.58	.93
2' overhang	.080	L.F.	.012	.46	.69	1.15
Wood board fascia, plywood soffit, 1' overhang	.080	L.F.	.010	.21	.48	.69
2' overhang	.080	L.F.	.014	.28	.75	1.03
Rake, trim, painted, 1" x 6"	.043	L.F.	.004	.06	.18	.24
1" x 8"	.043	L.F.	.004	.06	.18	.24
Gutter, 5" box, aluminum, seamless, painted	.040	L.F.	.003	.11	.15	.26
Vinyl	.040	L.F.	.003	.07	.15	.22
Downspout 2" x 3", aluminum, one story house	.020	L.F.	.001	.03	.05	.08
Two story house	.020	L.F.	.001	.05	.08	.13
Vinyl, one story house	.020	L.F.	.001	.03	.05	.08
Two story house	.020	L.F.	.001	.05	.08	.13

System Description	QUAN.	UNIT	LABOR HOURS	COST PER S.F.		
				MAT.	INST.	TOTAL
ASPHALT, ROOF SHINGLES, CLASS A						
Shingles, standard inorganic class A 210-235 lb./sq	1.400	S.F.	.020	1.25	1.02	2.27
Drip edge, metal, 5" wide	.220	L.F.	.004	.13	.24	.37
Building paper, #15 asphalt felt	1.500	S.F.	.002	.09	.10	.19
Ridge shingles, asphalt	.280	L.F.	.007	.62	.34	.96
Soffit & fascia, aluminum, vented	.220	L.F.	.032	1.01	1.73	2.74
Flashing, aluminum, mill finish, .013" thick	1.500	S.F.	.083	1.31	4.11	5.42
TOTAL		S.F.	.148	4.41	7.54	11.95
WOOD, CEDAR, NO. 1 PERFECTIONS						
Shingles, red cedar, No.1 perfections, 18" long, 5" exp.	1.400	S.F.	.041	3.50	2.20	5.70
Drip edge, metal, 5" wide	.220	L.F.	.004	.13	.24	.37
Building paper, #15 asphalt felt	1.500	S.F.	.002	.09	.10	.19
Ridge shingles, wood	.280	L.F.	.008	1.25	.43	1.68
Soffit & fascia, aluminum, vented	.220	L.F.	.032	1.01	1.73	2.74
Flashing, aluminum, mill finish, .013" thick	1.500	S.F.	.083	1.31	4.11	5.42
TOTAL		S.F.	.170	7.29	8.81	16.10
SLATE, BUCKINGHAM, BLACK						
Shingles, Buckingham, Virginia, black	1.400	S.F.	.064	7.35	3.21	10.56
Drip edge, metal, 5" wide	.220	L.F.	.004	.13	.24	.37
Building paper, #15 asphalt felt	1.500	S.F.	.002	.09	.10	.19
Ridge shingles, slate	.280	L.F.	.011	2.86	.56	3.42
Soffit & fascia, aluminum, vented	.220	L.F.	.032	1.01	1.73	2.74
Flashing, copper, 16 oz.	1.500	S.F.	.104	11.48	5.19	16.67
TOTAL		S.F.	.217	22.92	11.03	33.95

The prices in these systems are based on a square foot of plan area under the dormer roof.

Description	QUAN.	UNIT	LABOR HOURS	COST PER S.F.		
				MAT.	INST.	TOTAL

Gable Dormer Roofing Price Sheet	QUAN.	UNIT	LABOR HOURS	COST PER S.F.		
				MAT.	INST.	TOTAL
Shingles, asphalt, standard, inorganic, class A, 210-235 lb./sq.	1.400	S.F.	.020	1.25	1.02	2.27
Laminated, multi-layered, 240-260 lb./sq.	1.400	S.F.	.025	1.62	1.24	2.86
Premium laminated, multi-layered, 260-300 lb./sq.	1.400	S.F.	.032	2.53	1.60	4.13
Clay tile, Spanish tile, red	1.400	S.F.	.062	8.60	3.05	11.65
Mission tile, red	1.400	S.F.	.097	6.25	3.05	9.30
French tile, red	1.400	S.F.	.083	17.50	2.80	20.30
Slate Buckingham, Virginia, black	1.400	S.F.	.064	7.35	3.21	10.56
Vermont, black or grey	1.400	S.F.	.064	7.05	3.21	10.26
Wood, red cedar, No.1 5X, 16" long, 5" exposure	1.400	S.F.	.045	4.07	2.42	6.49
Fire retardant	1.400	S.F.	.045	4.92	2.42	7.34
18" long, No.1 perfections, 5" exposure	1.400	S.F.	.041	3.50	2.20	5.70
Fire retardant	1.400	S.F.	.041	4.35	2.20	6.55
Resquared & rebutted, 18" long, 5" exposure	1.400	S.F.	.037	4.34	2.02	6.36
Fire retardant	1.400	S.F.	.037	5.20	2.02	7.22
Shakes hand split, 24" long, 10" exposure	1.400	S.F.	.045	3.89	2.42	6.31
Fire retardant	1.400	S.F.	.045	4.74	2.42	7.16
18" long, 8" exposure	1.400	S.F.	.056	2.76	3.02	5.78
Fire retardant	1.400	S.F.	.056	3.61	3.02	6.63
Drip edge, metal, 5" wide	.220	L.F.	.004	.13	.24	.37
8" wide	.220	L.F.	.004	.17	.24	.41
Building paper, #15 asphalt felt	1.500	S.F.	.002	.09	.10	.19
Ridge shingles, asphalt	.280	L.F.	.007	.62	.34	.96
Clay	.280	L.F.	.011	1.69	1.68	3.37
Slate	.280	L.F.	.011	2.86	.56	3.42
Wood	.280	L.F.	.008	1.25	.43	1.68
Soffit & fascia, aluminum, vented	.220	L.F.	.032	1.01	1.73	2.74
Vinyl, vented	.220	L.F.	.029	.97	1.58	2.55
Wood, board fascia, plywood soffit	.220	L.F.	.026	.60	1.34	1.94
Flashing, aluminum, .013" thick	1.500	S.F.	.083	1.31	4.11	5.42
.032" thick	1.500	S.F.	.083	2.24	4.11	6.35
.040" thick	1.500	S.F.	.083	3.81	4.11	7.92
.050" thick	1.500	S.F.	.083	4.01	4.11	8.12
Copper, 16 oz.	1.500	S.F.	.104	11.50	5.20	16.70
20 oz.	1.500	S.F.	.109	16.30	5.45	21.75
24 oz.	1.500	S.F.	.114	20	5.70	25.70
32 oz.	1.500	S.F.	.120	26.50	5.95	32.45

Labels: Building Paper, Shingles, Drip Edge, Soffit & Fascia, Rake Boards, Flashing

System Description	QUAN.	UNIT	LABOR HOURS	COST PER S.F.		
				MAT.	INST.	TOTAL
ASPHALT, ROOF SHINGLES, CLASS A						
Shingles, standard inorganic class A 210-235 lb./sq.	1.100	S.F.	.016	.98	.80	1.78
Drip edge, aluminum, 5" wide	.250	L.F.	.005	.11	.27	.38
Building paper, #15 asphalt felt	1.200	S.F.	.002	.07	.08	.15
Soffit & fascia, aluminum, vented, 1' overhang	.250	L.F.	.036	1.15	1.96	3.11
Flashing, aluminum, mill finish, 0.013" thick	.800	L.F.	.044	.70	2.19	2.89
TOTAL		S.F.	.103	3.01	5.30	8.31
WOOD, CEDAR, NO. 1 PERFECTIONS, 18" LONG						
Shingles, wood, red cedar, #1 perfections, 5" exposure	1.100	S.F.	.032	2.75	1.73	4.48
Drip edge, aluminum, 5" wide	.250	L.F.	.005	.11	.27	.38
Building paper, #15 asphalt felt	1.200	S.F.	.002	.07	.08	.15
Soffit & fascia, aluminum, vented, 1' overhang	.250	L.F.	.036	1.15	1.96	3.11
Flashing, aluminum, mill finish, 0.013" thick	.800	L.F.	.044	.70	2.19	2.89
TOTAL		S.F.	.119	4.78	6.23	11.01
SLATE, BUCKINGHAM, BLACK						
Shingles, slate, Buckingham, black	1.100	S.F.	.050	5.78	2.52	8.30
Drip edge, aluminum, 5" wide	.250	L.F.	.005	.11	.27	.38
Building paper, #15 asphalt felt	1.200	S.F.	.002	.07	.08	.15
Soffit & fascia, aluminum, vented, 1' overhang	.250	L.F.	.036	1.15	1.96	3.11
Flashing, copper, 16 oz.	.800	L.F.	.056	6.12	2.77	8.89
TOTAL		S.F.	.149	13.23	7.60	20.83

The prices in this system are based on a square foot of plan area under the dormer roof.

Description	QUAN.	UNIT	LABOR HOURS	COST PER S.F.		
				MAT.	INST.	TOTAL

Shed Dormer Roofing Price Sheet	QUAN.	UNIT	LABOR HOURS	COST PER S.F.		
				MAT.	INST.	TOTAL
Shingles, asphalt, standard, inorganic, class A, 210-235 lb./sq.	1.100	S.F.	.016	.98	.80	1.78
Laminated, multi-layered, 240-260 lb./sq.	1.100	S.F.	.020	1.28	.97	2.25
Premium laminated, multi-layered, 260-300 lb./sq.	1.100	S.F.	.025	1.99	1.25	3.24
Clay tile, Spanish tile, red	1.100	S.F.	.049	6.75	2.40	9.15
Mission tile, red	1.100	S.F.	.077	4.90	2.40	7.30
French tile, red	1.100	S.F.	.065	13.75	2.20	15.95
Slate Buckingham, Virginia, black	1.100	S.F.	.050	5.80	2.52	8.32
Vermont, black or grey	1.100	S.F.	.050	5.55	2.52	8.07
Wood, red cedar, No. 1 5X, 16" long, 5" exposure	1.100	S.F.	.035	3.20	1.90	5.10
Fire retardant	1.100	S.F.	.035	3.87	1.90	5.77
18" long, No.1 perfections, 5" exposure	1.100	S.F.	.032	2.75	1.73	4.48
Fire retardant	1.100	S.F.	.032	3.42	1.73	5.15
Resquared & rebutted, 18" long, 5" exposure	1.100	S.F.	.029	3.41	1.58	4.99
Fire retardant	1.100	S.F.	.029	4.08	1.58	5.66
Shakes hand split, 24" long, 10" exposure	1.100	S.F.	.035	3.06	1.90	4.96
Fire retardant	1.100	S.F.	.035	3.73	1.90	5.63
18" long, 8" exposure	1.100	S.F.	.044	2.17	2.38	4.55
Fire retardant	1.100	S.F.	.044	2.84	2.38	5.22
Drip edge, metal, 5" wide	.250	L.F.	.005	.11	.27	.38
8" wide	.250	L.F.	.005	.19	.27	.46
Building paper, #15 asphalt felt	1.200	S.F.	.002	.07	.08	.15
Soffit & fascia, aluminum, vented	.250	L.F.	.036	1.15	1.96	3.11
Vinyl, vented	.250	L.F.	.033	1.10	1.80	2.90
Wood, board fascia, plywood soffit	.250	L.F.	.030	.69	1.53	2.22
Flashing, aluminum, .013" thick	.800	L.F.	.044	.70	2.19	2.89
.032" thick	.800	L.F.	.044	1.19	2.19	3.38
.040" thick	.800	L.F.	.044	2.03	2.19	4.22
.050" thick	.800	L.F.	.044	2.14	2.19	4.33
Copper, 16 oz.	.800	L.F.	.056	6.10	2.77	8.87
20 oz.	.800	L.F.	.058	8.70	2.90	11.60
24 oz.	.800	L.F.	.061	10.70	3.03	13.73
32 oz.	.800	L.F.	.064	14.25	3.18	17.43

System Description	QUAN.	UNIT	LABOR HOURS	COST EACH		
				MAT.	INST.	TOTAL
SKYLIGHT, FIXED, 32″ X 32″						
Skylight, fixed bubble, insulating, 32″ x 32″	1.000	Ea.	1.422	213.33	71.47	284.80
Trimmer rafters, 2″ x 6″	28.000	L.F.	.448	17.64	24.08	41.72
Headers, 2″ x 6″	6.000	L.F.	.267	3.78	14.40	18.18
Curb, 2″ x 4″	12.000	L.F.	.154	5.04	8.28	13.32
Flashing, aluminum, .013″ thick	13.500	S.F.	.745	11.75	36.99	48.74
Moldings, casing, ogee, 11/16″ x 2-1/2″, pine	12.000	L.F.	.384	20.04	20.76	40.80
Trim primer coat, oil base, brushwork	12.000	L.F.	.148	.48	6.84	7.32
Trim paint, 1 coat, brushwork	12.000	L.F.	.148	.72	6.84	7.56
TOTAL		Ea.	3.716	272.78	189.66	462.44
SKYLIGHT, FIXED, 48″ X 48″						
Skylight, fixed bubble, insulating, 48″ x 48″	1.000	Ea.	1.296	480	64.96	544.96
Trimmer rafters, 2″ x 6″	28.000	L.F.	.448	17.64	24.08	41.72
Headers, 2″ x 6″	8.000	L.F.	.356	5.04	19.20	24.24
Curb, 2″ x 4″	16.000	L.F.	.205	6.72	11.04	17.76
Flashing, aluminum, .013″ thick	16.000	S.F.	.883	13.92	43.84	57.76
Moldings, casing, ogee, 11/16″ x 2-1/2″, pine	16.000	L.F.	.512	26.72	27.68	54.40
Trim primer coat, oil base, brushwork	16.000	L.F.	.197	.64	9.12	9.76
Trim paint, 1 coat, brushwork	16.000	L.F.	.197	.96	9.12	10.08
TOTAL		Ea.	4.094	551.64	209.04	760.68
SKYWINDOW, OPERATING, 24″ X 48″						
Skywindow, operating, thermopane glass, 24″ x 48″	1.000	Ea.	3.200	635	160	795
Trimmer rafters, 2″ x 6″	28.000	L.F.	.448	17.64	24.08	41.72
Headers, 2″ x 6″	8.000	L.F.	.267	3.78	14.40	18.18
Curb, 2″ x 4″	14.000	L.F.	.179	5.88	9.66	15.54
Flashing, aluminum, .013″ thick	14.000	S.F.	.772	12.18	38.36	50.54
Moldings, casing, ogee, 11/16″ x 2-1/2″, pine	14.000	L.F.	.448	23.38	24.22	47.60
Trim primer coat, oil base, brushwork	14.000	L.F.	.172	.56	7.98	8.54
Trim paint, 1 coat, brushwork	14.000	L.F.	.172	.84	7.98	8.82
TOTAL		Ea.	5.658	699.26	286.68	985.94

The prices in these systems are on a cost each basis.

Description	QUAN.	UNIT	LABOR HOURS	COST EACH		
				MAT.	INST.	TOTAL

Skylight/Skywindow Price Sheet	QUAN.	UNIT	LABOR HOURS	COST EACH		
				MAT.	INST.	TOTAL
Skylight, fixed bubble insulating, 24" x 24"	1.000	Ea.	.800	120	40	160
32" x 32"	1.000	Ea.	1.422	213	71.50	284.50
32" x 48"	1.000	Ea.	.864	320	43.50	363.50
48" x 48"	1.000	Ea.	1.296	480	65	545
Ventilating bubble insulating, 36" x 36"	1.000	Ea.	2.667	530	134	664
52" x 52"	1.000	Ea.	2.667	725	134	859
28" x 52"	1.000	Ea.	3.200	535	160	695
36" x 52"	1.000	Ea.	3.200	595	160	755
Skywindow, operating, thermopane glass, 24" x 48"	1.000	Ea.	3.200	635	160	795
32" x 48"	1.000	Ea.	3.556	660	178	838
Trimmer rafters, 2" x 6"	28.000	L.F.	.448	17.65	24	41.65
2" x 8"	28.000	L.F.	.472	26.50	25.50	52
2" x 10"	28.000	L.F.	.711	35	38.50	73.50
Headers, 24" window, 2" x 6"	4.000	L.F.	.178	2.52	9.60	12.12
2" x 8"	4.000	L.F.	.188	3.76	10.15	13.91
2" x 10"	4.000	L.F.	.200	5	10.80	15.80
32" window, 2" x 6"	6.000	L.F.	.267	3.78	14.40	18.18
2" x 8"	6.000	L.F.	.282	5.65	15.25	20.90
2" x 10"	6.000	L.F.	.300	7.50	16.20	23.70
48" window, 2" x 6"	8.000	L.F.	.356	5.05	19.20	24.25
2" x 8"	8.000	L.F.	.376	7.50	20.50	28
2" x 10"	8.000	L.F.	.400	10	21.50	31.50
Curb, 2" x 4", skylight, 24" x 24"	8.000	L.F.	.102	3.36	5.50	8.86
32" x 32"	12.000	L.F.	.154	5.05	8.30	13.35
32" x 48"	14.000	L.F.	.179	5.90	9.65	15.55
48" x 48"	16.000	L.F.	.205	6.70	11.05	17.75
Flashing, aluminum .013" thick, skylight, 24" x 24"	9.000	S.F.	.497	7.85	24.50	32.35
32" x 32"	13.500	S.F.	.745	11.75	37	48.75
32" x 48"	14.000	S.F.	.772	12.20	38.50	50.70
48" x 48"	16.000	S.F.	.883	13.90	44	57.90
Copper 16 oz., skylight, 24" x 24"	9.000	S.F.	.626	69	31	100
32" x 32"	13.500	S.F.	.939	103	46.50	149.50
32" x 48"	14.000	S.F.	.974	107	48.50	155.50
48" x 48"	16.000	S.F.	1.113	122	55.50	177.50
Trim, interior casing painted, 24" x 24"	8.000	L.F.	.347	14.55	17.50	32.05
32" x 32"	12.000	L.F.	.520	22	26.50	48.50
32" x 48"	14.000	L.F.	.607	25.50	30.50	56
48" x 48"	16.000	L.F.	.693	29	35	64

System Description	QUAN.	UNIT	LABOR HOURS	COST PER S.F.		
				MAT.	INST.	TOTAL
ASPHALT, ORGANIC, 4-PLY, INSULATED DECK						
Membrane, asphalt, 4-plies #15 felt, gravel surfacing	1.000	S.F.	.025	1.42	1.47	2.89
Insulation board, 2-layers of 1-1/16″ glass fiber	2.000	S.F.	.012	2.22	.62	2.84
Roof deck insulation, fastening alternatives, low-rise polyurethane	.010	S.F	.002		.18	.18
Wood blocking, 2″ x 6″	.040	L.F.	.004	.08	.23	.31
Treated 4″ x 4″ cant strip	.040	L.F.	.001	.08	.05	.13
Flashing, aluminum, 0.040″ thick	.050	S.F.	.003	.13	.14	.27
TOTAL		S.F.	.047	3.93	2.69	6.62
ASPHALT, INORGANIC, 3-PLY, INSULATED DECK						
Membrane, asphalt, 3-plies type IV glass felt, gravel surfacing	1.000	S.F.	.028	1.41	1.62	3.03
Insulation board, 2-layers of 1-1/16″ glass fiber	2.000	S.F.	.012	2.22	.62	2.84
Roof deck insulation, fastening alternatives, low-rise polyurethane	.010	S.F	.002		.18	.18
Wood blocking, 2″ x 6″	.040	L.F.	.004	.08	.23	.31
Treated 4″ x 4″ cant strip	.040	L.F.	.001	.08	.05	.13
Flashing, aluminum, 0.040″ thick	.050	S.F.	.003	.13	.14	.27
TOTAL		S.F.	.050	3.92	2.84	6.76
COAL TAR, ORGANIC, 4-PLY, INSULATED DECK						
Membrane, coal tar, 4-plies #15 felt, gravel surfacing	1.000	S.F.	.027	2.57	1.53	4.10
Insulation board, 2-layers of 1-1/16″ glass fiber	2.000	S.F.	.012	2.22	.62	2.84
Roof deck insulation, fastening alternatives, low-rise polyurethane	.010	S.F	.002		.18	.18
Wood blocking, 2″ x 6″	.040	L.F.	.004	.08	.23	.31
Treated 4″ x 4″ cant strip	.040	L.F.	.001	.08	.05	.13
Flashing, aluminum, 0.040″ thick	.050	S.F.	.003	.13	.14	.27
TOTAL		S.F.	.049	5.08	2.75	7.83
COAL TAR, INORGANIC, 3-PLY, INSULATED DECK						
Membrane, coal tar, 3-plies type IV glass felt, gravel surfacing	1.000	S.F.	.029	2.12	1.69	3.81
Insulation board, 2-layers of 1-1/16″ glass fiber	2.000	S.F.	.012	2.22	.62	2.84
Roof deck insulation, fastening alternatives, low-rise polyurethane	.010	S.F	.002		.18	.18
Wood blocking, 2″ x 6″	.040	L.F.	.004	.08	.23	.31
Treated 4″ x 4″ cant strip	.040	L.F.	.001	.08	.05	.13
Flashing, aluminum, 0.040″ thick	.050	S.F.	.003	.13	.14	.27
TOTAL		S.F.	.051	4.63	2.91	7.54

Built-Up Roofing Price Sheet	QUAN.	UNIT	LABOR HOURS	COST PER S.F.		
				MAT.	INST.	TOTAL
Membrane, asphalt, 4-plies #15 organic felt, gravel surfacing	1.000	S.F.	.025	1.42	1.47	2.89
Asphalt base sheet & 3-plies #15 asphalt felt	1.000	S.F.	.025	1.09	1.47	2.56
3-plies type IV glass fiber felt	1.000	S.F.	.028	1.41	1.62	3.03
4-plies type IV glass fiber felt	1.000	S.F.	.028	1.75	1.62	3.37
Coal tar, 4-plies #15 organic felt, gravel surfacing	1.000	S.F.	.027			
4-plies tarred felt	1.000	S.F.	.027	2.57	1.53	4.10
3-plies type IV glass fiber felt	1.000	S.F.	.029	2.12	1.69	3.81
4-plies type IV glass fiber felt	1.000	S.F.	.027	2.91	1.53	4.44
Roll, asphalt, 1-ply #15 organic felt, 2-plies mineral surfaced	1.000	S.F.	.021	.82	1.20	2.02
3-plies type IV glass fiber, 1-ply mineral surfaced	1.000	S.F.	.022	1.38	1.29	2.67
Insulation boards, glass fiber, 1-1/16" thick	1.000	S.F.	.008	1.11	.49	1.60
2-1/16" thick	1.000	S.F.	.010	1.60	.56	2.16
2-7/16" thick	1.000	S.F.	.010	1.85	.56	2.41
Expanded perlite, 1" thick	1.000	S.F.	.010	.54	.56	1.10
1-1/2" thick	1.000	S.F.	.010	.79	.56	1.35
2" thick	1.000	S.F.	.011	1.09	.62	1.71
Fiberboard, 1" thick	1.000	S.F.	.010	.57	.56	1.13
1-1/2" thick	1.000	S.F.	.010	.88	.56	1.44
2" thick	1.000	S.F.	.010	1.17	.56	1.73
Extruded polystyrene, 15 PSI compressive strength, 2" thick R10	1.000	S.F.	.006	.76	.42	1.18
3" thick R15	1.000	S.F.	.008	1.52	.49	2.01
4" thick R20	1.000	S.F.	.008	2.04	.49	2.53
Tapered for drainage	1.000	S.F.	.005	.62	.38	1
40 PSI compressive strength, 1" thick R5	1.000	S.F.	.005	.56	.38	.94
2" thick R10	1.000	S.F.	.006	1.07	.42	1.49
3" thick R15	1.000	S.F.	.008	1.54	.49	2.03
4" thick R20	1.000	S.F.	.008	2.02	.49	2.51
Fiberboard high density, 1/2" thick R1.3	1.000	S.F.	.008	.32	.49	.81
1" thick R2.5	1.000	S.F.	.010	.66	.56	1.22
1 1/2" thick R3.8	1.000	S.F.	.010	.98	.56	1.54
Polyisocyanurate, 1 1/2" thick	1.000	S.F.	.006	.69	.42	1.11
2" thick	1.000	S.F.	.007	.87	.46	1.33
3 1/2" thick	1.000	S.F.	.008	2.15	.49	2.64
Tapered for drainage	1.000	S.F.	.006	.63	.40	1.03
Expanded polystyrene, 1" thick	1.000	S.F.	.005	.26	.38	.64
2" thick R10	1.000	S.F.	.006	.53	.42	.95
3" thick	1.000	S.F.	.006	.79	.42	1.21
Wood blocking, treated, 6" x 2" & 4" x 4" cant	.040	L.F.	.002	.13	.13	.26
6" x 4-1/2" & 4" x 4" cant	.040	L.F.	.005	.20	.28	.48
6" x 5" & 4" x 4" cant	.040	L.F.	.007	.22	.36	.58
Flashing, aluminum, 0.019" thick	.050	S.F.	.003	.06	.14	.20
0.032" thick	.050	S.F.	.003	.07	.14	.21
0.040" thick	.050	S.F.	.003	.13	.14	.27
Copper sheets, 16 oz., under 500 lbs.	.050	S.F.	.003	.38	.17	.55
Over 500 lbs.	.050	S.F.	.003	.38	.13	.51
20 oz., under 500 lbs.	.050	S.F.	.004	.54	.18	.72
Over 500 lbs.	.050	S.F.	.003	.52	.14	.66
Stainless steel, 32 gauge	.050	S.F.	.003	.17	.13	.30
28 gauge	.050	S.F.	.003	.22	.13	.35
26 gauge	.050	S.F.	.003	.23	.13	.36
24 gauge	.050	S.F.	.003	.26	.13	.39

System Description	QUAN.	UNIT	LABOR HOURS	COST PER S.F.		
				MAT.	INST.	TOTAL
1/2″ DRYWALL, TAPED & FINISHED						
Gypsum wallboard, 1/2″ thick, standard	1.000	S.F.	.008	.33	.43	.76
Finish, taped & finished joints	1.000	S.F.	.008	.05	.43	.48
Corners, taped & finished, 32 L.F. per 12′ x 12′ room	.083	L.F.	.002	.01	.08	.09
Painting, primer & 2 coats	1.000	S.F.	.011	.21	.49	.70
Paint trim, to 6″ wide, primer + 1 coat enamel	.125	L.F.	.001	.02	.06	.08
Moldings, base, ogee profile, 9/16″ x 4-1/2, red oak	.125	L.F.	.005	.48	.25	.73
TOTAL		S.F.	.035	1.10	1.74	2.84
THINCOAT, SKIM-COAT, ON 1/2″ BACKER DRYWALL						
Gypsum wallboard, 1/2″ thick, thincoat backer	1.000	S.F.	.008	.33	.43	.76
Thincoat plaster	1.000	S.F.	.011	.11	.55	.66
Corners, taped & finished, 32 L.F. per 12′ x 12′ room	.083	L.F.	.002	.01	.08	.09
Painting, primer & 2 coats	1.000	S.F.	.011	.21	.49	.70
Paint trim, to 6″ wide, primer + 1 coat enamel	.125	L.F.	.001	.02	.06	.08
Moldings, base, ogee profile, 9/16″ x 4-1/2, red oak	.125	L.F.	.005	.48	.25	.73
TOTAL		S.F.	.038	1.16	1.86	3.02
5/8″ DRYWALL, TAPED & FINISHED						
Gypsum wallboard, 5/8″ thick, standard	1.000	S.F.	.008	.35	.43	.78
Finish, taped & finished joints	1.000	S.F.	.008	.05	.43	.48
Corners, taped & finished, 32 L.F. per 12′ x 12′ room	.083	L.F.	.002	.01	.08	.09
Painting, primer & 2 coats	1.000	S.F.	.011	.21	.49	.70
Moldings, base, ogee profile, 9/16″ x 4-1/2, red oak	.125	L.F.	.005	.48	.25	.73
Paint trim, to 6″ wide, primer + 1 coat enamel	.125	L.F.	.001	.02	.06	.08
TOTAL		S.F.	.035	1.12	1.74	2.86

The costs in this system are based on a square foot of wall.
Do not deduct for openings.

Description	QUAN.	UNIT	LABOR HOURS	COST PER S.F.		
				MAT.	INST.	TOTAL

Drywall & Thincoat Wall Price Sheet	QUAN.	UNIT	LABOR HOURS	COST PER S.F.		
				MAT.	INST.	TOTAL
Gypsum wallboard, 1/2" thick, standard	1.000	S.F.	.008	.33	.43	.76
Fire resistant	1.000	S.F.	.008	.35	.43	.78
Water resistant	1.000	S.F.	.008	.42	.43	.85
5/8" thick, standard	1.000	S.F.	.008	.35	.43	.78
Fire resistant	1.000	S.F.	.008	.37	.43	.80
Water resistant	1.000	S.F.	.008	.50	.43	.93
Gypsum wallboard backer for thincoat system, 1/2" thick	1.000	S.F.	.008	.33	.43	.76
5/8" thick	1.000	S.F.	.008	.35	.43	.78
Gypsum wallboard, taped & finished	1.000	S.F.	.008	.05	.43	.48
Texture spray	1.000	S.F.	.010	.04	.46	.50
Thincoat plaster, including tape	1.000	S.F.	.011	.11	.55	.66
Gypsum wallboard corners, taped & finished, 32 L.F. per 4' x 4' room	.250	L.F.	.004	.03	.23	.26
6' x 6' room	.110	L.F.	.002	.01	.10	.11
10' x 10' room	.100	L.F.	.001	.01	.09	.10
12' x 12' room	.083	L.F.	.001	.01	.08	.09
16' x 16' room	.063	L.F.	.001	.01	.06	.07
Thincoat system, 32 L.F. per 4' x 4' room	.250	L.F.	.003	.03	.14	.17
6' x 6' room	.110	L.F.	.001	.01	.06	.07
10' x 10' room	.100	L.F.	.001	.01	.05	.06
12' x 12' room	.083	L.F.	.001	.01	.04	.05
16' x 16' room	.063	L.F.	.001	.01	.03	.04
Painting, primer, & 1 coat	1.000	S.F.	.008	.14	.38	.52
& 2 coats	1.000	S.F.	.011	.21	.49	.70
Wallpaper, $7/double roll	1.000	S.F.	.013	.47	.58	1.05
$17/double roll	1.000	S.F.	.015	1.08	.69	1.77
$40/double roll	1.000	S.F.	.018	2.13	.85	2.98
Wallcovering, medium weight vinyl		S.F.	.017	.99	.77	1.76
Tile, ceramic adhesive thin set, 4 1/4" x 4 1/4" tiles	1.000	S.F.	.084	2.48	3.58	6.06
6" x 6" tiles	1.000	S.F.	.080	3.43	3.88	7.31
Pregrouted sheets	1.000	S.F.	.067	5.55	2.83	8.38
Trim, painted or stained, baseboard	.125	L.F.	.006	.50	.31	.81
Base shoe	.125	L.F.	.005	.07	.29	.36
Chair rail	.125	L.F.	.005	.25	.26	.51
Cornice molding	.125	L.F.	.004	.19	.26	.45
Cove base, vinyl	.125	L.F.	.003	.17	.15	.32
Paneling, not including furring or trim						
Plywood, prefinished, 1/4" thick, 4' x 8' sheets, vert. grooves						
Birch faced, minimum	1.000	S.F.	.032	.45	1.73	2.18
Average	1.000	S.F.	.038	.91	2.06	2.97
Maximum	1.000	S.F.	.046	1.38	2.47	3.85
Mahogany, African	1.000	S.F.	.040	3.19	2.16	5.35
Philippine (lauan)	1.000	S.F.	.032	.66	1.73	2.39
Oak or cherry, minimum	1.000	S.F.	.032	.37	1.73	2.10
Maximum	1.000	S.F.	.040	2.27	2.16	4.43
Rosewood	1.000	S.F.	.050	3.19	2.70	5.89
Teak	1.000	S.F.	.040	3.19	2.16	5.35
Chestnut	1.000	S.F.	.043	5.35	2.30	7.65
Pecan	1.000	S.F.	.040	2.31	2.16	4.47
Walnut, minimum	1.000	S.F.	.032	2.27	1.73	4
Maximum	1.000	S.F.	.040	5.85	2.16	8.01

System Description	QUAN.	UNIT	LABOR HOURS	COST PER S.F.		
				MAT.	INST.	TOTAL
1/2" GYPSUM WALLBOARD, TAPED & FINISHED						
Gypsum wallboard, 1/2" thick, standard	1.000	S.F.	.008	.33	.43	.76
Finish, taped & finished	1.000	S.F.	.008	.05	.43	.48
Corners, taped & finished, 12' x 12' room	.333	L.F.	.006	.04	.30	.34
Paint, primer & 2 coats	1.000	S.F.	.011	.21	.49	.70
TOTAL		S.F.	.033	.63	1.65	2.28
THINCOAT, SKIM COAT ON 1/2" GYPSUM WALLBOARD						
Gypsum wallboard, 1/2" thick, thincoat backer	1.000	S.F.	.008	.33	.43	.76
Thincoat plaster	1.000	S.F.	.011	.11	.55	.66
Corners, taped & finished, 12' x 12' room	.333	L.F.	.006	.04	.30	.34
Paint, primer & 2 coats	1.000	S.F.	.011	.21	.49	.70
TOTAL		S.F.	.036	.69	1.77	2.46
WATER-RESISTANT GYPSUM WALLBOARD, 1/2" THICK, TAPED & FINISHED						
Gypsum wallboard, 1/2" thick, water-resistant	1.000	S.F.	.008	.42	.43	.85
Finish, taped & finished	1.000	S.F.	.008	.05	.43	.48
Corners, taped & finished, 12' x 12' room	.333	L.F.	.006	.04	.30	.34
Paint, primer & 2 coats	1.000	S.F.	.011	.21	.49	.70
TOTAL		S.F.	.033	.72	1.65	2.37
5/8" GYPSUM WALLBOARD, TAPED & FINISHED						
Gypsum wallboard, 5/8" thick, standard	1.000	S.F.	.008	.35	.43	.78
Finish, taped & finished	1.000	S.F.	.008	.05	.43	.48
Corners, taped & finished, 12' x 12' room	.333	L.F.	.006	.04	.30	.34
Paint, primer & 2 coats	1.000	S.F.	.011	.21	.49	.70
TOTAL		S.F.	.033	.65	1.65	2.30

The costs in this system are based on a square foot of ceiling.

Description	QUAN.	UNIT	LABOR HOURS	COST PER S.F.		
				MAT.	INST.	TOTAL

Drywall & Thincoat Ceilings	QUAN.	UNIT	LABOR HOURS	COST PER S.F.		
				MAT.	INST.	TOTAL
Gypsum wallboard ceilings, 1/2" thick, standard	1.000	S.F.	.008	.33	.43	.76
Fire resistant	1.000	S.F.	.008	.35	.43	.78
Water resistant	1.000	S.F.	.008	.42	.43	.85
5/8" thick, standard	1.000	S.F.	.008	.35	.43	.78
Fire resistant	1.000	S.F.	.008	.37	.43	.80
Water resistant	1.000	S.F.	.008	.50	.43	.93
Gypsum wallboard backer for thincoat ceiling system, 1/2" thick	1.000	S.F.	.016	.68	.86	1.54
5/8" thick	1.000	S.F.	.016	.70	.86	1.56
Gypsum wallboard ceilings, taped & finished	1.000	S.F.	.008	.05	.43	.48
Texture spray	1.000	S.F.	.010	.04	.46	.50
Thincoat plaster	1.000	S.F.	.011	.11	.55	.66
Corners taped & finished, 4' x 4' room	1.000	L.F.	.015	.12	.91	1.03
6' x 6' room	.667	L.F.	.010	.08	.61	.69
10' x 10' room	.400	L.F.	.006	.05	.36	.41
12' x 12' room	.333	L.F.	.005	.04	.30	.34
16' x 16' room	.250	L.F.	.003	.02	.17	.19
Thincoat system, 4' x 4' room	1.000	L.F.	.011	.11	.55	.66
6' x 6' room	.667	L.F.	.007	.07	.37	.44
10' x 10' room	.400	L.F.	.004	.04	.22	.26
12' x 12' room	.333	L.F.	.004	.04	.18	.22
16' x 16' room	.250	L.F.	.002	.02	.11	.13
Painting, primer & 1 coat	1.000	S.F.	.008	.14	.38	.52
& 2 coats	1.000	S.F.	.011	.21	.49	.70
Wallpaper, double roll, solid pattern, avg. workmanship	1.000	S.F.	.013	.47	.58	1.05
Basic pattern, avg. workmanship	1.000	S.F.	.015	1.08	.69	1.77
Basic pattern, quality workmanship	1.000	S.F.	.018	2.13	.85	2.98
Tile, ceramic adhesive thin set, 4 1/4" x 4 1/4" tiles	1.000	S.F.	.084	2.48	3.58	6.06
6" x 6" tiles	1.000	S.F.	.080	3.43	3.88	7.31
Pregrouted sheets	1.000	S.F.	.067	5.55	2.83	8.38

System Description	QUAN.	UNIT	LABOR HOURS	COST PER S.F.		
				MAT.	INST.	TOTAL
PLASTER ON GYPSUM LATH						
Plaster, gypsum or perlite, 2 coats	1.000	S.F.	.053	.41	2.67	3.08
Lath, 3/8" gypsum	1.000	S.F.	.010	.33	.48	.81
Corners, expanded metal, 32 L.F. per 12' x 12' room	.083	L.F.	.002	.01	.09	.10
Painting, primer & 2 coats	1.000	S.F.	.011	.21	.49	.70
Paint trim, to 6" wide, primer + 1 coat enamel	.125	L.F.	.001	.02	.06	.08
Moldings, base, ogee profile, 9/16" x 4-1/2, red oak	.125	L.F.	.005	.48	.25	.73
TOTAL		S.F.	.082	1.46	4.04	5.50
PLASTER ON METAL LATH						
Plaster, gypsum or perlite, 2 coats	1.000	S.F.	.053	.41	2.67	3.08
Lath, 2.5 Lb. diamond, metal	1.000	S.F.	.010	.47	.48	.95
Corners, expanded metal, 32 L.F. per 12' x 12' room	.083	L.F.	.002	.01	.09	.10
Painting, primer & 2 coats	1.000	S.F.	.011	.21	.49	.70
Paint trim, to 6" wide, primer + 1 coat enamel	.125	L.F.	.001	.02	.06	.08
Moldings, base, ogee profile, 9/16" x 4-1/2, red oak	.125	L.F.	.005	.48	.25	.73
TOTAL		S.F.	.082	1.60	4.04	5.64
STUCCO ON METAL LATH						
Stucco, 2 coats	1.000	S.F.	.041	.28	2.04	2.32
Lath, 2.5 Lb. diamond, metal	1.000	S.F.	.010	.47	.48	.95
Corners, expanded metal, 32 L.F. per 12' x 12' room	.083	L.F.	.002	.01	.09	.10
Painting, primer & 2 coats	1.000	S.F.	.011	.21	.49	.70
Paint trim, to 6" wide, primer + 1 coat enamel	.125	L.F.	.001	.02	.06	.08
Moldings, base, ogee profile, 9/16" x 4-1/2, red oak	.125	L.F.	.005	.48	.25	.73
TOTAL		S.F.	.070	1.47	3.41	4.88

The costs in these systems are based on a per square foot of wall area.
Do not deduct for openings.

Description	QUAN.	UNIT	LABOR HOURS	COST PER S.F.		
				MAT.	INST.	TOTAL

Plaster & Stucco Wall Price Sheet	QUAN.	UNIT	LABOR HOURS	COST PER S.F.		
				MAT.	INST.	TOTAL
Plaster, gypsum or perlite, 2 coats	1.000	S.F.	.053	.41	2.67	3.08
3 coats	1.000	S.F.	.065	.59	3.23	3.82
Lath, gypsum, standard, 3/8″ thick	1.000	S.F.	.010	.33	.48	.81
Fire resistant, 3/8″ thick	1.000	S.F.	.013	.30	.58	.88
1/2″ thick	1.000	S.F.	.014	.33	.63	.96
Metal, diamond, 2.5 Lb.	1.000	S.F.	.010	.47	.48	.95
3.4 Lb.	1.000	S.F.	.012	.47	.54	1.01
Rib, 2.75 Lb.	1.000	S.F.	.012	.36	.54	.90
3.4 Lb.	1.000	S.F.	.013	.48	.58	1.06
Corners, expanded metal, 32 L.F. per 4′ x 4′ room	.250	L.F.	.005	.04	.27	.31
6′ x 6′ room	.110	L.F.	.002	.02	.12	.14
10′ x 10′ room	.100	L.F.	.002	.02	.11	.13
12′ x 12′ room	.083	L.F.	.002	.01	.09	.10
16′ x 16′ room	.063	L.F.	.001	.01	.07	.08
Painting, primer & 1 coats	1.000	S.F.	.008	.14	.38	.52
Primer & 2 coats	1.000	S.F.	.011	.21	.49	.70
Wallpaper, low price double roll	1.000	S.F.	.013	.47	.58	1.05
Medium price double roll	1.000	S.F.	.015	1.08	.69	1.77
High price double roll	1.000	S.F.	.018	2.13	.85	2.98
Tile, ceramic thin set, 4-1/4″ x 4-1/4″ tiles	1.000	S.F.	.084	2.48	3.58	6.06
6″ x 6″ tiles	1.000	S.F.	.080	3.43	3.88	7.31
Pregrouted sheets	1.000	S.F.	.067	5.55	2.83	8.38
Trim, painted or stained, baseboard	.125	L.F.	.006	.50	.31	.81
Base shoe	.125	L.F.	.005	.07	.29	.36
Chair rail	.125	L.F.	.005	.25	.26	.51
Cornice molding	.125	L.F.	.004	.19	.26	.45
Cove base, vinyl	.125	L.F.	.003	.17	.15	.32
Paneling not including furring or trim						
Plywood, prefinished, 1/4″ thick, 4′ x 8′ sheets, vert. grooves						
Birch faced, minimum	1.000	S.F.	.032	.45	1.73	2.18
Average	1.000	S.F.	.038	.91	2.06	2.97
Maximum	1.000	S.F.	.046	1.38	2.47	3.85
Mahogany, African	1.000	S.F.	.040	3.19	2.16	5.35
Philippine (lauan)	1.000	S.F.	.032	.66	1.73	2.39
Oak or cherry, minimum	1.000	S.F.	.032	.37	1.73	2.10
Maximum	1.000	S.F.	.040	2.27	2.16	4.43
Rosewood	1.000	S.F.	.050	3.19	2.70	5.89
Teak	1.000	S.F.	.040	3.19	2.16	5.35
Chestnut	1.000	S.F.	.043	5.35	2.30	7.65
Pecan	1.000	S.F.	.040	2.31	2.16	4.47
Walnut, minimum	1.000	S.F.	.032	2.27	1.73	4
Maximum	1.000	S.F.	.040	5.85	2.16	8.01

System Description	QUAN.	UNIT	LABOR HOURS	COST PER S.F.		
				MAT.	INST.	TOTAL
PLASTER ON GYPSUM LATH						
Plaster, gypsum or perlite, 2 coats	1.000	S.F.	.061	.41	3.04	3.45
Gypsum lath, plain or perforated, nailed, 3/8" thick	1.000	S.F.	.010	.33	.48	.81
Gypsum lath, ceiling installation adder	1.000	S.F.	.004		.19	.19
Corners, expanded metal, 12' x 12' room	.330	L.F.	.007	.06	.36	.42
Painting, primer & 2 coats	1.000	S.F.	.011	.21	.49	.70
TOTAL		S.F.	.093	1.01	4.56	5.57
PLASTER ON METAL LATH						
Plaster, gypsum or perlite, 2 coats	1.000	S.F.	.061	.41	3.04	3.45
Lath, 2.5 Lb. diamond, metal	1.000	S.F.	.012	.47	.54	1.01
Corners, expanded metal, 12' x 12' room	.330	L.F.	.007	.06	.36	.42
Painting, primer & 2 coats	1.000	S.F.	.011	.21	.49	.70
TOTAL		S.F.	.091	1.15	4.43	5.58
STUCCO ON GYPSUM LATH						
Stucco, 2 coats	1.000	S.F.	.041	.28	2.04	2.32
Gypsum lath, plain or perforated, nailed, 3/8" thick	1.000	S.F.	.010	.33	.48	.81
Gypsum lath, ceiling installation adder	1.000	S.F.	.004		.19	.19
Corners, expanded metal, 12' x 12' room	.330	L.F.	.007	.06	.36	.42
Painting, primer & 2 coats	1.000	S.F.	.011	.21	.49	.70
TOTAL		S.F.	.073	.88	3.56	4.44
STUCCO ON METAL LATH						
Stucco, 2 coats	1.000	S.F.	.041	.28	2.04	2.32
Lath, 2.5 Lb. diamond, metal	1.000	S.F.	.012	.47	.54	1.01
Corners, expanded metal, 12' x 12' room	.330	L.F.	.007	.06	.36	.42
Painting, primer & 2 coats	1.000	S.F.	.011	.21	.49	.70
TOTAL		S.F.	.071	1.02	3.43	4.45

The costs in these systems are based on a square foot of ceiling area.

Description	QUAN.	UNIT	LABOR HOURS	COST PER S.F.		
				MAT.	INST.	TOTAL

Plaster & Stucco Ceiling Price Sheet	QUAN.	UNIT	LABOR HOURS	COST PER S.F.		
				MAT.	INST.	TOTAL
Plaster, gypsum or perlite, 2 coats	1.000	S.F.	.061	.41	3.04	3.45
3 coats	1.000	S.F.	.065	.59	3.23	3.82
Lath, gypsum, standard, 3/8" thick	1.000	S.F.	.014	.33	.67	1
Fire resistant, 3/8" thick	1.000	S.F.	.017	.30	.77	1.07
1/2" thick	1.000	S.F.	.018	.33	.82	1.15
Metal, diamond, 2.5 Lb.	1.000	S.F.	.012	.47	.54	1.01
3.4 Lb.	1.000	S.F.	.015	.47	.68	1.15
Rib, 2.75 Lb.	1.000	S.F.	.012	.36	.54	.90
3.4 Lb.	1.000	S.F.	.013	.48	.58	1.06
Corners expanded metal, 4' x 4' room	1.000	L.F.	.020	.17	1.08	1.25
6' x 6' room	.667	L.F.	.013	.11	.72	.83
10' x 10' room	.400	L.F.	.008	.07	.43	.50
12' x 12' room	.333	L.F.	.007	.06	.36	.42
16' x 16' room	.250	L.F.	.004	.03	.20	.23
Painting, primer & 1 coat	1.000	S.F.	.008	.14	.38	.52
Primer & 2 coats	1.000	S.F.	.011	.21	.49	.70

Suspension System · Carrier Channels · Hangers · Ceiling Board

System Description	QUAN.	UNIT	LABOR HOURS	COST PER S.F.		
				MAT.	INST.	TOTAL
2' X 2' GRID, FILM FACED FIBERGLASS, 5/8" THICK						
Suspension system, 2' x 2' grid, T bar	1.000	S.F.	.012	1	.66	1.66
Ceiling board, film faced fiberglass, 5/8" thick	1.000	S.F.	.013	1.12	.69	1.81
Carrier channels, 1-1/2" x 3/4"	1.000	S.F.	.017	.12	.92	1.04
Hangers, #12 wire	1.000	S.F.	.002		.09	.09
TOTAL		S.F.	.044	2.24	2.36	4.60
2' X 4' GRID, FILM FACED FIBERGLASS, 5/8" THICK						
Suspension system, 2' x 4' grid, T bar	1.000	S.F.	.010	.77	.54	1.31
Ceiling board, film faced fiberglass, 5/8" thick	1.000	S.F.	.013	1.12	.69	1.81
Carrier channels, 1-1/2" x 3/4"	1.000	S.F.	.017	.12	.92	1.04
Hangers, #12 wire	1.000	S.F.	.002		.09	.09
TOTAL		S.F.	.042	2.01	2.24	4.25
2' X 2' GRID, MINERAL FIBER, REVEAL EDGE, 1" THICK						
Suspension system, 2' x 2' grid, T bar	1.000	S.F.	.012	1	.66	1.66
Ceiling board, mineral fiber, reveal edge, 1" thick	1.000	S.F.	.013	1.69	.72	2.41
Carrier channels, 1-1/2" x 3/4"	1.000	S.F.	.017	.12	.92	1.04
Hangers, #12 wire	1.000	S.F.	.002		.09	.09
TOTAL		S.F.	.044	2.81	2.39	5.20
2' X 4' GRID, MINERAL FIBER, REVEAL EDGE, 1" THICK						
Suspension system, 2' x 4' grid, T bar	1.000	S.F.	.010	.77	.54	1.31
Ceiling board, mineral fiber, reveal edge, 1" thick	1.000	S.F.	.013	1.69	.72	2.41
Carrier channels, 1-1/2" x 3/4"	1.000	S.F.	.017	.12	.92	1.04
Hangers, #12 wire	1.000	S.F.	.002		.09	.09
TOTAL		S.F.	.042	2.58	2.27	4.85

Description	QUAN.	UNIT	LABOR HOURS	COST PER S.F.		
				MAT.	INST.	TOTAL

Suspended Ceiling Price Sheet	QUAN.	UNIT	LABOR HOURS	COST PER S.F.		
				MAT.	INST.	TOTAL
Suspension systems, T bar, 2' x 2' grid	1.000	S.F.	.012	1	.66	1.66
2' x 4' grid	1.000	S.F.	.010	.77	.54	1.31
Concealed Z bar, 12" module	1.000	S.F.	.015	.86	.83	1.69
Ceiling boards, fiberglass, film faced, 2' x 2' or 2' x 4', 5/8" thick	1.000	S.F.	.013	1.12	.69	1.81
3/4" thick	1.000	S.F.	.013	1.84	.72	2.56
3" thick thermal R11	1.000	S.F.	.018	2.09	.96	3.05
Glass cloth faced, 3/4" thick	1.000	S.F.	.016	2.21	.86	3.07
1" thick	1.000	S.F.	.016	3.01	.89	3.90
1-1/2" thick, nubby face	1.000	S.F.	.017	2.75	.91	3.66
Mineral fiber boards, 5/8" thick, aluminum face 2' x 2'	1.000	S.F.	.013	3.21	.72	3.93
2' x 4'	1.000	S.F.	.012	3.23	.66	3.89
Standard faced, 2' x 2' or 2' x 4'	1.000	S.F.	.012	.79	.64	1.43
Plastic coated face, 2' x 2' or 2' x 4'	1.000	S.F.	.020	1.21	1.08	2.29
Fire rated, 2 hour rating, 5/8" thick	1.000	S.F.	.012	1.05	.64	1.69
Tegular edge, 2' x 2' or 2' x 4', 5/8" thick, fine textured	1.000	S.F.	.013	1.80	.92	2.72
Rough textured	1.000	S.F.	.015	1.30	.92	2.22
3/4" thick, fine textured	1.000	S.F.	.016	2.97	.96	3.93
Rough textured	1.000	S.F.	.018	1.69	.96	2.65
Luminous panels, prismatic, acrylic	1.000	S.F.	.020	2.49	1.08	3.57
Polystyrene	1.000	S.F.	.020	1.28	1.08	2.36
Flat or ribbed, acrylic	1.000	S.F.	.020	4.33	1.08	5.41
Polystyrene	1.000	S.F.	.020	2.97	1.08	4.05
Drop pan, white, acrylic	1.000	S.F.	.020	6.35	1.08	7.43
Polystyrene	1.000	S.F.	.020	5.30	1.08	6.38
Carrier channels, 4'-0" on center, 3/4" x 1-1/2"	1.000	S.F.	.017	.12	.92	1.04
1-1/2" x 3-1/2"	1.000	S.F.	.017	.33	.92	1.25
Hangers, #12 wire	1.000	S.F.	.002		.09	.09

System Description	QUAN.	UNIT	LABOR HOURS	COST EACH		
				MAT.	INST.	TOTAL
LAUAN, FLUSH DOOR, HOLLOW CORE						
Door, flush, lauan, hollow core, 2'-8" wide x 6'-8" high	1.000	Ea.	.889	44	48	92
Frame, pine, 4-5/8" jamb	17.000	L.F.	.725	116.45	39.10	155.55
Moldings, casing, ogee, 11/16" x 2-1/2", pine	34.000	L.F.	1.088	56.78	58.82	115.60
Paint trim, to 6" wide, primer + 1 coat enamel	34.000	L.F.	.340	5.10	15.64	20.74
Butt hinges, chrome, 3-1/2" x 3-1/2"	1.500	Pr.		42.75		42.75
Lockset, passage	1.000	Ea.	.500	33	27	60
Prime door & frame, oil, brushwork	2.000	Face	1.600	7.32	74	81.32
Paint door and frame, oil, 2 coats	2.000	Face	2.667	10.10	123	133.10
TOTAL		Ea.	7.809	315.50	385.56	701.06
BIRCH, FLUSH DOOR, HOLLOW CORE						
Door, flush, birch, hollow core, 2'-8" wide x 6'-8" high	1.000	Ea.	.889	55.50	48	103.50
Frame, pine, 4-5/8" jamb	17.000	L.F.	.725	116.45	39.10	155.55
Moldings, casing, ogee, 11/16" x 2-1/2", pine	34.000	L.F.	1.088	56.78	58.82	115.60
Butt hinges, chrome, 3-1/2" x 3-1/2"	1.500	Pr.		42.75		42.75
Lockset, passage	1.000	Ea.	.500	33	27	60
Prime door & frame, oil, brushwork	2.000	Face	1.600	7.32	74	81.32
Paint door and frame, oil, 2 coats	2.000	Face	2.667	10.10	123	133.10
TOTAL		Ea.	7.469	321.90	369.92	691.82
RAISED PANEL, SOLID, PINE DOOR						
Door, pine, raised panel, 2'-8" wide x 6'-8" high	1.000	Ea.	.889	204	48	252
Frame, pine, 4-5/8" jamb	17.000	L.F.	.725	116.45	39.10	155.55
Moldings, casing, ogee, 11/16" x 2-1/2", pine	34.000	L.F.	1.088	56.78	58.82	115.60
Butt hinges, bronze, 3-1/2" x 3-1/2"	1.500	Pr.		49.50		49.50
Lockset, passage	1.000	Ea.	.500	33	27	60
Prime door & frame, oil, brushwork	2.000	Face	1.600	7.32	74	81.32
Paint door and frame, oil, 2 coats	2.000	Face	2.667	10.10	123	133.10
TOTAL		Ea.	7.469	477.15	369.92	847.07

The costs in these systems are based on a cost per each door.

Description	QUAN.	UNIT	LABOR HOURS	COST EACH		
				MAT.	INST.	TOTAL

Interior Door Price Sheet	QUAN.	UNIT	LABOR HOURS	COST EACH		
				MAT.	INST.	TOTAL
Door, hollow core, lauan 1-3/8" thick, 6'-8" high x 1'-6" wide	1.000	Ea.	.889	37.50	48	85.50
2'-0" wide	1.000	Ea.	.889	38.50	48	86.50
2'-6" wide	1.000	Ea.	.889	42.50	48	90.50
2'-8" wide	1.000	Ea.	.889	44	48	92
3'-0" wide	1.000	Ea.	.941	46.50	51	97.50
Birch 1-3/8" thick, 6'-8" high x 1'-6" wide	1.000	Ea.	.889	45	48	93
2'-0" wide	1.000	Ea.	.889	46.50	48	94.50
2'-6" wide	1.000	Ea.	.889	55	48	103
2'-8" wide	1.000	Ea.	.889	55.50	48	103.50
3'-0" wide	1.000	Ea.	.941	57.50	51	108.50
Louvered pine 1-3/8" thick, 6'-8" high x 1'-6" wide	1.000	Ea.	.842	132	45.50	177.50
2'-0" wide	1.000	Ea.	.889	144	48	192
2'-6" wide	1.000	Ea.	.889	165	48	213
2'-8" wide	1.000	Ea.	.889	177	48	225
3'-0" wide	1.000	Ea.	.941	192	51	243
Paneled pine 1-3/8" thick, 6'-8" high x 1'-6" wide	1.000	Ea.	.842	141	45.50	186.50
2'-0" wide	1.000	Ea.	.889	168	48	216
2'-6" wide	1.000	Ea.	.889	200	48	248
2'-8" wide	1.000	Ea.	.889	204	48	252
3'-0" wide	1.000	Ea.	.941	224	51	275
Frame, pine, 1'-6" thru 2'-0" wide door, 3-5/8" deep	16.000	L.F.	.683	107	37	144
4-5/8" deep	16.000	L.F.	.683	110	37	147
5-5/8" deep	16.000	L.F.	.683	109	37	146
2'-6" thru 3'0" wide door, 3-5/8" deep	17.000	L.F.	.725	114	39	153
4-5/8" deep	17.000	L.F.	.725	116	39	155
5-5/8" deep	17.000	L.F.	.725	116	39	155
Trim, casing, painted, both sides, 1'-6" thru 2'-6" wide door	32.000	L.F.	1.855	56.50	92	148.50
2'-6" thru 3'-0" wide door	34.000	L.F.	1.971	60	97.50	157.50
Butt hinges 3-1/2" x 3-1/2", steel plated, chrome	1.500	Pr.		43		43
Bronze	1.500	Pr.		49.50		49.50
Locksets, passage, minimum	1.000	Ea.	.500	33	27	60
Maximum	1.000	Ea.	.575	38	31	69
Privacy, miniumum	1.000	Ea.	.625	41.50	34	75.50
Maximum	1.000	Ea.	.675	44.50	36.50	81
Paint 2 sides, primer & 2 cts., flush door, 1'-6" to 2'-0" wide	2.000	Face	5.547	24.50	256	280.50
2'-6" thru 3'-0" wide	2.000	Face	6.933	31	320	351
Louvered door, 1'-6" thru 2'-0" wide	2.000	Face	6.400	23	295	318
2'-6" thru 3'-0" wide	2.000	Face	8.000	29	370	399
Paneled door, 1'-6" thru 2'-0" wide	2.000	Face	6.400	23	295	318
2'-6" thru 3'-0" wide	2.000	Face	8.000	29	370	399

Trim

Door

Frame

System Description	QUAN.	UNIT	LABOR HOURS	COST EACH		
				MAT.	INST.	TOTAL
BI-PASSING, FLUSH, LAUAN, HOLLOW CORE, 4'-0" X 6'-8"						
Door, flush, lauan, hollow core, 4'-0" x 6'-8" opening	1.000	Ea.	1.333	194	72	266
Frame, pine, 4-5/8" jamb	18.000	L.F.	.768	123.30	41.40	164.70
Moldings, casing, ogee, 11/16" x 2-1/2", pine	36.000	L.F.	1.152	60.12	62.28	122.40
Prime door & frame, oil, brushwork	2.000	Face	1.600	7.32	74	81.32
Paint door and frame, oil, 2 coats	2.000	Face	2.667	10.10	123	133.10
TOTAL		Ea.	7.520	394.84	372.68	767.52
BI-PASSING, FLUSH, BIRCH, HOLLOW CORE, 6'-0" X 6'-8"						
Door, flush, birch, hollow core, 6'-0" x 6'-8" opening	1.000	Ea.	1.600	286	86.50	372.50
Frame, pine, 4-5/8" jamb	19.000	L.F.	.811	130.15	43.70	173.85
Moldings, casing, ogee, 11/16" x 2-1/2", pine	38.000	L.F.	1.216	63.46	65.74	129.20
Prime door & frame, oil, brushwork	2.000	Face	2.000	9.15	92.50	101.65
Paint door and frame, oil, 2 coats	2.000	Face	3.333	12.63	153.75	166.38
TOTAL		Ea.	8.960	501.39	442.19	943.58
BI-FOLD, PINE, PANELED, 3'-0" X 6'-8"						
Door, pine, paneled, 3'-0" x 6'-8" opening	1.000	Ea.	1.231	228	66.50	294.50
Frame, pine, 4-5/8" jamb	17.000	L.F.	.725	116.45	39.10	155.55
Moldings, casing, ogee, 11/16" x 2-1/2", pine	34.000	L.F.	1.088	56.78	58.82	115.60
Prime door & frame, oil, brushwork	2.000	Face	1.600	7.32	74	81.32
Paint door and frame, oil, 2 coats	2.000	Face	2.667	10.10	123	133.10
TOTAL		Ea.	7.311	418.65	361.42	780.07
BI-FOLD, PINE, LOUVERED, 6'-0" X 6'-8"						
Door, pine, louvered, 6'-0" x 6'-8" opening	1.000	Ea.	1.600	320	86.50	406.50
Frame, pine, 4-5/8" jamb	19.000	L.F.	.811	130.15	43.70	173.85
Moldings, casing, ogee, 11/16" x 2-1/2", pine	38.000	L.F.	1.216	63.46	65.74	129.20
Prime door & frame, oil, brushwork	2.500	Face	2.000	9.15	92.50	101.65
Paint door and frame, oil, 2 coats	2.500	Face	3.333	12.63	153.75	166.38
TOTAL		Ea.	8.960	535.39	442.19	977.58

The costs in this system are based on a cost per each door.

Description	QUAN.	UNIT	LABOR HOURS	COST EACH		
				MAT.	INST.	TOTAL

Closet Door Price Sheet	QUAN.	UNIT	LABOR HOURS	COST EACH		
				MAT.	INST.	TOTAL
Doors, bi-passing, pine, louvered, 4'-0" x 6'-8" opening	1.000	Ea.	1.333	450	72	522
6'-0" x 6'-8" opening	1.000	Ea.	1.600	585	86.50	671.50
Paneled, 4'-0" x 6'-8" opening	1.000	Ea.	1.333	565	72	637
6'-0" x 6'-8" opening	1.000	Ea.	1.600	670	86.50	756.50
Flush, birch, hollow core, 4'-0" x 6'-8" opening	1.000	Ea.	1.333	245	72	317
6'-0" x 6'-8" opening	1.000	Ea.	1.600	286	86.50	372.50
Flush, lauan, hollow core, 4'-0" x 6'-8" opening	1.000	Ea.	1.333	194	72	266
6'-0" x 6'-8" opening	1.000	Ea.	1.600	230	86.50	316.50
Bi-fold, pine, louvered, 3'-0" x 6'-8" opening	1.000	Ea.	1.231	228	66.50	294.50
6'-0" x 6'-8" opening	1.000	Ea.	1.600	320	86.50	406.50
Paneled, 3'-0" x 6'-8" opening	1.000	Ea.	1.231	228	66.50	294.50
6'-0" x 6'-8" opening	1.000	Ea.	1.600	320	86.50	406.50
Flush, birch, hollow core, 3'-0" x 6'-8" opening	1.000	Ea.	1.231	78.50	66.50	145
6'-0" x 6'-8" opening	1.000	Ea.	1.600	141	86.50	227.50
Flush, lauan, hollow core, 3'-0" x 6'8" opening	1.000	Ea.	1.231	305	66.50	371.50
6'-0" x 6'-8" opening	1.000	Ea.	1.600	440	86.50	526.50
Frame pine, 3'-0" door, 3-5/8" deep	17.000	L.F.	.725	114	39	153
4-5/8" deep	17.000	L.F.	.725	116	39	155
5-5/8" deep	17.000	L.F.	.725	116	39	155
4'-0" door, 3-5/8" deep	18.000	L.F.	.768	121	41.50	162.50
4-5/8" deep	18.000	L.F.	.768	123	41.50	164.50
5-5/8" deep	18.000	L.F.	.768	122	41.50	163.50
6'-0" door, 3-5/8" deep	19.000	L.F.	.811	127	43.50	170.50
4-5/8" deep	19.000	L.F.	.811	130	43.50	173.50
5-5/8" deep	19.000	L.F.	.811	129	43.50	172.50
Trim both sides, painted 3'-0" x 6'-8" door	34.000	L.F.	1.971	60	97.50	157.50
4'-0" x 6'-8" door	36.000	L.F.	2.086	63.50	103	166.50
6'-0" x 6'-8" door	38.000	L.F.	2.203	67.50	109	176.50
Paint 2 sides, primer & 2 cts., flush door & frame, 3' x 6'-8" opng	2.000	Face	2.914	13.05	148	161.05
4'-0" x 6'-8" opening	2.000	Face	3.886	17.40	197	214.40
6'-0" x 6'-8" opening	2.000	Face	4.857	22	246	268
Paneled door & frame, 3'-0" x 6'-8" opening	2.000	Face	6.000	21.50	277	298.50
4'-0" x 6'-8" opening	2.000	Face	8.000	29	370	399
6'-0" x 6'-8" opening	2.000	Face	10.000	36	460	496
Louvered door & frame, 3'-0" x 6'-8" opening	2.000	Face	6.000	21.50	277	298.50
4'-0" x 6'-8" opening	2.000	Face	8.000	29	370	399
6'-0" x 6'-8" opening	2.000	Face	10.000	36	460	496

System Description	QUAN.	UNIT	LABOR HOURS	COST PER S.F.		
				MAT.	INST.	TOTAL
Carpet, direct glue-down, nylon, level loop, 26 oz.	1.000	S.F.	.018	3.67	.85	4.52
32 oz.	1.000	S.F.	.018	4.66	.85	5.51
40 oz.	1.000	S.F.	.018	6.85	.85	7.70
Nylon, plush, 20 oz.	1.000	S.F.	.018	2.41	.85	3.26
24 oz.	1.000	S.F.	.018	2.41	.85	3.26
30 oz.	1.000	S.F.	.018	3.62	.85	4.47
42 oz.	1.000	S.F.	.022	5.40	1.02	6.42
48 oz.	1.000	S.F.	.022	6.35	1.02	7.37
54 oz.	1.000	S.F.	.022	6.90	1.02	7.92
Olefin, 15 oz.	1.000	S.F.	.018	1.28	.85	2.13
22 oz.	1.000	S.F.	.018	1.53	.85	2.38
Tile, foam backed, needle punch	1.000	S.F.	.014	4.75	.66	5.41
Tufted loop or shag	1.000	S.F.	.014	3.41	.66	4.07
Wool, 36 oz., level loop	1.000	S.F.	.018	16.15	.85	17
32 oz., patterned	1.000	S.F.	.020	16	.95	16.95
48 oz., patterned	1.000	S.F.	.020	16.50	.95	17.45
Padding, sponge rubber cushion, minimum	1.000	S.F.	.006	.53	.28	.81
Maximum	1.000	S.F.	.006	1.25	.28	1.53
Felt, 32 oz. to 56 oz., minimum	1.000	S.F.	.006	.62	.28	.90
Maximum	1.000	S.F.	.006	.93	.28	1.21
Bonded urethane, 3/8" thick, minimum	1.000	S.F.	.006	.62	.28	.90
Maximum	1.000	S.F.	.006	1.12	.28	1.40
Prime urethane, 1/4" thick, minimum	1.000	S.F.	.006	.39	.28	.67
Maximum	1.000	S.F.	.006	.67	.28	.95
Stairs, for stairs, add to above carpet prices	1.000	Riser	.267		12.65	12.65
Underlayment plywood, 3/8" thick	1.000	S.F.	.011	1.02	.58	1.60
1/2" thick	1.000	S.F.	.011	1.17	.60	1.77
5/8" thick	1.000	S.F.	.011	1.30	.62	1.92
3/4" thick	1.000	S.F.	.012	1.54	.66	2.20
Particle board, 3/8" thick	1.000	S.F.	.011	.44	.58	1.02
1/2" thick	1.000	S.F.	.011	.46	.60	1.06
5/8" thick	1.000	S.F.	.011	.57	.62	1.19
3/4" thick	1.000	S.F.	.012	.68	.66	1.34
Hardboard, 4' x 4', 0.215" thick	1.000	S.F.	.011	.63	.58	1.21

System Description	QUAN.	UNIT	LABOR HOURS	COST PER S.F.		
				MAT.	INST.	TOTAL
Resilient flooring, asphalt tile on concrete, 1/8" thick						
Color group B	1.000	S.F.	.020	1.31	.95	2.26
Color group C & D	1.000	S.F.	.020	1.43	.95	2.38
Asphalt tile on wood subfloor, 1/8" thick						
Color group B	1.000	S.F.	.020	1.59	.95	2.54
Color group C & D	1.000	S.F.	.020	1.71	.95	2.66
Vinyl composition tile, 12" x 12", 1/16" thick	1.000	S.F.	.016	.95	.76	1.71
Embossed	1.000	S.F.	.016	2.43	.76	3.19
Marbleized	1.000	S.F.	.016	2.43	.76	3.19
Plain	1.000	S.F.	.016	3.14	.76	3.90
.080" thick, embossed	1.000	S.F.	.016	1.61	.76	2.37
Marbleized	1.000	S.F.	.016	2.79	.76	3.55
Plain	1.000	S.F.	.016	2.60	.76	3.36
1/8" thick, marbleized	1.000	S.F.	.016	2.44	.76	3.20
Plain	1.000	S.F.	.016	2.49	.76	3.25
Vinyl tile, 12" x 12", .050" thick, minimum	1.000	S.F.	.016	3.76	.76	4.52
Maximum	1.000	S.F.	.016	7.70	.76	8.46
1/8" thick, minimum	1.000	S.F.	.016	5.50	.76	6.26
Maximum	1.000	S.F.	.016	4.02	.76	4.78
1/8" thick, solid colors	1.000	S.F.	.016	6.50	.76	7.26
Florentine pattern	1.000	S.F.	.016	6.95	.76	7.71
Marbleized or travertine pattern	1.000	S.F.	.016	14.30	.76	15.06
Vinyl sheet goods, backed, .070" thick, minimum	1.000	S.F.	.032	4.51	1.52	6.03
Maximum	1.000	S.F.	.040	5.50	1.89	7.39
.093" thick, minimum	1.000	S.F.	.035	4.51	1.65	6.16
Maximum	1.000	S.F.	.040	6.50	1.89	8.39
.125" thick, minimum	1.000	S.F.	.035	4.68	1.65	6.33
Maximum	1.000	S.F.	.040	8.25	1.89	10.14
Wood, oak, finished in place, 25/32" x 2-1/2" clear	1.000	S.F.	.074	4.25	3.63	7.88
Select	1.000	S.F.	.074	5.65	3.63	9.28
No. 1 common	1.000	S.F.	.074	5.50	3.63	9.13
Prefinished, oak, 2-1/2" wide	1.000	S.F.	.047	5.15	2.54	7.69
3-1/4" wide	1.000	S.F.	.043	5.60	2.34	7.94
Ranch plank, oak, random width	1.000	S.F.	.055	7.85	2.98	10.83
Parquet, 5/16" thick, finished in place, oak, minimum	1.000	S.F.	.077	5.50	3.79	9.29
Maximum	1.000	S.F.	.107	8.65	5.40	14.05
Teak, minimum	1.000	S.F.	.077	6.30	3.79	10.09
Maximum	1.000	S.F.	.107	10.30	5.40	15.70
Sleepers, treated, 16" O.C., 1" x 2"	1.000	S.F.	.007	.30	.37	.67
1" x 3"	1.000	S.F.	.008	.50	.43	.93
2" x 4"	1.000	S.F.	.011	.58	.58	1.16
2" x 6"	1.000	S.F.	.012	.92	.66	1.58
Subfloor, plywood, 1/2" thick	1.000	S.F.	.011	.65	.58	1.23
5/8" thick	1.000	S.F.	.012	.82	.64	1.46
3/4" thick	1.000	S.F.	.013	.97	.69	1.66
Ceramic tile, color group 2, 1" x 1"	1.000	S.F.	.087	5.70	3.71	9.41
2" x 2" or 2" x 1"	1.000	S.F.	.084	6.55	3.58	10.13
Color group 1, 8" x 8"	1.000	S.F.	.064	4.89	2.27	7.16
12" x 12"	1.000	S.F.	.049	6.45	2.34	8.79
16" x 16"	1.000	S.F.	.029	7.40	2.43	9.83

System Description	QUAN.	UNIT	LABOR HOURS	COST EACH		
				MAT.	INST.	TOTAL
7 RISERS, OAK TREADS, BOX STAIRS						
Treads, oak, 1-1/4" x 10" wide, 3' long	6.000	Ea.	2.667	534	144	678
Risers, 3/4" thick, beech	7.000	Ea.	2.625	184.80	141.75	326.55
30" primed pine balusters	12.000	Ea.	1.000	39.60	54	93.60
Newels, 3" wide	2.000	Ea.	2.286	104	123	227
Handrails, oak laminated	7.000	L.F.	.933	266	50.40	316.40
Stringers, 2" x 10", 3 each	21.000	L.F.	.306	8.61	16.59	25.20
TOTAL		Ea.	9.817	1,137.01	529.74	1,666.75
14 RISERS, OAK TREADS, BOX STAIRS						
Treads, oak, 1-1/4" x 10" wide, 3' long	13.000	Ea.	5.778	1,157	312	1,469
Risers, 3/4" thick, beech	14.000	Ea.	5.250	369.60	283.50	653.10
30" primed pine balusters	26.000	Ea.	2.167	85.80	117	202.80
Newels, 3" wide	2.000	Ea.	2.286	104	123	227
Handrails, oak, laminated	14.000	L.F.	1.867	532	100.80	632.80
Stair stringers, 2" x 10"	42.000	L.F.	5.169	52.50	279.30	331.80
TOTAL		Ea.	22.517	2,300.90	1,215.60	3,516.50
14 RISERS, PINE TREADS, BOX STAIRS						
Treads, pine, 9-1/2" x 3/4" thick	13.000	Ea.	5.778	204.10	312	516.10
Risers, 3/4" thick, pine	14.000	Ea.	5.091	144.90	275.10	420
30" primed pine balusters	26.000	Ea.	2.167	85.80	117	202.80
Newels, 3" wide	2.000	Ea.	2.286	104	123	227
Handrails, oak, laminated	14.000	L.F.	1.867	532	100.80	632.80
Stair stringers, 2" x 10"	42.000	L.F.	5.169	52.50	279.30	331.80
TOTAL		Ea.	22.358	1,123.30	1,207.20	2,330.50

Description	QUAN.	UNIT	LABOR HOURS	COST EACH		
				MAT.	INST.	TOTAL

Stairway Price Sheet

Stairway Price Sheet	QUAN.	UNIT	LABOR HOURS	COST EACH MAT.	COST EACH INST.	COST EACH TOTAL
Treads, oak, 1-1/16" x 9-1/2", 3' long, 7 riser stair	6.000	Ea.	2.667	535	144	679
14 riser stair	13.000	Ea.	5.778	1,150	310	1,460
1-1/16" x 11-1/2", 3' long, 7 riser stair	6.000	Ea.	2.667	595	144	739
14 riser stair	13.000	Ea.	5.778	1,275	310	1,585
Pine, 3/4" x 9-1/2", 3' long, 7 riser stair	6.000	Ea.	2.667	94	144	238
14 riser stair	13.000	Ea.	5.778	204	310	514
3/4" x 11-1/4", 3' long, 7 riser stair	6.000	Ea.	2.667	106	144	250
14 riser stair	13.000	Ea.	5.778	229	310	539
Risers, oak, 3/4" x 7-1/2" high, 7 riser stair	7.000	Ea.	2.625	132	142	274
14 riser stair	14.000	Ea.	5.250	265	284	549
Beech, 3/4" x 7-1/2" high, 7 riser stair	7.000	Ea.	2.625	185	142	327
14 riser stair	14.000	Ea.	5.250	370	284	654
Baluster, turned, 30" high, primed pine, 7 riser stair	12.000	Ea.	3.429	39.50	54	93.50
14 riser stair	26.000	Ea.	7.428	86	117	203
30" birch, 7 riser stair	12.000	Ea.	3.429	36	49	85
14 riser stair	26.000	Ea.	7.428	78	106	184
42" pine, 7 riser stair	12.000	Ea.	3.556	58.50	54	112.50
14 riser stair	26.000	Ea.	7.704	126	117	243
42" birch, 7 riser stair	12.000	Ea.	3.556	58.50	54	112.50
14 riser stair	26.000	Ea.	7.704	126	117	243
Newels, 3-1/4" wide, starting, 7 riser stair	2.000	Ea.	2.286	104	123	227
14 riser stair	2.000	Ea.	2.286	104	123	227
Landing, 7 riser stair	2.000	Ea.	3.200	130	173	303
14 riser stair	2.000	Ea.	3.200	130	173	303
Handrails, oak, laminated, 7 riser stair	7.000	L.F.	.933	266	50.50	316.50
14 riser stair	14.000	L.F.	1.867	530	101	631
Stringers, fir, 2" x 10" 7 riser stair	21.000	L.F.	2.585	26.50	140	166.50
14 riser stair	42.000	L.F.	5.169	52.50	279	331.50
2" x 12", 7 riser stair	21.000	L.F.	2.585	35.50	140	175.50
14 riser stair	42.000	L.F.	5.169	71.50	279	350.50

Special Stairways

Special Stairways	QUAN.	UNIT	LABOR HOURS	COST EACH MAT.	COST EACH INST.	COST EACH TOTAL
Basement stairs, open risers	1.000	Flight	4.000	850	216	1,066
Spiral stairs, oak, 4'-6" diameter, prefabricated, 9' high	1.000	Flight	10.667	3,975	575	4,550
Aluminum, 5'-0" diameter stock unit	1.000	Flight	9.956	8,900	710	9,610
Custom unit	1.000	Flight	9.956	16,800	710	17,510
Cast iron, 4'-0" diameter, minimum	1.000	Flight	9.956	8,325	710	9,035
Maximum	1.000	Flight	17.920	11,300	1,275	12,575
Steel, industrial, pre-erected, 3'-6" wide, bar rail	1.000	Flight	7.724	8,475	765	9,240
Picket rail	1.000	Flight	7.724	9,525	765	10,290

Soffit Drywall
Soffit Framing
Top Cabinets
Counter Top
Bottom Cabinets

System Description	QUAN.	UNIT	LABOR HOURS	COST PER L.F.		
				MAT.	INST.	TOTAL
KITCHEN, ECONOMY GRADE						
Top cabinets, economy grade	1.000	L.F.	.171	59.20	9.28	68.48
Bottom cabinets, economy grade	1.000	L.F.	.256	88.80	13.92	102.72
Square edge, plastic face countertop	1.000	L.F.	.267	36	14.40	50.40
Blocking, wood, 2" x 4"	1.000	L.F.	.032	.42	1.73	2.15
Soffit, framing, wood, 2" x 4"	4.000	L.F.	.071	1.68	3.84	5.52
Soffit drywall	2.000	S.F.	.047	.80	2.56	3.36
Drywall painting	2.000	S.F.	.013	.12	.72	.84
TOTAL		L.F.	.857	187.02	46.45	233.47
AVERAGE GRADE						
Top cabinets, average grade	1.000	L.F.	.213	74	11.60	85.60
Bottom cabinets, average grade	1.000	L.F.	.320	111	17.40	128.40
Solid surface countertop, solid color	1.000	L.F.	.800	79.50	43	122.50
Blocking, wood, 2" x 4"	1.000	L.F.	.032	.42	1.73	2.15
Soffit framing, wood, 2" x 4"	4.000	L.F.	.071	1.68	3.84	5.52
Soffit drywall	2.000	S.F.	.047	.80	2.56	3.36
Drywall painting	2.000	S.F.	.013	.12	.72	.84
TOTAL		L.F.	1.496	267.52	80.85	348.37
CUSTOM GRADE						
Top cabinets, custom grade	1.000	L.F.	.256	166	13.80	179.80
Bottom cabinets, custom grade	1.000	L.F.	.384	249	20.70	269.70
Solid surface countertop, premium patterned color	1.000	L.F.	1.067	138	57.50	195.50
Blocking, wood, 2" x 4"	1.000	L.F.	.032	.42	1.73	2.15
Soffit framing, wood, 2" x 4"	4.000	L.F.	.071	1.68	3.84	5.52
Soffit drywall	2.000	S.F.	.047	.80	2.56	3.36
Drywall painting	2.000	S.F.	.013	.12	.72	.84
TOTAL		L.F.	1.870	556.02	100.85	656.87

Description	QUAN.	UNIT	LABOR HOURS	COST PER L.F.		
				MAT.	INST.	TOTAL

Kitchen Price Sheet	QUAN.	UNIT	LABOR HOURS	COST PER L.F.		
				MAT.	INST.	TOTAL
Top cabinets, economy grade	1.000	L.F.	.171	59	9.30	68.30
Average grade	1.000	L.F.	.213	74	11.60	85.60
Custom grade	1.000	L.F.	.256	166	13.80	179.80
Bottom cabinets, economy grade	1.000	L.F.	.256	89	13.90	102.90
Average grade	1.000	L.F.	.320	111	17.40	128.40
Custom grade	1.000	L.F.	.384	249	20.50	269.50
Counter top, laminated plastic, 7/8" thick, no splash	1.000	L.F.	.267	32.50	14.40	46.90
With backsplash	1.000	L.F.	.267	31.50	14.40	45.90
1-1/4" thick, no splash	1.000	L.F.	.286	38	15.45	53.45
With backsplash	1.000	L.F.	.286	45.50	15.45	60.95
Post formed, laminated plastic	1.000	L.F.	.267	11	14.40	25.40
Ceramic tile, with backsplash		L.F.	.427	18.15	8.65	26.80
Marble, with backsplash, minimum	1.000	L.F.	.471	45	25	70
Maximum	1.000	L.F.	.615	113	32.50	145.50
Maple, solid laminated, no backsplash	1.000	L.F.	.286	81.50	15.45	96.95
With backsplash	1.000	L.F.	.286	97	15.45	112.45
Solid Surface, with backsplash, minimum		L.F.	.842	87	45.50	132.50
Maximum		L.F.	1.067	138	57.50	195.50
Blocking, wood, 2" x 4"	1.000	L.F.	.032	.42	1.73	2.15
2" x 6"	1.000	L.F.	.036	.63	1.95	2.58
2" x 8"	1.000	L.F.	.040	.94	2.16	3.10
Soffit framing, wood, 2" x 3"	4.000	L.F.	.064	1.64	3.44	5.08
2" x 4"	4.000	L.F.	.071	1.68	3.84	5.52
Soffit, drywall, painted	2.000	S.F.	.060	.92	3.28	4.20
Paneling, standard	2.000	S.F.	.064	.90	3.46	4.36
Deluxe	2.000	S.F.	.091	2.76	4.94	7.70
Sinks, porcelain on cast iron, single bowl, 21" x 24"	1.000	Ea.	10.334	805	580	1,385
21" x 30"	1.000	Ea.	10.334	1,125	580	1,705
Double bowl, 20" x 32"	1.000	Ea.	10.810	880	610	1,490
Stainless steel, single bowl, 16" x 20"	1.000	Ea.	10.334	1,150	580	1,730
22" x 25"	1.000	Ea.	10.334	1,225	580	1,805
Double bowl, 20" x 32"	1.000	Ea.	10.810	1,050	610	1,660

Kitchen Price Sheet

	QUAN.	UNIT	LABOR HOURS	COST PER L.F. MAT.	COST PER L.F. INST.	COST PER L.F. TOTAL
Range, free standing, minimum	1.000	Ea.	3.600	565	181	746
Maximum	1.000	Ea.	6.000	2,275	277	2,552
Built-in, minimum	1.000	Ea.	3.333	825	195	1,020
Maximum	1.000	Ea.	10.000	1,550	545	2,095
Counter top range, 4-burner, minimum	1.000	Ea.	3.333	405	195	600
Maximum	1.000	Ea.	4.667	1,500	273	1,773
Compactor, built-in, minimum	1.000	Ea.	2.215	730	123	853
Maximum	1.000	Ea.	3.282	1,125	180	1,305
Dishwasher, built-in, minimum	1.000	Ea.	6.735	680	420	1,100
Maximum	1.000	Ea.	9.235	895	575	1,470
Garbage disposer, minimum	1.000	Ea.	2.810	295	176	471
Maximum	1.000	Ea.	2.810	440	176	616
Microwave oven, minimum	1.000	Ea.	2.615	154	153	307
Maximum	1.000	Ea.	4.615	530	270	800
Range hood, ducted, minimum	1.000	Ea.	4.658	114	261	375
Maximum	1.000	Ea.	5.991	885	335	1,220
Ductless, minimum	1.000	Ea.	2.615	120	146	266
Maximum	1.000	Ea.	3.948	890	219	1,109
Refrigerator, 16 cu.ft., minimum	1.000	Ea.	2.000	575	80	655
Maximum	1.000	Ea.	3.200	920	128	1,048
16 cu.ft. with icemaker, minimum	1.000	Ea.	4.210	890	210	1,100
Maximum	1.000	Ea.	5.410	1,225	258	1,483
19 cu.ft., minimum	1.000	Ea.	2.667	485	107	592
Maximum	1.000	Ea.	4.667	850	187	1,037
19 cu.ft. with icemaker, minimum	1.000	Ea.	5.143	805	247	1,052
Maximum	1.000	Ea.	7.143	1,175	330	1,505
Sinks, porcelain on cast iron single bowl, 21" x 24"	1.000	Ea.	10.334	805	580	1,385
21" x 30"	1.000	Ea.	10.334	1,125	580	1,705
Double bowl, 20" x 32"	1.000	Ea.	10.810	880	610	1,490
Stainless steel, single bowl 16" x 20"	1.000	Ea.	10.334	1,150	580	1,730
22" x 25"	1.000	Ea.	10.334	1,225	580	1,805
Double bowl, 20" x 32"	1.000	Ea.	10.810	1,050	610	1,660
Water heater, electric, 30 gallon	1.000	Ea.	3.636	525	228	753
40 gallon	1.000	Ea.	4.000	880	251	1,131
Gas, 30 gallon	1.000	Ea.	4.000	985	251	1,236
75 gallon	1.000	Ea.	5.333	1,500	335	1,835
Wall, packaged terminal heater/air conditioner cabinet, wall sleeve, louver, electric heat, thermostat, manual changeover, 208V		Ea.				
6000 BTUH cooling, 8800 BTU heating	1.000	Ea.	2.667	855	153	1,008
9000 BTUH cooling, 13,900 BTU heating	1.000	Ea.	3.200	935	184	1,119
12,000 BTUH cooling, 13,900 BTU heating	1.000	Ea.	4.000	1,000	229	1,229
15,000 BTUH cooling, 13,900 BTU heating	1.000	Ea.	5.333	1,275	305	1,580

System Description	QUAN.	UNIT	LABOR HOURS	COST EACH		
				MAT.	INST.	TOTAL
Curtain rods, stainless, 1" diameter, 3' long	1.000	Ea.	.615	29	33	62
5' long	1.000	Ea.	.615	29	33	62
Grab bar, 1" diameter, 12" long	1.000	Ea.	.283	27	15.30	42.30
36" long	1.000	Ea.	.340	36	18.30	54.30
1-1/4" diameter, 12" long	1.000	Ea.	.333	32	18	50
36" long	1.000	Ea.	.400	42.50	21.50	64
1-1/2" diameter, 12" long	1.000	Ea.	.383	37	20.50	57.50
36" long	1.000	Ea.	.460	49	24.50	73.50
Mirror, 18" x 24"	1.000	Ea.	.400	51.50	21.50	73
72" x 24"	1.000	Ea.	1.333	282	72	354
Medicine chest with mirror, 18" x 24"	1.000	Ea.	.400	205	21.50	226.50
36" x 24"	1.000	Ea.	.600	310	32.50	342.50
Toilet tissue dispenser, surface mounted, minimum	1.000	Ea.	.267	19.60	14.40	34
Maximum	1.000	Ea.	.400	29.50	21.50	51
Flush mounted, minimum	1.000	Ea.	.293	21.50	15.85	37.35
Maximum	1.000	Ea.	.427	31.50	23	54.50
Towel bar, 18" long, minimum	1.000	Ea.	.278	37	15.05	52.05
Maximum	1.000	Ea.	.348	46	18.80	64.80
24" long, minimum	1.000	Ea.	.313	41.50	16.90	58.40
Maximum	1.000	Ea.	.383	50.50	20.50	71
36" long, minimum	1.000	Ea.	.381	123	20.50	143.50
Maximum	1.000	Ea.	.419	135	22.50	157.50

System Description	QUAN.	UNIT	LABOR HOURS	COST EACH		
				MAT.	INST.	TOTAL
MASONRY FIREPLACE						
Footing, 8" thick, concrete, 4' x 7'	.700	C.Y.	2.800	126.70	142.30	269
Foundation, concrete block, 32" x 60" x 4' deep	1.000	Ea.	5.275	174.60	259.20	433.80
Fireplace, brick firebox, 30" x 29" opening	1.000	Ea.	40.000	605	1,925	2,530
Damper, cast iron, 30" opening	1.000	Ea.	1.333	137	71	208
Facing brick, standard size brick, 6' x 5'	30.000	S.F.	5.217	146.40	256.50	402.90
Hearth, standard size brick, 3' x 6'	1.000	Ea.	8.000	225	385	610
Chimney, standard size brick, 8" x 12" flue, one story house	12.000	V.L.F.	12.000	510	576	1,086
Mantle, 4" x 8", wood	6.000	L.F.	1.333	54.60	72	126.60
Cleanout, cast iron, 8" x 8"	1.000	Ea.	.667	45	35.50	80.50
TOTAL		Ea.	76.625	2,024.30	3,722.50	5,746.80

The costs in this system are on a cost each basis.

Description	QUAN.	UNIT	LABOR HOURS	COST EACH		
				MAT.	INST.	TOTAL

Masonry Fireplace Price Sheet	QUAN.	UNIT	LABOR HOURS	COST EACH		
				MAT.	INST.	TOTAL
Footing 8″ thick, 3′ x 6′	.440	C.Y.	1.326	79.50	89.50	169
4′ x 7′	.700	C.Y.	2.110	127	142	269
5′ x 8′	1.000	C.Y.	3.014	181	203	384
1′ thick, 3′ x 6′	.670	C.Y.	2.020	121	136	257
4′ x 7′	1.030	C.Y.	3.105	186	209	395
5′ x 8′	1.480	C.Y.	4.461	268	300	568
Foundation-concrete block, 24″ x 48″, 4′ deep	1.000	Ea.	4.267	140	207	347
8′ deep	1.000	Ea.	8.533	279	415	694
24″ x 60″, 4′ deep	1.000	Ea.	4.978	163	242	405
8′ deep	1.000	Ea.	9.956	325	485	810
32″ x 48″, 4′ deep	1.000	Ea.	4.711	154	229	383
8′ deep	1.000	Ea.	9.422	310	460	770
32″ x 60″, 4′ deep	1.000	Ea.	5.333	175	259	434
8′ deep	1.000	Ea.	10.845	355	525	880
32″ x 72″, 4′ deep	1.000	Ea.	6.133	201	298	499
8′ deep	1.000	Ea.	12.267	400	595	995
Fireplace, brick firebox 30″ x 29″ opening	1.000	Ea.	40.000	605	1,925	2,530
48″ x 30″ opening	1.000	Ea.	60.000	910	2,900	3,810
Steel fire box with registers, 25″ opening	1.000	Ea.	26.667	1,100	1,300	2,400
48″ opening	1.000	Ea.	44.000	1,850	2,125	3,975
Damper, cast iron, 30″ opening	1.000	Ea.	1.333	137	71	208
36″ opening	1.000	Ea.	1.556	160	83	243
Steel, 30″ opening	1.000	Ea.	1.333	131	71	202
36″ opening	1.000	Ea.	1.556	153	83	236
Facing for fireplace, standard size brick, 6′ x 5′	30.000	S.F.	5.217	146	257	403
7′ x 5′	35.000	S.F.	6.087	171	299	470
8′ x 6′	48.000	S.F.	8.348	234	410	644
Fieldstone, 6′ x 5′	30.000	S.F.	5.217	425	257	682
7′ x 5′	35.000	S.F.	6.087	500	299	799
8′ x 6′	48.000	S.F.	8.348	685	410	1,095
Sheetrock on metal, studs, 6′ x 5′	30.000	S.F.	.980	24	53	77
7′ x 5′	35.000	S.F.	1.143	28	61.50	89.50
8′ x 6′	48.000	S.F.	1.568	38.50	84.50	123
Hearth, standard size brick, 3′ x 6′	1.000	Ea.	8.000	225	385	610
3′ x 7′	1.000	Ea.	9.280	261	445	706
3′ x 8′	1.000	Ea.	10.640	299	510	809
Stone, 3′ x 6′	1.000	Ea.	8.000	232	385	617
3′ x 7′	1.000	Ea.	9.280	269	445	714
3′ x 8′	1.000	Ea.	10.640	310	510	820
Chimney, standard size brick , 8″ x 12″ flue, one story house	12.000	V.L.F.	12.000	510	575	1,085
Two story house	20.000	V.L.F.	20.000	850	960	1,810
Mantle wood, beams, 4″ x 8″	6.000	L.F.	1.333	54.50	72	126.50
4″ x 10″	6.000	L.F.	1.371	72	74	146
Ornate, prefabricated, 6′ x 3′-6″ opening, minimum	1.000	Ea.	1.600	273	86.50	359.50
Maximum	1.000	Ea.	1.600	490	86.50	576.50
Cleanout, door and frame, cast iron, 8″ x 8″	1.000	Ea.	.667	45	35.50	80.50
12″ x 12″	1.000	Ea.	.800	119	42.50	161.50

Chimney, Flue, Fittings & Framing

Framing

Mantle

Facing Brick

Prefabricated Fireplace

Hearth

System Description	QUAN.	UNIT	LABOR HOURS	COST EACH MAT.	COST EACH INST.	COST EACH TOTAL
PREFABRICATED FIREPLACE						
Prefabricated fireplace, metal, minimum	1.000	Ea.	6.154	1,325	330	1,655
Framing, 2" x 4" studs, 6' x 5'	35.000	L.F.	.509	14.35	27.65	42
Fire resistant gypsum drywall, unfinished	40.000	S.F.	.320	14	17.20	31.20
Drywall finishing adder	40.000	S.F.	.320	2	17.20	19.20
Facing, brick, standard size brick, 6' x 5'	30.000	S.F.	5.217	146.40	256.50	402.90
Hearth, standard size brick, 3' x 6'	1.000	Ea.	8.000	225	385	610
Chimney, one story house, framing, 2" x 4" studs	80.000	L.F.	1.164	32.80	63.20	96
Sheathing, plywood, 5/8" thick	32.000	S.F.	.758	85.44	40.96	126.40
Flue, 10" metal, insulated pipe	12.000	V.L.F.	4.000	480	216.60	696.60
Fittings, ceiling support	1.000	Ea.	.667	148	36	184
Fittings, joist shield	1.000	Ea.	.727	730	39.50	769.50
Fittings, roof flashing	1.000	Ea.	.667	415	36	451
Mantle beam, wood, 4" x 8"	6.000	L.F.	1.333	54.60	72	126.60
TOTAL		Ea.	29.836	3,672.59	1,537.81	5,210.40

The costs in this system are on a cost each basis.

Description	QUAN.	UNIT	LABOR HOURS	COST EACH MAT.	COST EACH INST.	COST EACH TOTAL

Prefabricated Fireplace Price Sheet	QUAN.	UNIT	LABOR HOURS	COST EACH		
				MAT.	INST.	TOTAL
Prefabricated fireplace, minimum	1.000	Ea.	6.154	1,325	330	1,655
Average	1.000	Ea.	8.000	1,600	430	2,030
Maximum	1.000	Ea.	8.889	3,000	480	3,480
Framing, 2" x 4" studs, fireplace, 6' x 5'	35.000	L.F.	.509	14.35	27.50	41.85
7' x 5'	40.000	L.F.	.582	16.40	31.50	47.90
8' x 6'	45.000	L.F.	.655	18.45	35.50	53.95
Sheetrock, 1/2" thick, fireplace, 6' x 5'	40.000	S.F.	.640	16	34.50	50.50
7' x 5'	45.000	S.F.	.720	18	38.50	56.50
8' x 6'	50.000	S.F.	.800	20	43	63
Facing for fireplace, brick, 6' x 5'	30.000	S.F.	5.217	146	257	403
7' x 5'	35.000	S.F.	6.087	171	299	470
8' x 6'	48.000	S.F.	8.348	234	410	644
Fieldstone, 6' x 5'	30.000	S.F.	5.217	355	257	612
7' x 5'	35.000	S.F.	6.087	410	299	709
8' x 6'	48.000	S.F.	8.348	565	410	975
Hearth, standard size brick, 3' x 6'	1.000	Ea.	8.000	225	385	610
3' x 7'	1.000	Ea.	9.280	261	445	706
3' x 8'	1.000	Ea.	10.640	299	510	809
Stone, 3' x 6'	1.000	Ea.	8.000	232	385	617
3' x 7'	1.000	Ea.	9.280	269	445	714
3' x 8'	1.000	Ea.	10.640	310	510	820
Chimney, framing, 2" x 4", one story house	80.000	L.F.	1.164	33	63	96
Two story house	120.000	L.F.	1.746	49	95	144
Sheathing, plywood, 5/8" thick	32.000	S.F.	.758	85.50	41	126.50
Stucco on plywood	32.000	S.F.	1.125	52	59	111
Flue, 10" metal pipe, insulated, one story house	12.000	V.L.F.	4.000	480	217	697
Two story house	20.000	V.L.F.	6.667	800	360	1,160
Fittings, ceiling support	1.000	Ea.	.667	148	36	184
Fittings joist sheild, one story house	1.000	Ea.	.667	730	39.50	769.50
Two story house	2.000	Ea.	1.333	1,450	79	1,529
Fittings roof flashing	1.000	Ea.	.667	415	36	451
Mantle, wood beam, 4" x 8"	6.000	L.F.	1.333	54.50	72	126.50
4" x 10"	6.000	L.F.	1.371	72	74	146
Ornate prefabricated, 6' x 3'-6" opening, minimum	1.000	Ea.	1.600	273	86.50	359.50
Maximum	1.000	Ea.	1.600	490	86.50	576.50

System Description	QUAN.	UNIT	LABOR HOURS	COST EACH MAT.	COST EACH INST.	COST EACH TOTAL
Economy, lean to, shell only, not including 2' stub wall, fndtn, flrs, heat						
4' x 16'	1.000	Ea.	26.212	2,250	1,425	3,675
4' x 24'	1.000	Ea.	30.259	2,600	1,650	4,250
6' x 10'	1.000	Ea.	16.552	2,950	895	3,845
6' x 16'	1.000	Ea.	23.034	4,100	1,250	5,350
6' x 24'	1.000	Ea.	29.793	5,300	1,600	6,900
8' x 10'	1.000	Ea.	22.069	3,925	1,200	5,125
8' x 16'	1.000	Ea.	38.400	6,825	2,075	8,900
8' x 24'	1.000	Ea.	49.655	8,825	2,675	11,500
Free standing, 8' x 8'	1.000	Ea.	17.356	2,250	940	3,190
8' x 16'	1.000	Ea.	30.211	3,900	1,625	5,525
8' x 24'	1.000	Ea.	39.051	5,050	2,100	7,150
10' x 10'	1.000	Ea.	18.824	2,650	1,025	3,675
10' x 16'	1.000	Ea.	24.095	3,400	1,300	4,700
10' x 24'	1.000	Ea.	31.624	4,450	1,700	6,150
14' x 10'	1.000	Ea.	20.741	3,650	1,125	4,775
14' x 16'	1.000	Ea.	24.889	4,375	1,350	5,725
14' x 24'	1.000	Ea.	33.349	5,850	1,800	7,650
Standard, lean to, shell only, not incl. 2' stub wall, fndtn, flrs, heat 4'x10'	1.000	Ea.	28.235	2,425	1,525	3,950
4' x 16'	1.000	Ea.	39.341	3,375	2,125	5,500
4' x 24'	1.000	Ea.	45.412	3,900	2,450	6,350
6' x 10'	1.000	Ea.	24.827	4,400	1,350	5,750
6' x 16'	1.000	Ea.	34.538	6,125	1,875	8,000
6' x 24'	1.000	Ea.	44.689	7,950	2,425	10,375
8' x 10'	1.000	Ea.	33.103	5,875	1,800	7,675
8' x 16'	1.000	Ea.	57.600	10,200	3,100	13,300
8' x 24'	1.000	Ea.	74.482	13,200	4,025	17,225
Free standing, 8' x 8'	1.000	Ea.	26.034	3,350	1,400	4,750
8' x 16'	1.000	Ea.	45.316	5,850	2,450	8,300
8' x 24'	1.000	Ea.	58.577	7,550	3,175	10,725
10' x 10'	1.000	Ea.	28.236	3,975	1,525	5,500
10' x 16'	1.000	Ea.	36.142	5,100	1,950	7,050
10' x 24'	1.000	Ea.	47.436	6,675	2,550	9,225
14' x 10'	1.000	Ea.	31.112	5,450	1,675	7,125
14' x 16'	1.000	Ea.	37.334	6,550	2,025	8,575
14' x 24'	1.000	Ea.	50.030	8,775	2,700	11,475
Deluxe, lean to, shell only, not incl. 2' stub wall, fndtn, flrs or heat, 4'x10'	1.000	Ea.	20.645	4,650	1,125	5,775
4' x 16'	1.000	Ea.	33.032	7,425	1,800	9,225
4' x 24'	1.000	Ea.	49.548	11,100	2,700	13,800
6' x 10'	1.000	Ea.	30.968	6,950	1,675	8,625
6' x 16'	1.000	Ea.	49.548	11,100	2,700	13,800
6' x 24'	1.000	Ea.	74.323	16,700	4,025	20,725
8' x 10'	1.000	Ea.	41.290	9,275	2,250	11,525
8' x 16'	1.000	Ea.	66.065	14,800	3,575	18,375
8' x 24'	1.000	Ea.	99.097	22,300	5,375	27,675
Freestanding, 8' x 8'	1.000	Ea.	18.618	4,150	1,000	5,150
8' x 16'	1.000	Ea.	37.236	8,325	2,000	10,325
8' x 24'	1.000	Ea.	55.855	12,500	3,025	15,525
10' x 10'	1.000	Ea.	29.091	6,500	1,575	8,075
10' x 16'	1.000	Ea.	46.546	10,400	2,500	12,900
10' x 24'	1.000	Ea.	69.818	15,600	3,775	19,375
14' x 10'	1.000	Ea.	40.727	9,100	2,200	11,300
14' x 16'	1.000	Ea.	65.164	14,600	3,525	18,125
14' x 24'	1.000	Ea.	97.746	21,800	5,275	27,075

System Description	QUAN.	UNIT	LABOR HOURS	COST EACH		
				MAT.	INST.	TOTAL
Swimming pools, vinyl lined, metal sides, sand bottom, 12' x 28'	1.000	Ea.	50.177	6,325	2,825	9,150
12' x 32'	1.000	Ea.	55.366	6,975	3,150	10,125
12' x 36'	1.000	Ea.	60.061	7,550	3,400	10,950
16' x 32'	1.000	Ea.	66.798	8,400	3,775	12,175
16' x 36'	1.000	Ea.	71.190	8,950	4,025	12,975
16' x 40'	1.000	Ea.	74.703	9,400	4,225	13,625
20' x 36'	1.000	Ea.	77.860	9,800	4,400	14,200
20' x 40'	1.000	Ea.	82.135	10,300	4,650	14,950
20' x 44'	1.000	Ea.	90.348	11,400	5,125	16,525
24' x 40'	1.000	Ea.	98.562	12,400	5,575	17,975
24' x 44'	1.000	Ea.	108.418	13,600	6,150	19,750
24' x 48'	1.000	Ea.	118.274	14,900	6,700	21,600
Vinyl lined, concrete sides, 12' x 28'	1.000	Ea.	79.447	10,000	4,500	14,500
12' x 32'	1.000	Ea.	88.818	11,200	5,025	16,225
12' x 36'	1.000	Ea.	97.656	12,300	5,550	17,850
16' x 32'	1.000	Ea.	111.393	14,000	6,325	20,325
16' x 36'	1.000	Ea.	121.354	15,300	6,875	22,175
16' x 40'	1.000	Ea.	130.445	16,400	7,400	23,800
28' x 36'	1.000	Ea.	140.585	17,700	7,975	25,675
20' x 40'	1.000	Ea.	149.336	18,800	8,475	27,275
20' x 44'	1.000	Ea.	164.270	20,700	9,325	30,025
24' x 40'	1.000	Ea.	179.203	22,600	10,200	32,800
24' x 44'	1.000	Ea.	197.124	24,800	11,200	36,000
24' x 48'	1.000	Ea.	215.044	27,100	12,200	39,300
Gunite, bottom and sides, 12' x 28'	1.000	Ea.	129.767	14,600	7,350	21,950
12' x 32'	1.000	Ea.	142.164	16,000	8,050	24,050
12' x 36'	1.000	Ea.	153.028	17,200	8,675	25,875
16' x 32'	1.000	Ea.	167.743	18,900	9,500	28,400
16' x 36'	1.000	Ea.	176.421	19,900	10,000	29,900
16' x 40'	1.000	Ea.	182.368	20,500	10,300	30,800
20' x 36'	1.000	Ea.	187.949	21,200	10,700	31,900
20' x 40'	1.000	Ea.	179.200	28,000	10,200	38,200
20' x 44'	1.000	Ea.	197.120	30,800	11,200	42,000
24' x 40'	1.000	Ea.	215.040	33,600	12,200	45,800
24' x 44'	1.000	Ea.	273.244	30,800	15,500	46,300
24' x 48'	1.000	Ea.	298.077	33,600	16,900	50,500

System Description	QUAN.	UNIT	LABOR HOURS	COST PER S.F.		
				MAT.	INST.	TOTAL
8′ X 12′ DECK, PRESSURE TREATED LUMBER, JOISTS 16″ O.C.						
4″ x 4″ Posts	.500	L.F.	.021	.67	1.11	1.78
Ledger, bolted 4′ O.C.	.125	L.F.	.005	.20	.28	.48
Joists, 2″ x 10″, 16″ O.C.	1.080	L.F.	.019	1.61	1.04	2.65
5/4″ x 6″ decking	1.000	S.F.	.025	2.24	1.35	3.59
2″ x 12″ stair stringers	.375	L.F.	.046	.67	2.49	3.16
5/4″ x 6″ stair treads	.500	L.F.	.050	.52	2.70	3.22
4′ x 4″ handrail posts	.210	L.F.	.009	.28	.47	.75
2″ x 6″ handrail cap	.520	L.F.	.014	.44	.75	1.19
2″ x 4″ baluster support	1.040	L.F.	.028	.57	1.50	2.07
2″ x 2″ balusters	3.850	L.F.	.093	1.42	5.04	6.46
Post footings	.042	Ea.	.134	1.03	6.34	7.37
Concrete step	.010	Ea.	.016	.73	.85	1.58
Joist hangers	.210	Ea.	.010	.32	.55	.87
TOTAL		S.F.	.470	10.70	24.47	35.17
12′ X 16′ DECK, PRESSURE TREATED LUMBER, JOISTS 24″ O.C.						
4″ x 4″ Posts	.312	L.F.	.013	.42	.69	1.11
Ledger, bolted 4′ O.C.	.083	L.F.	.003	.11	.18	.29
Joists, 2″ x 8″, 16″ O.C.	.810	L.F.	.014	1.21	.78	1.99
5/4″ x 6″ decking	1.000	S.F.	.025	2.24	1.35	3.59
2″ x 12″ stair stringers	.188	L.F.	.023	.34	1.25	1.59
5/4″ x 6″ stair treads	.250	L.F.	.025	1.22	1.35	2.57
4″ x 4″ handrail posts	.125	L.F.	.005	.17	.28	.45
2″ x 6″ handrail cap	.323	L.F.	.009	.27	.47	.74
2″ x 4″ baluster support	.650	L.F.	.017	.36	.94	1.30
2″ x 2″ balusters	2.440	L.F.	.059	.90	3.20	4.10
Post footings	.026	Ea.	.083	.64	3.93	4.57
Concrete step	.005	Ea.	.008	.37	.43	.80
Joist hangers	.135	Ea.	.007	.21	.35	.56
Deck support girder	.083	L.F.	.002	.25	.13	.38
TOTAL		S.F.	.293	8.71	15.33	24.04

The costs in this system are on a square foot basis.

System Description	QUAN.	UNIT	LABOR HOURS	COST PER S.F.		
				MAT.	INST.	TOTAL
12' X 24' DECK, REDWOOD OR CEDAR, JOISTS 16" O.C.						
4" x 4" redwood posts	.291	L.F.	.012	2.05	.65	2.70
Redwood joists, 2" x 8", 16" O.C.	.001	M.B.F.	.010	5.50	.54	6.04
5/4" x 6" redwood decking	1.000	S.F.	.025	5.25	1.35	6.60
Stair stringers	.125	L.F.	.015	.22	.83	1.05
Stringer trim	.083	L.F.	.003	.44	.18	.62
Stair treads	.135	S.F.	.003	.71	.18	.89
Handrail supports	.083	L.F.	.003	.59	.18	.77
Handrail cap	.152	L.F.	.004	1.25	.22	1.47
Baluster supports	.416	L.F.	.011	3.43	.60	4.03
Balusters	1.875	L.F.	.050	2.42	2.70	5.12
Post footings	.024	Ea.	.077	.59	3.62	4.21
Concrete step	.003	Ea.	.005	.22	.25	.47
Joist hangers	.132	Ea.	.006	.20	.35	.55
Deck support girder		M.B.F.	.003	1.50	.15	1.65
TOTAL		S.F.	.227	24.37	11.80	36.17

The costs in this system are on a square foot basis.

Wood Deck Price Sheet	QUAN.	UNIT	LABOR HOURS	COST PER S.F.		
				MAT.	INST.	TOTAL
Decking, treated lumber, 1" x 4"	3.430	L.F.	.031	7.35	5.40	12.75
2" x 4"	3.430	L.F.	.033	6.30	4.94	11.24
2" x 6"	2.200	L.F.	.041	4	2.97	6.97
5/4" x 6"	2.200	L.F.	.027	4.93	2.97	7.90
Redwood or cedar, 1" x 4"	3.430	L.F.	.035	6.85	5.40	12.25
2" x 4"	3.430	L.F.	.036	13.70	4.94	18.64
2" x 6"	2.200	L.F.	.028	15.95	2.97	18.92
5/4" x 6"	2.200	L.F.	.027	10.75	2.97	13.72
Joists for deck, treated lumber, 2" x 8", 16" O.C.	1.000	L.F.	.015	1.14	.79	1.93
24" O.C.	.750	L.F.	.012	.86	.59	1.45
2" x 10", 16" O.C.	1.000	L.F.	.018	1.49	.96	2.45
24" O.C.	.750	L.F.	.014	1.12	.72	1.84
Redwood or cedar, 2" x 8", 16" O.C.	1.000	L.F.	.015	5	.79	5.79
24" O.C.	.750	L.F.	.012	3.75	.59	4.34
2" x 10", 16" O.C.	1.000	L.F.	.018	8.35	.96	9.31
24" O.C.	.750	L.F.	.014	6.25	.72	6.97
Girder for joists, treated lumber, 2" x 10", 8' x 12' deck	.250	L.F.	.002	.37	.20	.57
12' x 16' deck	.167	L.F.	.001	.25	.13	.38
12' x 24' deck	.167	L.F.	.001	.25	.13	.38
Redwood or cedar, 2" x 10", 8' x 12' deck	.250	L.F.	.002	2.09	.24	2.33
12' x 16' deck	.167	L.F.	.001	1.39	.16	1.55
12' x 24' deck	.167	L.F.	.001	1.39	.16	1.55
Posts, 4" x 4", including concrete footing, 8' x 12' deck	.500	L.F.	.022	1.67	7.30	8.97
12' x 16' deck	.312	L.F.	.017	1.06	4.62	5.68
12' x 24' deck	.291	L.F.	.017	.98	4.27	5.25
Stairs 2" x 10" stringers, treated lumber, 8' x 12' deck	1.000	Set	.020	1.50	4.30	5.80
12' x 16' deck	1.000	Set	.012	.75	2.15	2.90
12' x 24' deck	1.000	Set	.008	.53	1.51	2.04
Redwood or cedar, 8' x 12' deck	1.000	Set	.040	3.90	4.30	8.20
12' x 16' deck	1.000	Set	.020	1.95	2.15	4.10
12' x 24' deck	1.000	Set	.012	1.37	1.51	2.88
Railings 2" x 4", treated lumber, 8' x 12' deck	.520	L.F.	.026	2.43	7.30	9.73
12' x 16' deck	.323	L.F.	.017	1.53	4.61	6.14
12' x 24' deck	.210	L.F.	.014	1.11	3.36	4.47
Redwood or cedar, 8' x 12' deck	1.000	L.F.	.009	10.60	7.80	18.40

Wood Deck Price Sheet	QUAN.	UNIT	LABOR HOURS	COST PER S.F.		
				MAT.	INST.	TOTAL
12' x 16' deck	.670	L.F.	.006	6.60	4.90	11.50
12' x 24' deck	.540	L.F.	.005	4.70	3.61	8.31
Alternative decking, wood/plastic composite, 5/4" x 6"	2.200	L.F.	.055	7.35	2.97	10.32
1" x 4" square edge fir	3.430	L.F.	.100	7.45	5.40	12.85
1" x 4" tongue and groove fir	3.430	L.F.	.122	4.94	6.60	11.54
1" x 4" mahogany	3.430	L.F.	.100	6.85	5.40	12.25
5/4" x 6" PVC	2.200	L.F.	.064	8.75	3.45	12.20

Lavatory
Vanity Top
Piping
Vanity Base Cabinet
Water Closet

System Description	QUAN.	UNIT	LABOR HOURS	COST EACH		
				MAT.	INST.	TOTAL
LAVATORY INSTALLED WITH VANITY, PLUMBING IN 2 WALLS						
Water closet, floor mounted, 2 piece, close coupled, white	1.000	Ea.	3.019	256	170	426
Rough-in, vent, 2″ diameter DWV piping	1.000	Ea.	.955	41.40	54	95.40
Waste, 4″ diameter DWV piping	1.000	Ea.	.828	55.95	46.65	102.60
Supply, 1/2″ diameter type "L" copper supply piping	1.000	Ea.	.593	22.26	37.20	59.46
Lavatory, 20″ x 18″, P.E. cast iron white	1.000	Ea.	2.500	360	141	501
Rough-in, vent, 1-1/2″ diameter DWV piping	1.000	Ea.	.901	40.20	50.80	91
Waste, 2″ diameter DWV piping	1.000	Ea.	.955	41.40	54	95.40
Supply, 1/2″ diameter type "L" copper supply piping	1.000	Ea.	.988	37.10	62	99.10
Piping, supply, 1/2″ diameter type "L" copper supply piping	10.000	L.F.	.988	37.10	62	99.10
Waste, 4″ diameter DWV piping	7.000	L.F.	1.931	130.55	108.85	239.40
Vent, 2″ diameter DWV piping	12.000	L.F.	2.866	124.20	162	286.20
Vanity base cabinet, 2 door, 30″ wide	1.000	Ea.	1.000	390	54	444
Vanity top, plastic & laminated, square edge	2.670	L.F.	.712	113.48	38.45	151.93
TOTAL		Ea.	18.236	1,649.64	1,040.95	2,690.59
LAVATORY WITH WALL-HUNG LAVATORY, PLUMBING IN 2 WALLS						
Water closet, floor mounted, 2 piece close coupled, white	1.000	Ea.	3.019	256	170	426
Rough-in, vent, 2″ diameter DWV piping	1.000	Ea.	.955	41.40	54	95.40
Waste, 4″ diameter DWV piping	1.000	Ea.	.828	55.95	46.65	102.60
Supply, 1/2″ diameter type "L" copper supply piping	1.000	Ea.	.593	22.26	37.20	59.46
Lavatory, 20″ x 18″, P.E. cast iron, wall hung, white	1.000	Ea.	2.000	305	113	418
Rough-in, vent, 1-1/2″ diameter DWV piping	1.000	Ea.	.901	40.20	50.80	91
Waste, 2″ diameter DWV piping	1.000	Ea.	.955	41.40	54	95.40
Supply, 1/2″ diameter type "L" copper supply piping	1.000	Ea.	.988	37.10	62	99.10
Piping, supply, 1/2″ diameter type "L" copper supply piping	10.000	L.F.	.988	37.10	62	99.10
Waste, 4″ diameter DWV piping	7.000	L.F.	1.931	130.55	108.85	239.40
Vent, 2″ diameter DWV piping	12.000	L.F.	2.866	124.20	162	286.20
Carrier, steel for studs, no arms	1.000	Ea.	1.143	91.50	71.50	163
TOTAL		Ea.	17.167	1,182.66	992	2,174.66

Description	QUAN.	UNIT	LABOR HOURS	COST EACH		
				MAT.	INST.	TOTAL

Two Fixture Lavatory Price Sheet	QUAN.	UNIT	LABOR HOURS	COST EACH		
				MAT.	INST.	TOTAL
Water closet, close coupled standard 2 piece, white	1.000	Ea.	3.019	256	170	426
Color	1.000	Ea.	3.019	445	170	615
One piece elongated bowl, white	1.000	Ea.	3.019	1,200	170	1,370
Color	1.000	Ea.	3.019	1,500	170	1,670
Low profile, one piece elongated bowl, white	1.000	Ea.	3.019	1,150	170	1,320
Color	1.000	Ea.	3.019	1,500	170	1,670
Rough-in for water closet						
1/2" copper supply, 4" cast iron waste, 2" cast iron vent	1.000	Ea.	2.376	120	138	258
4" PVC waste, 2" PVC vent	1.000	Ea.	2.678	64.50	155	219.50
4" copper waste , 2" copper vent	1.000	Ea.	2.520	300	150	450
3" cast iron waste, 1-1/2" cast iron vent	1.000	Ea.	2.244	106	130	236
3" PVC waste, 1-1/2" PVC vent	1.000	Ea.	2.388	55.50	144	199.50
3" copper waste, 1-1/2" copper vent	1.000	Ea.	2.524	292	146	438
1/2" PVC supply, 4" PVC waste, 2" PVC vent	1.000	Ea.	2.974	71.50	173	244.50
3" PVC waste, 1-1/2" PVC vent	1.000	Ea.	2.684	62.50	163	225.50
1/2" steel supply, 4" cast iron waste, 2" cast iron vent	1.000	Ea.	2.545	122	148	270
4" cast iron waste, 2" steel vent	1.000	Ea.	2.590	134	151	285
4" PVC waste, 2" PVC vent	1.000	Ea.	2.847	67	165	232
Lavatory, vanity top mounted, P.E. on cast iron 20" x 18" white	1.000	Ea.	2.500	360	141	501
Color	1.000	Ea.	2.500	625	141	766
Steel, enameled 10" x 17" white	1.000	Ea.	2.759	217	156	373
Color	1.000	Ea.	2.500	210	141	351
Vitreous china 20" x 16", white	1.000	Ea.	2.963	286	167	453
Color	1.000	Ea.	2.963	286	167	453
Wall hung, P.E. on cast iron, 20" x 18", white	1.000	Ea.	2.000	305	113	418
Color	1.000	Ea.	2.000	335	113	448
Vitreous china 19" x 17", white	1.000	Ea.	2.286	209	129	338
Color	1.000	Ea.	2.286	236	129	365
Rough-in supply waste and vent for lavatory						
1/2" copper supply, 2" cast iron waste, 1-1/2" cast iron vent	1.000	Ea.	2.844	119	167	286
2" PVC waste, 1-1/2" PVC vent	1.000	Ea.	2.962	65	179	244
2" copper waste, 1-1/2" copper vent	1.000	Ea.	2.308	167	145	312
1-1/2" PVC waste, 1-1/4" PVC vent	1.000	Ea.	2.639	65	166	231
1-1/2" copper waste, 1-1/4" copper vent	1.000	Ea.	2.114	136	133	269
1/2" PVC supply, 2" PVC waste, 1-1/2" PVC vent	1.000	Ea.	3.456	77	210	287
1-1/2" PVC waste, 1-1/4" PVC vent	1.000	Ea.	3.133	77	197	274
1/2" steel supply, 2" cast iron waste, 1-1/2" cast iron vent	1.000	Ea.	3.126	123	184	307
2" cast iron waste, 2" steel vent	1.000	Ea.	3.225	136	190	326
2" PVC waste, 1-1/2" PVC vent	1.000	Ea.	3.244	69.50	197	266.50
1-1/2" PVC waste, 1-1/4" PVC vent	1.000	Ea.	2.921	69.50	183	252.50
Piping, supply, 1/2" copper, type "L"	10.000	L.F.	.988	37	62	99
1/2" steel	10.000	L.F.	1.270	41.50	79.50	121
1/2" PVC	10.000	L.F.	1.482	49	93	142
Waste, 4" cast iron	7.000	L.F.	1.931	131	109	240
4" copper	7.000	L.F.	2.800	475	158	633
4" PVC	7.000	L.F.	2.333	64	132	196
Vent, 2" cast iron	12.000	L.F.	2.866	124	162	286
2" copper	12.000	L.F.	2.182	225	137	362
2" PVC	12.000	L.F.	3.254	45	184	229
2" steel	12.000	Ea.	3.000	160	169	329
Vanity base cabinet, 2 door, 24" x 30"	1.000	Ea.	1.000	390	54	444
24" x 36"	1.000	Ea.	1.200	380	65	445
Vanity top, laminated plastic, square edge 25" x 32"	2.670	L.F.	.712	113	38.50	151.50
25" x 38"	3.170	L.F.	.845	135	45.50	180.50
Post formed, laminated plastic, 25" x 32"	2.670	L.F.	.712	29.50	38.50	68
25" x 38"	3.170	L.F.	.845	35	45.50	80.50
Cultured marble, 25" x 32" with bowl	1.000	Ea.	2.500	236	141	377
25" x 38" with bowl	1.000	Ea.	2.500	270	141	411
Carrier for lavatory, steel for studs	1.000	Ea.	1.143	91.50	71.50	163
Wood 2" x 8" blocking	1.330	L.F.	.053	1.25	2.87	4.12

System Description	QUAN.	UNIT	LABOR HOURS	COST EACH		
				MAT.	INST.	TOTAL
BATHROOM INSTALLED WITH VANITY						
Water closet, floor mounted, 2 piece, close coupled, white	1.000	Ea.	3.019	256	170	426
Rough-in, waste, 4" diameter DWV piping	1.000	Ea.	.828	55.95	46.65	102.60
Vent, 2" diameter DWV piping	1.000	Ea.	.955	41.40	54	95.40
Supply, 1/2" diameter type "L" copper supply piping	1.000	Ea.	.593	22.26	37.20	59.46
Lavatory, 20" x 18", P.E. cast iron with accessories, white	1.000	Ea.	2.500	360	141	501
Rough-in, supply, 1/2" diameter type "L" copper supply piping	1.000	Ea.	.988	37.10	62	99.10
Waste, 1-1/2" diameter DWV piping	1.000	Ea.	1.803	80.40	101.60	182
Bathtub, P.E. cast iron, 5' long with accessories, white	1.000	Ea.	3.636	1,225	205	1,430
Rough-in, waste, 4" diameter DWV piping	1.000	Ea.	.828	55.95	46.65	102.60
Vent, 1-1/2" diameter DWV piping	1.000	Ea.	.593	54.80	37.20	92
Supply, 1/2" diameter type "L" copper supply piping	1.000	Ea.	.988	37.10	62	99.10
Piping, supply, 1/2" diameter type "L" copper supply piping	20.000	L.F.	1.975	74.20	124	198.20
Waste, 4" diameter DWV piping	9.000	L.F.	2.483	167.85	139.95	307.80
Vent, 2" diameter DWV piping	6.000	L.F.	1.500	80.10	84.60	164.70
Vanity base cabinet, 2 door, 30" wide	1.000	Ea.	1.000	390	54	444
Vanity top, plastic laminated square edge	2.670	L.F.	.712	96.12	38.45	134.57
TOTAL		Ea.	24.401	3,034.23	1,404.30	4,438.53
BATHROOM WITH WALL HUNG LAVATORY						
Water closet, floor mounted, 2 piece, close coupled, white	1.000	Ea.	3.019	256	170	426
Rough-in, vent, 2" diameter DWV piping	1.000	Ea.	.955	41.40	54	95.40
Waste, 4" diameter DWV piping	1.000	Ea.	.828	55.95	46.65	102.60
Supply, 1/2" diameter type "L" copper supply piping	1.000	Ea.	.593	22.26	37.20	59.46
Lavatory, 20" x 18" P.E. cast iron, wall hung, white	1.000	Ea.	2.000	305	113	418
Rough-in, waste, 1-1/2" diameter DWV piping	1.000	Ea.	1.803	80.40	101.60	182
Supply, 1/2" diameter type "L" copper supply piping	1.000	Ea.	.988	37.10	62	99.10
Bathtub, P.E. cast iron, 5' long with accessories, white	1.000	Ea.	3.636	1,225	205	1,430
Rough-in, waste, 4" diameter DWV piping	1.000	Ea.	.828	55.95	46.65	102.60
Supply, 1/2" diameter type "L" copper supply piping	1.000	Ea.	.988	37.10	62	99.10
Vent, 1-1/2" diameter DWV piping	1.000	Ea.	1.482	137	93	230
Piping, supply, 1/2" diameter type "L" copper supply piping	20.000	L.F.	1.975	74.20	124	198.20
Waste, 4" diameter DWV piping	9.000	L.F.	2.483	167.85	139.95	307.80
Vent, 2" diameter DWV piping	6.000	L.F.	1.500	80.10	84.60	164.70
Carrier, steel, for studs, no arms	1.000	Ea.	1.143	91.50	71.50	163
TOTAL		Ea.	24.221	2,666.81	1,411.15	4,077.96

The costs in this system are a cost each basis, all necessary piping is included.

Three Fixture Bathroom Price Sheet	QUAN.	UNIT	LABOR HOURS	COST EACH		
				MAT.	INST.	TOTAL
Water closet, close coupled standard 2 piece, white	1.000	Ea.	3.019	256	170	426
Color	1.000	Ea.	3.019	445	170	615
One piece, elongated bowl, white	1.000	Ea.	3.019	1,200	170	1,370
Color	1.000	Ea.	3.019	1,500	170	1,670
Low profile, one piece elongated bowl, white	1.000	Ea.	3.019	1,150	170	1,320
Color	1.000	Ea.	3.019	1,500	170	1,670
Rough-in, for water closet						
1/2" copper supply, 4" cast iron waste, 2" cast iron vent	1.000	Ea.	2.376	120	138	258
4" PVC/DWV waste, 2" PVC vent	1.000	Ea.	2.678	64.50	155	219.50
4" copper waste, 2" copper vent	1.000	Ea.	2.520	300	150	450
3" cast iron waste, 1-1/2" cast iron vent	1.000	Ea.	2.244	106	130	236
3" PVC waste, 1-1/2" PVC vent	1.000	Ea.	2.388	55.50	144	199.50
3" copper waste, 1-1/2" copper vent	1.000	Ea.	2.014	193	121	314
1/2" PVC supply, 4" PVC waste, 2" PVC vent	1.000	Ea.	2.974	71.50	173	244.50
3" PVC waste, 1-1/2" PVC supply	1.000	Ea.	2.684	62.50	163	225.50
1/2" steel supply, 4" cast iron waste, 2" cast iron vent	1.000	Ea.	2.545	122	148	270
4" cast iron waste, 2" steel vent	1.000	Ea.	2.590	134	151	285
4" PVC waste, 2" PVC vent	1.000	Ea.	2.847	67	165	232
Lavatory, wall hung, P.E. cast iron 20" x 18", white	1.000	Ea.	2.000	305	113	418
Color	1.000	Ea.	2.000	335	113	448
Vitreous china 19" x 17", white	1.000	Ea.	2.286	209	129	338
Color	1.000	Ea.	2.286	236	129	365
Lavatory, for vanity top, P.E. cast iron 20" x 18"", white	1.000	Ea.	2.500	360	141	501
Color	1.000	Ea.	2.500	625	141	766
Steel, enameled 20" x 17", white	1.000	Ea.	2.759	217	156	373
Color	1.000	Ea.	2.500	210	141	351
Vitreous china 20" x 16", white	1.000	Ea.	2.963	286	167	453
Color	1.000	Ea.	2.963	286	167	453
Rough-in, for lavatory						
1/2" copper supply, 1-1/2" C.I. waste, 1-1/2" C.I. vent	1.000	Ea.	2.791	118	164	282
1-1/2" PVC waste, 1-1/4" PVC vent	1.000	Ea.	2.639	65	166	231
1/2" steel supply, 1-1/4" cast iron waste, 1-1/4" steel vent	1.000	Ea.	2.890	116	171	287
1-1/4" PVC waste, 1-1/4" PVC vent	1.000	Ea.	2.794	71.50	175	246.50
1/2" PVC supply, 1-1/2" PVC waste, 1-1/2" PVC vent	1.000	Ea.	3.260	75	205	280
Bathtub, P.E. cast iron, 5' long corner with fittings, white	1.000	Ea.	3.636	1,225	205	1,430
Color	1.000	Ea.	3.636	1,500	205	1,705
Rough-in, for bathtub						
1/2" copper supply, 4" cast iron waste, 1-1/2" copper vent	1.000	Ea.	2.409	148	146	294
4" PVC waste, 1-1/2" PVC vent	1.000	Ea.	2.877	77.50	174	251.50
1/2" steel supply, 4" cast iron waste, 1-1/2" steel vent	1.000	Ea.	2.898	137	171	308
4" PVC waste, 1-1/2" PVC vent	1.000	Ea.	3.159	82	192	274
1/2" PVC supply, 4" PVC waste, 1-1/2" PVC vent	1.000	Ea.	3.371	89.50	205	294.50
Piping, supply 1/2" copper	20.000	L.F.	1.975	74	124	198
1/2" steel	20.000	L.F.	2.540	82.50	159	241.50
1/2" PVC	20.000	L.F.	2.963	98	186	284
Piping, waste, 4" cast iron no hub	9.000	L.F.	2.483	168	140	308
4" PVC/DWV	9.000	L.F.	3.000	82.50	169	251.50
4" copper/DWV	9.000	L.F.	3.600	610	203	813
Piping, vent 2" cast iron no hub	6.000	L.F.	1.433	62	81	143
2" copper/DWV	6.000	L.F.	1.091	113	68.50	181.50
2" PVC/DWV	6.000	L.F.	1.627	22.50	92	114.50
2" steel, galvanized	6.000	L.F.	1.500	80	84.50	164.50
Vanity base cabinet, 2 door, 24" x 30"	1.000	Ea.	1.000	390	54	444
24" x 36"	1.000	Ea.	1.200	380	65	445
Vanity top, laminated plastic square edge 25" x 32"	2.670	L.F.	.712	96	38.50	134.50
25" x 38"	3.160	L.F.	.843	114	45.50	159.50
Cultured marble, 25" x 32", with bowl	1.000	Ea.	2.500	236	141	377
25" x 38", with bowl	1.000	Ea.	2.500	270	141	411
Carrier, for lavatory, steel for studs, no arms	1.000	Ea.	1.143	91.50	71.50	163
Wood, 2" x 8" blocking	1.300	L.F.	.052	1.22	2.81	4.03

System Description	QUAN.	UNIT	LABOR HOURS	COST EACH		
				MAT.	INST.	TOTAL
BATHROOM WITH LAVATORY INSTALLED IN VANITY						
Water closet, floor mounted, 2 piece, close coupled, white	1.000	Ea.	3.019	256	170	426
Rough-in, waste, 4″ diameter DWV piping	1.000	Ea.	.828	55.95	46.65	102.60
Vent, 2″ diameter DWV piping	1.000	Ea.	.955	41.40	54	95.40
Supply, 1/2″ diameter type "L" copper supply piping	1.000	Ea.	.593	22.26	37.20	59.46
Lavatory, 20″ x 18″, P.E. cast iron with accessories, white	1.000	Ea.	2.500	360	141	501
Rough-in, waste, 1-1/2″ diameter DWV piping	1.000	Ea.	1.803	80.40	101.60	182
Supply, 1/2″ diameter type "L" copper supply piping	1.000	Ea.	.988	37.10	62	99.10
Bathtub, P.E. cast iron 5′ long with accessories, white	1.000	Ea.	3.636	1,225	205	1,430
Rough-in, waste, 4″ diameter DWV piping	1.000	Ea.	.828	55.95	46.65	102.60
Vent, 1-1/2″ diameter DWV piping	1.000	Ea.	.593	54.80	37.20	92
Supply, 1/2″ diameter type "L" copper supply piping	1.000	Ea.	.988	37.10	62	99.10
Piping, supply, 1/2″ diameter type "L" copper supply piping	10.000	L.F.	.988	37.10	62	99.10
Waste, 4″ diameter DWV piping	6.000	L.F.	1.655	111.90	93.30	205.20
Vent, 2″ diameter DWV piping	6.000	L.F.	1.500	80.10	84.60	164.70
Vanity base cabinet, 2 door, 30″ wide	1.000	Ea.	1.000	390	54	444
Vanity top, plastic laminated square edge	2.670	L.F.	.712	96.12	38.45	134.57
TOTAL		Ea.	22.586	2,941.18	1,295.65	4,236.83
BATHROOM WITH WALL HUNG LAVATORY						
Water closet, floor mounted, 2 piece, close coupled, white	1.000	Ea.	3.019	256	170	426
Rough-in, vent, 2″ diameter DWV piping	1.000	Ea.	.955	41.40	54	95.40
Waste, 4″ diameter DWV piping	1.000	Ea.	.828	55.95	46.65	102.60
Supply, 1/2″ diameter type "L" copper supply piping	1.000	Ea.	.593	22.26	37.20	59.46
Lavatory, 20″ x 18″ P.E. cast iron, wall hung, white	1.000	Ea.	2.000	305	113	418
Rough-in, waste, 1-1/2″ diameter DWV piping	1.000	Ea.	1.803	80.40	101.60	182
Supply, 1/2″ diameter type "L" copper supply piping	1.000	Ea.	.988	37.10	62	99.10
Bathtub, P.E. cast iron, 5′ long with accessories, white	1.000	Ea.	3.636	1,225	205	1,430
Rough-in, waste, 4″ diameter DWV piping	1.000	Ea.	.828	55.95	46.65	102.60
Supply, 1/2″ diameter type "L" copper supply piping	1.000	Ea.	.988	37.10	62	99.10
Vent, 1-1/2″ diameter DWV piping	1.000	Ea.	.593	54.80	37.20	92
Piping, supply, 1/2″ diameter type "L" copper supply piping	10.000	L.F.	.988	37.10	62	99.10
Waste, 4″ diameter DWV piping	6.000	L.F.	1.655	111.90	93.30	205.20
Vent, 2″ diameter DWV piping	6.000	L.F.	1.500	80.10	84.60	164.70
Carrier, steel, for studs, no arms	1.000	Ea.	1.143	91.50	71.50	163
TOTAL		Ea.	21.517	2,491.56	1,246.70	3,738.26

The costs in this system are on a cost each basis. All necessary piping is included.

Three Fixture Bathroom Price Sheet	QUAN.	UNIT	LABOR HOURS	COST EACH		
				MAT.	INST.	TOTAL
Water closet, close coupled standard 2 piece, white	1.000	Ea.	3.019	256	170	426
Color	1.000	Ea.	3.019	445	170	615
One piece elongated bowl, white	1.000	Ea.	3.019	1,200	170	1,370
Color	1.000	Ea.	3.019	1,500	170	1,670
Low profile, one piece elongated bowl, white	1.000	Ea.	3.019	1,150	170	1,320
Color	1.000	Ea.	3.019	1,500	170	1,670
Rough-in for water closet						
1/2" copper supply, 4" cast iron waste, 2" cast iron vent	1.000	Ea.	2.376	120	138	258
4" PVC/DWV waste, 2" PVC vent	1.000	Ea.	2.678	64.50	155	219.50
4" carrier waste, 2" copper vent	1.000	Ea.	2.520	300	150	450
3" cast iron waste, 1-1/2" cast iron vent	1.000	Ea.	2.244	106	130	236
3" PVC waste, 1-1/2" PVC vent	1.000	Ea.	2.388	55.50	144	199.50
3" copper waste, 1-1/2" copper vent	1.000	Ea.	2.014	193	121	314
1/2" PVC supply, 4" PVC waste, 2" PVC vent	1.000	Ea.	2.974	71.50	173	244.50
3" PVC waste, 1-1/2" PVC supply	1.000	Ea.	2.684	62.50	163	225.50
1/2" steel supply, 4" cast iron waste, 2" cast iron vent	1.000	Ea.	2.545	122	148	270
4" cast iron waste, 2" steel vent	1.000	Ea.	2.590	134	151	285
4" PVC waste, 2" PVC vent	1.000	Ea.	2.847	67	165	232
Lavatory, wall hung, PE cast iron 20" x 18", white	1.000	Ea.	2.000	305	113	418
Color	1.000	Ea.	2.000	335	113	448
Vitreous china 19" x 17", white	1.000	Ea.	2.286	209	129	338
Color	1.000	Ea.	2.286	236	129	365
Lavatory, for vanity top, PE cast iron 20" x 18", white	1.000	Ea.	2.500	360	141	501
Color	1.000	Ea.	2.500	625	141	766
Steel enameled 20" x 17", white	1.000	Ea.	2.759	217	156	373
Color	1.000	Ea.	2.500	210	141	351
Vitreous china 20" x 16", white	1.000	Ea.	2.963	286	167	453
Color	1.000	Ea.	2.963	286	167	453
Rough-in for lavatory						
1/2" copper supply, 1-1/2" cast iron waste, 1-1/2" cast iron vent	1.000	Ea.	2.791	118	164	282
1-1/2" PVC waste, 1-1/4" PVC vent	1.000	Ea.	2.639	65	166	231
1/2" steel supply, 1-1/4" cast iron waste, 1-1/4" steel vent	1.000	Ea.	2.890	116	171	287
1-1/4" PVC waste, 1-1/4" PVC vent	1.000	Ea.	2.794	71.50	175	246.50
1/2" PVC supply, 1-1/2" PVC waste, 1-1/2" PVC vent	1.000	Ea.	3.260	75	205	280
Bathtub, PE cast iron, 5' long corner with fittings, white	1.000	Ea.	3.636	1,225	205	1,430
Color	1.000	Ea.	3.636	1,500	205	1,705
Rough-in for bathtub						
1/2" copper supply, 4" cast iron waste, 1-1/2" copper vent	1.000	Ea.	2.409	148	146	294
4" PVC waste, 1/2" PVC vent	1.000	Ea.	2.877	77.50	174	251.50
1/2" steel supply, 4" cast iron waste, 1-1/2" steel vent	1.000	Ea.	2.898	137	171	308
4" PVC waste, 1-1/2" PVC vent	1.000	Ea.	3.159	82	192	274
1/2" PVC supply, 4" PVC waste, 1-1/2" PVC vent	1.000	Ea.	3.371	89.50	205	294.50
Piping supply, 1/2" copper	10.000	L.F.	.988	37	62	99
1/2" steel	10.000	L.F.	1.270	41.50	79.50	121
1/2" PVC	10.000	L.F.	1.482	49	93	142
Piping waste, 4" cast iron no hub	6.000	L.F.	1.655	112	93.50	205.50
4" PVC/DWV	6.000	L.F.	2.000	55	113	168
4" copper/DWV	6.000	L.F.	2.400	410	135	545
Piping vent 2" cast iron no hub	6.000	L.F.	1.433	62	81	143
2" copper/DWV	6.000	L.F.	1.091	113	68.50	181.50
2" PVC/DWV	6.000	L.F.	1.627	22.50	92	114.50
2" steel, galvanized	6.000	L.F.	1.500	80	84.50	164.50
Vanity base cabinet, 2 door, 24" x 30"	1.000	Ea.	1.000	390	54	444
24" x 36"	1.000	Ea.	1.200	380	65	445
Vanity top, laminated plastic square edge 25" x 32"	2.670	L.F.	.712	96	38.50	134.50
25" x 38"	3.160	L.F.	.843	114	45.50	159.50
Cultured marble, 25" x 32", with bowl	1.000	Ea.	2.500	236	141	377
25" x 38", with bowl	1.000	Ea.	2.500	270	141	411
Carrier, for lavatory, steel for studs, no arms	1.000	Ea.	1.143	91.50	71.50	163
Wood, 2" x 8" blocking	1.300	L.F.	.052	1.22	2.81	4.03

Bathtub — Water Closet — Lavatory — Vanity Top — Vanity Base Cabinet

System Description	QUAN.	UNIT	LABOR HOURS	COST EACH		
				MAT.	INST.	TOTAL
BATHROOM WITH LAVATORY INSTALLED IN VANITY						
Water closet, floor mounted, 2 piece, close coupled, white	1.000	Ea.	3.019	256	170	426
Rough-in, vent, 2" diameter DWV piping	1.000	Ea.	.955	41.40	54	95.40
Waste, 4" diameter DWV piping	1.000	Ea.	.828	55.95	46.65	102.60
Supply, 1/2" diameter type "L" copper supply piping	1.000	Ea.	.593	22.26	37.20	59.46
Lavatory, 20" x 18", PE cast iron with accessories, white	1.000	Ea.	2.500	360	141	501
Rough-in, vent, 1-1/2" diameter DWV piping	1.000	Ea.	1.803	80.40	101.60	182
Supply, 1/2" diameter type "L" copper supply piping	1.000	Ea.	.988	37.10	62	99.10
Bathtub, P.E. cast iron, 5' long with accessories, white	1.000	Ea.	3.636	1,225	205	1,430
Rough-in, waste, 4" diameter DWV piping	1.000	Ea.	.828	55.95	46.65	102.60
Supply, 1/2" diameter type "L" copper supply piping	1.000	Ea.	.988	37.10	62	99.10
Vent, 1-1/2" diameter DWV piping	1.000	Ea.	.593	54.80	37.20	92
Piping, supply, 1/2" diameter type "L" copper supply piping	32.000	L.F.	3.161	118.72	198.40	317.12
Waste, 4" diameter DWV piping	12.000	L.F.	3.310	223.80	186.60	410.40
Vent, 2" diameter DWV piping	6.000	L.F.	1.500	80.10	84.60	164.70
Vanity base cabinet, 2 door, 30" wide	1.000	Ea.	1.000	390	54	444
Vanity top, plastic laminated square edge	2.670	L.F.	.712	96.12	38.45	134.57
TOTAL		Ea.	26.414	3,134.70	1,525.35	4,660.05
BATHROOM WITH WALL HUNG LAVATORY						
Water closet, floor mounted, 2 piece, close coupled, white	1.000	Ea.	3.019	256	170	426
Rough-in, vent, 2" diameter DWV piping	1.000	Ea.	.955	41.40	54	95.40
Waste, 4" diameter DWV piping	1.000	Ea.	.828	55.95	46.65	102.60
Supply, 1/2" diameter type "L" copper supply piping	1.000	Ea.	.593	22.26	37.20	59.46
Lavatory, 20" x 18" P.E. cast iron, wall hung, white	1.000	Ea.	2.000	305	113	418
Rough-in, waste, 1-1/2" diameter DWV piping	1.000	Ea.	1.803	80.40	101.60	182
Supply, 1/2" diameter type "L" copper supply piping	1.000	Ea.	.988	37.10	62	99.10
Bathtub, P.E. cast iron, 5' long with accessories, white	1.000	Ea.	3.636	1,225	205	1,430
Rough-in, waste, 4" diameter DWV piping	1.000	Ea.	.828	55.95	46.65	102.60
Supply, 1/2" diameter type "L" copper supply piping	1.000	Ea.	.988	37.10	62	99.10
Vent, 1-1/2" diameter DWV piping	1.000	Ea.	.593	54.80	37.20	92
Piping, supply, 1/2" diameter type "L" copper supply piping	32.000	L.F.	3.161	118.72	198.40	317.12
Waste, 4" diameter DWV piping	12.000	L.F.	3.310	223.80	186.60	410.40
Vent, 2" diameter DWV piping	6.000	L.F.	1.500	80.10	84.60	164.70
Carrier steel, for studs, no arms	1.000	Ea.	1.143	91.50	71.50	163
TOTAL		Ea.	25.345	2,685.08	1,476.40	4,161.48

The costs in this system are on a cost each basis. All necessary piping is included.

Three Fixture Bathroom Price Sheet	QUAN.	UNIT	LABOR HOURS	COST EACH		
				MAT.	INST.	TOTAL
Water closet, close coupled, standard 2 piece, white	1.000	Ea.	3.019	256	170	426
Color	1.000	Ea.	3.019	445	170	615
One piece, elongated bowl, white	1.000	Ea.	3.019	1,200	170	1,370
Color	1.000	Ea.	3.019	1,500	170	1,670
Low profile, one piece, elongated bowl, white	1.000	Ea.	3.019	1,150	170	1,320
Color	1.000	Ea.	3.019	1,500	170	1,670
Rough-in, for water closet						
1/2" copper supply, 4" cast iron waste, 2" cast iron vent	1.000	Ea.	2.376	120	138	258
4" PVC/DWV waste, 2" PVC vent	1.000	Ea.	2.678	64.50	155	219.50
4" copper waste, 2" copper vent	1.000	Ea.	2.520	300	150	450
3" cast iron waste, 1-1/2" cast iron vent	1.000	Ea.	2.244	106	130	236
3" PVC waste, 1-1/2" PVC vent	1.000	Ea.	2.388	55.50	144	199.50
3" copper waste, 1-1/2" copper vent	1.000	Ea.	2.014	193	121	314
1/2" PVC supply, 4" PVC waste, 2" PVC vent	1.000	Ea.	2.974	71.50	173	244.50
3" PVC waste, 1-1/2" PVC supply	1.000	Ea.	2.684	62.50	163	225.50
1/2" steel supply, 4" cast iron waste, 2" cast iron vent	1.000	Ea.	2.545	122	148	270
4" cast iron waste, 2" steel vent	1.000	Ea.	2.590	134	151	285
4" PVC waste, 2" PVC vent	1.000	Ea.	2.847	67	165	232
Lavatory wall hung, P.E. cast iron, 20" x 18", white	1.000	Ea.	2.000	305	113	418
Color	1.000	Ea.	2.000	335	113	448
Vitreous china, 19" x 17", white	1.000	Ea.	2.286	209	129	338
Color	1.000	Ea.	2.286	236	129	365
Lavatory, for vanity top, P.E., cast iron, 20" x 18", white	1.000	Ea.	2.500	360	141	501
Color	1.000	Ea.	2.500	625	141	766
Steel, enameled, 20" x 17", white	1.000	Ea.	2.759	217	156	373
Color	1.000	Ea.	2.500	210	141	351
Vitreous china, 20" x 16", white	1.000	Ea.	2.963	286	167	453
Color	1.000	Ea.	2.963	286	167	453
Rough-in, for lavatory						
1/2" copper supply, 1-1/2" C.I. waste, 1-1/2" C.I. vent	1.000	Ea.	2.791	118	164	282
1-1/2" PVC waste, 1-1/4" PVC vent	1.000	Ea.	2.639	65	166	231
1/2" steel supply, 1-1/4" cast iron waste, 1-1/4" steel vent	1.000	Ea.	2.890	116	171	287
1-1/4" PVC waste, 1-1/4" PVC vent	1.000	Ea.	2.794	71.50	175	246.50
1/2" PVC supply, 1-1/2" PVC waste, 1-1/2" PVC vent	1.000	Ea.	3.260	75	205	280
Bathtub, P.E. cast iron, 5' long corner with fittings, white	1.000	Ea.	3.636	1,225	205	1,430
Color	1.000	Ea.	3.636	1,500	205	1,705
Rough-in, for bathtub						
1/2" copper supply, 4" cast iron waste, 1-1/2" copper vent	1.000	Ea.	2.409	148	146	294
4" PVC waste, 1/2" PVC vent	1.000	Ea.	2.877	77.50	174	251.50
1/2" steel supply, 4" cast iron waste, 1-1/2" steel vent	1.000	Ea.	2.898	137	171	308
4" PVC waste, 1-1/2" PVC vent	1.000	Ea.	3.159	82	192	274
1/2" PVC supply, 4" PVC waste, 1-1/2" PVC vent	1.000	Ea.	3.371	89.50	205	294.50
Piping, supply, 1/2" copper	32.000	L.F.	3.161	119	198	317
1/2" steel	32.000	L.F.	4.063	132	254	386
1/2" PVC	32.000	L.F.	4.741	156	298	454
Piping, waste, 4" cast iron no hub	12.000	L.F.	3.310	224	187	411
4" PVC/DWV	12.000	L.F.	4.000	110	226	336
4" copper/DWV	12.000	L.F.	4.800	815	270	1,085
Piping, vent, 2" cast iron no hub	6.000	L.F.	1.433	62	81	143
2" copper/DWV	6.000	L.F.	1.091	113	68.50	181.50
2" PVC/DWV	6.000	L.F.	1.627	22.50	92	114.50
2" steel, galvanized	6.000	L.F.	1.500	80	84.50	164.50
Vanity base cabinet, 2 door, 24" x 30"	1.000	Ea.	1.000	390	54	444
24" x 36"	1.000	Ea.	1.200	380	65	445
Vanity top, laminated plastic square edge, 25" x 32"	2.670	L.F.	.712	96	38.50	134.50
25" x 38"	3.160	L.F.	.843	114	45.50	159.50
Cultured marble, 25" x 32", with bowl	1.000	Ea.	2.500	236	141	377
25" x 38", with bowl	1.000	Ea.	2.500	270	141	411
Carrier, for lavatory, steel for studs, no arms	1.000	Ea.	1.143	91.50	71.50	163
Wood, 2" x 8" blocking	1.300	L.F.	.052	1.22	2.81	4.03

System Description	QUAN.	UNIT	LABOR HOURS	COST EACH		
				MAT.	INST.	TOTAL
BATHROOM WITH LAVATORY INSTALLED IN VANITY						
Water closet, floor mounted, 2 piece, close coupled, white	1.000	Ea.	3.019	256	170	426
Rough-in, vent, 2" diameter DWV piping	1.000	Ea.	.955	41.40	54	95.40
Waste, 4" diameter DWV piping	1.000	Ea.	.828	55.95	46.65	102.60
Supply, 1/2" diameter type "L" copper supply piping	1.000	Ea.	.593	22.26	37.20	59.46
Lavatory, 20" x 18", P.E. cast iron with fittings, white	1.000	Ea.	2.500	360	141	501
Rough-in, waste, 1-1/2" diameter DWV piping	1.000	Ea.	1.803	80.40	101.60	182
Supply, 1/2" diameter type "L" copper supply piping	1.000	Ea.	.988	37.10	62	99.10
Bathtub, P.E. cast iron, corner with fittings, white	1.000	Ea.	3.636	2,900	205	3,105
Rough-in, waste, 4" diameter DWV piping	1.000	Ea.	.828	55.95	46.65	102.60
Supply, 1/2" diameter type "L" copper supply piping	1.000	Ea.	.988	37.10	62	99.10
Vent, 1-1/2" diameter DWV piping	1.000	Ea.	.593	54.80	37.20	92
Piping, supply, 1/2" diameter type "L" copper supply piping	32.000	L.F.	3.161	118.72	198.40	317.12
Waste, 4" diameter DWV piping	12.000	L.F.	3.310	223.80	186.60	410.40
Vent, 2" diameter DWV piping	6.000	L.F.	1.500	80.10	84.60	164.70
Vanity base cabinet, 2 door, 30" wide	1.000	Ea.	1.000	390	54	444
Vanity top, plastic laminated, square edge	2.670	L.F.	.712	113.48	38.45	151.93
TOTAL		Ea.	26.414	4,827.06	1,525.35	6,352.41
BATHROOM WITH WALL HUNG LAVATORY						
Water closet, floor mounted, 2 piece, close coupled, white	1.000	Ea.	3.019	256	170	426
Rough-in, vent, 2" diameter DWV piping	1.000	Ea.	.955	41.40	54	95.40
Waste, 4" diameter DWV piping	1.000	Ea.	.828	55.95	46.65	102.60
Supply, 1/2" diameter type "L" copper supply piping	1.000	Ea.	.593	22.26	37.20	59.46
Lavatory, 20" x 18", P.E. cast iron, with fittings, white	1.000	Ea.	2.000	305	113	418
Rough-in, waste, 1-1/2" diameter DWV piping	1.000	Ea.	1.803	80.40	101.60	182
Supply, 1/2" diameter type "L" copper supply piping	1.000	Ea.	.988	37.10	62	99.10
Bathtub, P.E. cast iron, corner, with fittings, white	1.000	Ea.	3.636	2,900	205	3,105
Rough-in, waste, 4" diameter DWV piping	1.000	Ea.	.828	55.95	46.65	102.60
Supply, 1/2" diameter type "L" copper supply piping	1.000	Ea.	.988	37.10	62	99.10
Vent, 1-1/2" diameter DWV piping	1.000	Ea.	.593	54.80	37.20	92
Piping, supply, 1/2" diameter type "L" copper supply piping	32.000	L.F.	3.161	118.72	198.40	317.12
Waste, 4" diameter DWV piping	12.000	L.F.	3.310	223.80	186.60	410.40
Vent, 2" diameter DWV piping	6.000	L.F.	1.500	80.10	84.60	164.70
Carrier, steel, for studs, no arms	1.000	Ea.	1.143	91.50	71.50	163
TOTAL		Ea.	25.345	4,360.08	1,476.40	5,836.48

The costs in this system are on a cost each basis. All necessary piping is included.

Three Fixture Bathroom Price Sheet	QUAN.	UNIT	LABOR HOURS	COST EACH		
				MAT.	INST.	TOTAL
Water closet, close coupled, standard 2 piece, white	1.000	Ea.	3.019	256	170	426
Color	1.000	Ea.	3.019	445	170	615
One piece elongated bowl, white	1.000	Ea.	3.019	1,200	170	1,370
Color	1.000	Ea.	3.019	1,500	170	1,670
Low profile, one piece elongated bowl, white	1.000	Ea.	3.019	1,150	170	1,320
Color	1.000	Ea.	3.019	1,500	170	1,670
Rough-in, for water closet						
1/2" copper supply, 4" cast iron waste, 2" cast iron vent	1.000	Ea.	2.376	120	138	258
4" PVC/DWV waste, 2" PVC vent	1.000	Ea.	2.678	64.50	155	219.50
4" copper waste, 2" copper vent	1.000	Ea.	2.520	300	150	450
3" cast iron waste, 1-1/2" cast iron vent	1.000	Ea.	2.244	106	130	236
3" PVC waste, 1-1/2" PVC vent	1.000	Ea.	2.388	55.50	144	199.50
3" copper waste, 1-1/2" copper vent	1.000	Ea.	2.014	193	121	314
1/2" PVC supply, 4" PVC waste, 2" PVC vent	1.000	Ea.	2.974	71.50	173	244.50
3" PVC waste, 1-1/2" PVC supply	1.000	Ea.	2.684	62.50	163	225.50
1/2" steel supply, 4" cast iron waste, 2" cast iron vent	1.000	Ea.	2.545	122	148	270
4" cast iron waste, 2" steel vent	1.000	Ea.	2.590	134	151	285
4" PVC waste, 2" PVC vent	1.000	Ea.	2.847	67	165	232
Lavatory, wall hung P.E. cast iron 20" x 18", white	1.000	Ea.	2.000	305	113	418
Color	1.000	Ea.	2.000	335	113	448
Vitreous china 19" x 17", white	1.000	Ea.	2.286	209	129	338
Color	1.000	Ea.	2.286	236	129	365
Lavatory, for vanity top, P.E., cast iron, 20" x 18", white	1.000	Ea.	2.500	360	141	501
Color	1.000	Ea.	2.500	625	141	766
Steel enameled 20" x 17", white	1.000	Ea.	2.759	217	156	373
Color	1.000	Ea.	2.500	210	141	351
Vitreous china 20" x 16", white	1.000	Ea.	2.963	286	167	453
Color	1.000	Ea.	2.963	286	167	453
Rough-in, for lavatory						
1/2" copper supply, 1-1/2" cast iron waste, 1-1/2" cast iron vent	1.000	Ea.	2.791	118	164	282
1-1/2" PVC waste, 1-1/4" PVC vent	1.000	Ea.	2.639	65	166	231
1/2" steel supply, 1-1/4" cast iron waste, 1-1/4" steel vent	1.000	Ea.	2.890	116	171	287
1-1/4" PVC waste, 1-1/4" PVC vent	1.000	Ea.	2.794	71.50	175	246.50
1/2" PVC supply, 1-1/2" PVC waste, 1-1/2" PVC vent	1.000	Ea.	3.260	75	205	280
Bathtub, P.E. cast iron, corner with fittings, white	1.000	Ea.	3.636	2,900	205	3,105
Color	1.000	Ea.	4.000	3,300	226	3,526
Rough-in, for bathtub						
1/2" copper supply, 4" cast iron waste, 1-1/2" copper vent	1.000	Ea.	2.409	148	146	294
4" PVC waste, 1-1/2" PVC vent	1.000	Ea.	2.877	77.50	174	251.50
1/2" steel supply, 4" cast iron waste, 1-1/2" steel vent	1.000	Ea.	2.898	137	171	308
4" PVC waste, 1-1/2" PVC vent	1.000	Ea.	3.159	82	192	274
1/2" PVC supply, 4" PVC waste, 1-1/2" PVC vent	1.000	Ea.	3.371	89.50	205	294.50
Piping, supply, 1/2" copper	32.000	L.F.	3.161	119	198	317
1/2" steel	32.000	L.F.	4.063	132	254	386
1/2" PVC	32.000	L.F.	4.741	156	298	454
Piping, waste, 4" cast iron, no hub	12.000	L.F.	3.310	224	187	411
4" PVC/DWV	12.000	L.F.	4.000	110	226	336
4" copper/DWV	12.000	L.F.	4.800	815	270	1,085
Piping, vent 2" cast iron, no hub	6.000	L.F.	1.433	62	81	143
2" copper/DWV	6.000	L.F.	1.091	113	68.50	181.50
2" PVC/DWV	6.000	L.F.	1.627	22.50	92	114.50
2" steel, galvanized	6.000	L.F.	1.500	80	84.50	164.50
Vanity base cabinet, 2 door, 24" x 30"	1.000	Ea.	1.000	390	54	444
24" x 36"	1.000	Ea.	1.200	380	65	445
Vanity top, laminated plastic square edge 25" x 32"	2.670	L.F.	.712	113	38.50	151.50
25" x 38"	3.160	L.F.	.843	134	45.50	179.50
Cultured marble, 25" x 32", with bowl	1.000	Ea.	2.500	236	141	377
25" x 38", with bowl	1.000	Ea.	2.500	270	141	411
Carrier, for lavatory, steel for studs, no arms	1.000	Ea.	1.143	91.50	71.50	163
Wood, 2" x 8" blocking	1.300	L.F.	.053	1.25	2.87	4.12

System Description	QUAN.	UNIT	LABOR HOURS	COST EACH		
				MAT.	INST.	TOTAL
BATHROOM WITH SHOWER, LAVATORY INSTALLED IN VANITY						
Water closet, floor mounted, 2 piece, close coupled, white	1.000	Ea.	3.019	256	170	426
Rough-in, vent, 2" diameter DWV piping	1.000	Ea.	.955	41.40	54	95.40
Waste, 4" diameter DWV piping	1.000	Ea.	.828	55.95	46.65	102.60
Supply, 1/2" diameter type "L" copper supply piping	1.000	Ea.	.593	22.26	37.20	59.46
Lavatory, 20" x 18" P.E. cast iron with fittings, white	1.000	Ea.	2.500	360	141	501
Rough-in, waste, 1-1/2" diameter DWV piping	1.000	Ea.	1.803	80.40	101.60	182
Supply, 1/2" diameter type "L" copper supply piping	1.000	Ea.	.988	37.10	62	99.10
Shower, steel enameled, stone base, corner, white	1.000	Ea.	3.200	1,275	181	1,456
Shower mixing valve	1.000	Ea.	1.333	169	83.50	252.50
Shower door	1.000	Ea.	1.000	420	60	480
Rough-in, vent, 1-1/2" diameter DWV piping	1.000	Ea.	.225	10.05	12.70	22.75
Waste, 2" diameter DWV piping	1.000	Ea.	1.433	62.10	81	143.10
Supply, 1/2" diameter type "L" copper supply piping	1.000	Ea.	1.580	59.36	99.20	158.56
Piping, supply, 1/2" diameter type "L" copper supply piping	36.000	L.F.	4.148	155.82	260.40	416.22
Waste, 4" diameter DWV piping	7.000	L.F.	2.759	186.50	155.50	342
Vent, 2" diameter DWV piping	6.000	L.F.	2.250	120.15	126.90	247.05
Vanity base 2 door, 30" wide	1.000	Ea.	1.000	390	54	444
Vanity top, plastic laminated, square edge	2.170	L.F.	.712	84.11	38.45	122.56
TOTAL		Ea.	30.326	3,785.20	1,765.10	5,550.30
BATHROOM WITH SHOWER, WALL HUNG LAVATORY						
Water closet, floor mounted, close coupled	1.000	Ea.	3.019	256	170	426
Rough-in, vent, 2" diameter DWV piping	1.000	Ea.	.955	41.40	54	95.40
Waste, 4" diameter DWV piping	1.000	Ea.	.828	55.95	46.65	102.60
Supply, 1/2" diameter type "L" copper supply piping	1.000	Ea.	.593	22.26	37.20	59.46
Lavatory, 20" x 18" P.E. cast iron with fittings, white	1.000	Ea.	2.000	305	113	418
Rough-in, waste, 1-1/2" diameter DWV piping	1.000	Ea.	1.803	80.40	101.60	182
Supply, 1/2" diameter type "L" copper supply piping	1.000	Ea.	.988	37.10	62	99.10
Shower, steel enameled, stone base, white	1.000	Ea.	3.200	1,275	181	1,456
Mixing valve	1.000	Ea.	1.333	169	83.50	252.50
Shower door	1.000	Ea.	1.000	420	60	480
Rough-in, vent, 1-1/2" diameter DWV piping	1.000	Ea.	.225	10.05	12.70	22.75
Waste, 2" diameter DWV piping	1.000	Ea.	1.433	62.10	81	143.10
Supply, 1/2" diameter type "L" copper supply piping	1.000	Ea.	1.580	59.36	99.20	158.56
Piping, supply, 1/2" diameter type "L" copper supply piping	36.000	L.F.	4.148	155.82	260.40	416.22
Waste, 4" diameter DWV piping	7.000	L.F.	2.759	186.50	155.50	342
Vent, 2" diameter DWV piping	6.000	L.F.	2.250	120.15	126.90	247.05
Carrier, steel, for studs, no arms	1.000	Ea.	1.143	91.50	71.50	163
TOTAL		Ea.	29.257	3,347.59	1,716.15	5,063.74

The costs in this system are on a cost each basis. All necessary piping is included.

Three Fixture Bathroom Price Sheet	QUAN.	UNIT	LABOR HOURS	COST EACH		
				MAT.	INST.	TOTAL
Water closet, close coupled, standard 2 piece, white	1.000	Ea.	3.019	256	170	426
Color	1.000	Ea.	3.019	445	170	615
One piece elongated bowl, white	1.000	Ea.	3.019	1,200	170	1,370
Color	1.000	Ea.	3.019	1,500	170	1,670
Low profile, one piece elongated bowl, white	1.000	Ea.	3.019	1,150	170	1,320
Color	1.000	Ea.	3.019	1,500	170	1,670
Rough-in, for water closet						
1/2" copper supply, 4" cast iron waste, 2" cast iron vent	1.000	Ea.	2.376	120	138	258
4" PVC/DWV waste, 2" PVC vent	1.000	Ea.	2.678	64.50	155	219.50
4" copper waste, 2" copper vent	1.000	Ea.	2.520	300	150	450
3" cast iron waste, 1-1/2" cast iron vent	1.000	Ea.	2.244	106	130	236
3" PVC waste, 1-1/2" PVC vent	1.000	Ea.	2.388	55.50	144	199.50
3" copper waste, 1-1/2" copper vent	1.000	Ea.	2.014	193	121	314
1/2" PVC supply, 4" PVC waste, 2" PVC vent	1.000	Ea.	2.974	71.50	173	244.50
3" PVC waste, 1-1/2" PVC supply	1.000	Ea.	2.684	62.50	163	225.50
1/2" steel supply, 4" cast iron waste, 2" cast iron vent	1.000	Ea.	2.545	122	148	270
4" cast iron waste, 2" steel vent	1.000	Ea.	2.590	134	151	285
4" PVC waste, 2" PVC vent	1.000	Ea.	2.847	67	165	232
Lavatory, wall hung, P.E. cast iron 20" x 18", white	1.000	Ea.	2.000	305	113	418
Color	1.000	Ea.	2.000	335	113	448
Vitreous china 19" x 17", white	1.000	Ea.	2.286	209	129	338
Color	1.000	Ea.	2.286	236	129	365
Lavatory, for vanity top, P.E. cast iron 20" x 18", white	1.000	Ea.	2.500	360	141	501
Color	1.000	Ea.	2.500	625	141	766
Steel enameled 20" x 17", white	1.000	Ea.	2.759	217	156	373
Color	1.000	Ea.	2.500	210	141	351
Vitreous china 20" x 16", white	1.000	Ea.	2.963	286	167	453
Color	1.000	Ea.	2.963	286	167	453
Rough-in, for lavatory						
1/2" copper supply, 1-1/2" cast iron waste, 1-1/2" cast iron vent	1.000	Ea.	2.791	118	164	282
1-1/2" PVC waste, 1-1/2" PVC vent	1.000	Ea.	2.639	65	166	231
1/2" steel supply, 1-1/4" cast iron waste, 1-1/4" steel vent	1.000	Ea.	2.890	116	171	287
1-1/4" PVC waste, 1-1/4" PVC vent	1.000	Ea.	2.921	69.50	183	252.50
1/2" PVC supply, 1-1/2" PVC waste, 1-1/2" PVC vent	1.000	Ea.	3.260	75	205	280
Shower, steel enameled stone base, 32" x 32", white	1.000	Ea.	8.000	1,275	181	1,456
Color	1.000	Ea.	7.822	1,950	165	2,115
36" x 36" white	1.000	Ea.	8.889	1,625	188	1,813
Color	1.000	Ea.	8.889	2,225	188	2,413
Rough-in, for shower						
1/2" copper supply, 4" cast iron waste, 1-1/2" copper vent	1.000	Ea.	3.238	132	193	325
4" PVC waste, 1-1/2" PVC vent	1.000	Ea.	3.429	85	205	290
1/2" steel supply, 4" cast iron waste, 1-1/2" steel vent	1.000	Ea.	3.665	138	220	358
4" PVC waste, 1-1/2" PVC vent	1.000	Ea.	3.881	91.50	233	324.50
1/2" PVC supply, 4" PVC waste, 1-1/2" PVC vent	1.000	Ea.	4.219	104	255	359
Piping, supply, 1/2" copper	36.000	L.F.	4.148	156	260	416
1/2" steel	36.000	L.F.	5.333	173	335	508
1/2" PVC	36.000	L.F.	6.222	205	390	595
Piping, waste, 4" cast iron no hub	7.000	L.F.	2.759	187	156	343
4" PVC/DWV	7.000	L.F.	3.333	91.50	188	279.50
4" copper/DWV	7.000	L.F.	4.000	680	225	905
Piping, vent, 2" cast iron no hub	6.000	L.F.	2.149	93	122	215
2" copper/DWV	6.000	L.F.	1.636	169	103	272
2" PVC/DWV	6.000	L.F.	2.441	33.50	138	171.50
2" steel, galvanized	6.000	L.F.	2.250	120	127	247
Vanity base cabinet, 2 door, 24" x 30"	1.000	Ea.	1.000	390	54	444
24" x 36"	1.000	Ea.	1.200	380	65	445
Vanity top, laminated plastic square edge, 25" x 32"	2.170	L.F.	.712	84	38.50	122.50
25" x 38"	2.670	L.F.	.845	100	45.50	145.50
Carrier, for lavatory, steel for studs, no arms	1.000	Ea.	1.143	91.50	71.50	163
Wood, 2" x 8" blocking	1.300	L.F.	.052	1.22	2.81	4.03

Shower — Lavatory — Vanity Top — Water Closet — Vanity Base Cabinet

System Description	QUAN.	UNIT	LABOR HOURS	COST EACH		
				MAT.	INST.	TOTAL
BATHROOM WITH LAVATORY INSTALLED IN VANITY						
Water closet, floor mounted, 2 piece, close coupled, white	1.000	Ea.	3.019	256	170	426
Rough-in, vent, 2″ diameter DWV piping	1.000	Ea.	.955	41.40	54	95.40
Waste, 4″ diameter DWV piping	1.000	Ea.	.828	55.95	46.65	102.60
Supply, 1/2″ diameter type "L" copper supply piping	1.000	Ea.	.593	22.26	37.20	59.46
Lavatory, 20″ x 18″, P.E. cast iron with fittings, white	1.000	Ea.	2.500	360	141	501
Rough-in, waste, 1-1/2″ diameter DWV piping	1.000	Ea.	1.803	80.40	101.60	182
Supply, 1/2″ diameter type "L" copper supply piping	1.000	Ea.	.988	37.10	62	99.10
Shower, steel enameled, stone base, corner, white	1.000	Ea.	3.200	1,275	181	1,456
Mixing valve	1.000	Ea.	1.333	169	83.50	252.50
Shower door	1.000	Ea.	1.000	420	60	480
Rough-in, vent, 1-1/2″ diameter DWV piping	1.000	Ea.	.225	10.05	12.70	22.75
Waste, 2″ diameter DWV piping	1.000	Ea.	1.433	62.10	81	143.10
Supply, 1/2″ diameter type "L" copper supply piping	1.000	Ea.	1.580	59.36	99.20	158.56
Piping, supply, 1/2″ diameter type "L" copper supply piping	36.000	L.F.	3.556	133.56	223.20	356.76
Waste, 4″ diameter DWV piping	7.000	L.F.	1.931	130.55	108.85	239.40
Vent, 2″ diameter DWV piping	6.000	L.F.	1.500	80.10	84.60	164.70
Vanity base, 2 door, 30″ wide	1.000	Ea.	1.000	390	54	444
Vanity top, plastic laminated, square edge	2.670	L.F.	.712	96.12	38.45	134.57
TOTAL		Ea.	28.156	3,678.95	1,638.95	5,317.90
BATHROOM, WITH WALL HUNG LAVATORY						
Water closet, floor mounted, 2 piece, close coupled, white	1.000	Ea.	3.019	256	170	426
Rough-in, vent, 2″ diameter DWV piping	1.000	Ea.	.955	41.40	54	95.40
Waste, 4″ diameter DWV piping	1.000	Ea.	.828	55.95	46.65	102.60
Supply, 1/2″ diameter type "L" copper supply piping	1.000	Ea.	.593	22.26	37.20	59.46
Lavatory, wall hung, 20″ x 18″ P.E. cast iron with fittings, white	1.000	Ea.	2.000	305	113	418
Rough-in, waste, 1-1/2″ diameter DWV piping	1.000	Ea.	1.803	80.40	101.60	182
Supply, 1/2″ diameter type "L" copper supply piping	1.000	Ea.	.988	37.10	62	99.10
Shower, steel enameled, stone base, corner, white	1.000	Ea.	3.200	1,275	181	1,456
Mixing valve	1.000	Ea.	1.333	169	83.50	252.50
Shower door	1.000	Ea.	1.000	420	60	480
Rough-in, waste, 1-1/2″ diameter DWV piping	1.000	Ea.	.225	10.05	12.70	22.75
Waste, 2″ diameter DWV piping	1.000	Ea.	1.433	62.10	81	143.10
Supply, 1/2″ diameter type "L" copper supply piping	1.000	Ea.	1.580	59.36	99.20	158.56
Piping, supply, 1/2″ diameter type "L" copper supply piping	36.000	L.F.	3.556	133.56	223.20	356.76
Waste, 4″ diameter DWV piping	7.000	L.F.	1.931	130.55	108.85	239.40
Vent, 2″ diameter DWV piping	6.000	L.F.	1.500	80.10	84.60	164.70
Carrier, steel, for studs, no arms	1.000	Ea.	1.143	91.50	71.50	163
TOTAL		Ea.	27.087	3,229.33	1,590	4,819.33

The costs in this system are on a cost each basis. All necessary piping is included.

Three Fixture Bathroom Price Sheet	QUAN.	UNIT	LABOR HOURS	COST EACH		
				MAT.	INST.	TOTAL
Water closet, close coupled, standard 2 piece, white	1.000	Ea.	3.019	256	170	426
Color	1.000	Ea.	3.019	445	170	615
One piece elongated bowl, white	1.000	Ea.	3.019	1,200	170	1,370
Color	1.000	Ea.	3.019	1,500	170	1,670
Low profile one piece elongated bowl, white	1.000	Ea.	3.019	1,150	170	1,320
Color	1.000	Ea.	3.623	1,500	170	1,670
Rough-in, for water closet						
1/2″ copper supply, 4″ cast iron waste, 2″ cast iron vent	1.000	Ea.	2.376	120	138	258
4″ P.V.C./DWV waste, 2″ PVC vent	1.000	Ea.	2.678	64.50	155	219.50
4″ copper waste, 2″ copper vent	1.000	Ea.	2.520	300	150	450
3″ cast iron waste, 1-1/2″ cast iron vent	1.000	Ea.	2.244	106	130	236
3″ PVC waste, 1-1/2″ PVC vent	1.000	Ea.	2.388	55.50	144	199.50
3″ copper waste, 1-1/2″ copper vent	1.000	Ea.	2.014	193	121	314
1/2″ P.V.C. supply, 4″ P.V.C. waste, 2″ P.V.C. vent	1.000	Ea.	2.974	71.50	173	244.50
3″ P.V.C. waste, 1-1/2″ P.V.C. vent	1.000	Ea.	2.684	62.50	163	225.50
1/2″ steel supply, 4″ cast iron waste, 2″ cast iron vent	1.000	Ea.	2.545	122	148	270
4″ cast iron waste, 2″ steel vent	1.000	Ea.	2.590	134	151	285
4″ P.V.C. waste, 2″ P.V.C. vent	1.000	Ea.	2.847	67	165	232
Lavatory, wall hung P.E. cast iron 20″ x 18″, white	1.000	Ea.	2.000	305	113	418
Color	1.000	Ea.	2.000	335	113	448
Vitreous china 19″ x 17″, white	1.000	Ea.	2.286	209	129	338
Color	1.000	Ea.	2.286	236	129	365
Lavatory, for vanity top P.E. cast iron 20″ x 18″, white	1.000	Ea.	2.500	360	141	501
Color	1.000	Ea.	2.500	625	141	766
Steel enameled 20″ x 17″, white	1.000	Ea.	2.759	217	156	373
Color	1.000	Ea.	2.500	210	141	351
Vitreous china 20″ x 16″, white	1.000	Ea.	2.963	286	167	453
Color	1.000	Ea.	2.963	286	167	453
Rough-in, for lavatory						
1/2″ copper supply, 1-1/2″ cast iron waste, 1-1/2″ cast iron vent	1.000	Ea.	2.791	118	164	282
1-1/2″ P.V.C. waste, 1-1/2″ P.V.C. vent	1.000	Ea.	2.639	65	166	231
1/2″ steel supply, 1-1/2″ cast iron waste, 1-1/4″ steel vent	1.000	Ea.	2.890	116	171	287
1-1/2″ P.V.C. waste, 1-1/4″ P.V.C. vent	1.000	Ea.	2.921	69.50	183	252.50
1/2″ P.V.C. supply, 1-1/2″ P.V.C. waste, 1-1/2″ P.V.C. vent	1.000	Ea.	3.260	75	205	280
Shower, steel enameled stone base, 32″ x 32″, white	1.000	Ea.	8.000	1,275	181	1,456
Color	1.000	Ea.	7.822	1,950	165	2,115
36″ x 36″, white	1.000	Ea.	8.889	1,625	188	1,813
Color	1.000	Ea.	8.889	2,225	188	2,413
Rough-in, for shower						
1/2″ copper supply, 2″ cast iron waste, 1-1/2″ copper vent	1.000	Ea.	3.161	135	190	325
2″ P.V.C. waste, 1-1/2″ P.V.C. vent	1.000	Ea.	3.429	85	205	290
1/2″ steel supply, 2″ cast iron waste, 1-1/2″ steel vent	1.000	Ea.	3.887	188	232	420
2″ P.V.C. waste, 1-1/2″ P.V.C. vent	1.000	Ea.	3.881	91.50	233	324.50
1/2″ P.V.C. supply, 2″ P.V.C. waste, 1-1/2″ P.V.C. vent	1.000	Ea.	4.219	104	255	359
Piping, supply, 1/2″ copper	36.000	L.F.	3.556	134	223	357
1/2″ steel	36.000	L.F.	4.571	149	286	435
1/2″ P.V.C.	36.000	L.F.	5.333	176	335	511
Waste, 4″ cast iron, no hub	7.000	L.F.	1.931	131	109	240
4″ P.V.C./DWV	7.000	L.F.	2.333	64	132	196
4″ copper/DWV	7.000	L.F.	2.800	475	158	633
Vent, 2″ cast iron, no hub	6.000	L.F.	1.091	113	68.50	181.50
2″ copper/DWV	6.000	L.F.	1.091	113	68.50	181.50
2″ P.V.C./DWV	6.000	L.F.	1.627	22.50	92	114.50
2″ steel, galvanized	6.000	L.F.	1.500	80	84.50	164.50
Vanity base cabinet, 2 door, 24″ x 30″	1.000	Ea.	1.000	390	54	444
24″ x 36″	1.000	Ea.	1.200	380	65	445
Vanity top, laminated plastic square edge, 25″ x 32″	2.670	L.F.	.712	96	38.50	134.50
25″ x 38″	3.170	L.F.	.845	114	45.50	159.50
Carrier , for lavatory, steel, for studs, no arms	1.000	Ea.	1.143	91.50	71.50	163
Wood, 2″ x 8″ blocking	1.300	L.F.	.052	1.22	2.81	4.03

Shower — Lavatory
Bathtub — Vanity Top
— Vanity Base
— Water Closet

System Description	QUAN.	UNIT	LABOR HOURS	COST EACH		
				MAT.	INST.	TOTAL
BATHROOM WITH LAVATORY INSTALLED IN VANITY						
Water closet, floor mounted, 2 piece, close coupled, white	1.000	Ea.	3.019	256	170	426
Rough-in, vent, 2" diameter DWV piping	1.000	Ea.	.955	41.40	54	95.40
Waste, 4" diameter DWV piping	1.000	Ea.	.828	55.95	46.65	102.60
Supply, 1/2" diameter type "L" copper supply piping	1.000	Ea.	.593	22.26	37.20	59.46
Lavatory, 20" x 18" P.E. cast iron with fittings, white	1.000	Ea.	2.500	360	141	501
Shower, steel, enameled, stone base, corner, white	1.000	Ea.	3.333	1,900	188	2,088
Mixing valve	1.000	Ea.	1.333	169	83.50	252.50
Shower door	1.000	Ea.	1.000	420	60	480
Rough-in, waste, 1-1/2" diameter DWV piping	2.000	Ea.	4.507	201	254	455
Supply, 1/2" diameter type "L" copper supply piping	2.000	Ea.	3.161	118.72	198.40	317.12
Bathtub, P.E. cast iron, 5' long with fittings, white	1.000	Ea.	3.636	1,225	205	1,430
Rough-in, waste, 4" diameter DWV piping	1.000	Ea.	.828	55.95	46.65	102.60
Supply, 1/2" diameter type "L" copper supply piping	1.000	Ea.	.988	37.10	62	99.10
Vent, 1-1/2" diameter DWV piping	1.000	Ea.	.593	54.80	37.20	92
Piping, supply, 1/2" diameter type "L" copper supply piping	42.000	L.F.	4.148	155.82	260.40	416.22
Waste, 4" diameter DWV piping	10.000	L.F.	2.759	186.50	155.50	342
Vent, 2" diameter DWV piping	13.000	L.F.	3.250	173.55	183.30	356.85
Vanity base, 2 doors, 30" wide	1.000	Ea.	1.000	390	54	444
Vanity top, plastic laminated, square edge	2.670	L.F.	.712	96.12	38.45	134.57
TOTAL		Ea.	39.143	5,919.17	2,275.25	8,194.42
BATHROOM WITH WALL HUNG LAVATORY						
Water closet, floor mounted, 2 piece, close coupled, white	1.000	Ea.	3.019	256	170	426
Rough-in, vent, 2" diameter DWV piping	1.000	Ea.	.955	41.40	54	95.40
Waste, 4" diameter DWV piping	1.000	Ea.	.828	55.95	46.65	102.60
Supply, 1/2" diameter type "L" copper supply piping	1.000	Ea.	.593	22.26	37.20	59.46
Lavatory, 20" x 18" P.E. cast iron with fittings, white	1.000	Ea.	2.000	305	113	418
Shower, steel enameled, stone base, corner , white	1.000	Ea.	3.333	1,900	188	2,088
Mixing valve	1.000	Ea.	1.333	169	83.50	252.50
Shower door	1.000	Ea.	1.000	420	60	480
Rough-in, waste, 1-1/2" diameter DWV piping	2.000	Ea.	4.507	201	254	455
Supply, 1/2" diameter type "L" copper supply piping	2.000	Ea.	3.161	118.72	198.40	317.12
Bathtub, P.E. cast iron, 5' long with fittings, white	1.000	Ea.	3.636	1,225	205	1,430
Rough-in, waste, 4" diameter DWV piping	1.000	Ea.	.828	55.95	46.65	102.60
Supply, 1/2" diameter type "L" copper supply piping	1.000	Ea.	.988	37.10	62	99.10
Vent, 1-1/2" diameter copper DWV piping	1.000	Ea.	.593	54.80	37.20	92
Piping, supply, 1/2" diameter type "L" copper supply piping	42.000	L.F.	4.148	155.82	260.40	416.22
Waste, 4" diameter DWV piping	10.000	L.F.	2.759	186.50	155.50	342
Vent, 2" diameter DWV piping	13.000	L.F.	3.250	173.55	183.30	356.85
Carrier, steel, for studs, no arms	1.000	Ea.	1.143	91.50	71.50	163
TOTAL		Ea.	38.074	5,469.55	2,226.30	7,695.85

The costs in this system are on a cost each basis. All necessary piping is included.

Four Fixture Bathroom Price Sheet	QUAN.	UNIT	LABOR HOURS	COST EACH		
				MAT.	INST.	TOTAL
Water closet, close coupled, standard 2 piece, white	1.000	Ea.	3.019	256	170	426
Color	1.000	Ea.	3.019	445	170	615
One piece elongated bowl, white	1.000	Ea.	3.019	1,200	170	1,370
Color	1.000	Ea.	3.019	1,500	170	1,670
Low profile, one piece elongated bowl, white	1.000	Ea.	3.019	1,150	170	1,320
Color	1.000	Ea.	3.019	1,500	170	1,670
1/2" copper supply, 4" cast iron waste, 2" cast iron vent	1.000	Ea.	2.376	120	138	258
4" PVC/DWV waste, 2" PVC vent	1.000	Ea.	2.678	64.50	155	219.50
4" copper waste, 2" copper vent	1.000	Ea.	2.520	300	150	450
3" cast iron waste, 1-1/2" cast iron vent	1.000	Ea.	2.244	106	130	236
3" P.V.C. waste, 1-1/2" P.V.C. vent	1.000	Ea.	2.388	55.50	144	199.50
3" copper waste, 1-1/2" copper vent	1.000	Ea.	2.014	193	121	314
1/2" P.V.C. supply, 4" P.V.C. waste, 2" P.V.C. vent	1.000	Ea.	2.974	71.50	173	244.50
3" P.V.C. waste, 1-1/2" P.V.C. vent	1.000	Ea.	2.684	62.50	163	225.50
1/2" steel supply, 4" cast iron waste, 2" cast iron vent	1.000	Ea.	2.545	122	148	270
4" cast iron waste, 2" steel vent	1.000	Ea.	2.590	134	151	285
4" P.V.C. waste, 2" P.V.C. vent	1.000	Ea.	2.847	67	165	232
Lavatory, wall hung P.E. cast iron 20" x 18", white	1.000	Ea.	2.000	305	113	418
Color	1.000	Ea.	2.000	335	113	448
Vitreous china 19" x 17", white	1.000	Ea.	2.286	209	129	338
Color	1.000	Ea.	2.286	236	129	365
Lavatory for vanity top, P.E. cast iron 20" x 18", white	1.000	Ea.	2.500	360	141	501
Color	1.000	Ea.	2.500	625	141	766
Steel enameled, 20" x 17", white	1.000	Ea.	2.759	217	156	373
Color	1.000	Ea.	2.500	210	141	351
Vitreous china 20" x 16", white	1.000	Ea.	2.963	286	167	453
Color	1.000	Ea.	2.963	286	167	453
Shower, steel enameled stone base, 36" square, white	1.000	Ea.	8.889	1,900	188	2,088
Color	1.000	Ea.	8.889	1,950	188	2,138
Rough-in, for lavatory or shower						
1/2" copper supply, 1-1/2" cast iron waste, 1-1/2" cast iron vent	1.000	Ea.	3.834	160	226	386
1-1/2" P.V.C. waste, 1-1/4" P.V.C. vent	1.000	Ea.	3.675	94	231	325
1/2" steel supply, 1-1/4" cast iron waste, 1-1/4" steel vent	1.000	Ea.	4.103	160	244	404
1-1/4" P.V.C. waste, 1-1/4" P.V.C. vent	1.000	Ea.	3.937	104	247	351
1/2" P.V.C. supply, 1-1/2" P.V.C. waste, 1-1/2" P.V.C. vent	1.000	Ea.	4.592	111	288	399
Bathtub, P.E. cast iron, 5' long with fittings, white	1.000	Ea.	3.636	1,225	205	1,430
Color	1.000	Ea.	3.636	1,500	205	1,705
Steel, enameled 5' long with fittings, white	1.000	Ea.	2.909	570	164	734
Color	1.000	Ea.	2.909	570	164	734
Rough-in, for bathtub						
1/2" copper supply, 4" cast iron waste, 1-1/2" copper vent	1.000	Ea.	2.409	148	146	294
4" P.V.C. waste, 1-1/2" P.V.C. vent	1.000	Ea.	2.877	77.50	174	251.50
1/2" steel supply, 4" cast iron waste, 1-1/2" steel vent	1.000	Ea.	2.898	137	171	308
4" P.V.C. waste, 1-1/2" P.V.C. vent	1.000	Ea.	3.159	82	192	274
1/2" P.V.C. supply, 4" P.V.C. waste, 1-1/2" P.V.C. vent	1.000	Ea.	3.371	89.50	205	294.50
Piping, supply, 1/2" copper	42.000	L.F.	4.148	156	260	416
1/2" steel	42.000	L.F.	5.333	173	335	508
1/2" P.V.C.	42.000	L.F.	6.222	205	390	595
Waste, 4" cast iron, no hub	10.000	L.F.	2.759	187	156	343
4" P.V.C./DWV	10.000	L.F.	3.333	91.50	188	279.50
4" copper/DWV	10.000	Ea.	4.000	680	225	905
Vent 2" cast iron, no hub	13.000	L.F.	3.105	135	176	311
2" copper/DWV	13.000	L.F.	2.364	244	148	392
2" P.V.C./DWV	13.000	L.F.	3.525	48.50	199	247.50
2" steel, galvanized	13.000	L.F.	3.250	174	183	357
Vanity base cabinet, 2 doors, 30" wide	1.000	Ea.	1.000	390	54	444
Vanity top, plastic laminated, square edge	2.670	L.F.	.712	96	38.50	134.50
Carrier, steel for studs, no arms	1.000	Ea.	1.143	91.50	71.50	163
Wood, 2" x 8" blocking	1.300	L.F.	.052	1.22	2.81	4.03

263

Shower — Lavatory — Vanity Top — Cabinet — Bathtub — Water Closet

System Description	QUAN.	UNIT	LABOR HOURS	COST EACH		
				MAT.	INST.	TOTAL
BATHROOM WITH LAVATORY INSTALLED IN VANITY						
Water closet, floor mounted, 2 piece, close coupled, white	1.000	Ea.	3.019	256	170	426
Rough-in, vent, 2″ diameter DWV piping	1.000	Ea.	.955	41.40	54	95.40
Waste, 4″ diameter DWV piping	1.000	Ea.	.828	55.95	46.65	102.60
Supply, 1/2″ diameter type "L" copper supply piping	1.000	Ea.	.593	22.26	37.20	59.46
Lavatory, 20″ x 18″ P.E. cast iron with fittings, white	1.000	Ea.	2.500	360	141	501
Shower, steel, enameled, stone base, corner, white	1.000	Ea.	3.333	1,900	188	2,088
Mixing valve	1.000	Ea.	1.333	169	83.50	252.50
Shower door	1.000	Ea.	1.000	420	60	480
Rough-in, waste, 1-1/2″ diameter DWV piping	2.000	Ea.	4.507	201	254	455
Supply, 1/2″ diameter type "L" copper supply piping	2.000	Ea.	3.161	118.72	198.40	317.12
Bathtub, P.E. cast iron, 5′ long with fittings, white	1.000	Ea.	3.636	1,225	205	1,430
Rough-in, waste, 4″ diameter DWV piping	1.000	Ea.	.828	55.95	46.65	102.60
Supply, 1/2″ diameter type "L" copper supply piping	1.000	Ea.	.988	37.10	62	99.10
Vent, 1-1/2″ diameter DWV piping	1.000	Ea.	.593	54.80	37.20	92
Piping, supply, 1/2″ diameter type "L" copper supply piping	42.000	L.F.	4.939	185.50	310	495.50
Waste, 4″ diameter DWV piping	10.000	L.F.	4.138	279.75	233.25	513
Vent, 2″ diameter DWV piping	13.000	L.F.	4.500	240.30	253.80	494.10
Vanity base, 2 doors, 30″ wide	1.000	Ea.	1.000	390	54	444
Vanity top, plastic laminated, square edge	2.670	L.F.	.712	84.11	38.45	122.56
TOTAL		Ea.	42.563	6,096.84	2,473.10	8,569.94
BATHROOM WITH WALL HUNG LAVATORY						
Water closet, floor mounted, 2 piece, close coupled, white	1.000	Ea.	3.019	256	170	426
Rough-in, vent, 2″ diameter DWV piping	1.000	Ea.	.955	41.40	54	95.40
Waste, 4″ diameter DWV piping	1.000	Ea.	.828	55.95	46.65	102.60
Supply, 1/2″ diameter type "L" copper supply piping	1.000	Ea.	.593	22.26	37.20	59.46
Lavatory, 20″ x 18″ P.E. cast iron with fittings, white	1.000	Ea.	2.000	305	113	418
Shower, steel enameled, stone base, corner, white	1.000	Ea.	3.333	1,900	188	2,088
Mixing valve	1.000	Ea.	1.333	169	83.50	252.50
Shower door	1.000	Ea.	1.000	420	60	480
Rough-in, waste, 1-1/2″ diameter DWV piping	2.000	Ea.	4.507	201	254	455
Supply, 1/2″ diameter type "L" copper supply piping	2.000	Ea.	3.161	118.72	198.40	317.12
Bathtub, P.E. cast iron, 5′ long with fittings, white	1.000	Ea.	3.636	1,225	205	1,430
Rough-in, waste, 4″ diameter DWV piping	1.000	Ea.	.828	55.95	46.65	102.60
Supply, 1/2″ diameter type "L" copper supply piping	1.000	Ea.	.988	37.10	62	99.10
Vent, 1-1/2″ diameter DWV piping	1.000	Ea.	.593	54.80	37.20	92
Piping, supply, 1/2″ diameter type "L" copper supply piping	42.000	L.F.	4.939	185.50	310	495.50
Waste, 4″ diameter DWV piping	10.000	L.F.	4.138	279.75	233.25	513
Vent, 2″ diameter DWV piping	13.000	L.F.	4.500	240.30	253.80	494.10
Carrier, steel for studs, no arms	1.000	Ea.	1.143	91.50	71.50	163
TOTAL		Ea.	41.494	5,659.23	2,424.15	8,083.38

The costs in this system are on a cost each basis. All necessary piping is included.

Four Fixture Bathroom Price Sheet

	QUAN.	UNIT	LABOR HOURS	COST EACH MAT.	COST EACH INST.	COST EACH TOTAL
Water closet, close coupled, standard 2 piece, white	1.000	Ea.	3.019	256	170	426
Color	1.000	Ea.	3.019	445	170	615
One piece, elongated bowl, white	1.000	Ea.	3.019	1,200	170	1,370
Color	1.000	Ea.	3.019	1,500	170	1,670
Low profile, one piece elongated bowl, white	1.000	Ea.	3.019	1,150	170	1,320
Color	1.000	Ea.	3.019	1,500	170	1,670
Rough-in, for water closet						
1/2" copper supply, 4" cast iron waste, 2" cast iron vent	1.000	Ea.	2.376	120	138	258
4" PVC/DWV waste, 2" PVC vent	1.000	Ea.	2.678	64.50	155	219.50
4" copper waste, 2" copper vent	1.000	Ea.	2.520	300	150	450
3" cast iron waste, 1-1/2" cast iron vent	1.000	Ea.	2.244	106	130	236
3" PVC waste, 1-1/2" PVC vent	1.000	Ea.	2.388	55.50	144	199.50
3" PVC waste, 1-1/2" PVC vent	1.000	Ea.	2.014	193	121	314
1/2" PVC supply, 4" PVC waste, 2" PVC vent	1.000	Ea.	2.974	71.50	173	244.50
3" PVC waste, 1-1/2" PVC vent	1.000	Ea.	2.684	62.50	163	225.50
1/2" steel supply, 4" cast iron waste, 2" cast iron vent	1.000	Ea.	2.545	122	148	270
4" cast iron waste, 2" steel vent	1.000	Ea.	2.590	134	151	285
4" PVC waste, 2" PVC vent	1.000	Ea.	2.847	67	165	232
Lavatory wall hung, P.E. cast iron 20" x 18", white	1.000	Ea.	2.000	305	113	418
Color	1.000	Ea.	2.000	335	113	448
Vitreous china 19" x 17", white	1.000	Ea.	2.286	209	129	338
Color	1.000	Ea.	2.286	236	129	365
Lavatory for vanity top, P.E. cast iron, 20" x 18", white	1.000	Ea.	2.500	360	141	501
Color	1.000	Ea.	2.500	625	141	766
Steel, enameled 20" x 17", white	1.000	Ea.	2.759	217	156	373
Color	1.000	Ea.	2.500	210	141	351
Vitreous china 20" x 16", white	1.000	Ea.	2.963	286	167	453
Color	1.000	Ea.	2.963	286	167	453
Shower, steel enameled, stone base 36" square, white	1.000	Ea.	8.889	1,900	188	2,088
Color	1.000	Ea.	8.889	1,950	188	2,138
Rough-in, for lavatory and shower						
1/2" copper supply, 1-1/2" cast iron waste, 1-1/2" cast iron vent	1.000	Ea.	7.668	320	450	770
1-1/2" PVC waste, 1-1/4" PVC vent	1.000	Ea.	7.352	188	460	648
1/2" steel supply, 1-1/4" cast iron waste, 1-1/4" steel vent	1.000	Ea.	8.205	320	490	810
1-1/4" PVC waste, 1-1/4" PVC vent	1.000	Ea.	7.873	207	495	702
1/2" PVC supply, 1-1/2" PVC waste, 1-1/2" PVC vent	1.000	Ea.	9.185	222	575	797
Bathtub, P.E. cast iron, 5' long with fittings, white	1.000	Ea.	3.636	1,225	205	1,430
Color	1.000	Ea.	3.636	1,500	205	1,705
Steel enameled, 5' long with fittings, white	1.000	Ea.	2.909	570	164	734
Color	1.000	Ea.	2.909	570	164	734
Rough-in, for bathtub						
1/2" copper supply, 4" cast iron waste, 1-1/2" copper vent	1.000	Ea.	2.409	148	146	294
4" PVC waste, 1-1/2" PVC vent	1.000	Ea.	2.877	77.50	174	251.50
1/2" steel supply, 4" cast iron waste, 1-1/2" steel vent	1.000	Ea.	2.898	137	171	308
4" PVC waste, 1-1/2" PVC vent	1.000	Ea.	3.159	82	192	274
1/2" PVC supply, 4" PVC waste, 1-1/2" PVC vent	1.000	Ea.	3.371	89.50	205	294.50
Piping supply, 1/2" copper	42.000	L.F.	4.148	156	260	416
1/2" steel	42.000	L.F.	5.333	173	335	508
1/2" PVC	42.000	L.F.	6.222	205	390	595
Piping, waste, 4" cast iron, no hub	10.000	L.F.	3.586	242	202	444
4" PVC/DWV	10.000	L.F.	4.333	119	244	363
4" copper/DWV	10.000	L.F.	5.200	885	293	1,178
Piping, vent, 2" cast iron, no hub	13.000	L.F.	3.105	135	176	311
2" copper/DWV	13.000	L.F.	2.364	244	148	392
2" PVC/DWV	13.000	L.F.	3.525	48.50	199	247.50
2" steel, galvanized	13.000	L.F.	3.250	174	183	357
Vanity base cabinet, 2 doors, 30" wide	1.000	Ea.	1.000	390	54	444
Vanity top, plastic laminated, square edge	3.160	L.F.	.843	114	45.50	159.50
Carrier, steel, for studs, no arms	1.000	Ea.	1.143	91.50	71.50	163
Wood, 2" x 8" blocking	1.300	L.F.	.052	1.22	2.81	4.03

Shower — Vanity Top — Water Closet — Bathtub — Cabinet

System Description	QUAN.	UNIT	LABOR HOURS	COST EACH MAT.	COST EACH INST.	COST EACH TOTAL
BATHROOM WITH SHOWER, BATHTUB, LAVATORIES IN VANITY						
Water closet, floor mounted, 1 piece, white	1.000	Ea.	3.019	1,150	170	1,320
Rough-in, vent, 2″ diameter DWV piping	1.000	Ea.	.955	41.40	54	95.40
Waste, 4″ diameter DWV piping	1.000	Ea.	.828	55.95	46.65	102.60
Supply, 1/2″ diameter type "L" copper supply piping	1.000	Ea.	.593	22.26	37.20	59.46
Lavatory, 20″ x 16″, vitreous china oval, with fittings, white	2.000	Ea.	5.926	572	334	906
Shower, steel enameled, stone base, corner, white	1.000	Ea.	3.333	1,900	188	2,088
Mixing valve	1.000	Ea.	1.333	169	83.50	252.50
Shower door	1.000	Ea.	1.000	420	60	480
Rough-in, waste, 1-1/2″ diameter DWV piping	3.000	Ea.	5.408	241.20	304.80	546
Supply, 1/2″ diameter type "L" copper supply piping	3.000	Ea.	2.963	111.30	186	297.30
Bathtub, P.E. cast iron, 5′ long with fittings, white	1.000	Ea.	3.636	1,225	205	1,430
Rough-in, waste, 4″ diameter DWV piping	1.000	Ea.	1.103	74.60	62.20	136.80
Supply, 1/2″ diameter type "L" copper supply piping	1.000	Ea.	.988	37.10	62	99.10
Vent, 1-1/2″ diameter copper DWV piping	1.000	Ea.	.593	54.80	37.20	92
Piping, supply, 1/2″ diameter type "L" copper supply piping	42.000	L.F.	4.148	155.82	260.40	416.22
Waste, 4″ diameter DWV piping	10.000	L.F.	2.759	186.50	155.50	342
Vent, 2″ diameter DWV piping	13.000	L.F.	3.250	173.55	183.30	356.85
Vanity base, 2 door, 24″ x 48″	1.000	Ea.	1.400	495	75.50	570.50
Vanity top, plastic laminated, square edge	4.170	L.F.	1.112	150.12	60.05	210.17
TOTAL		Ea.	44.347	7,235.60	2,565.30	9,800.90

The costs in this system are on a cost each basis. All necessary piping is included.

Description	QUAN.	UNIT	LABOR HOURS	COST EACH MAT.	COST EACH INST.	COST EACH TOTAL

Five Fixture Bathroom Price Sheet	QUAN.	UNIT	LABOR HOURS	COST EACH		
				MAT.	INST.	TOTAL
Water closet, close coupled, standard 2 piece, white	1.000	Ea.	3.019	256	170	426
Color	1.000	Ea.	3.019	445	170	615
One piece elongated bowl, white	1.000	Ea.	3.019	1,200	170	1,370
Color	1.000	Ea.	3.019	1,500	170	1,670
Low profile, one piece elongated bowl, white	1.000	Ea.	3.019	1,150	170	1,320
Color	1.000	Ea.	3.019	1,500	170	1,670
Rough-in, supply, waste and vent for water closet						
1/2" copper supply, 4" cast iron waste, 2" cast iron vent	1.000	Ea.	2.376	120	138	258
4" P.V.C./DWV waste, 2" P.V.C. vent	1.000	Ea.	2.678	64.50	155	219.50
4" copper waste, 2" copper vent	1.000	Ea.	2.520	300	150	450
3" cast iron waste, 1-1/2" cast iron vent	1.000	Ea.	2.244	106	130	236
3" P.V.C. waste, 1-1/2" P.V.C. vent	1.000	Ea.	2.388	55.50	144	199.50
3" copper waste, 1-1/2" copper vent	1.000	Ea.	2.014	193	121	314
1/2" P.V.C. supply, 4" P.V.C. waste, 2" P.V.C. vent	1.000	Ea.	2.974	71.50	173	244.50
3" P.V.C. waste, 1-1/2" P.V.C. supply	1.000	Ea.	2.684	62.50	163	225.50
1/2" steel supply, 4" cast iron waste, 2" cast iron vent	1.000	Ea.	2.545	122	148	270
4" cast iron waste, 2" steel vent	1.000	Ea.	2.590	134	151	285
4" P.V.C. waste, 2" P.V.C. vent	1.000	Ea.	2.847	67	165	232
Lavatory, wall hung, P.E. cast iron 20" x 18", white	2.000	Ea.	4.000	610	226	836
Color	2.000	Ea.	4.000	670	226	896
Vitreous china, 19" x 17", white	2.000	Ea.	4.571	420	258	678
Color	2.000	Ea.	4.571	470	258	728
Lavatory, for vanity top, P.E. cast iron, 20" x 18", white	2.000	Ea.	5.000	720	282	1,002
Color	2.000	Ea.	5.000	1,250	282	1,532
Steel enameled 20" x 17", white	2.000	Ea.	5.517	435	310	745
Color	2.000	Ea.	5.000	420	282	702
Vitreous china 20" x 16", white	2.000	Ea.	5.926	570	335	905
Color	2.000	Ea.	5.926	570	335	905
Shower, steel enameled, stone base 36" square, white	1.000	Ea.	8.889	1,900	188	2,088
Color	1.000	Ea.	8.889	1,950	188	2,138
Rough-in, for lavatory or shower						
1/2" copper supply, 1-1/2" cast iron waste, 1-1/2" cast iron vent	3.000	Ea.	8.371	355	490	845
1-1/2" P.V.C. waste, 1-1/4" P.V.C. vent	3.000	Ea.	7.916	196	495	691
1/2" steel supply, 1-1/4" cast iron waste, 1-1/4" steel vent	3.000	Ea.	8.670	345	515	860
1-1/4" P.V.C. waste, 1-1/4" P.V.C. vent	3.000	Ea.	8.381	214	525	739
1/2" P.V.C. supply, 1-1/2" P.V.C. waste, 1-1/2" P.V.C. vent	3.000	Ea.	9.778	225	615	840
Bathtub, P.E. cast iron 5' long with fittings, white	1.000	Ea.	3.636	1,225	205	1,430
Color	1.000	Ea.	3.636	1,500	205	1,705
Steel, enameled 5' long with fittings, white	1.000	Ea.	2.909	570	164	734
Color	1.000	Ea.	2.909	570	164	734
Rough-in, for bathtub						
1/2" copper supply, 4" cast iron waste, 1-1/2" copper vent	1.000	Ea.	2.684	167	161	328
4" P.V.C. waste, 1-1/2" P.V.C. vent	1.000	Ea.	3.210	87	193	280
1/2" steel supply, 4" cast iron waste, 1-1/2" steel vent	1.000	Ea.	3.173	156	187	343
4" P.V.C. waste, 1-1/2" P.V.C. vent	1.000	Ea.	3.492	91	211	302
1/2" P.V.C. supply, 4" P.V.C. waste, 1-1/2" P.V.C. vent	1.000	Ea.	3.704	98.50	224	322.50
Piping, supply, 1/2" copper	42.000	L.F.	4.148	156	260	416
1/2" steel	42.000	L.F.	5.333	173	335	508
1/2" P.V.C.	42.000	L.F.	6.222	205	390	595
Piping, waste, 4" cast iron, no hub	10.000	L.F.	2.759	187	156	343
4" P.V.C./DWV	10.000	L.F.	3.333	91.50	188	279.50
4" copper/DWV	10.000	L.F.	4.000	680	225	905
Piping, vent, 2" cast iron, no hub	13.000	L.F.	3.105	135	176	311
2" copper/DWV	13.000	L.F.	2.364	244	148	392
2" P.V.C./DWV	13.000	L.F.	3.525	48.50	199	247.50
2" steel, galvanized	13.000	L.F.	3.250	174	183	357
Vanity base cabinet, 2 doors, 24" x 48"	1.000	Ea.	1.400	495	75.50	570.50
Vanity top, plastic laminated, square edge	4.170	L.F.	1.112	150	60	210
Carrier, steel, for studs, no arms	1.000	Ea.	1.143	91.50	71.50	163
Wood, 2" x 8" blocking	1.300	L.F.	.052	1.22	2.81	4.03

Floor Registers

Register Elbows

Lateral Ducts

Return Air Grille

Return Air Duct

Supply Duct

Plenum

Furnace

System Description	QUAN.	UNIT	LABOR HOURS	COST PER SYSTEM		
				MAT.	INST.	TOTAL
HEATING ONLY, GAS FIRED HOT AIR, ONE ZONE, 1200 S.F. BUILDING						
Furnace, gas, up flow	1.000	Ea.	5.000	690	271	961
Intermittent pilot	1.000	Ea.		166		166
Supply duct, rigid fiberglass	176.000	S.F.	12.068	149.60	677.60	827.20
Return duct, sheet metal, galvanized	158.000	Lb.	16.137	115.34	908.50	1,023.84
Lateral ducts, 6″ flexible fiberglass	144.000	L.F.	8.862	465.12	480.96	946.08
Register, elbows	12.000	Ea.	3.200	372	173.40	545.40
Floor registers, enameled steel	12.000	Ea.	3.000	118.80	180.60	299.40
Floor grille, return air	2.000	Ea.	.727	58	44	102
Thermostat	1.000	Ea.	1.000	51.50	63.50	115
Plenum	1.000	Ea.	1.000	96	54	150
TOTAL		System	50.994	2,282.36	2,853.56	5,135.92
HEATING/COOLING, GAS FIRED FORCED AIR, ONE ZONE, 1200 S.F. BUILDING						
Furnace, including plenum, compressor, coil	1.000	Ea.	14.720	5,727	795.80	6,522.80
Intermittent pilot	1.000	Ea.		166		166
Supply duct, rigid fiberglass	176.000	S.F.	12.068	149.60	677.60	827.20
Return duct, sheet metal, galvanized	158.000	Lb.	16.137	115.34	908.50	1,023.84
Lateral duct, 6″ flexible fiberglass	144.000	L.F.	8.862	465.12	480.96	946.08
Register elbows	12.000	Ea.	3.200	372	173.40	545.40
Floor registers, enameled steel	12.000	Ea.	3.000	118.80	180.60	299.40
Floor grille return air	2.000	Ea.	.727	58	44	102
Thermostat	1.000	Ea.	1.000	51.50	63.50	115
Refrigeration piping, 25 ft. (pre-charged)	1.000	Ea.		294		294
TOTAL		System	59.714	7,517.36	3,324.36	10,841.72

The costs in these systems are based on complete system basis. For larger buildings use the price sheet on the opposite page.

Description	QUAN.	UNIT	LABOR HOURS	COST PER SYSTEM		
				MAT.	INST.	TOTAL

Gas Heating/Cooling Price Sheet	QUAN.	UNIT	LABOR HOURS	COST EACH		
				MAT.	INST.	TOTAL
Furnace, heating only, 100 MBH, area to 1200 S.F.	1.000	Ea.	5.000	690	271	961
120 MBH, area to 1500 S.F.	1.000	Ea.	5.000	690	271	961
160 MBH, area to 2000 S.F.	1.000	Ea.	5.714	735	310	1,045
200 MBH, area to 2400 S.F.	1.000	Ea.	6.154	3,075	335	3,410
Heating/cooling, 100 MBH heat, 36 MBH cool, to 1200 S.F.	1.000	Ea.	16.000	6,225	865	7,090
120 MBH heat, 42 MBH cool, to 1500 S.F.	1.000	Ea.	18.462	6,625	1,050	7,675
144 MBH heat, 47 MBH cool, to 2000 S.F.	1.000	Ea.	20.000	7,650	1,125	8,775
200 MBH heat, 60 MBH cool, to 2400 S.F.	1.000	Ea.	34.286	8,050	1,925	9,975
Intermittent pilot, 100 MBH furnace	1.000	Ea.		166		166
200 MBH furnace	1.000	Ea.		166		166
Supply duct, rectangular, area to 1200 S.F., rigid fiberglass	176.000	S.F.	12.068	150	680	830
Sheet metal insulated	228.000	Lb.	31.331	340	1,725	2,065
Area to 1500 S.F., rigid fiberglass	176.000	S.F.	12.068	150	680	830
Sheet metal insulated	228.000	Lb.	31.331	340	1,725	2,065
Area to 2400 S.F., rigid fiberglass	205.000	S.F.	14.057	174	790	964
Sheet metal insulated	271.000	Lb.	37.048	400	2,050	2,450
Round flexible, insulated 6″ diameter, to 1200 S.F.	156.000	L.F.	9.600	505	520	1,025
To 1500 S.F.	184.000	L.F.	11.323	595	615	1,210
8″ diameter, to 2000 S.F.	269.000	L.F.	23.911	1,025	1,300	2,325
To 2400 S.F.	248.000	L.F.	22.045	950	1,200	2,150
Return duct, sheet metal galvanized, to 1500 S.F.	158.000	Lb.	16.137	115	910	1,025
To 2400 S.F.	191.000	Lb.	19.507	139	1,100	1,239
Lateral ducts, flexible round 6″ insulated, to 1200 S.F.	144.000	L.F.	8.862	465	480	945
To 1500 S.F.	172.000	L.F.	10.585	555	575	1,130
To 2000 S.F.	261.000	L.F.	16.062	845	870	1,715
To 2400 S.F.	300.000	L.F.	18.462	970	1,000	1,970
Spiral steel insulated, to 1200 S.F.	144.000	L.F.	20.067	555	1,050	1,605
To 1500 S.F.	172.000	L.F.	23.952	660	1,250	1,910
To 2000 S.F.	261.000	L.F.	36.352	1,000	1,925	2,925
To 2400 S.F.	300.000	L.F.	41.825	1,150	2,200	3,350
Rectangular sheet metal galvanized insulated, to 1200 S.F.	228.000	Lb.	39.056	505	2,125	2,630
To 1500 S.F.	344.000	Lb.	53.966	655	2,950	3,605
To 2000 S.F.	522.000	Lb.	81.926	995	4,475	5,470
To 2400 S.F.	600.000	Lb.	94.189	1,150	5,150	6,300
Register elbows, to 1500 S.F.	12.000	Ea.	3.200	370	173	543
To 2400 S.F.	14.000	Ea.	3.733	435	202	637
Floor registers, enameled steel w/damper, to 1500 S.F.	12.000	Ea.	3.000	119	181	300
To 2400 S.F.	14.000	Ea.	4.308	162	259	421
Return air grille, area to 1500 S.F. 12″ x 12″	2.000	Ea.	.727	58	44	102
Area to 2400 S.F. 8″ x 16″	2.000	Ea.	.444	39.50	27	66.50
Area to 2400 S.F. 8″ x 16″	2.000	Ea.	.727	58	44	102
16″ x 16″	1.000	Ea.	.364	37.50	22	59.50
Thermostat, manual, 1 set back	1.000	Ea.	1.000	51.50	63.50	115
Electric, timed, 1 set back	1.000	Ea.	1.000	39.50	63.50	103
2 set back	1.000	Ea.	1.000	197	63.50	260.50
Plenum, heating only, 100 M.B.H.	1.000	Ea.	1.000	96	54	150
120 MBH	1.000	Ea.	1.000	96	54	150
160 MBH	1.000	Ea.	1.000	96	54	150
200 MBH	1.000	Ea.	1.000	96	54	150
Refrigeration piping, 3/8″	25.000	L.F.		37.50		37.50
3/4″	25.000	L.F.		82.50		82.50
7/8″	25.000	L.F.		96		96
Refrigerant piping, 25 ft. (precharged)	1.000	Ea.		294		294
Diffusers, ceiling, 6″ diameter, to 1500 S.F.	10.000	Ea.	4.444	99	270	369
To 2400 S.F.	12.000	Ea.	6.000	126	360	486
Floor, aluminum, adjustable, 2-1/4″ x 12″ to 1500 S.F.	12.000	Ea.	3.000	86.50	181	267.50
To 2400 S.F.	14.000	Ea.	3.500	101	211	312
Side wall, aluminum, adjustable, 8″ x 4″, to 1500 S.F.	12.000	Ea.	3.000	214	181	395
5″ x 10″ to 2400 S.F.	12.000	Ea.	3.692	282	222	504

Floor Registers — Lateral Ducts — Supply Duct — Register Elbows — Return Air Grille — Return Air Duct — Furnace — Plenum

System Description	QUAN.	UNIT	LABOR HOURS	COST PER SYSTEM		
				MAT.	INST.	TOTAL
HEATING ONLY, OIL FIRED HOT AIR, ONE ZONE, 1200 S.F. BUILDING						
Furnace, oil fired, atomizing gun type burner	1.000	Ea.	4.571	2,050	248	2,298
3/8" diameter copper supply pipe	1.000	Ea.	2.759	87.60	172.50	260.10
Shut off valve	1.000	Ea.	.333	14.95	21	35.95
Oil tank, 275 gallon, on legs	1.000	Ea.	3.200	540	184	724
Supply duct, rigid fiberglass	176.000	S.F.	12.068	149.60	677.60	827.20
Return duct, sheet metal, galvanized	158.000	Lb.	16.137	115.34	908.50	1,023.84
Lateral ducts, 6" flexible fiberglass	144.000	L.F.	8.862	465.12	480.96	946.08
Register elbows	12.000	Ea.	3.200	372	173.40	545.40
Floor register, enameled steel	12.000	Ea.	3.000	118.80	180.60	299.40
Floor grille, return air	2.000	Ea.	.727	58	44	102
Thermostat	1.000	Ea.	1.000	51.50	63.50	115
TOTAL		System	55.857	4,022.91	3,154.06	7,176.97
HEATING/COOLING, OIL FIRED, FORCED AIR, ONE ZONE, 1200 S.F. BUILDING						
Furnace, including plenum, compressor, coil	1.000	Ea.	16.000	6,625	865	7,490
3/8" diameter copper supply pipe	1.000	Ea.	2.759	87.60	172.50	260.10
Shut off valve	1.000	Ea.	.333	14.95	21	35.95
Oil tank, 275 gallon on legs	1.000	Ea.	3.200	540	184	724
Supply duct, rigid fiberglass	176.000	S.F.	12.068	149.60	677.60	827.20
Return duct, sheet metal, galvanized	158.000	Lb.	16.137	115.34	908.50	1,023.84
Lateral ducts, 6" flexible fiberglass	144.000	L.F.	8.862	465.12	480.96	946.08
Register elbows	12.000	Ea.	3.200	372	173.40	545.40
Floor registers, enameled steel	12.000	Ea.	3.000	118.80	180.60	299.40
Floor grille, return air	2.000	Ea.	.727	58	44	102
Refrigeration piping (precharged)	25.000	L.F.		294		294
TOTAL		System	66.286	8,840.41	3,707.56	12,547.97

Description	QUAN.	UNIT	LABOR HOURS	COST EACH		
				MAT.	INST.	TOTAL

Oil Fired Heating/Cooling	QUAN.	UNIT	LABOR HOURS	COST EACH MAT.	COST EACH INST.	COST EACH TOTAL
Furnace, heating, 95.2 MBH, area to 1200 S.F.	1.000	Ea.	4.706	2,075	255	2,330
123.2 MBH, area to 1500 S.F.	1.000	Ea.	5.000	2,400	271	2,671
151.2 MBH, area to 2000 S.F.	1.000	Ea.	5.333	2,475	289	2,764
200 MBH, area to 2400 S.F.	1.000	Ea.	6.154	2,700	335	3,035
Heating/cooling, 95.2 MBH heat, 36 MBH cool, to 1200 S.F.	1.000	Ea.	16.000	6,625	865	7,490
112 MBH heat, 42 MBH cool, to 1500 S.F.	1.000	Ea.	24.000	9,950	1,300	11,250
151 MBH heat, 47 MBH cool, to 2000 S.F.	1.000	Ea.	20.800	8,625	1,125	9,750
184.8 MBH heat, 60 MBH cool, to 2400 S.F.	1.000	Ea.	24.000	3,175	1,350	4,525
Oil piping to furnace, 3/8" dia., copper	1.000	Ea.	3.412	235	211	446
Oil tank, on legs above ground, 275 gallons	1.000	Ea.	3.200	540	184	724
550 gallons	1.000	Ea.	5.926	3,750	340	4,090
Below ground, 275 gallons	1.000	Ea.	3.200	540	184	724
550 gallons	1.000	Ea.	5.926	3,750	340	4,090
1000 gallons	1.000	Ea.	6.400	6,150	365	6,515
Supply duct, rectangular, area to 1200 S.F., rigid fiberglass	176.000	S.F.	12.068	150	680	830
Sheet metal, insulated	228.000	Lb.	31.331	340	1,725	2,065
Area to 1500 S.F., rigid fiberglass	176.000	S.F.	12.068	150	680	830
Sheet metal, insulated	228.000	Lb.	31.331	340	1,725	2,065
Area to 2400 S.F., rigid fiberglass	205.000	S.F.	14.057	174	790	964
Sheet metal, insulated	271.000	Lb.	37.048	400	2,050	2,450
Round flexible, insulated, 6" diameter to 1200 S.F.	156.000	L.F.	9.600	505	520	1,025
To 1500 S.F.	184.000	L.F.	11.323	595	615	1,210
8" diameter to 2000 S.F.	269.000	L.F.	23.911	1,025	1,300	2,325
To 2400 S.F.	269.000	L.F.	22.045	950	1,200	2,150
Return duct, sheet metal galvanized, to 1500 S.F.	158.000	Lb.	16.137	115	910	1,025
To 2400 S.F.	191.000	Lb.	19.507	139	1,100	1,239
Lateral ducts, flexible round, 6", insulated to 1200 S.F.	144.000	L.F.	8.862	465	480	945
To 1500 S.F.	172.000	L.F.	10.585	555	575	1,130
To 2000 S.F.	261.000	L.F.	16.062	845	870	1,715
To 2400 S.F.	300.000	L.F.	18.462	970	1,000	1,970
Spiral steel, insulated to 1200 S.F.	144.000	L.F.	20.067	555	1,050	1,605
To 1500 S.F.	172.000	L.F.	23.952	660	1,250	1,910
To 2000 S.F.	261.000	L.F.	36.352	1,000	1,925	2,925
To 2400 S.F.	300.000	L.F.	41.825	1,150	2,200	3,350
Rectangular sheet metal galvanized insulated, to 1200 S.F.	288.000	Lb.	45.183	550	2,475	3,025
To 1500 S.F.	344.000	Lb.	53.966	655	2,950	3,605
To 2000 S.F.	522.000	Lb.	81.926	995	4,475	5,470
To 2400 S.F.	600.000	Lb.	94.189	1,150	5,150	6,300
Register elbows, to 1500 S.F.	12.000	Ea.	3.200	370	173	543
To 2400 S.F.	14.000	Ea.	3.733	435	202	637
Floor registers, enameled steel w/damper, to 1500 S.F.	12.000	Ea.	3.000	119	181	300
To 2400 S.F.	14.000	Ea.	4.308	162	259	421
Return air grille, area to 1500 S.F., 12" x 12"	2.000	Ea.	.727	58	44	102
12" x 24"	1.000	Ea.	.444	39.50	27	66.50
Area to 2400 S.F., 8" x 16"	2.000	Ea.	.727	58	44	102
16" x 16"	1.000	Ea.	.364	37.50	22	59.50
Thermostat, manual, 1 set back	1.000	Ea.	1.000	51.50	63.50	115
Electric, timed, 1 set back	1.000	Ea.	1.000	39.50	63.50	103
2 set back	1.000	Ea.	1.000	197	63.50	260.50
Refrigeration piping, 3/8"	25.000	L.F.		37.50		37.50
3/4"	25.000	L.F.		82.50		82.50
Diffusers, ceiling, 6" diameter, to 1500 S.F.	10.000	Ea.	4.444	99	270	369
To 2400 S.F.	12.000	Ea.	6.000	126	360	486
Floor, aluminum, adjustable, 2-1/4" x 12" to 1500 S.F.	12.000	Ea.	3.000	86.50	181	267.50
To 2400 S.F.	14.000	Ea.	3.500	101	211	312
Side wall, aluminum, adjustable, 8" x 4", to 1500 S.F.	12.000	Ea.	3.000	214	181	395
5" x 10" to 2400 S.F.	12.000	Ea.	3.692	282	222	504

System Description	QUAN.	UNIT	LABOR HOURS	COST EACH		
				MAT.	INST.	TOTAL
OIL FIRED HOT WATER HEATING SYSTEM, AREA TO 1200 S.F.						
Boiler package, oil fired, 97 MBH, area to 1200 S.F. building	1.000	Ea.	15.000	1,950	830	2,780
3/8" diameter copper supply pipe	1.000	Ea.	2.759	87.60	172.50	260.10
Shut off valve	1.000	Ea.	.333	14.95	21	35.95
Oil tank, 275 gallon, with black iron filler pipe	1.000	Ea.	3.200	540	184	724
Supply piping, 3/4" copper tubing	176.000	L.F.	18.526	994.40	1,161.60	2,156
Supply fittings, copper 3/4"	36.000	Ea.	15.158	273.60	954	1,227.60
Supply valves, 3/4"	2.000	Ea.	.800	296	50	346
Baseboard radiation, 3/4"	106.000	L.F.	35.333	731.40	2,024.60	2,756
Zone valve	1.000	Ea.	.400	182	25.50	207.50
TOTAL		Ea.	91.509	5,069.95	5,423.20	10,493.15
OIL FIRED HOT WATER HEATING SYSTEM, AREA TO 2400 S.F.						
Boiler package, oil fired, 225 MBH, area to 2400 S.F. building	1.000	Ea.	25.105	7,025	1,375	8,400
3/8" diameter copper supply pipe	1.000	Ea.	2.759	87.60	172.50	260.10
Shut off valve	1.000	Ea.	.333	14.95	21	35.95
Oil tank, 550 gallon, with black iron pipe filler pipe	1.000	Ea.	5.926	3,750	340	4,090
Supply piping, 3/4" copper tubing	228.000	L.F.	23.999	1,288.20	1,504.80	2,793
Supply fittings, copper	46.000	Ea.	19.368	349.60	1,219	1,568.60
Supply valves	2.000	Ea.	.800	296	50	346
Baseboard radiation	212.000	L.F.	70.666	1,462.80	4,049.20	5,512
Zone valve	1.000	Ea.	.400	182	25.50	207.50
TOTAL		Ea.	149.356	14,456.15	8,757	23,213.15

The costs in this system are on a cost each basis. The costs represent total cost for the system based on a gross square foot of plan area.

Description	QUAN.	UNIT	LABOR HOURS	COST EACH		
				MAT.	INST.	TOTAL

Hot Water Heating Price Sheet	QUAN.	UNIT	LABOR HOURS	COST EACH		
				MAT.	INST.	TOTAL
Boiler, oil fired, 97 MBH, area to 1200 S.F.	1.000	Ea.	15.000	1,950	830	2,780
118 MBH, area to 1500 S.F.	1.000	Ea.	16.506	2,075	910	2,985
161 MBH, area to 2000 S.F.	1.000	Ea.	18.405	2,325	1,025	3,350
215 MBH, area to 2400 S.F.	1.000	Ea.	19.704	3,875	2,150	6,025
Oil piping, (valve & filter), 3/8" copper	1.000	Ea.	3.289	103	194	297
1/4" copper	1.000	Ea.	3.242	122	202	324
Oil tank, filler pipe and cap on legs, 275 gallon	1.000	Ea.	3.200	540	184	724
550 gallon	1.000	Ea.	5.926	3,750	340	4,090
Buried underground, 275 gallon	1.000	Ea.	3.200	540	184	724
550 gallon	1.000	Ea.	5.926	3,750	340	4,090
1000 gallon	1.000	Ea.	6.400	6,150	365	6,515
Supply piping copper, area to 1200 S.F., 1/2" tubing	176.000	L.F.	17.384	655	1,100	1,755
3/4" tubing	176.000	L.F.	18.526	995	1,150	2,145
Area to 1500 S.F., 1/2" tubing	186.000	L.F.	18.371	690	1,150	1,840
3/4" tubing	186.000	L.F.	19.578	1,050	1,225	2,275
Area to 2000 S.F., 1/2" tubing	204.000	L.F.	20.149	755	1,275	2,030
3/4" tubing	204.000	L.F.	21.473	1,150	1,350	2,500
Area to 2400 S.F., 1/2" tubing	228.000	L.F.	22.520	845	1,425	2,270
3/4" tubing	228.000	L.F.	23.999	1,300	1,500	2,800
Supply pipe fittings copper, area to 1200 S.F., 1/2"	36.000	Ea.	14.400	122	900	1,022
3/4"	36.000	Ea.	15.158	274	955	1,229
Area to 1500 S.F., 1/2"	40.000	Ea.	16.000	136	1,000	1,136
3/4"	40.000	Ea.	16.842	305	1,050	1,355
Area to 2000 S.F., 1/2"	44.000	Ea.	17.600	149	1,100	1,249
3/4"	44.000	Ea.	18.526	335	1,175	1,510
Area to 2400, S.F., 1/2"	46.000	Ea.	18.400	156	1,150	1,306
3/4"	46.000	Ea.	19.368	350	1,225	1,575
Supply valves, 1/2" pipe size	2.000	Ea.	.667	222	42	264
3/4"	2.000	Ea.	.800	296	50	346
Baseboard radiation, area to 1200 S.F., 1/2" tubing	106.000	L.F.	28.267	1,300	1,625	2,925
3/4" tubing	106.000	L.F.	35.333	730	2,025	2,755
Area to 1500 S.F., 1/2" tubing	134.000	L.F.	35.734	1,650	2,050	3,700
3/4" tubing	134.000	L.F.	44.666	925	2,550	3,475
Area to 2000 S.F., 1/2" tubing	178.000	L.F.	47.467	2,200	2,725	4,925
3/4" tubing	178.000	L.F.	59.333	1,225	3,400	4,625
Area to 2400 S.F., 1/2" tubing	212.000	L.F.	56.534	2,600	3,250	5,850
3/4" tubing	212.000	L.F.	70.666	1,475	4,050	5,525
Zone valves, 1/2" tubing	1.000	Ea.	.400	182	25.50	207.50
3/4" tubing	1.000	Ea.	.400	183	25.50	208.50

System Description	QUAN.	UNIT	LABOR HOURS	COST EACH		
				MAT.	INST.	TOTAL
ROOFTOP HEATING/COOLING UNIT, AREA TO 2000 S.F.						
Rooftop unit, single zone, electric cool, gas heat, to 2000 S.F.	1.000	Ea.	28.521	5,800	1,625	7,425
Gas piping	34.500	L.F.	5.207	175.95	326.03	501.98
Duct, supply and return, galvanized steel	38.000	Lb.	3.881	27.74	218.50	246.24
Insulation, ductwork	33.000	S.F.	1.508	32.34	77.88	110.22
Lateral duct, flexible duct 12″ diameter, insulated	72.000	L.F.	11.520	388.80	622.80	1,011.60
Diffusers	4.000	Ea.	4.571	1,184	276	1,460
Return registers	1.000	Ea.	.727	71.50	44	115.50
TOTAL		Ea.	55.935	7,680.33	3,190.21	10,870.54
ROOFTOP HEATING/COOLING UNIT, AREA TO 5000 S.F.						
Rooftop unit, single zone, electric cool, gas heat, to 5000 S.F.	1.000	Ea.	42.032	18,700	2,325	21,025
Gas piping	86.250	L.F.	13.019	439.88	815.06	1,254.94
Duct supply and return, galvanized steel	95.000	Lb.	9.702	69.35	546.25	615.60
Insulation, ductwork	82.000	S.F.	3.748	80.36	193.52	273.88
Lateral duct, flexible duct, 12″ diameter, insulated	180.000	L.F.	28.800	972	1,557	2,529
Diffusers	10.000	Ea.	11.429	2,960	690	3,650
Return registers	3.000	Ea.	2.182	214.50	132	346.50
TOTAL		Ea.	110.912	23,436.09	6,258.83	29,694.92

Description	QUAN.	UNIT	LABOR HOURS	COST EACH		
				MAT.	INST.	TOTAL

Rooftop Price Sheet	QUAN.	UNIT	LABOR HOURS	COST EACH		
				MAT.	INST.	TOTAL
Rooftop unit, single zone, electric cool, gas heat to 2000 S.F.	1.000	Ea.	28.521	5,800	1,625	7,425
Area to 3000 S.F.	1.000	Ea.	35.982	12,800	1,975	14,775
Area to 5000 S.F.	1.000	Ea.	42.032	18,700	2,325	21,025
Area to 10000 S.F.	1.000	Ea.	68.376	31,500	3,925	35,425
Gas piping, area 2000 through 4000 S.F.	34.500	L.F.	5.207	176	325	501
Area 5000 to 10000 S.F.	86.250	L.F.	13.019	440	815	1,255
Duct, supply and return, galvanized steel, to 2000 S.F.	38.000	Lb.	3.881	27.50	219	246.50
Area to 3000 S.F.	57.000	Lb.	5.821	41.50	330	371.50
Area to 5000 S.F.	95.000	Lb.	9.702	69.50	545	614.50
Area to 10000 S.F.	190.000	Lb.	19.405	139	1,100	1,239
Rigid fiberglass, area to 2000 S.F.	33.000	S.F.	2.263	28	127	155
Area to 3000 S.F.	49.000	S.F.	3.360	41.50	189	230.50
Area to 5000 S.F.	82.000	S.F.	5.623	69.50	315	384.50
Area to 10000 S.F.	164.000	S.F.	11.245	139	630	769
Insulation, supply and return, blanket type, area to 2000 S.F.	33.000	S.F.	1.508	32.50	78	110.50
Area to 3000 S.F.	49.000	S.F.	2.240	48	116	164
Area to 5000 S.F.	82.000	S.F.	3.748	80.50	194	274.50
Area to 10000 S.F.	164.000	S.F.	7.496	161	385	546
Lateral ducts, flexible round, 12″ insulated, to 2000 S.F.	72.000	L.F.	11.520	390	625	1,015
Area to 3000 S.F.	108.000	L.F.	17.280	585	935	1,520
Area to 5000 S.F.	180.000	L.F.	28.800	970	1,550	2,520
Area to 10000 S.F.	360.000	L.F.	57.600	1,950	3,125	5,075
Rectangular, galvanized steel, to 2000 S.F.	239.000	Lb.	24.409	174	1,375	1,549
Area to 3000 S.F.	360.000	Lb.	36.767	263	2,075	2,338
Area to 5000 S.F.	599.000	Lb.	61.176	435	3,450	3,885
Area to 10000 S.F.	998.000	Lb.	101.926	730	5,750	6,480
Diffusers, ceiling, 1 to 4 way blow, 24″ x 24″, to 2000 S.F.	4.000	Ea.	4.571	1,175	276	1,451
Area to 3000 S.F.	6.000	Ea.	6.857	1,775	415	2,190
Area to 5000 S.F.	10.000	Ea.	11.429	2,950	690	3,640
Area to 10000 S.F.	20.000	Ea.	22.857	5,925	1,375	7,300
Return grilles, 24″ x 24″, to 2000 S.F.	1.000	Ea.	.727	71.50	44	115.50
Area to 3000 S.F.	2.000	Ea.	1.455	143	88	231
Area to 5000 S.F.	3.000	Ea.	2.182	215	132	347
Area to 10000 S.F.	5.000	Ea.	3.636	360	220	580

Weather Cap

Service Entrance Cable

Meter Socket

Panelboard, Including Breakers

Ground Cable

Ground Rod with Clamp

System Description	QUAN.	UNIT	LABOR HOURS	COST EACH		
				MAT.	INST.	TOTAL
100 AMP SERVICE						
Weather cap	1.000	Ea.	.667	11.35	39	50.35
Service entrance cable	10.000	L.F.	.762	40.20	44.60	84.80
Meter socket	1.000	Ea.	2.500	46	146	192
Ground rod with clamp	1.000	Ea.	1.455	22.50	85	107.50
Ground cable	5.000	L.F.	.250	8.05	14.65	22.70
Panel board, 12 circuit	1.000	Ea.	6.667	267	390	657
TOTAL		Ea.	12.301	395.10	719.25	1,114.35
200 AMP SERVICE						
Weather cap	1.000	Ea.	1.000	31.50	58.50	90
Service entrance cable	10.000	L.F.	1.143	72	67	139
Meter socket	1.000	Ea.	4.211	98.50	246	344.50
Ground rod with clamp	1.000	Ea.	1.818	43	106	149
Ground cable	10.000	L.F.	.500	16.10	29.30	45.40
3/4" EMT	5.000	L.F.	.308	4.70	18	22.70
Panel board, 24 circuit	1.000	Ea.	12.308	585	610	1,195
TOTAL		Ea.	21.288	850.80	1,134.80	1,985.60
400 AMP SERVICE						
Weather cap	1.000	Ea.	2.963	330	173	503
Service entrance cable	180.000	L.F.	5.760	784.80	336.60	1,121.40
Meter socket	1.000	Ea.	4.211	98.50	246	344.50
Ground rod with clamp	1.000	Ea.	2.000	69.50	117	186.50
Ground cable	20.000	L.F.	.485	55.40	28.40	83.80
3/4 Greenfield	20.000	L.F.	1.000	17.20	58.60	75.80
Current transformer cabinet	1.000	Ea.	6.154	183	360	543
Panel board, 42 circuit	1.000	Ea.	33.333	3,550	1,950	5,500
TOTAL		Ea.	55.906	5,088.40	3,269.60	8,358

Thermostat →

Electric Baseboard ———

System Description	QUAN.	UNIT	LABOR HOURS	COST EACH		
				MAT.	INST.	TOTAL
4' BASEBOARD HEATER						
Electric baseboard heater, 4' long	1.000	Ea.	1.194	45	70	115
Thermostat, integral	1.000	Ea.	.500	33	29.50	62.50
Romex, 12-3 with ground	40.000	L.F.	1.600	24	93.60	117.60
Panel board breaker, 20 Amp	1.000	Ea.	.300	10.50	17.55	28.05
TOTAL		Ea.	3.594	112.50	210.65	323.15
6' BASEBOARD HEATER						
Electric baseboard heater, 6' long	1.000	Ea.	1.600	61.50	93.50	155
Thermostat, integral	1.000	Ea.	.500	33	29.50	62.50
Romex, 12-3 with ground	40.000	L.F.	1.600	24	93.60	117.60
Panel board breaker, 20 Amp	1.000	Ea.	.400	14	23.40	37.40
TOTAL		Ea.	4.100	132.50	240	372.50
8' BASEBOARD HEATER						
Electric baseboard heater, 8' long	1.000	Ea.	2.000	76	117	193
Thermostat, integral	1.000	Ea.	.500	33	29.50	62.50
Romex, 12-3 with ground	40.000	L.F.	1.600	24	93.60	117.60
Panel board breaker, 20 Amp	1.000	Ea.	.500	17.50	29.25	46.75
TOTAL		Ea.	4.600	150.50	269.35	419.85
10' BASEBOARD HEATER						
Electric baseboard heater, 10' long	1.000	Ea.	2.424	212	142	354
Thermostat, integral	1.000	Ea.	.500	33	29.50	62.50
Romex, 12-3 with ground	40.000	L.F.	1.600	24	93.60	117.60
Panel board breaker, 20 Amp	1.000	Ea.	.750	26.25	43.88	70.13
TOTAL		Ea.	5.274	295.25	308.98	604.23

The costs in this system are on a cost each basis and include all
necessary conduit fittings.

Description	QUAN.	UNIT	LABOR HOURS	COST EACH		
				MAT.	INST.	TOTAL

System Description	QUAN.	UNIT	LABOR HOURS	COST EACH		
				MAT.	INST.	TOTAL
Air conditioning receptacles						
Using non-metallic sheathed cable	1.000	Ea.	.800	23	47	70
Using BX cable	1.000	Ea.	.964	32.50	56.50	89
Using EMT conduit	1.000	Ea.	1.194	43.50	70	113.50
Disposal wiring						
Using non-metallic sheathed cable	1.000	Ea.	.889	19.85	52	71.85
Using BX cable	1.000	Ea.	1.067	28.50	62.50	91
Using EMT conduit	1.000	Ea.	1.333	41.50	78	119.50
Dryer circuit						
Using non-metallic sheathed cable	1.000	Ea.	1.455	42.50	85	127.50
Using BX cable	1.000	Ea.	1.739	48	102	150
Using EMT conduit	1.000	Ea.	2.162	55	126	181
Duplex receptacles						
Using non-metallic sheathed cable	1.000	Ea.	.615	23	36	59
Using BX cable	1.000	Ea.	.741	32.50	43.50	76
Using EMT conduit	1.000	Ea.	.920	43.50	54	97.50
Exhaust fan wiring						
Using non-metallic sheathed cable	1.000	Ea.	.800	23.50	47	70.50
Using BX cable	1.000	Ea.	.964	33	56.50	89.50
Using EMT conduit	1.000	Ea.	1.194	44	70	114
Furnace circuit & switch						
Using non-metallic sheathed cable	1.000	Ea.	1.333	30.50	78	108.50
Using BX cable	1.000	Ea.	1.600	42.50	93.50	136
Using EMT conduit	1.000	Ea.	2.000	49.50	117	166.50
Ground fault						
Using non-metallic sheathed cable	1.000	Ea.	1.000	61	58.50	119.50
Using BX cable	1.000	Ea.	1.212	70.50	71	141.50
Using EMT conduit	1.000	Ea.	1.481	91.50	86.50	178
Heater circuits						
Using non-metallic sheathed cable	1.000	Ea.	1.000	27.50	58.50	86
Using BX cable	1.000	Ea.	1.212	32.50	71	103.50
Using EMT conduit	1.000	Ea.	1.481	43	86.50	129.50
Lighting wiring						
Using non-metallic sheathed cable	1.000	Ea.	.500	28	29.50	57.50
Using BX cable	1.000	Ea.	.602	33.50	35	68.50
Using EMT conduit	1.000	Ea.	.748	41	43.50	84.50
Range circuits						
Using non-metallic sheathed cable	1.000	Ea.	2.000	86	117	203
Using BX cable	1.000	Ea.	2.424	121	142	263
Using EMT conduit	1.000	Ea.	2.963	97	173	270
Switches, single pole						
Using non-metallic sheathed cable	1.000	Ea.	.500	23.50	29.50	53
Using BX cable	1.000	Ea.	.602	33	35	68
Using EMT conduit	1.000	Ea.	.748	44	43.50	87.50
Switches, 3-way						
Using non-metallic sheathed cable	1.000	Ea.	.667	26	39	65
Using BX cable	1.000	Ea.	.800	34	47	81
Using EMT conduit	1.000	Ea.	1.333	53	78	131
Water heater						
Using non-metallic sheathed cable	1.000	Ea.	1.600	33	93.50	126.50
Using BX cable	1.000	Ea.	1.905	48	111	159
Using EMT conduit	1.000	Ea.	2.353	48.50	138	186.50
Weatherproof receptacle						
Using non-metallic sheathed cable	1.000	Ea.	1.333	138	78	216
Using BX cable	1.000	Ea.	1.600	144	93.50	237.50
Using EMT conduit	1.000	Ea.	2.000	155	117	272

DESCRIPTION	QUAN.	UNIT	LABOR HOURS	COST EACH		
				MAT.	INST.	TOTAL
Fluorescent strip, 4' long, 1 light, average	1.000	Ea.	.941	30	55	85
Deluxe	1.000	Ea.	1.129	36	66	102
2 lights, average	1.000	Ea.	1.000	42	58.50	100.50
Deluxe	1.000	Ea.	1.200	50.50	70	120.50
8' long, 1 light, average	1.000	Ea.	1.194	52.50	70	122.50
Deluxe	1.000	Ea.	1.433	63	84	147
2 lights, average	1.000	Ea.	1.290	63	75.50	138.50
Deluxe	1.000	Ea.	1.548	75.50	90.50	166
Surface mounted, 4' x 1', economy	1.000	Ea.	.914	56	53.50	109.50
Average	1.000	Ea.	1.143	70	67	137
Deluxe	1.000	Ea.	1.371	84	80.50	164.50
4' x 2', economy	1.000	Ea.	1.208	71	71	142
Average	1.000	Ea.	1.509	89	88.50	177.50
Deluxe	1.000	Ea.	1.811	107	106	213
Recessed, 4'x 1', 2 lamps, economy	1.000	Ea.	1.123	41.50	65.50	107
Average	1.000	Ea.	1.404	52	82	134
Deluxe	1.000	Ea.	1.684	62.50	98.50	161
4' x 2', 4' lamps, economy	1.000	Ea.	1.362	51	79.50	130.50
Average	1.000	Ea.	1.702	63.50	99.50	163
Deluxe	1.000	Ea.	2.043	76	119	195
Incandescent, exterior, 150W, single spot	1.000	Ea.	.500	35	29.50	64.50
Double spot	1.000	Ea.	1.167	97	68.50	165.50
Recessed, 100W, economy	1.000	Ea.	.800	62.50	47	109.50
Average	1.000	Ea.	1.000	78	58.50	136.50
Deluxe	1.000	Ea.	1.200	93.50	70	163.50
150W, economy	1.000	Ea.	.800	90.50	47	137.50
Average	1.000	Ea.	1.000	113	58.50	171.50
Deluxe	1.000	Ea.	1.200	136	70	206
Surface mounted, 60W, economy	1.000	Ea.	.800	48.50	47	95.50
Average	1.000	Ea.	1.000	54.50	58.50	113
Deluxe	1.000	Ea.	1.194	76.50	70	146.50
Metal halide, recessed 2' x 2' 250W	1.000	Ea.	2.500	345	146	491
2' x 2', 400W	1.000	Ea.	2.759	400	161	561
Surface mounted, 2' x 2', 250W	1.000	Ea.	2.963	375	173	548
2' x 2', 400W	1.000	Ea.	3.333	440	195	635
High bay, single, unit, 400W	1.000	Ea.	3.478	450	203	653
Twin unit, 400W	1.000	Ea.	5.000	895	293	1,188
Low bay, 250W	1.000	Ea.	2.500	395	146	541

Unit Price Section

Table of Contents

Table of Contents (cont.)

How RSMeans Unit Price Data Works

All RSMeans unit price data is organized in the same way.

It is important to understand the structure, so that you can find information easily and use it correctly.

RSMeans **Line Numbers** consist of 12 characters, which identify a unique location in the database for each task. The first 6 or 8 digits conform to the Construction Specifications Institute MasterFormat® 2012. The remainder of the digits are a further breakdown by RSMeans in order to arrange items in understandable groups of similar tasks. Line numbers are consistent across all RSMeans publications, so a line number in any RSMeans product will always refer to the same unit of work.

RSMeans engineers have created **reference** information to assist you in your estimate. If there is information that applies to a section, it will be indicated at the start of the section. The Reference Section is located in the back of the book on the pages with a gray edge.

RSMeans **Descriptions** are shown in a hierarchical structure to make them readable. In order to read a complete description, read up through the indents to the top of the section. Include everything that is above and to the left that is not contradicted by information below. For instance, the complete description for line 03 30 53.40 3550 is "Concrete in place, including forms (4 uses), Grade 60 rebar, concrete (Portland cement Type 1), placement and finishing unless otherwise indicated; Equipment pad (3000 psi), 4' x 4' x 6" thick."

03 30 Cast-In-Place Concrete

03 30 53 – Miscellaneous Cast-In-Place Concrete

03 30 53.40 Concrete In Place

0010	**CONCRETE IN PLACE**	
0020	Including forms (4 uses), Grade 60 rebar, concrete (Portland cement	
0050	Type 1), placement and finishing unless otherwise indicated	
0500	Chimney foundations (5000 psi), over 5 C.Y.	C-14
0510	(3500 psi), under 5 C.Y.	"
3540	Equipment pad (3000 psi), 3' x 3' x 6" thick	C-14
3550	4' x 4' x 6" thick	
3560	5' x 5' x 8" thick	
3570	6' x 6' x 8" thick	
3580	8' x 8' x 10" thick	
3590	10' x 10' x 12" thick	
3800	Footings (3000 psi), spread under 1 C.Y.	C-14
3825	1 C.Y. to 5 C.Y.	
3850	Over 5 C.Y.	
3900	Footings, strip (3000 psi), 18" x 9", unreinforced	C-14

When using **RSMeans data**, it is important to read through an entire section to ensure that you use the data that most closely matches your work. Note that sometimes there is additional information shown in the section that may improve your price. There are frequently lines that further describe, add to, or adjust data for specific situations.

The data published in RSMeans print books represents a "national average" cost. This data should be modified to the project location using the **Location Factors** tables found in the reference section (see pages 698–703).

Use the location factors to adjust estimate totals.

Crews include labor or labor and equipment necessary to accomplish each task. In this case, Crew C-14H is used. RSMeans selects a crew to represent the workers and equipment that are typically used for that task. In this case, Crew C-14H consists of one carpenter foreman (outside), two carpenters, one rodman, one laborer, one cement finisher, and one gas engine vibrator. Details of all crews can be found in the reference section.

Crews

Crew No.	Bare Costs		Incl. Subs O&P		Cost Per Labor-Hour	
Crew C-14C	Hr.	Daily	Hr.	Daily	Bare Costs	Incl. O&P
1 Carpenter Foreman (outside)	$34.10	$272.80	$57.40	$459.20	$30.05	$50.55
6 Carpenters	32.10	1540.80	54.00	2592.00		
2 Rodmen (reinf.)	33.95	543.20	58.10	929.60		
4 Laborers	23.80	761.60	40.05	1281.60		
1 Cement Finisher	30.85	246.80	49.90	399.20		
1 Gas Engine Vibrator		33.00		36.30	0.29	0.32
112 L.H., Daily Totals		$3398.20		$5697.90	$30.34	$50.87

The **Daily Output** is the amount of work that the crew can do in a normal 8-hour workday, including mobilization, layout, movement of materials, and cleanup. In this case, crew C-14H can install thirty 4' x 4' x 6" thick concrete pads in a day. Daily output is variable, based on many factors, including the size of the job, location, and environmental conditions. RSMeans data represents work done in daylight (or adequate lighting) and temperate conditions.

Bare Costs are the costs of materials, labor, and equipment that the installing contractor pays. They represent the cost, in U.S. dollars, for one unit of work. They do not include any markups for profit or labor burden.

Crew	Daily Output	Labor-Hours	Unit	Material	2014 Bare Costs Labor	Equipment	Total	Total Incl O&P
C-14C	32.22	3.476	C.Y.	147	104	1.01	252.01	340
"	23.71	4.724	"	173	142	1.37	316.37	430
C-14H	45	1.067	Ea.	44.50	33	.74	78.24	105
	30	1.600		66.50	50	1.10	117.60	158
	18	2.667		119	83	1.84	203.84	272
	14	3.429		160	107	2.37	269.37	360
	8	6		335	187	4.14	526.14	690
	5	9.600		575	299	6.60	880.60	1,150
C-14C	28	4	C.Y.	164	120	1.16	285.16	385
	43	2.605		198	78.50	.76	277.26	350
	75	1.493		180	45	.43	225.43	274
C-14	40	2.400		120	70.50	.82	191.32	251

The **Total Incl O&P column** is the total cost, including overhead and profit, that the installing contractor will charge the customer. This represents the cost of materials plus 10% profit, the cost of labor plus labor burden and 10% profit, and the cost of equipment plus 10% profit. It does not include the general contractor's overhead and profit. Note: See the inside back cover for details of how RSMeans calculates labor burden.

The **Total column** represents the total bare cost for the installing contractor, in U.S. dollars. In this case, the sum of $66.50 for material + $50.00 for labor + $1.10 for equipment is $117.60.

The figure in the **Labor Hours** column is the amount of labor required to perform one unit of work—in this case the amount of labor required to construct one 4' x 4' equipment pad. This figure is calculated by dividing the number of hours of labor in the crew by the daily output (48 labor hours divided by 30 pads = 1.6 hours of labor per pad). Multiply 1.600 times 60 to see the value in minutes: 60 x 1.6 = 96 minutes. Note: the labor hour figure is not dependent on the crew size. A change in crew size will result in a corresponding change in daily output, but the labor hours per unit of work will not change.

All RSMeans unit cost data includes the typical **Unit of Measure** used for estimating that item. For concrete-in-place the typical unit is cubic yards (C.Y.) or each (Ea.). For installing broadloom carpet it is square yard, and for gypsum board it is square foot. The estimator needs to take special care that the unit in the data matches the unit in the take-off. Unit conversions may be found in the Reference Section.

Sample Estimate

This sample demonstrates the elements of an estimate, including a tally of the RSMeans data lines, and a summary of the markups on a contractor's work to arrive at a total cost to the owner. The RSMeans Location Factor is added at the bottom of the estimate to adjust the cost of the work to a specific location.

Work Performed: The body of the estimate shows the RSMeans data selected, including line number, a brief description of each item, its take-off unit and quantity, and the bare costs of materials, labor, and equipment. This estimate also includes a column titled "SubContract." This data is taken from the RSMeans column "Total Incl O&P," and represents the total that a subcontractor would charge a general contractor for the work, including the sub's markup for overhead and profit.

Division 1, General Requirements: This is the first division numerically, but the last division estimated. Division 1 includes project-wide needs provided by the general contractor. These requirements vary by project, but may include temporary facilities and utilities, security, testing, project cleanup, etc. For small projects a percentage can be used, typically between 5% and 15% of project cost. For large projects the costs may be itemized and priced individually.

Bonds: Bond costs should be added to the estimate. The figures here represent a typical performance bond, ensuring the owner that if the general contractor does not complete the obligations in the construction contract the bonding company will pay the cost for completion of the work.

Location Adjustment: RSMeans published data is based on national average costs. If necessary, adjust the total cost of the project using a location factor from the "Location Factor" table or the "City Cost Index" table. Use location factors if the work is general, covering multiple trades. If the work is by a single trade (e.g., masonry) use the more specific data found in the "City Cost Indexes."

This estimate is based on an interactive spreadsheet. A copy of this spreadsheet is located on the RSMeans website at **http://www.reedconstructiondata.com/rsmeans/extras/546011**. You are free to download it and adjust it to your methodology.

Project Name: Pre-Engineered Steel Building			Architect: As Shown		
Location:	**Anywhere, USA**				
Line Number	**Description**	**Qty**	**Unit**		**Material**
03 30 53.40 3940	Strip footing, 12" x 24", reinforced	34	C.Y.		$4,624.00
03 30 53.40 3950	Strip footing, 12" x 36", reinforced	15	C.Y.		$1,950.00
03 11 13.65 3000	Concrete slab edge forms	500	L.F.		$155.00
03 22 11.10 0200	Welded wire fabric reinforcing	150	C.S.F.		$2,580.00
03 31 13.35 0300	Ready mix concrete, 4000 psi for slab on grade	278	C.Y.		$28,912.00
03 31 13.70 4300	Place, strike off & consolidate concrete slab	278	C.Y.		$0.00
03 35 13.30 0250	Machine float & trowel concrete slab	15,000	S.F.		$0.00
03 15 16.20 0140	Cut control joints in concrete slab	950	L.F.		$57.00
03 39 23.13 0300	Sprayed concrete curing membrane	150	C.S.F.		$1,642.50
Division 03	**Subtotal**				**$39,920.50**
08 36 13.10 2650	Manual 10' x 10' steel sectional overhead door	8	Ea.		$8,800.00
08 36 13.10 2860	Insulation and steel back panel for OH door	800	S.F.		$3,760.00
Division 08	**Subtotal**				**$12,560.00**
13 34 19.50 1100	Pre-Engineered Steel Building, 100' x 150' x 24'	15,000	SF Flr.		$0.00
13 34 19.50 6050	Framing for PESB door opening, 3' x 7'	4	Opng.		$0.00
13 34 19.50 6100	Framing for PESB door opening, 10' x 10'	8	Opng.		$0.00
13 34 19.50 6200	Framing for PESB window opening, 4' x 3'	6	Opng.		$0.00
13 34 19.50 5750	PESB door, 3' x 7', single leaf	4	Opng.		$2,340.00
13 34 19.50 7750	PESB sliding window, 4' x 3' with screen	6	Opng.		$2,250.00
13 34 19.50 6550	PESB gutter, eave type, 26 ga., painted	300	L.F.		$2,010.00
13 34 19.50 8650	PESB roof vent, 12" wide x 10' long	15	Ea.		$540.00
13 34 19.50 6900	PESB insulation, vinyl faced, 4" thick	27,400	S.F.		$10,960.00
Division 13	**Subtotal**				**$18,100.00**
				Subtotal	$70,580.50
Division 01	**General Requirements @ 7%**				**4,940.64**
				Estimate Subtotal	$75,521.14
				Sales Tax @ 5%	3,776.06
				Subtotal A	79,297.19
				GC O & P	7,929.72
				Subtotal B	87,226.91
				Contingency @ 5%	
				Subtotal C	
				Bond @ $12/1000 +10% O&P	
				Subtotal D	
				Location Adjustment Factor	
				Grand Total	

This example shows the cost to construct a pre-engineered steel building. The foundation, doors, windows, and insulation will be installed by the general contractor. A subcontractor will install the structural steel, roofing, and siding.

Labor	Equipment	SubContract	Estimate Total	
		01/01/14	RESI	
$2,380.00	$23.12	$0.00		
$840.00	$8.10	$0.00		
$745.00	$0.00	$0.00		
$2,625.00	$0.00	$0.00		
$0.00	$0.00	$0.00		
$3,071.90	$166.80	$0.00		
$6,000.00	$450.00	$0.00		
$256.50	$95.00	$0.00		
$601.50	$0.00	$0.00		
$16,519.90	$743.02	$0.00	$57,183.42	Division 03
$2,280.00	$0.00	$0.00		
$0.00	$0.00	$0.00		
$2,280.00	$0.00	$0.00	$14,840.00	Division 08
$0.00	$0.00	$289,500.00		
$0.00	$0.00	$1,860.00		
$0.00	$0.00	$8,200.00		
$0.00	$0.00	$2,820.00		
$440.00	$0.00	$0.00		
$252.00	$65.70	$0.00		
$513.00	$0.00	$0.00		
$2,055.00	$0.00	$0.00		
$6,028.00	$0.00	$0.00		
$9,288.00	$65.70	$302,380.00	$329,833.70	Division 13
$28,087.90	$808.72	$302,380.00	$401,857.12	Subtotal
1,966.15	56.61	21,166.60		Gen. Requirements
$30,054.05	$865.33	$323,546.60	$401,857.12	Estimate Subtotal
	43.27	8,088.67		Sales tax
30,054.05	908.60	331,635.27		Subtotal
20,707.24	90.86	33,163.53		GC O&P
50,761.30	999.46	364,798.79	$503,786.45	Subtotal
			25,189.32	Contingency
			$528,975.78	Subtotal
			6,982.48	Bond
			$535,958.26	Subtotal
102.30			12,327.04	Location Adjustment
			$548,285.30	Grand Total

Sales Tax: If the work is subject to state or local sales taxes, the amount must be added to the estimate. Sales tax may be added to material costs, equipment costs, and subcontracted work. In this case, sales tax was added in all three categories. It was assumed that approximately half the subcontracted work would be material cost, so the tax was applied to 50% of the subcontract total.

GC O&P: This entry represents the general contractor's markup on material, labor, equipment, and subcontractor costs. RSMeans' standard markup on materials, equipment, and subcontracted work is 10%. In this estimate, the markup on the labor performed by the GC's workers uses "Skilled Workers Average" shown in Column F on the table "Installing Contractor's Overhead & Profit," which can be found on the inside-back cover of the book.

Contingency: A factor for contingency may be added to any estimate to represent the cost of unknowns that may occur between the time that the estimate is performed and the time the project is constructed. The amount of the allowance will depend on the stage of design at which the estimate is done, and the contractor's assessment of the risk involved. Refer to section 01 21 16.50 for contigency allowances.

Estimating Tips

01 20 00 Price and Payment Procedures

- Allowances that should be added to estimates to cover contingencies and job conditions that are not included in the national average material and labor costs are shown in section 01 21.

- When estimating historic preservation projects (depending on the condition of the existing structure and the owner's requirements), a 15%–20% contingency or allowance is recommended, regardless of the stage of the drawings.

01 30 00 Administrative Requirements

- Before determining a final cost estimate, it is a good practice to review all the items listed in Subdivisions 01 31 and 01 32 to make final adjustments for items that may need customizing to specific job conditions.

- Requirements for initial and periodic submittals can represent a significant cost to the General Requirements of a job. Thoroughly check the submittal specifications when estimating a project to determine any costs that should be included.

01 40 00 Quality Requirements

- All projects will require some degree of Quality Control. This cost is not included in the unit cost of construction listed in each division. Depending upon the terms of the contract, the various costs of inspection and testing can be the responsibility of either the owner or the contractor. Be sure to include the required costs in your estimate.

01 50 00 Temporary Facilities and Controls

- Barricades, access roads, safety nets, scaffolding, security, and many more requirements for the execution of a safe project are elements of direct cost. These costs can easily be overlooked when preparing an estimate. When looking through the major classifications of this subdivision, determine which items apply to each division in your estimate.

- Construction Equipment Rental Costs can be found in the Reference Section in section 01 54 33. Operators' wages are not included in equipment rental costs.

- Equipment mobilization and demobilization costs are not included in equipment rental costs and must be considered separately in section 01 54 36.50.

- The cost of small tools provided by the installing contractor for his workers is covered in the "Overhead" column on the "Installing Contractor's Overhead and Profit" table that lists labor trades, base rates and markups and, therefore, is included in the "Total Incl. O&P" cost of any Unit Price line item. For those users who are constrained by contract terms to use only bare costs, there are two line items in section 01 54 39.70 for small tools as a percentage of bare labor cost. If some of those users are further constrained by contract terms to refrain from using line items from Division 1, you are advised to cover the cost of small tools within your coefficient or multiplier.

01 70 00 Execution and Closeout Requirements

- When preparing an estimate, thoroughly read the specifications to determine the requirements for Contract Closeout. Final cleaning, record documentation, operation and maintenance data, warranties and bonds, and spare parts and maintenance materials can all be elements of cost for the completion of a contract. Do not overlook these in your estimate.

Reference Numbers

Reference numbers are shown in shaded boxes at the beginning of some major classifications. These numbers refer to related items in the Reference Section. The reference information may be an estimating procedure, an alternate pricing method, or technical information.

Note: Not all subdivisions listed here necessarily appear in this publication.

Division 1 - General Requirements

01 11 Summary of Work

01 11 31 – Professional Consultants

01 11 31.10 Architectural Fees		Crew	Daily Output	Labor-Hours	Unit	Material	2014 Bare Costs Labor	Equipment	Total	Total Incl O&P
0010	**ARCHITECTURAL FEES** R011110-10									
0020	For new construction									
0060	Minimum				Project				4.90%	4.90%
0090	Maximum								16%	16%
0100	For alteration work, to $500,000, add to new construction fee								50%	50%
0150	Over $500,000, add to new construction fee								25%	25%

01 11 31.20 Construction Management Fees										
0010	**CONSTRUCTION MANAGEMENT FEES**									
0060	For work to $100,000				Project				10%	10%
0070	To $250,000								9%	9%
0090	To $1,000,000								6%	6%

01 11 31.75 Renderings										
0010	**RENDERINGS** Color, matted, 20" x 30", eye level,									
0050	Average				Ea.	2,875			2,875	3,175

01 21 Allowances

01 21 16 – Contingency Allowances

01 21 16.50 Contingencies										
0010	**CONTINGENCIES**, Add to estimate									
0020	Conceptual stage				Project				20%	20%
0150	Final working drawing stage				"				3%	3%

01 21 55 – Job Conditions Allowance

01 21 55.50 Job Conditions										
0010	**JOB CONDITIONS** Modifications to applicable									
8000	Remove and reset contents of small room	1 Clab	6.50	1.231	Room		29.50		29.50	49.50
8010	Average room		4.70	1.702			40.50		40.50	68
8020	Large room		3.50	2.286			54.50		54.50	91.50
8030	Extra large room		2.40	3.333			79.50		79.50	134

01 21 63 – Taxes

01 21 63.10 Taxes										
0010	**TAXES** R012909-80									
0020	Sales tax, State, average				%	5.06%				
0050	Maximum R012909-85					7.25%				
0200	Social Security, on first $115,800 of wages						7.65%			
0300	Unemployment, combined Federal and State, minimum						.60%			
0350	Average						7.80%			
0400	Maximum						13.50%			

01 31 Project Management and Coordination

01 31 13 – Project Coordination

01 31 13.30 Insurance

		Crew	Daily Output	Labor-Hours	Unit	Material	2014 Bare Costs Labor	2014 Bare Costs Equipment	Total	Total Incl O&P
0010	**INSURANCE** R013113-40									
0020	Builders risk, standard, minimum				Job				.24%	.24%
0050	Maximum R013113-60								.64%	.64%
0200	All-risk type, minimum								.25%	.25%
0250	Maximum								.62%	.62%
0400	Contractor's equipment floater, minimum				Value				.50%	.50%
0450	Maximum				"				1.50%	1.50%
0600	Public liability, average				Job				2.02%	2.02%
0800	Workers' compensation & employer's liability, average									
0850	by trade, carpentry, general				Payroll		15.38%			
0900	Clerical						.51%			
0950	Concrete						13.15%			
1000	Electrical						5.83%			
1050	Excavation						9.69%			
1100	Glazing						13.15%			
1150	Insulation						11.67%			
1200	Lathing						8.12%			
1250	Masonry						13.49%			
1300	Painting & decorating						11.54%			
1350	Pile driving						14.65%			
1400	Plastering						11.55%			
1450	Plumbing						7.08%			
1500	Roofing						31.29%			
1550	Sheet metal work (HVAC)						8.79%			
1600	Steel erection, structural						34.64%			
1650	Tile work, interior ceramic						8.54%			
1700	Waterproofing, brush or hand caulking						6.86%			
1800	Wrecking						29.21%			
2000	Range of 35 trades in 50 states, excl. wrecking, min.						2.48%			
2100	Average						14%			
2200	Maximum						150%			

01 41 Regulatory Requirements

01 41 26 – Permit Requirements

01 41 26.50 Permits

		Crew	Daily Output	Labor-Hours	Unit	Material	2014 Bare Costs Labor	2014 Bare Costs Equipment	Total	Total Incl O&P
0010	**PERMITS**									
0020	Rule of thumb, most cities, minimum				Job				.50%	.50%
0100	Maximum				"				2%	2%

01 54 Construction Aids

01 54 16 – Temporary Hoists

01 54 16.50 Weekly Forklift Crew

		Crew	Daily Output	Labor-Hours	Unit	Material	2014 Bare Costs Labor	2014 Bare Costs Equipment	Total	Total Incl O&P
0010	**WEEKLY FORKLIFT CREW**									
0100	All-terrain forklift, 45' lift, 35' reach, 9000 lb. capacity	A-3P	.20	40	Week		1,300	2,650	3,950	5,075

01 54 19 – Temporary Cranes

01 54 19.50 Daily Crane Crews

		Crew	Daily Output	Labor-Hours	Unit	Material	2014 Bare Costs Labor	2014 Bare Costs Equipment	Total	Total Incl O&P
0010	**DAILY CRANE CREWS** for small jobs, portal to portal									
0100	12-ton truck-mounted hydraulic crane	A-3H	1	8	Day		277	875	1,152	1,425
0900	If crane is needed on a Saturday, Sunday or Holiday									

01 54 Construction Aids

01 54 19 – Temporary Cranes

01 54 19.50 Daily Crane Crews		Crew	Daily Output	Labor-Hours	Unit	Material	2014 Bare Costs Labor	Equipment	Total	Total Incl O&P
0910	At time-and-a-half, add				Day		50%			
0920	At double time, add				"		100%			

01 54 23 – Temporary Scaffolding and Platforms

01 54 23.60 Pump Staging

			Crew	Daily Output	Labor-Hours	Unit	Material	Labor	Equipment	Total	Total Incl O&P
0010	**PUMP STAGING**, Aluminum										
1300	System in place, 50' working height, per use based on 50 uses		2 Carp	84.80	.189	C.S.F.	6.10	6.05		12.15	16.90
1400	100 uses	R015423-20		84.80	.189		3.06	6.05		9.11	13.55
1500	150 uses			84.80	.189		2.05	6.05		8.10	12.45

01 54 23.70 Scaffolding

			Crew	Daily Output	Labor-Hours	Unit	Material	Labor	Equipment	Total	Total Incl O&P
0010	**SCAFFOLDING**	R015423-10									
0015	Steel tube, regular, no plank, labor only to erect & dismantle										
0091	Building exterior, wall face, 1 to 5 stories, 6'-4" x 5' frames		3 Clab	8	3	C.S.F.		71.50		71.50	120
0201	6 to 12 stories		4 Clab	8	4			95		95	160
0310	13 to 20 stories		5 Carp	8	5			161		161	270
0461	Building interior, walls face area, up to 16' high		3 Clab	12	2			47.50		47.50	80
0561	16' to 40' high			10	2.400			57		57	96
0801	Building interior floor area, up to 30' high			150	.160	C.C.F.		3.81		3.81	6.40
0901	Over 30' high		4 Clab	160	.200	"		4.76		4.76	8
0906	Complete system for face of walls, no plank, material only rent/mo					C.S.F.	35			35	38.50
0908	Interior spaces, no plank, material only rent/mo					C.C.F.	3.35			3.35	3.68
0910	Steel tubular, heavy duty shoring, buy										
0920	Frames 5' high 2' wide					Ea.	81.50			81.50	90
0925	5' high 4' wide						93			93	102
0930	6' high 2' wide						93.50			93.50	103
0935	6' high 4' wide						109			109	120
0940	Accessories										
0945	Cross braces					Ea.	15.50			15.50	17.05
0950	U-head, 8" x 8"						19.10			19.10	21
0955	J-head, 4" x 8"						13.90			13.90	15.30
0960	Base plate, 8" x 8"						15.50			15.50	17.05
0965	Leveling jack						33.50			33.50	36.50
1000	Steel tubular, regular, buy										
1100	Frames 3' high 5' wide					Ea.	72.50			72.50	80
1150	5' high 5' wide						86.50			86.50	95
1200	6'-4" high 5' wide						118			118	129
1350	7'-6" high 6' wide						158			158	173
1500	Accessories cross braces						15.50			15.50	17.05
1550	Guardrail post						16.40			16.40	18.05
1600	Guardrail 7' section						6.30			6.30	6.95
1650	Screw jacks & plates						21.50			21.50	24
1700	Sidearm brackets						25.50			25.50	28.50
1750	8" casters						31			31	34
1800	Plank 2" x 10" x 16'-0"						52			52	57.50
1900	Stairway section						276			276	305
1910	Stairway starter bar						32			32	35
1920	Stairway inside handrail						53			53	58
1930	Stairway outside handrail						81.50			81.50	90
1940	Walk-thru frame guardrail						41.50			41.50	46
2000	Steel tubular, regular, rent/mo.										
2100	Frames 3' high 5' wide					Ea.	5			5	5.50
2150	5' high 5' wide						5			5	5.50
2200	6'-4" high 5' wide						5.15			5.15	5.65

01 54 Construction Aids

01 54 23 – Temporary Scaffolding and Platforms

01 54 23.70 Scaffolding		Crew	Daily Output	Labor-Hours	Unit	Material	2014 Bare Costs Labor	Equipment	Total	Total Incl O&P
2250	7'-6" high 6' wide				Ea.	7			7	7.70
2500	Accessories, cross braces					1			1	1.10
2550	Guardrail post					1			1	1.10
2600	Guardrail 7' section					1			1	1.10
2650	Screw jacks & plates					2			2	2.20
2700	Sidearm brackets					2			2	2.20
2750	8" casters					8			8	8.80
2800	Outrigger for rolling tower					3			3	3.30
2850	Plank 2" x 10" x 16'-0"					6			6	6.60
2900	Stairway section					35.50			35.50	39
2940	Walk-thru frame guardrail				↓	2.50			2.50	2.75
3000	Steel tubular, heavy duty shoring, rent/mo.									
3250	5' high 2' & 4' wide				Ea.	5			5	5.50
3300	6' high 2' & 4' wide					5			5	5.50
3500	Accessories, cross braces					1			1	1.10
3600	U - head, 8" x 8"					1			1	1.10
3650	J - head, 4" x 8"					1			1	1.10
3700	Base plate, 8" x 8"					1			1	1.10
3750	Leveling jack					2			2	2.20
5700	Planks, 2" x 10" x 16'-0", labor only to erect & remove to 50' H	3 Carp	72	.333			10.70		10.70	18
5800	Over 50' high	4 Carp	80	.400	↓		12.85		12.85	21.50

01 54 23.80 Staging Aids

01 54 23.80 Staging Aids		Crew	Daily Output	Labor-Hours	Unit	Material	2014 Bare Costs Labor	Equipment	Total	Total Incl O&P
0010	**STAGING AIDS** and fall protection equipment									
0100	Sidewall staging bracket, tubular, buy				Ea.	51			51	56
0110	Cost each per day, based on 250 days use				Day	.20			.20	.22
0200	Guard post, buy				Ea.	48			48	53
0210	Cost each per day, based on 250 days use				Day	.19			.19	.21
0300	End guard chains, buy per pair				Pair	36			36	39.50
0310	Cost per set per day, based on 250 days use				Day	.20			.20	.22
1010	Cost each per day, based on 250 days use				"	.04			.04	.04
1100	Wood bracket, buy				Ea.	16.80			16.80	18.50
1110	Cost each per day, based on 250 days use				Day	.07			.07	.07
2010	Cost per pair per day, based on 250 days use				"	.47			.47	.52
2100	Steel siderail jack, buy per pair				Pair	97.50			97.50	107
2110	Cost per pair per day, based on 250 days use				Day	.39			.39	.43
3010	Cost each per day, based on 250 days use				"	.21			.21	.23
3100	Aluminum scaffolding plank, 20" wide x 24' long, buy				Ea.	820			820	900
3110	Cost each per day, based on 250 days use				Day	3.28			3.28	3.60
4010	Cost each per day, based on 250 days use				"	.70			.70	.77
4100	Rope for safety line, 5/8" x 100' nylon, buy				Ea.	56			56	61.50
4110	Cost each per day, based on 250 days use				Day	.22			.22	.25
4200	Permanent U-Bolt roof anchor, buy				Ea.	30			30	33
4300	Temporary (one use) roof ridge anchor, buy				"	32			32	35.50
5000	Installation (setup and removal) of staging aids									
5010	Sidewall staging bracket	2 Carp	64	.250	Ea.		8.05		8.05	13.50
5020	Guard post with 2 wood rails	"	64	.250			8.05		8.05	13.50
5030	End guard chains, set	1 Carp	64	.125			4.01		4.01	6.75
5100	Roof shingling bracket		96	.083			2.67		2.67	4.50
5200	Ladder jack	↓	64	.125			4.01		4.01	6.75
5300	Wood plank, 2" x 10" x 16'	2 Carp	80	.200			6.40		6.40	10.80
5310	Aluminum scaffold plank, 20" x 24'	"	40	.400			12.85		12.85	21.50
5410	Safety rope	1 Carp	40	.200	↓		6.40		6.40	10.80

01 54 Construction Aids

01 54 23 – Temporary Scaffolding and Platforms

01 54 23.80 Staging Aids	Crew	Daily Output	Labor-Hours	Unit	Material	2014 Bare Costs Labor	Equipment	Total	Total Incl O&P
5420	Permanent U-Bolt roof anchor (install only)	2 Carp	40	.400	Ea.		12.85		12.85	21.50
5430	Temporary roof ridge anchor (install only)	1 Carp	64	.125	↓		4.01		4.01	6.75

01 54 36 – Equipment Mobilization

01 54 36.50 Mobilization

		Crew	Daily Output	Labor-Hours	Unit	Material	Labor	Equipment	Total	Total Incl O&P
0010	**MOBILIZATION** (Use line item again for demobilization)									
0015	Up to 25 mi. haul dist. (50 mi. RT for mob/demob crew)									
0020	Dozer, loader, backhoe, excav., grader, paver, roller, 70 to 150 H.P.	B-34N	4	2	Ea.		53.50	142	195.50	246
0900	Shovel or dragline, 3/4 C.Y.	B-34K	3.60	2.222			59	267	326	395
1100	Small equipment, placed in rear of, or towed by pickup truck	A-3A	8	1			26	21	47	66
1150	Equip up to 70 HP, on flatbed trailer behind pickup truck	A-3D	4	2			52	70.50	122.50	164
2000	Crane, truck-mounted, up to 75 ton, (driver only, one-way)	1 Eqhv	7.20	1.111			38.50		38.50	64
2200	Crawler-mounted, up to 75 ton	A-3F	2	8	↓		245	500	745	955
2500	For each additional 5 miles haul distance, add						10%	10%		
3000	For large pieces of equipment, allow for assembly/knockdown									
3100	For mob/demob of micro-tunneling equip, see Section 33 05 23.19									

01 54 39 – Construction Equipment

01 54 39.70 Small Tools

		Crew	Daily Output	Labor-Hours	Unit	Material	Labor	Equipment	Total	Total Incl O&P
0010	**SMALL TOOLS**									
0020	As % of contractor's bare labor cost for project, minimum				Total		.50%			
0100	Maximum				"		2%			

01 56 Temporary Barriers and Enclosures

01 56 13 – Temporary Air Barriers

01 56 13.60 Tarpaulins

		Crew	Daily Output	Labor-Hours	Unit	Material	Labor	Equipment	Total	Total Incl O&P
0010	**TARPAULINS**									
0020	Cotton duck, 10 oz. to 13.13 oz. per S.Y., 6'x8'				S.F.	.75			.75	.83
0050	30'x30'					.43			.43	.47
0200	Reinforced polyethylene 3 mils thick, white					.03			.03	.03
0300	4 mils thick, white, clear or black					.09			.09	.10
0730	Polyester reinforced w/integral fastening system 11 mils thick				↓	.24			.24	.26

01 56 16 – Temporary Dust Barriers

01 56 16.10 Dust Barriers, Temporary

		Crew	Daily Output	Labor-Hours	Unit	Material	Labor	Equipment	Total	Total Incl O&P
0010	**DUST BARRIERS, TEMPORARY**									
0020	Spring loaded telescoping pole & head, to 12', erect and dismantle	1 Clab	240	.033	Ea.		.79		.79	1.33
0025	Cost per day (based upon 250 days)				Day	.24			.24	.26
0030	To 21', erect and dismantle	1 Clab	240	.033	Ea.		.79		.79	1.33
0035	Cost per day (based upon 250 days)				Day	.38			.38	.42
0040	Accessories, caution tape reel, erect and dismantle	1 Clab	480	.017	Ea.		.40		.40	.67
0045	Cost per day (based upon 250 days)				Day	.36			.36	.40
0060	Foam rail and connector, erect and dismantle	1 Clab	240	.033	Ea.		.79		.79	1.33
0065	Cost per day (based upon 250 days)				Day	.10			.10	.11
0070	Caution tape	1 Clab	384	.021	C.L.F.	2.70	.50		3.20	3.80
0080	Zipper, standard duty		60	.133	Ea.	15.95	3.17		19.12	23
0090	Heavy duty		48	.167	"	18.90	3.97		22.87	27.50
0100	Polyethylene sheet, 4 mil		37	.216	Sq.	2.91	5.15		8.06	11.85
0110	6 mil	↓	37	.216	"	3.98	5.15		9.13	13.05
1000	Dust partition, 6 mil polyethylene, 1" x 3" frame	2 Carp	2000	.008	S.F.	.29	.26		.55	.75
1080	2" x 4" frame	"	2000	.008	"	.32	.26		.58	.78

01 71 Examination and Preparation

01 71 23 – Field Engineering

01 71 23.13 Construction Layout	Crew	Daily Output	Labor-Hours	Unit	Material	2014 Bare Costs Labor	Equipment	Total	Total Incl O&P
0010 **CONSTRUCTION LAYOUT**									
1100 Crew for layout of building, trenching or pipe laying, 2 person crew	A-6	1	16	Day		510	71.50	581.50	935
1200 3 person crew	A-7	1	24	"		825	71.50	896.50	1,450

01 74 Cleaning and Waste Management

01 74 13 – Progress Cleaning

01 74 13.20 Cleaning Up	Crew	Daily Output	Labor-Hours	Unit	Material	2014 Bare Costs Labor	Equipment	Total	Total Incl O&P
0010 **CLEANING UP**									
0020 After job completion, allow, minimum				Job				.30%	.30%
0040 Maximum				"				1%	1%

01 76 Protecting Installed Construction

01 76 13 – Temporary Protection of Installed Construction

01 76 13.20 Temporary Protection	Crew	Daily Output	Labor-Hours	Unit	Material	2014 Bare Costs Labor	Equipment	Total	Total Incl O&P
0010 **TEMPORARY PROTECTION**									
0020 Flooring, 1/8" tempered hardboard, taped seams	2 Carp	1500	.011	S.F.	.39	.34		.73	1.01
0030 Peel away carpet protection	1 Clab	3200	.003	"	.11	.06		.17	.22

Division Notes

	CREW	DAILY OUTPUT	LABOR-HOURS	UNIT	BARE COSTS				TOTAL INCL O&P
					MAT.	LABOR	EQUIP.	TOTAL	

Estimating Tips

02 30 00 Subsurface Investigation

In preparing estimates on structures involving earthwork or foundations, all information concerning soil characteristics should be obtained. Look particularly for hazardous waste, evidence of prior dumping of debris, and previous stream beds.

02 40 00 Demolition and Structure Moving

The costs shown for selective demolition do not include rubbish handling or disposal. These items should be estimated separately using RSMeans data or other sources.

- Historic preservation often requires that the contractor remove materials from the existing structure, rehab them, and replace them. The estimator must be aware of any related measures and precautions that must be taken when doing selective demolition and cutting and patching. Requirements may include special handling and storage, as well as security.

- In addition to Subdivision 02 41 00, you can find selective demolition items in each division. Example: Roofing demolition is in Division 7.

02 40 00 Building Deconstruction

This section provides costs for the careful dismantling and recycling of most of low-rise building materials.

02 50 00 Containment of Hazardous Waste

This section addresses on-site hazardous waste disposal costs.

02 80 00 Hazardous Material Disposal/ Remediation

This subdivision includes information on hazardous waste handling, asbestos remediation, lead remediation, and mold remediation. See reference R028213-20 and R028319-60 for further guidance in using these unit price lines.

02 90 00 Monitoring Chemical Sampling, Testing Analysis

This section provides costs for on-site sampling and testing hazardous waste.

Reference Numbers

Reference numbers are shown in shaded boxes at the beginning of some major classifications. These numbers refer to related items in the Reference Section. The reference information may be an estimating procedure, an alternate pricing method, or technical information.

Note: Not all subdivisions listed here necessarily appear in this publication.

Division 2 - Existing Conditions

02 21 Surveys

02 21 13 – Site Surveys

02 21 13.09 Topographical Surveys

02 21 13.09 Topographical Surveys	Crew	Daily Output	Labor-Hours	Unit	Material	2014 Bare Costs Labor	2014 Bare Costs Equipment	Total	Total Incl O&P
0010 **TOPOGRAPHICAL SURVEYS**									
0020 Topographical surveying, conventional, minimum	A-7	3.30	7.273	Acre	19.20	250	21.50	290.70	465
0100 Maximum	A-8	.60	53.333	"	58.50	1,800	119	1,977.50	3,200

02 21 13.13 Boundary and Survey Markers

02 21 13.13 Boundary and Survey Markers	Crew	Daily Output	Labor-Hours	Unit	Material	2014 Bare Costs Labor	2014 Bare Costs Equipment	Total	Total Incl O&P
0010 **BOUNDARY AND SURVEY MARKERS**									
0300 Lot location and lines, large quantities, minimum	A-7	2	12	Acre	34	415	35.50	484.50	770
0320 Average	"	1.25	19.200		54	660	57	771	1,225
0400 Small quantities, maximum	A-8	1	32	↓	71.50	1,075	71.50	1,218	1,950
0600 Monuments, 3' long	A-7	10	2.400	Ea.	34	82.50	7.15	123.65	184
0800 Property lines, perimeter, cleared land	"	1000	.024	L.F.	.04	.83	.07	.94	1.51
0900 Wooded land	A-8	875	.037	"	.06	1.23	.08	1.37	2.22

02 32 Geotechnical Investigations

02 32 13 – Subsurface Drilling and Sampling

02 32 13.10 Boring and Exploratory Drilling

02 32 13.10 Boring and Exploratory Drilling	Crew	Daily Output	Labor-Hours	Unit	Material	2014 Bare Costs Labor	2014 Bare Costs Equipment	Total	Total Incl O&P
0010 **BORING AND EXPLORATORY DRILLING**									
0020 Borings, initial field stake out & determination of elevations	A-6	1	16	Day		510	71.50	581.50	935
0100 Drawings showing boring details				Total		335		335	425
0200 Report and recommendations from P.E.						775		775	970
0300 Mobilization and demobilization	B-55	4	4	↓		99.50	280	379.50	475
0350 For over 100 miles, per added mile		450	.036	Mile		.88	2.49	3.37	4.22
0600 Auger holes in earth, no samples, 2-1/2" diameter		78.60	.204	L.F.		5.05	14.25	19.30	24
0800 Cased borings in earth, with samples, 2-1/2" diameter		55.50	.288	"	22	7.15	20	49.15	58
1400 Borings, earth, drill rig and crew with truck mounted auger	↓	1	16	Day		400	1,125	1,525	1,900
1500 For inner city borings add, minimum								10%	10%
1510 Maximum								20%	20%

02 41 Demolition

02 41 13 – Selective Site Demolition

02 41 13.17 Demolish, Remove Pavement and Curb

02 41 13.17 Demolish, Remove Pavement and Curb	Crew	Daily Output	Labor-Hours	Unit	Material	2014 Bare Costs Labor	2014 Bare Costs Equipment	Total	Total Incl O&P
0010 **DEMOLISH, REMOVE PAVEMENT AND CURB** R024119-10									
5010 Pavement removal, bituminous roads, up to 3" thick	B-38	690	.035	S.Y.		.93	.79	1.72	2.42
5050 4" to 6" thick		420	.057			1.52	1.30	2.82	3.98
5100 Bituminous driveways		640	.038			1	.85	1.85	2.61
5200 Concrete to 6" thick, hydraulic hammer, mesh reinforced		255	.094			2.51	2.14	4.65	6.55
5300 Rod reinforced	↓	200	.120	↓		3.20	2.73	5.93	8.35
5600 With hand held air equipment, bituminous, to 6" thick	B-39	1900	.025	S.F.		.61	.12	.73	1.17
5700 Concrete to 6" thick, no reinforcing		1600	.030			.72	.15	.87	1.38
5800 Mesh reinforced		1400	.034			.83	.17	1	1.57
5900 Rod reinforced	↓	765	.063	↓		1.51	.31	1.82	2.89
6000 Curbs, concrete, plain	B-6	360	.067	L.F.		1.78	1.01	2.79	4.09
6100 Reinforced		275	.087			2.33	1.33	3.66	5.35
6200 Granite		360	.067			1.78	1.01	2.79	4.09
6300 Bituminous	↓	528	.045	↓		1.21	.69	1.90	2.79

02 41 13.33 Minor Site Demolition

02 41 13.33 Minor Site Demolition	Crew	Daily Output	Labor-Hours	Unit	Material	2014 Bare Costs Labor	2014 Bare Costs Equipment	Total	Total Incl O&P
0010 **MINOR SITE DEMOLITION** R024119-10									
0015 No hauling, abandon catch basin or manhole	B-6	7	3.429	Ea.		91.50	52	143.50	211
0020 Remove existing catch basin or manhole, masonry		4	6			160	91.50	251.50	370
0030 Catch basin or manhole frames and covers, stored	↓	13	1.846	↓		49.50	28	77.50	114

02 41 Demolition

02 41 13 – Selective Site Demolition

02 41 13.33 Minor Site Demolition

		Crew	Daily Output	Labor-Hours	Unit	Material	2014 Bare Costs Labor	2014 Bare Costs Equipment	Total	Total Incl O&P
0040	Remove and reset	B-6	7	3.429	Ea.		91.50	52	143.50	211
1000	Masonry walls, block, solid	B-5	1800	.022	C.F.		.58	.79	1.37	1.85
1200	Brick, solid		900	.044			1.16	1.58	2.74	3.69
1400	Stone, with mortar		900	.044			1.16	1.58	2.74	3.69
1500	Dry set		1500	.027			.70	.95	1.65	2.21
2900	Pipe removal, sewer/water, no excavation, 12" diameter	B-6	175	.137	L.F.		3.66	2.09	5.75	8.40
2930	15"-18" diameter	B-12Z	150	.160			4.39	10.90	15.29	19.35
2960	21"-24" diameter	"	120	.200			5.50	13.65	19.15	24
4000	Sidewalk removal, bituminous, 2" thick	B-6	350	.069	S.Y.		1.83	1.04	2.87	4.21
4010	2-1/2" thick		325	.074			1.97	1.12	3.09	4.54
4050	Brick, set in mortar		185	.130			3.46	1.97	5.43	7.95
4100	Concrete, plain, 4"		160	.150			4	2.28	6.28	9.20
4110	Plain, 5"		140	.171			4.57	2.61	7.18	10.50
4120	Plain, 6"		120	.200			5.35	3.04	8.39	12.25
4200	Mesh reinforced, concrete, 4"		150	.160			4.27	2.44	6.71	9.85
4210	5" thick		131	.183			4.89	2.79	7.68	11.20
4220	6" thick		112	.214			5.70	3.26	8.96	13.15
4300	Slab on grade removal, plain	B-5	45	.889	C.Y.		23.50	31.50	55	74
4310	Mesh reinforced		33	1.212			32	43	75	101
4320	Rod reinforced		25	1.600			42	57	99	133
4400	For congested sites or small quantities, add up to								200%	200%
4450	For disposal on site, add	B-11A	232	.069			1.99	5.70	7.69	9.60
4500	To 5 miles, add	B-34D	76	.105			2.81	9.90	12.71	15.55

02 41 13.60 Selective Demolition Fencing

			Crew	Daily Output	Labor-Hours	Unit	Material	Labor	Equipment	Total	Total Incl O&P
0010	**SELECTIVE DEMOLITION FENCING**	R024119-10									
1600	Fencing, barbed wire, 3 strand		2 Clab	430	.037	L.F.		.89		.89	1.49
1650	5 strand		"	280	.057			1.36		1.36	2.29
1700	Chain link, posts & fabric, 8' to 10' high, remove only		B-6	445	.054			1.44	.82	2.26	3.31
1750	Remove and reset		"	70	.343			9.15	5.20	14.35	21

02 41 16 – Structure Demolition

02 41 16.13 Building Demolition

			Crew	Daily Output	Labor-Hours	Unit	Material	Labor	Equipment	Total	Total Incl O&P
0010	**BUILDING DEMOLITION** Large urban projects, incl. 20 mi. haul	R024119-10									
0500	Small bldgs, or single bldgs, no salvage included, steel		B-3	14800	.003	C.F.		.09	.17	.26	.33
0600	Concrete		"	11300	.004	"		.11	.23	.34	.44
0605	Concrete, plain		B-5	33	1.212	C.Y.		32	43	75	101
0610	Reinforced			25	1.600			42	57	99	133
0615	Concrete walls			34	1.176			31	42	73	97.50
0620	Elevated slabs			26	1.538			40.50	55	95.50	128
0650	Masonry		B-3	14800	.003	C.F.		.09	.17	.26	.33
0700	Wood			14800	.003	"		.09	.17	.26	.33
1000	Demoliton single family house, one story, wood 1600 S.F.			1	48	Ea.		1,275	2,575	3,850	4,975
1020	3200 S.F.			.50	96			2,575	5,150	7,725	9,975
1200	Demoliton two family house, two story, wood 2400 S.F.			.67	71.964			1,925	3,850	5,775	7,475
1220	4200 S.F.			.38	128			3,425	6,875	10,300	13,300
1300	Demoliton three family house, three story, wood 3200 S.F.			.50	96			2,575	5,150	7,725	9,975
1320	5400 S.F.			.30	160			4,275	8,575	12,850	16,600

02 41 16.17 Building Demolition Footings and Foundations

			Crew	Daily Output	Labor-Hours	Unit	Material	Labor	Equipment	Total	Total Incl O&P
0010	**BUILDING DEMOLITION FOOTINGS AND FOUNDATIONS**	R024119-10									
0200	Floors, concrete slab on grade,										
0240	4" thick, plain concrete		B-9	500	.080	S.F.		1.94	.47	2.41	3.77
0280	Reinforced, wire mesh			470	.085			2.06	.50	2.56	4.02
0300	Rods			400	.100			2.42	.58	3	4.71

02 41 Demolition

02 41 16 – Structure Demolition

02 41 16.17 Building Demolition Footings and Foundations

02 41 16.17 Building Demolition Footings and Foundations		Crew	Daily Output	Labor-Hours	Unit	Material	2014 Bare Costs Labor	2014 Bare Costs Equipment	Total	Total Incl O&P
0400	6" thick, plain concrete	B-9	375	.107	S.F.		2.58	.62	3.20	5
0420	Reinforced, wire mesh		340	.118			2.85	.69	3.54	5.55
0440	Rods		300	.133			3.23	.78	4.01	6.30
1000	Footings, concrete, 1' thick, 2' wide	B-5	300	.133	L.F.		3.49	4.75	8.24	11.05
1080	1'-6" thick, 2' wide		250	.160			4.19	5.70	9.89	13.25
1120	3' wide		200	.200			5.25	7.10	12.35	16.65
1200	Average reinforcing, add								10%	10%
2000	Walls, block, 4" thick	1 Clab	180	.044	S.F.		1.06		1.06	1.78
2040	6" thick		170	.047			1.12		1.12	1.88
2080	8" thick		150	.053			1.27		1.27	2.14
2100	12" thick		150	.053			1.27		1.27	2.14
2400	Concrete, plain concrete, 6" thick	B-9	160	.250			6.05	1.46	7.51	11.80
2420	8" thick		140	.286			6.90	1.67	8.57	13.50
2440	10" thick		120	.333			8.05	1.95	10	15.70
2500	12" thick		100	.400			9.70	2.34	12.04	18.85
2600	For average reinforcing, add								10%	10%
4000	For congested sites or small quantities, add up to								200%	200%
4200	Add for disposal, on site	B-11A	232	.069	C.Y.		1.99	5.70	7.69	9.60
4250	To five miles	B-30	220	.109	"		3.17	11	14.17	17.35

02 41 19 – Selective Demolition

02 41 19.13 Selective Building Demolition

0010	**SELECTIVE BUILDING DEMOLITION**									
0020	Costs related to selective demolition of specific building components									
0025	are included under Common Work Results (XX 05)									
0030	in the component's appropriate division.									

02 41 19.16 Selective Demolition, Cutout

		Crew	Daily Output	Labor-Hours	Unit	Material	Labor	Equipment	Total	Total Incl O&P
0010	**SELECTIVE DEMOLITION, CUTOUT** R024119-10									
0020	Concrete, elev. slab, light reinforcement, under 6 C.F.	B-9	65	.615	C.F.		14.90	3.59	18.49	29
0050	Light reinforcing, over 6 C.F.		75	.533	"		12.90	3.11	16.01	25
0200	Slab on grade to 6" thick, not reinforced, under 8 S.F.		85	.471	S.F.		11.40	2.75	14.15	22
0250	8 – 16 S.F.		175	.229	"		5.55	1.33	6.88	10.75
0255	For over 16 S.F. see Line 02 41 16.17 0400									
0600	Walls, not reinforced, under 6 C.F.	B-9	60	.667	C.F.		16.15	3.89	20.04	31.50
0650	6 – 12 C.F.	"	80	.500	"		12.10	2.92	15.02	23.50
0655	For over 12 C.F. see Line 02 41 16.17 2500									
1000	Concrete, elevated slab, bar reinforced, under 6 C.F.	B-9	45	.889	C.F.		21.50	5.20	26.70	41.50
1050	Bar reinforced, over 6 C.F.		50	.800	"		19.35	4.67	24.02	37.50
1200	Slab on grade to 6" thick, bar reinforced, under 8 S.F.		75	.533	S.F.		12.90	3.11	16.01	25
1250	8 – 16 S.F.		150	.267	"		6.45	1.56	8.01	12.55
1255	For over 16 S.F. see Line 02 41 16.17 0440									
1400	Walls, bar reinforced, under 6 C.F.	B-9	50	.800	C.F.		19.35	4.67	24.02	37.50
1450	6 – 12 C.F.	"	70	.571	"		13.85	3.34	17.19	27
1455	For over 12 C.F. see Lines 02 41 16.17 2500 and 2600									
2000	Brick, to 4 S.F. opening, not including toothing									
2040	4" thick	B-9	30	1.333	Ea.		32.50	7.80	40.30	63
2060	8" thick		18	2.222			54	13	67	105
2080	12" thick		10	4			97	23.50	120.50	189
2400	Concrete block, to 4 S.F. opening, 2" thick		35	1.143			27.50	6.65	34.15	54
2420	4" thick		30	1.333			32.50	7.80	40.30	63
2440	8" thick		27	1.481			36	8.65	44.65	70
2460	12" thick		24	1.667			40.50	9.75	50.25	78.50
2600	Gypsum block, to 4 S.F. opening, 2" thick		80	.500			12.10	2.92	15.02	23.50

02 41 Demolition

02 41 19 - Selective Demolition

02 41 19.16 Selective Demolition, Cutout

		Crew	Daily Output	Labor-Hours	Unit	Material	2014 Bare Costs Labor	2014 Bare Costs Equipment	Total	Total Incl O&P
2620	4" thick	B-9	70	.571	Ea.		13.85	3.34	17.19	27
2640	8" thick		55	.727			17.60	4.25	21.85	34
2800	Terra cotta, to 4 S.F. opening, 4" thick		70	.571			13.85	3.34	17.19	27
2840	8" thick		65	.615			14.90	3.59	18.49	29
2880	12" thick		50	.800			19.35	4.67	24.02	37.50
3000	Toothing masonry cutouts, brick, soft old mortar	1 Brhe	40	.200	V.L.F.		5.20		5.20	8.60
3100	Hard mortar		30	.267			6.90		6.90	11.50
3200	Block, soft old mortar		70	.114			2.96		2.96	4.93
3400	Hard mortar		50	.160			4.14		4.14	6.90
6000	Walls, interior, not including re-framing,									
6010	openings to 5 S.F.									
6100	Drywall to 5/8" thick	1 Clab	24	.333	Ea.		7.95		7.95	13.35
6200	Paneling to 3/4" thick		20	.400			9.50		9.50	16
6300	Plaster, on gypsum lath		20	.400			9.50		9.50	16
6340	On wire lath		14	.571			13.60		13.60	23
7000	Wood frame, not including re-framing, openings to 5 S.F.									
7200	Floors, sheathing and flooring to 2" thick	1 Clab	5	1.600	Ea.		38		38	64
7310	Roofs, sheathing to 1" thick, not including roofing		6	1.333			31.50		31.50	53.50
7410	Walls, sheathing to 1" thick, not including siding		7	1.143			27		27	46

02 41 19.19 Selective Facility Services Demolition

		Crew	Daily Output	Labor-Hours	Unit	Material	2014 Bare Costs Labor	2014 Bare Costs Equipment	Total	Total Incl O&P
0010	**SELECTIVE FACILITY SERVICES DEMOLITION**, Rubbish Handling R024119-10									
0020	The following are to be added to the demolition prices									
0600	Dumpster, weekly rental, 1 dump/week, 6 C.Y. capacity (2 Tons)				Week	415			415	455
0700	10 C.Y. capacity (3 Tons)					480			480	530
0725	20 C.Y. capacity (5 Tons) R024119-20					565			565	625
0800	30 C.Y. capacity (7 Tons)					730			730	800
0840	40 C.Y. capacity (10 Tons)					775			775	850
2000	Load, haul, dump and return, 50' haul, hand carried	2 Clab	24	.667	C.Y.		15.85		15.85	26.50
2005	Wheeled		37	.432			10.30		10.30	17.30
2040	51' to 100' haul, hand carried		16.50	.970			23		23	39
2045	Wheeled		25	.640			15.25		15.25	25.50
2080	Over 100' haul, add per 100 L.F., hand carried		35.50	.451			10.75		10.75	18.05
2085	Wheeled		54	.296			7.05		7.05	11.85
2120	In elevators, per 10 floors, add		140	.114			2.72		2.72	4.58
2130	Load, haul, dump and return, up to 50' haul, incl. up to 5 rsr stair, hand		23	.696			16.55		16.55	28
2135	Wheeled		35	.457			10.90		10.90	18.30
2140	6 – 10 riser stairs, hand carried		22	.727			17.30		17.30	29
2145	Wheeled		34	.471			11.20		11.20	18.85
2150	11 – 20 riser stairs, hand carried		20	.800			19.05		19.05	32
2155	Wheeled		31	.516			12.30		12.30	20.50
2160	21 – 40 riser stairs, hand carried		16	1			24		24	40
2165	Wheeled		24	.667			15.85		15.85	26.50
2170	100' haul, incl. 5 riser stair, hand carried		15	1.067			25.50		25.50	42.50
2175	Wheeled		23	.696			16.55		16.55	28
2180	6 – 10 riser stair, hand carried		14	1.143			27		27	46
2185	Wheeled		21	.762			18.15		18.15	30.50
2190	11 – 20 riser stair, hand carried		12	1.333			31.50		31.50	53.50
2195	Wheeled		18	.889			21		21	35.50
2200	21 – 40 riser stair, hand carried		8	2			47.50		47.50	80
2205	Wheeled		12	1.333			31.50		31.50	53.50
2210	Over 100' haul, add per 100 L.F., hand carried		35.50	.451			10.75		10.75	18.05
2215	Wheeled		54	.296			7.05		7.05	11.85

02 41 Demolition

02 41 19 – Selective Demolition

02 41 19.19 Selective Facility Services Demolition		Crew	Daily Output	Labor-Hours	Unit	Material	2014 Bare Costs Labor	Equipment	Total	Total Incl O&P
2220	For each additional flight of stairs, up to 5 risers, add	2 Clab	550	.029	Flight		.69		.69	1.17
2225	6 – 10 risers, add		275	.058			1.38		1.38	2.33
2230	11 – 20 risers, add		138	.116			2.76		2.76	4.64
2235	21 – 40 risers, add		69	.232			5.50		5.50	9.30
3000	Loading & trucking, including 2 mile haul, chute loaded	B-16	45	.711	C.Y.		17.80	15.40	33.20	47
3040	Hand loading truck, 50' haul	"	48	.667			16.65	14.40	31.05	44
3080	Machine loading truck	B-17	120	.267			7.10	6.50	13.60	19.05
5000	Haul, per mile, up to 8 C.Y. truck	B-34B	1165	.007			.18	.59	.77	.96
5100	Over 8 C.Y. truck	"	1550	.005			.14	.45	.59	.72

02 41 19.20 Selective Demolition, Dump Charges

		Crew	Daily Output	Labor-Hours	Unit	Material	2014 Bare Costs Labor	Equipment	Total	Total Incl O&P
0010	**SELECTIVE DEMOLITION, DUMP CHARGES**	R024119-10								
0020	Dump charges, typical urban city, tipping fees only									
0100	Building construction materials				Ton	74			74	81
0200	Trees, brush, lumber					63			63	69.50
0300	Rubbish only					63			63	69.50
0500	Reclamation station, usual charge					74			74	81

02 41 19.21 Selective Demolition, Gutting

		Crew	Daily Output	Labor-Hours	Unit	Material	2014 Bare Costs Labor	Equipment	Total	Total Incl O&P
0010	**SELECTIVE DEMOLITION, GUTTING**	R024119-10								
0020	Building interior, including disposal, dumpster fees not included									
0500	Residential building									
0560	Minimum	B-16	400	.080	SF Flr.		2	1.73	3.73	5.25
0580	Maximum	"	360	.089	"		2.22	1.92	4.14	5.85
0900	Commercial building									
1000	Minimum	B-16	350	.091	SF Flr.		2.29	1.98	4.27	6
1020	Maximum	"	250	.128	"		3.20	2.77	5.97	8.40

02 83 Lead Remediation

02 83 19 – Lead-Based Paint Remediation

02 83 19.22 Preparation of Lead Containment Area

		Crew	Daily Output	Labor-Hours	Unit	Material	2014 Bare Costs Labor	Equipment	Total	Total Incl O&P
0010	**PREPARATION OF LEAD CONTAINMENT AREA**									
0020	Lead abatement work area, test kit, per swab	1 Skwk	16	.500	Ea.	4.13	16.25		20.38	32
0025	For dust barriers see Section 01 56 16.10									
0050	Caution sign	1 Skwk	48	.167	Ea.	10.45	5.40		15.85	20.50
0100	Pre-cleaning, HEPA vacuum and wet wipe, floor and wall surfaces	3 Skwk	5000	.005	S.F.	.02	.16		.18	.28
0105	Ceiling, 6' - 11' high		4100	.006		.09	.19		.28	.42
0108	12' - 15' high		3550	.007		.08	.22		.30	.45
0115	Over 15' high		3000	.008		.11	.26		.37	.56
0500	Cover surfaces with polyethylene sheeting									
0550	Floors, each layer, 6 mil	3 Skwk	8000	.003	S.F.	.04	.10		.14	.21
0560	Walls, each layer, 6 mil	"	6000	.004	"	.04	.13		.17	.27
0570	For heights above 12', add						20%			
2400	Post abatement cleaning of protective sheeting, HEPA vacuum & wet wipe	3 Skwk	5000	.005	S.F.	.02	.16		.18	.28
2450	Doff, bag and seal protective sheeting		12000	.002		.01	.06		.07	.12
2500	Post abatement cleaning, HEPA vacuum & wet wipe		5000	.005		.02	.16		.18	.28

02 83 19.23 Encapsulation of Lead-Based Paint

		Crew	Daily Output	Labor-Hours	Unit	Material	2014 Bare Costs Labor	Equipment	Total	Total Incl O&P
0010	**ENCAPSULATION OF LEAD-BASED PAINT**									
0020	Interior, brushwork, trim, under 6"	1 Pord	240	.033	L.F.	2.25	.94		3.19	4.02
0030	6" to 12" wide		180	.044		3	1.25		4.25	5.35
0040	Balustrades		300	.027		1.80	.75		2.55	3.21
0050	Pipe to 4" diameter		500	.016		1.10	.45		1.55	1.95

02 83 Lead Remediation

02 83 19 – Lead-Based Paint Remediation

02 83 19.23 Encapsulation of Lead-Based Paint	Crew	Daily Output	Labor-Hours	Unit	Material	2014 Bare Costs Labor	Equipment	Total	Total Incl O&P
0060	To 8" diameter	1 Pord	375	.021	L.F.	1.45	.60		2.05	2.59
0070	To 12" diameter		250	.032		2.15	.90		3.05	3.85
0080	To 16" diameter		170	.047		3.20	1.32		4.52	5.70
0090	Cabinets, ornate design		200	.040	S.F.	2.75	1.12		3.87	4.88
0100	Simple design		250	.032	"	2.20	.90		3.10	3.90
0110	Doors, 3' x 7', both sides, incl. frame & trim									
0120	Flush	1 Pord	6	1.333	Ea.	27.50	37.50		65	92
0130	French, 10 – 15 lite		3	2.667		5.55	75		80.55	129
0140	Panel		4	2		33.50	56		89.50	130
0150	Louvered		2.75	2.909		30.50	82		112.50	168
0160	Windows, per interior side, per 15 S.F.									
0170	1 to 6 lite	1 Pord	14	.571	Ea.	19	16.05		35.05	47.50
0180	7 to 10 lite		7.50	1.067		21	30		51	73
0190	12 lite		5.75	1.391		28.50	39		67.50	95.50
0200	Radiators		8	1		67.50	28		95.50	121
0210	Grilles, vents		275	.029	S.F.	2	.82		2.82	3.54
0220	Walls, roller, drywall or plaster		1000	.008		.55	.22		.77	.98
0230	With spunbonded reinforcing fabric		720	.011		.62	.31		.93	1.19
0240	Wood		800	.010		.68	.28		.96	1.21
0250	Ceilings, roller, drywall or plaster		900	.009		.62	.25		.87	1.09
0260	Wood		700	.011		.76	.32		1.08	1.37
0270	Exterior, brushwork, gutters and downspouts		300	.027	L.F.	1.80	.75		2.55	3.21
0280	Columns		400	.020	S.F.	1.35	.56		1.91	2.41
0290	Spray, siding		600	.013	"	.91	.37		1.28	1.62
0300	Miscellaneous									
0310	Electrical conduit, brushwork, to 2" diameter	1 Pord	500	.016	L.F.	1.10	.45		1.55	1.95
0320	Brick, block or concrete, spray		500	.016	S.F.	1.10	.45		1.55	1.95
0330	Steel, flat surfaces and tanks to 12"		500	.016		1.10	.45		1.55	1.95
0340	Beams, brushwork		400	.020		1.35	.56		1.91	2.41
0350	Trusses		400	.020		1.35	.56		1.91	2.41

02 83 19.26 Removal of Lead-Based Paint

		Crew	Daily Output	Labor-Hours	Unit	Material	Labor	Equipment	Total	Total Incl O&P
0010	**REMOVAL OF LEAD-BASED PAINT**									
0011	By chemicals, per application									
0050	Baseboard, to 6" wide	1 Pord	64	.125	L.F.	.71	3.51		4.22	6.60
0070	To 12" wide		32	.250	"	1.37	7.05		8.42	13.05
0200	Balustrades, one side		28	.286	S.F.	1.42	8.05		9.47	14.75
1400	Cabinets, simple design		32	.250		1.28	7.05		8.33	12.95
1420	Ornate design		25	.320		1.55	9		10.55	16.50
1600	Cornice, simple design		60	.133		1.47	3.75		5.22	7.75
1620	Ornate design		20	.400		5.25	11.25		16.50	24.50
2800	Doors, one side, flush		84	.095		1.84	2.68		4.52	6.40
2820	Two panel		80	.100		1.28	2.81		4.09	6.05
2840	Four panel		45	.178		1.37	5		6.37	9.70
2880	For trim, one side, add		64	.125	L.F.	.70	3.51		4.21	6.55
3000	Fence, picket, one side		30	.267	S.F.	1.28	7.50		8.78	13.70
3200	Grilles, one side, simple design		30	.267		1.30	7.50		8.80	13.75
3220	Ornate design		25	.320		1.40	9		10.40	16.35
3240	Handrails		90	.089	L.F.	1.30	2.50		3.80	5.55
4400	Pipes, to 4" diameter		90	.089		1.84	2.50		4.34	6.15
4420	To 8" diameter		50	.160		3.68	4.50		8.18	11.45
4440	To 12" diameter		36	.222		5.50	6.25		11.75	16.30
4460	To 16" diameter		20	.400		7.35	11.25		18.60	26.50

02 83 Lead Remediation

02 83 19 – Lead-Based Paint Remediation

02 83 19.26 Removal of Lead-Based Paint	Crew	Daily Output	Labor-Hours	Unit	Material	2014 Bare Costs Labor	Equipment	Total	Total Incl O&P
4500	For hangers, add	1 Pord	40	.200	Ea.	2.44	5.60		8.04	11.95
4800	Siding		90	.089	S.F.	1.22	2.50		3.72	5.45
5000	Trusses, open		55	.145	SF Face	1.92	4.09		6.01	8.80
6200	Windows, one side only, double hung, 1/1 light, 24" x 48" high		4	2	Ea.	23	56		79	118
6220	30" x 60" high		3	2.667		30.50	75		105.50	157
6240	36" x 72" high		2.50	3.200		36.50	90		126.50	188
6280	40" x 80" high		2	4		45.50	112		157.50	235
6400	Colonial window, 6/6 light, 24" x 48" high		2	4		45.50	112		157.50	235
6420	30" x 60" high		1.50	5.333		61	150		211	315
6440	36" x 72" high		1	8		91	225		316	470
6480	40" x 80" high		1	8		91	225		316	470
6600	8/8 light, 24" x 48" high		2	4		45.50	112		157.50	235
6620	40" x 80" high		1	8		91	225		316	470
6800	12/12 light, 24" x 48" high		1	8		91	225		316	470
6820	40" x 80" high		.75	10.667		122	300		422	630
6840	Window frame & trim items, included in pricing above									

Estimating Tips

General

- Carefully check all the plans and specifications. Concrete often appears on drawings other than structural drawings, including mechanical and electrical drawings for equipment pads. The cost of cutting and patching is often difficult to estimate. See Subdivision 03 81 for Concrete Cutting, Subdivision 02 41 19.16 for Cutout Demolition, Subdivision 03 05 05.10 for Concrete Demolition, and Subdivision 02 41 19.19 for Rubbish Handling (handling, loading and hauling of debris).
- Always obtain concrete prices from suppliers near the job site. A volume discount can often be negotiated, depending upon competition in the area. Remember to add for waste, particularly for slabs and footings on grade.

03 10 00 Concrete Forming and Accessories

- A primary cost for concrete construction is forming. Most jobs today are constructed with prefabricated forms. The selection of the forms best suited for the job and the total square feet of forms required for efficient concrete forming and placing are key elements in estimating concrete construction. Enough forms must be available for erection to make efficient use of the concrete placing equipment and crew.

- Concrete accessories for forming and placing depend upon the systems used. Study the plans and specifications to ensure that all special accessory requirements have been included in the cost estimate, such as anchor bolts, inserts, and hangers.
- Included within costs for forms-in-place are all necessary bracing and shoring.

03 20 00 Concrete Reinforcing

- Ascertain that the reinforcing steel supplier has included all accessories, cutting, bending, and an allowance for lapping, splicing, and waste. A good rule of thumb is 10% for lapping, splicing, and waste. Also, 10% waste should be allowed for welded wire fabric.
- The unit price items in the subdivisions for Reinforcing In Place, Glass Fiber Reinforcing, and Welded Wire Fabric include the labor to install accessories such as beam and slab bolsters, high chairs, and bar ties and tie wire. The material cost for these accessories is not included; they may be obtained from the Accessories Division.

03 30 00 Cast-In-Place Concrete

- When estimating structural concrete, pay particular attention to requirements for concrete additives, curing methods, and surface treatments. Special consideration for climate, hot or cold, must be included in your estimate. Be sure to include requirements for concrete placing equipment, and concrete finishing.

- For accurate concrete estimating, the estimator must consider each of the following major components individually: forms, reinforcing steel, ready-mix concrete, placement of the concrete, and finishing of the top surface. For faster estimating, Subdivision 03 30 53.40 for Concrete-In-Place can be used; here, various items of concrete work are presented that include the costs of all five major components (unless specifically stated otherwise).

03 40 00 Precast Concrete
03 50 00 Cast Decks and Underlayment

- The cost of hauling precast concrete structural members is often an important factor. For this reason, it is important to get a quote from the nearest supplier. It may become economically feasible to set up precasting beds on the site if the hauling costs are prohibitive.

Reference Numbers

Reference numbers are shown in shaded boxes at the beginning of some major classifications. These numbers refer to related items in the Reference Section. The reference information may be an estimating procedure, an alternate pricing method, or technical information.

Note: Not all subdivisions listed here necessarily appear in this publication.

03 01 Maintenance of Concrete

03 01 30 – Maintenance of Cast-In-Place Concrete

03 01 30.64 Floor Patching

		Crew	Daily Output	Labor-Hours	Unit	Material	2014 Bare Costs Labor	Equipment	Total	Total Incl O&P
0010	**FLOOR PATCHING**									
0012	Floor patching, 1/4" thick, small areas, regular	1 Cefi	170	.047	S.F.	2.39	1.45		3.84	4.97
0100	Epoxy	"	100	.080	"	7.25	2.47		9.72	12

03 05 Common Work Results for Concrete

03 05 13 – Basic Concrete Materials

03 05 13.85 Winter Protection

		Crew	Daily Output	Labor-Hours	Unit	Material	2014 Bare Costs Labor	Equipment	Total	Total Incl O&P
0010	**WINTER PROTECTION**									
0012	For heated ready mix, add				C.Y.	4.50			4.50	4.95
0100	Temporary heat to protect concrete, 24 hours	2 Clab	50	.320	M.S.F.	535	7.60		542.60	600
0200	Temporary shelter for slab on grade, wood frame/polyethylene sheeting									
0201	Build or remove, light framing for short spans	2 Carp	10	1.600	M.S.F.	284	51.50		335.50	395
0210	Large framing for long spans	"	3	5.333	"	380	171		551	710
0710	Electrically, heated pads, 15 watts/S.F., 20 uses				S.F.	.52			.52	.57

03 11 Concrete Forming

03 11 13 – Structural Cast-In-Place Concrete Forming

03 11 13.25 Forms In Place, Columns

			Crew	Daily Output	Labor-Hours	Unit	Material	2014 Bare Costs Labor	Equipment	Total	Total Incl O&P
0010	**FORMS IN PLACE, COLUMNS**										
1500	Round fiber tube, recycled paper, 1 use, 8" diameter	G	C-1	155	.206	L.F.	1.66	5.75		7.41	11.55
1550	10" diameter	G		155	.206		2.24	5.75		7.99	12.15
1600	12" diameter	G		150	.213		2.60	5.95		8.55	12.90
1650	14" diameter	G		145	.221		3.77	6.15		9.92	14.55
1700	16" diameter	G		140	.229		4.52	6.40		10.92	15.70
1720	18" diameter	G		140	.229		5.30	6.40		11.70	16.55
5000	Job-built plywood, 8" x 8" columns, 1 use			165	.194	SFCA	2.67	5.40		8.07	12.10
5500	12" x 12" columns, 1 use			180	.178	"	2.56	4.97		7.53	11.15
7400	Steel framed plywood, based on 50 uses of purchased										
7420	forms, and 4 uses of bracing lumber										
7500	8" x 8" column		C-1	340	.094	SFCA	2.11	2.63		4.74	6.75
7550	10" x 10"			350	.091		1.84	2.56		4.40	6.35
7600	12" x 12"			370	.086		1.56	2.42		3.98	5.80

03 11 13.45 Forms In Place, Footings

		Crew	Daily Output	Labor-Hours	Unit	Material	2014 Bare Costs Labor	Equipment	Total	Total Incl O&P
0010	**FORMS IN PLACE, FOOTINGS**									
0020	Continuous wall, plywood, 1 use	C-1	375	.085	SFCA	6.25	2.39		8.64	10.85
0150	4 use	"	485	.066	"	2.03	1.84		3.87	5.35
1500	Keyway, 4 use, tapered wood, 2" x 4"	1 Carp	530	.015	L.F.	.20	.48		.68	1.03
1550	2" x 6"	"	500	.016	"	.28	.51		.79	1.17
5000	Spread footings, job-built lumber, 1 use	C-1	305	.105	SFCA	2	2.93		4.93	7.15
5150	4 use	"	414	.077	"	.65	2.16		2.81	4.35

03 11 13.50 Forms In Place, Grade Beam

		Crew	Daily Output	Labor-Hours	Unit	Material	2014 Bare Costs Labor	Equipment	Total	Total Incl O&P
0010	**FORMS IN PLACE, GRADE BEAM**									
0020	Job-built plywood, 1 use	C-2	530	.091	SFCA	2.82	2.56		5.38	7.40
0150	4 use	"	605	.079	"	.92	2.25		3.17	4.79

03 11 13.65 Forms In Place, Slab On Grade

			Crew	Daily Output	Labor-Hours	Unit	Material	2014 Bare Costs Labor	Equipment	Total	Total Incl O&P
0010	**FORMS IN PLACE, SLAB ON GRADE**										
1000	Bulkhead forms w/keyway, wood, 6" high, 1 use		C-1	510	.063	L.F.	.93	1.75		2.68	3.97
1400	Bulkhead form for slab, 4-1/2" high, exp metal, incl keyway & stakes	G		1200	.027		.88	.75		1.63	2.23

03 11 Concrete Forming

03 11 13 – Structural Cast-In-Place Concrete Forming

03 11 13.65 Forms In Place, Slab On Grade

		Crew	Daily Output	Labor-Hours	Unit	Material	2014 Bare Costs Labor	Equipment	Total	Total Incl O&P
1410	5-1/2" high [G]	C-1	1100	.029	L.F.	1.01	.81		1.82	2.48
1420	7-1/2" high [G]		960	.033		1.25	.93		2.18	2.95
1430	9-1/2" high [G]		840	.038		1.36	1.07		2.43	3.29
2000	Curb forms, wood, 6" to 12" high, on grade, 1 use		215	.149	SFCA	2.43	4.16		6.59	9.65
2150	4 use		275	.116	"	.79	3.25		4.04	6.35
3000	Edge forms, wood, 4 use, on grade, to 6" high		600	.053	L.F.	.31	1.49		1.80	2.85
3050	7" to 12" high		435	.074	SFCA	.77	2.06		2.83	4.30
4000	For slab blockouts, to 12" high, 1 use		200	.160	L.F.	.71	4.47		5.18	8.35
4100	Plastic (extruded), to 6" high, multiple use, on grade		800	.040	"	8.20	1.12		9.32	10.90
8760	Void form, corrugated fiberboard, 4" x 12", 4' long [G]		3000	.011	S.F.	3.01	.30		3.31	3.81
8770	6" x 12", 4' long		3000	.011		3.59	.30		3.89	4.45
8780	1/4" thick hardboard protective cover for void form	2 Carp	1500	.011		.57	.34		.91	1.21

03 11 13.85 Forms In Place, Walls

		Crew	Daily Output	Labor-Hours	Unit	Material	2014 Bare Costs Labor	Equipment	Total	Total Incl O&P
0010	**FORMS IN PLACE, WALLS**									
0100	Box out for wall openings, to 16" thick, to 10 S.F.	C-2	24	2	Ea.	25	56.50		81.50	123
0150	Over 10 S.F. (use perimeter)	"	280	.171	L.F.	2.13	4.85		6.98	10.50
0250	Brick shelf, 4" w, add to wall forms, use wall area above shelf									
0260	1 use	C-2	240	.200	SFCA	2.28	5.65		7.93	12.05
0350	4 use		300	.160	"	.91	4.53		5.44	8.65
0500	Bulkhead, wood with keyway, 1 use, 2 piece		265	.181	L.F.	1.90	5.15		7.05	10.75
0600	Bulkhead forms with keyway, 1 piece expanded metal, 8" wall [G]	C-1	1000	.032		1.25	.89		2.14	2.89
0610	10" wall [G]	"	800	.040		1.36	1.12		2.48	3.38
2000	Wall, job-built plywood, to 8' high, 1 use	C-2	370	.130	SFCA	2.64	3.67		6.31	9.10
2050	2 use		435	.110		1.67	3.12		4.79	7.10
2100	3 use		495	.097		1.21	2.74		3.95	5.95
2150	4 use		505	.095		.99	2.69		3.68	5.60
2400	8' to 16' high, 1 use		280	.171		2.91	4.85		7.76	11.35
2450	2 use		345	.139		1.24	3.94		5.18	8
2500	3 use		375	.128		.89	3.62		4.51	7.05
2550	4 use		395	.122		.73	3.44		4.17	6.60
7800	Modular prefabricated plywood, based on 20 uses of purchased									
7820	forms, and 4 uses of bracing lumber									
7860	To 8' high	C-2	800	.060	SFCA	.85	1.70		2.55	3.80
8060	Over 8' to 16' high	"	600	.080	"	.90	2.26		3.16	4.80

03 11 19 – Insulating Concrete Forming

03 11 19.10 Insulating Forms, Left In Place

		Crew	Daily Output	Labor-Hours	Unit	Material	2014 Bare Costs Labor	Equipment	Total	Total Incl O&P
0010	**INSULATING FORMS, LEFT IN PLACE**									
0020	S.F. is for exterior face, but includes forms for both faces (total R22)									
2000	4" wall, straight block, 16" x 48" (5.33 S.F.) [G]	2 Carp	90	.178	Ea.	18.35	5.70		24.05	29.50
2010	90 corner block, exterior 16" x 38" x 22" (6.67 S.F.) [G]		75	.213		21.50	6.85		28.35	35.50
2020	45 corner block, exterior 16" x 34" x 18" (5.78 S.F.) [G]		75	.213		21.50	6.85		28.35	35.50
2100	6" wall, straight block, 16" x 48" (5.33 S.F.) [G]		90	.178		18.85	5.70		24.55	30
2110	90 corner block, exterior 16" x 32" x 24" (6.22 S.F.) [G]		75	.213		23.50	6.85		30.35	37.50
2120	45 corner block, exterior 16" x 26" x 18" (4.89 S.F.) [G]		75	.213		21	6.85		27.85	34.50
2130	Brick ledge block, 16" x 48" (5.33 S.F.) [G]		80	.200		24	6.40		30.40	37
2140	Taper top block, 16" x 48" (5.33 S.F.) [G]		80	.200		22	6.40		28.40	35.50
2200	8" wall, straight block, 16" x 48" (5.33 S.F.) [G]		90	.178		20	5.70		25.70	31.50
2210	90 corner block, exterior 16" x 34" x 26" (6.67 S.F.) [G]		75	.213		26	6.85		32.85	40
2220	45 corner block, exterior 16" x 28" x 20" (5.33 S.F.) [G]		75	.213		22	6.85		28.85	35.50
2230	Brick ledge block, 16" x 48" (5.33 S.F.) [G]		80	.200		25	6.40		31.40	38.50
2240	Taper top block, 16" x 48" (5.33 S.F.) [G]		80	.200		23	6.40		29.40	36.50

03 11 Concrete Forming

03 11 23 – Permanent Stair Forming

03 11 23.75 Forms In Place, Stairs

03 11 23.75 Forms In Place, Stairs	Crew	Daily Output	Labor-Hours	Unit	Material	2014 Bare Costs Labor	Equipment	Total	Total Incl O&P
0010 **FORMS IN PLACE, STAIRS**									
0015 (Slant length x width), 1 use	C-2	165	.291	S.F.	5.45	8.25		13.70	19.85
0150 4 use		190	.253		1.93	7.15		9.08	14.20
2000 Stairs, cast on sloping ground (length x width), 1 use		220	.218		2.14	6.15		8.29	12.75
2025 2 use		232	.207		1.17	5.85		7.02	11.15
2050 3 use		244	.197		.85	5.55		6.40	10.35
2100 4 use		256	.188		.69	5.30		5.99	9.70

03 15 Concrete Accessories

03 15 05 – Concrete Forming Accessories

03 15 05.12 Chamfer Strips

	Crew	Daily Output	Labor-Hours	Unit	Material	2014 Bare Costs Labor	Equipment	Total	Total Incl O&P
0010 **CHAMFER STRIPS**									
5000 Wood, 1/2" wide	1 Carp	535	.015	L.F.	.13	.48		.61	.95
5200 3/4" wide		525	.015		.16	.49		.65	1
5400 1" wide		515	.016		.33	.50		.83	1.20

03 15 05.15 Column Form Accessories

	Crew	Daily Output	Labor-Hours	Unit	Material	2014 Bare Costs Labor	Equipment	Total	Total Incl O&P
0010 **COLUMN FORM ACCESSORIES**									
1000 Column clamps, adjustable to 24" x 24", buy [G]				Set	137			137	150
1100 Rent per month [G]				"	13.70			13.70	15.05

03 15 05.75 Sleeves and Chases

	Crew	Daily Output	Labor-Hours	Unit	Material	2014 Bare Costs Labor	Equipment	Total	Total Incl O&P
0010 **SLEEVES AND CHASES**									
0100 Plastic, 1 use, 12" long, 2" diameter	1 Carp	100	.080	Ea.	2.44	2.57		5.01	7
0150 4" diameter		90	.089		6.65	2.85		9.50	12.10
0200 6" diameter		75	.107		14.25	3.42		17.67	21.50

03 15 05.80 Snap Ties

	Crew	Daily Output	Labor-Hours	Unit	Material	2014 Bare Costs Labor	Equipment	Total	Total Incl O&P
0010 **SNAP TIES**, 8-1/4" L&W (Lumber and wedge)									
0100 2250 lb., w/flat washer, 8" wall [G]				C	87			87	95.50
0150 10" wall [G]					127			127	140
0200 12" wall [G]					132			132	145
0500 With plastic cone, 8" wall [G]					78			78	86
0550 10" wall [G]					81			81	89
0600 12" wall [G]					86			86	94.50

03 15 05.95 Wall and Foundation Form Accessories

	Crew	Daily Output	Labor-Hours	Unit	Material	2014 Bare Costs Labor	Equipment	Total	Total Incl O&P
0010 **WALL AND FOUNDATION FORM ACCESSORIES**									
4000 Nail stakes, 3/4" diameter, 18" long [G]				Ea.	3.08			3.08	3.39
4050 24" long [G]					3.98			3.98	4.38
4200 30" long [G]					5.10			5.10	5.60
4250 36" long [G]					6.15			6.15	6.80

03 15 13 – Waterstops

03 15 13.50 Waterstops

	Crew	Daily Output	Labor-Hours	Unit	Material	2014 Bare Costs Labor	Equipment	Total	Total Incl O&P
0010 **WATERSTOPS**, PVC and Rubber									
0020 PVC, ribbed 3/16" thick, 4" wide	1 Carp	155	.052	L.F.	1.22	1.66		2.88	4.13
0050 6" wide		145	.055		2.16	1.77		3.93	5.35
0500 With center bulb, 6" wide, 3/16" thick		135	.059		1.88	1.90		3.78	5.25
0550 3/8" thick		130	.062		3.35	1.98		5.33	7
0600 9" wide x 3/8" thick		125	.064		5.45	2.05		7.50	9.45

03 15 Concrete Accessories

03 15 16 – Concrete Construction Joints

03 15 16.20 Control Joints, Saw Cut

03 15 16.20 Control Joints, Saw Cut		Crew	Daily Output	Labor-Hours	Unit	Material	2014 Bare Costs Labor	2014 Bare Costs Equipment	Total	Total Incl O&P
0010	**CONTROL JOINTS, SAW CUT**									
0100	Sawcut control joints in green concrete									
0120	1" depth	C-27	2000	.008	L.F.	.04	.25	.09	.38	.54
0140	1-1/2" depth		1800	.009		.06	.27	.10	.43	.61
0160	2" depth		1600	.010		.07	.31	.11	.49	.70
0180	Sawcut joint reservoir in cured concrete									
0182	3/8" wide x 3/4" deep, with single saw blade	C-27	1000	.016	L.F.	.06	.49	.18	.73	1.05
0184	1/2" wide x 1" deep, with double saw blades		900	.018		.11	.55	.19	.85	1.22
0186	3/4" wide x 1-1/2" deep, with double saw blades		800	.020		.22	.62	.22	1.06	1.49
0190	Water blast joint to wash away laitance, 2 passes	C-29	2500	.003			.08	.03	.11	.16
0200	Air blast joint to blow out debris and air dry, 2 passes	C-28	2000	.004			.12	.01	.13	.21
0300	For backer rod, see Section 07 91 23.10									
0340	For joint sealant, see Sections 03 15 16.30 or 07 92 13.20									

03 15 16.30 Expansion Joints

03 15 16.30 Expansion Joints			Crew	Daily Output	Labor-Hours	Unit	Material	Labor	Equipment	Total	Total Incl O&P
0010	**EXPANSION JOINTS**										
0020	Keyed, cold, 24 ga., incl. stakes, 3-1/2" high	G	1 Carp	200	.040	L.F.	.77	1.28		2.05	3.01
0050	4-1/2" high	G		200	.040		.88	1.28		2.16	3.13
0100	5-1/2" high	G		195	.041		1.01	1.32		2.33	3.33
2000	Premolded, bituminous fiber, 1/2" x 6"			375	.021		.43	.68		1.11	1.62
2050	1" x 12"			300	.027		1.95	.86		2.81	3.59
2140	Concrete expansion joint, recycled paper and fiber, 1/2" x 6"	G		390	.021		.42	.66		1.08	1.57
2150	1/2" x 12"	G		360	.022		.83	.71		1.54	2.12
2500	Neoprene sponge, closed cell, 1/2" x 6"			375	.021		2.37	.68		3.05	3.76
2550	1" x 12"			300	.027		8.25	.86		9.11	10.55
5000	For installation in walls, add							75%			
5250	For installation in boxouts, add							25%			

03 15 19 – Cast-In Concrete Anchors

03 15 19.05 Anchor Bolt Accessories

03 15 19.05 Anchor Bolt Accessories		Crew	Daily Output	Labor-Hours	Unit	Material	Labor	Equipment	Total	Total Incl O&P
0010	**ANCHOR BOLT ACCESSORIES**									
0015	For anchor bolts set in fresh concrete, see Section 03 15 19.10									
8150	Anchor bolt sleeve, plastic, 1" diam. bolts	1 Carp	60	.133	Ea.	8.10	4.28		12.38	16.10
8500	1-1/2" diameter		28	.286		14.35	9.15		23.50	31.50
8600	2" diameter		24	.333		18.10	10.70		28.80	38
8650	3" diameter		20	.400		33	12.85		45.85	58

03 15 19.10 Anchor Bolts

03 15 19.10 Anchor Bolts			Crew	Daily Output	Labor-Hours	Unit	Material	Labor	Equipment	Total	Total Incl O&P
0010	**ANCHOR BOLTS**										
0015	Made from recycled materials										
0025	Single bolts installed in fresh concrete, no templates										
0030	Hooked w/nut and washer, 1/2" diameter, 8" long	G	1 Carp	132	.061	Ea.	1.49	1.95		3.44	4.91
0040	12" long	G		131	.061		1.66	1.96		3.62	5.15
0070	3/4" diameter, 8" long	G		127	.063		4	2.02		6.02	7.80
0080	12" long	G		125	.064		5	2.05		7.05	8.95

03 15 19.30 Inserts

03 15 19.30 Inserts			Crew	Daily Output	Labor-Hours	Unit	Material	Labor	Equipment	Total	Total Incl O&P
0010	**INSERTS**										
1000	Inserts, slotted nut type for 3/4" bolts, 4" long	G	1 Carp	84	.095	Ea.	18.70	3.06		21.76	25.50
2100	6" long	G		84	.095		21	3.06		24.06	28
2150	8" long	G		84	.095		28	3.06		31.06	36
2200	Slotted, strap type, 4" long	G		84	.095		20	3.06		23.06	27
2300	8" long	G		84	.095		30	3.06		33.06	38

03 21 Reinforcement Bars

03 21 11 – Plain Steel Reinforcement Bars

03 21 11.60 Reinforcing In Place		Crew	Daily Output	Labor-Hours	Unit	Material	2014 Bare Costs Labor	2014 Bare Costs Equipment	Total	Total Incl O&P
0010	**REINFORCING IN PLACE**, 50-60 ton lots, A615 Grade 60									
0020	Includes labor, but not material cost, to install accessories									
0030	Made from recycled materials									
0502	Footings, #4 to #7	G 4 Rodm	4200	.008	Lb.	.50	.26		.76	.99
0550	#8 to #18	G	3.60	8.889	Ton	1,000	300		1,300	1,625
0702	Walls, #3 to #7	G	6000	.005	Lb.	.50	.18		.68	.86
0750	#8 to #18	G	4	8	Ton	1,000	272		1,272	1,575
0900	For other than 50 – 60 ton lots									
1000	Under 10 ton job, #3 to #7, add					25%	10%			
1010	#8 to #18, add					20%	10%			
1050	10 – 50 ton job, #3 to #7, add					10%				
1060	#8 to #18, add					5%				
1100	60 – 100 ton job, #3 to #7, deduct					5%				
1110	#8 to #18, deduct					10%				
1150	Over 100 ton job, #3 to #7, deduct					10%				
1160	#8 to #18, deduct					15%				
2400	Dowels, 2 feet long, deformed, #3	G 2 Rodm	520	.031	Ea.	.41	1.04		1.45	2.24
2410	#4	G	480	.033		.73	1.13		1.86	2.75
2420	#5	G	435	.037		1.15	1.25		2.40	3.40
2430	#6	G	360	.044		1.65	1.51		3.16	4.40
2600	Dowel sleeves for CIP concrete, 2-part system									
2610	Sleeve base, plastic, for 5/8" smooth dowel sleeve, fasten to edge form	1 Rodm	200	.040	Ea.	.52	1.36		1.88	2.89
2615	Sleeve, plastic, 12" long, for 5/8" smooth dowel, snap onto base		400	.020		1.16	.68		1.84	2.44
2620	Sleeve base, for 3/4" smooth dowel sleeve		175	.046		.52	1.55		2.07	3.23
2625	Sleeve, 12" long, for 3/4" smooth dowel		350	.023		1.30	.78		2.08	2.76
2630	Sleeve base, for 1" smooth dowel sleeve		150	.053		.66	1.81		2.47	3.83
2635	Sleeve, 12" long, for 1" smooth dowel		300	.027		1.37	.91		2.28	3.06
2700	Dowel caps, visual warning only, plastic, #3 to #8	2 Rodm	800	.020		.27	.68		.95	1.46
2720	#8 to #18		750	.021		.68	.72		1.40	1.99
2750	Impalement protective, plastic, #4 to #9		800	.020		1.50	.68		2.18	2.81

03 22 Fabric and Grid Reinforcing

03 22 11 – Plain Welded Wire Fabric Reinforcing

03 22 11.10 Welded Wire Fabric

		Crew	Daily Output	Labor-Hours	Unit	Material	Labor	Equipment	Total	Total Incl O&P
0011	**WELDED WIRE FABRIC**, 6 x 6 - W1.4 x W1.4 (10 x 10)	G 2 Rodm	3500	.005	S.F.	.15	.16		.31	.43
0301	6 x 6 - W2.9 x W2.9 (6 x 6) 42 lb. per C.S.F.	G	2900	.006		.22	.19		.41	.57
0501	4 x 4 - W1.4 x W1.4 (10 x 10) 31 lb. per C.S.F.	G	3100	.005		.20	.18		.38	.52
0750	Rolls									
0901	2 x 2 - #12 galv. for gunite reinforcing	G 2 Rodm	650	.025	S.F.	.63	.84		1.47	2.12

03 22 13 – Galvanized Welded Wire Fabric Reinforcing

03 22 13.10 Galvanized Welded Wire Fabric

		Crew	Daily Output	Labor-Hours	Unit	Material	Labor	Equipment	Total	Total Incl O&P
0010	**GALVANIZED WELDED WIRE FABRIC**									
0100	Add to plain welded wire pricing for galvanized welded wire				Lb.	.23			.23	.25

03 22 16 – Epoxy-Coated Welded Wire Fabric Reinforcing

03 22 16.10 Epoxy-Coated Welded Wire Fabric

		Crew	Daily Output	Labor-Hours	Unit	Material	Labor	Equipment	Total	Total Incl O&P
0010	**EPOXY-COATED WELDED WIRE FABRIC**									
0100	Add to plain welded wire pricing for epoxy-coated welded wire				Lb.	.21			.21	.23

03 23 Stressed Tendon Reinforcing

03 23 05 – Prestressing Tendons

03 23 05.50 Prestressing Steel

	03 23 05.50 Prestressing Steel	Crew	Daily Output	Labor-Hours	Unit	Material	2014 Bare Costs Labor	Equipment	Total	Total Incl O&P
0010	**PRESTRESSING STEEL**									
3000	Slabs on grade, 0.5-inch diam. non-bonded strands, HDPE sheathed,									
3050	attached dead-end anchors, loose stressing-end anchors									
3100	25' x 30' slab, strands @ 36" O.C., placing	2 Rodm	2940	.005	S.F.	.60	.18		.78	.98
3105	Stressing	C-4A	3750	.004			.15	.01	.16	.26
3110	42" O.C., placing	2 Rodm	3200	.005		.53	.17		.70	.88
3115	Stressing	C-4A	4040	.004			.13	.01	.14	.24
3120	48" O.C., placing	2 Rodm	3510	.005		.47	.15		.62	.77
3125	Stressing	C-4A	4390	.004			.12	.01	.13	.22
3150	25' x 40' slab, strands @ 36" O.C., placing	2 Rodm	3370	.005		.58	.16		.74	.92
3155	Stressing	C-4A	4360	.004			.12	.01	.13	.22
3160	42" O.C., placing	2 Rodm	3760	.004		.50	.14		.64	.80
3165	Stressing	C-4A	4820	.003			.11	.01	.12	.20
3170	48" O.C., placing	2 Rodm	4090	.004		.45	.13		.58	.72
3175	Stressing	C-4A	5190	.003			.10	.01	.11	.19
3200	30' x 30' slab, strands @ 36" O.C., placing	2 Rodm	3260	.005		.58	.17		.75	.93
3205	Stressing	C-4A	4190	.004			.13	.01	.14	.23
3210	42" O.C., placing	2 Rodm	3530	.005		.52	.15		.67	.84
3215	Stressing	C-4A	4500	.004			.12	.01	.13	.22
3220	48" O.C., placing	2 Rodm	3840	.004		.47	.14		.61	.75
3225	Stressing	C-4A	4850	.003			.11	.01	.12	.20
3230	30' x 40' slab, strands @ 36" O.C., placing	2 Rodm	3780	.004		.56	.14		.70	.87
3235	Stressing	C-4A	4920	.003			.11	.01	.12	.20
3240	42" O.C., placing	2 Rodm	4190	.004		.49	.13		.62	.76
3245	Stressing	C-4A	5410	.003			.10	.01	.11	.18
3250	48" O.C., placing	2 Rodm	4520	.004		.45	.12		.57	.70
3255	Stressing	C-4A	5790	.003			.09	.01	.10	.17
3260	30' x 50' slab, strands @ 36" O.C., placing	2 Rodm	4300	.004		.53	.13		.66	.81
3265	Stressing	C-4A	5650	.003			.10	.01	.11	.17
3270	42" O.C., placing	2 Rodm	4720	.003		.47	.12		.59	.72
3275	Stressing	C-4A	6150	.003			.09	.01	.10	.16
3280	48" O.C., placing	2 Rodm	5240	.003		.42	.10		.52	.64
3285	Stressing	C-4A	6760	.002			.08	.01	.09	.15

03 24 Fibrous Reinforcing

03 24 05 – Reinforcing Fibers

03 24 05.30 Synthetic Fibers

	03 24 05.30 Synthetic Fibers	Crew	Daily Output	Labor-Hours	Unit	Material	Labor	Equipment	Total	Total Incl O&P
0010	**SYNTHETIC FIBERS**									
0100	Synthetic fibers, add to concrete				Lb.	4.80			4.80	5.30
0110	1-1/2 lb. per C.Y.				C.Y.	7.40			7.40	8.15

03 24 05.70 Steel Fibers

	03 24 05.70 Steel Fibers		Crew	Daily Output	Labor-Hours	Unit	Material	Labor	Equipment	Total	Total Incl O&P
0010	**STEEL FIBERS**										
0140	ASTM A850, Type V, continuously deformed, 1-1/2" long x 0.045" diam.										
0150	Add to price of ready mix concrete	G				Lb.	1.25			1.25	1.38
0205	Alternate pricing, dosing at 5 lb. per C.Y., add to price of RMC	G				C.Y.	6.25			6.25	6.90
0210	10 lb. per C.Y.	G					12.50			12.50	13.75
0215	15 lb. per C.Y.	G					18.75			18.75	20.50
0220	20 lb. per C.Y.	G					25			25	27.50
0225	25 lb. per C.Y.	G					31.50			31.50	34.50
0230	30 lb. per C.Y.	G					37.50			37.50	41.50
0235	35 lb. per C.Y.	G					44			44	48

03 24 Fibrous Reinforcing

03 24 05 – Reinforcing Fibers

03 24 05.70 Steel Fibers		Crew	Daily Output	Labor-Hours	Unit	Material	2014 Bare Costs Labor	Equipment	Total	Total Incl O&P
0240	40 lb. per C.Y.	G			C.Y.	50			50	55
0250	50 lb. per C.Y.	G				62.50			62.50	69
0275	75 lb. per C.Y.	G				94			94	103
0300	100 lb. per C.Y.	G				125			125	138

03 30 Cast-In-Place Concrete

03 30 53 – Miscellaneous Cast-In-Place Concrete

03 30 53.40 Concrete In Place

		Crew	Daily Output	Labor-Hours	Unit	Material	2014 Bare Costs Labor	Equipment	Total	Total Incl O&P
0010	**CONCRETE IN PLACE**									
0020	Including forms (4 uses), Grade 60 rebar, concrete (Portland cement									
0050	Type I), placement and finishing unless otherwise indicated									
0500	Chimney foundations (5000 psi), over 5 C.Y.	C-14C	32.22	3.476	C.Y.	147	104	1.01	252.01	340
0510	(3500 psi), under 5 C.Y.	"	23.71	4.724	"	173	142	1.37	316.37	430
3540	Equipment pad (3000 psi), 3' x 3' x 6" thick	C-14H	45	1.067	Ea.	44.50	33	.74	78.24	105
3550	4' x 4' x 6" thick		30	1.600		66.50	50	1.10	117.60	158
3560	5' x 5' x 8" thick		18	2.667		119	83	1.84	203.84	272
3570	6' x 6' x 8" thick		14	3.429		160	107	2.37	269.37	360
3580	8' x 8' x 10" thick		8	6		335	187	4.14	526.14	690
3590	10' x 10' x 12" thick		5	9.600		575	299	6.60	880.60	1,150
3800	Footings (3000 psi), spread under 1 C.Y.	C-14C	28	4	C.Y.	164	120	1.16	285.16	385
3825	1 C.Y. to 5 C.Y.		43	2.605		198	78.50	.76	277.26	350
3850	Over 5 C.Y.		75	1.493		180	45	.43	225.43	274
3900	Footings, strip (3000 psi), 18" x 9", unreinforced	C-14L	40	2.400		120	70.50	.82	191.32	251
3920	18" x 9", reinforced	C-14C	35	3.200		144	96	.93	240.93	320
3925	20" x 10", unreinforced	C-14L	45	2.133		117	62.50	.73	180.23	234
3930	20" x 10", reinforced	C-14C	40	2.800		136	84	.81	220.81	293
3935	24" x 12", unreinforced	C-14L	55	1.745		116	51.50	.59	168.09	214
3940	24" x 12", reinforced	C-14C	48	2.333		136	70	.68	206.68	268
3945	36" x 12", unreinforced	C-14L	70	1.371		112	40.50	.47	152.97	191
3950	36" x 12", reinforced	C-14C	60	1.867		130	56	.54	186.54	238
4000	Foundation mat (3000 psi), under 10 C.Y.		38.67	2.896		204	87	.84	291.84	370
4050	Over 20 C.Y.		56.40	1.986		178	59.50	.58	238.08	297
4520	Handicap access ramp (4000 psi), railing both sides, 3' wide	C-14H	14.58	3.292	L.F.	315	103	2.27	420.27	525
4525	5' wide		12.22	3.928		330	122	2.71	454.71	570
4530	With 6" curb and rails both sides, 3' wide		8.55	5.614		325	175	3.87	503.87	655
4535	5' wide		7.31	6.566		330	205	4.53	539.53	715
4650	Slab on grade (3500 psi), not including finish, 4" thick	C-14E	60.75	1.449	C.Y.	120	44.50	.55	165.05	208
4700	6" thick	"	92	.957	"	115	29.50	.36	144.86	177
4701	Thickened slab edge (3500 psi), for slab on grade poured									
4702	monolithically with slab; depth is in addition to slab thickness;									
4703	formed vertical outside edge, earthen bottom and inside slope									
4705	8" deep x 8" wide bottom, unreinforced	C-14L	2190	.044	L.F.	3.33	1.29	.01	4.63	5.85
4710	8" x 8", reinforced	C-14C	1670	.067		5.70	2.02	.02	7.74	9.65
4715	12" deep x 12" wide bottom, unreinforced	C-14L	1800	.053		6.75	1.57	.02	8.34	10.10
4720	12" x 12", reinforced	C-14C	1310	.086		11.05	2.57	.02	13.64	16.50
4725	16" deep x 16" wide bottom, unreinforced	C-14L	1440	.067		11.40	1.96	.02	13.38	15.85
4730	16" x 16", reinforced	C-14C	1120	.100		16.50	3.01	.03	19.54	23
4735	20" deep x 20" wide bottom, unreinforced	C-14L	1150	.083		17.25	2.45	.03	19.73	23
4740	20" x 20", reinforced	C-14C	920	.122		24	3.66	.04	27.70	32
4745	24" deep x 24" wide bottom, unreinforced	C-14L	930	.103		24.50	3.04	.04	27.58	32
4750	24" x 24", reinforced	C-14C	740	.151		33	4.55	.04	37.59	43.50

03 30 Cast-In-Place Concrete

03 30 53 – Miscellaneous Cast-In-Place Concrete

03 30 53.40 Concrete In Place

		Crew	Daily Output	Labor-Hours	Unit	Material	2014 Bare Costs Labor	Equipment	Total	Total Incl O&P
4751	Slab on grade (3500 psi), incl. troweled finish, not incl. forms									
4760	or reinforcing, over 10,000 S.F., 4" thick	C-14F	3425	.021	S.F.	1.31	.60	.01	1.92	2.44
4820	6" thick	"	3350	.021	"	1.91	.62	.01	2.54	3.12
5000	Slab on grade (3000 psi), incl. broom finish, not incl. forms									
5001	or reinforcing, 4" thick	C-14G	2873	.019	S.F.	1.29	.55	.01	1.85	2.32
5010	6" thick		2590	.022		2.01	.61	.01	2.63	3.22
5020	8" thick		2320	.024		2.62	.68	.01	3.31	4.02
6800	Stairs (3500 psi), not including safety treads, free standing, 3'-6" wide	C-14H	83	.578	LF Nose	5.40	18	.40	23.80	36.50
6850	Cast on ground		125	.384	"	4.49	11.95	.27	16.71	25
7000	Stair landings, free standing		200	.240	S.F.	4.39	7.50	.17	12.06	17.55
7050	Cast on ground		475	.101	"	3.45	3.15	.07	6.67	9.15

03 31 Structural Concrete

03 31 13 – Heavyweight Structural Concrete

03 31 13.25 Concrete, Hand Mix

		Crew	Daily Output	Labor-Hours	Unit	Material	2014 Bare Costs Labor	Equipment	Total	Total Incl O&P
0010	**CONCRETE, HAND MIX** for small quantities or remote areas									
0050	Includes bulk local aggregate, bulk sand, bagged Portland									
0060	cement (Type I) and water, using gas powered cement mixer									
0125	2500 psi	C-30	135	.059	C.F.	3.14	1.41	1.31	5.86	7.25
0130	3000 psi		135	.059		3.37	1.41	1.31	6.09	7.50
0135	3500 psi		135	.059		3.50	1.41	1.31	6.22	7.65
0140	4000 psi		135	.059		3.66	1.41	1.31	6.38	7.85
0145	4500 psi		135	.059		3.83	1.41	1.31	6.55	8
0150	5000 psi		135	.059		4.09	1.41	1.31	6.81	8.30
0300	Using pre-bagged dry mix and wheelbarrow (80-lb. bag = 0.6 C.F.)									
0340	4000 psi	1 Clab	48	.167	C.F.	6.25	3.97		10.22	13.60

03 31 13.30 Concrete, Volumetric Site-Mixed

		Crew	Daily Output	Labor-Hours	Unit	Material	2014 Bare Costs Labor	Equipment	Total	Total Incl O&P
0010	**CONCRETE, VOLUMETRIC SITE-MIXED**									
0015	Mixed on-site in volumetric truck									
0020	Includes local aggregate, sand, Portland cement (Type I) and water									
0025	Excludes all additives and treatments									
0100	3000 psi, 1 C.Y. mixed and discharged				C.Y.	159			159	175
0110	2 C.Y.					136			136	150
0120	3 C.Y.					122			122	134
0130	4 C.Y.					114			114	125
0140	5 C.Y.					106			106	116
0200	For truck holding/waiting time past first 2 on-site hours, add				Hr.	72			72	79
0210	For trip charge beyond first 20 miles, each way, add				Mile	2.25			2.25	2.48
0220	For each additional increase of 500 psi, add				Ea.	4.17			4.17	4.59

03 31 13.35 Heavyweight Concrete, Ready Mix

		Crew	Daily Output	Labor-Hours	Unit	Material	2014 Bare Costs Labor	Equipment	Total	Total Incl O&P
0010	**HEAVYWEIGHT CONCRETE, READY MIX,** delivered									
0012	Includes local aggregate, sand, Portland cement (Type I) and water									
0015	Excludes all additives and treatments									
0020	2000 psi				C.Y.	93			93	102
0100	2500 psi					95.50			95.50	105
0150	3000 psi					99			99	109
0200	3500 psi					101			101	111
0300	4000 psi					104			104	114
0350	4500 psi					107			107	117
0400	5000 psi					110			110	121

03 31 Structural Concrete

03 31 13 – Heavyweight Structural Concrete

03 31 13.35 Heavyweight Concrete, Ready Mix

		Crew	Daily Output	Labor-Hours	Unit	Material	2014 Bare Costs Labor	Equipment	Total	Total Incl O&P
0411	6000 psi				C.Y.	113			113	124
0412	8000 psi					119			119	130
0413	10,000 psi					125			125	137
0414	12,000 psi					131			131	144
1000	For high early strength (Portland cement Type III), add					10%				
1300	For winter concrete (hot water), add					4.50			4.50	4.95
1400	For hot weather concrete (ice), add					7.65			7.65	8.40
1410	For mid-range water reducer, add					3.69			3.69	4.06
1420	For high-range water reducer/superplasticizer, add					5.70			5.70	6.30
1430	For retarder, add					3.06			3.06	3.37
1440	For non-Chloride accelerator, add					5.65			5.65	6.20
1450	For Chloride accelerator, per 1%, add					3.32			3.32	3.65
1460	For fiber reinforcing, synthetic (1 lb./C.Y.), add					6.95			6.95	7.60
1500	For Saturday delivery, add					4.93			4.93	5.40
1510	For truck holding/waiting time past 1st hour per load, add				Hr.	97			97	107
1520	For short load (less than 4 C.Y.), add per load				Ea.	77.50			77.50	85
2000	For all lightweight aggregate, add				C.Y.	45%				

03 31 13.70 Placing Concrete

		Crew	Daily Output	Labor-Hours	Unit	Material	2014 Bare Costs Labor	Equipment	Total	Total Incl O&P
0010	**PLACING CONCRETE**									
0020	Includes labor and equipment to place, level (strike off) and consolidate									
1900	Footings, continuous, shallow, direct chute	C-6	120	.400	C.Y.		10.10	.55	10.65	17.50
1950	Pumped	C-20	150	.427			11.15	5.20	16.35	24.50
2000	With crane and bucket	C-7	90	.800			21.50	13.60	35.10	50.50
2400	Footings, spread, under 1 C.Y., direct chute	C-6	55	.873			22	1.20	23.20	38.50
2600	Over 5 C.Y., direct chute		120	.400			10.10	.55	10.65	17.50
2900	Foundation mats, over 20 C.Y., direct chute		350	.137			3.47	.19	3.66	6
4300	Slab on grade, up to 6" thick, direct chute		110	.436			11.05	.60	11.65	19.10
4350	Pumped	C-20	130	.492			12.90	5.95	18.85	28
4400	With crane and bucket	C-7	110	.655			17.40	11.15	28.55	41.50
4900	Walls, 8" thick, direct chute	C-6	90	.533			13.50	.74	14.24	23.50
4950	Pumped	C-20	100	.640			16.75	7.75	24.50	36.50
5000	With crane and bucket	C-7	80	.900			24	15.35	39.35	57
5050	12" thick, direct chute	C-6	100	.480			12.15	.66	12.81	21
5100	Pumped	C-20	110	.582			15.25	7.05	22.30	33.50
5200	With crane and bucket	C-7	90	.800			21.50	13.60	35.10	50.50
5600	Wheeled concrete dumping, add to placing costs above									
5610	Walking cart, 50' haul, add	C-18	32	.281	C.Y.		6.75	1.88	8.63	13.40
5620	150' haul, add		24	.375			9	2.51	11.51	17.90
5700	250' haul, add		18	.500			12	3.35	15.35	23.50
5800	Riding cart, 50' haul, add	C-19	80	.113			2.70	1.26	3.96	5.95
5810	150' haul, add		60	.150			3.60	1.69	5.29	7.90
5900	250' haul, add		45	.200			4.80	2.25	7.05	10.55

03 35 Concrete Finishing

03 35 13 – High-Tolerance Concrete Floor Finishing

03 35 13.30 Finishing Floors, High Tolerance

		Crew	Daily Output	Labor-Hours	Unit	Material	2014 Bare Costs Labor	Equipment	Total	Total Incl O&P
0010	**FINISHING FLOORS, HIGH TOLERANCE**									
0012	Finishing requires that concrete first be placed, struck off & consolidated									
0015	Basic finishing for various unspecified flatwork									
0100	Bull float only	C-10	4000	.006	S.F.		.17		.17	.28
0125	Bull float & manual float		2000	.012			.34		.34	.56
0150	Bull float, manual float, & broom finish, w/edging & joints		1850	.013			.37		.37	.60
0200	Bull float, manual float & manual steel trowel		1265	.019			.54		.54	.88
0210	For specified Random Access Floors in ACI Classes 1, 2, 3 and 4 to achieve									
0215	Composite Overall Floor Flatness and Levelness values up to FF35/FL25									
0250	Bull float, machine float & machine trowel (walk-behind)	C-10C	1715	.014	S.F.		.40	.03	.43	.68
0300	Power screed, bull float, machine float & trowel (walk-behind)	C-10D	2400	.010			.29	.05	.34	.52
0350	Power screed, bull float, machine float & trowel (ride-on)	C-10E	4000	.006			.17	.07	.24	.35

03 35 23 – Exposed Aggregate Concrete Finishing

03 35 23.30 Finishing Floors, Exposed Aggregate

		Crew	Daily Output	Labor-Hours	Unit	Material	Labor	Equipment	Total	Total Incl O&P
0010	**FINISHING FLOORS, EXPOSED AGGREGATE**									
1600	Exposed local aggregate finish, 3 lb. per S.F.	1 Cefi	625	.013	S.F.	.43	.39		.82	1.11
1650	4 lb. per S.F.	"	465	.017	"	.81	.53		1.34	1.75

03 35 29 – Tooled Concrete Finishing

03 35 29.30 Finishing Floors, Tooled

		Crew	Daily Output	Labor-Hours	Unit	Material	Labor	Equipment	Total	Total Incl O&P
0010	**FINISHING FLOORS, TOOLED**									
4400	Stair finish, float	1 Cefi	275	.029	S.F.		.90		.90	1.45
4500	Steel trowel finish	"	200	.040	"		1.23		1.23	2

03 35 29.60 Finishing Walls

		Crew	Daily Output	Labor-Hours	Unit	Material	Labor	Equipment	Total	Total Incl O&P
0010	**FINISHING WALLS**									
0020	Break ties and patch voids	1 Cefi	540	.015	S.F.	.04	.46		.50	.78
0050	Burlap rub with grout	"	450	.018		.04	.55		.59	.93
0300	Bush hammer, green concrete	B-39	1000	.048			1.16	.23	1.39	2.21
0350	Cured concrete	"	650	.074			1.78	.36	2.14	3.40
0500	Acid etch	1 Cefi	575	.014		.14	.43		.57	.84
0850	Grind form fins flush	1 Clab	700	.011	L.F.		.27		.27	.46

03 35 33 – Stamped Concrete Finishing

03 35 33.50 Slab Texture Stamping

		Crew	Daily Output	Labor-Hours	Unit	Material	Labor	Equipment	Total	Total Incl O&P
0010	**SLAB TEXTURE STAMPING**									
0050	Stamping requires that concrete first be placed, struck off, consolidated,									
0060	bull floated and free of bleed water. Decorative stamping tasks include:									
0100	Step 1 - first application of dry shake colored hardener	1 Cefi	6400	.001	S.F.	.43	.04		.47	.53
0110	Step 2 - bull float		6400	.001			.04		.04	.06
0130	Step 3 - second application of dry shake colored hardener		6400	.001		.21	.04		.25	.29
0140	Step 4 - bull float, manual float & steel trowel	3 Cefi	1280	.019			.58		.58	.94
0150	Step 5 - application of dry shake colored release agent	1 Cefi	6400	.001		.10	.04		.14	.17
0160	Step 6 - place, tamp & remove mats	3 Cefi	2400	.010		1.43	.31		1.74	2.08
0170	Step 7 - touch up edges, mat joints & simulated grout lines	1 Cefi	1280	.006			.19		.19	.31
0300	Alternate stamping estimating method includes all tasks above	4 Cefi	800	.040		2.17	1.23		3.40	4.38
0400	Step 8 - pressure wash @ 3000 psi after 24 hours	1 Cefi	1600	.005			.15		.15	.25
0500	Step 9 - roll 2 coats cure/seal compound when dry	"	800	.010		.59	.31		.90	1.15

03 39 Concrete Curing

03 39 13 – Water Concrete Curing

03 39 13.50 Water Curing

		Crew	Daily Output	Labor-Hours	Unit	Material	2014 Bare Costs Labor	Equipment	Total	Total Incl O&P
0011	**WATER CURING**									
0020	With burlap, 4 uses assumed, 7.5 oz.	2 Clab	5500	.003	S.F.	.15	.07		.22	.28
0101	·10 oz.	"	5500	.003	"	.26	.07		.33	.41

03 39 23 – Membrane Concrete Curing

03 39 23.13 Chemical Compound Membrane Concrete Curing

		Crew	Daily Output	Labor-Hours	Unit	Material	2014 Bare Costs Labor	Equipment	Total	Total Incl O&P
0010	**CHEMICAL COMPOUND MEMBRANE CONCRETE CURING**									
0301	Sprayed membrane curing compound	2 Clab	9500	.002	S.F.	.11	.04		.15	.19

03 39 23.23 Sheet Membrane Concrete Curing

		Crew	Daily Output	Labor-Hours	Unit	Material	2014 Bare Costs Labor	Equipment	Total	Total Incl O&P
0010	**SHEET MEMBRANE CONCRETE CURING**									
0201	Curing blanket, burlap/poly, 2-ply	2 Clab	7000	.002	S.F.	.19	.05		.24	.30

03 41 Precast Structural Concrete

03 41 23 – Precast Concrete Stairs

03 41 23.50 Precast Stairs

		Crew	Daily Output	Labor-Hours	Unit	Material	2014 Bare Costs Labor	Equipment	Total	Total Incl O&P
0010	**PRECAST STAIRS**									
0020	Precast concrete treads on steel stringers, 3' wide	C-12	75	.640	Riser	134	20	8.85	162.85	191
0300	Front entrance, 5' wide with 48" platform, 2 risers		16	3	Flight	485	94.50	41.50	621	735
0350	5 risers		12	4		765	126	55	946	1,100
0500	6' wide, 2 risers		15	3.200		535	101	44	680	810
0550	5 risers		11	4.364		845	137	60.50	1,042.50	1,225
0700	7' wide, 2 risers		14	3.429		685	108	47.50	840.50	985
1200	Basement entrance stairwell, 6 steps, incl. steel bulkhead door	B-51	22	2.182		1,450	53.50	12.30	1,515.80	1,675
1250	14 steps	"	11	4.364		2,400	107	24.50	2,531.50	2,825

03 48 Precast Concrete Specialties

03 48 43 – Precast Concrete Trim

03 48 43.40 Precast Lintels

		Crew	Daily Output	Labor-Hours	Unit	Material	2014 Bare Costs Labor	Equipment	Total	Total Incl O&P
0010	**PRECAST LINTELS**, smooth gray, prestressed, stock units only									
0800	4" wide, 8" high, x 4' long	D-10	28	1.143	Ea.	23.50	36	17.20	76.70	105
0850	8' long		24	1.333		57	42	20	119	155
1000	6" wide, 8" high, x 4' long		26	1.231		33.50	39	18.50	91	122
1050	10' long		22	1.455		86	46	22	154	195

03 48 43.90 Precast Window Sills

		Crew	Daily Output	Labor-Hours	Unit	Material	2014 Bare Costs Labor	Equipment	Total	Total Incl O&P
0010	**PRECAST WINDOW SILLS**									
0600	Precast concrete, 4" tapers to 3", 9" wide	D-1	70	.229	L.F.	11.90	6.60		18.50	24
0650	11" wide		60	.267		15.55	7.70		23.25	30
0700	13" wide, 3 1/2" tapers to 2 1/2", 12" wall		50	.320		15.50	9.25		24.75	32.50

03 54 Cast Underlayment

03 54 13 – Gypsum Cement Underlayment

03 54 13.50 Poured Gypsum Underlayment	Crew	Daily Output	Labor-Hours	Unit	Material	2014 Bare Costs Labor	Equipment	Total	Total Incl O&P
0010 **POURED GYPSUM UNDERLAYMENT**									
0400 Underlayment, gypsum based, self-leveling 2500 psi, pumped, 1/2" thick	C-8	24000	.002	S.F.	.33	.06	.03	.42	.51
0500 3/4" thick		20000	.003		.50	.08	.04	.62	.72
0600 1" thick		16000	.004		.67	.10	.04	.81	.95
1400 Hand placed, 1/2" thick	C-18	450	.020		.33	.48	.13	.94	1.33
1500 3/4" thick	"	300	.030		.50	.72	.20	1.42	1.98

03 63 Epoxy Grouting

03 63 05 – Grouting of Dowels and Fasteners

03 63 05.10 Epoxy Only

	Crew	Daily Output	Labor-Hours	Unit	Material	2014 Bare Costs Labor	Equipment	Total	Total Incl O&P
0010 **EPOXY ONLY**									
1500 Chemical anchoring, epoxy cartridge, excludes layout, drilling, fastener									
1530 For fastener 3/4" diam. x 6" embedment	2 Skwk	72	.222	Ea.	5.55	7.20		12.75	18.30
1535 1" diam. x 8" embedment		66	.242		8.30	7.85		16.15	22.50
1540 1-1/4" diam. x 10" embedment		60	.267		16.60	8.65		25.25	33
1545 1-3/4" diam. x 12" embedment		54	.296		27.50	9.60		37.10	47
1550 14" embedment		48	.333		33	10.80		43.80	55
1555 2" diam. x 12" embedment		42	.381		44.50	12.35		56.85	69.50
1560 18" embedment		32	.500		55.50	16.25		71.75	88.50

03 82 Concrete Boring

03 82 16 – Concrete Drilling

03 82 16.10 Concrete Impact Drilling

	Crew	Daily Output	Labor-Hours	Unit	Material	2014 Bare Costs Labor	Equipment	Total	Total Incl O&P
0010 **CONCRETE IMPACT DRILLING**									
0020 Includes bit cost, layout and set-up time, no anchors									
0050 Up to 4" deep in concrete/brick floors/walls									
0100 Holes, 1/4" diameter	1 Carp	75	.107	Ea.	.06	3.42		3.48	5.80
0150 For each additional inch of depth in same hole, add		430	.019		.02	.60		.62	1.02
0200 3/8" diameter		63	.127		.05	4.08		4.13	6.90
0250 For each additional inch of depth in same hole, add		340	.024		.01	.76		.77	1.28
0300 1/2" diameter		50	.160		.05	5.15		5.20	8.70
0350 For each additional inch of depth in same hole, add		250	.032		.01	1.03		1.04	1.74
0400 5/8" diameter		48	.167		.08	5.35		5.43	9.10
0450 For each additional inch of depth in same hole, add		240	.033		.02	1.07		1.09	1.82
0500 3/4" diameter		45	.178		.11	5.70		5.81	9.70
0550 For each additional inch of depth in same hole, add		220	.036		.03	1.17		1.20	1.99
0600 7/8" diameter		43	.186		.15	5.95		6.10	10.20
0650 For each additional inch of depth in same hole, add		210	.038		.04	1.22		1.26	2.10
0700 1" diameter		40	.200		.16	6.40		6.56	11
0750 For each additional inch of depth in same hole, add		190	.042		.04	1.35		1.39	2.31
0800 1-1/4" diameter		38	.211		.23	6.75		6.98	11.60
0850 For each additional inch of depth in same hole, add		180	.044		.06	1.43		1.49	2.46
0900 1-1/2" diameter		35	.229		.32	7.35		7.67	12.70
0950 For each additional inch of depth in same hole, add		165	.048		.08	1.56		1.64	2.71
1000 For ceiling installations, add						40%			

Division Notes

		CREW	DAILY OUTPUT	LABOR-HOURS	UNIT	BARE COSTS				TOTAL INCL O&P
						MAT.	LABOR	EQUIP.	TOTAL	

Estimating Tips

04 05 00 Common Work Results for Masonry

- The terms *mortar* and *grout* are often used interchangeably, and incorrectly. Mortar is used to bed masonry units, seal the entry of air and moisture, provide architectural appearance, and allow for size variations in the units. Grout is used primarily in reinforced masonry construction and is used to bond the masonry to the reinforcing steel. Common mortar types are M(2500 psi), S(1800 psi), N(750 psi), and O(350 psi), and conform to ASTM C270. Grout is either fine or coarse and conforms to ASTM C476, and in-place strengths generally exceed 2500 psi. Mortar and grout are different components of masonry construction and are placed by entirely different methods. An estimator should be aware of their unique uses and costs.

- Mortar is included in all assembled masonry line items. The mortar cost, part of the assembled masonry material cost, includes all ingredients, all labor, and all equipment required. Please see reference number R040513-10.

- Waste, specifically the loss/ droppings of mortar and the breakage of brick and block, is included in all masonry assemblies in this division. A factor of 25% is added for mortar and 3% for brick and concrete masonry units.

- Scaffolding or staging is not included in any of the Division 4 costs. Refer to Subdivision 01 54 23 for scaffolding and staging costs.

04 20 00 Unit Masonry

- The most common types of unit masonry are brick and concrete masonry. The major classifications of brick are building brick (ASTM C62), facing brick (ASTM C216), glazed brick, fire brick, and pavers. Many varieties of texture and appearance can exist within these classifications, and the estimator would be wise to check local custom and availability within the project area. For repair and remodeling jobs, matching the existing brick may be the most important criteria.

- Brick and concrete block are priced by the piece and then converted into a price per square foot of wall. Openings less than two square feet are generally ignored by the estimator because any savings in units used is offset by the cutting and trimming required.

- It is often difficult and expensive to find and purchase small lots of historic brick. Costs can vary widely. Many design issues affect costs, selection of mortar mix, and repairs or replacement of masonry materials. Cleaning techniques must be reflected in the estimate.

- All masonry walls, whether interior or exterior, require bracing. The cost of bracing walls during construction should be included by the estimator, and this bracing must remain in place until permanent bracing is complete. Permanent bracing of masonry walls is accomplished by masonry itself, in the form of pilasters or abutting wall corners, or by anchoring the walls to the structural frame. Accessories in the form of anchors, anchor slots, and ties are used, but their supply and installation can be by different trades. For instance, anchor slots on spandrel beams and columns are supplied and welded in place by the steel fabricator, but the ties from the slots into the masonry are installed by the bricklayer. Regardless of the installation method, the estimator must be certain that these accessories are accounted for in pricing.

Reference Numbers

Reference numbers are shown in shaded boxes at the beginning of some major classifications. These numbers refer to related items in the Reference Section. The reference information may be an estimating procedure, an alternate pricing method, or technical information.
Note: Not all subdivisions listed here necessarily appear in this publication.

04 01 20 – Maintenance of Unit Masonry

04 01 20.20 Pointing Masonry

		Crew	Daily Output	Labor-Hours	Unit	Material	2014 Bare Costs Labor	Equipment	Total	Total Incl O&P
0010	**POINTING MASONRY**									
0300	Cut and repoint brick, hard mortar, running bond	1 Bric	80	.100	S.F.	.51	3.19		3.70	5.85
0320	Common bond		77	.104		.51	3.31		3.82	6.05
0360	Flemish bond		70	.114		.54	3.65		4.19	6.65
0400	English bond		65	.123		.54	3.93		4.47	7.15
0600	Soft old mortar, running bond		100	.080		.51	2.55		3.06	4.81
0620	Common bond		96	.083		.51	2.66		3.17	4.98
0640	Flemish bond		90	.089		.54	2.84		3.38	5.30
0680	English bond		82	.098		.54	3.11		3.65	5.80
0700	Stonework, hard mortar		140	.057	L.F.	.68	1.82		2.50	3.78
0720	Soft old mortar		160	.050	"	.68	1.60		2.28	3.41
1000	Repoint, mask and grout method, running bond		95	.084	S.F.	.68	2.69		3.37	5.20
1020	Common bond		90	.089		.68	2.84		3.52	5.45
1040	Flemish bond		86	.093		.72	2.97		3.69	5.75
1060	English bond		77	.104		.72	3.31		4.03	6.30
2000	Scrub coat, sand grout on walls, thin mix, brushed		120	.067		2.72	2.13		4.85	6.55
2020	Troweled		98	.082		3.79	2.60		6.39	8.50

04 01 20.30 Pointing CMU

		Crew	Daily Output	Labor-Hours	Unit	Material	2014 Bare Costs Labor	Equipment	Total	Total Incl O&P
0010	**POINTING CMU**									
0300	Cut and repoint block, hard mortar, running bond	1 Bric	190	.042	S.F.	.21	1.34		1.55	2.47
0310	Stacked bond		200	.040		.21	1.28		1.49	2.35
0600	Soft old mortar, running bond		230	.035		.21	1.11		1.32	2.08
0610	Stacked bond		245	.033		.21	1.04		1.25	1.96

04 01 30 – Unit Masonry Cleaning

04 01 30.60 Brick Washing

		Crew	Daily Output	Labor-Hours	Unit	Material	2014 Bare Costs Labor	Equipment	Total	Total Incl O&P
0010	**BRICK WASHING**	R040130-10								
0012	Acid cleanser, smooth brick surface	1 Bric	560	.014	S.F.	.06	.46		.52	.83
0050	Rough brick		400	.020		.09	.64		.73	1.16
0060	Stone, acid wash		600	.013		.10	.43		.53	.82
1000	Muriatic acid, price per gallon in 5 gallon lots				Gal.	13			13	14.30

04 05 05 – Selective Masonry Demolition

04 05 05.10 Selective Demolition

		Crew	Daily Output	Labor-Hours	Unit	Material	2014 Bare Costs Labor	Equipment	Total	Total Incl O&P
0010	**SELECTIVE DEMOLITION**	R024119-10								
0200	Bond beams, 8" block with #4 bar	2 Clab	32	.500	L.F.		11.90		11.90	20
0300	Concrete block walls, unreinforced, 2" thick		1200	.013	S.F.		.32		.32	.53
0310	4" thick		1150	.014			.33		.33	.56
0320	6" thick		1100	.015			.35		.35	.58
0330	8" thick		1050	.015			.36		.36	.61
0340	10" thick		1000	.016			.38		.38	.64
0360	12" thick		950	.017			.40		.40	.67
0380	Reinforced alternate courses, 2" thick		1130	.014			.34		.34	.57
0390	4" thick		1080	.015			.35		.35	.59
0400	6" thick		1035	.015			.37		.37	.62
0410	8" thick		990	.016			.38		.38	.65
0420	10" thick		940	.017			.41		.41	.68
0430	12" thick		890	.018			.43		.43	.72
0440	Reinforced alternate courses & vertically 48" OC, 4" thick		900	.018			.42		.42	.71
0450	6" thick		850	.019			.45		.45	.75

04 05 Common Work Results for Masonry

04 05 05 – Selective Masonry Demolition

04 05 05.10 Selective Demolition	Crew	Daily Output	Labor-Hours	Unit	Material	2014 Bare Costs Labor	Equipment	Total	Total Incl O&P
0460	8" thick	2 Clab	800	.020	S.F.		.48		.48	.80
0480	10" thick		750	.021			.51		.51	.85
0490	12" thick	▼	700	.023	▼		.54		.54	.92
1000	Chimney, 16" x 16", soft old mortar	1 Clab	55	.145	C.F.		3.46		3.46	5.85
1020	Hard mortar		40	.200			4.76		4.76	8
1030	16" x 20", soft old mortar		55	.145			3.46		3.46	5.85
1040	Hard mortar		40	.200			4.76		4.76	8
1050	16" x 24", soft old mortar		55	.145			3.46		3.46	5.85
1060	Hard mortar		40	.200			4.76		4.76	8
1080	20" x 20", soft old mortar		55	.145			3.46		3.46	5.85
1100	Hard mortar		40	.200			4.76		4.76	8
1110	20" x 24", soft old mortar		55	.145			3.46		3.46	5.85
1120	Hard mortar		40	.200			4.76		4.76	8
1140	20" x 32", soft old mortar		55	.145			3.46		3.46	5.85
1160	Hard mortar		40	.200			4.76		4.76	8
1200	48" x 48", soft old mortar		55	.145			3.46		3.46	5.85
1220	Hard mortar	▼	40	.200	▼		4.76		4.76	8
1250	Metal, high temp steel jacket, 24" diameter	E-2	130	.369	V.L.F.		12.80	11.75	24.55	37
1260	60" diameter	"	60	.800			27.50	25.50	53	79.50
1280	Flue lining, up to 12" x 12"	1 Clab	200	.040			.95		.95	1.60
1282	Up to 24" x 24"		150	.053			1.27		1.27	2.14
2000	Columns, 8" x 8", soft old mortar		48	.167			3.97		3.97	6.70
2020	Hard mortar		40	.200			4.76		4.76	8
2060	16" x 16", soft old mortar		16	.500			11.90		11.90	20
2100	Hard mortar		14	.571			13.60		13.60	23
2140	24" x 24", soft old mortar		8	1			24		24	40
2160	Hard mortar		6	1.333			31.50		31.50	53.50
2200	36" x 36", soft old mortar		4	2			47.50		47.50	80
2220	Hard mortar		3	2.667	▼		63.50		63.50	107
2230	Alternate pricing method, soft old mortar		30	.267	C.F.		6.35		6.35	10.70
2240	Hard mortar	▼	23	.348	"		8.30		8.30	13.95
3000	Copings, precast or masonry, to 8" wide									
3020	Soft old mortar	1 Clab	180	.044	L.F.		1.06		1.06	1.78
3040	Hard mortar	"	160	.050	"		1.19		1.19	2
3100	To 12" wide									
3120	Soft old mortar	1 Clab	160	.050	L.F.		1.19		1.19	2
3140	Hard mortar	"	140	.057	"		1.36		1.36	2.29
4000	Fireplace, brick, 30" x 24" opening									
4020	Soft old mortar	1 Clab	2	4	Ea.		95		95	160
4040	Hard mortar		1.25	6.400			152		152	256
4100	Stone, soft old mortar		1.50	5.333			127		127	214
4120	Hard mortar		1	8	▼		190		190	320
5000	Veneers, brick, soft old mortar		140	.057	S.F.		1.36		1.36	2.29
5020	Hard mortar		125	.064			1.52		1.52	2.56
5050	Glass block, up to 4" thick		500	.016			.38		.38	.64
5100	Granite and marble, 2" thick		180	.044			1.06		1.06	1.78
5120	4" thick		170	.047			1.12		1.12	1.88
5140	Stone, 4" thick		180	.044			1.06		1.06	1.78
5160	8" thick		175	.046	▼		1.09		1.09	1.83
5400	Alternate pricing method, stone, 4" thick		60	.133	C.F.		3.17		3.17	5.35
5420	8" thick	▼	85	.094	"		2.24		2.24	3.77

04 05 Common Work Results for Masonry

04 05 13 – Masonry Mortaring

04 05 13.10 Cement

04 05 13.10 Cement	Crew	Daily Output	Labor-Hours	Unit	Material	2014 Bare Costs Labor	Equipment	Total	Total Incl O&P
0010 **CEMENT** R040513-10									
0100 Masonry, 70 lb. bag, T.L. lots				Bag	11.05			11.05	12.15
0150 L.T.L. lots					11.70			11.70	12.90
0200 White, 70 lb. bag, T.L. lots					15.65			15.65	17.25
0250 L.T.L. lots					18.30			18.30	20

04 05 16 – Masonry Grouting

04 05 16.30 Grouting

04 05 16.30 Grouting	Crew	Daily Output	Labor-Hours	Unit	Material	2014 Bare Costs Labor	Equipment	Total	Total Incl O&P
0010 **GROUTING**									
0011 Bond beams & lintels, 8" deep, 6" thick, 0.15 C.F. per L.F.	D-4	1480	.027	L.F.	.66	.72	.09	1.47	2.02
0020 8" thick, 0.2 C.F. per L.F.		1400	.029		1.04	.76	.10	1.90	2.52
0050 10" thick, 0.25 C.F. per L.F.		1200	.033		1.09	.89	.11	2.09	2.80
0060 12" thick, 0.3 C.F. per L.F.		1040	.038		1.31	1.03	.13	2.47	3.29
0200 Concrete block cores, solid, 4" thk., by hand, 0.067 C.F./S.F. of wall	D-8	1100	.036	S.F.	.29	1.07		1.36	2.11
0210 6" thick, pumped, 0.175 C.F. per S.F.	D-4	720	.056		.76	1.48	.19	2.43	3.52
0250 8" thick, pumped, 0.258 C.F. per S.F.		680	.059		1.13	1.57	.20	2.90	4.08
0300 10" thick, pumped, 0.340 C.F. per S.F.		660	.061		1.49	1.62	.20	3.31	4.55
0350 12" thick, pumped, 0.422 C.F. per S.F.		640	.063		1.84	1.67	.21	3.72	5.05

04 05 19 – Masonry Anchorage and Reinforcing

04 05 19.05 Anchor Bolts

04 05 19.05 Anchor Bolts	Crew	Daily Output	Labor-Hours	Unit	Material	2014 Bare Costs Labor	Equipment	Total	Total Incl O&P
0010 **ANCHOR BOLTS**									
0015 Installed in fresh grout in CMU bond beams or filled cores, no templates									
0020 Hooked, with nut and washer, 1/2" diam., 8" long	1 Bric	132	.061	Ea.	1.49	1.93		3.42	4.86
0030 12" long		131	.061		1.66	1.95		3.61	5.05
0040 5/8" diameter, 8" long		129	.062		3.25	1.98		5.23	6.85
0050 12" long		127	.063		4	2.01		6.01	7.75
0060 3/4" diameter, 8" long		127	.063		4	2.01		6.01	7.75
0070 12" long		125	.064		5	2.04		7.04	8.90

04 05 19.16 Masonry Anchors

04 05 19.16 Masonry Anchors	Crew	Daily Output	Labor-Hours	Unit	Material	2014 Bare Costs Labor	Equipment	Total	Total Incl O&P
0010 **MASONRY ANCHORS**									
0020 For brick veneer, galv., corrugated, 7/8" x 7", 22 Ga.	1 Bric	10.50	.762	C	13.45	24.50		37.95	55.50
0100 24 Ga.		10.50	.762		9.50	24.50		34	51
0150 16 Ga.		10.50	.762		26.50	24.50		51	69.50
0200 Buck anchors, galv., corrugated, 16 ga., 2" bend, 8" x 2"		10.50	.762		49	24.50		73.50	94.50
0250 8" x 3"		10.50	.762		51	24.50		75.50	96.50
0660 Cavity wall, Z-type, galvanized, 6" long, 1/8" diam.		10.50	.762		23.50	24.50		48	66.50
0670 3/16" diameter		10.50	.762		27	24.50		51.50	70
0680 1/4" diameter		10.50	.762		40.50	24.50		65	85
0850 8" long, 3/16" diameter		10.50	.762		25	24.50		49.50	68
0855 1/4" diameter		10.50	.762		48.50	24.50		73	94
1000 Rectangular type, galvanized, 1/4" diameter, 2" x 6"		10.50	.762		70	24.50		94.50	118
1050 4" x 6"		10.50	.762		85	24.50		109.50	134
1100 3/16" diameter, 2" x 6"		10.50	.762		42	24.50		66.50	87
1150 4" x 6"		10.50	.762		48.50	24.50		73	93.50
1500 Rigid partition anchors, plain, 8" long, 1" x 1/8"		10.50	.762		235	24.50		259.50	300
1550 1" x 1/4"		10.50	.762		277	24.50		301.50	345
1580 1-1/2" x 1/8"		10.50	.762		259	24.50		283.50	325
1600 1-1/2" x 1/4"		10.50	.762		325	24.50		349.50	395
1650 2" x 1/8"		10.50	.762		305	24.50		329.50	375
1700 2" x 1/4"		10.50	.762		405	24.50		429.50	485

04 05 Common Work Results for Masonry

04 05 19 – Masonry Anchorage and Reinforcing

04 05 19.26 Masonry Reinforcing Bars

		Crew	Daily Output	Labor-Hours	Unit	Material	2014 Bare Costs Labor	Equipment	Total	Total Incl O&P
0010	**MASONRY REINFORCING BARS** R040519-50									
0015	Steel bars A615, placed horiz., #3 & #4 bars	1 Bric	450	.018	Lb.	.50	.57		1.07	1.49
0050	Placed vertical, #3 & #4 bars		350	.023		.50	.73		1.23	1.76
0060	#5 & #6 bars		650	.012		.50	.39		.89	1.20
0200	Joint reinforcing, regular truss, to 6" wide, mill std galvanized		30	.267	C.L.F.	21	8.50		29.50	37
0250	12" wide		20	.400		24.50	12.75		37.25	48
0400	Cavity truss with drip section, to 6" wide		30	.267		22.50	8.50		31	38.50
0450	12" wide		20	.400		26	12.75		38.75	49.50

04 21 Clay Unit Masonry

04 21 13 – Brick Masonry

04 21 13.13 Brick Veneer Masonry

		Crew	Daily Output	Labor-Hours	Unit	Material	2014 Bare Costs Labor	Equipment	Total	Total Incl O&P
0010	**BRICK VENEER MASONRY**, T.L. lots, excl. scaff., grout & reinforcing									
0015	Material costs incl. 3% brick and 25% mortar waste R042110-10									
2000	Standard, sel. common, 4" x 2-2/3" x 8", (6.75/S.F.) R042110-20	D-8	230	.174	S.F.	4.43	5.15		9.58	13.45
2020	Red, 4" x 2-2/3" x 8", running bond		220	.182		4	5.35		9.35	13.35
2050	Full header every 6th course (7.88/S.F.) R042110-50		185	.216		4.66	6.40		11.06	15.70
2100	English, full header every 2nd course (10.13/S.F.)		140	.286		5.95	8.45		14.40	20.50
2150	Flemish, alternate header every course (9.00/S.F.)		150	.267		5.30	7.85		13.15	18.95
2200	Flemish, alt. header every 6th course (7.13/S.F.)		205	.195		4.22	5.75		9.97	14.25
2250	Full headers throughout (13.50/S.F.)		105	.381		7.95	11.25		19.20	27.50
2300	Rowlock course (13.50/S.F.)		100	.400		7.95	11.80		19.75	28.50
2350	Rowlock stretcher (4.50/S.F.)		310	.129		2.69	3.81		6.50	9.30
2400	Soldier course (6.75/S.F.)		200	.200		4	5.90		9.90	14.20
2450	Sailor course (4.50/S.F.)		290	.138		2.69	4.07		6.76	9.70
2600	Buff or gray face, running bond, (6.75/S.F.)		220	.182		4.23	5.35		9.58	13.60
2700	Glazed face brick, running bond		210	.190		11.40	5.60		17	22
2750	Full header every 6th course (7.88/S.F.)		170	.235		13.30	6.95		20.25	26
3000	Jumbo, 6" x 4" x 12" running bond (3.00/S.F.)		435	.092		4.51	2.71		7.22	9.45
3050	Norman, 4" x 2-2/3" x 12" running bond, (4.5/S.F.)		320	.125		5.80	3.69		9.49	12.55
3100	Norwegian, 4" x 3-1/5" x 12" (3.75/S.F.)		375	.107		4.66	3.15		7.81	10.35
3150	Economy, 4" x 4" x 8" (4.50/S.F.)		310	.129		3.95	3.81		7.76	10.70
3200	Engineer, 4" x 3-1/5" x 8" (5.63/S.F.)		260	.154		3.48	4.54		8.02	11.40
3250	Roman, 4" x 2" x 12" (6.00/S.F.)		250	.160		7.70	4.72		12.42	16.35
3300	SCR, 6" x 2-2/3" x 12" (4.50/S.F.)		310	.129		6.55	3.81		10.36	13.55
3350	Utility, 4" x 4" x 12" (3.00/S.F.)		360	.111		4.56	3.28		7.84	10.45
3360	For less than truck load lots, add				M	15%				
3400	For cavity wall construction, add						15%			
3450	For stacked bond, add						10%			
3500	For interior veneer construction, add						15%			
3550	For curved walls, add						30%			

04 21 13.14 Thin Brick Veneer

		Crew	Daily Output	Labor-Hours	Unit	Material	2014 Bare Costs Labor	Equipment	Total	Total Incl O&P
0010	**THIN BRICK VENEER**									
0015	Material costs incl. 3% brick and 25% mortar waste									
0020	On & incl. metal panel support sys, modular, 2-2/3" x 5/8" x 8", red	D-7	92	.174	S.F.	8.75	4.58		13.33	17.05
0100	Closure, 4" x 5/8" x 8"		110	.145		8.75	3.83		12.58	15.85
0110	Norman, 2-2/3" x 5/8" x 12"		110	.145		8.95	3.83		12.78	16.05
0120	Utility, 4" x 5/8" x 12"		125	.128		8.95	3.37		12.32	15.30
0130	Emperor, 4" x 3/4" x 16"		175	.091		10.15	2.41		12.56	15.10
0140	Super emperor, 8" x 3/4" x 16"		195	.082		10.15	2.16		12.31	14.70

04 21 13.14 Thin Brick Veneer

		Crew	Daily Output	Labor-Hours	Unit	Material	2014 Bare Costs Labor	Equipment	Total	Total Incl O&P
0150	For L shaped corners with 4" return, add				L.F.	9.25			9.25	10.20
0200	On masonry/plaster back-up, modular, 2-2/3" x 5/8" x 8", red	D-7	137	.117	S.F.	3.95	3.08		7.03	9.30
0210	Closure, 4" x 5/8" x 8"		165	.097		3.95	2.55		6.50	8.45
0220	Norman, 2-2/3" x 5/8" x 12"		165	.097		4.15	2.55		6.70	8.70
0230	Utility, 4" x 5/8" x 12"		185	.086		4.15	2.28		6.43	8.25
0240	Emperor, 4" x 3/4" x 16"		260	.062		5.35	1.62		6.97	8.50
0250	Super emperor, 8" x 3/4" x 16"		285	.056		5.35	1.48		6.83	8.30
0260	For L shaped corners with 4" return, add				L.F.	9.25			9.25	10.20
0270	For embedment into pre-cast concrete panels, add				S.F.	14.40			14.40	15.85

04 21 13.15 Chimney

		Crew	Daily Output	Labor-Hours	Unit	Material	2014 Bare Costs Labor	Equipment	Total	Total Incl O&P
0010	CHIMNEY, excludes foundation, scaffolding, grout and reinforcing									
0100	Brick, 16" x 16", 8" flue	D-1	18.20	.879	V.L.F.	25	25.50		50.50	70
0150	16" x 20" with one 8" x 12" flue		16	1		38.50	29		67.50	90.50
0200	16" x 24" with two 8" x 8" flues		14	1.143		55.50	33		88.50	116
0250	20" x 20" with one 12" x 12" flue		13.70	1.168		50	34		84	111
0300	20" x 24" with two 8" x 12" flues		12	1.333		63	38.50		101.50	133
0350	20" x 32" with two 12" x 12" flues		10	1.600		87.50	46		133.50	174

04 21 13.18 Columns

		Crew	Daily Output	Labor-Hours	Unit	Material	2014 Bare Costs Labor	Equipment	Total	Total Incl O&P
0010	COLUMNS, solid, excludes scaffolding, grout and reinforcing									
0050	Brick, 8" x 8", 9 brick per V.L.F.	D-1	56	.286	V.L.F.	5.20	8.25		13.45	19.45
0100	12" x 8", 13.5 brick per V.L.F.		37	.432		7.80	12.50		20.30	29.50
0200	12" x 12", 20 brick per V.L.F.		25	.640		11.55	18.50		30.05	43.50
0300	16" x 12", 27 brick per V.L.F.		19	.842		15.60	24.50		40.10	57.50
0400	16" x 16", 36 brick per V.L.F.		14	1.143		21	33		54	78
0500	20" x 16", 45 brick per V.L.F.		11	1.455		26	42		68	98.50
0600	20" x 20", 56 brick per V.L.F.		9	1.778		32.50	51.50		84	121
0700	24" x 20", 68 brick per V.L.F.		7	2.286		39	66		105	153
0800	24" x 24", 81 brick per V.L.F.		6	2.667		46.50	77		123.50	180
1000	36" x 36", 182 brick per V.L.F.		3	5.333		105	154		259	375

04 21 13.30 Oversized Brick

		Crew	Daily Output	Labor-Hours	Unit	Material	2014 Bare Costs Labor	Equipment	Total	Total Incl O&P
0010	OVERSIZED BRICK, excludes scaffolding, grout and reinforcing									
0100	Veneer, 4" x 2.25" x 16"	D-8	387	.103	S.F.	5.05	3.05		8.10	10.65
0105	4" x 2.75" x 16"		412	.097		5.25	2.86		8.11	10.55
0110	4" x 4" x 16"		460	.087		5.90	2.57		8.47	10.75
0120	4" x 8" x 16"		533	.075		6	2.21		8.21	10.30
0125	Loadbearing, 6" x 4" x 16", grouted and reinforced		387	.103		14.10	3.05		17.15	20.50
0130	8" x 4" x 16", grouted and reinforced		327	.122		14.95	3.61		18.56	22.50
0135	6" x 8" x 16", grouted and reinforced		440	.091		13.40	2.68		16.08	19.20
0140	8" x 8" x 16", grouted and reinforced		400	.100		14.65	2.95		17.60	21
0145	Curtainwall/reinforced veneer, 6" x 4" x 16"		387	.103		18.35	3.05		21.40	25
0150	8" x 4" x 16"		327	.122		21.50	3.61		25.11	29.50
0155	6" x 8" x 16"		440	.091		18.15	2.68		20.83	24.50
0160	8" x 8" x 16"		400	.100		26	2.95		28.95	33.50
0200	For 1 to 3 slots in face, add					15%				
0210	For 4 to 7 slots in face, add					25%				
0220	For bond beams, add					20%				
0230	For bullnose shapes, add					20%				
0240	For open end knockout, add					10%				
0250	For white or gray color group, add					10%				
0260	For 135 degree corner, add					250%				

04 21 Clay Unit Masonry

04 21 13 – Brick Masonry

04 21 13.35 Common Building Brick

	Crew	Daily Output	Labor-Hours	Unit	Material	2014 Bare Costs Labor	Equipment	Total	Total Incl O&P
0010 **COMMON BUILDING BRICK**, C62, TL lots, material only R042110-20									
0020 Standard				M	490			490	540
0050 Select				"	550			550	605

04 21 13.45 Face Brick

	Crew	Daily Output	Labor-Hours	Unit	Material	2014 Bare Costs Labor	Equipment	Total	Total Incl O&P
0010 **FACE BRICK** Material Only, C216, TL lots R042110-20									
0300 Standard modular, 4" x 2-2/3" x 8", minimum				M	490			490	540
0350 Maximum					695			695	760
2170 For less than truck load lots, add					15			15	16.50
2180 For buff or gray brick, add				↓	16			16	17.60

04 22 Concrete Unit Masonry

04 22 10 – Concrete Masonry Units

04 22 10.11 Autoclave Aerated Concrete Block

	Crew	Daily Output	Labor-Hours	Unit	Material	2014 Bare Costs Labor	Equipment	Total	Total Incl O&P
0010 **AUTOCLAVE AERATED CONCRETE BLOCK**, excl. scaffolding, grout & reinforcing									
0050 Solid, 4" x 8" x 24", incl. mortar **G**	D-8	600	.067	S.F.	1.48	1.97		3.45	4.90
0060 6" x 8" x 24" **G**		600	.067		2.23	1.97		4.20	5.70
0070 8" x 8" x 24" **G**		575	.070		2.97	2.05		5.02	6.70
0080 10" x 8" x 24" **G**		575	.070		3.63	2.05		5.68	7.40
0090 12" x 8" x 24" **G**	↓	550	.073	↓	4.45	2.15		6.60	8.45

04 22 10.14 Concrete Block, Back-Up

	Crew	Daily Output	Labor-Hours	Unit	Material	2014 Bare Costs Labor	Equipment	Total	Total Incl O&P
0010 **CONCRETE BLOCK, BACK-UP**, C90, 2000 psi R042210-20									
0020 Normal weight, 8" x 16" units, tooled joint 1 side									
0050 Not-reinforced, 2000 psi, 2" thick	D-8	475	.084	S.F.	1.40	2.48		3.88	5.65
0200 4" thick		460	.087		1.66	2.57		4.23	6.10
0300 6" thick		440	.091		2.18	2.68		4.86	6.85
0350 8" thick		400	.100		2.45	2.95		5.40	7.60
0400 10" thick	↓	330	.121		2.95	3.58		6.53	9.20
0450 12" thick	D-9	310	.155		3.76	4.47		8.23	11.60
1000 Reinforced, alternate courses, 4" thick	D-8	450	.089		1.82	2.62		4.44	6.35
1100 6" thick		430	.093		2.34	2.74		5.08	7.15
1150 8" thick		395	.101		2.62	2.99		5.61	7.85
1200 10" thick	↓	320	.125		3.10	3.69		6.79	9.55
1250 12" thick	D-9	300	.160	↓	3.92	4.62		8.54	12

04 22 10.16 Concrete Block, Bond Beam

	Crew	Daily Output	Labor-Hours	Unit	Material	2014 Bare Costs Labor	Equipment	Total	Total Incl O&P
0010 **CONCRETE BLOCK, BOND BEAM**, C90, 2000 psi									
0020 Not including grout or reinforcing									
0125 Regular block, 6" thick	D-8	584	.068	L.F.	2.25	2.02		4.27	5.85
0130 8" high, 8" thick	"	565	.071		2.63	2.09		4.72	6.35
0150 12" thick	D-9	510	.094		3.91	2.72		6.63	8.85
0525 Lightweight, 6" thick	D-8	592	.068	↓	2.67	1.99		4.66	6.25

04 22 10.19 Concrete Block, Insulation Inserts

	Crew	Daily Output	Labor-Hours	Unit	Material	2014 Bare Costs Labor	Equipment	Total	Total Incl O&P
0010 **CONCRETE BLOCK, INSULATION INSERTS**									
0100 Styrofoam, plant installed, add to block prices									
0200 8" x 16" units, 6" thick				S.F.	1.20			1.20	1.32
0250 8" thick					1.35			1.35	1.49
0300 10" thick					1.50			1.50	1.65
0350 12" thick					1.65			1.65	1.82
0500 8" x 8" units, 8" thick					1.20			1.20	1.32
0550 12" thick				↓	1.20			1.20	1.32

04 22 10.23 Concrete Block, Decorative	Crew	Daily Output	Labor-Hours	Unit	Material	2014 Bare Costs Labor	Equipment	Total	Total Incl O&P
0010 **CONCRETE BLOCK, DECORATIVE**, C90, 2000 psi									
5000 Split rib profile units, 1" deep ribs, 8 ribs									
5100 8" x 16" x 4" thick	D-8	345	.116	S.F.	3.62	3.42		7.04	9.70
5150 6" thick		325	.123		4.17	3.63		7.80	10.65
5200 8" thick		300	.133		4.83	3.93		8.76	11.85
5250 12" thick	D-9	275	.175		5.65	5.05		10.70	14.60
5400 For special deeper colors, 4" thick, add					1.23			1.23	1.35
5450 12" thick, add					1.27			1.27	1.39
5600 For white, 4" thick, add					1.23			1.23	1.35
5650 6" thick, add					1.25			1.25	1.38
5700 8" thick, add					1.28			1.28	1.40
5750 12" thick, add					1.32			1.32	1.45

04 22 10.24 Concrete Block, Exterior	Crew	Daily Output	Labor-Hours	Unit	Material	2014 Bare Costs Labor	Equipment	Total	Total Incl O&P
0010 **CONCRETE BLOCK, EXTERIOR**, C90, 2000 psi									
0020 Reinforced alt courses, tooled joints 2 sides									
0100 Normal weight, 8" x 16" x 6" thick	D-8	395	.101	S.F.	2.27	2.99		5.26	7.45
0200 8" thick		360	.111		3.92	3.28		7.20	9.75
0250 10" thick		290	.138		4.08	4.07		8.15	11.25
0300 12" thick	D-9	250	.192		4.68	5.55		10.23	14.40

04 22 10.26 Concrete Block Foundation Wall	Crew	Daily Output	Labor-Hours	Unit	Material	2014 Bare Costs Labor	Equipment	Total	Total Incl O&P
0010 **CONCRETE BLOCK FOUNDATION WALL**, C90/C145									
0050 Normal-weight, cut joints, horiz joint reinf, no vert reinf.									
0200 Hollow, 8" x 16" x 6" thick	D-8	455	.088	S.F.	2.64	2.59		5.23	7.25
0250 8" thick		425	.094		2.93	2.78		5.71	7.85
0300 10" thick		350	.114		3.43	3.37		6.80	9.35
0350 12" thick	D-9	300	.160		4.25	4.62		8.87	12.40
0500 Solid, 8" x 16" block, 6" thick	D-8	440	.091		2.81	2.68		5.49	7.55
0550 8" thick	"	415	.096		4.12	2.84		6.96	9.25
0600 12" thick	D-9	350	.137		5.95	3.96		9.91	13.15

04 22 10.32 Concrete Block, Lintels	Crew	Daily Output	Labor-Hours	Unit	Material	2014 Bare Costs Labor	Equipment	Total	Total Incl O&P
0010 **CONCRETE BLOCK, LINTELS**, C90, normal weight									
0100 Including grout and horizontal reinforcing									
0200 8" x 8" x 8", 1 #4 bar	D-4	300	.133	L.F.	5.20	3.56	.45	9.21	12.20
0250 2 #4 bars		295	.136		5.45	3.62	.46	9.53	12.55
0400 8" x 16" x 8", 1 #4 bar		275	.145		3.65	3.88	.49	8.02	11
0450 2 #4 bars		270	.148		3.87	3.95	.50	8.32	11.40
1000 12" x 8" x 8", 1 #4 bar		275	.145		6.80	3.88	.49	11.17	14.50
1100 2 #4 bars		270	.148		7.05	3.95	.50	11.50	14.90
1150 2 #5 bars		270	.148		7.30	3.95	.50	11.75	15.15
1200 2 #6 bars		265	.151		7.60	4.03	.51	12.14	15.60
1500 12" x 16" x 8", 1 #4 bar		250	.160		7.40	4.27	.54	12.21	15.85
1600 2 #3 bars		245	.163		7.40	4.36	.55	12.31	16
1650 2 #4 bars		245	.163		7.60	4.36	.55	12.51	16.25
1700 2 #5 bars		240	.167		7.85	4.45	.56	12.86	16.65

04 22 10.33 Lintel Block	Crew	Daily Output	Labor-Hours	Unit	Material	2014 Bare Costs Labor	Equipment	Total	Total Incl O&P
0010 **LINTEL BLOCK**									
3481 Lintel block 6" x 8" x 8"	D-1	300	.053	Ea.	1.29	1.54		2.83	3.99
3501 6" x 16" x 8"		275	.058		2	1.68		3.68	5
3521 8" x 8" x 8"		275	.058		1.06	1.68		2.74	3.97
3561 8" x 16" x 8"		250	.064		1.84	1.85		3.69	5.10

04 22 Concrete Unit Masonry

04 22 10 – Concrete Masonry Units

04 22 10.34 Concrete Block, Partitions

		Crew	Daily Output	Labor-Hours	Unit	Material	2014 Bare Costs Labor	2014 Bare Costs Equipment	Total	Total Incl O&P
0010	**CONCRETE BLOCK, PARTITIONS**, excludes scaffolding									
1000	Lightweight block, tooled joints, 2 sides, hollow									
1100	Not reinforced, 8" x 16" x 4" thick	D-8	440	.091	S.F.	1.72	2.68		4.40	6.35
1150	6" thick		410	.098		2.45	2.88		5.33	7.50
1200	8" thick		385	.104		2.98	3.07		6.05	8.40
1250	10" thick		370	.108		3.61	3.19		6.80	9.25
1300	12" thick	D-9	350	.137		3.81	3.96		7.77	10.80
4000	Regular block, tooled joints, 2 sides, hollow									
4100	Not reinforced, 8" x 16" x 4" thick	D-8	430	.093	S.F.	1.58	2.74		4.32	6.30
4150	6" thick		400	.100		2.10	2.95		5.05	7.20
4200	8" thick		375	.107		2.37	3.15		5.52	7.85
4250	10" thick		360	.111		2.86	3.28		6.14	8.60
4300	12" thick	D-9	340	.141		3.67	4.08		7.75	10.85

04 23 Glass Unit Masonry

04 23 13 – Vertical Glass Unit Masonry

04 23 13.10 Glass Block

		Crew	Daily Output	Labor-Hours	Unit	Material	2014 Bare Costs Labor	2014 Bare Costs Equipment	Total	Total Incl O&P
0010	**GLASS BLOCK**									
0100	Plain, 4" thick, under 1,000 S.F., 6" x 6"	D-8	115	.348	S.F.	29	10.25		39.25	49
0150	8" x 8"		160	.250		16.65	7.40		24.05	30.50
0160	end block		160	.250		59	7.40		66.40	77.50
0170	90 deg corner		160	.250		53.50	7.40		60.90	71.50
0180	45 deg corner		160	.250		44	7.40		51.40	61
0200	12" x 12"		175	.229		23.50	6.75		30.25	37
0210	4" x 8"		160	.250		32	7.40		39.40	47.50
0220	6" x 8"		160	.250		22.50	7.40		29.90	37.50
0700	For solar reflective blocks, add					100%				
1000	Thinline, plain, 3-1/8" thick, under 1,000 S.F., 6" x 6"	D-8	115	.348	S.F.	21	10.25		31.25	40
1050	8" x 8"		160	.250		11.85	7.40		19.25	25.50
1400	For cleaning block after installation (both sides), add		1000	.040		.16	1.18		1.34	2.14

04 24 Adobe Unit Masonry

04 24 16 – Manufactured Adobe Unit Masonry

04 24 16.06 Adobe Brick

			Crew	Daily Output	Labor-Hours	Unit	Material	2014 Bare Costs Labor	2014 Bare Costs Equipment	Total	Total Incl O&P
0010	**ADOBE BRICK**, Semi-stabilized, with cement mortar										
0060	Brick, 10" x 4" x 14", 2.6/S.F.	G	D-8	560	.071	S.F.	4.17	2.11		6.28	8.10
0080	12" x 4" x 16", 2.3/S.F.	G		580	.069		6.85	2.03		8.88	10.95
0100	10" x 4" x 16", 2.3/S.F.	G		590	.068		6.30	2		8.30	10.30
0120	8" x 4" x 16", 2.3/S.F.	G		560	.071		4.82	2.11		6.93	8.80
0140	4" x 4" x 16", 2.3/S.F.	G		540	.074		4.75	2.19		6.94	8.90
0160	6" x 4" x 16", 2.3/S.F.	G		540	.074		4.39	2.19		6.58	8.45
0180	4" x 4" x 12", 3.0/S.F.	G		520	.077		5	2.27		7.27	9.30
0200	8" x 4" x 12", 3.0/S.F.	G		520	.077		3.98	2.27		6.25	8.15

04 27 Multiple-Wythe Unit Masonry

04 27 10 – Multiple-Wythe Masonry

04 27 10.10 Cornices

		Crew	Daily Output	Labor-Hours	Unit	Material	2014 Bare Costs Labor	Equipment	Total	Total Incl O&P
0010	**CORNICES**									
0110	Face bricks, 12 brick/S.F.	D-1	30	.533	SF Face	5.45	15.40		20.85	31.50
0150	15 brick/S.F.	"	23	.696	"	6.55	20		26.55	40.50

04 27 10.30 Brick Walls

		Crew	Daily Output	Labor-Hours	Unit	Material	2014 Bare Costs Labor	Equipment	Total	Total Incl O&P
0010	**BRICK WALLS**, including mortar, excludes scaffolding									
0800	Face brick, 4" thick wall, 6.75 brick/S.F.	D-8	215	.186	S.F.	3.93	5.50		9.43	13.50
0850	Common brick, 4" thick wall, 6.75 brick/S.F.		240	.167		3.94	4.92		8.86	12.55
0900	8" thick, 13.50 bricks per S.F.		135	.296		8.10	8.75		16.85	23.50
1000	12" thick, 20.25 bricks per S.F.		95	.421		12.20	12.40		24.60	34
1050	16" thick, 27.00 bricks per S.F.		75	.533		16.50	15.75		32.25	44
1200	Reinforced, face brick, 4" thick wall, 6.75 brick/S.F.		210	.190		4.10	5.60		9.70	13.85
1220	Common brick, 4" thick wall, 6.75 brick/S.F.		235	.170		4.11	5		9.11	12.85
1250	8" thick, 13.50 bricks per S.F.		130	.308		8.45	9.10		17.55	24.50
1300	12" thick, 20.25 bricks per S.F.		90	.444		12.75	13.10		25.85	36
1350	16" thick, 27.00 bricks per S.F.		70	.571		17.20	16.85		34.05	47

04 27 10.40 Steps

		Crew	Daily Output	Labor-Hours	Unit	Material	2014 Bare Costs Labor	Equipment	Total	Total Incl O&P
0010	**STEPS**									
0012	Entry steps, select common brick	D-1	.30	53.333	M	550	1,550		2,100	3,175

04 41 Dry-Placed Stone

04 41 10 – Dry Placed Stone

04 41 10.10 Rough Stone Wall

			Crew	Daily Output	Labor-Hours	Unit	Material	2014 Bare Costs Labor	Equipment	Total	Total Incl O&P
0011	**ROUGH STONE WALL**, Dry										
0012	Dry laid (no mortar), under 18" thick	G	D-1	60	.267	C.F.	12.40	7.70		20.10	26.50
0100	Random fieldstone, under 18" thick	G	D-12	60	.533		12.40	15.40		27.80	39
0150	Over 18" thick	G	"	63	.508		14.85	14.70		29.55	41
0500	Field stone veneer	G	D-8	120	.333	S.F.	11.45	9.85		21.30	29
0510	Valley stone veneer	G		120	.333		11.45	9.85		21.30	29
0520	River stone veneer	G		120	.333		11.45	9.85		21.30	29
0600	Rubble stone walls, in mortar bed, up to 18" thick	G	D-11	75	.320	C.F.	14.95	9.55		24.50	32.50

04 43 Stone Masonry

04 43 10 – Masonry with Natural and Processed Stone

04 43 10.45 Granite

		Crew	Daily Output	Labor-Hours	Unit	Material	2014 Bare Costs Labor	Equipment	Total	Total Incl O&P
0010	**GRANITE**, cut to size									
2500	Steps, copings, etc., finished on more than one surface									
2550	Minimum	D-10	50	.640	C.F.	91	20	9.65	120.65	144
2600	Maximum	"	50	.640	"	146	20	9.65	175.65	204
2800	Pavers, 4" x 4" x 4" blocks, split face and joints									
2850	Minimum	D-11	80	.300	S.F.	13.10	8.95		22.05	29.50
2900	Maximum	"	80	.300	"	29	8.95		37.95	47

04 43 10.55 Limestone

		Crew	Daily Output	Labor-Hours	Unit	Material	2014 Bare Costs Labor	Equipment	Total	Total Incl O&P
0010	**LIMESTONE**, cut to size									
0020	Veneer facing panels									
0500	Texture finish, light stick, 4-1/2" thick, 5' x 12'	D-4	300	.133	S.F.	47.50	3.56	.45	51.51	59
0750	5" thick, 5' x 14' panels	D-10	275	.116		51.50	3.68	1.75	56.93	65
1000	Sugarcube finish, 2" Thick, 3' x 5' panels		275	.116		35	3.68	1.75	40.43	46.50
1050	3" Thick, 4' x 9' panels		275	.116		38	3.68	1.75	43.43	49.50

04 43 Stone Masonry

04 43 10 – Masonry with Natural and Processed Stone

04 43 10.55 Limestone

		Crew	Daily Output	Labor-Hours	Unit	Material	2014 Bare Costs Labor	Equipment	Total	Total Incl O&P
1200	4" Thick, 5' x 11' panels	D-10	275	.116	S.F.	40.50	3.68	1.75	45.93	53
1400	Sugarcube, textured finish, 4-1/2" thick, 5' x 12'		275	.116		44.50	3.68	1.75	49.93	57
1450	5" thick, 5' x 14' panels		275	.116		53	3.68	1.75	58.43	66
2000	Coping, sugarcube finish, top & 2 sides		30	1.067	C.F.	67.50	33.50	16.05	117.05	148
2100	Sills, lintels, jambs, trim, stops, sugarcube finish, average		20	1.600		67.50	50.50	24	142	185
2150	Detailed		20	1.600		67.50	50.50	24	142	185
2300	Steps, extra hard, 14" wide, 6" rise		50	.640	L.F.	25	20	9.65	54.65	71.50
3000	Quoins, plain finish, 6" x 12" x 12"	D-12	25	1.280	Ea.	37.50	37		74.50	103
3050	6" x 16" x 24"	"	25	1.280	"	50	37		87	117

04 43 10.60 Marble

		Crew	Daily Output	Labor-Hours	Unit	Material	2014 Bare Costs Labor	Equipment	Total	Total Incl O&P
0011	**MARBLE**, ashlar, split face, 4" + or - thick, random									
0040	Lengths 1' to 4' & heights 2" to 7-1/2", average	D-8	175	.229	S.F.	14.25	6.75		21	27
0100	Base, polished, 3/4" or 7/8" thick, polished, 6" high	D-10	65	.492	L.F.	10.55	15.55	7.40	33.50	46
1000	Facing, polished finish, cut to size, 3/4" to 7/8" thick									
1050	Average	D-10	130	.246	S.F.	23.50	7.80	3.70	35	42.50
1100	Maximum	"	130	.246	"	33.50	7.80	3.70	45	54
2200	Window sills, 6" x 3/4" thick	D-1	85	.188	L.F.	10.45	5.45		15.90	20.50
2500	Flooring, polished tiles, 12" x 12" x 3/8" thick									
2510	Thin set, average	D-11	90	.267	S.F.	8.45	7.95		16.40	22.50
2600	Maximum		90	.267		86	7.95		93.95	108
2700	Mortar bed, average		65	.369		8.45	11.05		19.50	27.50
2740	Maximum		65	.369		90.50	11.05		101.55	118
2780	Travertine, 3/8" thick, average	D-10	130	.246		9.25	7.80	3.70	20.75	27
2790	Maximum	"	130	.246		25.50	7.80	3.70	37	45
3500	Thresholds, 3' long, 7/8" thick, 4" to 5" wide, plain	D-12	24	1.333	Ea.	31.50	38.50		70	98.50
3550	Beveled	"	24	1.333	"	67.50	38.50		106	138
3700	Window stools, polished, 7/8" thick, 5" wide		85	.376	L.F.	20.50	10.90		31.40	40.50

04 43 10.75 Sandstone or Brownstone

		Crew	Daily Output	Labor-Hours	Unit	Material	2014 Bare Costs Labor	Equipment	Total	Total Incl O&P
0011	**SANDSTONE OR BROWNSTONE**									
0100	Sawed face veneer, 2-1/2" thick, to 2' x 4' panels	D-10	130	.246	S.F.	19	7.80	3.70	30.50	38
0150	4" thick, to 3'-6" x 8' panels		100	.320		19	10.10	4.81	33.91	43
0300	Split face, random sizes		100	.320		13.65	10.10	4.81	28.56	37
0350	Cut stone trim (limestone)									
0360	Ribbon stone, 4" thick, 5' pieces	D-8	120	.333	Ea.	172	9.85		181.85	205
0370	Cove stone, 4" thick, 5' pieces		105	.381		173	11.25		184.25	209
0380	Cornice stone, 10" to 12" wide		90	.444		214	13.10		227.10	257
0390	Band stone, 4" thick, 5' pieces		145	.276		110	8.15		118.15	135
0410	Window and door trim, 3" to 4" wide		160	.250		93.50	7.40		100.90	115
0420	Key stone, 18" long		60	.667		98.50	19.65		118.15	141

04 43 10.80 Slate

		Crew	Daily Output	Labor-Hours	Unit	Material	2014 Bare Costs Labor	Equipment	Total	Total Incl O&P
0010	**SLATE**									
3100	Stair landings, 1" thick, black, clear	D-1	65	.246	S.F.	20	7.10		27.10	34
3200	Ribbon	"	65	.246	"	22	7.10		29.10	36
3500	Stair treads, sand finish, 1" thick x 12" wide									
3600	3 L.F. to 6 L.F.	D-10	120	.267	L.F.	24	8.40	4.01	36.41	44.50
3700	Ribbon, sand finish, 1" thick x 12" wide									
3750	To 6 L.F.	D-10	120	.267	L.F.	20	8.40	4.01	32.41	40.50

04 43 10.85 Window Sill

		Crew	Daily Output	Labor-Hours	Unit	Material	2014 Bare Costs Labor	Equipment	Total	Total Incl O&P
0010	**WINDOW SILL**									
0020	Bluestone, thermal top, 10" wide, 1-1/2" thick	D-1	85	.188	S.F.	9.25	5.45		14.70	19.25
0050	2" thick		75	.213	"	8.85	6.15		15	20
0100	Cut stone, 5" x 8" plain		48	.333	L.F.	11.90	9.65		21.55	29

04 43 Stone Masonry

04 43 10 – Masonry with Natural and Processed Stone

04 43 10.85 Window Sill

		Crew	Daily Output	Labor-Hours	Unit	Material	2014 Bare Costs Labor	2014 Bare Costs Equipment	Total	Total Incl O&P
0200	Face brick on edge, brick, 8" wide	D-1	80	.200	L.F.	5.30	5.80		11.10	15.40
0400	Marble, 9" wide, 1" thick		85	.188		8.50	5.45		13.95	18.40
0900	Slate, colored, unfading, honed, 12" wide, 1" thick		85	.188		8.50	5.45		13.95	18.40
0950	2" thick		70	.229		8.50	6.60		15.10	20.50

04 51 Flue Liner Masonry

04 51 10 – Clay Flue Lining

04 51 10.10 Flue Lining

		Crew	Daily Output	Labor-Hours	Unit	Material	2014 Bare Costs Labor	2014 Bare Costs Equipment	Total	Total Incl O&P
0010	**FLUE LINING**, including mortar									
0020	Clay, 8" x 8"	D-1	125	.128	V.L.F.	5.30	3.70		9	11.95
0100	8" x 12"		103	.155		7.85	4.49		12.34	16.10
0200	12" x 12"		93	.172		10.20	4.97		15.17	19.55
0300	12" x 18"		84	.190		20	5.50		25.50	31
0400	18" x 18"		75	.213		26	6.15		32.15	39.50
0500	20" x 20"		66	.242		40	7		47	55.50
0600	24" x 24"		56	.286		51.50	8.25		59.75	70.50
1000	Round, 18" diameter		66	.242		37	7		44	52
1100	24" diameter		47	.340		72	9.85		81.85	95.50

04 57 Masonry Fireplaces

04 57 10 – Brick or Stone Fireplaces

04 57 10.10 Fireplace

		Crew	Daily Output	Labor-Hours	Unit	Material	2014 Bare Costs Labor	2014 Bare Costs Equipment	Total	Total Incl O&P
0010	**FIREPLACE**									
0100	Brick fireplace, not incl. foundations or chimneys									
0110	30" x 29" opening, incl. chamber, plain brickwork	D-1	.40	40	Ea.	550	1,150		1,700	2,525
0200	Fireplace box only (110 brick)	"	2	8	"	157	231		388	555
0300	For elaborate brickwork and details, add					35%	35%			
0400	For hearth, brick & stone, add	D-1	2	8	Ea.	205	231		436	610
0410	For steel, damper, cleanouts, add		4	4		19.40	116		135.40	214
0600	Plain brickwork, incl. metal circulator		.50	32		985	925		1,910	2,625
0800	Face brick only, standard size, 8" x 2-2/3" x 4"		.30	53.333	M	550	1,550		2,100	3,175
0900	Stone fireplace, fieldstone, add				SF Face	8.50			8.50	9.35
1000	Cut stone, add				"	6.25			6.25	6.90

04 72 Cast Stone Masonry

04 72 10 – Cast Stone Masonry Features

04 72 10.10 Coping

		Crew	Daily Output	Labor-Hours	Unit	Material	2014 Bare Costs Labor	2014 Bare Costs Equipment	Total	Total Incl O&P
0010	**COPING**, stock units									
0050	Precast concrete, 10" wide, 4" tapers to 3-1/2", 8" wall	D-1	75	.213	L.F.	17.10	6.15		23.25	29
0100	12" wide, 3-1/2" tapers to 3", 10" wall		70	.229		18.45	6.60		25.05	31.50
0110	14" wide, 4" tapers to 3-1/2", 12" wall		65	.246		20.50	7.10		27.60	34.50
0150	16" wide, 4" tapers to 3-1/2", 14" wall		60	.267		22	7.70		29.70	37.50
0300	Limestone for 12" wall, 4" thick		90	.178		14.70	5.15		19.85	24.50
0350	6" thick		80	.200		22	5.80		27.80	34
0500	Marble, to 4" thick, no wash, 9" wide		90	.178		13.70	5.15		18.85	23.50
0550	12" wide		80	.200		15.70	5.80		21.50	27
0700	Terra cotta, 9" wide		90	.178		6.15	5.15		11.30	15.30

04 72 Cast Stone Masonry

04 72 10 – Cast Stone Masonry Features

04 72 10.10 Coping

04 72 10.10 Coping	Crew	Daily Output	Labor-Hours	Unit	Material	2014 Bare Costs Labor	Equipment	Total	Total Incl O&P
0750	12" wide	D-1	80	.200	L.F.	8.40	5.80		14.20	18.85
0800	Aluminum, for 12" wall	↓	80	.200	↓	8.90	5.80		14.70	19.35

04 72 20 – Cultured Stone Veneer

04 72 20.10 Cultured Stone Veneer Components

	04 72 20.10 Cultured Stone Veneer Components	Crew	Daily Output	Labor-Hours	Unit	Material	2014 Bare Costs Labor	Equipment	Total	Total Incl O&P
0010	**CULTURED STONE VENEER COMPONENTS**									
0110	On wood frame and sheathing substrate, random sized cobbles, corner stones	D-8	70	.571	V.L.F.	9.10	16.85		25.95	38
0120	Field stones		140	.286	S.F.	6.65	8.45		15.10	21.50
0130	Random sized flats, corner stones		70	.571	V.L.F.	9.35	16.85		26.20	38.50
0140	Field stones		140	.286	S.F.	7.55	8.45		16	22.50
0150	Horizontal lined ledgestones, corner stones		75	.533	V.L.F.	9.30	15.75		25.05	36
0160	Field stones		150	.267	S.F.	6.85	7.85		14.70	20.50
0170	Random shaped flats, corner stones		65	.615	V.L.F.	9.30	18.15		27.45	40
0180	Field stones		150	.267	S.F.	6.85	7.85		14.70	20.50
0190	Random shaped/textured face, corner stones		65	.615	V.L.F.	9.10	18.15		27.25	40
0200	Field stones		130	.308	S.F.	6.85	9.10		15.95	22.50
0210	Random shaped river rock, corner stones		65	.615	V.L.F.	9.10	18.15		27.25	40
0220	Field stones		130	.308	S.F.	6.85	9.10		15.95	22.50
0240	On concrete or CMU substrate, random sized cobbles, corner stones		70	.571	V.L.F.	8.45	16.85		25.30	37.50
0250	Field stones		140	.286	S.F.	6.30	8.45		14.75	21
0260	Random sized flats, corner stones		70	.571	V.L.F.	8.70	16.85		25.55	37.50
0270	Field stones		140	.286	S.F.	7.20	8.45		15.65	22
0280	Horizontal lined ledgestones, corner stones		75	.533	V.L.F.	8.60	15.75		24.35	35.50
0290	Field stones		150	.267	S.F.	6.50	7.85		14.35	20.50
0300	Random shaped flats, corner stones		70	.571	V.L.F.	8.60	16.85		25.45	37.50
0310	Field stones		140	.286	S.F.	6.50	8.45		14.95	21
0320	Random shaped/textured face, corner stones		65	.615	V.L.F.	8.45	18.15		26.60	39.50
0330	Field stones		130	.308	S.F.	6.55	9.10		15.65	22.50
0340	Random shaped river rock, corner stones		65	.615	V.L.F.	8.45	18.15		26.60	39.50
0350	Field stones	↓	130	.308	S.F.	6.55	9.10		15.65	22.50
0360	Cultured stone veneer, #15 felt weather resistant barrier	1 Clab	3700	.002	Sq.	5.40	.05		5.45	6.05
0390	Water table or window sill, 18" long	1 Bric	80	.100	Ea.	9.50	3.19		12.69	15.75

Division Notes

	CREW	DAILY OUTPUT	LABOR-HOURS	UNIT	BARE COSTS				TOTAL INCL O&P
					MAT.	LABOR	EQUIP.	TOTAL	

Estimating Tips

05 05 00 Common Work Results for Metals

- Nuts, bolts, washers, connection angles, and plates can add a significant amount to both the tonnage of a structural steel job and the estimated cost. As a rule of thumb, add 10% to the total weight to account for these accessories.

- Type 2 steel construction, commonly referred to as "simple construction," consists generally of field-bolted connections with lateral bracing supplied by other elements of the building, such as masonry walls or x-bracing. The estimator should be aware, however, that shop connections may be accomplished by welding or bolting. The method may be particular to the fabrication shop and may have an impact on the estimated cost.

05 10 00 Structural Steel

- Steel items can be obtained from two sources: a fabrication shop or a metals service center. Fabrication shops can fabricate items under more controlled conditions than can crews in the field. They are also more efficient and can produce items more economically. Metal service centers serve as a source of long mill shapes to both fabrication shops and contractors.

- Most line items in this structural steel subdivision, and most items in 05 50 00 Metal Fabrications, are indicated as being shop fabricated. The bare material cost for these shop fabricated items is the "Invoice Cost" from the shop and includes the mill base price of steel plus mill extras, transportation to the shop, shop drawings and detailing where warranted, shop fabrication and handling, sandblasting and a shop coat of primer paint, all necessary structural bolts, and delivery to the job site. The bare labor cost and bare equipment cost for these shop fabricated items is for field installation or erection.

- Line items in Subdivision 05 12 23.40 Lightweight Framing, and other items scattered in Division 5, are indicated as being field fabricated. The bare material cost for these field fabricated items is the "Invoice Cost" from the metals service center and includes the mill base price of steel plus mill extras, transportation to the metals service center, material handling, and delivery of long lengths of mill shapes to the job site. Material costs for structural bolts and welding rods should be added to the estimate. The bare labor cost and bare equipment cost for these items is for both field fabrication and field installation or erection, and include time for cutting, welding and drilling in the fabricated metal items. Drilling into concrete and fasteners to fasten field fabricated items to other work are not included and should be added to the estimate.

05 20 00 Steel Joist Framing

- In any given project the total weight of open web steel joists is determined by the loads to be supported and the design. However, economies can be realized in minimizing the amount of labor used to place the joists. This is done by maximizing the joist spacing, and therefore minimizing the number of joists required to be installed on the job. Certain spacings and locations may be required by the design, but in other cases maximizing the spacing and keeping it as uniform as possible will keep the costs down.

05 30 00 Steel Decking

- The takeoff and estimating of metal deck involves more than simply the area of the floor or roof and the type of deck specified or shown on the drawings. Many different sizes and types of openings may exist. Small openings for individual pipes or conduits may be drilled after the floor/roof is installed, but larger openings may require special deck lengths as well as reinforcing or structural support. The estimator should determine who will be supplying this reinforcing. Additionally, some deck terminations are part of the deck package, such as screed angles and pour stops, and others will be part of the steel contract, such as angles attached to structural members and cast-in-place angles and plates. The estimator must ensure that all pieces are accounted for in the complete estimate.

05 50 00 Metal Fabrications

- The most economical steel stairs are those that use common materials, standard details, and most importantly, a uniform and relatively simple method of field assembly. Commonly available A36 channels and plates are very good choices for the main stringers of the stairs, as are angles and tees for the carrier members. Risers and treads are usually made by specialty shops, and it is most economical to use a typical detail in as many places as possible. The stairs should be pre-assembled and shipped directly to the site. The field connections should be simple and straightforward to be accomplished efficiently, and with minimum equipment and labor.

Reference Numbers

Reference numbers are shown in shaded boxes at the beginning of some major classifications. These numbers refer to related items in the Reference Section. The reference information may be an estimating procedure, an alternate pricing method, or technical information. *Note:* Not all subdivisions listed here necessarily appear in this publication.

05 05 19.10 Chemical Anchors	Crew	Daily Output	Labor-Hours	Unit	Material	2014 Bare Costs Labor	Equipment	Total	Total Incl O&P
0010 **CHEMICAL ANCHORS**									
0020 Includes layout & drilling									
1430 Chemical anchor, w/rod & epoxy cartridge, 3/4" diam. x 9-1/2" long	B-89A	27	.593	Ea.	9.75	16.65	4.30	30.70	43.50
1435 1" diameter x 11-3/4" long		24	.667		16.70	18.75	4.84	40.29	55
1440 1-1/4" diameter x 14" long		21	.762		36	21.50	5.55	63.05	82
1445 1-3/4" diameter x 15" long		20	.800		64.50	22.50	5.80	92.80	115
1450 18" long		17	.941		77.50	26.50	6.85	110.85	137
1455 2" diameter x 18" long		16	1		102	28	7.25	137.25	168
1460 24" long		15	1.067		132	30	7.75	169.75	205

05 05 19.20 Expansion Anchors		Crew	Daily Output	Labor-Hours	Unit	Material	2014 Bare Costs Labor	Equipment	Total	Total Incl O&P
0010 **EXPANSION ANCHORS**										
0100 Anchors for concrete, brick or stone, no layout and drilling										
0200 Expansion shields, zinc, 1/4" diameter, 1-5/16" long, single	G	1 Carp	90	.089	Ea.	.48	2.85		3.33	5.35
0300 1-3/8" long, double	G		85	.094		.59	3.02		3.61	5.75
0400 3/8" diameter, 1-1/2" long, single	G		85	.094		.81	3.02		3.83	6
0500 2" long, double	G		80	.100		1.32	3.21		4.53	6.85
0600 1/2" diameter, 2-1/16" long, single	G		80	.100		1.62	3.21		4.83	7.20
0700 2-1/2" long, double	G		75	.107		2.10	3.42		5.52	8.05
0800 5/8" diameter, 2-5/8" long, single	G		75	.107		2.85	3.42		6.27	8.90
0900 2-3/4" long, double	G		70	.114		2.99	3.67		6.66	9.45
1000 3/4" diameter, 2-3/4" long, single	G		70	.114		3.25	3.67		6.92	9.75
1100 3-15/16" long, double	G		65	.123		5.80	3.95		9.75	13.05
2100 Hollow wall anchors for gypsum wall board, plaster or tile										
2500 3/16" diameter, short	G	1 Carp	150	.053	Ea.	.40	1.71		2.11	3.32
3000 Toggle bolts, bright steel, 1/8" diameter, 2" long	G		85	.094		.19	3.02		3.21	5.30
3100 4" long	G		80	.100		.25	3.21		3.46	5.70
3200 3/16" diameter, 3" long	G		80	.100		.26	3.21		3.47	5.70
3300 6" long	G		75	.107		.35	3.42		3.77	6.15
3400 1/4" diameter, 3" long	G		75	.107		.34	3.42		3.76	6.10
3500 6" long	G		70	.114		.50	3.67		4.17	6.70
3600 3/8" diameter, 3" long	G		70	.114		.82	3.67		4.49	7.05
3700 6" long	G		60	.133		1.24	4.28		5.52	8.55
3800 1/2" diameter, 4" long	G		60	.133		1.84	4.28		6.12	9.20
3900 6" long	G		50	.160		2.40	5.15		7.55	11.30
4000 Nailing anchors										
4100 Nylon nailing anchor, 1/4" diameter, 1" long		1 Carp	3.20	2.500	C	16.35	80.50		96.85	153
4200 1-1/2" long			2.80	2.857		21	91.50		112.50	178
4300 2" long			2.40	3.333		25.50	107		132.50	208
4400 Metal nailing anchor, 1/4" diameter, 1" long	G		3.20	2.500		17.60	80.50		98.10	154
4500 1-1/2" long	G		2.80	2.857		22.50	91.50		114	179
4600 2" long	G		2.40	3.333		28	107		135	211
5000 Screw anchors for concrete, masonry,										
5100 stone & tile, no layout or drilling included										
5700 Lag screw shields, 1/4" diameter, short	G	1 Carp	90	.089	Ea.	.37	2.85		3.22	5.20
5800 Long	G		85	.094		.41	3.02		3.43	5.55
5900 3/8" diameter, short	G		85	.094		.65	3.02		3.67	5.80
6000 Long	G		80	.100		.78	3.21		3.99	6.25
6100 1/2" diameter, short	G		80	.100		1.05	3.21		4.26	6.55
6200 Long	G		75	.107		1.18	3.42		4.60	7.05
6300 5/8" diameter, short	G		70	.114		1.81	3.67		5.48	8.15
6400 Long	G		65	.123		2	3.95		5.95	8.85
6600 Lead, #6 & #8, 3/4" long	G		260	.031		.18	.99		1.17	1.86

05 05 Common Work Results for Metals

05 05 19 – Post-Installed Concrete Anchors

05 05 19.20 Expansion Anchors

		Crew	Daily Output	Labor-Hours	Unit	Material	2014 Bare Costs Labor	Equipment	Total	Total Incl O&P
6700	#10 - #14, 1-1/2" long [G]	1 Carp	200	.040	Ea.	.29	1.28		1.57	2.48
6800	#16 & #18, 1-1/2" long [G]		160	.050		.39	1.61		2	3.13
6900	Plastic, #6 & #8, 3/4" long		260	.031		.04	.99		1.03	1.70
7000	#8 & #10, 7/8" long		240	.033		.04	1.07		1.11	1.84
7100	#10 & #12, 1" long		220	.036		.05	1.17		1.22	2.02
7200	#14 & #16, 1-1/2" long		160	.050		.07	1.61		1.68	2.78
8950	Self-drilling concrete screw, hex washer head, 3/16" diam. x 1-3/4" long [G]		300	.027		.20	.86		1.06	1.66
8960	2-1/4" long [G]		250	.032		.23	1.03		1.26	1.98
8970	Phillips flat head, 3/16" diam. x 1-3/4" long [G]		300	.027		.20	.86		1.06	1.66
8980	2-1/4" long [G]		250	.032		.23	1.03		1.26	1.98

05 05 21 – Fastening Methods for Metal

05 05 21.15 Drilling Steel

		Crew	Daily Output	Labor-Hours	Unit	Material	2014 Bare Costs Labor	Equipment	Total	Total Incl O&P
0010	**DRILLING STEEL**									
1910	Drilling & layout for steel, up to 1/4" deep, no anchor									
1920	Holes, 1/4" diameter	1 Sswk	112	.071	Ea.	.08	2.45		2.53	4.75
1925	For each additional 1/4" depth, add		336	.024		.08	.82		.90	1.64
1930	3/8" diameter		104	.077		.09	2.63		2.72	5.10
1935	For each additional 1/4" depth, add		312	.026		.09	.88		.97	1.77
1940	1/2" diameter		96	.083		.09	2.85		2.94	5.55
1945	For each additional 1/4" depth, add		288	.028		.09	.95		1.04	1.91
1950	5/8" diameter		88	.091		.13	3.11		3.24	6.10
1955	For each additional 1/4" depth, add		264	.030		.13	1.04		1.17	2.13
1960	3/4" diameter		80	.100		.17	3.43		3.60	6.75
1965	For each additional 1/4" depth, add		240	.033		.17	1.14		1.31	2.35
1970	7/8" diameter		72	.111		.22	3.81		4.03	7.50
1975	For each additional 1/4" depth, add		216	.037		.22	1.27		1.49	2.66
1980	1" diameter		64	.125		.23	4.28		4.51	8.40
1985	For each additional 1/4" depth, add		192	.042		.23	1.43		1.66	2.97
1990	For drilling up, add						40%			

05 05 23 – Metal Fastenings

05 05 23.10 Bolts and Hex Nuts

		Crew	Daily Output	Labor-Hours	Unit	Material	2014 Bare Costs Labor	Equipment	Total	Total Incl O&P
0010	**BOLTS & HEX NUTS**, Steel, A307									
0100	1/4" diameter, 1/2" long [G]	1 Sswk	140	.057	Ea.	.06	1.96		2.02	3.80
0200	1" long [G]		140	.057		.07	1.96		2.03	3.81
0300	2" long [G]		130	.062		.10	2.11		2.21	4.13
0400	3" long [G]		130	.062		.15	2.11		2.26	4.19
0500	4" long [G]		120	.067		.17	2.28		2.45	4.53
0600	3/8" diameter, 1" long [G]		130	.062		.14	2.11		2.25	4.18
0700	2" long [G]		130	.062		.18	2.11		2.29	4.22
0800	3" long [G]		120	.067		.24	2.28		2.52	4.61
0900	4" long [G]		120	.067		.30	2.28		2.58	4.68
1000	5" long [G]		115	.070		.38	2.38		2.76	4.95
1100	1/2" diameter, 1-1/2" long [G]		120	.067		.40	2.28		2.68	4.79
1200	2" long [G]		120	.067		.46	2.28		2.74	4.86
1300	4" long [G]		115	.070		.75	2.38		3.13	5.35
1400	6" long [G]		110	.073		1.05	2.49		3.54	5.90
1500	8" long [G]		105	.076		1.38	2.61		3.99	6.50
1600	5/8" diameter, 1-1/2" long [G]		120	.067		.98	2.28		3.26	5.45
1700	2" long [G]		120	.067		1.09	2.28		3.37	5.55
1800	4" long [G]		115	.070		1.59	2.38		3.97	6.30
1900	6" long [G]		110	.073		2.05	2.49		4.54	7
2000	8" long [G]		105	.076		3.06	2.61		5.67	8.35

337

05 05 23 – Metal Fastenings

05 05 23.10 Bolts and Hex Nuts

			Crew	Daily Output	Labor-Hours	Unit	Material	2014 Bare Costs Labor	Equipment	Total	Total Incl O&P
2100	10" long	G	1 Sswk	100	.080	Ea.	3.87	2.74		6.61	9.45
2200	3/4" diameter, 2" long	G		120	.067		1.15	2.28		3.43	5.60
2300	4" long	G		110	.073		1.65	2.49		4.14	6.55
2400	6" long	G		105	.076		2.12	2.61		4.73	7.30
2500	8" long	G		95	.084		3.20	2.88		6.08	9
2600	10" long	G		85	.094		4.20	3.22		7.42	10.75
2700	12" long	G		80	.100		4.92	3.43		8.35	11.95
2800	1" diameter, 3" long	G		105	.076		2.69	2.61		5.30	7.95
2900	6" long	G		90	.089		3.94	3.04		6.98	10.15
3000	12" long	G		75	.107		7.10	3.65		10.75	14.75
3100	For galvanized, add						75%				
3200	For stainless, add						350%				

05 05 23.30 Lag Screws

			Crew	Daily Output	Labor-Hours	Unit	Material	2014 Bare Costs Labor	Equipment	Total	Total Incl O&P
0010	**LAG SCREWS**										
0020	Steel, 1/4" diameter, 2" long	G	1 Carp	200	.040	Ea.	.09	1.28		1.37	2.26
0100	3/8" diameter, 3" long	G		150	.053		.29	1.71		2	3.20
0200	1/2" diameter, 3" long	G		130	.062		.63	1.98		2.61	4.01
0300	5/8" diameter, 3" long	G		120	.067		1.13	2.14		3.27	4.84

05 05 23.50 Powder Actuated Tools and Fasteners

			Crew	Daily Output	Labor-Hours	Unit	Material	2014 Bare Costs Labor	Equipment	Total	Total Incl O&P
0010	**POWDER ACTUATED TOOLS & FASTENERS**										
0020	Stud driver, .22 caliber, single shot					Ea.	147			147	161
0100	.27 caliber, semi automatic, strip					"	435			435	475
0300	Powder load, single shot, .22 cal, power level 2, brown					C	5.30			5.30	5.80
0400	Strip, .27 cal, power level 4, red						7.60			7.60	8.35
0600	Drive pin, .300 x 3/4" long	G	1 Carp	4.80	1.667		4.86	53.50		58.36	95.50
0700	.300 x 3" long with washer	G	"	4	2		12.50	64		76.50	122

05 05 23.55 Rivets

			Crew	Daily Output	Labor-Hours	Unit	Material	2014 Bare Costs Labor	Equipment	Total	Total Incl O&P
0010	**RIVETS**										
0100	Aluminum rivet & mandrel, 1/2" grip length x 1/8" diameter	G	1 Carp	4.80	1.667	C	7.65	53.50		61.15	98.50
0200	3/16" diameter	G		4	2		11.40	64		75.40	121
0300	Aluminum rivet, steel mandrel, 1/8" diameter	G		4.80	1.667		10.25	53.50		63.75	101
0400	3/16" diameter	G		4	2		16.45	64		80.45	126
0500	Copper rivet, steel mandrel, 1/8" diameter	G		4.80	1.667		9.10	53.50		62.60	100
0800	Stainless rivet & mandrel, 1/8" diameter	G		4.80	1.667		26	53.50		79.50	119
0900	3/16" diameter	G		4	2		36	64		100	148
1000	Stainless rivet, steel mandrel, 1/8" diameter	G		4.80	1.667		15.65	53.50		69.15	107
1100	3/16" diameter	G		4	2		25.50	64		89.50	136
1200	Steel rivet and mandrel, 1/8" diameter	G		4.80	1.667		7.40	53.50		60.90	98
1300	3/16" diameter	G		4	2		12	64		76	121
1400	Hand riveting tool, standard					Ea.	71.50			71.50	78.50
1500	Deluxe						380			380	420
1600	Power riveting tool, standard						570			570	625
1700	Deluxe						3,600			3,600	3,950

05 12 Structural Steel Framing

05 12 23 – Structural Steel for Buildings

05 12 23.10 Ceiling Supports

		Crew	Daily Output	Labor-Hours	Unit	Material	2014 Bare Costs Labor	Equipment	Total	Total Incl O&P
0010	**CEILING SUPPORTS**									
1000	Entrance door/folding partition supports, shop fabricated [G]	E-4	60	.533	L.F.	26.50	18.55	2.37	47.42	67
1100	Linear accelerator door supports [G]		14	2.286		121	79.50	10.15	210.65	295
1200	Lintels or shelf angles, hung, exterior hot dipped galv. [G]		267	.120		18.10	4.16	.53	22.79	28.50
1250	Two coats primer paint instead of galv. [G]		267	.120		15.65	4.16	.53	20.34	26
1400	Monitor support, ceiling hung, expansion bolted [G]		4	8	Ea.	420	278	35.50	733.50	1,025
1450	Hung from pre-set inserts [G]		6	5.333		450	185	23.50	658.50	875
1600	Motor supports for overhead doors [G]		4	8		214	278	35.50	527.50	805
1700	Partition support for heavy folding partitions, without pocket [G]		24	1.333	L.F.	60.50	46.50	5.90	112.90	162
1750	Supports at pocket only [G]		12	2.667		121	92.50	11.85	225.35	325
2000	Rolling grilles & fire door supports [G]		34	.941		51.50	32.50	4.18	88.18	124
2100	Spider-leg light supports, expansion bolted to ceiling slab [G]		8	4	Ea.	172	139	17.75	328.75	475
2150	Hung from pre-set inserts [G]		12	2.667	"	186	92.50	11.85	290.35	395
2400	Toilet partition support [G]		36	.889	L.F.	60.50	31	3.95	95.45	130
2500	X-ray travel gantry support [G]		12	2.667	"	207	92.50	11.85	311.35	415

05 12 23.15 Columns, Lightweight

		Crew	Daily Output	Labor-Hours	Unit	Material	2014 Bare Costs Labor	Equipment	Total	Total Incl O&P
0010	**COLUMNS, LIGHTWEIGHT**									
8000	Lally columns, to 8', 3-1/2" diameter	2 Carp	24	.667	Ea.	66	21.50		87.50	109
8080	4" diameter	"	20	.800	"	81	25.50		106.50	132

05 12 23.17 Columns, Structural

		Crew	Daily Output	Labor-Hours	Unit	Material	2014 Bare Costs Labor	Equipment	Total	Total Incl O&P
0010	**COLUMNS, STRUCTURAL**									
0015	Made from recycled materials									
0020	Shop fab'd for 100-ton, 1-2 story project, bolted connections									
0800	Steel, concrete filled, extra strong pipe, 3-1/2" diameter	E-2	660	.073	L.F.	43.50	2.52	2.32	48.34	55.50
0830	4" diameter		780	.062		48.50	2.13	1.96	52.59	59.50
0890	5" diameter		1020	.047		58	1.63	1.50	61.13	68.50
0930	6" diameter		1200	.040		77	1.39	1.27	79.66	88.50
0940	8" diameter		1100	.044		77	1.51	1.39	79.90	89
1100	For galvanizing, add				Lb.	.25			.25	.28
1300	For web ties, angles, etc., add per added lb.	1 Sswk	945	.008		1.33	.29		1.62	2.01
1500	Steel pipe, extra strong, no concrete, 3" to 5" diameter [G]	E-2	16000	.003		1.33	.10	.10	1.53	1.76
1600	6" to 12" diameter [G]		14000	.003		1.33	.12	.11	1.56	1.80
5100	Structural tubing, rect., 5" to 6" wide, light section [G]		8000	.006		1.33	.21	.19	1.73	2.06
5200	Heavy section [G]		12000	.004		1.33	.14	.13	1.60	1.86
8090	For projects 75 to 99 tons, add				All	10%				
8092	50 to 74 tons, add					20%				
8094	25 to 49 tons, add					30%	10%			
8096	10 to 24 tons, add					50%	25%			
8098	2 to 9 tons, add					75%	50%			
8099	Less than 2 tons, add					100%	100%			

05 12 23.45 Lintels

		Crew	Daily Output	Labor-Hours	Unit	Material	2014 Bare Costs Labor	Equipment	Total	Total Incl O&P
0010	**LINTELS**									
0015	Made from recycled materials									
0020	Plain steel angles, shop fabricated, under 500 lb. [G]	1 Bric	550	.015	Lb.	1.02	.46		1.48	1.89
0100	500 to 1000 lb. [G]		640	.013	"	.99	.40		1.39	1.75
2000	Steel angles, 3-1/2" x 3", 1/4" thick, 2'-6" long [G]		47	.170	Ea.	14.30	5.45		19.75	25
2100	4'-6" long [G]		26	.308		26	9.80		35.80	45
2600	4" x 3-1/2", 1/4" thick, 5'-0" long [G]		21	.381		33	12.15		45.15	56
2700	9'-0" long [G]		12	.667		59	21.50		80.50	101

05 12 Structural Steel Framing

05 12 23 – Structural Steel for Buildings

05 12 23.65 Plates

05 12 23.65 Plates		Crew	Daily Output	Labor-Hours	Unit	Material	2014 Bare Costs Labor	Equipment	Total	Total Incl O&P
0010	**PLATES**									
0015	Made from recycled materials									
0020	For connections & stiffener plates, shop fabricated									
0050	1/8" thick (5.1 lb./S.F.)	G			S.F.	6.75			6.75	7.45
0100	1/4" thick (10.2 lb./S.F.)	G				13.50			13.50	14.85
0300	3/8" thick (15.3 lb./S.F.)	G				20.50			20.50	22.50
0400	1/2" thick (20.4 lb./S.F.)	G				27			27	29.50
0450	3/4" thick (30.6 lb./S.F.)	G				40.50			40.50	44.50
0500	1" thick (40.8 lb./S.F.)	G				54			54	59.50
2000	Steel plate, warehouse prices, no shop fabrication									
2100	1/4" thick (10.2 lb./S.F.)	G			S.F.	8.05			8.05	8.85

05 12 23.79 Structural Steel

05 12 23.79 Structural Steel		Crew	Daily Output	Labor-Hours	Unit	Material	2014 Bare Costs Labor	Equipment	Total	Total Incl O&P
0010	**STRUCTURAL STEEL**									
0020	Shop fab'd for 100-ton, 1-2 story project, bolted conn's.									
0050	Beams, W 6 x 9	G	E-2	720	.067	L.F.	14.30	2.31	2.12	18.73	22.50
0100	W 8 x 10	G		720	.067		15.90	2.31	2.12	20.33	24
0200	Columns, W 6 x 15	G		540	.089		26	3.08	2.83	31.91	37.50
0250	W 8 x 31	G		540	.089		53.50	3.08	2.83	59.41	67.50
7990	For projects 75 to 99 tons, add					All	10%				
7992	50 to 75 tons, add						20%				
7994	25 to 49 tons, add						30%	10%			
7996	10 to 24 tons, add						50%	25%			
7998	2 to 9 tons, add						75%	50%			
7999	Less than 2 tons, add						100%	100%			

05 31 Steel Decking

05 31 23 – Steel Roof Decking

05 31 23.50 Roof Decking

05 31 23.50 Roof Decking		Crew	Daily Output	Labor-Hours	Unit	Material	2014 Bare Costs Labor	Equipment	Total	Total Incl O&P
0010	**ROOF DECKING**									
0015	Made from recycled materials									
2100	Open type, 1-1/2" deep, Type B, wide rib, galv., 22 ga., under 50 sq.	G	E-4	4500	.007	S.F.	1.97	.25	.03	2.25	2.67
2600	20 ga., under 50 squares	G		3865	.008		2.30	.29	.04	2.63	3.13
2900	18 ga., under 50 squares	G		3800	.008		2.97	.29	.04	3.30	3.87
3050	16 ga., under 50 squares	G		3700	.009		4	.30	.04	4.34	5

05 31 33 – Steel Form Decking

05 31 33.50 Form Decking

05 31 33.50 Form Decking		Crew	Daily Output	Labor-Hours	Unit	Material	2014 Bare Costs Labor	Equipment	Total	Total Incl O&P
0010	**FORM DECKING**									
0015	Made from recycled materials									
6100	Slab form, steel, 28 ga., 9/16" deep, Type UFS, uncoated	G	E-4	4000	.008	S.F.	1.49	.28	.04	1.81	2.21
6200	Galvanized	G		4000	.008		1.32	.28	.04	1.64	2.02
6220	24 ga., 1" deep, Type UF1X, uncoated	G		3900	.008		1.43	.29	.04	1.76	2.15
6240	Galvanized	G		3900	.008		1.68	.29	.04	2.01	2.43
6300	24 ga., 1-5/16" deep, Type UFX, uncoated	G		3800	.008		1.52	.29	.04	1.85	2.27
6400	Galvanized	G		3800	.008		1.79	.29	.04	2.12	2.57
6500	22 ga., 1-5/16" deep, uncoated	G		3700	.009		1.92	.30	.04	2.26	2.72
6600	Galvanized	G		3700	.009		1.96	.30	.04	2.30	2.77
6700	22 ga., 2" deep, uncoated	G		3600	.009		2.50	.31	.04	2.85	3.38
6800	Galvanized	G		3600	.009		2.45	.31	.04	2.80	3.33

05 41 13 – Load-Bearing Metal Stud Framing

05 41 13.05 Bracing

		Crew	Daily Output	Labor-Hours	Unit	Material	2014 Bare Costs Labor	2014 Bare Costs Equipment	Total	Total Incl O&P
0010	**BRACING**, shear wall X-bracing, per 10' x 10' bay, one face									
0015	Made of recycled materials									
0120	Metal strap, 20 ga. x 4" wide [G]	2 Carp	18	.889	Ea.	17.55	28.50		46.05	67.50
0130	6" wide [G]		18	.889		29.50	28.50		58	80
0160	18 ga. x 4" wide [G]		16	1		30.50	32		62.50	87.50
0170	6" wide [G]		16	1		45	32		77	104
0410	Continuous strap bracing, per horizontal row on both faces									
0420	Metal strap, 20 ga. x 2" wide, studs 12" O.C. [G]	1 Carp	7	1.143	C.L.F.	53	36.50		89.50	120
0430	16" O.C. [G]		8	1		53	32		85	112
0440	24" O.C. [G]		10	.800		53	25.50		78.50	101
0450	18 ga. x 2" wide, studs 12" O.C. [G]		6	1.333		75	43		118	155
0460	16" O.C. [G]		7	1.143		75	36.50		111.50	144
0470	24" O.C. [G]		8	1		75	32		107	137

05 41 13.10 Bridging

		Crew	Daily Output	Labor-Hours	Unit	Material	2014 Bare Costs Labor	2014 Bare Costs Equipment	Total	Total Incl O&P
0010	**BRIDGING**, solid between studs w/1-1/4" leg track, per stud bay									
0015	Made from recycled materials									
0200	Studs 12" O.C., 18 ga. x 2-1/2" wide [G]	1 Carp	125	.064	Ea.	.89	2.05		2.94	4.44
0210	3-5/8" wide [G]		120	.067		1.07	2.14		3.21	4.78
0220	4" wide [G]		120	.067		1.13	2.14		3.27	4.85
0230	6" wide [G]		115	.070		1.48	2.23		3.71	5.40
0240	8" wide [G]		110	.073		1.84	2.33		4.17	5.95
0300	16 ga. x 2-1/2" wide [G]		115	.070		1.13	2.23		3.36	5
0310	3-5/8" wide [G]		110	.073		1.38	2.33		3.71	5.45
0320	4" wide [G]		110	.073		1.47	2.33		3.80	5.55
0330	6" wide [G]		105	.076		1.87	2.45		4.32	6.15
0340	8" wide [G]		100	.080		2.34	2.57		4.91	6.90
1200	Studs 16" O.C., 18 ga. x 2-1/2" wide [G]		125	.064		1.14	2.05		3.19	4.71
1210	3-5/8" wide [G]		120	.067		1.37	2.14		3.51	5.10
1220	4" wide [G]		120	.067		1.45	2.14		3.59	5.20
1230	6" wide [G]		115	.070		1.90	2.23		4.13	5.85
1240	8" wide [G]		110	.073		2.36	2.33		4.69	6.55
1300	16 ga. x 2-1/2" wide [G]		115	.070		1.45	2.23		3.68	5.35
1310	3-5/8" wide [G]		110	.073		1.77	2.33		4.10	5.85
1320	4" wide [G]		110	.073		1.88	2.33		4.21	6
1330	6" wide [G]		105	.076		2.39	2.45		4.84	6.75
1340	8" wide [G]		100	.080		3	2.57		5.57	7.60
2200	Studs 24" O.C., 18 ga. x 2-1/2" wide [G]		125	.064		1.65	2.05		3.70	5.25
2210	3-5/8" wide [G]		120	.067		1.98	2.14		4.12	5.80
2220	4" wide [G]		120	.067		2.10	2.14		4.24	5.90
2230	6" wide [G]		115	.070		2.75	2.23		4.98	6.80
2240	8" wide [G]		110	.073		3.41	2.33		5.74	7.70
2300	16 ga. x 2-1/2" wide [G]		115	.070		2.10	2.23		4.33	6.05
2310	3-5/8" wide [G]		110	.073		2.55	2.33		4.88	6.75
2320	4" wide [G]		110	.073		2.72	2.33		5.05	6.90
2330	6" wide [G]		105	.076		3.46	2.45		5.91	7.90
2340	8" wide [G]		100	.080		4.34	2.57		6.91	9.10
3000	Continuous bridging, per row									
3100	16 ga. x 1-1/2" channel thru studs 12" O.C. [G]	1 Carp	6	1.333	C.L.F.	48	43		91	125
3110	16" O.C. [G]		7	1.143		48	36.50		84.50	115
3120	24" O.C. [G]		8.80	.909		48	29		77	102
4100	2" x 2" angle x 18 ga., studs 12" O.C. [G]		7	1.143		75	36.50		111.50	144
4110	16" O.C. [G]		9	.889		75	28.50		103.50	131

05 41 Structural Metal Stud Framing

05 41 13 – Load-Bearing Metal Stud Framing

05 41 13.10 Bridging

			Crew	Daily Output	Labor-Hours	Unit	Material	2014 Bare Costs Labor	Equipment	Total	Total Incl O&P
4120	24" O.C.	G	1 Carp	12	.667	C.L.F.	75	21.50		96.50	119
4200	16 ga., studs 12" O.C.	G		5	1.600		94.50	51.50		146	191
4210	16" O.C.	G		7	1.143		94.50	36.50		131	166
4220	24" O.C.	G		10	.800		94.50	25.50		120	147

05 41 13.25 Framing, Boxed Headers/Beams

			Crew	Daily Output	Labor-Hours	Unit	Material	2014 Bare Costs Labor	Equipment	Total	Total Incl O&P
0010	**FRAMING, BOXED HEADERS/BEAMS**										
0015	Made from recycled materials										
0200	Double, 18 ga. x 6" deep	G	2 Carp	220	.073	L.F.	5.10	2.33		7.43	9.55
0210	8" deep	G		210	.076		5.65	2.45		8.10	10.30
0220	10" deep	G		200	.080		6.90	2.57		9.47	11.90
0230	12" deep	G		190	.084		7.55	2.70		10.25	12.85
0300	16 ga. x 8" deep	G		180	.089		6.50	2.85		9.35	11.95
0310	10" deep	G		170	.094		7.90	3.02		10.92	13.75
0320	12" deep	G		160	.100		8.60	3.21		11.81	14.85
0400	14 ga. x 10" deep	G		140	.114		9.10	3.67		12.77	16.15
0410	12" deep	G		130	.123		10	3.95		13.95	17.60
1210	Triple, 18 ga. x 8" deep	G		170	.094		8.20	3.02		11.22	14.10
1220	10" deep	G		165	.097		9.85	3.11		12.96	16.10
1230	12" deep	G		160	.100		10.85	3.21		14.06	17.30
1300	16 ga. x 8" deep	G		145	.110		9.50	3.54		13.04	16.35
1310	10" deep	G		140	.114		11.35	3.67		15.02	18.60
1320	12" deep	G		135	.119		12.40	3.80		16.20	20
1400	14 ga. x 10" deep	G		115	.139		12.40	4.47		16.87	21
1410	12" deep	G		110	.145		13.70	4.67		18.37	23

05 41 13.30 Framing, Stud Walls

			Crew	Daily Output	Labor-Hours	Unit	Material	2014 Bare Costs Labor	Equipment	Total	Total Incl O&P
0010	**FRAMING, STUD WALLS** w/top & bottom track, no openings,										
0020	Headers, beams, bridging or bracing										
0025	Made from recycled materials										
4100	8' high walls, 18 ga. x 2-1/2" wide, studs 12" O.C.	G	2 Carp	54	.296	L.F.	8.50	9.50		18	25.50
4110	16" O.C.	G		77	.208		6.80	6.65		13.45	18.65
4120	24" O.C.	G		107	.150		5.10	4.80		9.90	13.65
4130	3-5/8" wide, studs 12" O.C.	G		53	.302		10.05	9.70		19.75	27.50
4140	16" O.C.	G		76	.211		8.05	6.75		14.80	20
4150	24" O.C.	G		105	.152		6.05	4.89		10.94	14.90
4160	4" wide, studs 12" O.C.	G		52	.308		10.55	9.90		20.45	28
4170	16" O.C.	G		74	.216		8.45	6.95		15.40	21
4180	24" O.C.	G		103	.155		6.35	4.99		11.34	15.40
4190	6" wide, studs 12" O.C.	G		51	.314		13.40	10.05		23.45	31.50
4200	16" O.C.	G		73	.219		10.75	7.05		17.80	23.50
4210	24" O.C.	G		101	.158		8.10	5.10		13.20	17.45
4220	8" wide, studs 12" O.C.	G		50	.320		16.30	10.25		26.55	35.50
4230	16" O.C.	G		72	.222		13.10	7.15		20.25	26.50
4240	24" O.C.	G		100	.160		9.90	5.15		15.05	19.55
4300	16 ga. x 2-1/2" wide, studs 12" O.C.	G		47	.340		10.10	10.95		21.05	29.50
4310	16" O.C.	G		68	.235		8	7.55		15.55	21.50
4320	24" O.C.	G		94	.170		5.90	5.45		11.35	15.70
4330	3-5/8" wide, studs 12" O.C.	G		46	.348		12.05	11.15		23.20	32
4340	16" O.C.	G		66	.242		9.55	7.80		17.35	23.50
4350	24" O.C.	G		92	.174		7.05	5.60		12.65	17.15
4360	4" wide, studs 12" O.C.	G		45	.356		12.65	11.40		24.05	33
4370	16" O.C.	G		65	.246		10	7.90		17.90	24.50
4380	24" O.C.	G		90	.178		7.40	5.70		13.10	17.75

05 41 Structural Metal Stud Framing

05 41 13 – Load-Bearing Metal Stud Framing

05 41 13.30 Framing, Stud Walls

		Crew	Daily Output	Labor-Hours	Unit	Material	2014 Bare Costs Labor	Equipment	Total	Total Incl O&P
4390	6" wide, studs 12" O.C. [G]	2 Carp	44	.364	L.F.	15.80	11.65		27.45	37
4400	16" O.C. [G]		64	.250		12.55	8.05		20.60	27.50
4410	24" O.C. [G]		88	.182		9.30	5.85		15.15	20
4420	8" wide, studs 12" O.C. [G]		43	.372		19.50	11.95		31.45	41.50
4430	16" O.C. [G]		63	.254		15.50	8.15		23.65	31
4440	24" O.C. [G]		86	.186		11.50	5.95		17.45	22.50
5100	10' high walls, 18 ga. x 2-1/2" wide, studs 12" O.C. [G]		54	.296		10.20	9.50		19.70	27
5110	16" O.C. [G]		77	.208		8.05	6.65		14.70	20
5120	24" O.C. [G]		107	.150		5.95	4.80		10.75	14.60
5130	3-5/8" wide, studs 12" O.C. [G]		53	.302		12.05	9.70		21.75	29.50
5140	16" O.C. [G]		76	.211		9.55	6.75		16.30	22
5150	24" O.C. [G]		105	.152		7.05	4.89		11.94	16
5160	4" wide, studs 12" O.C. [G]		52	.308		12.65	9.90		22.55	30.50
5170	16" O.C. [G]		74	.216		10.05	6.95		17	23
5180	24" O.C. [G]		103	.155		7.40	4.99		12.39	16.55
5190	6" wide, studs 12" O.C. [G]		51	.314		16	10.05		26.05	34.50
5200	16" O.C. [G]		73	.219		12.70	7.05		19.75	26
5210	24" O.C. [G]		101	.158		9.40	5.10		14.50	18.90
5220	8" wide, studs 12" O.C. [G]		50	.320		19.50	10.25		29.75	39
5230	16" O.C. [G]		72	.222		15.50	7.15		22.65	29
5240	24" O.C. [G]		100	.160		11.50	5.15		16.65	21.50
5300	16 ga. x 2-1/2" wide, studs 12" O.C. [G]		47	.340		12.20	10.95		23.15	32
5310	16" O.C. [G]		68	.235		9.55	7.55		17.10	23
5320	24" O.C. [G]		94	.170		6.95	5.45		12.40	16.85
5330	3-5/8" wide, studs 12" O.C. [G]		46	.348		14.55	11.15		25.70	35
5340	16" O.C. [G]		66	.242		11.40	7.80		19.20	25.50
5350	24" O.C. [G]		92	.174		8.30	5.60		13.90	18.50
5360	4" wide, studs 12" O.C. [G]		45	.356		15.25	11.40		26.65	36
5370	16" O.C. [G]		65	.246		12	7.90		19.90	26.50
5380	24" O.C. [G]		90	.178		8.70	5.70		14.40	19.20
5390	6" wide, studs 12" O.C. [G]		44	.364		19	11.65		30.65	40.50
5400	16" O.C. [G]		64	.250		14.95	8.05		23	30
5410	24" O.C. [G]		88	.182		10.90	5.85		16.75	22
5420	8" wide, studs 12" O.C. [G]		43	.372		23.50	11.95		35.45	46
5430	16" O.C. [G]		63	.254		18.50	8.15		26.65	34
5440	24" O.C. [G]		86	.186		13.50	5.95		19.45	25
6190	12' high walls, 18 ga. x 6" wide, studs 12" O.C. [G]		41	.390		18.65	12.55		31.20	41.50
6200	16" O.C. [G]		58	.276		14.70	8.85		23.55	31
6210	24" O.C. [G]		81	.198		10.75	6.35		17.10	22.50
6220	8" wide, studs 12" O.C. [G]		40	.400		22.50	12.85		35.35	46.50
6230	16" O.C. [G]		57	.281		17.90	9		26.90	35
6240	24" O.C. [G]		80	.200		13.10	6.40		19.50	25
6390	16 ga. x 6" wide, studs 12" O.C. [G]		35	.457		22.50	14.65		37.15	49
6400	16" O.C. [G]		51	.314		17.40	10.05		27.45	36
6410	24" O.C. [G]		70	.229		12.55	7.35		19.90	26
6420	8" wide, studs 12" O.C. [G]		34	.471		27.50	15.10		42.60	56
6430	16" O.C. [G]		50	.320		21.50	10.25		31.75	41
6440	24" O.C. [G]		69	.232		15.50	7.45		22.95	29.50
6530	14 ga. x 3-5/8" wide, studs 12" O.C. [G]		34	.471		21	15.10		36.10	49
6540	16" O.C. [G]		48	.333		16.55	10.70		27.25	36.50
6550	24" O.C. [G]		65	.246		11.90	7.90		19.80	26.50
6560	4" wide, studs 12" O.C. [G]		33	.485		22.50	15.55		38.05	50.50
6570	16" O.C. [G]		47	.340		17.55	10.95		28.50	37.50

05 41 Structural Metal Stud Framing

05 41 13 – Load-Bearing Metal Stud Framing

05 41 13.30 Framing, Stud Walls		Crew	Daily Output	Labor-Hours	Unit	Material	2014 Bare Costs Labor	Equipment	Total	Total Incl O&P
6580	24" O.C.	2 Carp	64	.250	L.F.	12.65	8.05		20.70	27.50
6730	12 ga. x 3-5/8" wide, studs 12" O.C.		31	.516		29.50	16.55		46.05	60.50
6740	16" O.C.		43	.372		23	11.95		34.95	45
6750	24" O.C.		59	.271		16.05	8.70		24.75	32.50
6760	4" wide, studs 12" O.C.		30	.533		31.50	17.10		48.60	63.50
6770	16" O.C.		42	.381		24.50	12.25		36.75	47
6780	24" O.C.		58	.276		17.15	8.85		26	34
7390	16' high walls, 16 ga. x 6" wide, studs 12" O.C.		33	.485		28.50	15.55		44.05	57.50
7400	16" O.C.		48	.333		22.50	10.70		33.20	42.50
7410	24" O.C.		67	.239		15.80	7.65		23.45	30.50
7420	8" wide, studs 12" O.C.		32	.500		35.50	16.05		51.55	66
7430	16" O.C.		47	.340		27.50	10.95		38.45	49
7440	24" O.C.		66	.242		19.50	7.80		27.30	34.50
7560	14 ga. x 4" wide, studs 12" O.C.		31	.516		29	16.55		45.55	60
7570	16" O.C.		45	.356		22.50	11.40		33.90	43.50
7580	24" O.C.		61	.262		15.90	8.40		24.30	31.50
7590	6" wide, studs 12" O.C.		30	.533		36.50	17.10		53.60	69
7600	16" O.C.		44	.364		28.50	11.65		40.15	50.50
7610	24" O.C.		60	.267		20	8.55		28.55	36.50
7760	12 ga. x 4" wide, studs 12" O.C.		29	.552		41	17.70		58.70	75
7770	16" O.C.		40	.400		31.50	12.85		44.35	56
7780	24" O.C.		55	.291		22	9.35		31.35	39.50
7790	6" wide, studs 12" O.C.		28	.571		51.50	18.35		69.85	88
7800	16" O.C.		39	.410		39.50	13.15		52.65	65.50
7810	24" O.C.		54	.296		27.50	9.50		37	46.50
8590	20' high walls, 14 ga. x 6" wide, studs 12" O.C.		29	.552		45	17.70		62.70	79
8600	16" O.C.		42	.381		34.50	12.25		46.75	58.50
8610	24" O.C.		57	.281		24	9		33	41.50
8620	8" wide, studs 12" O.C.		28	.571		48.50	18.35		66.85	84.50
8630	16" O.C.		41	.390		37.50	12.55		50.05	62
8640	24" O.C.		56	.286		26.50	9.15		35.65	44.50
8790	12 ga. x 6" wide, studs 12" O.C.		27	.593		64	19		83	102
8800	16" O.C.		37	.432		48.50	13.90		62.40	77
8810	24" O.C.		51	.314		33.50	10.05		43.55	54
8820	8" wide, studs 12" O.C.		26	.615		77.50	19.75		97.25	118
8830	16" O.C.		36	.444		59	14.25		73.25	89
8840	24" O.C.		50	.320		41	10.25		51.25	62.50

05 42 Cold-Formed Metal Joist Framing

05 42 13 – Cold-Formed Metal Floor Joist Framing

05 42 13.05 Bracing		Crew	Daily Output	Labor-Hours	Unit	Material	2014 Bare Costs Labor	Equipment	Total	Total Incl O&P
0010	**BRACING**, continuous, per row, top & bottom									
0015	Made from recycled materials									
0120	Flat strap, 20 ga. x 2" wide, joists at 12" O.C.	1 Carp	4.67	1.713	C.L.F.	55	55		110	153
0130	16" O.C.		5.33	1.501		53.50	48		101.50	140
0140	24" O.C.		6.66	1.201		51.50	38.50		90	122
0150	18 ga. x 2" wide, joists at 12" O.C.		4	2		74	64		138	190
0160	16" O.C.		4.67	1.713		73	55		128	173
0170	24" O.C.		5.33	1.501		71.50	48		119.50	160

05 42 Cold-Formed Metal Joist Framing

05 42 13 – Cold-Formed Metal Floor Joist Framing

05 42 13.10 Bridging

		Crew	Daily Output	Labor-Hours	Unit	Material	2014 Bare Costs Labor	Equipment	Total	Total Incl O&P
0010	**BRIDGING**, solid between joists w/1-1/4" leg track, per joist bay									
0015	Made from recycled materials									
0230	Joists 12" O.C., 18 ga. track x 6" wide	G	1 Carp	80	.100	Ea.	1.48	3.21		4.69	7.05
0240	8" wide	G		75	.107		1.84	3.42		5.26	7.75
0250	10" wide	G		70	.114		2.29	3.67		5.96	8.65
0260	12" wide	G		65	.123		2.60	3.95		6.55	9.50
0330	16 ga. track x 6" wide	G		70	.114		1.87	3.67		5.54	8.20
0340	8" wide	G		65	.123		2.34	3.95		6.29	9.25
0350	10" wide	G		60	.133		2.91	4.28		7.19	10.40
0360	12" wide	G		55	.145		3.35	4.67		8.02	11.55
0440	14 ga. track x 8" wide	G		60	.133		2.93	4.28		7.21	10.45
0450	10" wide	G		55	.145		3.64	4.67		8.31	11.85
0460	12" wide	G		50	.160		4.20	5.15		9.35	13.25
0550	12 ga. track x 10" wide	G		45	.178		5.35	5.70		11.05	15.45
0560	12" wide	G		40	.200		5.45	6.40		11.85	16.80
1230	16" O.C., 18 ga. track x 6" wide	G		80	.100		1.90	3.21		5.11	7.50
1240	8" wide	G		75	.107		2.36	3.42		5.78	8.35
1250	10" wide	G		70	.114		2.94	3.67		6.61	9.40
1260	12" wide	G		65	.123		3.33	3.95		7.28	10.30
1330	16 ga. track x 6" wide	G		70	.114		2.39	3.67		6.06	8.80
1340	8" wide	G		65	.123		3	3.95		6.95	9.95
1350	10" wide	G		60	.133		3.73	4.28		8.01	11.30
1360	12" wide	G		55	.145		4.29	4.67		8.96	12.55
1440	14 ga. track x 8" wide	G		60	.133		3.76	4.28		8.04	11.35
1450	10" wide	G		55	.145		4.67	4.67		9.34	13
1460	12" wide	G		50	.160		5.40	5.15		10.55	14.55
1550	12 ga. track x 10" wide	G		45	.178		6.85	5.70		12.55	17.10
1560	12" wide	G		40	.200		7	6.40		13.40	18.50
2230	24" O.C., 18 ga. track x 6" wide	G		80	.100		2.75	3.21		5.96	8.40
2240	8" wide	G		75	.107		3.41	3.42		6.83	9.50
2250	10" wide	G		70	.114		4.25	3.67		7.92	10.80
2260	12" wide	G		65	.123		4.82	3.95		8.77	11.95
2330	16 ga. track x 6" wide	G		70	.114		3.46	3.67		7.13	9.95
2340	8" wide	G		65	.123		4.34	3.95		8.29	11.45
2350	10" wide	G		60	.133		5.40	4.28		9.68	13.15
2360	12" wide	G		55	.145		6.20	4.67		10.87	14.70
2440	14 ga. track x 8" wide	G		60	.133		5.45	4.28		9.73	13.20
2450	10" wide	G		55	.145		6.75	4.67		11.42	15.30
2460	12" wide	G		50	.160		7.80	5.15		12.95	17.20
2550	12 ga. track x 10" wide	G		45	.178		9.90	5.70		15.60	20.50
2560	12" wide	G		40	.200		10.10	6.40		16.50	22

05 42 13.25 Framing, Band Joist

		Crew	Daily Output	Labor-Hours	Unit	Material	2014 Bare Costs Labor	Equipment	Total	Total Incl O&P
0010	**FRAMING, BAND JOIST** (track) fastened to bearing wall									
0015	Made from recycled materials									
0220	18 ga. track x 6" deep	G	2 Carp	1000	.016	L.F.	1.21	.51		1.72	2.19
0230	8" deep	G		920	.017		1.50	.56		2.06	2.59
0240	10" deep	G		860	.019		1.87	.60		2.47	3.06
0320	16 ga. track x 6" deep	G		900	.018		1.52	.57		2.09	2.63
0330	8" deep	G		840	.019		1.91	.61		2.52	3.13
0340	10" deep	G		780	.021		2.37	.66		3.03	3.72
0350	12" deep	G		740	.022		2.73	.69		3.42	4.17
0430	14 ga. track x 8" deep	G		750	.021		2.39	.68		3.07	3.78

05 42 Cold-Formed Metal Joist Framing

05 42 13 – Cold-Formed Metal Floor Joist Framing

05 42 13.25 Framing, Band Joist

			Crew	Daily Output	Labor-Hours	Unit	Material	2014 Bare Costs Labor	Equipment	Total	Total Incl O&P
0440	10" deep	G	2 Carp	720	.022	L.F.	2.97	.71		3.68	4.47
0450	12" deep	G		700	.023		3.42	.73		4.15	5
0540	12 ga. track x 10" deep	G		670	.024		4.35	.77		5.12	6.05
0550	12" deep	G		650	.025		4.45	.79		5.24	6.25

05 42 13.30 Framing, Boxed Headers/Beams

			Crew	Daily Output	Labor-Hours	Unit	Material	2014 Bare Costs Labor	Equipment	Total	Total Incl O&P
0010	**FRAMING, BOXED HEADERS/BEAMS**										
0015	Made from recycled materials										
0200	Double, 18 ga. x 6" deep	G	2 Carp	220	.073	L.F.	5.10	2.33		7.43	9.55
0210	8" deep	G		210	.076		5.65	2.45		8.10	10.30
0220	10" deep	G		200	.080		6.90	2.57		9.47	11.90
0230	12" deep	G		190	.084		7.55	2.70		10.25	12.85
0300	16 ga. x 8" deep	G		180	.089		6.50	2.85		9.35	11.95
0310	10" deep	G		170	.094		7.90	3.02		10.92	13.75
0320	12" deep	G		160	.100		8.60	3.21		11.81	14.85
0400	14 ga. x 10" deep	G		140	.114		9.10	3.67		12.77	16.15
0410	12" deep	G		130	.123		10	3.95		13.95	17.60
0500	12 ga. x 10" deep	G		110	.145		12	4.67		16.67	21
0510	12" deep	G		100	.160		13.25	5.15		18.40	23.50
1210	Triple, 18 ga. x 8" deep	G		170	.094		8.20	3.02		11.22	14.10
1220	10" deep	G		165	.097		9.85	3.11		12.96	16.10
1230	12" deep	G		160	.100		10.85	3.21		14.06	17.30
1300	16 ga. x 8" deep	G		145	.110		9.50	3.54		13.04	16.35
1310	10" deep	G		140	.114		11.35	3.67		15.02	18.60
1320	12" deep	G		135	.119		12.40	3.80		16.20	20
1400	14 ga. x 10" deep	G		115	.139		13.15	4.47		17.62	22
1410	12" deep	G		110	.145		14.50	4.67		19.17	24
1500	12 ga. x 10" deep	G		90	.178		17.50	5.70		23.20	29
1510	12" deep	G		85	.188		19.40	6.05		25.45	31.50

05 42 13.40 Framing, Joists

			Crew	Daily Output	Labor-Hours	Unit	Material	2014 Bare Costs Labor	Equipment	Total	Total Incl O&P
0010	**FRAMING, JOISTS**, no band joists (track), web stiffeners, headers,										
0020	Beams, bridging or bracing										
0025	Made from recycled materials										
0030	Joists (2" flange) and fasteners, materials only										
0220	18 ga. x 6" deep	G				L.F.	1.58			1.58	1.73
0230	8" deep	G					1.86			1.86	2.04
0240	10" deep	G					2.18			2.18	2.40
0320	16 ga. x 6" deep	G					1.93			1.93	2.13
0330	8" deep	G					2.31			2.31	2.54
0340	10" deep	G					2.70			2.70	2.97
0350	12" deep	G					3.07			3.07	3.37
0430	14 ga. x 8" deep	G					2.90			2.90	3.19
0440	10" deep	G					3.34			3.34	3.67
0450	12" deep	G					3.80			3.80	4.18
0540	12 ga. x 10" deep	G					4.86			4.86	5.35
0550	12" deep	G					5.50			5.50	6.10
1010	Installation of joists to band joists, beams & headers, labor only										
1220	18 ga. x 6" deep		2 Carp	110	.145	Ea.		4.67		4.67	7.85
1230	8" deep			90	.178			5.70		5.70	9.60
1240	10" deep			80	.200			6.40		6.40	10.80
1320	16 ga. x 6" deep			95	.168			5.40		5.40	9.10
1330	8" deep			70	.229			7.35		7.35	12.35
1340	10" deep			60	.267			8.55		8.55	14.40

05 42 Cold-Formed Metal Joist Framing

05 42 13 – Cold-Formed Metal Floor Joist Framing

05 42 13.40 Framing, Joists

		Crew	Daily Output	Labor-Hours	Unit	Material	2014 Bare Costs Labor	Equipment	Total	Total Incl O&P
1350	12" deep	2 Carp	55	.291	Ea.		9.35		9.35	15.70
1430	14 ga. x 8" deep		65	.246			7.90		7.90	13.30
1440	10" deep		45	.356			11.40		11.40	19.20
1450	12" deep		35	.457			14.65		14.65	24.50
1540	12 ga. x 10" deep		40	.400			12.85		12.85	21.50
1550	12" deep		30	.533			17.10		17.10	29

05 42 13.45 Framing, Web Stiffeners

			Crew	Daily Output	Labor-Hours	Unit	Material	2014 Bare Costs Labor	Equipment	Total	Total Incl O&P
0010	**FRAMING, WEB STIFFENERS** at joist bearing, fabricated from										
0020	Stud piece (1-5/8" flange) to stiffen joist (2" flange)										
0025	Made from recycled materials										
2120	For 6" deep joist, with 18 ga. x 2-1/2" stud	G	1 Carp	120	.067	Ea.	.85	2.14		2.99	4.54
2130	3-5/8" stud	G		110	.073		1	2.33		3.33	5.05
2140	4" stud	G		105	.076		1.05	2.45		3.50	5.25
2150	6" stud	G		100	.080		1.32	2.57		3.89	5.75
2160	8" stud	G		95	.084		1.60	2.70		4.30	6.30
2220	8" deep joist, with 2-1/2" stud	G		120	.067		1.14	2.14		3.28	4.85
2230	3-5/8" stud	G		110	.073		1.34	2.33		3.67	5.40
2240	4" stud	G		105	.076		1.41	2.45		3.86	5.65
2250	6" stud	G		100	.080		1.77	2.57		4.34	6.25
2260	8" stud	G		95	.084		2.14	2.70		4.84	6.90
2320	10" deep joist, with 2-1/2" stud	G		110	.073		1.41	2.33		3.74	5.50
2330	3-5/8" stud	G		100	.080		1.66	2.57		4.23	6.15
2340	4" stud	G		95	.084		1.74	2.70		4.44	6.45
2350	6" stud	G		90	.089		2.19	2.85		5.04	7.20
2360	8" stud	G		85	.094		2.66	3.02		5.68	8
2420	12" deep joist, with 2-1/2" stud	G		110	.073		1.70	2.33		4.03	5.80
2430	3-5/8" stud	G		100	.080		2	2.57		4.57	6.50
2440	4" stud	G		95	.084		2.10	2.70		4.80	6.85
2450	6" stud	G		90	.089		2.64	2.85		5.49	7.70
2460	8" stud	G		85	.094		3.20	3.02		6.22	8.60
3130	For 6" deep joist, with 16 ga. x 3-5/8" stud	G		100	.080		1.25	2.57		3.82	5.70
3140	4" stud	G		95	.084		1.31	2.70		4.01	6
3150	6" stud	G		90	.089		1.62	2.85		4.47	6.60
3160	8" stud	G		85	.094		2	3.02		5.02	7.30
3230	8" deep joist, with 3-5/8" stud	G		100	.080		1.68	2.57		4.25	6.15
3240	4" stud	G		95	.084		1.76	2.70		4.46	6.50
3250	6" stud	G		90	.089		2.17	2.85		5.02	7.20
3260	8" stud	G		85	.094		2.68	3.02		5.70	8.05
3330	10" deep joist, with 3-5/8" stud	G		85	.094		2.08	3.02		5.10	7.40
3340	4" stud	G		80	.100		2.17	3.21		5.38	7.80
3350	6" stud	G		75	.107		2.69	3.42		6.11	8.70
3360	8" stud	G		70	.114		3.32	3.67		6.99	9.80
3430	12" deep joist, with 3-5/8" stud	G		85	.094		2.50	3.02		5.52	7.85
3440	4" stud	G		80	.100		2.62	3.21		5.83	8.30
3450	6" stud	G		75	.107		3.24	3.42		6.66	9.30
3460	8" stud	G		70	.114		4	3.67		7.67	10.55
4230	For 8" deep joist, with 14 ga. x 3-5/8" stud	G		90	.089		2.08	2.85		4.93	7.10
4240	4" stud	G		85	.094		2.20	3.02		5.22	7.50
4250	6" stud	G		80	.100		2.76	3.21		5.97	8.45
4260	8" stud	G		75	.107		2.95	3.42		6.37	9
4330	10" deep joist, with 3-5/8" stud	G		75	.107		2.57	3.42		5.99	8.60
4340	4" stud	G		70	.114		2.72	3.67		6.39	9.15

05 42 Cold-Formed Metal Joist Framing

05 42 13 – Cold-Formed Metal Floor Joist Framing

05 42 13.45 Framing, Web Stiffeners

			Crew	Daily Output	Labor-Hours	Unit	Material	2014 Bare Costs Labor	Equipment	Total	Total Incl O&P
4350	6" stud	G	1 Carp	65	.123	Ea.	3.42	3.95		7.37	10.40
4360	8" stud	G		60	.133		3.65	4.28		7.93	11.20
4430	12" deep joist, with 3-5/8" stud	G		75	.107		3.10	3.42		6.52	9.15
4440	4" stud	G		70	.114		3.28	3.67		6.95	9.75
4450	6" stud	G		65	.123		4.12	3.95		8.07	11.20
4460	8" stud	G		60	.133		4.40	4.28		8.68	12.05
5330	For 10" deep joist, with 12 ga. x 3-5/8" stud	G		65	.123		3.72	3.95		7.67	10.75
5340	4" stud	G		60	.133		3.97	4.28		8.25	11.55
5350	6" stud	G		55	.145		5	4.67		9.67	13.35
5360	8" stud	G		50	.160		6.05	5.15		11.20	15.30
5430	12" deep joist, with 3-5/8" stud	G		65	.123		4.48	3.95		8.43	11.60
5440	4" stud	G		60	.133		4.78	4.28		9.06	12.45
5450	6" stud	G		55	.145		6	4.67		10.67	14.45
5460	8" stud	G		50	.160		7.30	5.15		12.45	16.65

05 42 23 – Cold-Formed Metal Roof Joist Framing

05 42 23.05 Framing, Bracing

			Crew	Daily Output	Labor-Hours	Unit	Material	2014 Bare Costs Labor	Equipment	Total	Total Incl O&P
0010	**FRAMING, BRACING**										
0015	Made from recycled materials										
0020	Continuous bracing, per row										
0100	16 ga. x 1-1/2" channel thru rafters/trusses @ 16" O.C.	G	1 Carp	4.50	1.778	C.L.F.	48	57		105	149
0120	24" O.C.	G		6	1.333		48	43		91	125
0300	2" x 2" angle x 18 ga., rafters/trusses @ 16" O.C.	G		6	1.333		75	43		118	155
0320	24" O.C.	G		8	1		75	32		107	137
0400	16 ga., rafters/trusses @ 16" O.C.	G		4.50	1.778		94.50	57		151.50	200
0420	24" O.C.	G		6.50	1.231		94.50	39.50		134	171

05 42 23.10 Framing, Bridging

			Crew	Daily Output	Labor-Hours	Unit	Material	2014 Bare Costs Labor	Equipment	Total	Total Incl O&P
0010	**FRAMING, BRIDGING**										
0015	Made from recycled materials										
0020	Solid, between rafters w/1-1/4" leg track, per rafter bay										
1200	Rafters 16" O.C., 18 ga. x 4" deep	G	1 Carp	60	.133	Ea.	1.45	4.28		5.73	8.80
1210	6" deep	G		57	.140		1.90	4.51		6.41	9.70
1220	8" deep	G		55	.145		2.36	4.67		7.03	10.45
1230	10" deep	G		52	.154		2.94	4.94		7.88	11.55
1240	12" deep	G		50	.160		3.33	5.15		8.48	12.30
2200	24" O.C., 18 ga. x 4" deep	G		60	.133		2.10	4.28		6.38	9.50
2210	6" deep	G		57	.140		2.75	4.51		7.26	10.60
2220	8" deep	G		55	.145		3.41	4.67		8.08	11.60
2230	10" deep	G		52	.154		4.25	4.94		9.19	12.95
2240	12" deep	G		50	.160		4.82	5.15		9.97	13.95

05 42 23.50 Framing, Parapets

			Crew	Daily Output	Labor-Hours	Unit	Material	2014 Bare Costs Labor	Equipment	Total	Total Incl O&P
0010	**FRAMING, PARAPETS**										
0015	Made from recycled materials										
0100	3' high installed on 1st story, 18 ga. x 4" wide studs, 12" O.C.	G	2 Carp	100	.160	L.F.	5.30	5.15		10.45	14.50
0110	16" O.C.	G		150	.107		4.52	3.42		7.94	10.70
0120	24" O.C.	G		200	.080		3.73	2.57		6.30	8.40
0200	6" wide studs, 12" O.C.	G		100	.160		6.80	5.15		11.95	16.10
0210	16" O.C.	G		150	.107		5.80	3.42		9.22	12.10
0220	24" O.C.	G		200	.080		4.80	2.57		7.37	9.60
1100	Installed on 2nd story, 18 ga. x 4" wide studs, 12" O.C.	G		95	.168		5.30	5.40		10.70	14.95
1110	16" O.C.	G		145	.110		4.52	3.54		8.06	10.90
1120	24" O.C.	G		190	.084		3.73	2.70		6.43	8.65
1200	6" wide studs, 12" O.C.	G		95	.168		6.80	5.40		12.20	16.55

05 42 Cold-Formed Metal Joist Framing

05 42 23 – Cold-Formed Metal Roof Joist Framing

05 42 23.50 Framing, Parapets

		Crew	Daily Output	Labor-Hours	Unit	Material	2014 Bare Costs Labor	Equipment	Total	Total Incl O&P
1210	16" O.C.	G 2 Carp	145	.110	L.F.	5.80	3.54		9.34	12.30
1220	24" O.C.	G	190	.084		4.80	2.70		7.50	9.85
2100	Installed on gable, 18 ga. x 4" wide studs, 12" O.C.	G	85	.188		5.30	6.05		11.35	16
2110	16" O.C.	G	130	.123		4.52	3.95		8.47	11.60
2120	24" O.C.	G	170	.094		3.73	3.02		6.75	9.20
2200	6" wide studs, 12" O.C.	G	85	.188		6.80	6.05		12.85	17.60
2210	16" O.C.	G	130	.123		5.80	3.95		9.75	13
2220	24" O.C.	G	170	.094		4.80	3.02		7.82	10.40

05 42 23.60 Framing, Roof Rafters

		Crew	Daily Output	Labor-Hours	Unit	Material	2014 Bare Costs Labor	Equipment	Total	Total Incl O&P
0010	**FRAMING, ROOF RAFTERS**									
0015	Made from recycled materials									
0100	Boxed ridge beam, double, 18 ga. x 6" deep	G 2 Carp	160	.100	L.F.	5.10	3.21		8.31	11
0110	8" deep	G	150	.107		5.65	3.42		9.07	11.95
0120	10" deep	G	140	.114		6.90	3.67		10.57	13.75
0130	12" deep	G	130	.123		7.55	3.95		11.50	14.95
0200	16 ga. x 6" deep	G	150	.107		5.80	3.42		9.22	12.10
0210	8" deep	G	140	.114		6.50	3.67		10.17	13.30
0220	10" deep	G	130	.123		7.90	3.95		11.85	15.30
0230	12" deep	G	120	.133		8.60	4.28		12.88	16.65
1100	Rafters, 2" flange, material only, 18 ga. x 6" deep	G				1.58			1.58	1.73
1110	8" deep	G				1.86			1.86	2.04
1120	10" deep	G				2.18			2.18	2.40
1130	12" deep	G				2.52			2.52	2.77
1200	16 ga. x 6" deep	G				1.93			1.93	2.13
1210	8" deep	G				2.31			2.31	2.54
1220	10" deep	G				2.70			2.70	2.97
1230	12" deep	G				3.07			3.07	3.37
2100	Installation only, ordinary rafter to 4:12 pitch, 18 ga. x 6" deep	2 Carp	35	.457	Ea.		14.65		14.65	24.50
2110	8" deep		30	.533			17.10		17.10	29
2120	10" deep		25	.640			20.50		20.50	34.50
2130	12" deep		20	.800			25.50		25.50	43
2200	16 ga. x 6" deep		30	.533			17.10		17.10	29
2210	8" deep		25	.640			20.50		20.50	34.50
2220	10" deep		20	.800			25.50		25.50	43
2230	12" deep		15	1.067			34		34	57.50
8100	Add to labor, ordinary rafters on steep roofs						25%			
8110	Dormers & complex roofs						50%			
8200	Hip & valley rafters to 4:12 pitch						25%			
8210	Steep roofs						50%			
8220	Dormers & complex roofs						75%			
8300	Hip & valley jack rafters to 4:12 pitch						50%			
8310	Steep roofs						75%			
8320	Dormers & complex roofs						100%			

05 42 23.70 Framing, Soffits and Canopies

		Crew	Daily Output	Labor-Hours	Unit	Material	2014 Bare Costs Labor	Equipment	Total	Total Incl O&P
0010	**FRAMING, SOFFITS & CANOPIES**									
0015	Made from recycled materials									
0130	Continuous ledger track @ wall, studs @ 16" O.C., 18 ga. x 4" wide	G 2 Carp	535	.030	L.F.	.97	.96		1.93	2.68
0140	6" wide	G	500	.032		1.27	1.03		2.30	3.12
0150	8" wide	G	465	.034		1.57	1.10		2.67	3.59
0160	10" wide	G	430	.037		1.96	1.19		3.15	4.16
0230	Studs @ 24" O.C., 18 ga. x 4" wide	G	800	.020		.92	.64		1.56	2.10
0240	6" wide	G	750	.021		1.21	.68		1.89	2.48

05 42 Cold-Formed Metal Joist Framing

05 42 23 – Cold-Formed Metal Roof Joist Framing

05 42 23.70 Framing, Soffits and Canopies		Crew	Daily Output	Labor-Hours	Unit	Material	2014 Bare Costs Labor	Equipment	Total	Total Incl O&P
0250	8" wide	G 2 Carp	700	.023	L.F.	1.50	.73		2.23	2.88
0260	10" wide	G ↓	650	.025	↓	1.87	.79		2.66	3.39
1000	Horizontal soffit and canopy members, material only									
1030	1-5/8" flange studs, 18 ga. x 4" deep	G			L.F.	1.26			1.26	1.39
1040	6" deep	G				1.58			1.58	1.74
1050	8" deep	G				1.92			1.92	2.11
1140	2" flange joists, 18 ga. x 6" deep	G				1.80			1.80	1.98
1150	8" deep	G				2.12			2.12	2.34
1160	10" deep	G			↓	2.50			2.50	2.75
4030	Installation only, 18 ga., 1-5/8" flange x 4" deep	2 Carp	130	.123	Ea.		3.95		3.95	6.65
4040	6" deep		110	.145			4.67		4.67	7.85
4050	8" deep		90	.178			5.70		5.70	9.60
4140	2" flange, 18 ga. x 6" deep		110	.145			4.67		4.67	7.85
4150	8" deep		90	.178			5.70		5.70	9.60
4160	10" deep	↓	80	.200			6.40		6.40	10.80
6010	Clips to attach facia to rafter tails, 2" x 2" x 18 ga. angle	G 1 Carp	120	.067		.88	2.14		3.02	4.57
6020	16 ga. angle	G "	100	.080	↓	1.12	2.57		3.69	5.55

05 44 Cold-Formed Metal Trusses

05 44 13 – Cold-Formed Metal Roof Trusses

05 44 13.60 Framing, Roof Trusses		Crew	Daily Output	Labor-Hours	Unit	Material	2014 Bare Costs Labor	Equipment	Total	Total Incl O&P
0010	**FRAMING, ROOF TRUSSES**									
0015	Made from recycled materials									
0020	Fabrication of trusses on ground, Fink (W) or King Post, to 4:12 pitch									
0120	18 ga. x 4" chords, 16' span	G 2 Carp	12	1.333	Ea.	59	43		102	137
0130	20' span	G	11	1.455		73.50	46.50		120	160
0140	24' span	G	11	1.455		88	46.50		134.50	176
0150	28' span	G	10	1.600		103	51.50		154.50	200
0160	32' span	G	10	1.600		118	51.50		169.50	216
0250	6" chords, 28' span	G	9	1.778		129	57		186	238
0260	32' span	G	9	1.778		148	57		205	259
0270	36' span	G	8	2		166	64		230	291
0280	40' span	G	8	2		185	64		249	310
1120	5:12 to 8:12 pitch, 18 ga. x 4" chords, 16' span	G	10	1.600		67	51.50		118.50	161
1130	20' span	G	9	1.778		84	57		141	189
1140	24' span	G	9	1.778		101	57		158	207
1150	28' span	G	8	2		118	64		182	237
1160	32' span	G	8	2		134	64		198	256
1250	6" chords, 28' span	G	7	2.286		148	73.50		221.50	286
1260	32' span	G	7	2.286		169	73.50		242.50	310
1270	36' span	G	6	2.667		190	85.50		275.50	355
1280	40' span	G	6	2.667		211	85.50		296.50	375
2120	9:12 to 12:12 pitch, 18 ga. x 4" chords, 16' span	G	8	2		84	64		148	201
2130	20' span	G	7	2.286		105	73.50		178.50	239
2140	24' span	G	7	2.286		126	73.50		199.50	262
2150	28' span	G	6	2.667		147	85.50		232.50	305
2160	32' span	G	6	2.667		168	85.50		253.50	330
2250	6" chords, 28' span	G	5	3.200		185	103		288	375
2260	32' span	G	5	3.200		211	103		314	405
2270	36' span	G	4	4		238	128		366	475
2280	40' span	G ↓	4	4	↓	264	128		392	505

05 44 Cold-Formed Metal Trusses

05 44 13 – Cold-Formed Metal Roof Trusses

05 44 13.60 Framing, Roof Trusses	Crew	Daily Output	Labor-Hours	Unit	Material	2014 Bare Costs Labor	Equipment	Total	Total Incl O&P
5120	Erection only of roof trusses, to 4:12 pitch, 16' span	F-6	48	.833	Ea.		24.50	13.80	38.30	56
5130	20' span		46	.870			25.50	14.40	39.90	58.50
5140	24' span		44	.909			26.50	15.05	41.55	61
5150	28' span		42	.952			28	15.80	43.80	64.50
5160	32' span		40	1			29.50	16.60	46.10	67.50
5170	36' span		38	1.053			31	17.45	48.45	70.50
5180	40' span		36	1.111			32.50	18.40	50.90	75
5220	5:12 to 8:12 pitch, 16' span		42	.952			28	15.80	43.80	64.50
5230	20' span		40	1			29.50	16.60	46.10	67.50
5240	24' span		38	1.053			31	17.45	48.45	70.50
5250	28' span		36	1.111			32.50	18.40	50.90	75
5260	32' span		34	1.176			34.50	19.50	54	79.50
5270	36' span		32	1.250			36.50	20.50	57	84.50
5280	40' span		30	1.333			39	22	61	90
5320	9:12 to 12:12 pitch, 16' span		36	1.111			32.50	18.40	50.90	75
5330	20' span		34	1.176			34.50	19.50	54	79.50
5340	24' span		32	1.250			36.50	20.50	57	84.50
5350	28' span		30	1.333			39	22	61	90
5360	32' span		28	1.429			42	23.50	65.50	96
5370	36' span		26	1.538			45	25.50	70.50	104
5380	40' span		24	1.667			49	27.50	76.50	113

05 51 Metal Stairs

05 51 13 – Metal Pan Stairs

05 51 13.50 Pan Stairs

			Crew	Daily Output	Labor-Hours	Unit	Material	Labor	Equipment	Total	Total Incl O&P
0010	PAN STAIRS, shop fabricated, steel stringers										
0015	Made from recycled materials										
1700	Pre-erected, steel pan tread, 3'-6" wide, 2 line pipe rail	G	E-2	87	.552	Riser	550	19.10	17.55	586.65	660
1800	With flat bar picket rail	G	"	87	.552	"	615	19.10	17.55	651.65	735

05 51 23 – Metal Fire Escapes

05 51 23.50 Fire Escape Stairs

						Unit	Material			Total	Total Incl O&P
0010	FIRE ESCAPE STAIRS, portable										
0100	Portable ladder					Ea.	128			128	141

05 52 Metal Railings

05 52 13 – Pipe and Tube Railings

05 52 13.50 Railings, Pipe

			Crew	Daily Output	Labor-Hours	Unit	Material	Labor	Equipment	Total	Total Incl O&P
0010	RAILINGS, PIPE, shop fab'd, 3'-6" high, posts @ 5' O.C.										
0015	Made from recycled materials										
0020	Aluminum, 2 rail, satin finish, 1-1/4" diameter	G	E-4	160	.200	L.F.	36	6.95	.89	43.84	53.50
0030	Clear anodized	G		160	.200		44	6.95	.89	51.84	62.50
0040	Dark anodized	G		160	.200		49	6.95	.89	56.84	68
0080	1-1/2" diameter, satin finish	G		160	.200		42.50	6.95	.89	50.34	60.50
0090	Clear anodized	G		160	.200		47.50	6.95	.89	55.34	66
0100	Dark anodized	G		160	.200		52.50	6.95	.89	60.34	71.50
0140	Aluminum, 3 rail, 1-1/4" diam., satin finish	G		137	.234		54.50	8.10	1.04	63.64	76
0150	Clear anodized	G		137	.234		67.50	8.10	1.04	76.64	91
0160	Dark anodized	G		137	.234		75	8.10	1.04	84.14	99
0200	1-1/2" diameter, satin finish	G		137	.234		64.50	8.10	1.04	73.64	87.50

05 52 Metal Railings

05 52 13 – Pipe and Tube Railings

05 52 13.50 Railings, Pipe		Crew	Daily Output	Labor-Hours	Unit	Material	2014 Bare Costs Labor	Equipment	Total	Total Incl O&P
0210	Clear anodized	G	E-4	137	.234	L.F.	74	8.10	1.04	83.14	97.50
0220	Dark anodized	G		137	.234		80.50	8.10	1.04	89.64	105
0500	Steel, 2 rail, on stairs, primed, 1-1/4" diameter	G		160	.200		25	6.95	.89	32.84	41.50
0520	1-1/2" diameter	G		160	.200		27	6.95	.89	34.84	44
0540	Galvanized, 1-1/4" diameter	G		160	.200		34	6.95	.89	41.84	51.50
0560	1-1/2" diameter	G		160	.200		38.50	6.95	.89	46.34	56
0580	Steel, 3 rail, primed, 1-1/4" diameter	G		137	.234		37.50	8.10	1.04	46.64	57.50
0600	1-1/2" diameter	G		137	.234		39	8.10	1.04	48.14	59.50
0620	Galvanized, 1-1/4" diameter	G		137	.234		52.50	8.10	1.04	61.64	74
0640	1-1/2" diameter	G		137	.234		60.50	8.10	1.04	69.64	83
0700	Stainless steel, 2 rail, 1-1/4" diam. #4 finish	G		137	.234		110	8.10	1.04	119.14	138
0720	High polish	G		137	.234		178	8.10	1.04	187.14	213
0740	Mirror polish	G		137	.234		223	8.10	1.04	232.14	262
0760	Stainless steel, 3 rail, 1-1/2" diam., #4 finish	G		120	.267		166	9.25	1.18	176.43	202
0770	High polish	G		120	.267		275	9.25	1.18	285.43	325
0780	Mirror finish	G		120	.267		335	9.25	1.18	345.43	390
0900	Wall rail, alum. pipe, 1-1/4" diam., satin finish	G		213	.150		20	5.20	.67	25.87	32.50
0905	Clear anodized	G		213	.150		25	5.20	.67	30.87	38
0910	Dark anodized	G		213	.150		29.50	5.20	.67	35.37	43
0915	1-1/2" diameter, satin finish	G		213	.150		22.50	5.20	.67	28.37	35.50
0920	Clear anodized	G		213	.150		28	5.20	.67	33.87	41.50
0925	Dark anodized	G		213	.150		35	5.20	.67	40.87	49
0930	Steel pipe, 1-1/4" diameter, primed	G		213	.150		15	5.20	.67	20.87	27
0935	Galvanized	G		213	.150		22	5.20	.67	27.87	34.50
0940	1-1/2" diameter	G		176	.182		15.50	6.30	.81	22.61	30
0945	Galvanized	G		213	.150		22	5.20	.67	27.87	34.50
0955	Stainless steel pipe, 1-1/2" diam., #4 finish	G		107	.299		88	10.40	1.33	99.73	118
0960	High polish	G		107	.299		179	10.40	1.33	190.73	218
0965	Mirror polish	G		107	.299		212	10.40	1.33	223.73	254
2000	2-line pipe rail (1-1/2" T&B) with 1/2" pickets @ 4-1/2" O.C.,										
2005	attached handrail on brackets										
2010	42" high aluminum, satin finish, straight & level	G	E-4	120	.267	L.F.	198	9.25	1.18	208.43	237
2050	42" high steel, primed, straight & level	G	"	120	.267		127	9.25	1.18	137.43	159
4000	For curved and level rails, add						10%	10%			
4100	For sloped rails for stairs, add						30%	30%			

05 58 Formed Metal Fabrications

05 58 25 – Formed Lamp Posts

05 58 25.40 Lamp Posts

		Crew	Daily Output	Labor-Hours	Unit	Material	2014 Bare Costs Labor	Equipment	Total	Total Incl O&P
0010	**LAMP POSTS**										
0020	Aluminum, 7' high, stock units, post only	G	1 Carp	16	.500	Ea.	82	16.05		98.05	117
0100	Mild steel, plain	G	"	16	.500	"	71	16.05		87.05	105

05 71 Decorative Metal Stairs

05 71 13 – Fabricated Metal Spiral Stairs

05 71 13.50 Spiral Stairs		Crew	Daily Output	Labor-Hours	Unit	Material	2014 Bare Costs Labor	Equipment	Total	Total Incl O&P
0010	**SPIRAL STAIRS**									
1805	Shop fabricated, custom ordered									
1810	Aluminum, 5'-0" diameter, plain units ▢G	E-4	45	.711	Riser	575	24.50	3.16	602.66	685
1820	Fancy units ▢G		45	.711		1,100	24.50	3.16	1,127.66	1,250
1900	Cast iron, 4'-0" diameter, plain units ▢G		45	.711		540	24.50	3.16	567.66	645
1920	Fancy Units ▢G		25	1.280		735	44.50	5.70	785.20	900
3100	Spiral stair kits, 12 stacking risers to fit exact floor height									

Division Notes

	CREW	DAILY OUTPUT	LABOR-HOURS	UNIT	BARE COSTS				TOTAL INCL O&P
					MAT.	LABOR	EQUIP.	TOTAL	

Estimating Tips

06 05 00 Common Work Results for Wood, Plastics, and Composites

- Common to any wood-framed structure are the accessory connector items such as screws, nails, adhesives, hangers, connector plates, straps, angles, and hold-downs. For typical wood-framed buildings, such as residential projects, the aggregate total for these items can be significant, especially in areas where seismic loading is a concern. For floor and wall framing, the material cost is based on 10 to 25 lbs. per MBF. Hold-downs, hangers, and other connectors should be taken off by the piece.

  Included with material costs are fasteners for a normal installation. RSMeans engineers use manufacturer's recommendations, written specifications, and/or standard construction practice for size and spacing of fasteners. Prices for various fasteners are shown for informational purposes only. Adjustments should be made if unusual fastening conditions exist.

06 10 00 Carpentry

- Lumber is a traded commodity and therefore sensitive to supply and demand in the marketplace. Even in "budgetary" estimating of wood-framed projects, it is advisable to call local suppliers for the latest market pricing.

- Common quantity units for wood-framed projects are "thousand board feet" (MBF). A board foot is a volume of wood, 1" x 1' x 1', or 144 cubic inches. Board-foot quantities are generally calculated using nominal material dimensions—dressed sizes are ignored. Board foot per lineal foot of any stick of lumber can be calculated by dividing the nominal cross-sectional area by 12. As an example, 2,000 lineal feet of 2 x 12 equates to 4 MBF by dividing the nominal area, 2 x 12, by 12, which equals 2, and multiplying by 2,000 to give 4,000 board feet. This simple rule applies to all nominal dimensioned lumber.

- Waste is an issue of concern at the quantity takeoff for any area of construction. Framing lumber is sold in even foot lengths, i.e., 10', 12', 14', 16', and depending on spans, wall heights, and the grade of lumber, waste is inevitable. A rule of thumb for lumber waste is 5%–10% depending on material quality and the complexity of the framing.

- Wood in various forms and shapes is used in many projects, even where the main structural framing is steel, concrete, or masonry. Plywood as a back-up partition material and 2x boards used as blocking and cant strips around roof edges are two common examples. The estimator should ensure that the costs of all wood materials are included in the final estimate.

06 20 00 Finish Carpentry

- It is necessary to consider the grade of workmanship when estimating labor costs for erecting millwork and interior finish. In practice, there are three grades: premium, custom, and economy. The RSMeans daily output for base and case moldings is in the range of 200 to 250 L.F. per carpenter per day. This is appropriate for most average custom-grade projects. For premium projects, an adjustment to productivity of 25%–50% should be made, depending on the complexity of the job.

Reference Numbers

Reference numbers are shown in shaded boxes at the beginning of some major classifications. These numbers refer to related items in the Reference Section. The reference information may be an estimating procedure, an alternate pricing method, or technical information.

Note: Not all subdivisions listed here necessarily appear in this publication.

Division 6 - Wood, Plastics, and Composites

	06 05 05.10 Selective Demolition Wood Framing	Crew	Daily Output	Labor-Hours	Unit	Material	2014 Bare Costs Labor	Equipment	Total	Total Incl O&P
0010	**SELECTIVE DEMOLITION WOOD FRAMING** R024119-10									
0100	Timber connector, nailed, small	1 Clab	96	.083	Ea.		1.98		1.98	3.34
0110	Medium		60	.133			3.17		3.17	5.35
0120	Large		48	.167			3.97		3.97	6.70
0130	Bolted, small		48	.167			3.97		3.97	6.70
0140	Medium		32	.250			5.95		5.95	10
0150	Large		24	.333			7.95		7.95	13.35
2958	Beams, 2" x 6"	2 Clab	1100	.015	L.F.		.35		.35	.58
2960	2" x 8"		825	.019			.46		.46	.78
2965	2" x 10"		665	.024			.57		.57	.96
2970	2" x 12"		550	.029			.69		.69	1.17
2972	2" x 14"		470	.034			.81		.81	1.36
2975	4" x 8"	B-1	413	.058			1.42		1.42	2.39
2980	4" x 10"		330	.073			1.78		1.78	2.99
2985	4" x 12"		275	.087			2.14		2.14	3.59
3000	6" x 8"		275	.087			2.14		2.14	3.59
3040	6" x 10"		220	.109			2.67		2.67	4.49
3080	6" x 12"		185	.130			3.17		3.17	5.35
3120	8" x 12"		140	.171			4.19		4.19	7.05
3160	10" x 12"		110	.218			5.35		5.35	9
3162	Alternate pricing method		1.10	21.818	M.B.F.		535		535	900
3170	Blocking, in 16" OC wall framing, 2" x 4"	1 Clab	600	.013	L.F.		.32		.32	.53
3172	2" x 6"		400	.020			.48		.48	.80
3174	In 24" OC wall framing, 2" x 4"		600	.013			.32		.32	.53
3176	2" x 6"		400	.020			.48		.48	.80
3178	Alt method, wood blocking removal from wood framing		.40	20	M.B.F.		475		475	800
3179	Wood blocking removal from steel framing		.36	22.222	"		530		530	890
3180	Bracing, let in, 1" x 3", studs 16" OC		1050	.008	L.F.		.18		.18	.31
3181	Studs 24" OC		1080	.007			.18		.18	.30
3182	1" x 4", studs 16" OC		1050	.008			.18		.18	.31
3183	Studs 24" OC		1080	.007			.18		.18	.30
3184	1" x 6", studs 16" OC		1050	.008			.18		.18	.31
3185	Studs 24" OC		1080	.007			.18		.18	.30
3186	2" x 3", studs 16" OC		800	.010			.24		.24	.40
3187	Studs 24" OC		830	.010			.23		.23	.39
3188	2" x 4", studs 16" OC		800	.010			.24		.24	.40
3189	Studs 24" OC		830	.010			.23		.23	.39
3190	2" x 6", studs 16" OC		800	.010			.24		.24	.40
3191	Studs 24" OC		830	.010			.23		.23	.39
3192	2" x 8", studs 16" OC		800	.010			.24		.24	.40
3193	Studs 24" OC		830	.010			.23		.23	.39
3194	"T" shaped metal bracing, studs at 16" OC		1060	.008			.18		.18	.30
3195	Studs at 24" OC		1200	.007			.16		.16	.27
3196	Metal straps, studs at 16" OC		1200	.007			.16		.16	.27
3197	Studs at 24" OC		1240	.006			.15		.15	.26
3200	Columns, round, 8' to 14' tall		40	.200	Ea.		4.76		4.76	8
3202	Dimensional lumber sizes	2 Clab	1.10	14.545	M.B.F.		345		345	585
3250	Blocking, between joists	1 Clab	320	.025	Ea.		.60		.60	1
3252	Bridging, metal strap, between joists		320	.025	Pr.		.60		.60	1
3254	Wood, between joists		320	.025	"		.60		.60	1
3260	Door buck, studs, header & access., 8' high 2" x 4" wall, 3' wide		32	.250	Ea.		5.95		5.95	10
3261	4' wide		32	.250			5.95		5.95	10
3262	5' wide		32	.250			5.95		5.95	10

06 05 Common Work Results for Wood, Plastics, and Composites

06 05 05 – Selective Wood and Plastics Demolition

06 05 05.10 Selective Demolition Wood Framing	Crew	Daily Output	Labor-Hours	Unit	Material	2014 Bare Costs Labor	2014 Bare Costs Equipment	Total	Total Incl O&P
3263	6' wide	1 Clab	32	.250	Ea.		5.95		5.95	10
3264	8' wide		30	.267			6.35		6.35	10.70
3265	10' wide		30	.267			6.35		6.35	10.70
3266	12' wide		30	.267			6.35		6.35	10.70
3267	2" x 6" wall, 3' wide		32	.250			5.95		5.95	10
3268	4' wide		32	.250			5.95		5.95	10
3269	5' wide		32	.250			5.95		5.95	10
3270	6' wide		32	.250			5.95		5.95	10
3271	8' wide		30	.267			6.35		6.35	10.70
3272	10' wide		30	.267			6.35		6.35	10.70
3273	12' wide		30	.267			6.35		6.35	10.70
3274	Window buck, studs, header & access, 8' high 2" x 4" wall, 2' wide		24	.333			7.95		7.95	13.35
3275	3' wide		24	.333			7.95		7.95	13.35
3276	4' wide		24	.333			7.95		7.95	13.35
3277	5' wide		24	.333			7.95		7.95	13.35
3278	6' wide		24	.333			7.95		7.95	13.35
3279	7' wide		24	.333			7.95		7.95	13.35
3280	8' wide		22	.364			8.65		8.65	14.55
3281	10' wide		22	.364			8.65		8.65	14.55
3282	12' wide		22	.364			8.65		8.65	14.55
3283	2" x 6" wall, 2' wide		24	.333			7.95		7.95	13.35
3284	3' wide		24	.333			7.95		7.95	13.35
3285	4' wide		24	.333			7.95		7.95	13.35
3286	5' wide		24	.333			7.95		7.95	13.35
3287	6' wide		24	.333			7.95		7.95	13.35
3288	7' wide		24	.333			7.95		7.95	13.35
3289	8' wide		22	.364			8.65		8.65	14.55
3290	10' wide		22	.364			8.65		8.65	14.55
3291	12' wide		22	.364	▼		8.65		8.65	14.55
3360	Deck or porch decking		825	.010	L.F.		.23		.23	.39
3400	Fascia boards, 1" x 6"		500	.016			.38		.38	.64
3440	1" x 8"		450	.018			.42		.42	.71
3480	1" x 10"		400	.020			.48		.48	.80
3490	2" x 6"		450	.018			.42		.42	.71
3500	2" x 8"		400	.020			.48		.48	.80
3510	2" x 10"		350	.023	▼		.54		.54	.92
3610	Furring, on wood walls or ceiling		4000	.002	S.F.		.05		.05	.08
3620	On masonry or concrete walls or ceiling		1200	.007	"		.16		.16	.27
3800	Headers over openings, 2 @ 2" x 6"		110	.073	L.F.		1.73		1.73	2.91
3840	2 @ 2" x 8"		100	.080			1.90		1.90	3.20
3880	2 @ 2" x 10"		90	.089	▼		2.12		2.12	3.56
3885	Alternate pricing method		.26	30.651	M.B.F.		730		730	1,225
3920	Joists, 1" x 4"		1250	.006	L.F.		.15		.15	.26
3930	1" x 6"		1135	.007			.17		.17	.28
3940	1" x 8"		1000	.008			.19		.19	.32
3950	1" x 10"		895	.009			.21		.21	.36
3960	1" x 12"	▼	765	.010			.25		.25	.42
4200	2" x 4"	2 Clab	1000	.016			.38		.38	.64
4230	2" x 6"		970	.016			.39		.39	.66
4240	2" x 8"		940	.017			.41		.41	.68
4250	2" x 10"		910	.018			.42		.42	.70
4280	2" x 12"		880	.018			.43		.43	.73
4281	2" x 14"	▼	850	.019	▼		.45		.45	.75

06 05 05.10 Selective Demolition Wood Framing		Crew	Daily Output	Labor-Hours	Unit	Material	2014 Bare Costs Labor	2014 Bare Costs Equipment	Total	Total Incl O&P
4282	Composite joists, 9-1/2"	2 Clab	960	.017	L.F.		.40		.40	.67
4283	11-7/8"		930	.017			.41		.41	.69
4284	14"		897	.018			.42		.42	.71
4285	16"		865	.019			.44		.44	.74
4290	Wood joists, alternate pricing method		1.50	10.667	M.B.F.		254		254	425
4500	Open web joist, 12" deep		500	.032	L.F.		.76		.76	1.28
4505	14" deep		475	.034			.80		.80	1.35
4510	16" deep		450	.036			.85		.85	1.42
4520	18" deep		425	.038			.90		.90	1.51
4530	24" deep		400	.040			.95		.95	1.60
4550	Ledger strips, 1" x 2"	1 Clab	1200	.007			.16		.16	.27
4560	1" x 3"		1200	.007			.16		.16	.27
4570	1" x 4"		1200	.007			.16		.16	.27
4580	2" x 2"		1100	.007			.17		.17	.29
4590	2" x 4"		1000	.008			.19		.19	.32
4600	2" x 6"		1000	.008			.19		.19	.32
4601	2" x 8" or 2" x 10"		800	.010			.24		.24	.40
4602	4" x 6"		600	.013			.32		.32	.53
4604	4" x 8"		450	.018			.42		.42	.71
5400	Posts, 4" x 4"	2 Clab	800	.020			.48		.48	.80
5405	4" x 6"		550	.029			.69		.69	1.17
5410	4" x 8"		440	.036			.87		.87	1.46
5425	4" x 10"		390	.041			.98		.98	1.64
5430	4" x 12"		350	.046			1.09		1.09	1.83
5440	6" x 6"		400	.040			.95		.95	1.60
5445	6" x 8"		350	.046			1.09		1.09	1.83
5450	6" x 10"		320	.050			1.19		1.19	2
5455	6" x 12"		290	.055			1.31		1.31	2.21
5480	8" x 8"		300	.053			1.27		1.27	2.14
5500	10" x 10"		240	.067			1.59		1.59	2.67
5660	Tongue and groove floor planks		2	8	M.B.F.		190		190	320
5682	Rafters, ordinary, 16" OC, 2" x 4"		880	.018	S.F.		.43		.43	.73
5683	2" x 6"		840	.019			.45		.45	.76
5684	2" x 8"		820	.020			.46		.46	.78
5685	2" x 10"		820	.020			.46		.46	.78
5686	2" x 12"		810	.020			.47		.47	.79
5687	24" OC, 2" x 4"		1170	.014			.33		.33	.55
5688	2" x 6"		1117	.014			.34		.34	.57
5689	2" x 8"		1091	.015			.35		.35	.59
5690	2" x 10"		1091	.015			.35		.35	.59
5691	2" x 12"		1077	.015			.35		.35	.60
5795	Rafters, ordinary, 2" x 4" (alternate method)		862	.019	L.F.		.44		.44	.74
5800	2" x 6" (alternate method)		850	.019			.45		.45	.75
5840	2" x 8" (alternate method)		837	.019			.46		.46	.77
5855	2" x 10" (alternate method)		825	.019			.46		.46	.78
5865	2" x 12" (alternate method)		812	.020			.47		.47	.79
5870	Sill plate, 2" x 4"	1 Clab	1170	.007			.16		.16	.27
5871	2" x 6"		780	.010			.24		.24	.41
5872	2" x 8"		586	.014			.32		.32	.55
5873	Alternate pricing method		.78	10.256	M.B.F.		244		244	410
5885	Ridge board, 1" x 4"	2 Clab	900	.018	L.F.		.42		.42	.71
5886	1" x 6"		875	.018			.44		.44	.73
5887	1" x 8"		850	.019			.45		.45	.75

06 05 05 – Selective Wood and Plastics Demolition

06 05 05.10 Selective Demolition Wood Framing	Crew	Daily Output	Labor-Hours	Unit	Material	2014 Bare Costs Labor	Equipment	Total	Total Incl O&P
5888	1" x 10"	2 Clab	825	.019	L.F.		.46		.46	.78
5889	1" x 12"		800	.020			.48		.48	.80
5890	2" x 4"		900	.018			.42		.42	.71
5892	2" x 6"		875	.018			.44		.44	.73
5894	2" x 8"		850	.019			.45		.45	.75
5896	2" x 10"		825	.019			.46		.46	.78
5898	2" x 12"		800	.020			.48		.48	.80
6050	Rafter tie, 1" x 4"		1250	.013			.30		.30	.51
6052	1" x 6"		1135	.014			.34		.34	.56
6054	2" x 4"		1000	.016			.38		.38	.64
6056	2" x 6"		970	.016			.39		.39	.66
6070	Sleepers, on concrete, 1" x 2"	1 Clab	4700	.002			.04		.04	.07
6075	1" x 3"		4000	.002			.05		.05	.08
6080	2" x 4"		3000	.003			.06		.06	.11
6085	2" x 6"		2600	.003			.07		.07	.12
6086	Sheathing from roof, 5/16"	2 Clab	1600	.010	S.F.		.24		.24	.40
6088	3/8"		1525	.010			.25		.25	.42
6090	1/2"		1400	.011			.27		.27	.46
6092	5/8"		1300	.012			.29		.29	.49
6094	3/4"		1200	.013			.32		.32	.53
6096	Board sheathing from roof		1400	.011			.27		.27	.46
6100	Sheathing, from walls, 1/4"		1200	.013			.32		.32	.53
6110	5/16"		1175	.014			.32		.32	.55
6120	3/8"		1150	.014			.33		.33	.56
6130	1/2"		1125	.014			.34		.34	.57
6140	5/8"		1100	.015			.35		.35	.58
6150	3/4"		1075	.015			.35		.35	.60
6152	Board sheathing from walls		1500	.011			.25		.25	.43
6158	Subfloor, with boards		1050	.015			.36		.36	.61
6160	Plywood, 1/2" thick		768	.021			.50		.50	.83
6162	5/8" thick		760	.021			.50		.50	.84
6164	3/4" thick		750	.021			.51		.51	.85
6165	1-1/8" thick		720	.022			.53		.53	.89
6166	Underlayment, particle board, 3/8" thick	1 Clab	780	.010			.24		.24	.41
6168	1/2" thick		768	.010			.25		.25	.42
6170	5/8" thick		760	.011			.25		.25	.42
6172	3/4" thick		750	.011			.25		.25	.43
6200	Stairs and stringers, minimum	2 Clab	40	.400	Riser		9.50		9.50	16
6240	Maximum	"	26	.615	"		14.65		14.65	24.50
6300	Components, tread	1 Clab	110	.073	Ea.		1.73		1.73	2.91
6320	Riser		80	.100	"		2.38		2.38	4.01
6390	Stringer, 2" x 10"		260	.031	L.F.		.73		.73	1.23
6400	2" x 12"		260	.031			.73		.73	1.23
6410	3" x 10"		250	.032			.76		.76	1.28
6420	3" x 12"		250	.032			.76		.76	1.28
6590	Wood studs, 2" x 3"	2 Clab	3076	.005			.12		.12	.21
6600	2" x 4"		2000	.008			.19		.19	.32
6640	2" x 6"		1600	.010			.24		.24	.40
6720	Wall framing, including studs, plates and blocking, 2" x 4"	1 Clab	600	.013	S.F.		.32		.32	.53
6740	2" x 6"		480	.017	"		.40		.40	.67
6750	Headers, 2" x 4"		1125	.007	L.F.		.17		.17	.28
6755	2" x 6"		1125	.007			.17		.17	.28
6760	2" x 8"		1050	.008			.18		.18	.31

06 05 05 – Selective Wood and Plastics Demolition

06 05 05.10 Selective Demolition Wood Framing

		Crew	Daily Output	Labor-Hours	Unit	Material	2014 Bare Costs Labor	2014 Bare Costs Equipment	Total	Total Incl O&P
6765	2" x 10"	1 Clab	1050	.008	L.F.		.18		.18	.31
6770	2" x 12"		1000	.008			.19		.19	.32
6780	4" x 10"		525	.015			.36		.36	.61
6785	4" x 12"		500	.016			.38		.38	.64
6790	6" x 8"		560	.014			.34		.34	.57
6795	6" x 10"		525	.015			.36		.36	.61
6797	6" x 12"		500	.016			.38		.38	.64
7000	Trusses									
7050	12' span	2 Clab	74	.216	Ea.		5.15		5.15	8.65
7150	24' span	F-3	66	.606			17.75	10.05	27.80	41
7200	26' span		64	.625			18.30	10.35	28.65	42.50
7250	28' span		62	.645			18.90	10.70	29.60	43.50
7300	30' span		58	.690			20	11.45	31.45	46.50
7350	32' span		56	.714			21	11.85	32.85	48
7400	34' span		54	.741			21.50	12.30	33.80	50
7450	36' span		52	.769			22.50	12.75	35.25	52
8000	Soffit, T & G wood	1 Clab	520	.015	S.F.		.37		.37	.62
8010	Hardboard, vinyl or aluminum	"	640	.013			.30		.30	.50
8030	Plywood	2 Carp	315	.051			1.63		1.63	2.74
9500	See Section 02 41 19.19 for rubbish handling									

06 05 05.20 Selective Demolition Millwork and Trim

		Crew	Daily Output	Labor-Hours	Unit	Material	2014 Bare Costs Labor	2014 Bare Costs Equipment	Total	Total Incl O&P
0010	**SELECTIVE DEMOLITION MILLWORK AND TRIM** R024119-10									
1000	Cabinets, wood, base cabinets, per L.F.	2 Clab	80	.200	L.F.		4.76		4.76	8
1020	Wall cabinets, per L.F.	"	80	.200	"		4.76		4.76	8
1060	Remove and reset, base cabinets	2 Carp	18	.889	Ea.		28.50		28.50	48
1070	Wall cabinets	"	20	.800	"		25.50		25.50	43
1100	Steel, painted, base cabinets	2 Clab	60	.267	L.F.		6.35		6.35	10.70
1120	Wall cabinets		60	.267	"		6.35		6.35	10.70
1200	Casework, large area		320	.050	S.F.		1.19		1.19	2
1220	Selective		200	.080	"		1.90		1.90	3.20
1500	Counter top, minimum		200	.080	L.F.		1.90		1.90	3.20
1510	Maximum		120	.133	"		3.17		3.17	5.35
2000	Paneling, 4' x 8' sheets		2000	.008	S.F.		.19		.19	.32
2100	Boards, 1" x 4"		700	.023			.54		.54	.92
2120	1" x 6"		750	.021			.51		.51	.85
2140	1" x 8"		800	.020			.48		.48	.80
3000	Trim, baseboard, to 6" wide		1200	.013	L.F.		.32		.32	.53
3040	Greater than 6" and up to 12" wide		1000	.016			.38		.38	.64
3080	Remove and reset, minimum	2 Carp	400	.040			1.28		1.28	2.16
3090	Maximum	"	300	.053			1.71		1.71	2.88
3100	Ceiling trim	2 Clab	1000	.016			.38		.38	.64
3120	Chair rail		1200	.013			.32		.32	.53
3140	Railings with balusters		240	.067			1.59		1.59	2.67
3160	Wainscoting		700	.023	S.F.		.54		.54	.92
4000	Curtain rod	1 Clab	80	.100	L.F.		2.38		2.38	4.01

06 05 23 – Wood, Plastic, and Composite Fastenings

06 05 23.10 Nails

		Crew	Daily Output	Labor-Hours	Unit	Material	2014 Bare Costs Labor	2014 Bare Costs Equipment	Total	Total Incl O&P
0010	**NAILS**, material only, based upon 50# box purchase									
0020	Copper nails, plain				Lb.	9.65			9.65	10.60
0400	Stainless steel, plain					9.25			9.25	10.15
0500	Box, 3d to 20d, bright					1.28			1.28	1.41
0520	Galvanized					1.76			1.76	1.94

06 05 23 – Wood, Plastic, and Composite Fastenings

06 05 23.10 Nails

		Crew	Daily Output	Labor-Hours	Unit	Material	2014 Bare Costs Labor	2014 Bare Costs Equipment	Total	Total Incl O&P
0600	Common, 3d to 60d, plain				Lb.	1.10			1.10	1.21
0700	Galvanized					1.97			1.97	2.17
0800	Aluminum					5.85			5.85	6.45
1000	Annular or spiral thread, 4d to 60d, plain					2.56			2.56	2.82
1200	Galvanized					3.03			3.03	3.33
1400	Drywall nails, plain					1.37			1.37	1.51
1600	Galvanized					2			2	2.20
1800	Finish nails, 4d to 10d, plain					1.25			1.25	1.38
2000	Galvanized					1.86			1.86	2.05
2100	Aluminum					5.85			5.85	6.45
2300	Flooring nails, hardened steel, 2d to 10d, plain					2.63			2.63	2.89
2400	Galvanized					4.04			4.04	4.44
2500	Gypsum lath nails, 1-1/8", 13 ga. flathead, blued					2			2	2.20
2600	Masonry nails, hardened steel, 3/4" to 3" long, plain					1.71			1.71	1.88
2700	Galvanized					3.79			3.79	4.17
2900	Roofing nails, threaded, galvanized					1.76			1.76	1.94
3100	Aluminum					4.85			4.85	5.35
3300	Compressed lead head, threaded, galvanized					2.49			2.49	2.74
3600	Siding nails, plain shank, galvanized					2.02			2.02	2.22
3800	Aluminum					5.85			5.85	6.45
5000	Add to prices above for cement coating					.11			.11	.12
5200	Zinc or tin plating					.14			.14	.15
5500	Vinyl coated sinkers, 8d to 16d					2.50			2.50	2.75

06 05 23.50 Wood Screws

		Crew	Daily Output	Labor-Hours	Unit	Material	2014 Bare Costs Labor	2014 Bare Costs Equipment	Total	Total Incl O&P
0010	**WOOD SCREWS**									
0020	#8 x 1" long, steel				C	2.70			2.70	2.97
0100	Brass					12.20			12.20	13.40
0200	#8, 2" long, steel					4.16			4.16	4.58
0300	Brass					22			22	24
0400	#10, 1" long, steel					3.30			3.30	3.63
0500	Brass					15.60			15.60	17.15
0600	#10, 2" long, steel					5.30			5.30	5.85
0700	Brass					27			27	29.50
0800	#10, 3" long, steel					8.85			8.85	9.75
1000	#12, 2" long, steel					7.30			7.30	8.05
1100	Brass					34.50			34.50	38
1500	#12, 3" long, steel					11.15			11.15	12.30
2000	#12, 4" long, steel					18.75			18.75	20.50

06 05 23.60 Timber Connectors

		Crew	Daily Output	Labor-Hours	Unit	Material	2014 Bare Costs Labor	2014 Bare Costs Equipment	Total	Total Incl O&P
0010	**TIMBER CONNECTORS**									
0020	Add up cost of each part for total cost of connection									
0100	Connector plates, steel, with bolts, straight	2 Carp	75	.213	Ea.	30.50	6.85		37.35	45
0110	Tee, 7 ga.		50	.320		35	10.25		45.25	56
0120	T-Strap, 14 ga., 12" x 8" x 2"		50	.320		35	10.25		45.25	56
0150	Anchor plates, 7 ga., 9" x 7"		75	.213		30.50	6.85		37.35	45
0200	Bolts, machine, sq. hd. with nut & washer, 1/2" diameter, 4" long	1 Carp	140	.057		.75	1.83		2.58	3.92
0300	7-1/2" long		130	.062		1.37	1.98		3.35	4.83
0500	3/4" diameter, 7-1/2" long		130	.062		3.20	1.98		5.18	6.85
0610	Machine bolts, w/nut, washer, 3/4" diam., 15" L, HD's & beam hangers		95	.084		5.95	2.70		8.65	11.10
0720	Machine bolts, sq. hd. w/nut & wash		150	.053	Lb.	3.45	1.71		5.16	6.70
0800	Drilling bolt holes in timber, 1/2" diameter		450	.018	Inch		.57		.57	.96
0900	1" diameter		350	.023	"		.73		.73	1.23

06 05 23.60 Timber Connectors	Crew	Daily Output	Labor-Hours	Unit	Material	2014 Bare Costs Labor	Equipment	Total	Total Incl O&P
1100 Framing anchor, angle, 3" x 3" x 1-1/2", 12 ga	1 Carp	175	.046	Ea.	2.61	1.47		4.08	5.35
1150 Framing anchors, 18 ga., 4-1/2" x 2-3/4"		175	.046		2.61	1.47		4.08	5.35
1160 Framing anchors, 18 ga., 4-1/2" x 3"		175	.046		2.61	1.47		4.08	5.35
1170 Clip anchors plates, 18 ga., 12" x 1-1/8"		175	.046		2.61	1.47		4.08	5.35
1250 Holdowns, 3 ga. base, 10 ga. body		8	1		25	32		57	81.50
1260 Holdowns, 7 ga. 11-1/16" x 3-1/4"		8	1		25	32		57	81.50
1270 Holdowns, 7 ga. 14-3/8" x 3-1/8"		8	1		25	32		57	81.50
1275 Holdowns, 12 ga. 8" x 2-1/2"		8	1		25	32		57	81.50
1300 Joist and beam hangers, 18 ga. galv., for 2" x 4" joist		175	.046		.73	1.47		2.20	3.27
1400 2" x 6" to 2" x 10" joist		165	.048		1.39	1.56		2.95	4.15
1600 16 ga. galv., 3" x 6" to 3" x 10" joist		160	.050		2.96	1.61		4.57	5.95
1700 3" x 10" to 3" x 14" joist		160	.050		4.92	1.61		6.53	8.10
1800 4" x 6" to 4" x 10" joist		155	.052		3.07	1.66		4.73	6.15
1900 4" x 10" to 4" x 14" joist		155	.052		5	1.66		6.66	8.30
2000 Two-2" x 6" to two-2" x 10" joists		150	.053		4.19	1.71		5.90	7.50
2100 Two-2" x 10" to two-2" x 14" joists		150	.053		4.68	1.71		6.39	8.05
2300 3/16" thick, 6" x 8" joist		145	.055		65	1.77		66.77	74.50
2400 6" x 10" joist		140	.057		67.50	1.83		69.33	77.50
2500 6" x 12" joist		135	.059		70.50	1.90		72.40	80.50
2700 1/4" thick, 6" x 14" joist	▼	130	.062		73	1.98		74.98	84
2900 Plywood clips, extruded aluminum H clip, for 3/4" panels					.24			.24	.26
3000 Galvanized 18 ga. back-up clip					.18			.18	.20
3200 Post framing, 16 ga. galv. for 4" x 4" base, 2 piece	1 Carp	130	.062		16.40	1.98		18.38	21.50
3300 Cap		130	.062		23	1.98		24.98	28.50
3500 Rafter anchors, 18 ga. galv., 1-1/2" wide, 5-1/4" long		145	.055		.49	1.77		2.26	3.52
3600 10-3/4" long		145	.055		1.46	1.77		3.23	4.59
3800 Shear plates, 2-5/8" diameter		120	.067		2.38	2.14		4.52	6.20
3900 4" diameter		115	.070		5.65	2.23		7.88	9.95
4000 Sill anchors, embedded in concrete or block, 25-1/2" long		115	.070		12.70	2.23		14.93	17.70
4100 Spike grids, 3" x 6"		120	.067		.96	2.14		3.10	4.66
4400 Split rings, 2-1/2" diameter		120	.067		1.96	2.14		4.10	5.75
4500 4" diameter		110	.073		2.97	2.33		5.30	7.20
4550 Tie plate, 20 ga., 7" x 3 1/8"		110	.073		2.97	2.33		5.30	7.20
4560 Tie plate, 20 ga., 5" x 4 1/8"		110	.073		2.97	2.33		5.30	7.20
4575 Twist straps, 18 ga., 12" x 1 1/4"		110	.073		2.97	2.33		5.30	7.20
4580 Twist straps, 18 ga., 16" x 1 1/4"		110	.073		2.97	2.33		5.30	7.20
4600 Strap ties, 20 ga., 2 -1/16" wide, 12 13/16" long		180	.044		.94	1.43		2.37	3.43
4700 Strap ties, 16 ga., 1-3/8" wide, 12" long		180	.044		.94	1.43		2.37	3.43
4800 21-5/8" x 1-1/4"		160	.050		2.96	1.61		4.57	5.95
5000 Toothed rings, 2-5/8" or 4" diameter		90	.089	▼	1.78	2.85		4.63	6.75
5200 Truss plates, nailed, 20 ga., up to 32' span	▼	17	.471	Truss	12.90	15.10		28	39.50
5400 Washers, 2" x 2" x 1/8"				Ea.	.40			.40	.44
5500 3" x 3" x 3/16"				"	1.06			1.06	1.17
6000 Angles and gussets, painted									
6012 7 ga., 3-1/4" x 3-1/4" x 2-1/2" long	1 Carp	1.90	4.211	C	1,100	135		1,235	1,450
6014 3-1/4" x 3-1/4" x 5" long		1.90	4.211		2,150	135		2,285	2,600
6016 3-1/4" x 3-1/4" x 7-1/2" long		1.85	4.324		4,075	139		4,214	4,700
6018 5-3/4" x 5-3/4" x 2-1/2" long		1.85	4.324		2,625	139		2,764	3,125
6020 5-3/4" x 5-3/4" x 5" long		1.85	4.324		4,175	139		4,314	4,825
6022 5-3/4" x 5-3/4" x 7-1/2" long		1.80	4.444		6,175	143		6,318	7,050
6024 3 ga., 4-1/4" x 4-1/4" x 3" long		1.85	4.324		2,800	139		2,939	3,300
6026 4-1/4" x 4-1/4" x 6" long		1.85	4.324		6,000	139		6,139	6,825
6028 4-1/4" x 4-1/4" x 9" long	▼	1.80	4.444	▼	6,750	143		6,893	7,675

06 05 23.60 Timber Connectors	Crew	Daily Output	Labor-Hours	Unit	Material	2014 Bare Costs Labor	Equipment	Total	Total Incl O&P
6030	7-1/4" x 7-1/4" x 3" long	1 Carp	1.80	4.444	C	4,825	143		4,968	5,575
6032	7-1/4" x 7-1/4" x 6" long		1.80	4.444		6,525	143		6,668	7,425
6034	7-1/4" x 7-1/4" x 9" long	↓	1.75	4.571	↓	14,600	147		14,747	16,300
6036	Gussets									
6038	7 ga., 8-1/8" x 8-1/8" x 2-3/4" long	1 Carp	1.80	4.444	C	4,625	143		4,768	5,325
6040	3 ga., 9-3/4" x 9-3/4" x 3-1/4" long	"	1.80	4.444	"	6,400	143		6,543	7,300
6101	Beam hangers, polymer painted									
6102	Bolted, 3 ga., (W x H x L)									
6104	3-1/4" x 9" x 12" top flange	1 Carp	1	8	C	19,600	257		19,857	22,000
6106	5-1/4" x 9" x 12" top flange		1	8		20,500	257		20,757	22,900
6108	5-1/4" x 11" x 11-3/4" top flange		1	8		23,200	257		23,457	26,000
6110	6-7/8" x 9" x 12" top flange		1	8		21,200	257		21,457	23,700
6112	6-7/8" x 11" x 13-1/2" top flange		1	8		24,400	257		24,657	27,300
6114	8-7/8" x 11" x 15-1/2" top flange	↓	1	8	↓	26,100	257		26,357	29,100
6116	Nailed, 3 ga., (W x H x L)									
6118	3-1/4" x 10-1/2" x 10" top flange	1 Carp	1.80	4.444	C	20,500	143		20,643	22,700
6120	3-1/4" x 10-1/2" x 12" top flange		1.80	4.444		20,500	143		20,643	22,700
6122	5-1/4" x 9-1/2" x 10" top flange		1.80	4.444		20,900	143		21,043	23,200
6124	5-1/4" x 9-1/2" x 12" top flange		1.80	4.444		20,900	143		21,043	23,200
6128	6-7/8" x 8-1/2" x 12" top flange	↓	1.80	4.444	↓	21,400	143		21,543	23,700
6134	Saddle hangers, glu-lam (W x H x L)									
6136	3-1/4" x 10-1/2" x 5-1/4" x 6" saddle	1 Carp	.50	16	C	15,300	515		15,815	17,700
6138	3-1/4" x 10-1/2" x 6-7/8" x 6" saddle		.50	16		16,100	515		16,615	18,600
6140	3-1/4" x 10-1/2" x 8-7/8" x 6" saddle		.50	16		16,900	515		17,415	19,500
6142	3-1/4" x 19-1/2" x 5-1/4" x 10-1/8" saddle		.40	20		15,300	640		15,940	17,900
6144	3-1/4" x 19-1/2" x 6-7/8" x 10-1/8" saddle		.40	20		16,100	640		16,740	18,800
6146	3-1/4" x 19-1/2" x 8-7/8" x 10-1/8" saddle		.40	20		16,900	640		17,540	19,700
6148	5-1/4" x 9-1/2" x 5-1/4" x 12" saddle		.50	16		18,300	515		18,815	21,000
6150	5-1/4" x 9-1/2" x 6-7/8" x 9" saddle		.50	16		20,000	515		20,515	22,900
6152	5-1/4" x 10-1/2" x spec x 12" saddle		.50	16		21,800	515		22,315	24,800
6154	5-1/4" x 18" x 5-1/4" x 12-1/8" saddle		.40	20		18,300	640		18,940	21,200
6156	5-1/4" x 18" x 6-7/8" x 12-1/8" saddle		.40	20		20,000	640		20,640	23,100
6158	5-1/4" x 18" x spec x 12-1/8" saddle		.40	20		21,800	640		22,440	25,000
6160	6-7/8" x 8-1/2" x 6-7/8" x 12" saddle		.50	16		21,800	515		22,315	24,900
6162	6-7/8" x 8-1/2" x 8-7/8" x 12" saddle		.50	16		22,600	515		23,115	25,700
6164	6-7/8" x 10-1/2" x spec x 12" saddle		.50	16		21,800	515		22,315	24,900
6166	6-7/8" x 18" x 6-7/8" x 13-3/4" saddle		.40	20		21,800	640		22,440	25,100
6168	6-7/8" x 18" x 8-7/8" x 13-3/4" saddle		.40	20		22,600	640		23,240	25,900
6170	6-7/8" x 18" x spec x 13-3/4" saddle		.40	20		24,400	640		25,040	27,900
6172	8-7/8" x 18" x spec x 15-3/4" saddle	↓	.40	20	↓	38,000	640		38,640	42,900
6201	Beam and purlin hangers, galvanized, 12 ga.									
6202	Purlin or joist size, 3" x 8"	1 Carp	1.70	4.706	C	2,025	151		2,176	2,475
6204	3" x 10"		1.70	4.706		2,175	151		2,326	2,650
6206	3" x 12"		1.65	4.848		2,500	156		2,656	3,000
6208	3" x 14"		1.65	4.848		2,675	156		2,831	3,175
6210	3" x 16"		1.65	4.848		2,825	156		2,981	3,350
6212	4" x 8"		1.65	4.848		2,025	156		2,181	2,500
6214	4" x 10"		1.65	4.848		2,200	156		2,356	2,675
6216	4" x 12"		1.60	5		2,600	161		2,761	3,125
6218	4" x 14"		1.60	5		2,750	161		2,911	3,300
6220	4" x 16"		1.60	5		2,925	161		3,086	3,500
6222	6" x 8"		1.60	5		2,625	161		2,786	3,150
6224	6" x 10"	↓	1.55	5.161	↓	2,675	166		2,841	3,225

06 05 23.60 Timber Connectors	Crew	Daily Output	Labor-Hours	Unit	Material	2014 Bare Costs Labor	Equipment	Total	Total Incl O&P
6226	6" x 12"	1 Carp	1.55	5.161	C	4,575	166		4,741	5,325
6228	6" x 14"		1.50	5.333		4,850	171		5,021	5,650
6230	6" x 16"		1.50	5.333		5,125	171		5,296	5,950
6250	Beam seats									
6252	Beam size, 5-1/4" wide									
6254	5" x 7" x 1/4"	1 Carp	1.80	4.444	C	7,725	143		7,868	8,725
6256	6" x 7" x 3/8"		1.80	4.444		8,650	143		8,793	9,775
6258	7" x 7" x 3/8"		1.80	4.444		9,250	143		9,393	10,400
6260	8" x 7" x 3/8"		1.80	4.444		10,900	143		11,043	12,200
6262	Beam size, 6-7/8" wide									
6264	5" x 9" x 1/4"	1 Carp	1.80	4.444	C	9,225	143		9,368	10,300
6266	6" x 9" x 3/8"		1.80	4.444		12,000	143		12,143	13,400
6268	7" x 9" x 3/8"		1.80	4.444		12,200	143		12,343	13,600
6270	8" x 9" x 3/8"		1.80	4.444		14,400	143		14,543	16,100
6272	Special beams, over 6-7/8" wide									
6274	5" x 10" x 3/8"	1 Carp	1.80	4.444	C	12,500	143		12,643	13,900
6276	6" x 10" x 3/8"		1.80	4.444		14,600	143		14,743	16,200
6278	7" x 10" x 3/8"		1.80	4.444		15,200	143		15,343	16,900
6280	8" x 10" x 3/8"		1.75	4.571		16,300	147		16,447	18,100
6282	5-1/4" x 12" x 5/16"		1.75	4.571		12,600	147		12,747	14,100
6284	6-1/2" x 12" x 3/8"		1.75	4.571		20,900	147		21,047	23,200
6286	5-1/4" x 16" x 5/16"		1.70	4.706		18,600	151		18,751	20,700
6288	6-1/2" x 16" x 3/8"		1.70	4.706		24,200	151		24,351	27,000
6290	5-1/4" x 20" x 5/16"		1.70	4.706		21,800	151		21,951	24,300
6292	6-1/2" x 20" x 3/8"		1.65	4.848		28,500	156		28,656	31,700
6300	Column bases									
6302	4 x 4, 16 ga.	1 Carp	1.80	4.444	C	780	143		923	1,100
6306	7 ga.		1.80	4.444		2,850	143		2,993	3,400
6308	4 x 6, 16 ga.		1.80	4.444		1,825	143		1,968	2,250
6312	7 ga.		1.80	4.444		2,975	143		3,118	3,525
6314	6 x 6, 16 ga.		1.75	4.571		2,050	147		2,197	2,525
6318	7 ga.		1.75	4.571		4,075	147		4,222	4,725
6320	6 x 8, 7 ga.		1.70	4.706		3,175	151		3,326	3,725
6322	6 x 10, 7 ga.		1.70	4.706		3,400	151		3,551	3,975
6324	6 x 12, 7 ga.		1.70	4.706		3,675	151		3,826	4,300
6326	8 x 8, 7 ga.		1.65	4.848		6,200	156		6,356	7,075
6330	8 x 10, 7 ga.		1.65	4.848		7,425	156		7,581	8,425
6332	8 x 12, 7 ga.		1.60	5		8,075	161		8,236	9,150
6334	10 x 10, 3 ga.		1.60	5		8,225	161		8,386	9,325
6336	10 x 12, 3 ga.		1.60	5		9,475	161		9,636	10,700
6338	12 x 12, 3 ga.		1.55	5.161		10,300	166		10,466	11,600
6350	Column caps, painted, 3 ga.									
6352	3-1/4" x 3-5/8"	1 Carp	1.80	4.444	C	10,400	143		10,543	11,700
6354	3-1/4" x 5-1/2"		1.80	4.444		10,400	143		10,543	11,700
6356	3-5/8" x 3-5/8"		1.80	4.444		8,550	143		8,693	9,650
6358	3-5/8" x 5-1/2"		1.80	4.444		8,550	143		8,693	9,650
6360	5-1/4" x 5-1/2"		1.75	4.571		11,200	147		11,347	12,500
6362	5-1/4" x 7-1/2"		1.75	4.571		11,200	147		11,347	12,500
6364	5-1/2" x 3-5/8"		1.75	4.571		12,100	147		12,247	13,500
6366	5-1/2" x 5-1/2"		1.75	4.571		12,100	147		12,247	13,500
6368	5-1/2" x 7-1/2"		1.70	4.706		12,100	151		12,251	13,600
6370	6-7/8" x 5-1/2"		1.70	4.706		12,600	151		12,751	14,100
6372	6-7/8" x 6-7/8"		1.70	4.706		12,600	151		12,751	14,100

06 05 23.60 Timber Connectors		Crew	Daily Output	Labor-Hours	Unit	Material	2014 Bare Costs Labor	Equipment	Total	Total Incl O&P
6374	6-7/8" x 7-1/2"	1 Carp	1.70	4.706	C	12,600	151		12,751	14,100
6376	7-1/2" x 5-1/2"		1.65	4.848		13,100	156		13,256	14,800
6378	7-1/2" x 7-1/2"		1.65	4.848		13,100	156		13,256	14,800
6380	8-7/8" x 5-1/2"		1.60	5		13,900	161		14,061	15,600
6382	8-7/8" x 7-1/2"		1.60	5		13,900	161		14,061	15,600
6384	9-1/2" x 5-1/2"		1.60	5		18,800	161		18,961	20,900
6400	Floor tie anchors, polymer paint									
6402	10 ga., 3" x 37-1/2"	1 Carp	1.80	4.444	C	5,000	143		5,143	5,750
6404	3-1/2" x 45-1/2"		1.75	4.571		5,250	147		5,397	6,025
6406	3 ga., 3-1/2" x 56"		1.70	4.706		9,250	151		9,401	10,500
6410	Girder hangers									
6412	6" wall thickness, 4" x 6"	1 Carp	1.80	4.444	C	2,800	143		2,943	3,350
6414	4" x 8"		1.80	4.444		3,150	143		3,293	3,700
6416	8" wall thickness, 4" x 6"		1.80	4.444		3,250	143		3,393	3,825
6418	4" x 8"		1.80	4.444		3,250	143		3,393	3,825
6420	Hinge connections, polymer painted									
6422	3/4" thick top plate									
6424	5-1/4" x 12" w/5" x 5" top	1 Carp	1	8	C	35,900	257		36,157	39,900
6426	5-1/4" x 15" w/6" x 6" top		.80	10		38,100	320		38,420	42,400
6428	5-1/4" x 18" w/7" x 7" top		.70	11.429		40,100	365		40,465	44,700
6430	5-1/4" x 26" w/9" x 9" top		.60	13.333		42,700	430		43,130	47,600
6432	1" thick top plate									
6434	6-7/8" x 14" w/5" x 5" top	1 Carp	.80	10	C	43,700	320		44,020	48,600
6436	6-7/8" x 17" w/6" x 6" top		.80	10		48,600	320		48,920	54,000
6438	6-7/8" x 21" w/7" x 7" top		.70	11.429		53,000	365		53,365	59,000
6440	6-7/8" x 31" w/9" x 9" top		.60	13.333		58,000	430		58,430	64,500
6442	1-1/4" thick top plate									
6444	8-7/8" x 16" w/5" x 5" top	1 Carp	.60	13.333	C	54,500	430		54,930	60,500
6446	8-7/8" x 21" w/6" x 6" top		.50	16		60,000	515		60,515	67,000
6448	8-7/8" x 26" w/7" x 7" top		.40	20		68,000	640		68,640	75,500
6450	8-7/8" x 39" w/9" x 9" top		.30	26.667		84,500	855		85,355	94,500
6460	Holddowns									
6462	Embedded along edge									
6464	26" long, 12 ga.	1 Carp	.90	8.889	C	1,375	285		1,660	1,975
6466	35" long, 12 ga.		.85	9.412		1,800	300		2,100	2,500
6468	35" long, 10 ga.		.85	9.412		1,450	300		1,750	2,075
6470	Embedded away from edge									
6472	Medium duty, 12 ga.									
6474	18-1/2" long	1 Carp	.95	8.421	C	825	270		1,095	1,350
6476	23-3/4" long		.90	8.889		965	285		1,250	1,525
6478	28" long		.85	9.412		985	300		1,285	1,575
6480	35" long		.85	9.412		1,350	300		1,650	1,975
6482	Heavy duty, 10 ga.									
6484	28" long	1 Carp	.85	9.412	C	1,750	300		2,050	2,450
6486	35" long	"	.85	9.412	"	1,925	300		2,225	2,600
6490	Surface mounted (W x H)									
6492	2-1/2" x 5-3/4", 7 ga.	1 Carp	1	8	C	2,000	257		2,257	2,625
6494	2-1/2" x 8", 12 ga.		1	8		1,225	257		1,482	1,775
6496	2-7/8" x 6-3/8", 7 ga.		1	8		4,425	257		4,682	5,300
6498	2-7/8" x 12-1/2", 3 ga.		1	8		4,550	257		4,807	5,425
6500	3-3/16" x 9-3/8", 10 ga.		1	8		3,025	257		3,282	3,775
6502	3-1/2" x 11-5/8", 3 ga.		1	8		5,525	257		5,782	6,525
6504	3-1/2" x 14-3/4", 3 ga.		1	8		7,000	257		7,257	8,125

06 05 23.60 Timber Connectors		Crew	Daily Output	Labor-Hours	Unit	Material	2014 Bare Costs Labor	Equipment	Total	Total Incl O&P
6506	3-1/2" x 16-1/2", 3 ga.	1 Carp	1	8	C	8,450	257		8,707	9,725
6508	3-1/2" x 20-1/2", 3 ga.		.90	8.889		8,650	285		8,935	10,000
6510	3-1/2" x 24-1/2", 3 ga.		.90	8.889		10,900	285		11,185	12,500
6512	4-1/4" x 20-3/4", 3 ga.	▼	.90	8.889	▼	7,450	285		7,735	8,675
6520	Joist hangers									
6522	Sloped, field adjustable, 18 ga.									
6524	2" x 6"	1 Carp	1.65	4.848	C	545	156		701	860
6526	2" x 8"		1.65	4.848		980	156		1,136	1,325
6528	2" x 10" and up		1.65	4.848		1,625	156		1,781	2,050
6530	3" x 10" and up		1.60	5		1,225	161		1,386	1,625
6532	4" x 10" and up	▼	1.55	5.161	▼	1,475	166		1,641	1,900
6536	Skewed 45°, 16 ga.									
6538	2" x 4"	1 Carp	1.75	4.571	C	870	147		1,017	1,200
6540	2" x 6" or 2" x 8"		1.65	4.848		885	156		1,041	1,225
6542	2" x 10" or 2" x 12"		1.65	4.848		1,025	156		1,181	1,375
6544	2" x 14" or 2" x 16"		1.60	5		1,825	161		1,986	2,275
6546	(2) 2" x 6" or (2) 2" x 8"		1.60	5		1,650	161		1,811	2,075
6548	(2) 2" x 10" or (2) 2" x 12"		1.55	5.161		1,750	166		1,916	2,225
6550	(2) 2" x 14" or (2) 2" x 16"		1.50	5.333		2,775	171		2,946	3,350
6552	4" x 6" or 4" x 8"		1.60	5		1,375	161		1,536	1,775
6554	4" x 10" or 4" x 12"		1.55	5.161		1,600	166		1,766	2,050
6556	4" x 14" or 4" x 16"	▼	1.55	5.161	▼	2,475	166		2,641	3,000
6560	Skewed 45°, 14 ga.									
6562	(2) 2" x 6" or (2) 2" x 8"	1 Carp	1.60	5	C	1,900	161		2,061	2,350
6564	(2) 2" x 10" or (2) 2" x 12"		1.55	5.161		2,625	166		2,791	3,150
6566	(2) 2" x 14" or (2) 2" x 16"		1.50	5.333		3,850	171		4,021	4,525
6568	4" x 6" or 4" x 8"		1.60	5		2,250	161		2,411	2,750
6570	4" x 10" or 4" x 12"		1.55	5.161		2,375	166		2,541	2,875
6572	4" x 14" or 4" x 16"	▼	1.55	5.161	▼	3,175	166		3,341	3,775
6590	Joist hangers, heavy duty 12 ga., galvanized									
6592	2" x 4"	1 Carp	1.75	4.571	C	1,275	147		1,422	1,650
6594	2" x 6"		1.65	4.848		1,400	156		1,556	1,775
6595	2" x 6", 16 ga.		1.65	4.848		1,325	156		1,481	1,700
6596	2" x 8"		1.65	4.848		2,100	156		2,256	2,575
6597	2" x 8", 16 ga.		1.65	4.848		2,000	156		2,156	2,450
6598	2" x 10"		1.65	4.848		2,175	156		2,331	2,625
6600	2" x 12"		1.65	4.848		2,675	156		2,831	3,175
6602	2" x 14"		1.65	4.848		2,775	156		2,931	3,300
6604	2" x 16"		1.65	4.848		2,925	156		3,081	3,475
6606	3" x 4"		1.65	4.848		1,775	156		1,931	2,200
6608	3" x 6"		1.65	4.848		2,375	156		2,531	2,850
6610	3" x 8"		1.65	4.848		2,400	156		2,556	2,900
6612	3" x 10"		1.60	5		2,775	161		2,936	3,350
6614	3" x 12"		1.60	5		3,350	161		3,511	3,950
6616	3" x 14"		1.60	5		3,900	161		4,061	4,575
6618	3" x 16"		1.60	5		4,300	161		4,461	5,025
6620	(2) 2" x 4"		1.75	4.571		2,075	147		2,222	2,525
6622	(2) 2" x 6"		1.60	5		2,500	161		2,661	3,025
6624	(2) 2" x 8"		1.60	5		2,550	161		2,711	3,075
6626	(2) 2" x 10"		1.55	5.161		2,750	166		2,916	3,300
6628	(2) 2" x 12"		1.55	5.161		3,525	166		3,691	4,150
6630	(2) 2" x 14"		1.50	5.333		3,550	171		3,721	4,225
6632	(2) 2" x 16"	▼	1.50	5.333	▼	3,600	171		3,771	4,250

06 05 23 – Wood, Plastic, and Composite Fastenings

06 05 23.60 Timber Connectors		Crew	Daily Output	Labor-Hours	Unit	Material	2014 Bare Costs Labor	Equipment	Total	Total Incl O&P
6634	4" x 4"	1 Carp	1.65	4.848	C	1,500	156		1,656	1,900
6636	4" x 6"		1.60	5		1,650	161		1,811	2,100
6638	4" x 8"		1.60	5		1,900	161		2,061	2,375
6640	4" x 10"		1.55	5.161		2,350	166		2,516	2,850
6642	4" x 12"		1.55	5.161		2,500	166		2,666	3,025
6644	4" x 14"		1.55	5.161		2,975	166		3,141	3,550
6646	4" x 16"		1.55	5.161		3,275	166		3,441	3,875
6648	(3) 2" x 10"		1.50	5.333		3,625	171		3,796	4,275
6650	(3) 2" x 12"		1.50	5.333		4,025	171		4,196	4,750
6652	(3) 2" x 14"		1.45	5.517		4,325	177		4,502	5,050
6654	(3) 2" x 16"		1.45	5.517		4,400	177		4,577	5,150
6656	6" x 6"		1.60	5		1,950	161		2,111	2,425
6658	6" x 8"		1.60	5		2,000	161		2,161	2,475
6660	6" x 10"		1.55	5.161		2,400	166		2,566	2,900
6662	6" x 12"		1.55	5.161		2,725	166		2,891	3,275
6664	6" x 14"		1.50	5.333		3,425	171		3,596	4,050
6666	6" x 16"	▼	1.50	5.333	▼	4,025	171		4,196	4,725
6690	Knee braces, galvanized, 12 ga.									
6692	Beam depth, 10" x 15" x 5' long	1 Carp	1.80	4.444	C	5,225	143		5,368	6,000
6694	15" x 22-1/2" x 7' long		1.70	4.706		6,000	151		6,151	6,850
6696	22-1/2" x 28-1/2" x 8' long		1.60	5		6,450	161		6,611	7,375
6698	28-1/2" x 36" x 10' long		1.55	5.161		6,725	166		6,891	7,675
6700	36" x 42" x 12' long	▼	1.50	5.333	▼	7,425	171		7,596	8,450
6710	Mudsill anchors									
6714	2" x 4" or 3" x 4"	1 Carp	115	.070	C	1,350	2.23		1,352.23	1,475
6716	2" x 6" or 3" x 6"		115	.070		1,350	2.23		1,352.23	1,475
6718	Block wall, 13-1/4" long		115	.070		85	2.23		87.23	97.50
6720	21-1/4" long	▼	115	.070	▼	126	2.23		128.23	143
6730	Post bases, 12 ga. galvanized									
6732	Adjustable, 3-9/16" x 3-9/16"	1 Carp	1.30	6.154	C	1,075	198		1,273	1,500
6734	3-9/16" x 5-1/2"		1.30	6.154		2,025	198		2,223	2,550
6736	4" x 4"		1.30	6.154		930	198		1,128	1,350
6738	4" x 6"		1.30	6.154		2,700	198		2,898	3,300
6740	5-1/2" x 5-1/2"		1.30	6.154		3,325	198		3,523	3,975
6742	6" x 6"		1.30	6.154		3,325	198		3,523	3,975
6744	Elevated, 3-9/16" x 3-1/4"		1.30	6.154		1,150	198		1,348	1,600
6746	5-1/2" x 3-5/16"		1.30	6.154		1,650	198		1,848	2,125
6748	5-1/2" x 5"		1.30	6.154		2,475	198		2,673	3,025
6750	Regular, 3-9/16" x 3-3/8"		1.30	6.154		885	198		1,083	1,300
6752	4" x 3-3/8"		1.30	6.154		1,250	198		1,448	1,700
6754	18 ga., 5-1/4" x 3-1/8"		1.30	6.154		1,300	198		1,498	1,750
6755	5-1/2" x 3-3/8"		1.30	6.154		1,300	198		1,498	1,750
6756	5-1/2" x 5-3/8"		1.30	6.154		1,875	198		2,073	2,375
6758	6" x 3-3/8"		1.30	6.154		2,250	198		2,448	2,800
6760	6" x 5-3/8"	▼	1.30	6.154	▼	2,500	198		2,698	3,100
6762	Post combination cap/bases									
6764	3-9/16" x 3-9/16"	1 Carp	1.20	6.667	C	460	214		674	870
6766	3-9/16" x 5-1/2"		1.20	6.667		1,050	214		1,264	1,500
6768	4" x 4"		1.20	6.667		2,075	214		2,289	2,650
6770	5-1/2" x 5-1/2"		1.20	6.667		1,150	214		1,364	1,625
6772	6" x 6"		1.20	6.667		4,175	214		4,389	4,950
6774	7-1/2" x 7-1/2"		1.20	6.667		4,575	214		4,789	5,375
6776	8" x 8"	▼	1.20	6.667	▼	4,725	214		4,939	5,550

06 05 23.60 Timber Connectors		Crew	Daily Output	Labor-Hours	Unit	Material	2014 Bare Costs Labor	Equipment	Total	Total Incl O&P
6790	Post-beam connection caps									
6792	Beam size 3-9/16"									
6794	12 ga. post, 4" x 4"	1 Carp	1	8	C	2,900	257		3,157	3,600
6796	4" x 6"		1	8		3,850	257		4,107	4,675
6798	4" x 8"		1	8		5,700	257		5,957	6,700
6800	16 ga. post, 4" x 4"		1	8		1,200	257		1,457	1,725
6802	4" x 6"		1	8		2,000	257		2,257	2,625
6804	4" x 8"		1	8		3,350	257		3,607	4,125
6805	18 ga. post, 2-7/8" x 3"		1	8		3,350	257		3,607	4,125
6806	Beam size 5-1/2"									
6808	12 ga. post, 6" x 4"	1 Carp	1	8	C	3,450	257		3,707	4,225
6810	6" x 6"		1	8		5,450	257		5,707	6,425
6812	6" x 8"		1	8		3,750	257		4,007	4,550
6816	16 ga. post, 6" x 4"		1	8		1,875	257		2,132	2,500
6818	6" x 6"		1	8		2,000	257		2,257	2,625
6820	Beam size 7-1/2"									
6822	12 ga. post, 8" x 4"	1 Carp	1	8	C	4,775	257		5,032	5,700
6824	8" x 6"		1	8		5,025	257		5,282	5,950
6826	8" x 8"		1	8		7,550	257		7,807	8,725
6840	Purlin anchors, embedded									
6842	Heavy duty, 10 ga.									
6844	Straight, 28" long	1 Carp	1.60	5	C	1,450	161		1,611	1,850
6846	35" long		1.50	5.333		1,775	171		1,946	2,250
6848	Twisted, 28" long		1.60	5		1,450	161		1,611	1,850
6850	35" long		1.50	5.333		1,775	171		1,946	2,250
6852	Regular duty, 12 ga.									
6854	Straight, 18-1/2" long	1 Carp	1.80	4.444	C	825	143		968	1,150
6856	23-3/4" long		1.70	4.706		1,025	151		1,176	1,400
6858	29" long		1.60	5		1,050	161		1,211	1,450
6860	35" long		1.50	5.333		1,450	171		1,621	1,900
6862	Twisted, 18" long		1.80	4.444		825	143		968	1,150
6866	28" long		1.60	5		980	161		1,141	1,350
6868	35" long		1.50	5.333		1,450	171		1,621	1,900
6870	Straight, plastic coated									
6872	23-1/2" long	1 Carp	1.60	5	C	2,025	161		2,186	2,500
6874	26-7/8" long		1.60	5		2,375	161		2,536	2,875
6876	32-1/2" long		1.50	5.333		2,525	171		2,696	3,075
6878	35-7/8" long		1.50	5.333		2,625	171		2,796	3,200
6890	Purlin hangers, painted									
6892	12 ga., 2" x 6"	1 Carp	1.80	4.444	C	1,850	143		1,993	2,300
6894	2" x 8"		1.80	4.444		2,025	143		2,168	2,475
6896	2" x 10"		1.80	4.444		2,175	143		2,318	2,650
6898	2" x 12"		1.75	4.571		2,350	147		2,497	2,825
6900	2" x 14"		1.75	4.571		2,500	147		2,647	3,000
6902	2" x 16"		1.75	4.571		2,650	147		2,797	3,175
6904	3" x 6"		1.70	4.706		1,875	151		2,026	2,300
6906	3" x 8"		1.70	4.706		2,025	151		2,176	2,475
6908	3" x 10"		1.70	4.706		2,175	151		2,326	2,650
6910	3" x 12"		1.65	4.848		2,500	156		2,656	3,000
6912	3" x 14"		1.65	4.848		2,675	156		2,831	3,175
6914	3" x 16"		1.65	4.848		2,825	156		2,981	3,350
6916	4" x 6"		1.65	4.848		1,875	156		2,031	2,325
6918	4" x 8"		1.65	4.848		2,025	156		2,181	2,500

06 05 23 – Wood, Plastic, and Composite Fastenings

06 05 23.60 Timber Connectors	Crew	Daily Output	Labor-Hours	Unit	Material	2014 Bare Costs Labor	Equipment	Total	Total Incl O&P
6920	4" x 10"	1 Carp	1.65	4.848	C	2,200	156		2,356	2,675
6922	4" x 12"		1.60	5		2,600	161		2,761	3,125
6924	4" x 14"		1.60	5		2,750	161		2,911	3,300
6926	4" x 16"		1.60	5		2,925	161		3,086	3,500
6928	6" x 6"		1.60	5		2,475	161		2,636	3,000
6930	6" x 8"		1.60	5		2,625	161		2,786	3,150
6932	6" x 10"		1.55	5.161		2,675	166		2,841	3,225
6934	double 2" x 6"		1.70	4.706		2,025	151		2,176	2,475
6936	double 2" x 8"		1.70	4.706		2,175	151		2,326	2,650
6938	double 2" x 10"		1.70	4.706		2,350	151		2,501	2,825
6940	double 2" x 12"		1.65	4.848		2,500	156		2,656	3,000
6942	double 2" x 14"		1.65	4.848		2,675	156		2,831	3,175
6944	double 2" x 16"		1.65	4.848		2,825	156		2,981	3,350
6960	11 ga., 4" x 6"		1.65	4.848		3,700	156		3,856	4,325
6962	4" x 8"		1.65	4.848		3,975	156		4,131	4,625
6964	4" x 10"		1.65	4.848		4,250	156		4,406	4,925
6966	6" x 6"		1.60	5		3,750	161		3,911	4,400
6968	6" x 8"		1.60	5		4,025	161		4,186	4,700
6970	6" x 10"		1.55	5.161		4,300	166		4,466	5,000
6972	6" x 12"		1.55	5.161		4,575	166		4,741	5,325
6974	6" x 14"		1.55	5.161		4,850	166		5,016	5,625
6976	6" x 16"		1.50	5.333		5,125	171		5,296	5,950
6978	7 ga., 8" x 6"		1.60	5		4,075	161		4,236	4,750
6980	8" x 8"		1.60	5		4,350	161		4,511	5,050
6982	8" x 10"		1.55	5.161		4,625	166		4,791	5,375
6984	8" x 12"		1.55	5.161		4,900	166		5,066	5,675
6986	8" x 14"		1.50	5.333		5,175	171		5,346	6,000
6988	8" x 16"	▼	1.50	5.333	▼	5,450	171		5,621	6,300
7000	Strap connectors, galvanized									
7002	12 ga., 2-1/16" x 36"	1 Carp	1.55	5.161	C	1,175	166		1,341	1,575
7004	2-1/16" x 47"		1.50	5.333		1,650	171		1,821	2,100
7005	10 ga., 2-1/16" x 72"		1.50	5.333		1,725	171		1,896	2,200
7006	7 ga., 2-1/16" x 34"		1.55	5.161		2,925	166		3,091	3,500
7008	2-1/16" x 45"		1.50	5.333		3,825	171		3,996	4,500
7010	3 ga., 3" x 32"		1.55	5.161		4,925	166		5,091	5,700
7012	3" x 41"		1.55	5.161		5,125	166		5,291	5,925
7014	3" x 50"		1.50	5.333		7,825	171		7,996	8,900
7016	3" x 59"		1.50	5.333		9,525	171		9,696	10,800
7018	3-1/2" x 68"	▼	1.45	5.517	▼	9,675	177		9,852	10,900
7030	Tension ties									
7032	19-1/8" long, 16 ga., 3/4" anchor bolt	1 Carp	1.80	4.444	C	1,350	143		1,493	1,750
7034	20" long, 12 ga., 1/2" anchor bolt		1.80	4.444		1,750	143		1,893	2,175
7036	20" long, 12 ga., 3/4" anchor bolt		1.80	4.444		1,750	143		1,893	2,175
7038	27-3/4" long, 12 ga., 3/4" anchor bolt	▼	1.75	4.571	▼	3,100	147		3,247	3,675
7050	Truss connectors, galvanized									
7052	Adjustable hanger									
7054	18 ga., 2" x 6"	1 Carp	1.65	4.848	C	530	156		686	845
7056	4" x 6"		1.65	4.848		700	156		856	1,025
7058	16 ga., 4" x 10"		1.60	5		1,025	161		1,186	1,400
7060	(2) 2" x 10"	▼	1.60	5	▼	1,025	161		1,186	1,400
7062	Connectors to plate									
7064	16 ga., 2" x 4" plate	1 Carp	1.80	4.444	C	525	143		668	815
7066	2" x 6" plate	"	1.80	4.444	"	675	143		818	985

06 05 Common Work Results for Wood, Plastics, and Composites

06 05 23 – Wood, Plastic, and Composite Fastenings

06 05 23.60 Timber Connectors		Crew	Daily Output	Labor-Hours	Unit	Material	2014 Bare Costs Labor	Equipment	Total	Total Incl O&P
7068	Hip jack connector									
7070	14 ga.	1 Carp	1.50	5.333	C	2,750	171		2,921	3,325

06 05 23.70 Rough Hardware

0010	**ROUGH HARDWARE**, average percent of carpentry material									
0020	Minimum				Job	.50%				
0200	Maximum					1.50%				
0210	In seismic or hurricane areas, up to				↓	10%				

06 05 23.80 Metal Bracing

0010	**METAL BRACING**									
0302	Let-in, "T" shaped, 22 ga. galv. steel, studs at 16" O.C.	1 Carp	580	.014	L.F.	.81	.44		1.25	1.63
0402	Studs at 24" O.C.		600	.013		.81	.43		1.24	1.61
0502	16 ga. galv. steel straps, studs at 16" O.C.		600	.013		1.05	.43		1.48	1.88
0602	Studs at 24" O.C.	↓	620	.013	↓	1.05	.41		1.46	1.86

06 11 Wood Framing

06 11 10 – Framing with Dimensional, Engineered or Composite Lumber

06 11 10.01 Forest Stewardship Council Certification

0010	**FOREST STEWARDSHIP COUNCIL CERTIFICATION**									
0020	For Forest Stewardship Council (FSC) cert dimension lumber, add G					65%				

06 11 10.02 Blocking

0010	**BLOCKING**									
1790	Bolted to concrete									
1798	Ledger board, 2" x 4"	1 Carp	180	.044	L.F.	4.32	1.43		5.75	7.15
1800	2" x 6"		160	.050		4.32	1.61		5.93	7.45
1810	4" x 6"		140	.057		7.50	1.83		9.33	11.35
1820	4" x 8"	↓	120	.067	↓	8.40	2.14		10.54	12.85
1950	Miscellaneous, to wood construction									
2000	2" x 4"	1 Carp	250	.032	L.F.	.38	1.03		1.41	2.15
2005	Pneumatic nailed		305	.026		.38	.84		1.22	1.84
2050	2" x 6"		222	.036		.57	1.16		1.73	2.58
2055	Pneumatic nailed		271	.030		.58	.95		1.53	2.22
2100	2" x 8"		200	.040		.86	1.28		2.14	3.10
2105	Pneumatic nailed		244	.033		.87	1.05		1.92	2.72
2150	2" x 10"		178	.045		1.14	1.44		2.58	3.68
2155	Pneumatic nailed		217	.037		1.15	1.18		2.33	3.25
2200	2" x 12"		151	.053		1.54	1.70		3.24	4.56
2205	Pneumatic nailed	↓	185	.043	↓	1.55	1.39		2.94	4.05
2300	To steel construction									
2320	2" x 4"	1 Carp	208	.038	L.F.	.38	1.23		1.61	2.50
2340	2" x 6"		180	.044		.57	1.43		2	3.03
2360	2" x 8"		158	.051		.86	1.63		2.49	3.68
2380	2" x 10"		136	.059		1.14	1.89		3.03	4.43
2400	2" x 12"	↓	109	.073	↓	1.54	2.36		3.90	5.65

06 11 10.04 Wood Bracing

0010	**WOOD BRACING**									
0012	Let-in, with 1" x 6" boards, studs @ 16" O.C.	1 Carp	150	.053	L.F.	.80	1.71		2.51	3.76
0202	Studs @ 24" O.C.	"	230	.035	"	.80	1.12		1.92	2.76

06 11 Wood Framing

06 11 10 – Framing with Dimensional, Engineered or Composite Lumber

06 11 10.06 Bridging

		Crew	Daily Output	Labor-Hours	Unit	Material	2014 Bare Costs Labor	Equipment	Total	Total Incl O&P
0010	**BRIDGING**									
0012	Wood, for joists 16" O.C., 1" x 3"	1 Carp	130	.062	Pr.	.62	1.98		2.60	4
0017	Pneumatic nailed		170	.047		.68	1.51		2.19	3.29
0102	2" x 3" bridging		130	.062		.64	1.98		2.62	4.02
0107	Pneumatic nailed		170	.047		.66	1.51		2.17	3.27
0302	Steel, galvanized, 18 ga., for 2" x 10" joists at 12" O.C.		130	.062		.90	1.98		2.88	4.31
0352	16" O.C.		135	.059		.93	1.90		2.83	4.22
0402	24" O.C.		140	.057		1.90	1.83		3.73	5.20
0602	For 2" x 14" joists at 16" O.C.		130	.062		1.40	1.98		3.38	4.86
0902	Compression type, 16" O.C., 2" x 8" joists		200	.040		.93	1.28		2.21	3.18
1002	2" x 12" joists	▼	200	.040	▼	.93	1.28		2.21	3.18

06 11 10.10 Beam and Girder Framing

		Crew	Daily Output	Labor-Hours	Unit	Material	2014 Bare Costs Labor	Equipment	Total	Total Incl O&P
0010	**BEAM AND GIRDER FRAMING** R061110-30									
1000	Single, 2" x 6"	2 Carp	700	.023	L.F.	.57	.73		1.30	1.86
1005	Pneumatic nailed		812	.020		.58	.63		1.21	1.69
1020	2" x 8"		650	.025		.86	.79		1.65	2.27
1025	Pneumatic nailed		754	.021		.87	.68		1.55	2.10
1040	2" x 10"		600	.027		1.14	.86		2	2.69
1045	Pneumatic nailed		696	.023		1.15	.74		1.89	2.50
1060	2" x 12"		550	.029		1.54	.93		2.47	3.27
1065	Pneumatic nailed		638	.025		1.55	.81		2.36	3.06
1080	2" x 14"		500	.032		1.80	1.03		2.83	3.71
1085	Pneumatic nailed		580	.028		1.81	.89		2.70	3.48
1100	3" x 8"		550	.029		2.55	.93		3.48	4.37
1120	3" x 10"		500	.032		3.21	1.03		4.24	5.25
1140	3" x 12"		450	.036		3.86	1.14		5	6.15
1160	3" x 14"	▼	400	.040		4.50	1.28		5.78	7.10
1170	4" x 6"	F-3	1100	.036		2.59	1.07	.60	4.26	5.30
1180	4" x 8"		1000	.040		3.49	1.17	.66	5.32	6.55
1200	4" x 10"		950	.042		4.28	1.23	.70	6.21	7.55
1220	4" x 12"		900	.044		5.15	1.30	.74	7.19	8.65
1240	4" x 14"		850	.047		6.75	1.38	.78	8.91	10.60
1250	6" x 8"		525	.076		6.35	2.23	1.26	9.84	12.15
1260	6" x 10"		500	.080		7.95	2.34	1.33	11.62	14.15
1290	8" x 12"	▼	300	.133		14.10	3.91	2.21	20.22	24.50
2000	Double, 2" x 6"	2 Carp	625	.026		1.14	.82		1.96	2.63
2005	Pneumatic nailed		725	.022		1.15	.71		1.86	2.46
2020	2" x 8"		575	.028		1.72	.89		2.61	3.39
2025	Pneumatic nailed		667	.024		1.73	.77		2.50	3.21
2040	2" x 10"		550	.029		2.27	.93		3.20	4.07
2045	Pneumatic nailed		638	.025		2.30	.81		3.11	3.88
2060	2" x 12"		525	.030		3.08	.98		4.06	5.05
2065	Pneumatic nailed		610	.026		3.11	.84		3.95	4.84
2080	2" x 14"		475	.034		3.60	1.08		4.68	5.80
2085	Pneumatic nailed		551	.029		3.63	.93		4.56	5.55
3000	Triple, 2" x 6"		550	.029		1.71	.93		2.64	3.45
3005	Pneumatic nailed		638	.025		1.73	.81		2.54	3.25
3020	2" x 8"		525	.030		2.58	.98		3.56	4.48
3025	Pneumatic nailed		609	.026		2.60	.84		3.44	4.28
3040	2" x 10"		500	.032		3.41	1.03		4.44	5.50
3045	Pneumatic nailed		580	.028		3.44	.89		4.33	5.30
3060	2" x 12"	▼	475	.034	▼	4.62	1.08		5.70	6.90

06 11 Wood Framing

06 11 10 - Framing with Dimensional, Engineered or Composite Lumber

06 11 10.10 Beam and Girder Framing	Crew	Daily Output	Labor-Hours	Unit	Material	2014 Bare Costs Labor	2014 Bare Costs Equipment	Total	Total Incl O&P
3065 Pneumatic nailed	2 Carp	551	.029	L.F.	4.66	.93		5.59	6.70
3080 2" x 14"		450	.036		5.95	1.14		7.09	8.45
3085 Pneumatic nailed		522	.031		5.45	.98		6.43	7.65

06 11 10.12 Ceiling Framing

	Crew	Daily Output	Labor-Hours	Unit	Material	2014 Bare Costs Labor	2014 Bare Costs Equipment	Total	Total Incl O&P
0010 **CEILING FRAMING**									
6000 Suspended, 2" x 3"	2 Carp	1000	.016	L.F.	.37	.51		.88	1.27
6050 2" x 4"		900	.018		.38	.57		.95	1.38
6100 2" x 6"		800	.020		.57	.64		1.21	1.71
6150 2" x 8"		650	.025		.86	.79		1.65	2.27

06 11 10.14 Posts and Columns

	Crew	Daily Output	Labor-Hours	Unit	Material	2014 Bare Costs Labor	2014 Bare Costs Equipment	Total	Total Incl O&P
0010 **POSTS AND COLUMNS**									
0100 4" x 4"	2 Carp	390	.041	L.F.	1.71	1.32		3.03	4.10
0150 4" x 6"		275	.058		2.59	1.87		4.46	6
0200 4" x 8"		220	.073		3.49	2.33		5.82	7.75
0250 6" x 6"		215	.074		4.76	2.39		7.15	9.25
0300 6" x 8"		175	.091		6.35	2.93		9.28	11.95
0350 6" x 10"		150	.107		7.95	3.42		11.37	14.50

06 11 10.18 Joist Framing

	Crew	Daily Output	Labor-Hours	Unit	Material	2014 Bare Costs Labor	2014 Bare Costs Equipment	Total	Total Incl O&P
0010 **JOIST FRAMING**									
2000 Joists, 2" x 4"	2 Carp	1250	.013	L.F.	.38	.41		.79	1.11
2005 Pneumatic nailed		1438	.011		.38	.36		.74	1.02
2100 2" x 6"		1250	.013		.57	.41		.98	1.32
2105 Pneumatic nailed		1438	.011		.58	.36		.94	1.23
2150 2" x 8"		1100	.015		.86	.47		1.33	1.73
2155 Pneumatic nailed		1265	.013		.87	.41		1.28	1.63
2200 2" x 10"		900	.018		1.14	.57		1.71	2.21
2205 Pneumatic nailed		1035	.015		1.15	.50		1.65	2.09
2250 2" x 12"		875	.018		1.54	.59		2.13	2.69
2255 Pneumatic nailed		1006	.016		1.55	.51		2.06	2.57
2300 2" x 14"		770	.021		1.80	.67		2.47	3.10
2305 Pneumatic nailed		886	.018		1.81	.58		2.39	2.97
2350 3" x 6"		925	.017		1.41	.56		1.97	2.48
2400 3" x 10"		780	.021		3.21	.66		3.87	4.64
2450 3" x 12"		600	.027		3.86	.86		4.72	5.70
2500 4" x 6"		800	.020		2.59	.64		3.23	3.93
2550 4" x 10"		600	.027		4.28	.86		5.14	6.15
2600 4" x 12"		450	.036		5.15	1.14		6.29	7.55
2605 Sister joist, 2" x 6"		800	.020		.57	.64		1.21	1.71
2606 Pneumatic nailed		960	.017		.58	.54		1.12	1.53
3000 Composite wood joist 9-1/2" deep		.90	17.778	M.L.F.	1,725	570		2,295	2,850
3010 11-1/2" deep		.88	18.182		1,950	585		2,535	3,125
3020 14" deep		.82	19.512		2,325	625		2,950	3,600
3030 16" deep		.78	20.513		3,425	660		4,085	4,875
4000 Open web joist 12" deep		.88	18.182		3,100	585		3,685	4,375
4002 Per linear foot		880	.018	L.F.	3.10	.58		3.68	4.39
4004 Treated, per linear foot		880	.018	"	3.97	.58		4.55	5.35
4010 14" deep		.82	19.512	M.L.F.	3,275	625		3,900	4,650
4012 Per linear foot		820	.020	L.F.	3.27	.63		3.90	4.65
4014 Treated, per linear foot		820	.020	"	4.28	.63		4.91	5.75
4020 16" deep		.78	20.513	M.L.F.	3,650	660		4,310	5,125
4022 Per linear foot		780	.021	L.F.	3.66	.66		4.32	5.15
4024 Treated, per linear foot		780	.021	"	4.81	.66		5.47	6.40

06 11 Wood Framing

06 11 10 – Framing with Dimensional, Engineered or Composite Lumber

06 11 10.18 Joist Framing

		Crew	Daily Output	Labor-Hours	Unit	Material	2014 Bare Costs Labor	Equipment	Total	Total Incl O&P
4030	18" deep	2 Carp	.74	21.622	M.L.F.	4,000	695		4,695	5,575
4032	Per linear foot		740	.022	L.F.	3.99	.69		4.68	5.55
4034	Treated, per linear foot		740	.022	"	5.30	.69		5.99	6.95
6000	Composite rim joist, 1-1/4" x 9-1/2"		.90	17.778	M.L.F.	1,875	570		2,445	3,000
6010	1-1/4" x 11-1/2"		.88	18.182		2,300	585		2,885	3,500
6020	1-1/4" x 14-1/2"		.82	19.512		2,775	625		3,400	4,100
6030	1-1/4" x 16-1/2"		.78	20.513		3,300	660		3,960	4,725

06 11 10.24 Miscellaneous Framing

		Crew	Daily Output	Labor-Hours	Unit	Material	2014 Bare Costs Labor	Equipment	Total	Total Incl O&P
0010	**MISCELLANEOUS FRAMING**									
2000	Firestops, 2" x 4"	2 Carp	780	.021	L.F.	.38	.66		1.04	1.53
2005	Pneumatic nailed		952	.017		.38	.54		.92	1.33
2100	2" x 6"		600	.027		.57	.86		1.43	2.07
2105	Pneumatic nailed		732	.022		.58	.70		1.28	1.81
5000	Nailers, treated, wood construction, 2" x 4"		800	.020		.49	.64		1.13	1.62
5005	Pneumatic nailed		960	.017		.50	.54		1.04	1.44
5100	2" x 6"		750	.021		.76	.68		1.44	1.98
5105	Pneumatic nailed		900	.018		.77	.57		1.34	1.80
5120	2" x 8"		700	.023		1.01	.73		1.74	2.34
5125	Pneumatic nailed		840	.019		1.02	.61		1.63	2.15
5200	Steel construction, 2" x 4"		750	.021		.49	.68		1.17	1.69
5220	2" x 6"		700	.023		.76	.73		1.49	2.07
5240	2" x 8"		650	.025		1.01	.79		1.80	2.45
7000	Rough bucks, treated, for doors or windows, 2" x 6"		400	.040		.76	1.28		2.04	2.99
7005	Pneumatic nailed		480	.033		.77	1.07		1.84	2.64
7100	2" x 8"		380	.042		1.01	1.35		2.36	3.38
7105	Pneumatic nailed		456	.035		1.02	1.13		2.15	3.01
8000	Stair stringers, 2" x 10"		130	.123		1.14	3.95		5.09	7.90
8100	2" x 12"		130	.123		1.54	3.95		5.49	8.35
8150	3" x 10"		125	.128		3.21	4.11		7.32	10.45
8200	3" x 12"		125	.128		3.86	4.11		7.97	11.15
8870	Laminated structural lumber, 1-1/4" x 11-1/2"		130	.123		2.30	3.95		6.25	9.20
8880	1-1/4" x 14-1/2"		130	.123		2.76	3.95		6.71	9.70

06 11 10.26 Partitions

		Crew	Daily Output	Labor-Hours	Unit	Material	2014 Bare Costs Labor	Equipment	Total	Total Incl O&P
0010	**PARTITIONS**									
0020	Single bottom and double top plate, no waste, std. & better lumber									
0180	2" x 4" studs, 8' high, studs 12" O.C.	2 Carp	80	.200	L.F.	4.17	6.40		10.57	15.40
0185	12" O.C., pneumatic nailed		96	.167		4.22	5.35		9.57	13.65
0200	16" O.C.		100	.160		3.41	5.15		8.56	12.40
0205	16" O.C., pneumatic nailed		120	.133		3.45	4.28		7.73	11
0300	24" O.C.		125	.128		2.65	4.11		6.76	9.80
0305	24" O.C., pneumatic nailed		150	.107		2.68	3.42		6.10	8.70
0380	10' high, studs 12" O.C.		80	.200		4.93	6.40		11.33	16.20
0385	12" O.C., pneumatic nailed		96	.167		4.98	5.35		10.33	14.50
0400	16" O.C.		100	.160		3.98	5.15		9.13	13.05
0405	16" O.C., pneumatic nailed		120	.133		4.03	4.28		8.31	11.65
0500	24" O.C.		125	.128		3.03	4.11		7.14	10.25
0505	24" O.C., pneumatic nailed		150	.107		3.07	3.42		6.49	9.10
0580	12' high, studs 12" O.C.		65	.246		5.70	7.90		13.60	19.55
0585	12" O.C., pneumatic nailed		78	.205		5.75	6.60		12.35	17.45
0600	16" O.C.		80	.200		4.55	6.40		10.95	15.80
0605	16" O.C., pneumatic nailed		96	.167		4.60	5.35		9.95	14.05
0700	24" O.C.		100	.160		3.41	5.15		8.56	12.40

06 11 Wood Framing

06 11 10 – Framing with Dimensional, Engineered or Composite Lumber

06 11 10.26 Partitions

		Crew	Daily Output	Labor-Hours	Unit	Material	2014 Bare Costs Labor	Equipment	Total	Total Incl O&P
0705	24" O.C., pneumatic nailed	2 Carp	120	.133	L.F.	3.45	4.28		7.73	11
0780	2" x 6" studs, 8' high, studs 12" O.C.		70	.229		6.25	7.35		13.60	19.25
0785	12" O.C., pneumatic nailed		84	.190		6.35	6.10		12.45	17.25
0800	16" O.C.		90	.178		5.10	5.70		10.80	15.25
0805	16" O.C., pneumatic nailed		108	.148		5.20	4.76		9.96	13.70
0900	24" O.C.		115	.139		3.98	4.47		8.45	11.90
0905	24" O.C., pneumatic nailed		138	.116		4.03	3.72		7.75	10.70
0980	10' high, studs 12" O.C.		70	.229		7.40	7.35		14.75	20.50
0985	12" O.C., pneumatic nailed		84	.190		7.50	6.10		13.60	18.55
1000	16" O.C.		90	.178		5.95	5.70		11.65	16.15
1005	16" O.C., pneumatic nailed		108	.148		6.05	4.76		10.81	14.65
1100	24" O.C.		115	.139		4.55	4.47		9.02	12.50
1105	24" O.C., pneumatic nailed		138	.116		4.60	3.72		8.32	11.30
1180	12' high, studs 12" O.C.		55	.291		8.55	9.35		17.90	25
1185	12" O.C., pneumatic nailed		66	.242		8.65	7.80		16.45	22.50
1200	16" O.C.		70	.229		6.85	7.35		14.20	19.85
1205	16" O.C., pneumatic nailed		84	.190		6.90	6.10		13	17.90
1300	24" O.C.		90	.178		5.10	5.70		10.80	15.25
1305	24" O.C., pneumatic nailed		108	.148		5.20	4.76		9.96	13.70
1400	For horizontal blocking, 2" x 4", add		600	.027		.38	.86		1.24	1.86
1500	2" x 6", add		600	.027		.57	.86		1.43	2.07
1600	For openings, add	▼	250	.064	▼		2.05		2.05	3.46
1702	Headers for above openings, material only, add				B.F.	.71			.71	.78

06 11 10.28 Porch or Deck Framing

		Crew	Daily Output	Labor-Hours	Unit	Material	2014 Bare Costs Labor	Equipment	Total	Total Incl O&P
0010	**PORCH OR DECK FRAMING**									
0100	Treated lumber, posts or columns, 4" x 4"	2 Carp	390	.041	L.F.	1.22	1.32		2.54	3.56
0110	4" x 6"		275	.058		1.77	1.87		3.64	5.10
0120	4" x 8"		220	.073		3.07	2.33		5.40	7.30
0130	Girder, single, 4" x 4"		675	.024		1.22	.76		1.98	2.62
0140	4" x 6"		600	.027		1.77	.86		2.63	3.38
0150	4" x 8"		525	.030		3.07	.98		4.05	5.05
0160	Double, 2" x 4"		625	.026		1.01	.82		1.83	2.49
0170	2" x 6"		600	.027		1.56	.86		2.42	3.16
0180	2" x 8"		575	.028		2.08	.89		2.97	3.79
0190	2" x 10"		550	.029		2.72	.93		3.65	4.56
0200	2" x 12"		525	.030		4.07	.98		5.05	6.15
0210	Triple, 2" x 4"		575	.028		1.51	.89		2.40	3.16
0220	2" x 6"		550	.029		2.34	.93		3.27	4.14
0230	2" x 8"		525	.030		3.12	.98		4.10	5.10
0240	2" x 10"		500	.032		4.08	1.03		5.11	6.20
0250	2" x 12"		475	.034		6.10	1.08		7.18	8.50
0260	Ledger, bolted 4' O.C., 2" x 4"		400	.040		.64	1.28		1.92	2.87
0270	2" x 6"		395	.041		.91	1.30		2.21	3.19
0280	2" x 8"		390	.041		1.16	1.32		2.48	3.49
0290	2" x 10"		385	.042		1.47	1.33		2.80	3.86
0300	2" x 12"		380	.042		2.13	1.35		3.48	4.62
0310	Joists, 2" x 4"		1250	.013		.50	.41		.91	1.24
0320	2" x 6"		1250	.013		.78	.41		1.19	1.54
0330	2" x 8"		1100	.015		1.04	.47		1.51	1.93
0340	2" x 10"		900	.018		1.36	.57		1.93	2.45
0350	2" x 12"		875	.018		1.63	.59		2.22	2.78
0360	Railings and trim , 1" x 4"	1 Carp	300	.027	▼	.47	.86		1.33	1.96

06 11 Wood Framing

06 11 10 – Framing with Dimensional, Engineered or Composite Lumber

06 11 10.28 Porch or Deck Framing		Crew	Daily Output	Labor-Hours	Unit	Material	2014 Bare Costs Labor	Equipment	Total	Total Incl O&P
0370	2" x 2"	1 Carp	300	.027	L.F.	.33	.86		1.19	1.81
0380	2" x 4"		300	.027		.50	.86		1.36	1.99
0390	2" x 6"		300	.027		.77	.86		1.63	2.28
0400	Decking, 1" x 4"		275	.029	S.F.	1.95	.93		2.88	3.72
0410	2" x 4"		300	.027		1.67	.86		2.53	3.28
0420	2" x 6"		320	.025		1.65	.80		2.45	3.17
0430	5/4" x 6"		320	.025		2.04	.80		2.84	3.59
0440	Balusters, square, 2" x 2"	2 Carp	660	.024	L.F.	.34	.78		1.12	1.68
0450	Turned, 2" x 2"		420	.038		.45	1.22		1.67	2.55
0460	Stair stringer, 2" x 10"		130	.123		1.36	3.95		5.31	8.15
0470	2" x 12"		130	.123		1.63	3.95		5.58	8.45
0480	Stair treads, 1" x 4"		140	.114		1.96	3.67		5.63	8.30
0490	2" x 4"		140	.114		.50	3.67		4.17	6.70
0500	2" x 6"		160	.100		.75	3.21		3.96	6.25
0510	5/4" x 6"		160	.100		.95	3.21		4.16	6.45
0520	Turned handrail post, 4" x 4"		64	.250	Ea.	31	8.05		39.05	47.50
0530	Lattice panel, 4' x 8', 1/2"		1600	.010	S.F.	.80	.32		1.12	1.42
0535	3/4"		1600	.010	"	1.20	.32		1.52	1.86
0540	Cedar, posts or columns, 4" x 4"		390	.041	L.F.	3.80	1.32		5.12	6.40
0550	4" x 6"		275	.058		5.90	1.87		7.77	9.60
0560	4" x 8"		220	.073		10	2.33		12.33	14.95
0800	Decking, 1" x 4"		550	.029		1.81	.93		2.74	3.56
0810	2" x 4"		600	.027		3.63	.86		4.49	5.45
0820	2" x 6"		640	.025		6.60	.80		7.40	8.60
0830	5/4" x 6"		640	.025		4.45	.80		5.25	6.25
0840	Railings and trim, 1" x 4"		600	.027		1.81	.86		2.67	3.43
0860	2" x 4"		600	.027		3.63	.86		4.49	5.45
0870	2" x 6"		600	.027		6.60	.86		7.46	8.70
0920	Stair treads, 1" x 4"		140	.114		1.81	3.67		5.48	8.15
0930	2" x 4"		140	.114		3.63	3.67		7.30	10.15
0940	2" x 6"		160	.100		6.60	3.21		9.81	12.65
0950	5/4" x 6"		160	.100		4.45	3.21		7.66	10.30
0980	Redwood, posts or columns, 4" x 4"		390	.041		6.45	1.32		7.77	9.25
0990	4" x 6"		275	.058		11.20	1.87		13.07	15.45
1000	4" x 8"		220	.073		20.50	2.33		22.83	26.50
1240	Redwood decking, 1" x 4"	1 Carp	275	.029	S.F.	3.97	.93		4.90	5.95
1260	2" x 6"		340	.024		7.50	.76		8.26	9.50
1270	5/4" x 6"		320	.025		4.77	.80		5.57	6.60
1280	Railings and trim, 1" x 4"	2 Carp	600	.027	L.F.	1.17	.86		2.03	2.73
1310	2" x 6"		600	.027		7.50	.86		8.36	9.70
1420	Alternative decking, wood/plastic composite, 5/4" x 6" [G]		640	.025		3.04	.80		3.84	4.69
1440	1" x 4" square edge fir		550	.029		1.97	.93		2.90	3.74
1450	1" x 4" tongue and groove fir		450	.036		1.31	1.14		2.45	3.36
1460	1" x 4" mahogany		550	.029		1.81	.93		2.74	3.56
1462	5/4" x 6" PVC		550	.029		3.62	.93		4.55	5.55
1465	Framing, porch or deck, alt deck fastening, screws, add	1 Carp	240	.033	S.F.		1.07		1.07	1.80
1470	Accessories, joist hangers, 2" x 4"		160	.050	Ea.	.73	1.61		2.34	3.50
1480	2" x 6" through 2" x 12"		150	.053		1.39	1.71		3.10	4.41
1530	Post footing, incl excav, backfill, tube form & concrete, 4' deep, 8" dia	F-7	12	2.667		11.60	74.50		86.10	138
1540	10" diameter		11	2.909		16.90	81.50		98.40	156
1550	12" diameter		10	3.200		22.50	89.50		112	176

06 11 Wood Framing

06 11 10 – Framing with Dimensional, Engineered or Composite Lumber

06 11 10.30 Roof Framing		Crew	Daily Output	Labor-Hours	Unit	Material	2014 Bare Costs Labor	Equipment	Total	Total Incl O&P
0010	**ROOF FRAMING**									
1900	Rough fascia, 2" x 6"	2 Carp	250	.064	L.F.	.57	2.05		2.62	4.09
2000	2" x 8"		225	.071		.86	2.28		3.14	4.78
2100	2" x 10"		180	.089		1.14	2.85		3.99	6.05
5002	Rafters, to 4 in 12 pitch, 2" x 6", ordinary		1000	.016		.57	.51		1.08	1.49
5021	On steep roofs		800	.020		.57	.64		1.21	1.71
5041	On dormers or complex roofs		590	.027		.57	.87		1.44	2.09
5062	2" x 8", ordinary		950	.017		.86	.54		1.40	1.85
5081	On steep roofs		750	.021		.86	.68		1.54	2.09
5101	On dormers or complex roofs		540	.030		.86	.95		1.81	2.54
5122	2" x 10", ordinary		630	.025		1.14	.82		1.96	2.62
5141	On steep roofs		495	.032		1.14	1.04		2.18	3
5161	On dormers or complex roofs		425	.038		1.14	1.21		2.35	3.28
5182	2" x 12", ordinary		575	.028		1.54	.89		2.43	3.20
5201	On steep roofs		455	.035		1.54	1.13		2.67	3.60
5221	On dormers or complex roofs		395	.041		1.54	1.30		2.84	3.89
5250	Composite rafter, 9-1/2" deep		575	.028		1.72	.89		2.61	3.40
5260	11-1/2" deep		575	.028		1.95	.89		2.84	3.65
5301	Hip and valley rafters, 2" x 6", ordinary		760	.021		.57	.68		1.25	1.77
5321	On steep roofs		585	.027		.57	.88		1.45	2.11
5341	On dormers or complex roofs		510	.031		.57	1.01		1.58	2.32
5361	2" x 8", ordinary		720	.022		.86	.71		1.57	2.14
5381	On steep roofs		545	.029		.86	.94		1.80	2.53
5401	On dormers or complex roofs		470	.034		.86	1.09		1.95	2.78
5421	2" x 10", ordinary		570	.028		1.14	.90		2.04	2.77
5441	On steep roofs		440	.036		1.14	1.17		2.31	3.21
5461	On dormers or complex roofs		380	.042		1.14	1.35		2.49	3.52
5481	2" x 12", ordinary		525	.030		1.54	.98		2.52	3.35
5501	On steep roofs		410	.039		1.54	1.25		2.79	3.81
5521	On dormers or complex roofs		355	.045		1.54	1.45		2.99	4.13
5541	Hip and valley jacks, 2" x 6", ordinary		600	.027		.57	.86		1.43	2.07
5561	On steep roofs		475	.034		.57	1.08		1.65	2.45
5581	On dormers or complex roofs		410	.039		.57	1.25		1.82	2.74
5601	2" x 8", ordinary		490	.033		.86	1.05		1.91	2.70
5621	On steep roofs		385	.042		.86	1.33		2.19	3.18
5641	On dormers or complex roofs		335	.048		.86	1.53		2.39	3.52
5661	2" x 10", ordinary		450	.036		1.14	1.14		2.28	3.17
5681	On steep roofs		350	.046		1.14	1.47		2.61	3.72
5701	On dormers or complex roofs		305	.052		1.14	1.68		2.82	4.08
5721	2" x 12", ordinary		375	.043		1.54	1.37		2.91	4
5741	On steep roofs		295	.054		1.54	1.74		3.28	4.63
5762	On dormers or complex roofs		255	.063		1.54	2.01		3.55	5.10
5781	Rafter tie, 1" x 4", #3		800	.020		.47	.64		1.11	1.59
5791	2" x 4", #3		800	.020		.38	.64		1.02	1.50
5801	Ridge board, #2 or better, 1" x 6"		600	.027		.80	.86		1.66	2.32
5821	1" x 8"		550	.029		1.20	.93		2.13	2.89
5841	1" x 10"		500	.032		1.55	1.03		2.58	3.44
5861	2" x 6"		500	.032		.57	1.03		1.60	2.36
5881	2" x 8"		450	.036		.86	1.14		2	2.86
5901	2" x 10"		400	.040		1.14	1.28		2.42	3.41
5921	Roof cants, split, 4" x 4"		650	.025		1.71	.79		2.50	3.21
5941	6" x 6"		600	.027		4.76	.86		5.62	6.70

06 11 Wood Framing

06 11 10 – Framing with Dimensional, Engineered or Composite Lumber

06 11 10.30 Roof Framing

		Crew	Daily Output	Labor-Hours	Unit	Material	2014 Bare Costs Labor	Equipment	Total	Total Incl O&P
5961	Roof curbs, untreated, 2" x 6"	2 Carp	520	.031	L.F.	.57	.99		1.56	2.29
5981	2" x 12"		400	.040		1.54	1.28		2.82	3.86
6001	Sister rafters, 2" x 6"		800	.020		.57	.64		1.21	1.71
6021	2" x 8"		640	.025		.85	.80		1.65	2.28
6041	2" x 10"		535	.030		1.14	.96		2.10	2.87
6061	2" x 12"		455	.035		1.54	1.13		2.67	3.60

06 11 10.32 Sill and Ledger Framing

		Crew	Daily Output	Labor-Hours	Unit	Material	2014 Bare Costs Labor	Equipment	Total	Total Incl O&P
0010	**SILL AND LEDGER FRAMING**									
2002	Ledgers, nailed, 2" x 4"	2 Carp	755	.021	L.F.	.38	.68		1.06	1.56
2052	2" x 6"		600	.027		.57	.86		1.43	2.07
2102	Bolted, not including bolts, 3" x 6"		325	.049		1.39	1.58		2.97	4.19
2152	3" x 12"		233	.069		3.83	2.20		6.03	7.90
2602	Mud sills, redwood, construction grade, 2" x 4"		895	.018		2.26	.57		2.83	3.46
2622	2" x 6"		780	.021		3.40	.66		4.06	4.85
4002	Sills, 2" x 4"		600	.027		.37	.86		1.23	1.85
4052	2" x 6"		550	.029		.56	.93		1.49	2.19
4082	2" x 8"		500	.032		.85	1.03		1.88	2.66
4101	2" x 10"		450	.036		1.12	1.14		2.26	3.15
4121	2" x 12"		400	.040		1.52	1.28		2.80	3.84
4202	Treated, 2" x 4"		550	.029		.48	.93		1.41	2.10
4222	2" x 6"		500	.032		.75	1.03		1.78	2.56
4242	2" x 8"		450	.036		1	1.14		2.14	3.02
4261	2" x 10"		400	.040		1.31	1.28		2.59	3.60
4281	2" x 12"		350	.046		1.98	1.47		3.45	4.64
4402	4" x 4"		450	.036		1.18	1.14		2.32	3.22
4422	4" x 6"		350	.046		1.71	1.47		3.18	4.35
4462	4" x 8"		300	.053		2.99	1.71		4.70	6.15
4480	4" x 10"		260	.062		4.64	1.98		6.62	8.40

06 11 10.34 Sleepers

		Crew	Daily Output	Labor-Hours	Unit	Material	2014 Bare Costs Labor	Equipment	Total	Total Incl O&P
0010	**SLEEPERS**									
0100	On concrete, treated, 1" x 2"	2 Carp	2350	.007	L.F.	.27	.22		.49	.67
0150	1" x 3"		2000	.008		.45	.26		.71	.93
0200	2" x 4"		1500	.011		.53	.34		.87	1.16
0250	2" x 6"		1300	.012		.84	.40		1.24	1.58

06 11 10.36 Soffit and Canopy Framing

		Crew	Daily Output	Labor-Hours	Unit	Material	2014 Bare Costs Labor	Equipment	Total	Total Incl O&P
0010	**SOFFIT AND CANOPY FRAMING**									
1002	Canopy or soffit framing , 1" x 4"	2 Carp	900	.018	L.F.	.47	.57		1.04	1.47
1021	1" x 6"		850	.019		.80	.60		1.40	1.90
1042	1" x 8"		750	.021		1.20	.68		1.88	2.47
1102	2" x 4"		620	.026		.38	.83		1.21	1.81
1121	2" x 6"		560	.029		.57	.92		1.49	2.17
1142	2" x 8"		500	.032		.86	1.03		1.89	2.67
1202	3" x 4"		500	.032		1.07	1.03		2.10	2.91
1221	3" x 6"		400	.040		1.41	1.28		2.69	3.71
1242	3" x 10"		300	.053		3.21	1.71		4.92	6.40

06 11 10.38 Treated Lumber Framing Material

		Crew	Daily Output	Labor-Hours	Unit	Material	2014 Bare Costs Labor	Equipment	Total	Total Incl O&P
0010	**TREATED LUMBER FRAMING MATERIAL**									
0100	2" x 4"				M.B.F.	725			725	800
0110	2" x 6"					750			750	825
0120	2" x 8"					750			750	825
0130	2" x 10"					785			785	865
0140	2" x 12"					990			990	1,075

06 11 10 – Framing with Dimensional, Engineered or Composite Lumber

06 11 10.38 Treated Lumber Framing Material		Crew	Daily Output	Labor-Hours	Unit	Material	2014 Bare Costs Labor	Equipment	Total	Total Incl O&P
0200	4" x 4"				M.B.F.	885			885	975
0210	4" x 6"					855			855	940
0220	4" x 8"					1,125			1,125	1,225

06 11 10.40 Wall Framing

		Crew	Daily Output	Labor-Hours	Unit	Material	2014 Bare Costs Labor	Equipment	Total	Total Incl O&P
0010	**WALL FRAMING** R061110-30									
0100	Door buck, studs, header, access, 8' H, 2" x 4" wall, 3' W	1 Carp	32	.250	Ea.	15.80	8.05		23.85	31
0110	4' wide		32	.250		16.95	8.05		25	32
0120	5' wide		32	.250		21	8.05		29.05	36.50
0130	6' wide		32	.250		23	8.05		31.05	38.50
0140	8' wide		30	.267		30.50	8.55		39.05	48.50
0150	10' wide		30	.267		43.50	8.55		52.05	62.50
0160	12' wide		30	.267		56	8.55		64.55	76
0170	2" x 6" wall, 3' wide		32	.250		22	8.05		30.05	37.50
0180	4' wide		32	.250		23	8.05		31.05	39
0190	5' wide		32	.250		27	8.05		35.05	43.50
0200	6' wide		32	.250		29	8.05		37.05	45.50
0210	8' wide		30	.267		37	8.55		45.55	55
0220	10' wide		30	.267		49.50	8.55		58.05	69
0230	12' wide		30	.267		62	8.55		70.55	82.50
0240	Window buck, studs, header & access, 8' high 2" x 4" wall, 2' wide		24	.333		16.85	10.70		27.55	36.50
0250	3' wide		24	.333		19.60	10.70		30.30	39.50
0260	4' wide		24	.333		21.50	10.70		32.20	41.50
0270	5' wide		24	.333		25.50	10.70		36.20	46
0280	6' wide		24	.333		28.50	10.70		39.20	49.50
0290	7' wide		24	.333		35	10.70		45.70	56.50
0300	8' wide		22	.364		38.50	11.65		50.15	62
0310	10' wide		22	.364		52.50	11.65		64.15	77.50
0320	12' wide		22	.364		67	11.65		78.65	93.50
0330	2" x 6" wall, 2' wide		24	.333		24.50	10.70		35.20	45
0340	3' wide		24	.333		27	10.70		37.70	48
0350	4' wide		24	.333		29.50	10.70		40.20	50.50
0360	5' wide		24	.333		34	10.70		44.70	55.50
0370	6' wide		24	.333		37.50	10.70		48.20	59
0380	7' wide		24	.333		45	10.70		55.70	67.50
0390	8' wide		22	.364		49	11.65		60.65	73
0400	10' wide		22	.364		63.50	11.65		75.15	89
0410	12' wide		22	.364		79	11.65		90.65	107
2002	Headers over openings, 2" x 6"	2 Carp	360	.044	L.F.	.57	1.43		2	3.03
2007	2" x 6", pneumatic nailed		432	.037		.58	1.19		1.77	2.63
2052	2" x 8"		340	.047		.86	1.51		2.37	3.48
2057	2" x 8", pneumatic nailed		408	.039		.87	1.26		2.13	3.07
2101	2" x 10"		320	.050		1.14	1.61		2.75	3.95
2106	2" x 10", pneumatic nailed		384	.042		1.15	1.34		2.49	3.51
2152	2" x 12"		300	.053		1.54	1.71		3.25	4.58
2157	2" x 12", pneumatic nailed		360	.044		1.55	1.43		2.98	4.11
2180	4" x 8"		260	.062		3.49	1.98		5.47	7.15
2185	4" x 8", pneumatic nailed		312	.051		3.51	1.65		5.16	6.65
2191	4" x 10"		240	.067		4.28	2.14		6.42	8.30
2196	4" x 10", pneumatic nailed		288	.056		4.30	1.78		6.08	7.75
2202	4" x 12"		190	.084		5.15	2.70		7.85	10.20
2207	4" x 12", pneumatic nailed		228	.070		5.15	2.25		7.40	9.50
2241	6" x 10"		165	.097		7.95	3.11		11.06	14

06 11 Wood Framing

06 11 10 – Framing with Dimensional, Engineered or Composite Lumber

06 11 10.40 Wall Framing	Crew	Daily Output	Labor-Hours	Unit	Material	2014 Bare Costs Labor	Equipment	Total	Total Incl O&P
2246	6" x 10", pneumatic nailed	2 Carp	198	.081	L.F.	8	2.59		10.59	13.10
2251	6" x 12"		140	.114		9.55	3.67		13.22	16.65
2256	6" x 12", pneumatic nailed		168	.095		9.55	3.06		12.61	15.70
5002	Plates, untreated, 2" x 3"		850	.019		.37	.60		.97	1.43
5007	2" x 3", pneumatic nailed		1020	.016		.38	.50		.88	1.26
5022	2" x 4"		800	.020		.38	.64		1.02	1.50
5027	2" x 4", pneumatic nailed		960	.017		.38	.54		.92	1.32
5041	2" x 6"		750	.021		.57	.68		1.25	1.78
5045	2" x 6", pneumatic nailed		900	.018		.58	.57		1.15	1.59
5061	Treated, 2" x 3"		850	.019		.42	.60		1.02	1.48
5066	2" x 3", treated, pneumatic nailed		1020	.016		.42	.50		.92	1.31
5081	2" x 4"		800	.020		.49	.64		1.13	1.62
5086	2" x 4", treated, pneumatic nailed		960	.017		.50	.54		1.04	1.44
5101	2" x 6"		750	.021		.76	.68		1.44	1.98
5106	2" x 6", treated, pneumatic nailed		900	.018		.77	.57		1.34	1.80
5122	Studs, 8' high wall, 2" x 3"		1200	.013		.37	.43		.80	1.13
5127	2" x 3", pneumatic nailed		1440	.011		.38	.36		.74	1.01
5142	2" x 4"		1100	.015		.37	.47		.84	1.20
5147	2" x 4", pneumatic nailed		1320	.012		.38	.39		.77	1.07
5162	2" x 6"		1000	.016		.57	.51		1.08	1.49
5167	2" x 6", pneumatic nailed		1200	.013		.58	.43		1.01	1.35
5182	3" x 4"		800	.020		1.07	.64		1.71	2.26
5187	3" x 4", pneumatic nailed		960	.017		1.08	.54		1.62	2.08
5201	Installed on second story, 2" x 3"		1170	.014		.37	.44		.81	1.15
5206	2" x 3", pneumatic nailed		1200	.013		.38	.43		.81	1.13
5221	2" x 4"		1015	.016		.38	.51		.89	1.27
5226	2" x 4", pneumatic nailed		1080	.015		.38	.48		.86	1.22
5241	2" x 6"		890	.018		.57	.58		1.15	1.60
5246	2" x 6", pneumatic nailed		1020	.016		.58	.50		1.08	1.48
5261	3" x 4"		800	.020		1.07	.64		1.71	2.26
5266	3" x 4", pneumatic nailed		960	.017		1.08	.54		1.62	2.08
5281	Installed on dormer or gable, 2" x 3"		1045	.015		.37	.49		.86	1.24
5286	2" x 3", pneumatic nailed		1254	.013		.38	.41		.79	1.10
5301	2" x 4"		905	.018		.38	.57		.95	1.37
5306	2" x 4", pneumatic nailed		1086	.015		.38	.47		.85	1.22
5321	2" x 6"		800	.020		.57	.64		1.21	1.71
5326	2" x 6", pneumatic nailed		960	.017		.58	.54		1.12	1.53
5341	3" x 4"		700	.023		1.07	.73		1.80	2.41
5346	3" x 4", pneumatic nailed		840	.019		1.08	.61		1.69	2.21
5361	6' high wall, 2" x 3"		970	.016		.37	.53		.90	1.30
5366	2" x 3", pneumatic nailed		1164	.014		.38	.44		.82	1.15
5381	2" x 4"		850	.019		.38	.60		.98	1.44
5386	2" x 4", pneumatic nailed		1020	.016		.38	.50		.88	1.27
5401	2" x 6"		740	.022		.57	.69		1.26	1.80
5406	2" x 6", pneumatic nailed		888	.018		.58	.58		1.16	1.60
5421	3" x 4"		600	.027		1.07	.86		1.93	2.62
5426	3" x 4", pneumatic nailed		720	.022		1.08	.71		1.79	2.38
5441	Installed on second story, 2" x 3"		950	.017		.38	.54		.92	1.32
5446	2" x 3", pneumatic nailed		1140	.014		.38	.45		.83	1.17
5461	2" x 4"		810	.020		.38	.63		1.01	1.49
5466	2" x 4", pneumatic nailed		972	.016		.38	.53		.91	1.31
5481	2" x 6"		700	.023		.57	.73		1.30	1.86
5486	2" x 6", pneumatic nailed		840	.019		.58	.61		1.19	1.66

06 11 Wood Framing

06 11 10 – Framing with Dimensional, Engineered or Composite Lumber

06 11 10.40 Wall Framing

		Crew	Daily Output	Labor-Hours	Unit	Material	2014 Bare Costs Labor	Equipment	Total	Total Incl O&P
5501	3" x 4"	2 Carp	550	.029	L.F.	1.07	.93		2	2.75
5506	3" x 4", pneumatic nailed		660	.024		1.08	.78		1.86	2.49
5521	Installed on dormer or gable, 2" x 3"		850	.019		.37	.60		.97	1.43
5526	2" x 3", pneumatic nailed		1020	.016		.38	.50		.88	1.26
5541	2" x 4"		720	.022		.38	.71		1.09	1.62
5546	2" x 4", pneumatic nailed		864	.019		.38	.59		.97	1.42
5561	2" x 6"		620	.026		.57	.83		1.40	2.02
5566	2" x 6", pneumatic nailed		744	.022		.58	.69		1.27	1.79
5581	3" x 4"		480	.033		1.07	1.07		2.14	2.98
5586	3" x 4", pneumatic nailed		576	.028		1.08	.89		1.97	2.68
5601	3' high wall, 2" x 3"		740	.022		.37	.69		1.06	1.58
5606	2" x 3", pneumatic nailed		888	.018		.38	.58		.96	1.38
5621	2" x 4"		640	.025		.38	.80		1.18	1.77
5626	2" x 4", pneumatic nailed		768	.021		.38	.67		1.05	1.54
5641	2" x 6"		550	.029		.57	.93		1.50	2.20
5646	2" x 6", pneumatic nailed		660	.024		.58	.78		1.36	1.94
5661	3" x 4"		440	.036		1.07	1.17		2.24	3.14
5666	3" x 4", pneumatic nailed		528	.030		1.08	.97		2.05	2.82
5681	Installed on second story, 2" x 3"		700	.023		.37	.73		1.10	1.64
5686	2" x 3", pneumatic nailed		840	.019		.38	.61		.99	1.44
5701	2" x 4"		610	.026		.38	.84		1.22	1.84
5706	2" x 4", pneumatic nailed		732	.022		.38	.70		1.08	1.60
5721	2" x 6"		520	.031		.57	.99		1.56	2.29
5726	2" x 6", pneumatic nailed		624	.026		.58	.82		1.40	2.01
5741	3" x 4"		430	.037		1.07	1.19		2.26	3.19
5746	3" x 4", pneumatic nailed		516	.031		1.08	1		2.08	2.85
5761	Installed on dormer or gable, 2" x 3"		625	.026		.37	.82		1.19	1.79
5766	2" x 3", pneumatic nailed		750	.021		.38	.68		1.06	1.56
5781	2" x 4"		545	.029		.38	.94		1.32	2.01
5786	2" x 4", pneumatic nailed		654	.024		.38	.79		1.17	1.74
5801	2" x 6"		465	.034		.57	1.10		1.67	2.49
5806	2" x 6", pneumatic nailed		558	.029		.58	.92		1.50	2.18
5821	3" x 4"		380	.042		1.07	1.35		2.42	3.45
5826	3" x 4", pneumatic nailed		456	.035		1.08	1.13		2.21	3.07
8250	For second story & above, add						5%			
8300	For dormer & gable, add						15%			

06 11 10.42 Furring

		Crew	Daily Output	Labor-Hours	Unit	Material	2014 Bare Costs Labor	Equipment	Total	Total Incl O&P
0010	**FURRING**									
0012	Wood strips, 1" x 2", on walls, on wood	1 Carp	550	.015	L.F.	.24	.47		.71	1.05
0015	On wood, pneumatic nailed		710	.011		.24	.36		.60	.87
0300	On masonry		495	.016		.26	.52		.78	1.16
0400	On concrete		260	.031		.26	.99		1.25	1.95
0600	1" x 3", on walls, on wood		550	.015		.38	.47		.85	1.21
0605	On wood, pneumatic nailed		710	.011		.39	.36		.75	1.03
0700	On masonry		495	.016		.42	.52		.94	1.33
0800	On concrete		260	.031		.42	.99		1.41	2.12
0850	On ceilings, on wood		350	.023		.38	.73		1.11	1.65
0855	On wood, pneumatic nailed		450	.018		.39	.57		.96	1.38
0900	On masonry		320	.025		.42	.80		1.22	1.81
0950	On concrete		210	.038		.42	1.22		1.64	2.52

06 11 Wood Framing

06 11 10 – Framing with Dimensional, Engineered or Composite Lumber

06 11 10.44 Grounds		Crew	Daily Output	Labor-Hours	Unit	Material	2014 Bare Costs Labor	Equipment	Total	Total Incl O&P
0010	**GROUNDS**									
0020	For casework, 1" x 2" wood strips, on wood	1 Carp	330	.024	L.F.	.24	.78		1.02	1.57
0100	On masonry		285	.028		.26	.90		1.16	1.81
0200	On concrete		250	.032		.26	1.03		1.29	2.02
0400	For plaster, 3/4" deep, on wood		450	.018		.24	.57		.81	1.22
0500	On masonry		225	.036		.26	1.14		1.40	2.21
0600	On concrete		175	.046		.26	1.47		1.73	2.76
0700	On metal lath		200	.040		.26	1.28		1.54	2.45

06 12 Structural Panels

06 12 10 – Structural Insulated Panels

06 12 10.10 OSB Faced Panels

			Crew	Daily Output	Labor-Hours	Unit	Material	2014 Bare Costs Labor	Equipment	Total	Total Incl O&P
0010	**OSB FACED PANELS**										
0100	Structural insul. panels, 7/16" OSB both faces, EPS insul, 3-5/8" T	G	F-3	2075	.019	S.F.	3.06	.57	.32	3.95	4.67
0110	5-5/8" thick	G		1725	.023		3.43	.68	.38	4.49	5.35
0120	7-3/8" thick	G		1425	.028		3.73	.82	.47	5.02	6
0130	9-3/8" thick	G		1125	.036		4.08	1.04	.59	5.71	6.90
0140	7/16" OSB one face, EPS insul, 3-5/8" thick	G		2175	.018		3.25	.54	.30	4.09	4.82
0150	5-5/8" thick	G		1825	.022		3.72	.64	.36	4.72	5.55
0160	7-3/8" thick	G		1525	.026		4.15	.77	.43	5.35	6.35
0170	9-3/8" thick	G		1225	.033		4.62	.96	.54	6.12	7.30
0190	7/16" OSB - 1/2" GWB faces , EPS insul, 3-5/8" T	G		2075	.019		3.22	.57	.32	4.11	4.84
0200	5-5/8" thick	G		1725	.023		3.69	.68	.38	4.75	5.60
0210	7-3/8" thick	G		1425	.028		4.11	.82	.47	5.40	6.40
0220	9-3/8" thick	G		1125	.036		4.82	1.04	.59	6.45	7.70
0240	7/16" OSB - 1/2" MRGWB faces , EPS insul, 3-5/8" T	G		2075	.019		3.22	.57	.32	4.11	4.84
0250	5-5/8" thick	G		1725	.023		3.69	.68	.38	4.75	5.60
0260	7-3/8" thick	G		1425	.028		4.11	.82	.47	5.40	6.40
0270	9-3/8" thick	G		1125	.036		4.82	1.04	.59	6.45	7.70
0300	For 1/2" GWB added to OSB skin, add	G					.68			.68	.75
0310	For 1/2" MRGWB added to OSB skin, add	G					.68			.68	.75
0320	For one T1-11 skin, add to OSB-OSB	G					1.55			1.55	1.71
0330	For one 19/32" CDX skin, add to OSB-OSB	G					.79			.79	.87
0500	Structural insulated panel, 7/16" OSB both sides, straw core										
0510	4-3/8" T, walls (w/sill, splines, plates)	G	F-6	2400	.017	S.F.	7.40	.49	.28	8.17	9.20
0520	Floors (w/splines)	G		2400	.017		7.40	.49	.28	8.17	9.20
0530	Roof (w/splines)	G		2400	.017		7.40	.49	.28	8.17	9.20
0550	7-7/8" T, walls (w/sill, splines, plates)	G		2400	.017		11.20	.49	.28	11.97	13.40
0560	Floors (w/splines)	G		2400	.017		11.20	.49	.28	11.97	13.40
0570	Roof (w/splines)	G		2400	.017		11.20	.49	.28	11.97	13.40

06 12 19 – Composite Shearwall Panels

06 12 19.10 Steel and Wood Composite Shearwall Panels

		Crew	Daily Output	Labor-Hours	Unit	Material	2014 Bare Costs Labor	Equipment	Total	Total Incl O&P
0010	**STEEL & WOOD COMPOSITE SHEARWALL PANELS**									
0020	Anchor bolts, 36" long (must be placed in wet concrete)	1 Carp	150	.053	Ea.	35	1.71		36.71	41.50
0030	On concrete, 2 x 4 & 2 x 6 walls, 7' - 10' high, 360 lb. shear, 12" wide	2 Carp	8	2		465	64		529	620
0040	715 lb. shear, 15" wide		8	2		560	64		624	725
0050	1860 lb. shear, 18" wide		8	2		580	64		644	745
0060	2780 lb. shear, 21" wide		8	2		685	64		749	865
0070	3790 lb. shear, 24" wide		8	2		790	64		854	975
0080	2 x 6 walls, 11' to 13' high, 1180 lb. shear, 18" wide		6	2.667		705	85.50		790.50	920

06 12 Structural Panels

06 12 19 – Composite Shearwall Panels

06 12 19.10 Steel and Wood Composite Shearwall Panels	Crew	Daily Output	Labor-Hours	Unit	Material	2014 Bare Costs Labor	Equipment	Total	Total Incl O&P
0090	1555 lb. shear, 21" wide	2 Carp	6	2.667	Ea.	890	85.50		975.50	1,125
0100	2280 lb. shear, 24" wide	"	6	2.667	"	995	85.50		1,080.50	1,250
0110	For installing above on wood floor frame, add									
0120	Coupler nuts, threaded rods, bolts, shear transfer plate kit	1 Carp	16	.500	Ea.	70	16.05		86.05	104
0130	Framing anchors, angle (2 required)	"	96	.083	"	2.61	2.67		5.28	7.35
0140	For blocking see Section 06 11 10.02									
0150	For installing above, first floor to second floor, wood floor frame, add									
0160	Add stack option to first floor wall panel				Ea.	77			77	84.50
0170	Threaded rods, bolts, shear transfer plate kit	1 Carp	16	.500		84	16.05		100.05	120
0180	Framing anchors, angle (2 required)	"	96	.083		2.61	2.67		5.28	7.35
0190	For blocking see 06 11 10.02									
0200	For installing stacked panels, balloon framing									
0210	Add stack option to first floor wall panel				Ea.	77			77	84.50
0220	Threaded rods, bolts kit	1 Carp	16	.500	"	49	16.05		65.05	81

06 13 Heavy Timber Construction

06 13 13 – Log Construction

06 13 13.10 Log Structures

		Crew	Daily Output	Labor-Hours	Unit	Material	Labor	Equipment	Total	Total Incl O&P
0010	**LOG STRUCTURES**									
0020	Exterior walls, pine, D logs, with double T & G, 6" x 6"	2 Carp	500	.032	L.F.	4.31	1.03		5.34	6.45
0030	6" x 8"		375	.043		4.91	1.37		6.28	7.70
0040	8" x 6"		375	.043		4.31	1.37		5.68	7.05
0050	8" x 7"		322	.050		4.31	1.60		5.91	7.40
0060	Square/rectangular logs, with double T & G, 6" x 6"		500	.032		4.31	1.03		5.34	6.45
0070	6" x 8"		375	.043		4.31	1.37		5.68	7.05
0080	8" x 6"		375	.043		4.31	1.37		5.68	7.05
0090	8" x 7"		322	.050		4.31	1.60		5.91	7.40
0100	Round logs, with double T & G, 6" x 8"		375	.043		4.31	1.37		5.68	7.05
0110	8" x 7"		322	.050		4.31	1.60		5.91	7.40
0120	Log siding, ship lapped, 2" x 6"		225	.071	S.F.	3.49	2.28		5.77	7.70
0130	2" x 8"		200	.080		2.56	2.57		5.13	7.15
0140	2" x 12"		180	.089		2.92	2.85		5.77	8
0150	Foam sealant strip, 3/8" x 3/8"	1 Carp	1920	.004	L.F.	.17	.13		.30	.42
0152	Chinking, 2" - 3" wide joint, 1/4" to 3/8" deep		600	.013		1.29	.43		1.72	2.14
0154	Caulking, 1/4" to 1/2" joint		900	.009		.50	.29		.79	1.03
0156	Backer rod, 1/4"		900	.009		.19	.29		.48	.69
0157	Penetrating wood preservative	1 Pord	2000	.004	S.F.	.13	.11		.24	.33
0158	Insect treatment	"	4000	.002	"	.34	.06		.40	.47
0160	Upper floor framing, pine, posts/columns, 4" x 6"	2 Carp	750	.021	L.F.	2.58	.68		3.26	3.98
0180	4" x 8"		562	.028		3.47	.91		4.38	5.35
0190	6" x 6"		500	.032		4.73	1.03		5.76	6.95
0200	6" x 8"		375	.043		6.30	1.37		7.67	9.25
0210	8" x 8"		281	.057		8.95	1.83		10.78	12.90
0220	8" x 10"		225	.071		11.20	2.28		13.48	16.15
0230	Beams, 4" x 8"		562	.028		3.47	.91		4.38	5.35
0240	4" x 10"		449	.036		4.25	1.14		5.39	6.60
0250	4" x 12"		375	.043		5.10	1.37		6.47	7.90
0260	6" x 8"		375	.043		6.30	1.37		7.67	9.25
0270	6" x 10"		300	.053		7.90	1.71		9.61	11.60
0280	6" x 12"		250	.064		9.50	2.05		11.55	13.90
0290	8" x 10"		225	.071		11.20	2.28		13.48	16.15

06 13 Heavy Timber Construction

06 13 13 – Log Construction

06 13 13.10 Log Structures

		Crew	Daily Output	Labor-Hours	Unit	Material	2014 Bare Costs Labor	Equipment	Total	Total Incl O&P
0300	8" x 12"	2 Carp	188	.085	L.F.	14	2.73		16.73	20
0310	Joists, 4" x 8"		562	.028		3.47	.91		4.38	5.35
0320	4" x 10"		449	.036		4.25	1.14		5.39	6.60
0330	4" x 12"		375	.043		5.10	1.37		6.47	7.90
0340	6" x 8"		375	.043		6.30	1.37		7.67	9.25
0350	6" x 10"		300	.053		7.90	1.71		9.61	11.60
0360	6" x 12"		250	.064		9.50	2.05		11.55	13.90
0370	8" x 10"		225	.071		11.20	2.28		13.48	16.15
0380	8" x 12"		188	.085	▼	13.45	2.73		16.18	19.40
0390	Decking, 1" x 6" T & G		964	.017	S.F.	1.64	.53		2.17	2.70
0400	1" x 8" T & G		700	.023		1.44	.73		2.17	2.81
0410	2" x 6" T & G		482	.033	▼	2.73	1.07		3.80	4.79
0420	Gable end roof framing, rafters, 4" x 8"		562	.028	L.F.	3.47	.91		4.38	5.35
0430	4" x 10"		449	.036		4.25	1.14		5.39	6.60
0450	4" x 12"		375	.043		5.10	1.37		6.47	7.90
0460	6" x 8"		375	.043		6.30	1.37		7.67	9.25
0470	6" x 10"		300	.053		7.90	1.71		9.61	11.60
0480	6" x 12"		250	.064		9.50	2.05		11.55	13.90
0490	8" x 10"		225	.071		11.20	2.28		13.48	16.15
0500	8" x 12"		188	.085		13.45	2.73		16.18	19.40
0510	Purlins, 4" x 8"		562	.028		3.47	.91		4.38	5.35
0520	6" x 8"		375	.043	▼	6.30	1.37		7.67	9.25
0530	Roof decking, 1" x 6" T & G		640	.025	S.F.	1.64	.80		2.44	3.15
0540	1" x 8" T & G		430	.037		1.44	1.19		2.63	3.59
0550	2" x 6" T & G	▼	320	.050	▼	2.73	1.61		4.34	5.70

06 13 23 – Heavy Timber Framing

06 13 23.10 Heavy Framing

		Crew	Daily Output	Labor-Hours	Unit	Material	2014 Bare Costs Labor	Equipment	Total	Total Incl O&P
0010	**HEAVY FRAMING**									
0020	Beams, single 6" x 10"	2 Carp	1.10	14.545	M.B.F.	1,600	465		2,065	2,525
0100	Single 8" x 16"		1.20	13.333	"	2,000	430		2,430	2,925
0202	Built from 2" lumber, multiple 2" x 14"		900	.018	B.F.	.76	.57		1.33	1.80
0212	Built from 3" lumber, multiple 3" x 6"		700	.023		.93	.73		1.66	2.25
0222	Multiple 3" x 8"		800	.020		1.27	.64		1.91	2.47
0232	Multiple 3" x 10"		900	.018		1.28	.57		1.85	2.36
0242	Multiple 3" x 12"		1000	.016		1.28	.51		1.79	2.26
0252	Built from 4" lumber, multiple 4" x 6"		800	.020		1.29	.64		1.93	2.50
0262	Multiple 4" x 8"		900	.018		1.30	.57		1.87	2.39
0272	Multiple 4" x 10"		1000	.016		1.28	.51		1.79	2.26
0282	Multiple 4" x 12"		1100	.015	▼	1.28	.47		1.75	2.19
0292	Columns, structural grade, 1500f, 4" x 4"		450	.036	L.F.	1.70	1.14		2.84	3.79
0302	6" x 6"		225	.071		4.21	2.28		6.49	8.45
0402	8" x 8"		240	.067		7.20	2.14		9.34	11.50
0502	10" x 10"		90	.178		12.10	5.70		17.80	23
0602	12" x 12"		70	.229	▼	18.35	7.35		25.70	32.50
0802	Floor planks, 2" thick, T & G, 2" x 6"		1050	.015	B.F.	1.59	.49		2.08	2.57
0902	2" x 10"		1100	.015		1.59	.47		2.06	2.54
1102	3" thick, 3" x 6"		1050	.015		1.59	.49		2.08	2.57
1202	3" x 10"		1100	.015		1.59	.47		2.06	2.54
1402	Girders, structural grade, 12" x 12"		800	.020		1.53	.64		2.17	2.76
1502	10" x 16"		1000	.016		2.40	.51		2.91	3.50
2302	Roof purlins, 4" thick, structural grade	▼	1050	.015	▼	1.30	.49		1.79	2.25

383

06 15 Wood Decking

06 15 16 – Wood Roof Decking

06 15 16.10 Solid Wood Roof Decking		Crew	Daily Output	Labor-Hours	Unit	Material	2014 Bare Costs Labor	Equipment	Total	Total Incl O&P
0010	**SOLID WOOD ROOF DECKING**									
0350	Cedar planks, 2" thick	2 Carp	350	.046	S.F.	5.35	1.47		6.82	8.30
0400	3" thick		320	.050		8	1.61		9.61	11.50
0500	4" thick		250	.064		10.65	2.05		12.70	15.20
0550	6" thick		200	.080		16	2.57		18.57	22
0650	Douglas fir, 2" thick		350	.046		2.69	1.47		4.16	5.45
0700	3" thick		320	.050		4.04	1.61		5.65	7.15
0800	4" thick		250	.064		5.40	2.05		7.45	9.35
0850	6" thick		200	.080		8.05	2.57		10.62	13.20
0950	Hemlock, 2" thick		350	.046		2.74	1.47		4.21	5.50
1000	3" thick		320	.050		4.11	1.61		5.72	7.20
1100	4" thick		250	.064		5.50	2.05		7.55	9.45
1150	6" thick		200	.080		8.20	2.57		10.77	13.35
1250	Western white spruce, 2" thick		350	.046		1.75	1.47		3.22	4.39
1300	3" thick		320	.050		2.62	1.61		4.23	5.60
1400	4" thick		250	.064		3.50	2.05		5.55	7.30
1450	6" thick		200	.080		5.25	2.57		7.82	10.05

06 15 23 – Laminated Wood Decking

06 15 23.10 Laminated Roof Deck

		Crew	Daily Output	Labor-Hours	Unit	Material	2014 Bare Costs Labor	Equipment	Total	Total Incl O&P
0010	**LAMINATED ROOF DECK**									
0020	Pine or hemlock, 3" thick	2 Carp	425	.038	S.F.	6.30	1.21		7.51	9
0100	4" thick		325	.049		8.70	1.58		10.28	12.20
0300	Cedar, 3" thick		425	.038		6.85	1.21		8.06	9.60
0400	4" thick		325	.049		9.15	1.58		10.73	12.75
0600	Fir, 3" thick		425	.038		6.30	1.21		7.51	9
0700	4" thick		325	.049		8.70	1.58		10.28	12.20

06 16 Sheathing

06 16 13 – Insulating Sheathing

06 16 13.10 Insulating Sheathing

			Crew	Daily Output	Labor-Hours	Unit	Material	2014 Bare Costs Labor	Equipment	Total	Total Incl O&P
0010	**INSULATING SHEATHING**										
0020	Expanded polystyrene, 1#/C.F. density, 3/4" thick R2.89	G	2 Carp	1400	.011	S.F.	.32	.37		.69	.98
0030	1" thick R3.85	G		1300	.012		.38	.40		.78	1.08
0040	2" thick R7.69	G		1200	.013		.62	.43		1.05	1.41
0050	Extruded polystyrene, 15 PSI compressive strength, 1" thick, R5	G		1300	.012		.67	.40		1.07	1.40
0060	2" thick, R10	G		1200	.013		.83	.43		1.26	1.64
0070	Polyisocyanurate, 2#/C.F. density, 3/4" thick	G		1400	.011		.58	.37		.95	1.26
0080	1" thick	G		1300	.012		.64	.40		1.04	1.37
0090	1-1/2" thick	G		1250	.013		.77	.41		1.18	1.54
0100	2" thick	G		1200	.013		.93	.43		1.36	1.75

06 16 23 – Subflooring

06 16 23.10 Subfloor

		Crew	Daily Output	Labor-Hours	Unit	Material	2014 Bare Costs Labor	Equipment	Total	Total Incl O&P
0010	**SUBFLOOR**									
0011	Plywood, CDX, 1/2" thick	2 Carp	1500	.011	SF Flr.	.60	.34		.94	1.23
0015	Pneumatic nailed		1860	.009		.60	.28		.88	1.11
0017	Pneumatic nailed		1860	.009		.60	.28		.88	1.11
0102	5/8" thick		1350	.012		.74	.38		1.12	1.46
0107	Pneumatic nailed		1674	.010		.74	.31		1.05	1.34
0202	3/4" thick		1250	.013		.88	.41		1.29	1.66
0207	Pneumatic nailed		1550	.010		.88	.33		1.21	1.53

06 16 Sheathing

06 16 23 – Subflooring

06 16 23.10 Subfloor

		Crew	Daily Output	Labor-Hours	Unit	Material	2014 Bare Costs Labor	Equipment	Total	Total Incl O&P
0302	1-1/8" thick, 2-4-1 including underlayment	2 Carp	1050	.015	SF Flr.	2.23	.49		2.72	3.27
0440	With boards, 1" x 6", S4S, laid regular		900	.018		1.74	.57		2.31	2.88
0452	1" x 8", laid regular		1000	.016		1.90	.51		2.41	2.95
0462	Laid diagonal		850	.019		1.90	.60		2.50	3.11
0502	1" x 10", laid regular		1100	.015		1.95	.47		2.42	2.93
0602	Laid diagonal		900	.018		1.95	.57		2.52	3.10
1500	OSB, 5/8" thick		1330	.012	S.F.	.52	.39		.91	1.22
1600	3/4" thick		1230	.013	"	.62	.42		1.04	1.38
8990	Subfloor adhesive, 3/8" bead	1 Carp	2300	.003	L.F.	.12	.11		.23	.32

06 16 26 – Underlayment

06 16 26.10 Wood Product Underlayment

		Crew	Daily Output	Labor-Hours	Unit	Material	2014 Bare Costs Labor	Equipment	Total	Total Incl O&P
0010	**WOOD PRODUCT UNDERLAYMENT**									
0015	Plywood, underlayment grade, 1/4" thick	2 Carp	1500	.011	S.F.	.84	.34		1.18	1.50
0018	Pneumatic nailed		1860	.009		.84	.28		1.12	1.38
0030	3/8" thick		1500	.011		.93	.34		1.27	1.60
0070	Pneumatic nailed		1860	.009		.93	.28		1.21	1.48
0102	1/2" thick		1450	.011		1.06	.35		1.41	1.77
0107	Pneumatic nailed		1798	.009		1.06	.29		1.35	1.65
0202	5/8" thick		1400	.011		1.18	.37		1.55	1.92
0207	Pneumatic nailed		1736	.009		1.18	.30		1.48	1.80
0302	3/4" thick		1300	.012		1.40	.40		1.80	2.20
0306	Pneumatic nailed		1612	.010		1.40	.32		1.72	2.08
0502	Particle board, 3/8" thick		1500	.011		.40	.34		.74	1.02
0507	Pneumatic nailed		1860	.009		.40	.28		.68	.90
0602	1/2" thick		1450	.011		.42	.35		.77	1.06
0607	Pneumatic nailed		1798	.009		.42	.29		.71	.94
0802	5/8" thick		1400	.011		.52	.37		.89	1.19
0807	Pneumatic nailed		1736	.009		.52	.30		.82	1.07
0902	3/4" thick		1300	.012		.62	.40		1.02	1.34
0907	Pneumatic nailed		1612	.010		.62	.32		.94	1.22
0955	Particleboard, 100% recycled straw/wheat, 4' x 8' x 1/4" [G]		1450	.011		.29	.35		.64	.92
0960	4' x 8' x 3/8" [G]		1450	.011		.42	.35		.77	1.06
0965	4' x 8' x 1/2" [G]		1350	.012		.59	.38		.97	1.29
0970	4' x 8' x 5/8" [G]		1300	.012		.71	.40		1.11	1.44
0975	4' x 8' x 3/4" [G]		1250	.013		.81	.41		1.22	1.58
0980	4' x 8' x 1" [G]		1150	.014		1.08	.45		1.53	1.94
0985	4' x 8' x 1-1/4" [G]		1100	.015		1.24	.47		1.71	2.15
1100	Hardboard, underlayment grade, 4' x 4', .215" thick [G]		1500	.011		.57	.34		.91	1.21

06 16 33 – Wood Board Sheathing

06 16 33.10 Board Sheathing

		Crew	Daily Output	Labor-Hours	Unit	Material	2014 Bare Costs Labor	Equipment	Total	Total Incl O&P
0009	**BOARD SHEATHING**									
0010	Roof, 1" x 6" boards, laid horizontal	2 Carp	725	.022	S.F.	1.74	.71		2.45	3.11
0020	On steep roof		520	.031		1.74	.99		2.73	3.58
0040	On dormers, hips, & valleys		480	.033		1.74	1.07		2.81	3.72
0050	Laid diagonal		650	.025		1.74	.79		2.53	3.25
0070	1" x 8" boards, laid horizontal		875	.018		1.90	.59		2.49	3.08
0080	On steep roof		635	.025		1.90	.81		2.71	3.45
0090	On dormers, hips, & valleys		580	.028		1.95	.89		2.84	3.63
0100	Laid diagonal		725	.022		1.90	.71		2.61	3.28
0110	Skip sheathing, 1" x 4", 7" OC	1 Carp	1200	.007		.58	.21		.79	1
0120	1" x 6", 9" OC	"	1450	.006		.80	.18		.98	1.18
0200	Walls, 1" x 6" boards, laid regular	2 Carp	650	.025		1.74	.79		2.53	3.25

06 16 Sheathing

06 16 33 – Wood Board Sheathing

06 16 33.10 Board Sheathing		Crew	Daily Output	Labor-Hours	Unit	Material	2014 Bare Costs Labor	Equipment	Total	Total Incl O&P
0210	Laid diagonal	2 Carp	585	.027	S.F.	1.74	.88		2.62	3.40
0220	1" x 8" boards, laid regular		765	.021		1.90	.67		2.57	3.22
0230	Laid diagonal	↓	650	.025	↓	1.90	.79		2.69	3.42

06 16 36 – Wood Panel Product Sheathing

06 16 36.10 Sheathing

			Crew	Daily Output	Labor-Hours	Unit	Material	2014 Bare Costs Labor	Equipment	Total	Total Incl O&P
0010	**SHEATHING**	R061636-20									
0012	Plywood on roofs, CDX										
0032	5/16" thick		2 Carp	1600	.010	S.F.	.55	.32		.87	1.15
0037	Pneumatic nailed			1952	.008		.55	.26		.81	1.05
0052	3/8" thick			1525	.010		.50	.34		.84	1.12
0057	Pneumatic nailed			1860	.009		.50	.28		.78	1.01
0102	1/2" thick			1400	.011		.60	.37		.97	1.27
0103	Pneumatic nailed			1708	.009		.60	.30		.90	1.16
0202	5/8" thick			1300	.012		.74	.40		1.14	1.48
0207	Pneumatic nailed			1586	.010		.74	.32		1.06	1.36
0302	3/4" thick			1200	.013		.88	.43		1.31	1.69
0307	Pneumatic nailed			1464	.011		.88	.35		1.23	1.56
0502	Plywood on walls, with exterior CDX, 3/8" thick			1200	.013		.50	.43		.93	1.27
0507	Pneumatic nailed			1488	.011		.50	.35		.85	1.13
0603	1/2" thick			1125	.014		.60	.46		1.06	1.42
0608	Pneumatic nailed			1395	.011		.60	.37		.97	1.27
0702	5/8" thick			1050	.015		.74	.49		1.23	1.64
0707	Pneumatic nailed			1302	.012		.74	.39		1.13	1.48
0803	3/4" thick			975	.016		.88	.53		1.41	1.86
0808	Pneumatic nailed		↓	1209	.013	↓	.88	.42		1.30	1.68
1000	For shear wall construction, add							20%			
1200	For structural 1 exterior plywood, add					S.F.	10%				
3000	Wood fiber, regular, no vapor barrier, 1/2" thick		2 Carp	1200	.013		.60	.43		1.03	1.38
3100	5/8" thick			1200	.013		.76	.43		1.19	1.56
3300	No vapor barrier, in colors, 1/2" thick			1200	.013		.73	.43		1.16	1.52
3400	5/8" thick			1200	.013		.77	.43		1.20	1.57
3600	With vapor barrier one side, white, 1/2" thick			1200	.013		.59	.43		1.02	1.37
3700	Vapor barrier 2 sides, 1/2" thick			1200	.013		.82	.43		1.25	1.62
3800	Asphalt impregnated, 25/32" thick			1200	.013		.32	.43		.75	1.07
3850	Intermediate, 1/2" thick			1200	.013		.24	.43		.67	.98
4500	Oriented strand board, on roof, 7/16" thick	G		1460	.011		.50	.35		.85	1.14
4505	Pneumatic nailed	G		1780	.009		.50	.29		.79	1.04
4550	1/2" thick	G		1400	.011		.50	.37		.87	1.17
4555	Pneumatic nailed	G		1736	.009		.50	.30		.80	1.05
4600	5/8" thick	G		1300	.012		.69	.40		1.09	1.42
4605	Pneumatic nailed	G		1586	.010		.69	.32		1.01	1.30
4610	On walls, 7/16" thick			1200	.013		.50	.43		.93	1.27
4615	Pneumatic nailed			1488	.011		.50	.35		.85	1.13
4620	1/2" thick			1195	.013		.50	.43		.93	1.27
4625	Pneumatic nailed			1325	.012		.50	.39		.89	1.20
4630	5/8" thick			1050	.015		.69	.49		1.18	1.58
4635	Pneumatic nailed			1302	.012		.69	.39		1.08	1.42
4700	Oriented strand board, factory laminated W.R. barrier, on roof, 1/2" thick	G		1400	.011		.62	.37		.99	1.30
4705	Pneumatic nailed	G		1736	.009		.62	.30		.92	1.18
4720	5/8" thick	G		1300	.012		.77	.40		1.17	1.51
4725	Pneumatic nailed	G		1586	.010		.77	.32		1.09	1.39
4730	5/8" thick, T&G	G	↓	1150	.014	↓	.78	.45		1.23	1.61

06 16 Sheathing

06 16 36 – Wood Panel Product Sheathing

06 16 36.10 Sheathing

06 16 36.10 Sheathing		Crew	Daily Output	Labor-Hours	Unit	Material	2014 Bare Costs Labor	Equipment	Total	Total Incl O&P
4735	Pneumatic nailed, T&G	[G] 2 Carp	1400	.011	S.F.	.78	.37		1.15	1.48
4740	On walls, 7/16" thick	[G]	1200	.013		.56	.43		.99	1.34
4745	Pneumatic nailed	[G]	1488	.011		.56	.35		.91	1.20
4750	1/2" thick	[G]	1195	.013		.62	.43		1.05	1.40
4755	Pneumatic nailed	[G]	1325	.012		.62	.39		1.01	1.33
4800	Joint sealant tape, 3-1/2"		7600	.002	L.F.	.28	.07		.35	.42
4810	Joint sealant tape, 6"		7600	.002	"	.44	.07		.51	.59

06 16 43 – Gypsum Sheathing

06 16 43.10 Gypsum Sheathing

		Crew	Daily Output	Labor-Hours	Unit	Material	Labor	Equipment	Total	Total Incl O&P
0010	**GYPSUM SHEATHING**									
0020	Gypsum, weatherproof, 1/2" thick	2 Carp	1125	.014	S.F.	.44	.46		.90	1.25
0040	With embedded glass mats	"	1100	.015	"	.77	.47		1.24	1.64

06 17 Shop-Fabricated Structural Wood

06 17 33 – Wood I-Joists

06 17 33.10 Wood and Composite I-Joists

		Crew	Daily Output	Labor-Hours	Unit	Material	Labor	Equipment	Total	Total Incl O&P
0010	**WOOD AND COMPOSITE I-JOISTS**									
0100	Plywood webs, incl. bridging & blocking, panels 24" O.C.									
1200	15' to 24' span, 50 psf live load	F-5	2400	.013	SF Flr.	1.95	.37		2.32	2.77
1300	55 psf live load		2250	.014		2.21	.40		2.61	3.10
1400	24' to 30' span, 45 psf live load		2600	.012		2.61	.34		2.95	3.46
1500	55 psf live load		2400	.013		3.89	.37		4.26	4.91

06 17 53 – Shop-Fabricated Wood Trusses

06 17 53.10 Roof Trusses

		Crew	Daily Output	Labor-Hours	Unit	Material	Labor	Equipment	Total	Total Incl O&P
0010	**ROOF TRUSSES**									
5000	Common wood, 2" x 4" metal plate connected, 24" O.C., 4/12 slope									
5010	1' overhang, 12' span	F-5	55	.582	Ea.	43	16.30		59.30	75
5050	20' span	F-6	62	.645		68.50	18.90	10.70	98.10	118
5100	24' span		60	.667		77	19.55	11.05	107.60	129
5150	26' span		57	.702		80	20.50	11.65	112.15	135
5200	28' span		53	.755		92.50	22	12.50	127	153
5240	30' span		51	.784		101	23	13	137	164
5250	32' span		50	.800		109	23.50	13.25	145.75	173
5280	34' span		48	.833		117	24.50	13.80	155.30	184
5350	8/12 pitch, 1' overhang, 20' span		57	.702		76.50	20.50	11.65	108.65	131
5400	24' span		55	.727		97	21.50	12.05	130.55	156
5450	26' span		52	.769		101	22.50	12.75	136.25	163
5500	28' span		49	.816		111	24	13.55	148.55	178
5550	32' span		45	.889		134	26	14.75	174.75	207
5600	36' span		41	.976		167	28.50	16.20	211.70	249
5650	38' span		40	1		182	29.50	16.60	228.10	267
5700	40' span		40	1		188	29.50	16.60	234.10	273

06 18 Glued-Laminated Construction

06 18 13 – Glued-Laminated Beams

06 18 13.10 Laminated Beams

		Crew	Daily Output	Labor-Hours	Unit	Material	2014 Bare Costs Labor	2014 Bare Costs Equipment	Total	Total Incl O&P
0010	**LAMINATED BEAMS**									
0050	3-1/2" x 18"	F-3	480	.083	L.F.	29	2.44	1.38	32.82	37
0100	5-1/4" x 11-7/8"		450	.089		28.50	2.61	1.47	32.58	37
0150	5-1/4" x 16"		360	.111		38.50	3.26	1.84	43.60	49.50
0200	5-1/4" x 18"		290	.138		43	4.04	2.29	49.33	57
0250	5-1/4" x 24"		220	.182		57.50	5.35	3.01	65.86	75.50
0300	7" x 11-7/8"		320	.125		38	3.66	2.07	43.73	50
0350	7" x 16"		260	.154		51	4.51	2.55	58.06	66.50
0400	7" x 18"		210	.190		57.50	5.60	3.16	66.26	76.50
0500	For premium appearance, add to S.F. prices					5%				
0550	For industrial type, deduct					15%				
0600	For stain and varnish, add					5%				
0650	For 3/4" laminations, add					25%				

06 18 13.20 Laminated Framing

		Crew	Daily Output	Labor-Hours	Unit	Material	2014 Bare Costs Labor	2014 Bare Costs Equipment	Total	Total Incl O&P
0010	**LAMINATED FRAMING**									
0020	30 lb., short term live load, 15 lb. dead load									
0200	Straight roof beams, 20' clear span, beams 8' O.C.	F-3	2560	.016	SF Flr.	1.91	.46	.26	2.63	3.15
0300	Beams 16' O.C.		3200	.013		1.38	.37	.21	1.96	2.37
0500	40' clear span, beams 8' O.C.		3200	.013		3.65	.37	.21	4.23	4.87
0600	Beams 16' O.C.		3840	.010		2.99	.31	.17	3.47	3.99
0800	60' clear span, beams 8' O.C.	F-4	2880	.014		6.30	.41	.39	7.10	8
0900	Beams 16' O.C.	"	3840	.010		4.68	.31	.30	5.29	6
1100	Tudor arches, 30' to 40' clear span, frames 8' O.C.	F-3	1680	.024		8.20	.70	.39	9.29	10.60
1200	Frames 16' O.C.	"	2240	.018		6.40	.52	.30	7.22	8.25
1400	50' to 60' clear span, frames 8' O.C.	F-4	2200	.018		8.85	.53	.52	9.90	11.15
1500	Frames 16' O.C.		2640	.015		7.50	.44	.43	8.37	9.45
1700	Radial arches, 60' clear span, frames 8' O.C.		1920	.021		8.25	.61	.59	9.45	10.75
1800	Frames 16' O.C.		2880	.014		6.35	.41	.39	7.15	8.10
2000	100' clear span, frames 8' O.C.		1600	.025		8.55	.73	.71	9.99	11.40
2100	Frames 16' O.C.		2400	.017		7.50	.49	.47	8.46	9.60
2300	120' clear span, frames 8' O.C.		1440	.028		11.35	.81	.79	12.95	14.75
2400	Frames 16' O.C.		1920	.021		10.35	.61	.59	11.55	13.05
2600	Bowstring trusses, 20' O.C., 40' clear span	F-3	2400	.017		5.10	.49	.28	5.87	6.75
2700	60' clear span	F-4	3600	.011		4.60	.33	.32	5.25	5.95
2800	100' clear span		4000	.010		6.50	.29	.28	7.07	7.95
2900	120' clear span		3600	.011		7	.33	.32	7.65	8.60
3100	For premium appearance, add to S.F. prices					5%				
3300	For industrial type, deduct					15%				
3500	For stain and varnish, add					5%				
3900	For 3/4" laminations, add to straight					25%				
4100	Add to curved					15%				
4300	Alternate pricing method: (use nominal footage of									
4310	components). Straight beams, camber less than 6"	F-3	3.50	11.429	M.B.F.	2,825	335	189	3,349	3,900
4400	Columns, including hardware		2	20		3,050	585	330	3,965	4,700
4600	Curved members, radius over 32'		2.50	16		3,125	470	265	3,860	4,500
4700	Radius 10' to 32'		3	13.333		3,075	390	221	3,686	4,300
4900	For complicated shapes, add maximum					100%				
5100	For pressure treating, add to straight					35%				
5200	Add to curved					45%				
6000	Laminated veneer members, southern pine or western species									
6050	1-3/4" wide x 5-1/2" deep	2 Carp	480	.033	L.F.	2.94	1.07		4.01	5.05
6100	9-1/2" deep		480	.033		4.35	1.07		5.42	6.60

06 18 13 – Glued-Laminated Beams

06 18 13.20 Laminated Framing	Crew	Daily Output	Labor-Hours	Unit	Material	2014 Bare Costs Labor	Equipment	Total	Total Incl O&P
6150	14" deep	2 Carp	450	.036	L.F.	6.75	1.14		7.89	9.30
6200	18" deep	↓	450	.036	↓	9.50	1.14		10.64	12.35
6300	Parallel strand members, southern pine or western species									
6350	1-3/4" wide x 9-1/4" deep	2 Carp	480	.033	L.F.	4.35	1.07		5.42	6.60
6400	11-1/4" deep		450	.036		4.93	1.14		6.07	7.30
6450	14" deep		400	.040		6.75	1.28		8.03	9.55
6500	3-1/2" wide x 9-1/4" deep		480	.033		15.15	1.07		16.22	18.45
6550	11-1/4" deep		450	.036		18.10	1.14		19.24	22
6600	14" deep		400	.040		22.50	1.28		23.78	26.50
6650	7" wide x 9-1/4" deep		450	.036		30.50	1.14		31.64	35.50
6700	11-1/4" deep		420	.038		38	1.22		39.22	43.50
6750	14" deep	↓	400	.040	↓	44.50	1.28		45.78	51
8000	Straight beams									
8102	20' span									
8104	3-1/8" x 9"	F-3	30	1.333	Ea.	133	39	22	194	236
8106	X 10-1/2"		30	1.333		155	39	22	216	260
8108	X 12"		30	1.333		177	39	22	238	285
8110	X 13-1/2"		30	1.333		199	39	22	260	310
8112	X 15"		29	1.379		221	40.50	23	284.50	335
8114	5-1/8" x 10-1/2"		30	1.333		254	39	22	315	370
8116	X 12"		30	1.333		290	39	22	351	410
8118	X 13-1/2"		30	1.333		325	39	22	386	450
8120	X 15"		29	1.379		365	40.50	23	428.50	495
8122	X 16-1/2"		29	1.379		400	40.50	23	463.50	535
8124	X 18"		29	1.379		435	40.50	23	498.50	575
8126	X 19-1/2"		29	1.379		470	40.50	23	533.50	615
8128	X 21"		28	1.429		510	42	23.50	575.50	655
8130	X 22-1/2"		28	1.429		545	42	23.50	610.50	695
8132	X 24"		28	1.429		580	42	23.50	645.50	735
8134	6-3/4" x 12"		29	1.379		380	40.50	23	443.50	515
8136	X 13-1/2"		29	1.379		430	40.50	23	493.50	570
8138	X 15"		29	1.379		480	40.50	23	543.50	620
8140	X 16-1/2"		28	1.429		525	42	23.50	590.50	675
8142	X 18"		28	1.429		575	42	23.50	640.50	725
8144	X 19-1/2"		28	1.429		620	42	23.50	685.50	780
8146	X 21"		27	1.481		670	43.50	24.50	738	835
8148	X 22-1/2"		27	1.481		715	43.50	24.50	783	890
8150	X 24"		27	1.481		765	43.50	24.50	833	940
8152	X 25-1/2"		27	1.481		810	43.50	24.50	878	995
8154	X 27"		26	1.538		860	45	25.50	930.50	1,050
8156	X 28-1/2"		26	1.538		910	45	25.50	980.50	1,100
8158	X 30"	↓	26	1.538	↓	955	45	25.50	1,025.50	1,150
8200	30' span									
8250	3-1/8" x 9"	F-3	30	1.333	Ea.	199	39	22	260	310
8252	X 10-1/2"		30	1.333		232	39	22	293	345
8254	X 12"		30	1.333		266	39	22	327	380
8256	X 13-1/2"		30	1.333		299	39	22	360	420
8258	X 15"		29	1.379		330	40.50	23	393.50	460
8260	5-1/8" x 10-1/2"		30	1.333		380	39	22	441	510
8262	X 12"		30	1.333		435	39	22	496	570
8264	X 13-1/2"		30	1.333		490	39	22	551	630
8266	X 15"		29	1.379		545	40.50	23	608.50	695
8268	X 16-1/2"		29	1.379		600	40.50	23	663.50	755

06 18 13.20 Laminated Framing		Crew	Daily Output	Labor-Hours	Unit	Material	2014 Bare Costs			Total Incl O&P
							Labor	Equipment	Total	
8270	X 18"	F-3	29	1.379	Ea.	655	40.50	23	718.50	815
8272	X 19-1/2"		29	1.379		710	40.50	23	773.50	875
8274	X 21"		28	1.429		760	42	23.50	825.50	935
8276	X 22-1/2"		28	1.429		815	42	23.50	880.50	995
8278	X 24"		28	1.429		870	42	23.50	935.50	1,050
8280	6-3/4" x 12"		29	1.379		575	40.50	23	638.50	725
8282	X 13-1/2"		29	1.379		645	40.50	23	708.50	805
8284	X 15"		29	1.379		715	40.50	23	778.50	885
8286	X 16-1/2"		28	1.429		790	42	23.50	855.50	960
8288	X 18"		28	1.429		860	42	23.50	925.50	1,050
8290	X 19-1/2"		28	1.429		930	42	23.50	995.50	1,125
8292	X 21"		27	1.481		1,000	43.50	24.50	1,068	1,200
8294	X 22-1/2"		27	1.481		1,075	43.50	24.50	1,143	1,275
8296	X 24"		27	1.481		1,150	43.50	24.50	1,218	1,350
8298	X 25-1/2"		27	1.481		1,225	43.50	24.50	1,293	1,450
8300	X 27"		26	1.538		1,300	45	25.50	1,370.50	1,525
8302	X 28-1/2"		26	1.538		1,350	45	25.50	1,420.50	1,600
8304	X 30"	▼	26	1.538	▼	1,425	45	25.50	1,495.50	1,675
8400	40' span									
8402	3-1/8" x 9"	F-3	30	1.333	Ea.	266	39	22	327	380
8404	X 10-1/2"		30	1.333		310	39	22	371	430
8406	X 12"		30	1.333		355	39	22	416	480
8408	X 13-1/2"		30	1.333		400	39	22	461	530
8410	X 15"		29	1.379		445	40.50	23	508.50	580
8412	5-1/8" x 10-1/2"		30	1.333		510	39	22	571	650
8414	X 12"		30	1.333		580	39	22	641	730
8416	X 13-1/2"		30	1.333		655	39	22	716	810
8418	X 15"		29	1.379		725	40.50	23	788.50	895
8420	X 16-1/2"		29	1.379		800	40.50	23	863.50	975
8422	X 18"		29	1.379		870	40.50	23	933.50	1,050
8424	X 19-1/2"		29	1.379		945	40.50	23	1,008.50	1,150
8426	X 21"		28	1.429		1,025	42	23.50	1,090.50	1,225
8428	X 22-1/2"		28	1.429		1,100	42	23.50	1,165.50	1,300
8430	X 24"		28	1.429		1,150	42	23.50	1,215.50	1,375
8432	6-3/4" x 12"		29	1.379		765	40.50	23	828.50	935
8434	X 13-1/2"		29	1.379		860	40.50	23	923.50	1,050
8436	X 15"		29	1.379		955	40.50	23	1,018.50	1,150
8438	X 16-1/2"		28	1.429		1,050	42	23.50	1,115.50	1,250
8440	X 18"		28	1.429		1,150	42	23.50	1,215.50	1,350
8442	X 19-1/2"		28	1.429		1,250	42	23.50	1,315.50	1,475
8444	X 21"		27	1.481		1,350	43.50	24.50	1,418	1,575
8446	X 22-1/2"		27	1.481		1,425	43.50	24.50	1,493	1,675
8448	X 24"		27	1.481		1,525	43.50	24.50	1,593	1,775
8450	X 25-1/2"		27	1.481		1,625	43.50	24.50	1,693	1,875
8452	X 27"		26	1.538		1,725	45	25.50	1,795.50	2,000
8454	X 28-1/2"		26	1.538		1,825	45	25.50	1,895.50	2,100
8456	X 30"	▼	26	1.538	▼	1,900	45	25.50	1,970.50	2,200

06 22 13 – Standard Pattern Wood Trim

06 22 13.10 Millwork	Crew	Daily Output	Labor-Hours	Unit	Material	2014 Bare Costs Labor	Equipment	Total	Total Incl O&P
0010 **MILLWORK**									
0020 Rule of thumb, milled material equals rough lumber cost x 3									
1020 1" x 12", custom birch				L.F.	5.35			5.35	5.90
1040 Cedar					7			7	7.70
1060 Oak					3.89			3.89	4.28
1080 Redwood					4.71			4.71	5.20
1100 Southern yellow pine					3.83			3.83	4.21
1120 Sugar pine					3.51			3.51	3.86
1140 Teak					30.50			30.50	33.50
1160 Walnut					6.50			6.50	7.15
1180 White pine					4.56			4.56	5

06 22 13.15 Moldings, Base

	Crew	Daily Output	Labor-Hours	Unit	Material	2014 Bare Costs Labor	Equipment	Total	Total Incl O&P
0010 **MOLDINGS, BASE**									
5100 Classic profile, 5/8" x 5-1/2", finger jointed and primed	1 Carp	250	.032	L.F.	1.39	1.03		2.42	3.26
5105 Poplar		240	.033		1.47	1.07		2.54	3.42
5110 Red oak		220	.036		2.15	1.17		3.32	4.32
5115 Maple		220	.036		3.40	1.17		4.57	5.70
5120 Cherry		220	.036		4.04	1.17		5.21	6.40
5125 3/4 x 7-1/2", finger jointed and primed		250	.032		1.76	1.03		2.79	3.66
5130 Poplar		240	.033		2.34	1.07		3.41	4.37
5135 Red oak		220	.036		3.12	1.17		4.29	5.40
5140 Maple		220	.036		4.52	1.17		5.69	6.95
5145 Cherry		220	.036		5.40	1.17		6.57	7.90
5150 Modern profile, 5/8" x 3-1/2", finger jointed and primed		250	.032		.93	1.03		1.96	2.75
5155 Poplar		240	.033		.93	1.07		2	2.82
5160 Red oak		220	.036		1.47	1.17		2.64	3.58
5165 Maple		220	.036		2.38	1.17		3.55	4.58
5170 Cherry		220	.036		2.57	1.17		3.74	4.79
5175 Ogee profile, 7/16" x 3", finger jointed and primed		250	.032		.56	1.03		1.59	2.34
5180 Poplar		240	.033		.61	1.07		1.68	2.47
5185 Red oak		220	.036		.82	1.17		1.99	2.86
5200 9/16" x 3-1/2", finger jointed and primed		250	.032		.62	1.03		1.65	2.41
5205 Pine		240	.033		1.44	1.07		2.51	3.38
5210 Red oak		220	.036		2.32	1.17		3.49	4.51
5215 9/16" x 4-1/2", red oak		220	.036		3.47	1.17		4.64	5.80
5220 5/8" x 3-1/2", finger jointed and primed		250	.032		.85	1.03		1.88	2.66
5225 Poplar		240	.033		.93	1.07		2	2.82
5230 Red oak		220	.036		1.47	1.17		2.64	3.58
5235 Maple		220	.036		2.38	1.17		3.55	4.58
5240 Cherry		220	.036		2.57	1.17		3.74	4.79
5245 5/8" x 4", finger jointed and primed		250	.032		1.10	1.03		2.13	2.94
5250 Poplar		240	.033		1.20	1.07		2.27	3.12
5255 Red oak		220	.036		1.65	1.17		2.82	3.77
5260 Maple		220	.036		2.66	1.17		3.83	4.88
5265 Cherry		220	.036		2.79	1.17		3.96	5.05
5270 Rectangular profile, oak, 3/8" x 1-1/4"		260	.031		1.25	.99		2.24	3.04
5275 1/2" x 2-1/2"		255	.031		1.91	1.01		2.92	3.79
5280 1/2" x 3-1/2"		250	.032		2.31	1.03		3.34	4.27
5285 1" x 6"		240	.033		3.64	1.07		4.71	5.80
5290 1" x 8"		240	.033		5.10	1.07		6.17	7.40
5295 Pine, 3/8" x 1-3/4"		260	.031		.62	.99		1.61	2.34
5300 7/16" x 2-1/2"		255	.031		.90	1.01		1.91	2.68

06 22 13 – Standard Pattern Wood Trim

06 22 13.15 Moldings, Base	Crew	Daily Output	Labor-Hours	Unit	Material	2014 Bare Costs Labor	Equipment	Total	Total Incl O&P
5305	1" x 6"	1 Carp	240	.033	L.F.	.88	1.07		1.95	2.77
5310	1" x 8"		240	.033		1.18	1.07		2.25	3.10
5315	Shoe, 1/2" x 3/4", primed		260	.031		.46	.99		1.45	2.16
5320	Pine		240	.033		.37	1.07		1.44	2.21
5325	Poplar		240	.033		.36	1.07		1.43	2.19
5330	Red oak		220	.036		.47	1.17		1.64	2.48
5335	Maple		220	.036		.66	1.17		1.83	2.68
5340	Cherry		220	.036		.74	1.17		1.91	2.77
5345	11/16" x 1-1/2", pine		240	.033		.80	1.07		1.87	2.68
5350	Caps, 11/16" x 1-3/8", pine		240	.033		.84	1.07		1.91	2.72
5355	3/4" x 1-3/4", finger jointed and primed		260	.031		.67	.99		1.66	2.40
5360	Poplar		240	.033		.94	1.07		2.01	2.83
5365	Red oak		220	.036		1.08	1.17		2.25	3.15
5370	Maple		220	.036		1.48	1.17		2.65	3.59
5375	Cherry		220	.036		3.12	1.17		4.29	5.40
5380	Combination base & shoe, 9/16" x 3-1/2" & 1/2" x 3/4", pine		125	.064		1.81	2.05		3.86	5.45
5385	Three piece oak, 6" high		80	.100		5.20	3.21		8.41	11.10
5390	Including 3/4" x 1" base shoe		70	.114		5.50	3.67		9.17	12.20
5395	Flooring cant strip, 3/4" x 3/4", pre-finished pine		260	.031		.47	.99		1.46	2.18
5400	For pre-finished, stain and clear coat, add					.50			.50	.55
5405	Clear coat only, add					.40			.40	.44

06 22 13.30 Moldings, Casings

		Crew	Daily Output	Labor-Hours	Unit	Material	2014 Bare Costs Labor	Equipment	Total	Total Incl O&P
0010	**MOLDINGS, CASINGS**									
0085	Apron, 9/16" x 2-1/2", pine	1 Carp	250	.032	L.F.	1.58	1.03		2.61	3.47
0090	5/8" x 2-1/2", pine		250	.032		1.64	1.03		2.67	3.53
0110	5/8" x 3-1/2", pine		220	.036		2.45	1.17		3.62	4.65
0300	Band, 11/16" x 1-1/8", pine		270	.030		1	.95		1.95	2.70
0310	11/16" x 1-1/2", finger jointed and primed		270	.030		.67	.95		1.62	2.34
0320	Pine		270	.030		1.24	.95		2.19	2.96
0330	11/16" x 1-3/4", finger jointed and primed		270	.030		.75	.95		1.70	2.42
0350	Pine		270	.030		1.25	.95		2.20	2.97
0355	Beaded, 3/4" x 3-1/2", finger jointed and primed		220	.036		1.04	1.17		2.21	3.10
0360	Poplar		220	.036		1.04	1.17		2.21	3.10
0365	Red oak		220	.036		1.47	1.17		2.64	3.58
0370	Maple		220	.036		2.38	1.17		3.55	4.58
0375	Cherry		220	.036		2.88	1.17		4.05	5.15
0380	3/4" x 4", finger jointed and primed		220	.036		1.10	1.17		2.27	3.17
0385	Poplar		220	.036		1.34	1.17		2.51	3.43
0390	Red oak		220	.036		1.80	1.17		2.97	3.94
0395	Maple		220	.036		2.48	1.17		3.65	4.69
0400	Cherry		220	.036		3.13	1.17		4.30	5.40
0405	3/4" x 5-1/2", finger jointed and primed		200	.040		1.07	1.28		2.35	3.34
0410	Poplar		200	.040		1.80	1.28		3.08	4.14
0415	Red oak		200	.040		2.53	1.28		3.81	4.94
0420	Maple		200	.040		3.49	1.28		4.77	6
0425	Cherry		200	.040		4.02	1.28		5.30	6.60
0430	Classic profile, 3/4" x 2-3/4", finger jointed and primed		250	.032		.73	1.03		1.76	2.53
0435	Poplar		250	.032		.93	1.03		1.96	2.75
0440	Red oak		250	.032		1.30	1.03		2.33	3.16
0445	Maple		250	.032		1.95	1.03		2.98	3.87
0450	Cherry		250	.032		2.21	1.03		3.24	4.16
0455	Fluted, 3/4" x 3-1/2", poplar		220	.036		1.04	1.17		2.21	3.10

06 22 13 – Standard Pattern Wood Trim

06 22 13.30 Moldings, Casings		Crew	Daily Output	Labor-Hours	Unit	Material	2014 Bare Costs Labor	Equipment	Total	Total Incl O&P
0460	Red oak	1 Carp	220	.036	L.F.	1.47	1.17		2.64	3.58
0465	Maple		220	.036		2.38	1.17		3.55	4.58
0470	Cherry		220	.036		2.88	1.17		4.05	5.15
0475	3/4" x 4", poplar		220	.036		1.34	1.17		2.51	3.43
0480	Red oak		220	.036		1.80	1.17		2.97	3.94
0485	Maple		220	.036		2.48	1.17		3.65	4.69
0490	Cherry		220	.036		3.13	1.17		4.30	5.40
0495	3/4" x 5-1/2", poplar		200	.040		1.80	1.28		3.08	4.14
0500	Red oak		200	.040		2.53	1.28		3.81	4.94
0505	Maple		200	.040		3.49	1.28		4.77	6
0510	Cherry		200	.040		4.02	1.28		5.30	6.60
0515	3/4" x 7-1/2", poplar		190	.042		1.27	1.35		2.62	3.66
0520	Red oak		190	.042		3.50	1.35		4.85	6.10
0525	Maple		190	.042		5.30	1.35		6.65	8.05
0530	Cherry		190	.042		6.30	1.35		7.65	9.20
0535	3/4" x 9-1/2", poplar		180	.044		3.85	1.43		5.28	6.65
0540	Red oak		180	.044		5.85	1.43		7.28	8.85
0545	Maple		180	.044		8.40	1.43		9.83	11.65
0550	Cherry		180	.044		9.15	1.43		10.58	12.45
0555	Modern profile, 9/16" x 2-1/4", poplar		250	.032		.53	1.03		1.56	2.31
0560	Red oak		250	.032		.69	1.03		1.72	2.49
0565	11/16" x 2-1/2", finger jointed & primed		250	.032		.72	1.03		1.75	2.52
0570	Pine		250	.032		1.55	1.03		2.58	3.43
0575	3/4" x 2-1/2", poplar		250	.032		.82	1.03		1.85	2.63
0580	Red oak		250	.032		1.06	1.03		2.09	2.89
0585	Maple		250	.032		1.68	1.03		2.71	3.58
0590	Cherry		250	.032		2.12	1.03		3.15	4.06
0595	Mullion, 5/16" x 2", pine		270	.030		.99	.95		1.94	2.69
0600	9/16" x 2-1/2", fingerjointed and primed		250	.032		.83	1.03		1.86	2.64
0605	Pine		250	.032		1.64	1.03		2.67	3.53
0610	Red oak		250	.032		2.80	1.03		3.83	4.81
0615	1-1/16" x 3-3/4", red oak		220	.036		6.85	1.17		8.02	9.45
0620	Ogee, 7/16" x 2-1/2", poplar		250	.032		.51	1.03		1.54	2.29
0625	Red oak		250	.032		.67	1.03		1.70	2.47
0630	9/16" x 2-1/4", finger jointed and primed		250	.032		.47	1.03		1.50	2.25
0635	Poplar		250	.032		.53	1.03		1.56	2.31
0640	Red oak		250	.032		.69	1.03		1.72	2.49
0645	11/16" x 2-1/2", finger jointed and primed		250	.032		.67	1.03		1.70	2.47
0700	Pine		250	.032		1.52	1.03		2.55	3.40
0701	Red oak		250	.032		2.59	1.03		3.62	4.58
0730	11/16" x 3-1/2", finger jointed and primed		220	.036		2.12	1.17		3.29	4.29
0750	Pine		220	.036		2.18	1.17		3.35	4.36
0755	3/4" x 2-1/2", finger jointed and primed		250	.032		.67	1.03		1.70	2.47
0760	Poplar		250	.032		.82	1.03		1.85	2.63
0765	Red oak		250	.032		1.06	1.03		2.09	2.89
0770	Maple		250	.032		1.68	1.03		2.71	3.58
0775	Cherry		250	.032		2.12	1.03		3.15	4.06
0780	3/4" x 3-1/2", finger jointed and primed		220	.036		.85	1.17		2.02	2.89
0785	Poplar		220	.036		1.04	1.17		2.21	3.10
0790	Red oak		220	.036		1.47	1.17		2.64	3.58
0795	Maple		220	.036		2.38	1.17		3.55	4.58
0800	Cherry		220	.036		2.88	1.17		4.05	5.15
4700	Square profile, 1" x 1", teak		215	.037		2.01	1.19		3.20	4.22

06 22 Millwork

06 22 13 – Standard Pattern Wood Trim

06 22 13.30 Moldings, Casings	Crew	Daily Output	Labor-Hours	Unit	Material	2014 Bare Costs Labor	Equipment	Total	Total Incl O&P
4800	Rectangular profile, 1" x 3", teak	1 Carp	200	.040	L.F.	6	1.28		7.28	8.75
06 22 13.35 Moldings, Ceilings									
0010	**MOLDINGS, CEILINGS**									
0600	Bed, 9/16" x 1-3/4", pine	1 Carp	270	.030	L.F.	1.20	.95		2.15	2.92
0650	9/16" x 2", pine		270	.030		1.43	.95		2.38	3.17
0710	9/16" x 1-3/4", oak		270	.030		1.96	.95		2.91	3.75
1200	Cornice, 9/16" x 1-3/4", pine		270	.030		1.21	.95		2.16	2.93
1300	9/16" x 2-1/4", pine		265	.030		1.47	.97		2.44	3.24
1350	Cove, 1/2" x 2-1/4", poplar		265	.030		.92	.97		1.89	2.64
1360	Red oak		265	.030		1.18	.97		2.15	2.92
1370	Hard maple		265	.030		1.69	.97		2.66	3.49
1380	Cherry		265	.030		2.07	.97		3.04	3.90
2400	9/16" x 1-3/4", pine		270	.030		1.12	.95		2.07	2.83
2401	Oak		270	.030		1.11	.95		2.06	2.82
2500	11/16" x 2-3/4", pine		265	.030		2.21	.97		3.18	4.06
2510	Crown, 5/8" x 5/8", poplar		300	.027		.41	.86		1.27	1.89
2520	Red oak		300	.027		.46	.86		1.32	1.94
2530	Hard maple		300	.027		.66	.86		1.52	2.16
2540	Cherry		300	.027		.70	.86		1.56	2.21
2600	9/16" x 3-5/8", pine		250	.032		2.70	1.03		3.73	4.70
2700	11/16" x 4-1/4", pine		250	.032		4.55	1.03		5.58	6.75
2705	Oak		250	.032		6.30	1.03		7.33	8.70
2710	3/4" x 1-3/4", poplar		270	.030		.65	.95		1.60	2.31
2720	Red oak		270	.030		.91	.95		1.86	2.60
2730	Hard maple		270	.030		1.26	.95		2.21	2.98
2740	Cherry		270	.030		1.55	.95		2.50	3.30
2750	3/4" x 2", poplar		270	.030		.85	.95		1.80	2.53
2760	Red oak		270	.030		1.10	.95		2.05	2.81
2770	Hard maple		270	.030		1.52	.95		2.47	3.27
2780	Cherry		270	.030		1.70	.95		2.65	3.47
2790	3/4" x 2-3/4", poplar		265	.030		.92	.97		1.89	2.64
2800	Red oak		265	.030		1.36	.97		2.33	3.12
2810	Hard maple		265	.030		1.89	.97		2.86	3.71
2820	Cherry		265	.030		2.18	.97		3.15	4.02
2830	3/4" x 3-1/2", poplar		250	.032		1.18	1.03		2.21	3.02
2840	Red oak		250	.032		1.70	1.03		2.73	3.60
2850	Hard maple		250	.032		2.32	1.03		3.35	4.28
2860	Cherry		250	.032		2.72	1.03		3.75	4.72
2870	FJP poplar		250	.032		.84	1.03		1.87	2.65
2880	3/4" x 5", poplar		245	.033		1.75	1.05		2.80	3.68
2890	Red oak		245	.033		2.47	1.05		3.52	4.47
2900	Hard maple		245	.033		3.40	1.05		4.45	5.50
2910	Cherry		245	.033		3.92	1.05		4.97	6.05
2920	FJP poplar		245	.033		1.19	1.05		2.24	3.07
2930	3/4" x 6-1/4", poplar		240	.033		2.09	1.07		3.16	4.09
2940	Red oak		240	.033		3	1.07		4.07	5.10
2950	Hard maple		240	.033		4.11	1.07		5.18	6.30
2960	Cherry		240	.033		4.87	1.07		5.94	7.15
2970	7/8" x 8-3/4", poplar		220	.036		3.24	1.17		4.41	5.50
2980	Red oak		220	.036		4.71	1.17		5.88	7.15
2990	Hard maple		220	.036		6.80	1.17		7.97	9.45
3000	Cherry		220	.036		7.80	1.17		8.97	10.50

06 22 Millwork

06 22 13 – Standard Pattern Wood Trim

06 22 13.35 Moldings, Ceilings

		Crew	Daily Output	Labor-Hours	Unit	Material	2014 Bare Costs Labor	Equipment	Total	Total Incl O&P
3010	1" x 7-1/4", poplar	1 Carp	220	.036	L.F.	3.43	1.17		4.60	5.75
3020	Red oak		220	.036		5.10	1.17		6.27	7.55
3030	Hard maple		220	.036		7.40	1.17		8.57	10.05
3040	Cherry		220	.036		8.60	1.17		9.77	11.45
3050	1-1/16" x 4-1/4", poplar		250	.032		2.08	1.03		3.11	4.01
3060	Red oak		250	.032		2.33	1.03		3.36	4.29
3070	Hard maple		250	.032		3.22	1.03		4.25	5.25
3080	Cherry		250	.032		4.60	1.03		5.63	6.80
3090	Dentil crown, 3/4" x 5", poplar		250	.032		1.75	1.03		2.78	3.65
3100	Red oak		250	.032		2.47	1.03		3.50	4.44
3110	Hard maple		250	.032		3.30	1.03		4.33	5.35
3120	Cherry		250	.032		3.92	1.03		4.95	6.05
3130	Dentil piece for above, 1/2" x 1/2", poplar		300	.027		2.48	.86		3.34	4.16
3140	Red oak		300	.027		2.72	.86		3.58	4.43
3150	Hard maple		300	.027		3.23	.86		4.09	4.99
3160	Cherry		300	.027		3.52	.86		4.38	5.30

06 22 13.40 Moldings, Exterior

		Crew	Daily Output	Labor-Hours	Unit	Material	2014 Bare Costs Labor	Equipment	Total	Total Incl O&P
0010	**MOLDINGS, EXTERIOR**									
0100	Band board, cedar, rough sawn, 1" x 2"	1 Carp	300	.027	L.F.	.54	.86		1.40	2.04
0110	1" x 3"		300	.027		.81	.86		1.67	2.33
0120	1" x 4"		250	.032		1.07	1.03		2.10	2.91
0130	1" x 6"		250	.032		1.61	1.03		2.64	3.50
0140	1" x 8"		225	.036		2.15	1.14		3.29	4.29
0150	1" x 10"		225	.036		2.67	1.14		3.81	4.86
0160	1" x 12"		200	.040		3.21	1.28		4.49	5.70
0240	STK, 1" x 2"		300	.027		.43	.86		1.29	1.92
0250	1" x 3"		300	.027		.48	.86		1.34	1.96
0260	1" x 4"		250	.032		.62	1.03		1.65	2.41
0270	1" x 6"		250	.032		.96	1.03		1.99	2.78
0280	1" x 8"		225	.036		1.41	1.14		2.55	3.47
0290	1" x 10"		225	.036		2.08	1.14		3.22	4.21
0300	1" x 12"		200	.040		3.21	1.28		4.49	5.70
0310	Pine, #2, 1" x 2"		300	.027		.25	.86		1.11	1.72
0320	1" x 3"		300	.027		.40	.86		1.26	1.88
0330	1" x 4"		250	.032		.49	1.03		1.52	2.27
0340	1" x 6"		250	.032		.83	1.03		1.86	2.64
0350	1" x 8"		225	.036		1.22	1.14		2.36	3.26
0360	1" x 10"		225	.036		1.59	1.14		2.73	3.67
0370	1" x 12"		200	.040		2.05	1.28		3.33	4.41
0380	D & better, 1" x 2"		300	.027		.41	.86		1.27	1.90
0390	1" x 3"		300	.027		.61	.86		1.47	2.12
0400	1" x 4"		250	.032		.82	1.03		1.85	2.63
0410	1" x 6"		250	.032		1.12	1.03		2.15	2.96
0420	1" x 8"		225	.036		1.62	1.14		2.76	3.70
0430	1" x 10"		225	.036		2.03	1.14		3.17	4.16
0440	1" x 12"		200	.040		2.63	1.28		3.91	5.05
0450	Redwood, clear all heart, 1" x 2"		300	.027		.63	.86		1.49	2.14
0460	1" x 3"		300	.027		.94	.86		1.80	2.48
0470	1" x 4"		250	.032		1.19	1.03		2.22	3.04
0480	1" x 6"		252	.032		1.78	1.02		2.80	3.67
0490	1" x 8"		225	.036		2.36	1.14		3.50	4.51
0500	1" x 10"		225	.036		3.96	1.14		5.10	6.30

06 22 13.40 Moldings, Exterior		Crew	Daily Output	Labor-Hours	Unit	Material	2014 Bare Costs Labor	Equipment	Total	Total Incl O&P
0510	1" x 12"	1 Carp	200	.040	L.F.	4.75	1.28		6.03	7.40
0530	Corner board, cedar, rough sawn, 1" x 2"		225	.036		.54	1.14		1.68	2.52
0540	1" x 3"		225	.036		.81	1.14		1.95	2.81
0550	1" x 4"		200	.040		1.07	1.28		2.35	3.34
0560	1" x 6"		200	.040		1.61	1.28		2.89	3.93
0570	1" x 8"		200	.040		2.15	1.28		3.43	4.53
0580	1" x 10"		175	.046		2.67	1.47		4.14	5.40
0590	1" x 12"		175	.046		3.21	1.47		4.68	6
0670	STK, 1" x 2"		225	.036		.43	1.14		1.57	2.40
0680	1" x 3"		225	.036		.48	1.14		1.62	2.44
0690	1" x 4"		200	.040		.60	1.28		1.88	2.82
0700	1" x 6"		200	.040		.96	1.28		2.24	3.21
0710	1" x 8"		200	.040		1.41	1.28		2.69	3.71
0720	1" x 10"		175	.046		2.08	1.47		3.55	4.76
0730	1" x 12"		175	.046		3.21	1.47		4.68	6
0740	Pine, #2, 1" x 2"		225	.036		.25	1.14		1.39	2.20
0750	1" x 3"		225	.036		.40	1.14		1.54	2.36
0760	1" x 4"		200	.040		.49	1.28		1.77	2.70
0770	1" x 6"		200	.040		.83	1.28		2.11	3.07
0780	1" x 8"		200	.040		1.22	1.28		2.50	3.50
0790	1" x 10"		175	.046		1.59	1.47		3.06	4.22
0800	1" x 12"		175	.046		2.05	1.47		3.52	4.72
0810	D & better, 1" x 2"		225	.036		.41	1.14		1.55	2.38
0820	1" x 3"		225	.036		.61	1.14		1.75	2.60
0830	1" x 4"		200	.040		.82	1.28		2.10	3.06
0840	1" x 6"		200	.040		1.12	1.28		2.40	3.39
0850	1" x 8"		200	.040		1.62	1.28		2.90	3.94
0860	1" x 10"		175	.046		2.03	1.47		3.50	4.71
0870	1" x 12"		175	.046		2.63	1.47		4.10	5.35
0880	Redwood, clear all heart, 1" x 2"		225	.036		.63	1.14		1.77	2.62
0890	1" x 3"		225	.036		.94	1.14		2.08	2.96
0900	1" x 4"		200	.040		1.19	1.28		2.47	3.47
0910	1" x 6"		200	.040		1.78	1.28		3.06	4.12
0920	1" x 8"		200	.040		2.36	1.28		3.64	4.75
0930	1" x 10"		175	.046		3.96	1.47		5.43	6.85
0940	1" x 12"		175	.046		4.75	1.47		6.22	7.70
0950	Cornice board, cedar, rough sawn, 1" x 2"		330	.024		.54	.78		1.32	1.91
0960	1" x 3"		290	.028		.81	.89		1.70	2.38
0970	1" x 4"		250	.032		1.07	1.03		2.10	2.91
0980	1" x 6"		250	.032		1.61	1.03		2.64	3.50
0990	1" x 8"		200	.040		2.15	1.28		3.43	4.53
1000	1" x 10"		180	.044		2.67	1.43		4.10	5.35
1010	1" x 12"		180	.044		3.21	1.43		4.64	5.95
1020	STK, 1" x 2"		330	.024		.43	.78		1.21	1.79
1030	1" x 3"		290	.028		.48	.89		1.37	2.01
1040	1" x 4"		250	.032		.62	1.03		1.65	2.41
1050	1" x 6"		250	.032		.96	1.03		1.99	2.78
1060	1" x 8"		200	.040		1.41	1.28		2.69	3.71
1070	1" x 10"		180	.044		2.08	1.43		3.51	4.69
1080	1" x 12"		180	.044		3.21	1.43		4.64	5.95
1500	Pine, #2, 1" x 2"		330	.024		.25	.78		1.03	1.59
1510	1" x 3"		290	.028		.27	.89		1.16	1.79
1600	1" x 4"		250	.032		.49	1.03		1.52	2.27

06 22 Millwork

06 22 13 – Standard Pattern Wood Trim

06 22 13.40 Moldings, Exterior		Crew	Daily Output	Labor-Hours	Unit	Material	2014 Bare Costs Labor	Equipment	Total	Total Incl O&P
1700	1" x 6"	1 Carp	250	.032	L.F.	.83	1.03		1.86	2.64
1800	1" x 8"		200	.040		1.22	1.28		2.50	3.50
1900	1" x 10"		180	.044		1.59	1.43		3.02	4.15
2000	1" x 12"		180	.044		2.05	1.43		3.48	4.65
2020	D & better, 1" x 2"		330	.024		.41	.78		1.19	1.77
2030	1" x 3"		290	.028		.61	.89		1.50	2.17
2040	1" x 4"		250	.032		.82	1.03		1.85	2.63
2050	1" x 6"		250	.032		1.12	1.03		2.15	2.96
2060	1" x 8"		200	.040		1.62	1.28		2.90	3.94
2070	1" x 10"		180	.044		2.03	1.43		3.46	4.64
2080	1" x 12"		180	.044		2.63	1.43		4.06	5.30
2090	Redwood, clear all heart, 1" x 2"		330	.024		.63	.78		1.41	2.01
2100	1" x 3"		290	.028		.94	.89		1.83	2.53
2110	1" x 4"		250	.032		1.19	1.03		2.22	3.04
2120	1" x 6"		250	.032		1.78	1.03		2.81	3.69
2130	1" x 8"		200	.040		2.36	1.28		3.64	4.75
2140	1" x 10"		180	.044		3.96	1.43		5.39	6.75
2150	1" x 12"		180	.044		4.75	1.43		6.18	7.65
2160	3 piece, 1" x 2", 1" x 4", 1" x 6", rough sawn cedar		80	.100		3.24	3.21		6.45	8.95
2180	STK cedar		80	.100		2.01	3.21		5.22	7.60
2200	#2 pine		80	.100		1.57	3.21		4.78	7.15
2210	D & better pine		80	.100		2.35	3.21		5.56	8
2220	Clear all heart redwood		80	.100		3.60	3.21		6.81	9.35
2230	1" x 8", 1" x 10", 1" x 12", rough sawn cedar		65	.123		8	3.95		11.95	15.45
2240	STK cedar		65	.123		6.65	3.95		10.60	14
2300	#2 pine		65	.123		4.83	3.95		8.78	11.95
2320	D & better pine		65	.123		6.25	3.95		10.20	13.55
2330	Clear all heart redwood		65	.123		11.05	3.95		15	18.80
2340	Door/window casing, cedar, rough sawn, 1" x 2"		275	.029		.54	.93		1.47	2.17
2350	1" x 3"		275	.029		.81	.93		1.74	2.46
2360	1" x 4"		250	.032		1.07	1.03		2.10	2.91
2370	1" x 6"		250	.032		1.61	1.03		2.64	3.50
2380	1" x 8"		230	.035		2.15	1.12		3.27	4.25
2390	1" x 10"		230	.035		2.67	1.12		3.79	4.82
2395	1" x 12"		210	.038		3.21	1.22		4.43	5.60
2410	STK, 1" x 2"		275	.029		.43	.93		1.36	2.05
2420	1" x 3"		275	.029		.48	.93		1.41	2.09
2430	1" x 4"		250	.032		.62	1.03		1.65	2.41
2440	1" x 6"		250	.032		.96	1.03		1.99	2.78
2450	1" x 8"		230	.035		1.41	1.12		2.53	3.43
2460	1" x 10"		230	.035		2.08	1.12		3.20	4.17
2470	1" x 12"		210	.038		3.21	1.22		4.43	5.60
2550	Pine, #2, 1" x 2"		275	.029		.25	.93		1.18	1.85
2560	1" x 3"		275	.029		.40	.93		1.33	2.01
2570	1" x 4"		250	.032		.49	1.03		1.52	2.27
2580	1" x 6"		250	.032		.83	1.03		1.86	2.64
2590	1" x 8"		230	.035		1.22	1.12		2.34	3.22
2600	1" x 10"		230	.035		1.59	1.12		2.71	3.63
2610	1" x 12"		210	.038		2.05	1.22		3.27	4.31
2620	Pine, D & better, 1" x 2"		275	.029		.41	.93		1.34	2.03
2630	1" x 3"		275	.029		.61	.93		1.54	2.25
2640	1" x 4"		250	.032		.82	1.03		1.85	2.63
2650	1" x 6"		250	.032		1.12	1.03		2.15	2.96

06 22 13.40 Moldings, Exterior		Crew	Daily Output	Labor-Hours	Unit	Material	2014 Bare Costs Labor	Equipment	Total	Total Incl O&P
2660	1" x 8"	1 Carp	230	.035	L.F.	1.62	1.12		2.74	3.66
2670	1" x 10"		230	.035		2.03	1.12		3.15	4.12
2680	1" x 12"		210	.038		2.63	1.22		3.85	4.96
2690	Redwood, clear all heart, 1" x 2"		275	.029		.63	.93		1.56	2.27
2695	1" x 3"		275	.029		.94	.93		1.87	2.61
2710	1" x 4"		250	.032		1.19	1.03		2.22	3.04
2715	1" x 6"		250	.032		1.78	1.03		2.81	3.69
2730	1" x 8"		230	.035		2.36	1.12		3.48	4.47
2740	1" x 10"		230	.035		3.96	1.12		5.08	6.25
2750	1" x 12"		210	.038		4.75	1.22		5.97	7.30
3500	Bellyband, 11/16" x 4-1/4"		250	.032		3.23	1.03		4.26	5.30
3610	Brickmold, pine, 1-1/4" x 2"		200	.040		2.50	1.28		3.78	4.91
3620	FJP, 1-1/4" x 2"		200	.040		1.06	1.28		2.34	3.33
5100	Fascia, cedar, rough sawn, 1" x 2"		275	.029		.54	.93		1.47	2.17
5110	1" x 3"		275	.029		.81	.93		1.74	2.46
5120	1" x 4"		250	.032		1.07	1.03		2.10	2.91
5200	1" x 6"		250	.032		1.61	1.03		2.64	3.50
5300	1" x 8"		230	.035		2.15	1.12		3.27	4.25
5310	1" x 10"		230	.035		2.67	1.12		3.79	4.82
5320	1" x 12"		210	.038		3.21	1.22		4.43	5.60
5400	2" x 4"		220	.036		1.05	1.17		2.22	3.12
5500	2" x 6"		220	.036		1.58	1.17		2.75	3.70
5600	2" x 8"		200	.040		2.11	1.28		3.39	4.48
5700	2" x 10"		180	.044		2.62	1.43		4.05	5.30
5800	2" x 12"		170	.047		6.25	1.51		7.76	9.45
6120	STK, 1" x 2"		275	.029		.43	.93		1.36	2.05
6130	1" x 3"		275	.029		.48	.93		1.41	2.09
6140	1" x 4"		250	.032		.62	1.03		1.65	2.41
6150	1" x 6"		250	.032		.96	1.03		1.99	2.78
6160	1" x 8"		230	.035		1.41	1.12		2.53	3.43
6170	1" x 10"		230	.035		2.08	1.12		3.20	4.17
6180	1" x 12"		210	.038		3.21	1.22		4.43	5.60
6185	2" x 2"		260	.031		.56	.99		1.55	2.28
6190	Pine, #2, 1" x 2"		275	.029		.25	.93		1.18	1.85
6200	1" x 3"		275	.029		.40	.93		1.33	2.01
6210	1" x 4"		250	.032		.49	1.03		1.52	2.27
6220	1" x 6"		250	.032		.83	1.03		1.86	2.64
6230	1" x 8"		230	.035		1.22	1.12		2.34	3.22
6240	1" x 10"		230	.035		1.59	1.12		2.71	3.63
6250	1" x 12"		210	.038		2.05	1.22		3.27	4.31
6260	D & better, 1" x 2"		275	.029		.41	.93		1.34	2.03
6270	1" x 3"		275	.029		.61	.93		1.54	2.25
6280	1" x 4"		250	.032		.82	1.03		1.85	2.63
6290	1" x 6"		250	.032		1.12	1.03		2.15	2.96
6300	1" x 8"		230	.035		1.62	1.12		2.74	3.66
6310	1" x 10"		230	.035		2.03	1.12		3.15	4.12
6312	1" x 12"		210	.038		2.63	1.22		3.85	4.96
6330	Southern yellow, 1-1/4" x 5"		240	.033		2.27	1.07		3.34	4.29
6340	1-1/4" x 6"		240	.033		2.52	1.07		3.59	4.57
6350	1-1/4" x 8"		215	.037		3.43	1.19		4.62	5.80
6360	1-1/4" x 12"		190	.042		5.05	1.35		6.40	7.80
6370	Redwood, clear all heart, 1" x 2"		275	.029		.63	.93		1.56	2.27
6380	1" x 3"		275	.029		1.19	.93		2.12	2.88

06 22 13 – Standard Pattern Wood Trim

06 22 13.40 Moldings, Exterior		Crew	Daily Output	Labor-Hours	Unit	Material	2014 Bare Costs Labor	Equipment	Total	Total Incl O&P
6390	1" x 4"	1 Carp	250	.032	L.F.	1.19	1.03		2.22	3.04
6400	1" x 6"		250	.032		1.78	1.03		2.81	3.69
6410	1" x 8"		230	.035		2.36	1.12		3.48	4.47
6420	1" x 10"		230	.035		3.96	1.12		5.08	6.25
6430	1" x 12"		210	.038		4.75	1.22		5.97	7.30
6440	1-1/4" x 5"		240	.033		1.86	1.07		2.93	3.84
6450	1-1/4" x 6"		240	.033		2.22	1.07		3.29	4.24
6460	1-1/4" x 8"		215	.037		3.53	1.19		4.72	5.90
6470	1-1/4" x 12"		190	.042		7.10	1.35		8.45	10.10
6580	Frieze, cedar, rough sawn, 1" x 2"		275	.029		.54	.93		1.47	2.17
6590	1" x 3"		275	.029		.81	.93		1.74	2.46
6600	1" x 4"		250	.032		1.07	1.03		2.10	2.91
6610	1" x 6"		250	.032		1.61	1.03		2.64	3.50
6620	1" x 8"		250	.032		2.15	1.03		3.18	4.10
6630	1" x 10"		225	.036		2.67	1.14		3.81	4.86
6640	1" x 12"		200	.040		3.18	1.28		4.46	5.65
6650	STK, 1" x 2"		275	.029		.43	.93		1.36	2.05
6660	1" x 3"		275	.029		.48	.93		1.41	2.09
6670	1" x 4"		250	.032		.62	1.03		1.65	2.41
6680	1" x 6"		250	.032		.96	1.03		1.99	2.78
6690	1" x 8"		250	.032		1.41	1.03		2.44	3.28
6700	1" x 10"		225	.036		2.08	1.14		3.22	4.21
6710	1" x 12"		200	.040		3.21	1.28		4.49	5.70
6790	Pine, #2, 1" x 2"		275	.029		.25	.93		1.18	1.85
6800	1" x 3"		275	.029		.40	.93		1.33	2.01
6810	1" x 4"		250	.032		.49	1.03		1.52	2.27
6820	1" x 6"		250	.032		.83	1.03		1.86	2.64
6830	1" x 8"		250	.032		1.22	1.03		2.25	3.07
6840	1" x 10"		225	.036		1.59	1.14		2.73	3.67
6850	1" x 12"		200	.040		2.05	1.28		3.33	4.41
6860	D & better, 1" x 2"		275	.029		.41	.93		1.34	2.03
6870	1" x 3"		275	.029		.61	.93		1.54	2.25
6880	1" x 4"		250	.032		.82	1.03		1.85	2.63
6890	1" x 6"		250	.032		1.12	1.03		2.15	2.96
6900	1" x 8"		250	.032		1.62	1.03		2.65	3.51
6910	1" x 10"		225	.036		2.03	1.14		3.17	4.16
6920	1" x 12"		200	.040		2.63	1.28		3.91	5.05
6930	Redwood, clear all heart, 1" x 2"		275	.029		.63	.93		1.56	2.27
6940	1" x 3"		275	.029		.94	.93		1.87	2.61
6950	1" x 4"		250	.032		1.19	1.03		2.22	3.04
6960	1" x 6"		250	.032		1.78	1.03		2.81	3.69
6970	1" x 8"		250	.032		2.36	1.03		3.39	4.32
6980	1" x 10"		225	.036		3.96	1.14		5.10	6.30
6990	1" x 12"		200	.040		4.75	1.28		6.03	7.40
7000	Grounds, 1" x 1", cedar, rough sawn		300	.027		.28	.86		1.14	1.74
7010	STK		300	.027		.27	.86		1.13	1.73
7020	Pine, #2		300	.027		.16	.86		1.02	1.61
7030	D & better		300	.027		.25	.86		1.11	1.72
7050	Redwood		300	.027		.39	.86		1.25	1.86
7060	Rake/verge board, cedar, rough sawn, 1" x 2"		225	.036		.54	1.14		1.68	2.52
7070	1" x 3"		225	.036		.81	1.14		1.95	2.81
7080	1" x 4"		200	.040		1.07	1.28		2.35	3.34
7090	1" x 6"		200	.040		1.61	1.28		2.89	3.93

06 22 13 – Standard Pattern Wood Trim

06 22 13.40 Moldings, Exterior		Crew	Daily Output	Labor-Hours	Unit	Material	2014 Bare Costs Labor	Equipment	Total	Total Incl O&P
7100	1" x 8"	1 Carp	190	.042	L.F.	2.15	1.35		3.50	4.64
7110	1" x 10"		190	.042		2.67	1.35		4.02	5.20
7120	1" x 12"		180	.044		3.21	1.43		4.64	5.95
7130	STK, 1" x 2"		225	.036		.43	1.14		1.57	2.40
7140	1" x 3"		225	.036		.48	1.14		1.62	2.44
7150	1" x 4"		200	.040		.62	1.28		1.90	2.84
7160	1" x 6"		200	.040		.96	1.28		2.24	3.21
7170	1" x 8"		190	.042		1.41	1.35		2.76	3.82
7180	1" x 10"		190	.042		2.08	1.35		3.43	4.56
7190	1" x 12"		180	.044		3.21	1.43		4.64	5.95
7200	Pine, #2, 1" x 2"		225	.036		.25	1.14		1.39	2.20
7210	1" x 3"		225	.036		.40	1.14		1.54	2.36
7220	1" x 4"		200	.040		.49	1.28		1.77	2.70
7230	1" x 6"		200	.040		.83	1.28		2.11	3.07
7240	1" x 8"		190	.042		1.22	1.35		2.57	3.61
7250	1" x 10"		190	.042		1.59	1.35		2.94	4.02
7260	1" x 12"		180	.044		2.05	1.43		3.48	4.65
7340	D & better, 1" x 2"		225	.036		.41	1.14		1.55	2.38
7350	1" x 3"		225	.036		.61	1.14		1.75	2.60
7360	1" x 4"		200	.040		.82	1.28		2.10	3.06
7370	1" x 6"		200	.040		1.12	1.28		2.40	3.39
7380	1" x 8"		190	.042		1.62	1.35		2.97	4.05
7390	1" x 10"		190	.042		2.03	1.35		3.38	4.51
7400	1" x 12"		180	.044		2.63	1.43		4.06	5.30
7410	Redwood, clear all heart, 1" x 2"		225	.036		.63	1.14		1.77	2.62
7420	1" x 3"		225	.036		.94	1.14		2.08	2.96
7430	1" x 4"		200	.040		1.19	1.28		2.47	3.47
7440	1" x 6"		200	.040		1.78	1.28		3.06	4.12
7450	1" x 8"		190	.042		2.36	1.35		3.71	4.86
7460	1" x 10"		190	.042		3.96	1.35		5.31	6.65
7470	1" x 12"		180	.044		4.75	1.43		6.18	7.65
7480	2" x 4"		200	.040		2.29	1.28		3.57	4.68
7490	2" x 6"		182	.044		3.43	1.41		4.84	6.15
7500	2" x 8"	▼	165	.048		4.56	1.56		6.12	7.60
7630	Soffit, cedar, rough sawn, 1" x 2"	2 Carp	440	.036		.54	1.17		1.71	2.56
7640	1" x 3"		440	.036		.81	1.17		1.98	2.85
7650	1" x 4"		420	.038		1.07	1.22		2.29	3.24
7660	1" x 6"		420	.038		1.61	1.22		2.83	3.83
7670	1" x 8"		420	.038		2.15	1.22		3.37	4.43
7680	1" x 10"		400	.040		2.67	1.28		3.95	5.10
7690	1" x 12"		400	.040		3.21	1.28		4.49	5.70
7700	STK, 1" x 2"		440	.036		.43	1.17		1.60	2.44
7710	1" x 3"		440	.036		.48	1.17		1.65	2.48
7720	1" x 4"		420	.038		.62	1.22		1.84	2.74
7730	1" x 6"		420	.038		.96	1.22		2.18	3.11
7740	1" x 8"		420	.038		1.41	1.22		2.63	3.61
7750	1" x 10"		400	.040		2.08	1.28		3.36	4.45
7760	1" x 12"		400	.040		3.21	1.28		4.49	5.70
7770	Pine, #2, 1" x 2"		440	.036		.25	1.17		1.42	2.24
7780	1" x 3"		440	.036		.40	1.17		1.57	2.40
7790	1" x 4"		420	.038		.49	1.22		1.71	2.60
7800	1" x 6"		420	.038		.83	1.22		2.05	2.97
7810	1" x 8"	▼	420	.038	▼	1.22	1.22		2.44	3.40

06 22 Millwork

06 22 13 – Standard Pattern Wood Trim

06 22 13.40 Moldings, Exterior

		Crew	Daily Output	Labor-Hours	Unit	Material	2014 Bare Costs Labor	Equipment	Total	Total Incl O&P
7820	1" x 10"	2 Carp	400	.040	L.F.	1.59	1.28		2.87	3.91
7830	1" x 12"		400	.040		2.05	1.28		3.33	4.41
7840	D & better, 1" x 2"		440	.036		.41	1.17		1.58	2.42
7850	1" x 3"		440	.036		.61	1.17		1.78	2.64
7860	1" x 4"		420	.038		.82	1.22		2.04	2.96
7870	1" x 6"		420	.038		1.12	1.22		2.34	3.29
7880	1" x 8"		420	.038		1.62	1.22		2.84	3.84
7890	1" x 10"		400	.040		2.03	1.28		3.31	4.40
7900	1" x 12"		400	.040		2.63	1.28		3.91	5.05
7910	Redwood, clear all heart, 1" x 2"		440	.036		.63	1.17		1.80	2.66
7920	1" x 3"		440	.036		.94	1.17		2.11	3
7930	1" x 4"		420	.038		1.19	1.22		2.41	3.37
7940	1" x 6"		420	.038		1.78	1.22		3	4.02
7950	1" x 8"		420	.038		2.36	1.22		3.58	4.65
7960	1" x 10"		400	.040		3.96	1.28		5.24	6.50
7970	1" x 12"		400	.040		4.75	1.28		6.03	7.40
8050	Trim, crown molding, pine, 11/16" x 4-1/4"	1 Carp	250	.032		4.54	1.03		5.57	6.70
8060	Back band, 11/16" x 1-1/16"		250	.032		.99	1.03		2.02	2.82
8070	Insect screen frame stock, 1-1/16" x 1-3/4"		395	.020		2.39	.65		3.04	3.72
8080	Dentils, 2-1/2" x 2-1/2" x 4", 6" O.C.		30	.267		1.22	8.55		9.77	15.75
8100	Fluted, 5-1/2"		165	.048		4.52	1.56		6.08	7.60
8110	Stucco bead, 1-3/8" x 1-5/8"		250	.032		2.50	1.03		3.53	4.48

06 22 13.45 Moldings, Trim

		Crew	Daily Output	Labor-Hours	Unit	Material	2014 Bare Costs Labor	Equipment	Total	Total Incl O&P
0010	**MOLDINGS, TRIM**									
0200	Astragal, stock pine, 11/16" x 1-3/4"	1 Carp	255	.031	L.F.	1.42	1.01		2.43	3.25
0250	1-5/16" x 2-3/16"		240	.033		2.10	1.07		3.17	4.11
0800	Chair rail, stock pine, 5/8" x 2-1/2"		270	.030		1.68	.95		2.63	3.45
0900	5/8" x 3-1/2"		240	.033		2.65	1.07		3.72	4.72
1000	Closet pole, stock pine, 1-1/8" diameter		200	.040		1.22	1.28		2.50	3.50
1100	Fir, 1-5/8" diameter		200	.040		2.36	1.28		3.64	4.76
1150	Corner, inside, 5/16" x 1"		225	.036		.40	1.14		1.54	2.36
1160	Outside, 1-1/16" x 1-1/16"		240	.033		1.56	1.07		2.63	3.52
1161	1-5/16" x 1-5/16"		240	.033		2.14	1.07		3.21	4.15
3300	Half round, stock pine, 1/4" x 1/2"		270	.030		.31	.95		1.26	1.94
3350	1/2" x 1"		255	.031		.74	1.01		1.75	2.50
3400	Handrail, fir, single piece, stock, hardware not included									
3450	1-1/2" x 1-3/4"	1 Carp	80	.100	L.F.	2.50	3.21		5.71	8.15
3470	Pine, 1-1/2" x 1-3/4"		80	.100		2.38	3.21		5.59	8
3500	1-1/2" x 2-1/2"		76	.105		2.67	3.38		6.05	8.65
3600	Lattice, stock pine, 1/4" x 1-1/8"		270	.030		.51	.95		1.46	2.16
3700	1/4" x 1-3/4"		250	.032		.92	1.03		1.95	2.74
3800	Miscellaneous, custom, pine, 1" x 1"		270	.030		.38	.95		1.33	2.02
3850	1" x 2"		265	.030		.76	.97		1.73	2.47
3900	1" x 3"		240	.033		1.14	1.07		2.21	3.05
4100	Birch or oak, nominal 1" x 1"		240	.033		.45	1.07		1.52	2.29
4200	Nominal 1" x 3"		215	.037		1.34	1.19		2.53	3.48
4400	Walnut, nominal 1" x 1"		215	.037		.54	1.19		1.73	2.61
4500	Nominal 1" x 3"		200	.040		1.63	1.28		2.91	3.95
4700	Teak, nominal 1" x 1"		215	.037		2.54	1.19		3.73	4.80
4800	Nominal 1" x 3"		200	.040		7.60	1.28		8.88	10.50
4900	Quarter round, stock pine, 1/4" x 1/4"		275	.029		.31	.93		1.24	1.91
4950	3/4" x 3/4"		255	.031		.71	1.01		1.72	2.47

06 22 Millwork

06 22 13 – Standard Pattern Wood Trim

06 22 13.45 Moldings, Trim		Crew	Daily Output	Labor-Hours	Unit	Material	2014 Bare Costs Labor	Equipment	Total	Total Incl O&P
5600	Wainscot moldings, 1-1/8" x 9/16", 2' high, minimum	1 Carp	76	.105	S.F.	12.35	3.38		15.73	19.30
5700	Maximum	↓	65	.123	"	15.65	3.95		19.60	24

06 22 13.50 Moldings, Window and Door

		Crew	Daily Output	Labor-Hours	Unit	Material	2014 Bare Costs Labor	Equipment	Total	Total Incl O&P
0010	**MOLDINGS, WINDOW AND DOOR**									
2800	Door moldings, stock, decorative, 1-1/8" wide, plain	1 Carp	17	.471	Set	51.50	15.10		66.60	82
2900	Detailed		17	.471	"	87.50	15.10		102.60	122
2960	Clear pine door jamb, no stops, 11/16" x 4-9/16"		240	.033	L.F.	5.15	1.07		6.22	7.50
3150	Door trim set, 1 head and 2 sides, pine, 2-1/2 wide		12	.667	Opng.	25.50	21.50		47	64
3170	3-1/2" wide		11	.727	"	37	23.50		60.50	80
3250	Glass beads, stock pine, 3/8" x 1/2"		275	.029	L.F.	.37	.93		1.30	1.98
3270	3/8" x 7/8"		270	.030		.50	.95		1.45	2.15
4850	Parting bead, stock pine, 3/8" x 3/4"		275	.029		.45	.93		1.38	2.07
4870	1/2" x 3/4"		255	.031		.57	1.01		1.58	2.32
5000	Stool caps, stock pine, 11/16" x 3-1/2"		200	.040		2.65	1.28		3.93	5.10
5100	1-1/16" x 3-1/4"		150	.053	↓	4.15	1.71		5.86	7.45
5300	Threshold, oak, 3' long, inside, 5/8" x 3-5/8"		32	.250	Ea.	6.40	8.05		14.45	20.50
5400	Outside, 1-1/2" x 7-5/8"	↓	16	.500	"	38	16.05		54.05	69
5900	Window trim sets, including casings, header, stops,									
5910	stool and apron, 2-1/2" wide, minimum	1 Carp	13	.615	Opng.	37	19.75		56.75	73.50
5950	Average		10	.800		43.50	25.50		69	91
6000	Maximum	↓	6	1.333	↓	62.50	43		105.50	141

06 22 13.60 Moldings, Soffits

		Crew	Daily Output	Labor-Hours	Unit	Material	2014 Bare Costs Labor	Equipment	Total	Total Incl O&P
0010	**MOLDINGS, SOFFITS**									
0200	Soffits, pine, 1" x 4"	2 Carp	420	.038	L.F.	.47	1.22		1.69	2.57
0210	1" x 6"		420	.038		.80	1.22		2.02	2.94
0220	1" x 8"		420	.038		1.19	1.22		2.41	3.37
0230	1" x 10"		400	.040		1.55	1.28		2.83	3.86
0240	1" x 12"		400	.040		2.01	1.28		3.29	4.37
0250	STK cedar, 1" x 4"		420	.038		.59	1.22		1.81	2.71
0260	1" x 6"		420	.038		.93	1.22		2.15	3.08
0270	1" x 8"		420	.038		1.38	1.22		2.60	3.58
0280	1" x 10"		400	.040		2.04	1.28		3.32	4.40
0290	1" x 12"		400	.040	↓	3.17	1.28		4.45	5.65
1000	Exterior AC plywood, 1/4" thick		400	.040	S.F.	.62	1.28		1.90	2.84
1050	3/8" thick		400	.040		.93	1.28		2.21	3.18
1100	1/2" thick	↓	400	.040		1.06	1.28		2.34	3.33
1150	Polyvinyl chloride, white, solid	1 Carp	230	.035		2.04	1.12		3.16	4.12
1160	Perforated	"	230	.035	↓	2.04	1.12		3.16	4.12
1170	Accessories, "J" channel 5/8"	2 Carp	700	.023	L.F.	.43	.73		1.16	1.70

06 25 Prefinished Paneling

06 25 13 – Prefinished Hardboard Paneling

06 25 13.10 Paneling, Hardboard

			Crew	Daily Output	Labor-Hours	Unit	Material	2014 Bare Costs Labor	Equipment	Total	Total Incl O&P
0010	**PANELING, HARDBOARD**										
0050	Not incl. furring or trim, hardboard, tempered, 1/8" thick	G	2 Carp	500	.032	S.F.	.39	1.03		1.42	2.16
0100	1/4" thick	G		500	.032		.63	1.03		1.66	2.42
0300	Tempered pegboard, 1/8" thick	G		500	.032		.40	1.03		1.43	2.17
0400	1/4" thick	G		500	.032		.65	1.03		1.68	2.45
0600	Untempered hardboard, natural finish, 1/8" thick	G		500	.032		.41	1.03		1.44	2.18
0700	1/4" thick	G		500	.032	↓	.50	1.03		1.53	2.28

06 25 Prefinished Paneling

06 25 13 – Prefinished Hardboard Paneling

06 25 13.10 Paneling, Hardboard

			Crew	Daily Output	Labor-Hours	Unit	Material	2014 Bare Costs Labor	Equipment	Total	Total Incl O&P
0900	Untempered pegboard, 1/8" thick	G	2 Carp	500	.032	S.F.	.42	1.03		1.45	2.19
1000	1/4" thick	G		500	.032		.46	1.03		1.49	2.24
1200	Plastic faced hardboard, 1/8" thick	G		500	.032		.63	1.03		1.66	2.42
1300	1/4" thick	G		500	.032		.86	1.03		1.89	2.68
1500	Plastic faced pegboard, 1/8" thick	G		500	.032		.64	1.03		1.67	2.43
1600	1/4" thick	G		500	.032		.82	1.03		1.85	2.63
1800	Wood grained, plain or grooved, 1/4" thick, minimum	G		500	.032		.66	1.03		1.69	2.46
1900	Maximum	G		425	.038		1.35	1.21		2.56	3.52
2100	Moldings for hardboard, wood or aluminum, minimum			500	.032	L.F.	.39	1.03		1.42	2.16
2200	Maximum			425	.038	"	1.29	1.21		2.50	3.45

06 25 16 – Prefinished Plywood Paneling

06 25 16.10 Paneling, Plywood

		Crew	Daily Output	Labor-Hours	Unit	Material	2014 Bare Costs Labor	Equipment	Total	Total Incl O&P
0010	**PANELING, PLYWOOD**									
2400	Plywood, prefinished, 1/4" thick, 4' x 8' sheets									
2410	with vertical grooves. Birch faced, minimum	2 Carp	500	.032	S.F.	.41	1.03		1.44	2.18
2420	Average		420	.038		.83	1.22		2.05	2.97
2430	Maximum		350	.046		1.25	1.47		2.72	3.85
2600	Mahogany, African		400	.040		2.90	1.28		4.18	5.35
2700	Philippine (Lauan)		500	.032		.60	1.03		1.63	2.39
2900	Oak or Cherry, minimum		500	.032		.34	1.03		1.37	2.10
3000	Maximum		400	.040		2.06	1.28		3.34	4.43
3200	Rosewood		320	.050		2.90	1.61		4.51	5.90
3400	Teak		400	.040		2.90	1.28		4.18	5.35
3600	Chestnut		375	.043		4.87	1.37		6.24	7.65
3800	Pecan		400	.040		2.10	1.28		3.38	4.47
3900	Walnut, minimum		500	.032		2.06	1.03		3.09	4
3950	Maximum		400	.040		5.30	1.28		6.58	8
4000	Plywood, prefinished, 3/4" thick, stock grades, minimum		320	.050		1.56	1.61		3.17	4.42
4100	Maximum		224	.071		4.68	2.29		6.97	9
4300	Architectural grade, minimum		224	.071		4.68	2.29		6.97	9
4400	Maximum		160	.100		4.68	3.21		7.89	10.55
4600	Plywood, "A" face, birch, VC, 1/2" thick, natural		450	.036		2.18	1.14		3.32	4.32
4700	Select		450	.036		2.18	1.14		3.32	4.32
4900	Veneer core, 3/4" thick, natural		320	.050		2.03	1.61		3.64	4.93
5000	Select		320	.050		2.27	1.61		3.88	5.20
5200	Lumber core, 3/4" thick, natural		320	.050		3.05	1.61		4.66	6.05
5500	Plywood, knotty pine, 1/4" thick, A2 grade		450	.036		1.67	1.14		2.81	3.76
5600	A3 grade		450	.036		2.10	1.14		3.24	4.23
5800	3/4" thick, veneer core, A2 grade		320	.050		2.15	1.61		3.76	5.05
5900	A3 grade		320	.050		2.42	1.61		4.03	5.35
6100	Aromatic cedar, 1/4" thick, plywood		400	.040		2.12	1.28		3.40	4.49
6200	1/4" thick, particle board		400	.040		1.03	1.28		2.31	3.29

06 25 26 – Panel System

06 25 26.10 Panel Systems

		Crew	Daily Output	Labor-Hours	Unit	Material	2014 Bare Costs Labor	Equipment	Total	Total Incl O&P
0010	**PANEL SYSTEMS**									
0100	Raised panel, eng. wood core w/wood veneer, std., paint grade	2 Carp	300	.053	S.F.	10.35	1.71		12.06	14.30
0110	Oak veneer		300	.053		24	1.71		25.71	29
0120	Maple veneer		300	.053		30	1.71		31.71	36
0130	Cherry veneer		300	.053		34.50	1.71		36.21	40.50
0300	Class I fire rated, paint grade		300	.053		12	1.71		13.71	16.10
0310	Oak veneer		300	.053		28	1.71		29.71	33.50
0320	Maple veneer		300	.053		37.50	1.71		39.21	44

06 25 Prefinished Paneling

06 25 26 – Panel System

06 25 26.10 Panel Systems	Crew	Daily Output	Labor-Hours	Unit	Material	2014 Bare Costs Labor	Equipment	Total	Total Incl O&P
0330	Cherry veneer	2 Carp	300	.053	S.F.	45	1.71		46.71	52.50
0510	Beadboard, 5/8" MDF, standard, primed		300	.053		7.85	1.71		9.56	11.50
0520	Oak veneer, unfinished		300	.053		12.40	1.71		14.11	16.55
0530	Maple veneer, unfinished		300	.053		13.55	1.71		15.26	17.80
0610	Rustic paneling, 5/8" MDF, standard, maple veneer, unfinished	▼	300	.053	▼	13.60	1.71		15.31	17.85

06 26 Board Paneling

06 26 13 – Profile Board Paneling

06 26 13.10 Paneling, Boards

		Crew	Daily Output	Labor-Hours	Unit	Material	2014 Bare Costs Labor	Equipment	Total	Total Incl O&P
0010	**PANELING, BOARDS**									
6400	Wood board paneling, 3/4" thick, knotty pine	2 Carp	300	.053	S.F.	1.91	1.71		3.62	4.98
6500	Rough sawn cedar		300	.053		3.09	1.71		4.80	6.30
6700	Redwood, clear, 1" x 4" boards		300	.053		4.96	1.71		6.67	8.35
6900	Aromatic cedar, closet lining, boards	▼	275	.058	▼	2.02	1.87		3.89	5.35

06 43 Wood Stairs and Railings

06 43 13 – Wood Stairs

06 43 13.20 Prefabricated Wood Stairs

		Crew	Daily Output	Labor-Hours	Unit	Material	2014 Bare Costs Labor	Equipment	Total	Total Incl O&P
0010	**PREFABRICATED WOOD STAIRS**									
0100	Box stairs, prefabricated, 3'-0" wide									
0110	Oak treads, up to 14 risers	2 Carp	39	.410	Riser	92.50	13.15		105.65	124
0600	With pine treads for carpet, up to 14 risers	"	39	.410	"	59.50	13.15		72.65	87.50
1100	For 4' wide stairs, add				Flight	25%				
1550	Stairs, prefabricated stair handrail with balusters	1 Carp	30	.267	L.F.	74	8.55		82.55	96
1700	Basement stairs, prefabricated, pine treads									
1710	Pine risers, 3' wide, up to 14 risers	2 Carp	52	.308	Riser	59.50	9.90		69.40	82
4000	Residential, wood, oak treads, prefabricated		1.50	10.667	Flight	1,200	340		1,540	1,900
4200	Built in place	▼	.44	36.364	"	1,900	1,175		3,075	4,075
4400	Spiral, oak, 4'-6" diameter, unfinished, prefabricated,									
4500	incl. railing, 9' high	2 Carp	1.50	10.667	Flight	3,625	340		3,965	4,550

06 43 13.40 Wood Stair Parts

		Crew	Daily Output	Labor-Hours	Unit	Material	2014 Bare Costs Labor	Equipment	Total	Total Incl O&P
0010	**WOOD STAIR PARTS**									
0020	Pin top balusters, 1-1/4", oak, 34"	1 Carp	96	.083	Ea.	7.80	2.67		10.47	13.10
0030	38"		96	.083		9.85	2.67		12.52	15.35
0040	42"		96	.083		12.10	2.67		14.77	17.80
0050	Poplar, 34"		96	.083		3.05	2.67		5.72	7.85
0060	38"		96	.083		3.88	2.67		6.55	8.75
0070	42"		96	.083		8.85	2.67		11.52	14.20
0080	Maple, 34"		96	.083		4.90	2.67		7.57	9.90
0090	38"		96	.083		5.60	2.67		8.27	10.70
0100	42"		96	.083		6.50	2.67		9.17	11.65
0130	Primed, 34"		96	.083		3	2.67		5.67	7.80
0140	38"		96	.083		3.62	2.67		6.29	8.50
0150	42"		96	.083		4.42	2.67		7.09	9.35
0180	Box top balusters, 1-1/4", oak, 34"		60	.133		10.85	4.28		15.13	19.15
0190	38"		60	.133		12.50	4.28		16.78	21
0200	42"		60	.133		12.95	4.28		17.23	21.50
0210	Poplar, 34"		60	.133		8.65	4.28		12.93	16.70
0220	38"	▼	60	.133	▼	9.50	4.28		13.78	17.65

06 43 Wood Stairs and Railings

06 43 13 – Wood Stairs

06 43 13.40 Wood Stair Parts	Crew	Daily Output	Labor-Hours	Unit	Material	2014 Bare Costs Labor	Equipment	Total	Total Incl O&P
0230	42"	1 Carp	60	.133	Ea.	10	4.28		14.28	18.20
0240	Maple, 34"		60	.133		11.90	4.28		16.18	20.50
0250	38"		60	.133		13.80	4.28		18.08	22.50
0260	42"		60	.133		14.20	4.28		18.48	23
0290	Primed, 34"		60	.133		7	4.28		11.28	14.90
0300	38"		60	.133		8	4.28		12.28	16
0310	42"		60	.133	▼	8.35	4.28		12.63	16.40
0340	Square balusters, cut from lineal stock, pine, 1-1/16" x 1-1/16"		180	.044	L.F.	1.49	1.43		2.92	4.04
0350	1-5/16" x 1-5/16"		180	.044		2	1.43		3.43	4.60
0360	1-5/8" x 1-5/8"		180	.044	▼	3.29	1.43		4.72	6
0370	Turned newel, oak, 3-1/2" square, 48" high		8	1	Ea.	94.50	32		126.50	158
0380	62" high		8	1		138	32		170	206
0390	Poplar, 3-1/2" square, 48" high		8	1		55	32		87	115
0400	62" high		8	1		75	32		107	137
0410	Maple, 3-1/2" square, 48" high		8	1		66	32		98	127
0420	62" high		8	1		93	32		125	156
0430	Square newel, oak, 3-1/2" square, 48" high		8	1		50	32		82	109
0440	58" high		8	1		70	32		102	131
0450	Poplar, 3-1/2" square, 48" high		8	1		35	32		67	92.50
0460	58" high		8	1		39	32		71	97
0470	Maple, 3" square, 48" high		8	1		50	32		82	109
0480	58" high		8	1	▼	62	32		94	122
0490	Railings, oak, minimum		96	.083	L.F.	9.50	2.67		12.17	14.95
0500	Average		96	.083		12.90	2.67		15.57	18.65
0510	Maximum		96	.083		13.50	2.67		16.17	19.35
0520	Maple, minimum		96	.083		15	2.67		17.67	21
0530	Average		96	.083		15.25	2.67		17.92	21.50
0540	Maximum		96	.083		15.50	2.67		18.17	21.50
0550	Oak, for bending rail, minimum		48	.167		22	5.35		27.35	33
0560	Average		48	.167		25	5.35		30.35	36.50
0570	Maximum		48	.167		28	5.35		33.35	40
0580	Maple, for bending rail, minimum		48	.167		25	5.35		30.35	36
0590	Average		48	.167		27	5.35		32.35	39
0600	Maximum		48	.167	▼	29.50	5.35		34.85	41.50
0610	Risers, oak, 3/4" x 8", 36" long		80	.100	Ea.	18	3.21		21.21	25
0620	42" long		80	.100		21	3.21		24.21	28.50
0630	48" long		80	.100		24	3.21		27.21	32
0640	54" long		80	.100		27	3.21		30.21	35
0650	60" long		80	.100		30	3.21		33.21	38.50
0660	72" long		80	.100		36	3.21		39.21	45
0670	Poplar, 3/4" x 8", 36" long		80	.100		12	3.21		15.21	18.60
0680	42" long		80	.100		14	3.21		17.21	21
0690	48" long		80	.100		16	3.21		19.21	23
0700	54" long		80	.100		18	3.21		21.21	25
0710	60" long		80	.100		20	3.21		23.21	27.50
0720	72" long		80	.100		24	3.21		27.21	32
0730	Pine, 1" x 8", 36" long		80	.100		3.57	3.21		6.78	9.35
0740	42" long		80	.100		4.17	3.21		7.38	10
0750	48" long		80	.100		4.76	3.21		7.97	10.65
0760	54" long		80	.100		5.35	3.21		8.56	11.30
0770	60" long		80	.100		5.95	3.21		9.16	11.95
0780	72" long		80	.100		7.15	3.21		10.36	13.25
0790	Treads, oak, no returns, 1-1/32" x 11-1/2" x 36" long	▼	32	.250	▼	29	8.05		37.05	45.50

06 43 Wood Stairs and Railings

06 43 13 – Wood Stairs

06 43 13.40 Wood Stair Parts

06 43 13.40 Wood Stair Parts	Crew	Daily Output	Labor-Hours	Unit	Material	2014 Bare Costs Labor	Equipment	Total	Total Incl O&P
0800	42" long	1 Carp	32	.250	Ea.	34	8.05		42.05	50.50
0810	48" long		32	.250		38.50	8.05		46.55	56
0820	54" long		32	.250		43.50	8.05		51.55	61.50
0830	60" long		32	.250		48.50	8.05		56.55	66.50
0840	72" long		32	.250		58	8.05		66.05	77.50
0850	Mitred return one end, 1-1/32" x 11-1/2" x 36" long		24	.333		52	10.70		62.70	75
0860	42" long		24	.333		60.50	10.70		71.20	84.50
0870	48" long		24	.333		69.50	10.70		80.20	94.50
0880	54" long		24	.333		78	10.70		88.70	104
0890	60" long		24	.333		86.50	10.70		97.20	114
0900	72" long		24	.333		104	10.70		114.70	132
0910	Mitred return two ends, 1-1/32" x 11-1/2" x 36" long		12	.667		53	21.50		74.50	94.50
0920	42" long		12	.667		62	21.50		83.50	104
0930	48" long		12	.667		70.50	21.50		92	114
0940	54" long		12	.667		79.50	21.50		101	124
0950	60" long		12	.667		88.50	21.50		110	133
0960	72" long		12	.667		106	21.50		127.50	153
0970	Starting step, oak, 48", bullnose		8	1		195	32		227	269
0980	Double end bullnose		8	1		345	32		377	435
1030	Skirt board, pine, 1" x 10"		55	.145	L.F.	1.55	4.67		6.22	9.55
1040	1" x 12"		52	.154	"	2.01	4.94		6.95	10.50
1050	Oak landing tread, 1-1/16" thick		54	.148	S.F.	9	4.76		13.76	17.90
1060	Oak cove molding		96	.083	L.F.	1.45	2.67		4.12	6.10
1070	Oak stringer molding		96	.083	"	3.25	2.67		5.92	8.10
1090	Rail bolt, 5/16" x 3-1/2"		48	.167	Ea.	2.75	5.35		8.10	12.05
1100	5/16" x 4-1/2"		48	.167		2.75	5.35		8.10	12.05
1120	Newel post anchor		16	.500		9.75	16.05		25.80	38
1130	Tapered plug, 1/2"		240	.033		1	1.07		2.07	2.90
1140	1"		240	.033		.99	1.07		2.06	2.89

06 43 16 – Wood Railings

06 43 16.10 Wood Handrails and Railings

06 43 16.10 Wood Handrails and Railings	Crew	Daily Output	Labor-Hours	Unit	Material	Labor	Equipment	Total	Total Incl O&P
0010	**WOOD HANDRAILS AND RAILINGS**									
0020	Custom design, architectural grade, hardwood, minimum	1 Carp	38	.211	L.F.	10	6.75		16.75	22.50
0100	Maximum		30	.267		62.50	8.55		71.05	83.50
0300	Stock interior railing with spindles 4" O.C., 4' long		40	.200		41	6.40		47.40	56
0400	8' long		48	.167		41	5.35		46.35	54

06 44 Ornamental Woodwork

06 44 19 – Wood Grilles

06 44 19.10 Grilles

06 44 19.10 Grilles	Crew	Daily Output	Labor-Hours	Unit	Material	Labor	Equipment	Total	Total Incl O&P
0010	**GRILLES** and panels, hardwood, sanded									
0020	2' x 4' to 4' x 8', custom designs, unfinished, minimum	1 Carp	38	.211	S.F.	61	6.75		67.75	78.50
0050	Average		30	.267		67.50	8.55		76.05	89
0100	Maximum		19	.421		70.50	13.50		84	100

06 44 33 – Wood Mantels

06 44 33.10 Fireplace Mantels

06 44 33.10 Fireplace Mantels	Crew	Daily Output	Labor-Hours	Unit	Material	Labor	Equipment	Total	Total Incl O&P
0010	**FIREPLACE MANTELS**									
0015	6" molding, 6' x 3'-6" opening, minimum	1 Carp	5	1.600	Opng.	248	51.50		299.50	360
0100	Maximum		5	1.600		445	51.50		496.50	575
0300	Prefabricated pine, colonial type, stock, deluxe		2	4		1,500	128		1,628	1,875

06 44 Ornamental Woodwork

06 44 33 – Wood Mantels

06 44 33.10 Fireplace Mantels

06 44 33.10 Fireplace Mantels	Crew	Daily Output	Labor-Hours	Unit	Material	2014 Bare Costs Labor	Equipment	Total	Total Incl O&P
0400	Economy	1 Carp	3	2.667	Opng.	690	85.50		775.50	905

06 44 33.20 Fireplace Mantel Beam

06 44 33.20 Fireplace Mantel Beam	Crew	Daily Output	Labor-Hours	Unit	Material	Labor	Equipment	Total	Total Incl O&P
0010	**FIREPLACE MANTEL BEAM**									
0020	Rough texture wood, 4" x 8"	1 Carp	36	.222	L.F.	8.30	7.15		15.45	21
0100	4" x 10"		35	.229	"	10.90	7.35		18.25	24.50
0300	Laminated hardwood, 2-1/4" x 10-1/2" wide, 6' long		5	1.600	Ea.	110	51.50		161.50	208
0400	8' long		5	1.600	"	150	51.50		201.50	252
0600	Brackets for above, rough sawn		12	.667	Pr.	10	21.50		31.50	47
0700	Laminated		12	.667	"	15	21.50		36.50	52.50

06 44 39 – Wood Posts and Columns

06 44 39.10 Decorative Beams

06 44 39.10 Decorative Beams	Crew	Daily Output	Labor-Hours	Unit	Material	Labor	Equipment	Total	Total Incl O&P
0010	**DECORATIVE BEAMS**									
0020	Rough sawn cedar, non-load bearing, 4" x 4"	2 Carp	180	.089	L.F.	1.20	2.85		4.05	6.10
0100	4" x 6"		170	.094		1.79	3.02		4.81	7.05
0200	4" x 8"		160	.100		2.39	3.21		5.60	8.05
0300	4" x 10"		150	.107		3.63	3.42		7.05	9.75
0400	4" x 12"		140	.114		4.61	3.67		8.28	11.20
0500	8" x 8"		130	.123		4.78	3.95		8.73	11.90
0600	Plastic beam, "hewn finish", 6" x 2"		240	.067		3.20	2.14		5.34	7.10
0601	6" x 4"		220	.073		3.60	2.33		5.93	7.90

06 44 39.20 Columns

06 44 39.20 Columns	Crew	Daily Output	Labor-Hours	Unit	Material	Labor	Equipment	Total	Total Incl O&P
0010	**COLUMNS**									
0050	Aluminum, round colonial, 6" diameter	2 Carp	80	.200	V.L.F.	18.60	6.40		25	31.50
0100	8" diameter		62.25	.257		21.50	8.25		29.75	37.50
0200	10" diameter		55	.291		25.50	9.35		34.85	43.50
0250	Fir, stock units, hollow round, 6" diameter		80	.200		20	6.40		26.40	33
0300	8" diameter		80	.200		25	6.40		31.40	38
0350	10" diameter		70	.229		32.50	7.35		39.85	48.50
0360	12" diameter		65	.246		38.50	7.90		46.40	55.50
0400	Solid turned, to 8' high, 3-1/2" diameter		80	.200		9.10	6.40		15.50	21
0500	4-1/2" diameter		75	.213		13.60	6.85		20.45	26.50
0600	5-1/2" diameter		70	.229		17.75	7.35		25.10	32
0800	Square columns, built-up, 5" x 5"		65	.246		15.50	7.90		23.40	30.50
0900	Solid, 3-1/2" x 3-1/2"		130	.123		9.10	3.95		13.05	16.70
1600	Hemlock, tapered, T & G, 12" diam., 10' high		100	.160		36.50	5.15		41.65	49
1700	16' high		65	.246		71.50	7.90		79.40	92.50
1900	10' high, 14" diameter		100	.160		112	5.15		117.15	132
2000	18' high		65	.246		91	7.90		98.90	113
2200	18" diameter, 12' high		65	.246		163	7.90		170.90	193
2300	20' high		50	.320		115	10.25		125.25	143
2500	20" diameter, 14' high		40	.400		184	12.85		196.85	224
2600	20' high		35	.457		172	14.65		186.65	214
2800	For flat pilasters, deduct					33%				
3000	For splitting into halves, add				Ea.	105			105	116
4000	Rough sawn cedar posts, 4" x 4"	2 Carp	250	.064	V.L.F.	3.33	2.05		5.38	7.10
4100	4" x 6"		235	.068		7.25	2.19		9.44	11.65
4200	6" x 6"		220	.073		11.70	2.33		14.03	16.80
4300	8" x 8"		200	.080		20.50	2.57		23.07	27

06 48 Wood Frames

06 48 13 – Exterior Wood Door Frames

06 48 13.10 Exterior Wood Door Frames and Accessories	Crew	Daily Output	Labor-Hours	Unit	Material	2014 Bare Costs Labor	Equipment	Total	Total Incl O&P
0010 **EXTERIOR WOOD DOOR FRAMES AND ACCESSORIES**									
0400 Exterior frame, incl. ext. trim, pine, 5/4 x 4-9/16" deep	2 Carp	375	.043	L.F.	6.60	1.37		7.97	9.60
0420 5-3/16" deep		375	.043		7.80	1.37		9.17	10.90
0440 6-9/16" deep		375	.043		7.90	1.37		9.27	11
0600 Oak, 5/4 x 4-9/16" deep		350	.046		16.90	1.47		18.37	21
0620 5-3/16" deep		350	.046		18.55	1.47		20.02	23
0640 6-9/16" deep		350	.046		20	1.47		21.47	24.50
1000 Sills, 8/4 x 8" deep, oak, no horns		100	.160		6.40	5.15		11.55	15.65
1020 2" horns		100	.160		17.10	5.15		22.25	27.50
1040 3" horns		100	.160		17.10	5.15		22.25	27.50
1100 8/4 x 10" deep, oak, no horns		90	.178		6	5.70		11.70	16.20
1120 2" horns		90	.178		22.50	5.70		28.20	34
1140 3" horns		90	.178		22.50	5.70		28.20	34
2000 Exterior, colonial, frame & trim, 3' opng., in-swing, minimum		22	.727	Ea.	355	23.50		378.50	430
2010 Average		21	.762		580	24.50		604.50	675
2020 Maximum		20	.800		1,200	25.50		1,225.50	1,375
2100 5'-4" opening, in-swing, minimum		17	.941		420	30		450	515
2120 Maximum		15	1.067		1,200	34		1,234	1,375
2140 Out-swing, minimum		17	.941		420	30		450	515
2160 Maximum		15	1.067		1,200	34		1,234	1,375
2400 6'-0" opening, in-swing, minimum		16	1		420	32		452	520
2420 Maximum		10	1.600		1,200	51.50		1,251.50	1,400
2460 Out-swing, minimum		16	1		420	32		452	520
2480 Maximum		10	1.600		1,200	51.50		1,251.50	1,400
2600 For two sidelights, add, minimum		30	.533	Opng.	67	17.10		84.10	103
2620 Maximum		20	.800	"	845	25.50		870.50	970
2700 Custom birch frame, 3'-0" opening		16	1	Ea.	230	32		262	305
2750 6'-0" opening		16	1		350	32		382	440
2900 Exterior, modern, plain trim, 3' opng., in-swing, minimum		26	.615		45	19.75		64.75	82.50
2920 Average		24	.667		53.50	21.50		75	94.50
2940 Maximum		22	.727		61.50	23.50		85	107

06 48 16 – Interior Wood Door Frames

06 48 16.10 Interior Wood Door Jamb and Frames

	Crew	Daily Output	Labor-Hours	Unit	Material	2014 Bare Costs Labor	Equipment	Total	Total Incl O&P
0010 **INTERIOR WOOD DOOR JAMB AND FRAMES**									
3000 Interior frame, pine, 11/16" x 3-5/8" deep	2 Carp	375	.043	L.F.	6.10	1.37		7.47	9
3020 4-9/16" deep		375	.043		6.25	1.37		7.62	9.15
3040 5-3/16" deep		375	.043		6.20	1.37		7.57	9.10
3200 Oak, 11/16" x 3-5/8" deep		350	.046		9	1.47		10.47	12.35
3220 4-9/16" deep		350	.046		9	1.47		10.47	12.35
3240 5-3/16" deep		350	.046		12.75	1.47		14.22	16.50
3400 Walnut, 11/16" x 3-5/8" deep		350	.046		8.25	1.47		9.72	11.55
3420 4-9/16" deep		350	.046		9	1.47		10.47	12.35
3440 5-3/16" deep		350	.046		9	1.47		10.47	12.35
3600 Pocket door frame		16	1	Ea.	82	32		114	144
3800 Threshold, oak, 5/8" x 3-5/8" deep		200	.080	L.F.	3.56	2.57		6.13	8.25
3820 4-5/8" deep		190	.084		4.13	2.70		6.83	9.10
3840 5-5/8" deep		180	.089		6.50	2.85		9.35	11.95

06 49 Wood Screens and Exterior Wood Shutters

06 49 19 – Exterior Wood Shutters

06 49 19.10 Shutters, Exterior	Crew	Daily Output	Labor-Hours	Unit	Material	2014 Bare Costs Labor	Equipment	Total	Total Incl O&P
0010 **SHUTTERS, EXTERIOR**									
0012 Aluminum, louvered, 1'-4" wide, 3'-0" long	1 Carp	10	.800	Pr.	75	25.50		100.50	126
0200 4'-0" long		10	.800		89.50	25.50		115	142
0300 5'-4" long		10	.800		118	25.50		143.50	173
0400 6'-8" long		9	.889		150	28.50		178.50	214
1000 Pine, louvered, primed, each 1'-2" wide, 3'-3" long		10	.800		215	25.50		240.50	280
1100 4'-7" long		10	.800		282	25.50		307.50	355
1250 Each 1'-4" wide, 3'-0" long		10	.800		224	25.50		249.50	289
1350 5'-3" long		10	.800		355	25.50		380.50	435
1500 Each 1'-6" wide, 3'-3" long		10	.800		262	25.50		287.50	330
1600 4'-7" long		10	.800		350	25.50		375.50	430
1620 Cedar, louvered, 1'-2" wide, 5'-7" long		10	.800		335	25.50		360.50	410
1630 Each 1'-4" wide, 2'-2" long		10	.800		176	25.50		201.50	237
1640 3'-0" long		10	.800		224	25.50		249.50	289
1650 3'-3" long		10	.800		238	25.50		263.50	305
1660 3'-11" long		10	.800		277	25.50		302.50	350
1670 4'-3" long		10	.800		296	25.50		321.50	370
1680 5'-3" long		10	.800		355	25.50		380.50	435
1690 5'-11" long		10	.800		390	25.50		415.50	475
1700 Door blinds, 6'-9" long, each 1'-3" wide		9	.889		415	28.50		443.50	510
1710 1'-6" wide		9	.889		490	28.50		518.50	590
1720 Cedar, solid raised panel, each 1'-4" wide, 3'-3" long		10	.800		335	25.50		360.50	410
1730 3'-11" long		10	.800		385	25.50		410.50	470
1740 4'-3" long		10	.800		415	25.50		440.50	500
1750 4'-7" long		10	.800		440	25.50		465.50	530
1760 4'-11" long		10	.800		465	25.50		490.50	560
1770 5'-11" long		10	.800		550	25.50		575.50	650
1800 Door blinds, 6'-9" long, each 1'-3" wide		9	.889		415	28.50		443.50	510
1900 1'-6" wide		9	.889		490	28.50		518.50	590
2500 Polystyrene, solid raised panel, each 1'-4" wide, 3'-3" long		10	.800		72	25.50		97.50	122
2600 3'-11" long		10	.800		97	25.50		122.50	150
2700 4'-7" long		10	.800		109	25.50		134.50	163
2800 5'-3" long		10	.800		126	25.50		151.50	182
2900 6'-8" long		9	.889		161	28.50		189.50	225
4500 Polystyrene, louvered, each 1'-2" wide, 3'-3" long		10	.800		65	25.50		90.50	115
4600 4'-7" long		10	.800		88	25.50		113.50	140
4750 5'-3" long		10	.800		102	25.50		127.50	155
4850 6'-8" long		9	.889		126	28.50		154.50	187
6000 Vinyl, louvered, each 1'-2" x 4'-7" long		10	.800		88	25.50		113.50	140
6200 Each 1'-4" x 6'-8" long		9	.889		126	28.50		154.50	187
8000 PVC exterior rolling shutters									
8100 including crank control	1 Carp	8	1	Ea.	510	32		542	620
8500 Insulative - 6' x 6'8" stock unit	"	8	1	"	730	32		762	855

06 51 Structural Plastic Shapes and Plates

06 51 13 – Plastic Lumber

06 51 13.10 Recycled Plastic Lumber		Crew	Daily Output	Labor-Hours	Unit	Material	2014 Bare Costs Labor	Equipment	Total	Total Incl O&P
0010	**RECYCLED PLASTIC LUMBER**									
4000	Sheeting, recycled plastic, black or white, 4' x 8' x 1/8" G	2 Carp	1100	.015	S.F.	1.58	.47		2.05	2.53
4010	4' x 8' x 3/16" G		1100	.015		2.27	.47		2.74	3.29
4020	4' x 8' x 1/4" G		950	.017		2.36	.54		2.90	3.51
4030	4' x 8' x 3/8" G		950	.017		3.67	.54		4.21	4.95
4040	4' x 8' x 1/2" G		900	.018		4.85	.57		5.42	6.30
4050	4' x 8' x 5/8" G		900	.018		6.55	.57		7.12	8.15
4060	4' x 8' x 3/4" G		850	.019		8.25	.60		8.85	10.10
4070	Add for colors G				Ea.	5%				
8500	100% recycled plastic, var colors, NLB, 2" x 2" G				L.F.	1.76			1.76	1.94
8510	2" x 4" G					3.67			3.67	4.04
8520	2" x 6" G					5.75			5.75	6.35
8530	2" x 8" G					7.90			7.90	8.70
8540	2" x 10" G					11.50			11.50	12.65
8550	5/4" x 4" G					4.26			4.26	4.69
8560	5/4" x 6" G					5.05			5.05	5.55
8570	1" x 6" G					2.86			2.86	3.15
8580	1/2" x 8" G					3.41			3.41	3.75
8590	2" x 10" T & G G					11.50			11.50	12.65
8600	3" x 10" T & G G					13.65			13.65	15
8610	Add for premium colors G					20%				

06 63 Plastic Railings

06 63 10 – Plastic (PVC) Railings

06 63 10.10 Plastic Railings		Crew	Daily Output	Labor-Hours	Unit	Material	2014 Bare Costs Labor	Equipment	Total	Total Incl O&P
0010	**PLASTIC RAILINGS**									
0100	Horizontal PVC handrail with balusters, 3-1/2" wide, 36" high	1 Carp	96	.083	L.F.	25	2.67		27.67	32
0150	42" high		96	.083		28	2.67		30.67	35.50
0200	Angled PVC handrail with balusters, 3-1/2" wide, 36" high		72	.111		28.50	3.57		32.07	37
0250	42" high		72	.111		31.50	3.57		35.07	41
0300	Post sleeve for 4 x 4 post		96	.083		14	2.67		16.67	19.90
0400	Post cap for 4 x 4 post, flat profile		48	.167	Ea.	13.90	5.35		19.25	24.50
0450	Newel post style profile		48	.167		23.50	5.35		28.85	35
0500	Raised corbeled profile		48	.167		28.50	5.35		33.85	40
0550	Post base trim for 4 x 4 post		96	.083		18.25	2.67		20.92	24.50

06 65 Plastic Simulated Wood Trim

06 65 10 – PVC Trim

06 65 10.10 PVC Trim, Exterior		Crew	Daily Output	Labor-Hours	Unit	Material	2014 Bare Costs Labor	Equipment	Total	Total Incl O&P
0010	**PVC TRIM, EXTERIOR**									
0100	Cornerboards, 5/4" x 6" x 6"	1 Carp	240	.033	L.F.	8.90	1.07		9.97	11.60
0110	Door/window casing, 1" x 4"		200	.040		1.35	1.28		2.63	3.65
0120	1" x 6"		200	.040		2.12	1.28		3.40	4.49
0130	1" x 8"		195	.041		2.80	1.32		4.12	5.30
0140	1" x 10"		195	.041		3.55	1.32		4.87	6.15
0150	1" x 12"		190	.042		4.34	1.35		5.69	7.05
0160	5/4" x 4"		195	.041		1.72	1.32		3.04	4.11
0170	5/4" x 6"		195	.041		2.72	1.32		4.04	5.20
0180	5/4" x 8"		190	.042		3.57	1.35		4.92	6.20

06 65 Plastic Simulated Wood Trim

06 65 10 – PVC Trim

06 65 10.10 PVC Trim, Exterior		Crew	Daily Output	Labor-Hours	Unit	Material	2014 Bare Costs Labor	Equipment	Total	Total Incl O&P
0190	5/4" x 10"	1 Carp	190	.042	L.F.	4.57	1.35		5.92	7.30
0200	5/4" x 12"		185	.043		5	1.39		6.39	7.85
0210	Fascia, 1" x 4"		250	.032		1.35	1.03		2.38	3.22
0220	1" x 6"		250	.032		2.12	1.03		3.15	4.06
0230	1" x 8"		225	.036		2.80	1.14		3.94	5
0240	1" x 10"		225	.036		3.55	1.14		4.69	5.85
0250	1" x 12"		200	.040		4.34	1.28		5.62	6.95
0260	5/4" x 4"		240	.033		1.72	1.07		2.79	3.69
0270	5/4" x 6"		240	.033		2.72	1.07		3.79	4.79
0280	5/4" x 8"		215	.037		3.57	1.19		4.76	5.95
0290	5/4" x 10"		215	.037		4.57	1.19		5.76	7.05
0300	5/4" x 12"		190	.042		5	1.35		6.35	7.75
0310	Frieze, 1" x 4"		250	.032		1.35	1.03		2.38	3.22
0320	1" x 6"		250	.032		2.12	1.03		3.15	4.06
0330	1" x 8"		225	.036		2.80	1.14		3.94	5
0340	1" x 10"		225	.036		3.55	1.14		4.69	5.85
0350	1" x 12"		200	.040		4.34	1.28		5.62	6.95
0360	5/4" x 4"		240	.033		1.72	1.07		2.79	3.69
0370	5/4" x 6"		240	.033		2.72	1.07		3.79	4.79
0380	5/4" x 8"		215	.037		3.57	1.19		4.76	5.95
0390	5/4" x 10"		215	.037		4.57	1.19		5.76	7.05
0400	5/4" x 12"		190	.042		5	1.35		6.35	7.75
0410	Rake, 1" x 4"		200	.040		1.35	1.28		2.63	3.65
0420	1" x 6"		200	.040		2.12	1.28		3.40	4.49
0430	1" x 8"		190	.042		2.80	1.35		4.15	5.35
0440	1" x 10"		190	.042		3.55	1.35		4.90	6.20
0450	1" x 12"		180	.044		4.34	1.43		5.77	7.15
0460	5/4" x 4"		195	.041		1.72	1.32		3.04	4.11
0470	5/4" x 6"		195	.041		2.72	1.32		4.04	5.20
0480	5/4" x 8"		185	.043		3.57	1.39		4.96	6.25
0490	5/4" x 10"		185	.043		4.57	1.39		5.96	7.40
0500	5/4" x 12"		175	.046		5	1.47		6.47	7.95
0510	Rake trim, 1" x 4"		225	.036		1.35	1.14		2.49	3.41
0520	1" x 6"		225	.036		2.12	1.14		3.26	4.25
0560	5/4" x 4"		220	.036		1.72	1.17		2.89	3.85
0570	5/4" x 6"	▼	220	.036		2.72	1.17		3.89	4.95
0610	Soffit, 1" x 4"	2 Carp	420	.038		1.35	1.22		2.57	3.55
0620	1" x 6"		420	.038		2.12	1.22		3.34	4.39
0630	1" x 8"		420	.038		2.80	1.22		4.02	5.15
0640	1" x 10"		400	.040		3.55	1.28		4.83	6.05
0650	1" x 12"		400	.040		4.34	1.28		5.62	6.95
0660	5/4" x 4"		410	.039		1.72	1.25		2.97	4
0670	5/4" x 6"		410	.039		2.72	1.25		3.97	5.10
0680	5/4" x 8"		410	.039		3.57	1.25		4.82	6.05
0690	5/4" x 10"		390	.041		4.57	1.32		5.89	7.25
0700	5/4" x 12"	▼	390	.041	▼	5	1.32		6.32	7.70

Division Notes

	CREW	DAILY OUTPUT	LABOR-HOURS	UNIT	BARE COSTS				TOTAL INCL O&P
					MAT.	LABOR	EQUIP.	TOTAL	

Estimating Tips

07 10 00 Dampproofing and Waterproofing

- Be sure of the job specifications before pricing this subdivision. The difference in cost between waterproofing and dampproofing can be great. Waterproofing will hold back standing water. Dampproofing prevents the transmission of water vapor. Also included in this section are vapor retarding membranes.

07 20 00 Thermal Protection

- Insulation and fireproofing products are measured by area, thickness, volume or R-value. Specifications may give only what the specific R-value should be in a certain situation. The estimator may need to choose the type of insulation to meet that R-value.

07 30 00 Steep Slope Roofing
07 40 00 Roofing and Siding Panels

- Many roofing and siding products are bought and sold by the square. One square is equal to an area that measures 100 square feet.

This simple change in unit of measure could create a large error if the estimator is not observant. Accessories necessary for a complete installation must be figured into any calculations for both material and labor.

07 50 00 Membrane Roofing
07 60 00 Flashing and Sheet Metal
07 70 00 Roofing and Wall Specialties and Accessories

- The items in these subdivisions compose a roofing system. No one component completes the installation, and all must be estimated. Built-up or single-ply membrane roofing systems are made up of many products and installation trades. Wood blocking at roof perimeters or penetrations, parapet coverings, reglets, roof drains, gutters, downspouts, sheet metal flashing, skylights, smoke vents, and roof hatches all need to be considered along with the roofing material. Several different installation trades will need to work together on the roofing system. Inherent difficulties in the scheduling and coordination of various trades must be accounted for when estimating labor costs.

07 90 00 Joint Protection

- To complete the weather-tight shell, the sealants and caulkings must be estimated. Where different materials meet—at expansion joints, at flashing penetrations, and at hundreds of other locations throughout a construction project—they provide another line of defense against water penetration. Often, an entire system is based on the proper location and placement of caulking or sealants. The detailed drawings that are included as part of a set of architectural plans show typical locations for these materials. When caulking or sealants are shown at typical locations, this means the estimator must include them for all the locations where this detail is applicable. Be careful to keep different types of sealants separate, and remember to consider backer rods and primers if necessary.

Reference Numbers

Reference numbers are shown in shaded boxes at the beginning of some major classifications. These numbers refer to related items in the Reference Section. The reference information may be an estimating procedure, an alternate pricing method, or technical information.

Note: Not all subdivisions listed here necessarily appear in this publication.

07 01 50 – Maintenance of Membrane Roofing

07 01 50.10 Roof Coatings	Crew	Daily Output	Labor-Hours	Unit	Material	2014 Bare Costs Labor	Equipment	Total	Total Incl O&P
0010 **ROOF COATINGS**									
0012 Asphalt, brush grade, material only				Gal.	9.15			9.15	10.10
0800 Glass fibered roof & patching cement, 5 gallon					7.65			7.65	8.40
1100 Roof patch & flashing cement, 5 gallon					8.30			8.30	9.10

07 05 05 – Selective Demolition

07 05 05.10 Selective Demo., Thermal and Moist. Protection

		Crew	Daily Output	Labor-Hours	Unit	Material	2014 Bare Costs Labor	Equipment	Total	Total Incl O&P
0010	**SELECTIVE DEMO., THERMAL AND MOISTURE PROTECTION**									
0020	Caulking/sealant, to 1" x 1" joint R024119-10	1 Clab	600	.013	L.F.		.32		.32	.53
0120	Downspouts, including hangers		350	.023	"		.54		.54	.92
0220	Flashing, sheet metal		290	.028	S.F.		.66		.66	1.11
0420	Gutters, aluminum or wood, edge hung		240	.033	L.F.		.79		.79	1.33
0520	Built-in		100	.080	"		1.90		1.90	3.20
0620	Insulation, air/vapor barrier		3500	.002	S.F.		.05		.05	.09
0670	Batts or blankets		1400	.006	C.F.		.14		.14	.23
0720	Foamed or sprayed in place	2 Clab	1000	.016	B.F.		.38		.38	.64
0770	Loose fitting	1 Clab	3000	.003	C.F.		.06		.06	.11
0870	Rigid board		3450	.002	B.F.		.06		.06	.09
1120	Roll roofing, cold adhesive		12	.667	Sq.		15.85		15.85	26.50
1170	Roof accessories, adjustable metal chimney flashing		9	.889	Ea.		21		21	35.50
1325	Plumbing vent flashing		32	.250	"		5.95		5.95	10
1375	Ridge vent strip, aluminum		310	.026	L.F.		.61		.61	1.03
1620	Skylight to 10 S.F.		8	1	Ea.		24		24	40
2120	Roof edge, aluminum soffit and fascia		570	.014	L.F.		.33		.33	.56
2170	Concrete coping, up to 12" wide	2 Clab	160	.100			2.38		2.38	4.01
2220	Drip edge	1 Clab	1000	.008			.19		.19	.32
2270	Gravel stop		950	.008			.20		.20	.34
2370	Sheet metal coping, up to 12" wide		240	.033			.79		.79	1.33
2470	Roof insulation board, over 2" thick	B-2	7800	.005	B.F.		.12		.12	.21
2520	Up to 2" thick	"	3900	.010	S.F.		.25		.25	.42
2620	Roof ventilation, louvered gable vent	1 Clab	16	.500	Ea.		11.90		11.90	20
2670	Remove, roof hatch	G-3	15	2.133			64		64	107
2675	Rafter vents	1 Clab	960	.008			.20		.20	.33
2720	Soffit vent and/or fascia vent		575	.014	L.F.		.33		.33	.56
2775	Soffit vent strip, aluminum, 3" to 4" wide		160	.050			1.19		1.19	2
2820	Roofing accessories, shingle moulding, to 1" x 4"		1600	.005			.12		.12	.20
2870	Cant strip	B-2	2000	.020			.48		.48	.81
2920	Concrete block walkway	1 Clab	230	.035			.83		.83	1.39
3070	Roofing, felt paper, 15#		70	.114	Sq.		2.72		2.72	4.58
3125	#30 felt		30	.267	"		6.35		6.35	10.70
3170	Asphalt shingles, 1 layer	B-2	3500	.011	S.F.		.28		.28	.47
3180	2 layers		1750	.023	"		.55		.55	.93
3370	Modified bitumen		26	1.538	Sq.		37		37	62.50
3420	Built-up, no gravel, 3 ply		25	1.600			38.50		38.50	65
3470	4 ply		21	1.905			46		46	77.50
3620	5 ply		1600	.025	S.F.		.61		.61	1.02
3720	5 ply, with gravel		890	.045			1.09		1.09	1.83
3725	Gravel removal, minimum		5000	.008			.19		.19	.33
3730	Maximum		2000	.020			.48		.48	.81
3870	Fiberglass sheet		1200	.033			.81		.81	1.36

07 05 Common Work Results for Thermal and Moisture Protection

07 05 05 – Selective Demolition

07 05 05.10 Selective Demo., Thermal and Moist. Protection

		Crew	Daily Output	Labor-Hours	Unit	Material	2014 Bare Costs Labor	Equipment	Total	Total Incl O&P
4120	Slate shingles	B-2	1900	.021	S.F.		.51		.51	.86
4170	Ridge shingles, clay or slate		2000	.020	L.F.		.48		.48	.81
4320	Single ply membrane, attached at seams		52	.769	Sq.		18.60		18.60	31.50
4370	Ballasted		75	.533			12.90		12.90	21.50
4420	Fully adhered	↓	39	1.026	↓		25		25	42
4550	Roof hatch, 2'-6" x 3'-0"	1 Clab	10	.800	Ea.		19.05		19.05	32
4670	Wood shingles	B-2	2200	.018	S.F.		.44		.44	.74
4820	Sheet metal roofing	"	2150	.019			.45		.45	.76
4970	Siding, horizontal wood clapboards	1 Clab	380	.021			.50		.50	.84
5025	Exterior insulation finish system	"	120	.067			1.59		1.59	2.67
5070	Tempered hardboard, remove and reset	1 Carp	380	.021			.68		.68	1.14
5120	Tempered hardboard sheet siding	"	375	.021	↓		.68		.68	1.15
5170	Metal, corner strips	1 Clab	850	.009	L.F.		.22		.22	.38
5225	Horizontal strips		444	.018	S.F.		.43		.43	.72
5320	Vertical strips		400	.020			.48		.48	.80
5520	Wood shingles		350	.023			.54		.54	.92
5620	Stucco siding		360	.022			.53		.53	.89
5670	Textured plywood		725	.011			.26		.26	.44
5720	Vinyl siding		510	.016	↓		.37		.37	.63
5770	Corner strips		900	.009	L.F.		.21		.21	.36
5870	Wood, boards, vertical	↓	400	.020	S.F.		.48		.48	.80
5920	Waterproofing, protection/drain board	2 Clab	3900	.004	B.F.		.10		.10	.16
5970	Over 1/2" thick		1750	.009	S.F.		.22		.22	.37
6020	To 1/2" thick	↓	2000	.008	"		.19		.19	.32

07 11 Dampproofing

07 11 13 – Bituminous Dampproofing

07 11 13.10 Bituminous Asphalt Coating

		Crew	Daily Output	Labor-Hours	Unit	Material	2014 Bare Costs Labor	Equipment	Total	Total Incl O&P
0010	**BITUMINOUS ASPHALT COATING**									
0030	Brushed on, below grade, 1 coat	1 Rofc	665	.012	S.F.	.23	.32		.55	.85
0100	2 coat		500	.016		.46	.43		.89	1.30
0300	Sprayed on, below grade, 1 coat		830	.010		.23	.26		.49	.73
0400	2 coat	↓	500	.016	↓	.45	.43		.88	1.29
0500	Asphalt coating, with fibers				Gal.	7.65			7.65	8.40
0600	Troweled on, asphalt with fibers, 1/16" thick	1 Rofc	500	.016	S.F.	.33	.43		.76	1.17
0700	1/8" thick		400	.020		.59	.54		1.13	1.65
1000	1/2" thick	↓	350	.023	↓	1.91	.62		2.53	3.24

07 11 16 – Cementitious Dampproofing

07 11 16.20 Cementitious Parging

		Crew	Daily Output	Labor-Hours	Unit	Material	2014 Bare Costs Labor	Equipment	Total	Total Incl O&P
0010	**CEMENTITIOUS PARGING**									
0020	Portland cement, 2 coats, 1/2" thick	D-1	250	.064	S.F.	.30	1.85		2.15	3.41
0100	Waterproofed Portland cement, 1/2" thick, 2 coats	"	250	.064	"	3.73	1.85		5.58	7.20

07 19 Water Repellents

07 19 19 – Silicone Water Repellents

07 19 19.10 Silicone Based Water Repellents		Crew	Daily Output	Labor-Hours	Unit	Material	2014 Bare Costs Labor	Equipment	Total	Total Incl O&P
0010	**SILICONE BASED WATER REPELLENTS**									
0020	Water base liquid, roller applied	2 Rofc	7000	.002	S.F.	.49	.06		.55	.65
0200	Silicone or stearate, sprayed on CMU, 1 coat	1 Rofc	4000	.002	↓	.35	.05		.40	.49
0300	2 coats	"	3000	.003	↓	.71	.07		.78	.91

07 21 Thermal Insulation

07 21 13 – Board Insulation

07 21 13.10 Rigid Insulation

07 21 13.10 Rigid Insulation			Crew	Daily Output	Labor-Hours	Unit	Material	Labor	Equipment	Total	Total Incl O&P
0010	**RIGID INSULATION**, for walls										
0040	Fiberglass, 1.5#/C.F., unfaced, 1" thick, R4.1	G	1 Carp	1000	.008	S.F.	.27	.26		.53	.73
0060	1-1/2" thick, R6.2	G		1000	.008		.40	.26		.66	.87
0080	2" thick, R8.3	G		1000	.008		.45	.26		.71	.93
0120	3" thick, R12.4	G		800	.010		.56	.32		.88	1.16
0370	3#/C.F., unfaced, 1" thick, R4.3	G		1000	.008		.52	.26		.78	1
0390	1-1/2" thick, R6.5	G		1000	.008		.78	.26		1.04	1.29
0400	2" thick, R8.7	G		890	.009		1.05	.29		1.34	1.65
0420	2-1/2" thick, R10.9	G		800	.010		1.10	.32		1.42	1.75
0440	3" thick, R13	G		800	.010		1.59	.32		1.91	2.29
0520	Foil faced, 1" thick, R4.3	G		1000	.008		.90	.26		1.16	1.42
0540	1-1/2" thick, R6.5	G		1000	.008		1.35	.26		1.61	1.92
0560	2" thick, R8.7	G		890	.009		1.69	.29		1.98	2.35
0580	2-1/2" thick, R10.9	G		800	.010		1.98	.32		2.30	2.72
0600	3" thick, R13	G	↓	800	.010	↓	2.18	.32		2.50	2.94
1600	Isocyanurate, 4' x 8' sheet, foil faced, both sides										
1610	1/2" thick	G	1 Carp	800	.010	S.F.	.29	.32		.61	.86
1620	5/8" thick	G		800	.010		.32	.32		.64	.89
1630	3/4" thick	G		800	.010		.33	.32		.65	.90
1640	1" thick	G		800	.010		.51	.32		.83	1.10
1650	1-1/2" thick	G		730	.011		.63	.35		.98	1.28
1660	2" thick	G		730	.011		.79	.35		1.14	1.46
1670	3" thick	G		730	.011		1.78	.35		2.13	2.55
1680	4" thick	G		730	.011		2	.35		2.35	2.79
1700	Perlite, 1" thick, R2.77	G		800	.010		.36	.32		.68	.94
1750	2" thick, R5.55	G		730	.011		.72	.35		1.07	1.38
1900	Extruded polystyrene, 25 PSI compressive strength, 1" thick, R5	G		800	.010		.52	.32		.84	1.11
1940	2" thick R10	G		730	.011		1.05	.35		1.40	1.75
1960	3" thick, R15	G		730	.011		1.49	.35		1.84	2.23
2100	Expanded polystyrene, 1" thick, R3.85	G		800	.010		.24	.32		.56	.80
2120	2" thick, R7.69	G		730	.011		.48	.35		.83	1.12
2140	3" thick, R11.49	G	↓	730	.011	↓	.72	.35		1.07	1.38

07 21 13.13 Foam Board Insulation

07 21 13.13 Foam Board Insulation			Crew	Daily Output	Labor-Hours	Unit	Material	Labor	Equipment	Total	Total Incl O&P
0010	**FOAM BOARD INSULATION**										
0600	Polystyrene, expanded, 1" thick, R4	G	1 Carp	680	.012	S.F.	.24	.38		.62	.90
0700	2" thick, R8	G	"	675	.012	"	.48	.38		.86	1.17

07 21 16 – Blanket Insulation

07 21 16.10 Blanket Insulation for Floors/Ceilings

07 21 16.10 Blanket Insulation for Floors/Ceilings			Crew	Daily Output	Labor-Hours	Unit	Material	Labor	Equipment	Total	Total Incl O&P
0010	**BLANKET INSULATION FOR FLOORS/CEILINGS**										
0020	Including spring type wire fasteners										
2000	Fiberglass, blankets or batts, paper or foil backing										
2100	3-1/2" thick, R13	G	1 Carp	700	.011	S.F.	.37	.37		.74	1.03

07 21 Thermal Insulation

07 21 16 – Blanket Insulation

07 21 16.10 Blanket Insulation for Floors/Ceilings

		Crew	Daily Output	Labor-Hours	Unit	Material	2014 Bare Costs Labor	Equipment	Total	Total Incl O&P
2150	6-1/4" thick, R19 [G]	1 Carp	600	.013	S.F.	.48	.43		.91	1.25
2210	9-1/2" thick, R30 [G]		500	.016		.70	.51		1.21	1.63
2220	12" thick, R38 [G]		475	.017		.89	.54		1.43	1.89
3000	Unfaced, 3-1/2" thick, R13 [G]		600	.013		.32	.43		.75	1.07
3010	6-1/4" thick, R19 [G]		500	.016		.37	.51		.88	1.27
3020	9-1/2" thick, R30 [G]		450	.018		.60	.57		1.17	1.62
3030	12" thick, R38 [G]		425	.019		.75	.60		1.35	1.85

07 21 16.20 Blanket Insulation for Walls

		Crew	Daily Output	Labor-Hours	Unit	Material	2014 Bare Costs Labor	Equipment	Total	Total Incl O&P
0010	**BLANKET INSULATION FOR WALLS**									
0020	Kraft faced fiberglass, 3-1/2" thick, R11, 15" wide [G]	1 Carp	1350	.006	S.F.	.26	.19		.45	.61
0030	23" wide [G]		1600	.005		.26	.16		.42	.56
0080	15" wide [G]		1350	.006		.31	.19		.50	.66
0110	R15, 11" wide [G]		1150	.007		.51	.22		.73	.94
0120	15" wide [G]		1350	.006		.51	.19		.70	.88
0140	6" thick, R19, 11" wide [G]		1150	.007		.42	.22		.64	.84
0160	15" wide [G]		1350	.006		.42	.19		.61	.78
0180	23" wide [G]		1600	.005		.42	.16		.58	.73
0201	9" thick, R30, 15" wide [G]		1350	.006		.70	.19		.89	1.09
0241	12" thick, R38, 15" wide [G]		1350	.006		.89	.19		1.08	1.30
0410	Foil faced fiberglass, 3-1/2" thick, R13, 11" wide [G]		1150	.007		.44	.22		.66	.86
0420	15" wide [G]		1350	.006		.44	.19		.63	.80
0442	R15, 11" wide [G]		1150	.007		.48	.22		.70	.91
0444	15" wide [G]		1350	.006		.48	.19		.67	.85
0461	6" thick, R19, 15" wide [G]		1600	.005		.57	.16		.73	.90
0482	R21, 11" wide [G]		1150	.007		.60	.22		.82	1.04
0501	9" thick, R30, 15" wide [G]		1350	.006		.89	.19		1.08	1.30
0620	Unfaced fiberglass, 3-1/2" thick, R13, 11" wide [G]		1150	.007		.32	.22		.54	.73
0821	3-1/2" thick, R13, 15" wide [G]		1600	.005		.32	.16		.48	.62
0832	R15, 11" wide [G]		1150	.007		.46	.22		.68	.89
0834	15" wide [G]		1350	.006		.46	.19		.65	.83
0861	6" thick, R19, 15" wide [G]		1350	.006		.37	.19		.56	.73
0901	9" thick, R30, 15" wide [G]		1150	.007		.60	.22		.82	1.04
0941	12" thick, R38, 15" wide [G]		1150	.007		.75	.22		.97	1.21
1300	Wall or ceiling insulation, mineral wool batts									
1320	3-1/2" thick, R15 [G]	1 Carp	1600	.005	S.F.	.60	.16		.76	.93
1340	5-1/2" thick, R23 [G]		1600	.005		.94	.16		1.10	1.31
1380	7-1/4" thick, R30 [G]		1350	.006		1.24	.19		1.43	1.69
1850	Friction fit wire insulation supports, 16" O.C.		960	.008	Ea.	.06	.27		.33	.52

07 21 19 – Foamed In Place Insulation

07 21 19.10 Masonry Foamed In Place Insulation

		Crew	Daily Output	Labor-Hours	Unit	Material	2014 Bare Costs Labor	Equipment	Total	Total Incl O&P
0010	**MASONRY FOAMED IN PLACE INSULATION**									
0100	Amino-plast foam, injected into block core, 6" block [G]	G-2A	6000	.004	Ea.	.15	.09	.12	.36	.48
0110	8" block [G]		5000	.005		.19	.11	.15	.45	.56
0120	10" block [G]		4000	.006		.23	.14	.19	.56	.71
0130	12" block [G]		3000	.008		.31	.19	.25	.75	.95
0140	Injected into cavity wall [G]		13000	.002	B.F.	.05	.04	.06	.15	.20
0150	Preparation, drill holes into mortar joint every 4 VLF, 5/8" dia	1 Clab	960	.008	Ea.		.20		.20	.33
0160	7/8" dia		680	.012			.28		.28	.47
0170	Patch drilled holes, 5/8" diameter		1800	.004		.03	.11		.14	.21
0180	7/8" diameter		1200	.007		.04	.16		.20	.32

07 21 Thermal Insulation

07 21 23 – Loose-Fill Insulation

07 21 23.10 Poured Loose-Fill Insulation

		Crew	Daily Output	Labor-Hours	Unit	Material	2014 Bare Costs Labor	Equipment	Total	Total Incl O&P
0010	**POURED LOOSE-FILL INSULATION**									
0020	Cellulose fiber, R3.8 per inch	G	1 Carp	200	.040	C.F.	.69	1.28		1.97	2.92
0021	4" thick	G		1000	.008	S.F.	.17	.26		.43	.61
0022	6" thick	G		800	.010	"	.28	.32		.60	.85
0080	Fiberglass wool, R4 per inch	G		200	.040	C.F.	.53	1.28		1.81	2.75
0081	4" thick	G		600	.013	S.F.	.18	.43		.61	.92
0082	6" thick	G		400	.020	"	.26	.64		.90	1.36
0100	Mineral wool, R3 per inch	G		200	.040	C.F.	.39	1.28		1.67	2.59
0101	4" thick	G		600	.013	S.F.	.13	.43		.56	.86
0102	6" thick	G		400	.020	"	.20	.64		.84	1.29
0300	Polystyrene, R4 per inch	G		200	.040	C.F.	2.50	1.28		3.78	4.91
0301	4" thick	G		600	.013	S.F.	.83	.43		1.26	1.63
0302	6" thick	G		400	.020	"	1.25	.64		1.89	2.46
0400	Perlite, R2.78 per inch	G		200	.040	C.F.	5.40	1.28		6.68	8.10
0401	4" thick	G		1000	.008	S.F.	1.80	.26		2.06	2.41
0402	6" thick	G		800	.010	"	2.70	.32		3.02	3.51

07 21 23.20 Masonry Loose-Fill Insulation

		Crew	Daily Output	Labor-Hours	Unit	Material	2014 Bare Costs Labor	Equipment	Total	Total Incl O&P
0010	**MASONRY LOOSE-FILL INSULATION**, vermiculite or perlite										
0100	In cores of concrete block, 4" thick wall, .115 C.F./S.F.	G	D-1	4800	.003	S.F.	.62	.10		.72	.84
0700	Foamed in place, urethane in 2-5/8" cavity	G	G-2A	1035	.023		1.38	.55	.72	2.65	3.29
0800	For each 1" added thickness, add	G	"	2372	.010		.53	.24	.31	1.08	1.35

07 21 26 – Blown Insulation

07 21 26.10 Blown Insulation

		Crew	Daily Output	Labor-Hours	Unit	Material	2014 Bare Costs Labor	Equipment	Total	Total Incl O&P
0010	**BLOWN INSULATION** Ceilings, with open access										
0020	Cellulose, 3-1/2" thick, R13	G	G-4	5000	.005	S.F.	.24	.12	.09	.45	.55
0030	5-3/16" thick, R19	G		3800	.006		.35	.15	.11	.61	.77
0050	6-1/2" thick, R22	G		3000	.008		.45	.20	.14	.79	.99
0100	8-11/16" thick, R30	G		2600	.009		.61	.23	.16	1	1.23
0120	10-7/8" thick, R38	G		1800	.013		.78	.33	.24	1.35	1.66
1000	Fiberglass, 5.5" thick, R11	G		3800	.006		.18	.15	.11	.44	.58
1050	6" thick, R12	G		3000	.008		.26	.20	.14	.60	.77
1100	8.8" thick, R19	G		2200	.011		.32	.27	.19	.78	1.01
1200	10" thick, R22	G		1800	.013		.37	.33	.24	.94	1.22
1300	11.5" thick, R26	G		1500	.016		.44	.39	.29	1.12	1.46
1350	13" thick, R30	G		1400	.017		.52	.42	.31	1.25	1.62
1450	16" thick, R38	G		1145	.021		.66	.51	.37	1.54	2
1500	20" thick, R49	G		920	.026		.87	.64	.46	1.97	2.54

07 21 27 – Reflective Insulation

07 21 27.10 Reflective Insulation Options

		Crew	Daily Output	Labor-Hours	Unit	Material	2014 Bare Costs Labor	Equipment	Total	Total Incl O&P
0010	**REFLECTIVE INSULATION OPTIONS**										
0020	Aluminum foil on reinforced scrim	G	1 Carp	19	.421	C.S.F.	14.20	13.50		27.70	38
0100	Reinforced with woven polyolefin	G		19	.421		22	13.50		35.50	46.50
0500	With single bubble air space, R8.8	G		15	.533		26	17.10		43.10	57.50
0600	With double bubble air space, R9.8	G		15	.533		29	17.10		46.10	60.50

07 21 29 – Sprayed Insulation

07 21 29.10 Sprayed-On Insulation

		Crew	Daily Output	Labor-Hours	Unit	Material	2014 Bare Costs Labor	Equipment	Total	Total Incl O&P
0010	**SPRAYED-ON INSULATION**										
0300	Closed cell, spray polyurethane foam, 2 pounds per cubic foot density										
0310	1" thick	G	G-2A	6000	.004	S.F.	.53	.09	.12	.74	.89
0320	2" thick	G		3000	.008		1.05	.19	.25	1.49	1.77

07 21 Thermal Insulation

07 21 29 – Sprayed Insulation

07 21 29.10 Sprayed-On Insulation		Crew	Daily Output	Labor-Hours	Unit	Material	2014 Bare Costs Labor	Equipment	Total	Total Incl O&P
0330	3" thick	G	G-2A	2000	.012	S.F.	1.58	.28	.37	2.23	2.65
0335	3-1/2" thick	G		1715	.014		1.84	.33	.43	2.60	3.09
0340	4" thick	G		1500	.016		2.10	.38	.49	2.97	3.53
0350	5" thick	G		1200	.020		2.63	.47	.62	3.72	4.42
0355	5-1/2" thick	G		1090	.022		2.89	.52	.68	4.09	4.86
0360	6" thick	G		1000	.024		3.15	.57	.74	4.46	5.30

07 22 Roof and Deck Insulation

07 22 16 – Roof Board Insulation

07 22 16.10 Roof Deck Insulation

			Crew	Daily Output	Labor-Hours	Unit	Material	2014 Bare Costs Labor	Equipment	Total	Total Incl O&P
0010	**ROOF DECK INSULATION**, fastening excluded										
0020	Fiberboard low density, 1/2" thick R1.39	G	1 Rofc	1300	.006	S.F.	.30	.17		.47	.64
0030	1" thick R2.78	G		1040	.008		.52	.21		.73	.95
0080	1 1/2" thick R4.17	G		1040	.008		.80	.21		1.01	1.26
0100	2" thick R5.56	G		1040	.008		1.06	.21		1.27	1.55
0110	Fiberboard high density, 1/2" thick R1.3	G		1300	.006		.29	.17		.46	.63
0120	1" thick R2.5	G		1040	.008		.60	.21		.81	1.04
0130	1-1/2" thick R3.8	G		1040	.008		.89	.21		1.10	1.36
0200	Fiberglass, 3/4" thick R2.78	G		1300	.006		.61	.17		.78	.98
0400	15/16" thick R3.70	G		1300	.006		.81	.17		.98	1.20
0460	1-1/16" thick R4.17	G		1300	.006		1.01	.17		1.18	1.42
0600	1-5/16" thick R5.26	G		1300	.006		1.37	.17		1.54	1.82
0650	2-1/16" thick R8.33	G		1040	.008		1.45	.21		1.66	1.98
0700	2-7/16" thick R10	G		1040	.008		1.68	.21		1.89	2.23
1650	Perlite, 1/2" thick R1.32	G		1365	.006		.31	.16		.47	.63
1655	3/4" thick R2.08	G		1040	.008		.35	.21		.56	.77
1660	1" thick R2.78	G		1040	.008		.49	.21		.70	.92
1670	1-1/2" thick R4.17	G		1040	.008		.72	.21		.93	1.17
1680	2" thick R5.56	G		910	.009		.99	.24		1.23	1.53
1685	2-1/2" thick R6.67	G		910	.009		1.30	.24		1.54	1.87
1690	Tapered for drainage	G		1040	.008	B.F.	1.01	.21		1.22	1.49
1700	Polyisocyanurate, 2#/C.F. density, 3/4" thick	G		1950	.004	S.F.	.44	.11		.55	.68
1705	1" thick	G		1820	.004		.50	.12		.62	.77
1715	1-1/2" thick	G		1625	.005		.63	.13		.76	.93
1725	2" thick	G		1430	.006		.79	.15		.94	1.15
1735	2-1/2" thick	G		1365	.006		1.01	.16		1.17	1.40
1745	3" thick	G		1300	.006		1.22	.17		1.39	1.65
1755	3-1/2" thick	G		1300	.006		1.95	.17		2.12	2.46
1765	Tapered for drainage	G		1820	.004	B.F.	.57	.12		.69	.85
1900	Extruded Polystyrene										
1910	15 PSI compressive strength, 1" thick, R5	G	1 Rofc	1950	.004	S.F.	.53	.11		.64	.78
1920	2" thick, R10	G		1625	.005		.69	.13		.82	1
1930	3" thick R15	G		1300	.006		1.38	.17		1.55	1.83
1932	4" thick R20	G		1300	.006		1.86	.17		2.03	2.35
1934	Tapered for drainage	G		1950	.004	B.F.	.56	.11		.67	.82
1940	25 PSI compressive strength, 1" thick R5	G		1950	.004	S.F.	.66	.11		.77	.93
1942	2" thick R10	G		1625	.005		1.25	.13		1.38	1.62
1944	3" thick R15	G		1300	.006		1.91	.17		2.08	2.42
1946	4" thick R20	G		1300	.006		2.64	.17		2.81	3.21
1948	Tapered for drainage	G		1950	.004	B.F.	.58	.11		.69	.84
1950	40 psi compressive strength, 1" thick R5	G		1950	.004	S.F.	.51	.11		.62	.76

07 22 Roof and Deck Insulation

07 22 16 – Roof Board Insulation

07 22 16.10 Roof Deck Insulation		Crew	Daily Output	Labor-Hours	Unit	Material	2014 Bare Costs Labor	Equipment	Total	Total Incl O&P
1952	2" thick R10	G 1 Rofc	1625	.005	S.F.	.97	.13		1.10	1.31
1954	3" thick R15	G	1300	.006		1.40	.17		1.57	1.85
1956	4" thick R20	G	1300	.006		1.84	.17		2.01	2.33
1958	Tapered for drainage	G	1820	.004	B.F.	.73	.12		.85	1.02
1960	60 PSI compressive strength, 1" thick R5	G	1885	.004	S.F.	.71	.11		.82	.99
1962	2" thick R10	G	1560	.005		1.35	.14		1.49	1.74
1964	3" thick R15	G	1270	.006		2.20	.17		2.37	2.73
1966	4" thick R20	G	1235	.006		2.73	.18		2.91	3.33
1968	Tapered for drainage	G	1820	.004	B.F.	.93	.12		1.05	1.24
2010	Expanded polystyrene, 1#/C.F. density, 3/4" thick R2.89	G	1950	.004	S.F.	.18	.11		.29	.40
2020	1" thick R3.85	G	1950	.004		.24	.11		.35	.46
2100	2" thick R7.69	G	1625	.005		.48	.13		.61	.77
2110	3" thick R11.49	G	1625	.005		.72	.13		.85	1.03
2120	4" thick R15.38	G	1625	.005		.96	.13		1.09	1.30
2130	5" thick R19.23	G	1495	.005		1.20	.14		1.34	1.59
2140	6" thick R23.26	G	1495	.005		1.44	.14		1.58	1.85
2150	Tapered for drainage	G	1950	.004	B.F.	.51	.11		.62	.76
2400	Composites with 2" EPS									
2410	1" fiberboard	G 1 Rofc	1325	.006	S.F.	1.33	.16		1.49	1.76
2420	7/16" oriented strand board	G	1040	.008		1.07	.21		1.28	1.56
2430	1/2" plywood	G	1040	.008		1.32	.21		1.53	1.83
2440	1" perlite	G	1040	.008		1.09	.21		1.30	1.58
2450	Composites with 1-1/2" polyisocyanurate									
2460	1" fiberboard	G 1 Rofc	1040	.008	S.F.	1.13	.21		1.34	1.62
2470	1" perlite	G	1105	.007		1.01	.20		1.21	1.47
2480	7/16" oriented strand board	G	1040	.008		.89	.21		1.10	1.36
3000	Fastening alternatives, coated screws, 2"		3744	.002	Ea.	.05	.06		.11	.17
3010	4"		3120	.003		.10	.07		.17	.24
3020	6"		2675	.003		.17	.08		.25	.34
3030	8"		2340	.003		.25	.09		.34	.45
3040	10"		1872	.004		.43	.12		.55	.68
3050	Pre-drill and drive wedge spike, 2-1/2"		1248	.006		.37	.17		.54	.73
3060	3-1/2"		1101	.007		.48	.20		.68	.89
3070	4-1/2"		936	.009		.60	.23		.83	1.09
3075	3" galvanized deck plates		7488	.001		.07	.03		.10	.13
3080	Spot mop asphalt	G-1	295	.190	Sq.	5.50	4.80	1.88	12.18	16.95
3090	Full mop asphalt	"	192	.292		11	7.40	2.88	21.28	29
3100	Low-rise polyurethane adhesive	G-2A	100	.240		.18	5.65	7.40	13.23	18.50

07 24 Exterior Insulation and Finish Systems

07 24 13 – Polymer-Based Exterior Insulation and Finish System

07 24 13.10 Exterior Insulation and Finish Systems

0010	EXTERIOR INSULATION AND FINISH SYSTEMS		Crew	Daily Output	Labor-Hours	Unit	Material	Labor	Equipment	Total	Total Incl O&P
0095	Field applied, 1" EPS insulation	G J-1	390	.103	S.F.	1.92	2.87	.37	5.16	7.25
0100	With 1/2" cement board sheathing	G	268	.149		2.65	4.18	.54	7.37	10.40
0105	2" EPS insulation	G	390	.103		2.16	2.87	.37	5.40	7.50
0110	With 1/2" cement board sheathing	G	268	.149		2.89	4.18	.54	7.61	10.65
0115	3" EPS insulation	G	390	.103		2.40	2.87	.37	5.64	7.80
0120	With 1/2" cement board sheathing	G	268	.149		3.13	4.18	.54	7.85	10.95
0125	4" EPS insulation	G	390	.103		2.64	2.87	.37	5.88	8.05
0130	With 1/2" cement board sheathing	G	268	.149		4.11	4.18	.54	8.83	12

07 24 Exterior Insulation and Finish Systems

07 24 13 – Polymer-Based Exterior Insulation and Finish System

07 24 13.10 Exterior Insulation and Finish Systems	Crew	Daily Output	Labor-Hours	Unit	Material	2014 Bare Costs Labor	Equipment	Total	Total Incl O&P
0140	Premium finish add	J-1	1265	.032	S.F.	.31	.89	.11	1.31	1.92
0150	Heavy duty reinforcement add	↓	914	.044	↓	.81	1.23	.16	2.20	3.08
0160	2.5#/S.Y. metal lath substrate add	1 Lath	75	.107	S.Y.	3.05	3.03		6.08	8.25
0170	3.4#/S.Y. metal lath substrate add	"	75	.107	"	3.80	3.03		6.83	9.05
0180	Color or texture change,	J-1	1265	.032	S.F.	.75	.89	.11	1.75	2.41
0190	With substrate leveling base coat	1 Plas	530	.015		.75	.44		1.19	1.56
0210	With substrate sealing base coat	1 Pord	1224	.007	↓	.08	.18		.26	.39
0370	V groove shape in panel face				L.F.	.60			.60	.66
0380	U groove shape in panel face				"	.79			.79	.87

07 25 Weather Barriers

07 25 10 – Weather Barriers or Wraps

07 25 10.10 Weather Barriers

		Crew	Daily Output	Labor-Hours	Unit	Material	2014 Bare Costs Labor	Equipment	Total	Total Incl O&P
0010	**WEATHER BARRIERS**									
0400	Asphalt felt paper, 15#	1 Carp	37	.216	Sq.	5.40	6.95		12.35	17.65
0401	Per square foot	"	3700	.002	S.F.	.05	.07		.12	.18
0450	Housewrap, exterior, spun bonded polypropylene									
0470	Small roll	1 Carp	3800	.002	S.F.	.14	.07		.21	.27
0480	Large roll	"	4000	.002	"	.14	.06		.20	.26
2100	Asphalt felt roof deck vapor barrier, class 1 metal decks	1 Rofc	37	.216	Sq.	22	5.85		27.85	35
2200	For all other decks	"	37	.216		16.40	5.85		22.25	29
2800	Asphalt felt, 50% recycled content, 15 lb., 4 sq. per roll	1 Carp	36	.222		5.40	7.15		12.55	17.95
2810	30 lb., 2 sq. per roll	"	36	.222	↓	10.80	7.15		17.95	24
3000	Building wrap, spunbonded polyethylene	2 Carp	8000	.002	S.F.	.14	.06		.20	.26

07 26 Vapor Retarders

07 26 10 – Above-Grade Vapor Retarders

07 26 10.10 Building Paper

			Crew	Daily Output	Labor-Hours	Unit	Material	2014 Bare Costs Labor	Equipment	Total	Total Incl O&P
0011	**BUILDING PAPER** Aluminum and kraft laminated, foil 1 side		1 Carp	3700	.002	S.F.	.11	.07		.18	.24
0101	Foil 2 sides	G		3700	.002		.13	.07		.20	.26
0601	Polyethylene vapor barrier, standard, .002" thick	G		3700	.002		.02	.07		.09	.14
0701	.004" thick	G		3700	.002		.03	.07		.10	.15
0901	.006" thick	G		3700	.002		.04	.07		.11	.16
1201	.010" thick	G		3700	.002		.09	.07		.16	.22
1801	Reinf. waterproof, .002" polyethylene backing, 1 side			3700	.002		.06	.07		.13	.19
1901	2 sides		↓	3700	.002	↓	.08	.07		.15	.21

07 27 Air Barriers

07 27 26 – Fluid-Applied Membrane Air Barriers

07 27 26.10 Fluid Applied Membrane Air Barrier

		Crew	Daily Output	Labor-Hours	Unit	Material	2014 Bare Costs Labor	Equipment	Total	Total Incl O&P
0010	**FLUID APPLIED MEMBRANE AIR BARRIER**									
0100	Spray applied vapor barrier, 25 S.F./gallon	1 Pord	1375	.006	S.F.	.01	.16		.17	.29

07 31 Shingles and Shakes

07 31 13 – Asphalt Shingles

07 31 13.10 Asphalt Roof Shingles

		Crew	Daily Output	Labor-Hours	Unit	Material	2014 Bare Costs Labor	Equipment	Total	Total Incl O&P
0010	**ASPHALT ROOF SHINGLES**									
0100	Standard strip shingles									
0150	Inorganic, class A, 210-235 lb./sq.	1 Rofc	5.50	1.455	Sq.	81	39.50		120.50	162
0155	Pneumatic nailed		7	1.143		81	31		112	146
0200	235-240 lb./sq.		5	1.600		96	43		139	186
0205	Pneumatic nailed		6.25	1.280		96	34.50		130.50	170
0250	Standard, laminated multi-layered shingles									
0300	Class A, 240-260 lb./sq.	1 Rofc	4.50	1.778	Sq.	106	48		154	205
0305	Pneumatic nailed		5.63	1.422		106	38.50		144.50	187
0350	Class A, 260-300 lb./square, 4 bundles/square		4	2		106	54		160	216
0355	Pneumatic nailed		5	1.600		106	43		149	196
0400	Premium, laminated multi-layered shingles									
0450	Class A, 260-300 lb., 4 bundles/sq.	1 Rofc	3.50	2.286	Sq.	165	61.50		226.50	295
0455	Pneumatic nailed		4.37	1.831		165	49.50		214.50	272
0500	Class A, 300-385 lb./square, 5 bundles/square		3	2.667		219	72		291	375
0505	Pneumatic nailed		3.75	2.133		219	57.50		276.50	345
0800	#15 felt underlayment		64	.125		5.40	3.38		8.78	12.15
0825	#30 felt underlayment		58	.138		10.80	3.72		14.52	18.75
0850	Self adhering polyethylene and rubberized asphalt underlayment		22	.364		77	9.80		86.80	103
0900	Ridge shingles		330	.024	L.F.	2	.65		2.65	3.41
0905	Pneumatic nailed		412.50	.019	"	2	.52		2.52	3.16
1000	For steep roofs (7 to 12 pitch or greater), add						50%			

07 31 26 – Slate Shingles

07 31 26.10 Slate Roof Shingles

			Crew	Daily Output	Labor-Hours	Unit	Material	2014 Bare Costs Labor	Equipment	Total	Total Incl O&P
0010	**SLATE ROOF SHINGLES**	R073126-20									
0100	Buckingham Virginia black, 3/16" - 1/4" thick	G	1 Rots	1.75	4.571	Sq.	475	124		599	755
0200	1/4" thick	G		1.75	4.571		475	124		599	755
0900	Pennsylvania black, Bangor, #1 clear	G		1.75	4.571		490	124		614	770
1200	Vermont, unfading, green, mottled green	G		1.75	4.571		480	124		604	755
1300	Semi-weathering green & gray	G		1.75	4.571		350	124		474	610
1400	Purple	G		1.75	4.571		425	124		549	695
1500	Black or gray	G		1.75	4.571		460	124		584	735
2700	Ridge shingles, slate			200	.040	L.F.	9.30	1.09		10.39	12.20

07 31 29 – Wood Shingles and Shakes

07 31 29.13 Wood Shingles

		Crew	Daily Output	Labor-Hours	Unit	Material	2014 Bare Costs Labor	Equipment	Total	Total Incl O&P
0010	**WOOD SHINGLES**									
0012	16" No. 1 red cedar shingles, 5" exposure, on roof	1 Carp	2.50	3.200	Sq.	264	103		367	465
0015	Pneumatic nailed		3.25	2.462		264	79		343	425
0200	7-1/2" exposure, on walls		2.05	3.902		176	125		301	405
0205	Pneumatic nailed		2.67	2.996		176	96		272	355
0300	18" No. 1 red cedar perfections, 5-1/2" exposure, on roof		2.75	2.909		227	93.50		320.50	405
0305	Pneumatic nailed		3.57	2.241		227	72		299	370
0500	7-1/2" exposure, on walls		2.25	3.556		167	114		281	375
0505	Pneumatic nailed		2.92	2.740		167	88		255	330
0600	Resquared, and rebutted, 5-1/2" exposure, on roof		3	2.667		280	85.50		365.50	455
0605	Pneumatic nailed		3.90	2.051		280	66		346	420
0900	7-1/2" exposure, on walls		2.45	3.265		206	105		311	405
0905	Pneumatic nailed		3.18	2.516		206	81		287	365
1000	Add to above for fire retardant shingles					55			55	60.50
1060	Preformed ridge shingles	1 Carp	400	.020	L.F.	4.50	.64		5.14	6.05
2000	White cedar shingles, 16" long, extras, 5" exposure, on roof		2.40	3.333	Sq.	173	107		280	370
2005	Pneumatic nailed		3.12	2.564		173	82.50		255.50	330

07 31 Shingles and Shakes

07 31 29 – Wood Shingles and Shakes

07 31 29.13 Wood Shingles

		Crew	Daily Output	Labor-Hours	Unit	Material	2014 Bare Costs Labor	Equipment	Total	Total Incl O&P
2050	5" exposure on walls	1 Carp	2	4	Sq.	173	128		301	405
2055	Pneumatic nailed		2.60	3.077		173	99		272	355
2100	7-1/2" exposure, on walls		2	4		123	128		251	350
2105	Pneumatic nailed		2.60	3.077		123	99		222	300
2150	"B" grade, 5" exposure on walls		2	4		150	128		278	380
2155	Pneumatic nailed		2.60	3.077		150	99		249	330
2300	For 15# organic felt underlayment on roof, 1 layer, add		64	.125		5.40	4.01		9.41	12.70
2400	2 layers, add	▼	32	.250		10.80	8.05		18.85	25.50
2600	For steep roofs (7/12 pitch or greater), add to above				▼		50%			
2700	Panelized systems, No.1 cedar shingles on 5/16" CDX plywood									
2800	On walls, 8' strips, 7" or 14" exposure	2 Carp	700	.023	S.F.	6	.73		6.73	7.85
3000	Ridge shakes or shingle wood	1 Carp	280	.029	L.F.	4.05	.92		4.97	6

07 31 29.16 Wood Shakes

		Crew	Daily Output	Labor-Hours	Unit	Material	2014 Bare Costs Labor	Equipment	Total	Total Incl O&P
0010	**WOOD SHAKES**									
1100	Hand-split red cedar shakes, 1/2" thick x 24" long, 10" exp. on roof	1 Carp	2.50	3.200	Sq.	253	103		356	450
1105	Pneumatic nailed		3.25	2.462		253	79		332	410
1110	3/4" thick x 24" long, 10" exp. on roof		2.25	3.556		253	114		367	470
1115	Pneumatic nailed		2.92	2.740		253	88		341	425
1200	1/2" thick, 18" long, 8-1/2" exp. on roof		2	4		179	128		307	415
1205	Pneumatic nailed		2.60	3.077		179	99		278	365
1210	3/4" thick x 18" long, 8 1/2" exp. on roof		1.80	4.444		179	143		322	435
1215	Pneumatic nailed		2.34	3.419		179	110		289	380
1255	10" exp. on walls		2	4		173	128		301	405
1260	10" exposure on walls, pneumatic nailed	▼	2.60	3.077		173	99		272	355
1700	Add to above for fire retardant shakes, 24" long					55			55	60.50
1800	18" long				▼	55			55	60.50
1810	Ridge shakes	1 Carp	350	.023	L.F.	4.50	.73		5.23	6.20

07 32 Roof Tiles

07 32 13 – Clay Roof Tiles

07 32 13.10 Clay Tiles

		Crew	Daily Output	Labor-Hours	Unit	Material	2014 Bare Costs Labor	Equipment	Total	Total Incl O&P
0010	**CLAY TILES**, including accessories									
0300	Flat shingle, interlocking, 15", 166 pcs/sq, fireflashed blend	3 Rots	6	4	Sq.	510	109		619	760
0500	Terra cotta red		6	4		510	109		619	760
0600	Roman pan and top, 18", 102 pcs/sq, fireflashed blend	▼	5.50	4.364		560	118		678	835
0640	Terra cotta red	1 Rots	2.40	3.333		560	90.50		650.50	780
1100	Barrel mission tile, 18", 166 pcs/sq, fireflashed blend	3 Rots	5.50	4.364		405	118		523	665
1140	Terra cotta red		5.50	4.364		405	118		523	665
1700	Scalloped edge flat shingle, 14", 145 pcs/sq, fireflashed blend		6	4		1,125	109		1,234	1,450
1800	Terra cotta red	▼	6	4		1,125	109		1,234	1,450
3010	#15 felt underlayment	1 Rofc	64	.125		5.40	3.38		8.78	12.15
3020	#30 felt underlayment		58	.138		10.80	3.72		14.52	18.75
3040	Polyethylene and rubberized asph. underlayment	▼	22	.364	▼	77	9.80		86.80	103

07 32 16 – Concrete Roof Tiles

07 32 16.10 Concrete Tiles

		Crew	Daily Output	Labor-Hours	Unit	Material	2014 Bare Costs Labor	Equipment	Total	Total Incl O&P
0010	**CONCRETE TILES**									
0020	Corrugated, 13" x 16-1/2", 90 per sq., 950 lb. per sq.									
0050	Earthtone colors, nailed to wood deck	1 Rots	1.35	5.926	Sq.	104	161		265	410
0150	Blues		1.35	5.926		104	161		265	410
0200	Greens	▼	1.35	5.926	▼	108	161		269	415

07 32 Roof Tiles

07 32 16 – Concrete Roof Tiles

07 32 16.10 Concrete Tiles		Crew	Daily Output	Labor-Hours	Unit	Material	2014 Bare Costs Labor	Equipment	Total	Total Incl O&P
0250	Premium colors	1 Rots	1.35	5.926	Sq.	108	161		269	415
0500	Shakes, 13" x 16-1/2", 90 per sq., 950 lb. per sq.									
0600	All colors, nailed to wood deck	1 Rots	1.50	5.333	Sq.	88.50	145		233.50	365
1500	Accessory pieces, ridge & hip, 10" x 16-1/2", 8 lb. each	"	120	.067	Ea.	3.88	1.81		5.69	7.60
1700	Rake, 6-1/2" x 16-3/4", 9 lb. each					3.88			3.88	4.27
1800	Mansard hip, 10" x 16-1/2", 9.2 lb. each					3.88			3.88	4.27
1900	Hip starter, 10" x 16-1/2", 10.5 lb. each					12.20			12.20	13.40
2000	3 or 4 way apex, 10" each side, 11.5 lb. each					14.10			14.10	15.50

07 33 Natural Roof Coverings

07 33 63 – Vegetated Roofing

07 33 63.10 Green Roof Systems

			Crew	Daily Output	Labor-Hours	Unit	Material	2014 Bare Costs Labor	Equipment	Total	Total Incl O&P
0010	**GREEN ROOF SYSTEMS**										
0020	Soil mixture for green roof 30% sand, 55% gravel, 15% soil										
0100	Hoist and spread soil mixture 4 inch depth up to five stories tall roof	G	B-13B	4000	.014	S.F.	.25	.37	.28	.90	1.20
0150	6 inch depth	G		2667	.021		.37	.56	.43	1.36	1.81
0200	8 inch depth	G		2000	.028		.50	.74	.57	1.81	2.42
0250	10 inch depth	G		1600	.035		.62	.93	.71	2.26	3.01
0300	12 inch depth	G		1335	.042		.75	1.11	.85	2.71	3.62
0310	Alt. man-made soil mix, hoist & spread, 4" deep up to 5 stories tall roof	G		4000	.014		1.80	.37	.28	2.45	2.91
0350	Mobilization 55 ton crane to site	G	1 Eqhv	3.60	2.222	Ea.		77		77	128
0355	Hoisting cost to five stories per day (Avg. 28 picks per day)	G	B-13B	1	56	Day		1,475	1,125	2,600	3,725
0360	Mobilization or demobilization, 100 ton crane to site driver & escort	G	A-3E	2.50	6.400	Ea.		196	67.50	263.50	400
0365	Hoisting cost six to ten stories per day (Avg. 21 picks per day)	G	B-13C	1	56	Day		1,475	1,700	3,175	4,350
0370	Hoist and spread soil mixture 4 inch depth six to ten stories tall roof	G		4000	.014	S.F.	.25	.37	.43	1.05	1.36
0375	6 inch depth	G		2667	.021		.37	.56	.64	1.57	2.04
0380	8 inch depth	G		2000	.028		.50	.74	.85	2.09	2.73
0385	10 inch depth	G		1600	.035		.62	.93	1.06	2.61	3.40
0390	12 inch depth	G		1335	.042		.75	1.11	1.28	3.14	4.08
0400	Green roof edging treated lumber 4" x 4" no hoisting included	G	2 Carp	400	.040	L.F.	1.22	1.28		2.50	3.50
0410	4" x 6"	G		400	.040		1.77	1.28		3.05	4.10
0420	4" x 8"	G		360	.044		3.07	1.43		4.50	5.80
0430	4" x 6" double stacked	G		300	.053		3.53	1.71		5.24	6.75
0500	Green roof edging redwood lumber 4" x 4" no hoisting included	G		400	.040		6.45	1.28		7.73	9.20
0510	4" x 6"	G		400	.040		11.20	1.28		12.48	14.45
0520	4" x 8"	G		360	.044		20.50	1.43		21.93	25
0530	4" x 6" double stacked	G		300	.053		22.50	1.71		24.21	27.50
0550	Components, not including membrane or insulation:										
0560	Fluid applied rubber membrane, reinforced, 215 mil thick	G	G-5	350	.114	S.F.	.26	2.82	.57	3.65	6.10
0570	Root barrier	G	2 Rofc	775	.021		.55	.56		1.11	1.64
0580	Moisture retention barrier and reservoir	G	"	900	.018		2.20	.48		2.68	3.30
0600	Planting sedum, light soil, potted, 2-1/4" diameter, two per S.F.	G	1 Clab	420	.019		5.20	.45		5.65	6.45
0610	one per S.F.	G	"	840	.010		2.60	.23		2.83	3.24
0630	Planting sedum mat per S.F. including shipping (4000 S.F. min)	G	4 Clab	4000	.008		6.25	.19		6.44	7.15
0640	Installation sedum mat system (no soil required) per S.F. (4000 S.F. min)	G	"	4000	.008		8.70	.19		8.89	9.85
0645	Note: pricing of sedum mats shipped in full truck loads (4000-5000 S.F.)										

07 41 Roof Panels

07 41 13 – Metal Roof Panels

07 41 13.10 Aluminum Roof Panels	Crew	Daily Output	Labor-Hours	Unit	Material	2014 Bare Costs Labor	Equipment	Total	Total Incl O&P
0010 **ALUMINUM ROOF PANELS**									
0020 Corrugated or ribbed, .0155" thick, natural	G-3	1200	.027	S.F.	.99	.80		1.79	2.43
0300 Painted	"	1200	.027	"	1.44	.80		2.24	2.92

07 41 33 – Plastic Roof Panels

07 41 33.10 Fiberglass Panels	Crew	Daily Output	Labor-Hours	Unit	Material	2014 Bare Costs Labor	Equipment	Total	Total Incl O&P
0010 **FIBERGLASS PANELS**									
0012 Corrugated panels, roofing, 8 oz. per S.F.	G-3	1000	.032	S.F.	2.08	.96		3.04	3.89
0100 12 oz. per S.F.		1000	.032		3.55	.96		4.51	5.50
0300 Corrugated siding, 6 oz. per S.F.		880	.036		1.75	1.09		2.84	3.75
0400 8 oz. per S.F.		880	.036		2.08	1.09		3.17	4.11
0500 Fire retardant		880	.036		3.51	1.09		4.60	5.70
0600 12 oz. siding, textured		880	.036		3.60	1.09		4.69	5.80
0700 Fire retardant		880	.036		4.20	1.09		5.29	6.45
0900 Flat panels, 6 oz. per S.F., clear or colors		880	.036		2.20	1.09		3.29	4.24
1100 Fire retardant, class A		880	.036		3.30	1.09		4.39	5.45
1300 8 oz. per S.F., clear or colors	▼	880	.036	▼	2.42	1.09		3.51	4.48

07 42 Wall Panels

07 42 13 – Metal Wall Panels

07 42 13.20 Aluminum Siding	Crew	Daily Output	Labor-Hours	Unit	Material	2014 Bare Costs Labor	Equipment	Total	Total Incl O&P
0011 **ALUMINUM SIDING**									
6040 .024 thick smooth white single 8" wide	2 Carp	515	.031	S.F.	2.44	1		3.44	4.36
6060 Double 4" pattern		515	.031		2.51	1		3.51	4.44
6080 Double 5" pattern		550	.029		2.45	.93		3.38	4.27
6120 Embossed white, 8" wide		515	.031		2.44	1		3.44	4.36
6140 Double 4" pattern		515	.031		2.51	1		3.51	4.44
6160 Double 5" pattern		550	.029		2.49	.93		3.42	4.31
6170 Vertical, embossed white, 12" wide		590	.027		2.49	.87		3.36	4.20
6320 .019 thick, insulated, smooth white, 8" wide		515	.031		2.20	1		3.20	4.10
6340 Double 4" pattern		515	.031		2.18	1		3.18	4.08
6360 Double 5" pattern		550	.029		2.18	.93		3.11	3.97
6400 Embossed white, 8" wide		515	.031		2.54	1		3.54	4.47
6420 Double 4" pattern		515	.031		2.57	1		3.57	4.51
6440 Double 5" pattern		550	.029		2.57	.93		3.50	4.40
6500 Shake finish 10" wide white		550	.029		2.75	.93		3.68	4.60
6600 Vertical pattern, 12" wide, white	▼	590	.027		2.10	.87		2.97	3.77
6640 For colors add				▼	.13			.13	.14
6700 Accessories, white									
6720 Starter strip 2-1/8"	2 Carp	610	.026	L.F.	.44	.84		1.28	1.90
6740 Sill trim		450	.036		.59	1.14		1.73	2.57
6760 Inside corner		610	.026		1.53	.84		2.37	3.10
6780 Outside corner post		610	.026		3.25	.84		4.09	5
6800 Door & window trim	▼	440	.036		.56	1.17		1.73	2.58
6820 For colors add					.12			.12	.13
6900 Soffit & fascia 1' overhang solid	2 Carp	110	.145		4.18	4.67		8.85	12.45
6920 Vented		110	.145		4.18	4.67		8.85	12.45
6940 2' overhang solid		100	.160		6.20	5.15		11.35	15.45
6960 Vented	▼	100	.160	▼	6.20	5.15		11.35	15.45

07 42 Wall Panels

07 42 13 – Metal Wall Panels

07 42 13.30 Steel Siding

		Crew	Daily Output	Labor-Hours	Unit	Material	2014 Bare Costs Labor	Equipment	Total	Total Incl O&P
0010	**STEEL SIDING**									
0020	Beveled, vinyl coated, 8" wide	1 Carp	265	.030	S.F.	1.91	.97		2.88	3.73
0050	10" wide	"	275	.029		2.04	.93		2.97	3.81
0081	Galv., corrugated or ribbed, on steel frame, 30 ga.	G-3	775	.041		1.31	1.24		2.55	3.51
0101	28 ga.		775	.041		1.38	1.24		2.62	3.59
0301	26 ga.		775	.041		1.91	1.24		3.15	4.17
0401	24 ga.		775	.041		1.94	1.24		3.18	4.20
0601	22 ga.		775	.041		2.24	1.24		3.48	4.53
0701	Colored, corrugated/ribbed, on steel frame, 10 yr. finish, 28 ga.		775	.041		2.04	1.24		3.28	4.31
0901	26 ga.		775	.041		2.13	1.24		3.37	4.41
1001	24 ga.		775	.041		2.49	1.24		3.73	4.81

07 46 Siding

07 46 23 – Wood Siding

07 46 23.10 Wood Board Siding

		Crew	Daily Output	Labor-Hours	Unit	Material	2014 Bare Costs Labor	Equipment	Total	Total Incl O&P
0010	**WOOD BOARD SIDING**									
2000	Board & batten, cedar, "B" grade, 1" x 10"	1 Carp	375	.021	S.F.	5.10	.68		5.78	6.75
2200	Redwood, clear, vertical grain, 1" x 10"		375	.021		5.30	.68		5.98	7
2400	White pine, #2 & better, 1" x 10"		375	.021		3.18	.68		3.86	4.65
2410	Board & batten siding, white pine #2, 1" x 12"		420	.019		3.18	.61		3.79	4.53
3200	Wood, cedar bevel, A grade, 1/2" x 6"		295	.027		4.14	.87		5.01	6
3300	1/2" x 8"		330	.024		5.90	.78		6.68	7.80
3500	3/4" x 10", clear grade		375	.021		6.30	.68		6.98	8.05
3600	"B" grade		375	.021		3.79	.68		4.47	5.30
3800	Cedar, rough sawn, 1" x 4", A grade, natural		220	.036		6.35	1.17		7.52	8.95
3900	Stained		220	.036		6.50	1.17		7.67	9.10
4100	1" x 12", board & batten, #3 & Btr., natural		420	.019		4.35	.61		4.96	5.80
4200	Stained		420	.019		4.67	.61		5.28	6.20
4400	1" x 8" channel siding, #3 & Btr., natural		330	.024		4.43	.78		5.21	6.20
4500	Stained		330	.024		4.78	.78		5.56	6.55
4700	Redwood, clear, beveled, vertical grain, 1/2" x 4"		220	.036		4.11	1.17		5.28	6.50
4750	1/2" x 6"		295	.027		4.49	.87		5.36	6.40
4800	1/2" x 8"		330	.024		4.89	.78		5.67	6.70
5000	3/4" x 10"		375	.021		4.50	.68		5.18	6.10
5200	Channel siding, 1" x 10", B grade		375	.021		4.12	.68		4.80	5.70
5250	Redwood, T&G boards, B grade, 1" x 4"		220	.036		2.54	1.17		3.71	4.75
5270	1" x 8"		330	.024		4.10	.78		4.88	5.80
5400	White pine, rough sawn, 1" x 8", natural		330	.024		2.19	.78		2.97	3.72
5500	Stained		330	.024		2.19	.78		2.97	3.72
5600	Tongue and groove, 1" x 8"		330	.024		2.19	.78		2.97	3.72

07 46 29 – Plywood Siding

07 46 29.10 Plywood Siding Options

		Crew	Daily Output	Labor-Hours	Unit	Material	2014 Bare Costs Labor	Equipment	Total	Total Incl O&P
0010	**PLYWOOD SIDING OPTIONS**									
0900	Plywood, medium density overlaid, 3/8" thick	2 Carp	750	.021	S.F.	1.15	.68		1.83	2.42
1000	1/2" thick		700	.023		1.36	.73		2.09	2.73
1100	3/4" thick		650	.025		1.74	.79		2.53	3.24
1600	Texture 1-11, cedar, 5/8" thick, natural		675	.024		2.43	.76		3.19	3.95
1700	Factory stained		675	.024		2.69	.76		3.45	4.24
1900	Texture 1-11, fir, 5/8" thick, natural		675	.024		1.57	.76		2.33	3.01
2000	Factory stained		675	.024		1.80	.76		2.56	3.26

07 46 Siding

07 46 29 – Plywood Siding

07 46 29.10 Plywood Siding Options		Crew	Daily Output	Labor-Hours	Unit	Material	2014 Bare Costs Labor	Equipment	Total	Total Incl O&P
2050	Texture 1-11, S.Y.P., 5/8" thick, natural	2 Carp	675	.024	S.F.	1.19	.76		1.95	2.59
2100	Factory stained		675	.024		1.24	.76		2	2.64
2200	Rough sawn cedar, 3/8" thick, natural		675	.024		1.20	.76		1.96	2.60
2300	Factory stained		675	.024		1.46	.76		2.22	2.89
2500	Rough sawn fir, 3/8" thick, natural		675	.024		.82	.76		1.58	2.18
2600	Factory stained		675	.024		1.04	.76		1.80	2.42
2800	Redwood, textured siding, 5/8" thick		675	.024		1.92	.76		2.68	3.39

07 46 33 – Plastic Siding

07 46 33.10 Vinyl Siding

		Crew	Daily Output	Labor-Hours	Unit	Material	2014 Bare Costs Labor	Equipment	Total	Total Incl O&P
0010	**VINYL SIDING**									
3995	Clapboard profile, woodgrain texture, .048 thick, double 4	2 Carp	495	.032	S.F.	.97	1.04		2.01	2.82
4000	Double 5		550	.029		.97	.93		1.90	2.64
4005	Single 8		495	.032		1.08	1.04		2.12	2.94
4010	Single 10		550	.029		1.30	.93		2.23	3
4015	.044 thick, double 4		495	.032		.95	1.04		1.99	2.80
4020	Double 5		550	.029		.95	.93		1.88	2.62
4025	.042 thick, double 4		495	.032		.90	1.04		1.94	2.75
4030	Double 5		550	.029		.90	.93		1.83	2.57
4035	Cross sawn texture, .040 thick, double 4		495	.032		.64	1.04		1.68	2.46
4040	Double 5		550	.029		.64	.93		1.57	2.28
4045	Smooth texture, .042 thick, double 4		495	.032		.72	1.04		1.76	2.55
4050	Double 5		550	.029		.72	.93		1.65	2.37
4055	Single 8		495	.032		.72	1.04		1.76	2.55
4060	Cedar texture, .044 thick, double 4		495	.032		.95	1.04		1.99	2.80
4065	Double 6		600	.027		.96	.86		1.82	2.50
4070	Dutch lap profile, woodgrain texture, .048 thick, double 5		550	.029		.97	.93		1.90	2.64
4075	.044 thick, double 4.5		525	.030		.95	.98		1.93	2.70
4080	.042 thick, double 4.5		525	.030		.80	.98		1.78	2.54
4085	.040 thick, double 4.5		525	.030		.64	.98		1.62	2.36
4100	Shake profile, 10" wide		400	.040		3.26	1.28		4.54	5.75
4105	Vertical pattern, .046 thick, double 5		550	.029		1.29	.93		2.22	2.99
4110	.044 thick, triple 3		550	.029		1.47	.93		2.40	3.19
4115	.040 thick, triple 4		550	.029		1.47	.93		2.40	3.19
4120	.040 thick, triple 2.66		550	.029		1.62	.93		2.55	3.36
4125	Insulation, fan folded extruded polystyrene, 1/4"		2000	.008		.27	.26		.53	.73
4130	3/8"		2000	.008		.30	.26		.56	.76
4135	Accessories, J channel, 5/8" pocket		700	.023	L.F.	.44	.73		1.17	1.71
4140	3/4" pocket		695	.023		.46	.74		1.20	1.74
4145	1-1/4" pocket		680	.024		.70	.76		1.46	2.04
4150	Flexible, 3/4" pocket		600	.027		2.20	.86		3.06	3.86
4155	Under sill finish trim		500	.032		.49	1.03		1.52	2.27
4160	Vinyl starter strip		700	.023		.50	.73		1.23	1.78
4165	Aluminum starter strip		700	.023		.26	.73		.99	1.51
4170	Window casing, 2-1/2" wide, 3/4" pocket		510	.031		1.46	1.01		2.47	3.29
4175	Outside corner, woodgrain finish, 4" face, 3/4" pocket		700	.023		1.82	.73		2.55	3.24
4180	5/8" pocket		700	.023		1.82	.73		2.55	3.24
4185	Smooth finish, 4" face, 3/4" pocket		700	.023		1.82	.73		2.55	3.24
4190	7/8" pocket		690	.023		1.82	.74		2.56	3.26
4195	1-1/4" pocket		700	.023		1.28	.73		2.01	2.64
4200	Soffit and fascia, 1' overhang, solid		120	.133		4	4.28		8.28	11.60
4205	Vented		120	.133		4	4.28		8.28	11.60
4207	18" overhang, solid		110	.145		4.65	4.67		9.32	12.95

07 46 Siding

07 46 33 – Plastic Siding

07 46 33.10 Vinyl Siding

		Crew	Daily Output	Labor-Hours	Unit	Material	2014 Bare Costs Labor	2014 Bare Costs Equipment	Total	Total Incl O&P
4208	Vented	2 Carp	110	.145	L.F.	4.65	4.67		9.32	12.95
4210	2' overhang, solid		100	.160		5.30	5.15		10.45	14.45
4215	Vented		100	.160		5.30	5.15		10.45	14.45
4217	3' overhang, solid		100	.160		6.55	5.15		11.70	15.90
4218	Vented		100	.160		6.55	5.15		11.70	15.90
4220	Colors for siding and soffits, add				S.F.	.14			.14	.15
4225	Colors for accessories and trim, add				L.F.	.29			.29	.32

07 46 33.20 Polypropylene Siding

		Crew	Daily Output	Labor-Hours	Unit	Material	2014 Bare Costs Labor	2014 Bare Costs Equipment	Total	Total Incl O&P
0010	**POLYPROPYLENE SIDING**									
4090	Shingle profile, random grooves, double 7	2 Carp	400	.040	S.F.	2.87	1.28		4.15	5.30
4092	Cornerpost for above	1 Carp	365	.022	L.F.	11.15	.70		11.85	13.45
4095	Triple 5	2 Carp	400	.040	S.F.	2.87	1.28		4.15	5.30
4097	Cornerpost for above	1 Carp	365	.022	L.F.	10.50	.70		11.20	12.70
5000	Staggered butt, double 7"	2 Carp	400	.040	S.F.	3.26	1.28		4.54	5.75
5002	Cornerpost for above	1 Carp	365	.022	L.F.	11.30	.70		12	13.65
5010	Half round, double 6-1/4"	2 Carp	360	.044	S.F.	3.25	1.43		4.68	6
5020	Shake profile, staggered butt, double 9"	"	510	.031	"	3.25	1.01		4.26	5.25
5022	Cornerpost for above	1 Carp	365	.022	L.F.	8.35	.70		9.05	10.35
5030	Straight butt, double 7"	2 Carp	400	.040	S.F.	3.25	1.28		4.53	5.75
5032	Cornerpost for above	1 Carp	365	.022	L.F.	11.20	.70		11.90	13.50
6000	Accessories, J channel, 5/8" pocket	2 Carp	700	.023		.44	.73		1.17	1.71
6010	3/4" pocket		695	.023		.46	.74		1.20	1.74
6020	1-1/4" pocket		680	.024		.70	.76		1.46	2.04
6030	Aluminum starter strip		700	.023		.26	.73		.99	1.51

07 46 46 – Fiber Cement Siding

07 46 46.10 Fiber Cement Siding

		Crew	Daily Output	Labor-Hours	Unit	Material	2014 Bare Costs Labor	2014 Bare Costs Equipment	Total	Total Incl O&P
0010	**FIBER CEMENT SIDING**									
0020	Lap siding, 5/16" thick, 6" wide, 4-3/4" exposure, smooth texture	2 Carp	415	.039	S.F.	1.21	1.24		2.45	3.41
0025	Woodgrain texture		415	.039		1.21	1.24		2.45	3.41
0030	7-1/2" wide, 6-1/4" exposure, smooth texture		425	.038		1.42	1.21		2.63	3.59
0035	Woodgrain texture		425	.038		1.42	1.21		2.63	3.59
0040	8" wide, 6-3/4" exposure, smooth texture		425	.038		1.55	1.21		2.76	3.73
0045	Roughsawn texture		425	.038		1.55	1.21		2.76	3.73
0050	9-1/2" wide, 8-1/4" exposure, smooth texture		440	.036		1.54	1.17		2.71	3.66
0055	Woodgrain texture		440	.036		1.54	1.17		2.71	3.66
0060	12" wide, 10-3/8" exposure, smooth texture		455	.035		1.34	1.13		2.47	3.37
0065	Woodgrain texture		455	.035		1.34	1.13		2.47	3.37
0070	Panel siding, 5/16" thick, smooth texture		750	.021		1.31	.68		1.99	2.59
0075	Stucco texture		750	.021		1.31	.68		1.99	2.59
0080	Grooved woodgrain texture		750	.021		1.31	.68		1.99	2.59
0085	V - grooved woodgrain texture		750	.021		1.31	.68		1.99	2.59
0088	Shingle siding, 48" x 15-1/4" panels, 7" exposure		700	.023		4	.73		4.73	5.65
0090	Wood starter strip		400	.040	L.F.	.42	1.28		1.70	2.62
0200	Fiber cement siding, accessories, fascia, 5/4" x 3-1/2"		275	.058		1.10	1.87		2.97	4.35
0210	5/4 x 5-1/2"		250	.064		1.75	2.05		3.80	5.40
0220	5/4 x 7-1/2"		225	.071		2.30	2.28		4.58	6.35
0230	5/4" x 9-1/2"		210	.076		2.76	2.45		5.21	7.15

07 46 Siding

07 46 73 – Soffit

07 46 73.10 Soffit Options	Crew	Daily Output	Labor-Hours	Unit	Material	2014 Bare Costs Labor	Equipment	Total	Total Incl O&P
0010 **SOFFIT OPTIONS**									
0012 Aluminum, residential, .020" thick	1 Carp	210	.038	S.F.	1.87	1.22		3.09	4.12
0100 Baked enamel on steel, 16 or 18 ga.		105	.076		5.80	2.45		8.25	10.50
0300 Polyvinyl chloride, white, solid		230	.035		2.04	1.12		3.16	4.12
0400 Perforated	↓	230	.035		2.04	1.12		3.16	4.12
0500 For colors, add				↓	.12			.12	.13

07 51 Built-Up Bituminous Roofing

07 51 13 – Built-Up Asphalt Roofing

07 51 13.10 Built-Up Roofing Components

	Crew	Daily Output	Labor-Hours	Unit	Material	2014 Bare Costs Labor	Equipment	Total	Total Incl O&P
0010 **BUILT-UP ROOFING COMPONENTS**									
0012 Asphalt saturated felt, #30, 2 square per roll	1 Rofc	58	.138	Sq.	10.80	3.72		14.52	18.75
0200 #15, 4 sq. per roll, plain or perforated, not mopped		58	.138		5.40	3.72		9.12	12.80
0250 Perforated		58	.138		5.40	3.72		9.12	12.80
0300 Roll roofing, smooth, #65		15	.533		9.65	14.40		24.05	37
0500 #90		12	.667		35	18		53	71.50
0520 Mineralized		12	.667		35	18		53	71.50
0540 D.C. (Double coverage), 19" selvage edge	↓	10	.800	↓	52	21.50		73.50	97.50
0580 Adhesive (lap cement)				Gal.	8.50			8.50	9.35

07 51 13.20 Built-Up Roofing Systems

	Crew	Daily Output	Labor-Hours	Unit	Material	2014 Bare Costs Labor	Equipment	Total	Total Incl O&P
0010 **BUILT-UP ROOFING SYSTEMS**									
0120 Asphalt flood coat with gravel/slag surfacing, not including									
0140 Insulation, flashing or wood nailers									
0200 Asphalt base sheet, 3 plies #15 asphalt felt, mopped	G-1	22	2.545	Sq.	98.50	64.50	25	188	256
0350 On nailable decks		21	2.667		101	67.50	26.50	195	264
0500 4 plies #15 asphalt felt, mopped		20	2.800		134	71	27.50	232.50	310
0550 On nailable decks	↓	19	2.947	↓	119	74.50	29	222.50	300
2000 Asphalt flood coat, smooth surface									
2200 Asphalt base sheet & 3 plies #15 asphalt felt, mopped	G-1	24	2.333	Sq.	104	59	23	186	249
2400 On nailable decks		23	2.435		96	61.50	24	181.50	247
2600 4 plies #15 asphalt felt, mopped		24	2.333		122	59	23	204	269
2700 On nailable decks	↓	23	2.435	↓	114	61.50	24	199.50	267
4500 Coal tar pitch with gravel/slag surfacing									
4600 4 plies #15 tarred felt, mopped	G-1	21	2.667	Sq.	234	67.50	26.50	328	410
4800 3 plies glass fiber felt (type IV), mopped	"	19	2.947	"	193	74.50	29	296.50	380

07 51 13.30 Cants

	Crew	Daily Output	Labor-Hours	Unit	Material	2014 Bare Costs Labor	Equipment	Total	Total Incl O&P
0010 **CANTS**									
0012 Lumber, treated, 4" x 4" cut diagonally	1 Rofc	325	.025	L.F.	1.75	.66		2.41	3.15
0300 Mineral or fiber, trapezoidal, 1" x 4" x 48"		325	.025		.24	.66		.90	1.48
0400 1-1/2" x 5-5/8" x 48"	↓	325	.025	↓	.42	.66		1.08	1.68

07 52 Modified Bituminous Membrane Roofing

07 52 13 – Atactic-Polypropylene-Modified Bituminous Membrane Roofing

07 52 13.10 APP Modified Bituminous Membrane		Crew	Daily Output	Labor-Hours	Unit	Material	2014 Bare Costs Labor	Equipment	Total	Total Incl O&P
0010	**APP MODIFIED BITUMINOUS MEMBRANE** R075213-30									
0020	Base sheet, #15 glass fiber felt, nailed to deck	1 Rofc	58	.138	Sq.	10.65	3.72		14.37	18.55
0030	Spot mopped to deck	G-1	295	.190		15.15	4.80	1.88	21.83	27.50
0040	Fully mopped to deck	"	192	.292		20.50	7.40	2.88	30.78	39.50
0050	#15 organic felt, nailed to deck	1 Rofc	58	.138		6.40	3.72		10.12	13.90
0060	Spot mopped to deck	G-1	295	.190		10.90	4.80	1.88	17.58	23
0070	Fully mopped to deck	"	192	.292		16.40	7.40	2.88	26.68	35
2100	APP mod., smooth surf. cap sheet, poly. reinf., torched, 160 mils	G-5	2100	.019	S.F.	.68	.47	.09	1.24	1.71
2150	170 mils		2100	.019		.70	.47	.09	1.26	1.73
2200	Granule surface cap sheet, poly. reinf., torched, 180 mils		2000	.020		.89	.49	.10	1.48	2
2250	Smooth surface flashing, torched, 160 mils		1260	.032		.68	.78	.16	1.62	2.36
2300	170 mils		1260	.032		.70	.78	.16	1.64	2.38
2350	Granule surface flashing, torched, 180 mils		1260	.032		.89	.78	.16	1.83	2.59
2400	Fibrated aluminum coating	1 Rofc	3800	.002		.08	.06		.14	.19

07 52 16 – Styrene-Butadiene-Styrene Modified Bituminous Membrane Roofing

07 52 16.10 SBS Modified Bituminous Membrane

		Crew	Daily Output	Labor-Hours	Unit	Material	2014 Bare Costs Labor	Equipment	Total	Total Incl O&P
0010	**SBS MODIFIED BITUMINOUS MEMBRANE**									
0080	SBS modified, granule surf cap sheet, polyester reinf., mopped									
0600	150 mils	G-1	2000	.028	S.F.	.65	.71	.28	1.64	2.33
1100	160 mils		2000	.028		.71	.71	.28	1.70	2.39
1500	Glass fiber reinforced, mopped, 160 mils		2000	.028		.71	.71	.28	1.70	2.39
1600	Smooth surface cap sheet, mopped, 145 mils		2100	.027		.78	.68	.26	1.72	2.39
1700	Smooth surface flashing, 145 mils		1260	.044		.78	1.12	.44	2.34	3.41
1800	150 mils		1260	.044		.49	1.12	.44	2.05	3.09
1900	Granular surface flashing, 150 mils		1260	.044		.65	1.12	.44	2.21	3.27
2000	160 mils		1260	.044		.71	1.12	.44	2.27	3.33

07 57 Coated Foamed Roofing

07 57 13 – Sprayed Polyurethane Foam Roofing

07 57 13.10 Sprayed Polyurethane Foam Roofing (S.P.F.)

		Crew	Daily Output	Labor-Hours	Unit	Material	2014 Bare Costs Labor	Equipment	Total	Total Incl O&P
0010	**SPRAYED POLYURETHANE FOAM ROOFING (S.P.F.)**									
0100	Primer for metal substrate (when required)	G-2A	3000	.008	S.F.	.42	.19	.25	.86	1.07
0200	Primer for non-metal substrate (when required)		3000	.008		.16	.19	.25	.60	.79
0300	Closed cell spray, polyurethane foam, 3 lb. per C.F. density, 1", R6.7		15000	.002		.66	.04	.05	.75	.85
0400	2", R13.4		13125	.002		1.32	.04	.06	1.42	1.59
0500	3", R18.6		11485	.002		1.98	.05	.06	2.09	2.34
0550	4", R24.8		10080	.002		2.64	.06	.07	2.77	3.09
0700	Spray-on silicone coating		2500	.010		.95	.23	.30	1.48	1.78
0800	Warranty 5-20 year manufacturer's									.15
0900	Warranty 20 year, no dollar limit									.20

07 58 Roll Roofing

07 58 10 – Asphalt Roll Roofing

07 58 10.10 Roll Roofing

07 58 10.10 Roll Roofing	Crew	Daily Output	Labor-Hours	Unit	Material	2014 Bare Costs Labor	Equipment	Total	Total Incl O&P
0010 **ROLL ROOFING**									
0100 Asphalt, mineral surface									
0200 1 ply #15 organic felt, 1 ply mineral surfaced									
0300 Selvage roofing, lap 19", nailed & mopped	G-1	27	2.074	Sq.	74	52.50	20.50	147	201
0400 3 plies glass fiber felt (type IV), 1 ply mineral surfaced									
0500 Selvage roofing, lapped 19", mopped	G-1	25	2.240	Sq.	125	56.50	22	203.50	267
0600 Coated glass fiber base sheet, 2 plies of glass fiber									
0700 Felt (type IV), 1 ply mineral surfaced selvage									
0800 Roofing, lapped 19", mopped	G-1	25	2.240	Sq.	133	56.50	22	211.50	275
0900 On nailable decks	"	24	2.333	"	122	59	23	204	269
1000 3 plies glass fiber felt (type III), 1 ply mineral surfaced									
1100 Selvage roofing, lapped 19", mopped	G-1	25	2.240	Sq.	125	56.50	22	203.50	267

07 61 Sheet Metal Roofing

07 61 13 – Standing Seam Sheet Metal Roofing

07 61 13.10 Standing Seam Sheet Metal Roofing, Field Fab.

	Crew	Daily Output	Labor-Hours	Unit	Material	2014 Bare Costs Labor	Equipment	Total	Total Incl O&P
0010 **STANDING SEAM SHEET METAL ROOFING, FIELD FABRICATED**									
0400 Copper standing seam roofing, over 10 squares, 16 oz., 125 lb. per sq.	1 Shee	1.30	6.154	Sq.	870	222		1,092	1,325
0600 18 oz., 140 lb. per sq.	"	1.20	6.667		975	241		1,216	1,475
1200 For abnormal conditions or small areas, add					25%	100%			
1300 For lead-coated copper, add					25%				

07 61 16 – Batten Seam Sheet Metal Roofing

07 61 16.10 Batten Seam Sheet Metal Roofing, Field Fabricated

	Crew	Daily Output	Labor-Hours	Unit	Material	2014 Bare Costs Labor	Equipment	Total	Total Incl O&P
0010 **BATTEN SEAM SHEET METAL ROOFING, FIELD FABRICATED**									
0012 Copper batten seam roofing, over 10 sq., 16 oz., 130 lb. per sq.	1 Shee	1.10	7.273	Sq.	1,100	263		1,363	1,650
0100 Zinc/copper alloy batten seam roofing, .020 thick		1.20	6.667		1,150	241		1,391	1,675
0200 Copper roofing, batten seam, over 10 sq., 18 oz., 145 lb. per sq.		1	8		1,225	289		1,514	1,825
0800 Zinc, copper alloy roofing, batten seam, .027" thick		1.15	6.957		1,450	251		1,701	2,025
0900 .032" thick		1.10	7.273		1,850	263		2,113	2,500
1000 .040" thick		1.05	7.619		2,325	275		2,600	3,000

07 61 19 – Flat Seam Sheet Metal Roofing

07 61 19.10 Flat Seam Sheet Metal Roofing, Field Fabricated

	Crew	Daily Output	Labor-Hours	Unit	Material	2014 Bare Costs Labor	Equipment	Total	Total Incl O&P
0010 **FLAT SEAM SHEET METAL ROOFING, FIELD FABRICATED**									
0900 Copper flat seam roofing, over 10 squares, 16 oz., 115 lb./sq.	1 Shee	1.20	6.667	Sq.	805	241		1,046	1,300
0950 18 oz., 130 lb./sq.		1.15	6.957		905	251		1,156	1,425
1000 20 oz., 145 lb./sq.		1.10	7.273		1,150	263		1,413	1,700
1008 Zinc flat seam roofing, .020" thick		1.20	6.667		990	241		1,231	1,500
1010 .027" thick		1.15	6.957		1,250	251		1,501	1,800
1020 .032" thick		1.12	7.143		1,575	258		1,833	2,175
1030 .040" thick		1.05	7.619		1,975	275		2,250	2,625
1100 Lead flat seam roofing, 5 lb. per S.F.		1.30	6.154		1,150	222		1,372	1,650

07 62 Sheet Metal Flashing and Trim

07 62 10 – Sheet Metal Trim

07 62 10.10 Sheet Metal Cladding	Crew	Daily Output	Labor-Hours	Unit	Material	2014 Bare Costs Labor	2014 Bare Costs Equipment	Total	Total Incl O&P
0010 **SHEET METAL CLADDING**									
0100 Aluminum, up to 6 bends, .032" thick, window casing	1 Carp	180	.044	S.F.	1.39	1.43		2.82	3.93
0200 Window sill		72	.111	L.F.	1.39	3.57		4.96	7.55
0300 Door casing		180	.044	S.F.	1.39	1.43		2.82	3.93
0400 Fascia		250	.032		1.39	1.03		2.42	3.26
0500 Rake trim		225	.036		1.39	1.14		2.53	3.45
0700 .024" thick, window casing		180	.044	↓	1.52	1.43		2.95	4.07
0800 Window sill		72	.111	L.F.	1.52	3.57		5.09	7.65
0900 Door casing		180	.044	S.F.	1.52	1.43		2.95	4.07
1000 Fascia		250	.032		1.52	1.03		2.55	3.40
1100 Rake trim		225	.036		1.52	1.14		2.66	3.59
1200 Vinyl coated aluminum, up to 6 bends, window casing		180	.044	↓	1.18	1.43		2.61	3.70
1300 Window sill		72	.111	L.F.	1.18	3.57		4.75	7.30
1400 Door casing		180	.044	S.F.	1.18	1.43		2.61	3.70
1500 Fascia		250	.032		1.18	1.03		2.21	3.03
1600 Rake trim	↓	225	.036	↓	1.18	1.14		2.32	3.22

07 65 Flexible Flashing

07 65 10 – Sheet Metal Flashing

07 65 10.10 Sheet Metal Flashing and Counter Flashing

07 65 10.10 Sheet Metal Flashing and Counter Flashing	Crew	Daily Output	Labor-Hours	Unit	Material	2014 Bare Costs Labor	2014 Bare Costs Equipment	Total	Total Incl O&P
0010 **SHEET METAL FLASHING AND COUNTER FLASHING**									
0011 Including up to 4 bends									
0020 Aluminum, mill finish, .013" thick	1 Rofc	145	.055	S.F.	.79	1.49		2.28	3.61
0030 .016" thick		145	.055		.91	1.49		2.40	3.74
0060 .019" thick		145	.055		1.15	1.49		2.64	4.01
0100 .032" thick		145	.055		1.35	1.49		2.84	4.23
0200 .040" thick		145	.055		2.31	1.49		3.80	5.30
0300 .050" thick		145	.055		2.43	1.49		3.92	5.40
0325 Mill finish 5" x 7" step flashing, .016" thick		1920	.004	Ea.	.15	.11		.26	.38
0350 Mill finish 12" x 12" step flashing, .016" thick	↓	1600	.005	"	.50	.14		.64	.80
0400 Painted finish, add				S.F.	.29			.29	.32
1600 Copper, 16 oz., sheets, under 1000 lb.	1 Rofc	115	.070		6.95	1.88		8.83	11.10
1900 20 oz. sheets, under 1000 lb.		110	.073		9.85	1.96		11.81	14.45
2200 24 oz. sheets, under 1000 lb.		105	.076		12.10	2.06		14.16	17.15
2500 32 oz. sheets, under 1000 lb.		100	.080	↓	16.15	2.16		18.31	22
2700 W shape for valleys, 16 oz., 24" wide		100	.080	L.F.	14	2.16		16.16	19.40
5800 Lead, 2.5 lb. per S.F., up to 12" wide		135	.059	S.F.	4.99	1.60		6.59	8.45
5900 Over 12" wide		135	.059		3.99	1.60		5.59	7.35
8900 Stainless steel sheets, 32 ga., .010" thick		155	.052		3	1.39		4.39	5.85
9000 28 ga., .015" thick		155	.052		3.99	1.39		5.38	6.95
9100 26 ga., .018" thick		155	.052		4.25	1.39		5.64	7.25
9200 24 ga., .025" thick	↓	155	.052	↓	4.75	1.39		6.14	7.80
9290 For mechanically keyed flashing, add					40%				
9320 Steel sheets, galvanized, 20 ga.	1 Rofc	130	.062	S.F.	1.25	1.66		2.91	4.44
9322 22 ga.		135	.059		1.21	1.60		2.81	4.28
9324 24 ga.		140	.057		.92	1.54		2.46	3.85
9326 26 ga.		145	.055		.80	1.49		2.29	3.62
9328 28 ga.		155	.052		.69	1.39		2.08	3.33
9340 30 ga.		160	.050		.58	1.35		1.93	3.13
9400 Terne coated stainless steel, .015" thick, 28 ga		155	.052		7.35	1.39		8.74	10.65
9500 .018" thick, 26 ga	↓	155	.052	↓	8.30	1.39		9.69	11.65

07 65 Flexible Flashing

07 65 10 – Sheet Metal Flashing

07 65 10.10 Sheet Metal Flashing and Counter Flashing	Crew	Daily Output	Labor-Hours	Unit	Material	2014 Bare Costs Labor	Equipment	Total	Total Incl O&P
9600	Zinc and copper alloy (brass), .020" thick	1 Rofc	155	.052	S.F.	8.55	1.39		9.94	11.95
9700	.027" thick		155	.052		10.70	1.39		12.09	14.30
9800	.032" thick		155	.052		13.65	1.39		15.04	17.60
9900	.040" thick	▼	155	.052	▼	17.10	1.39		18.49	21.50

07 65 13 – Laminated Sheet Flashing

07 65 13.10 Laminated Sheet Flashing

		Crew	Daily Output	Labor-Hours	Unit	Material	Labor	Equipment	Total	Total Incl O&P
0010	**LAMINATED SHEET FLASHING**, Including up to 4 bends									
8550	Shower pan, 3 ply copper and fabric, 3 oz.	1 Rofc	155	.052	S.F.	3.13	1.39		4.52	6
8600	7 oz.	"	155	.052	"	3.99	1.39		5.38	6.95

07 65 19 – Plastic Sheet Flashing

07 65 19.10 Plastic Sheet Flashing and Counter Flashing

		Crew	Daily Output	Labor-Hours	Unit	Material	Labor	Equipment	Total	Total Incl O&P
0010	**PLASTIC SHEET FLASHING AND COUNTER FLASHING**									
7300	Polyvinyl chloride, black, .010" thick	1 Rofc	285	.028	S.F.	.21	.76		.97	1.63
7400	.020" thick		285	.028		.28	.76		1.04	1.71
7600	.030" thick		285	.028		.35	.76		1.11	1.79
7700	.056" thick	▼	285	.028	▼	.85	.76		1.61	2.34
8060	PVC tape, 5" x 45 mils, for joint covers, 100 L.F./roll				Ea.	170			170	187

07 65 23 – Rubber Sheet Flashing

07 65 23.10 Rubber Sheet Flashing and Counterflashing

		Crew	Daily Output	Labor-Hours	Unit	Material	Labor	Equipment	Total	Total Incl O&P
0010	**RUBBER SHEET FLASHING AND COUNTERFLASHING**									
4810	EPDM 90 mils, 1" diameter pipe flashing	1 Rofc	32	.250	Ea.	19.45	6.75		26.20	34
4820	2" diameter		30	.267		19.45	7.20		26.65	35
4830	3" diameter		28	.286		21	7.70		28.70	37
4840	4" diameter		24	.333		24	9		33	43
4850	6" diameter		22	.364	▼	24	9.80		33.80	44.50
8100	Rubber, butyl, 1/32" thick		285	.028	S.F.	1.92	.76		2.68	3.51
8200	1/16" thick		285	.028		2.60	.76		3.36	4.26
8300	Neoprene, cured, 1/16" thick		285	.028		2.23	.76		2.99	3.85
8400	1/8" thick	▼	285	.028	▼	6.05	.76		6.81	8.05

07 71 Roof Specialties

07 71 19 – Manufactured Gravel Stops and Fasciae

07 71 19.10 Gravel Stop

		Crew	Daily Output	Labor-Hours	Unit	Material	Labor	Equipment	Total	Total Incl O&P
0010	**GRAVEL STOP**									
0020	Aluminum, .050" thick, 4" face height, mill finish	1 Shee	145	.055	L.F.	6	1.99		7.99	9.90
0080	Duranodic finish		145	.055		6.50	1.99		8.49	10.45
0100	Painted		145	.055		6.85	1.99		8.84	10.80
1200	Copper, 16 oz., 3" face height		145	.055		39.50	1.99		41.49	46.50
1300	6" face height		135	.059		39.50	2.14		41.64	46.50
1350	Galv steel, 24 ga., 4" leg, plain, with continuous cleat, 4" face		145	.055		6	1.99		7.99	9.90
1360	6" face height		145	.055		6	1.99		7.99	9.90
1500	Polyvinyl chloride, 6" face height		135	.059		4.90	2.14		7.04	8.95
1800	Stainless steel, 24 ga., 6" face height	▼	135	.059	▼	9.85	2.14		11.99	14.35

07 71 19.30 Fascia

		Crew	Daily Output	Labor-Hours	Unit	Material	Labor	Equipment	Total	Total Incl O&P
0010	**FASCIA**									
0100	Aluminum, reverse board and batten, .032" thick, colored, no furring incl	1 Shee	145	.055	S.F.	6.25	1.99		8.24	10.20
0200	Residential type, aluminum	1 Carp	200	.040	L.F.	1.72	1.28		3	4.05
0220	Vinyl	"	200	.040	"	1.92	1.28		3.20	4.27
0300	Steel, galv and enameled, stock, no furring, long panels	1 Shee	145	.055	S.F.	3.91	1.99		5.90	7.60

07 71 19 – Manufactured Gravel Stops and Fasciae

07 71 19.30 Fascia		Crew	Daily Output	Labor-Hours	Unit	Material	2014 Bare Costs Labor	Equipment	Total	Total Incl O&P
0600	Short panels	1 Shee	115	.070	S.F.	5.30	2.51		7.81	10.05

07 71 23 – Manufactured Gutters and Downspouts

07 71 23.10 Downspouts

		Crew	Daily Output	Labor-Hours	Unit	Material	2014 Bare Costs Labor	Equipment	Total	Total Incl O&P
0010	**DOWNSPOUTS**									
0020	Aluminum 2" x 3", .020" thick, embossed	1 Shee	190	.042	L.F.	.97	1.52		2.49	3.61
0100	Enameled		190	.042		1.32	1.52		2.84	3.99
0300	Enameled, .024" thick, 2" x 3"		180	.044		2.05	1.60		3.65	4.94
0400	3" x 4"		140	.057		2.88	2.06		4.94	6.60
0600	Round, corrugated aluminum, 3" diameter, .020" thick		190	.042		1.57	1.52		3.09	4.27
0700	4" diameter, .025" thick		140	.057		2.33	2.06		4.39	6
0900	Wire strainer, round, 2" diameter		155	.052	Ea.	3.92	1.86		5.78	7.40
1000	4" diameter		155	.052		7.20	1.86		9.06	11.05
1200	Rectangular, perforated, 2" x 3"		145	.055		2.30	1.99		4.29	5.85
1300	3" x 4"		145	.055		3.32	1.99		5.31	6.95
1500	Copper, round, 16 oz., stock, 2" diameter		190	.042	L.F.	8.55	1.52		10.07	11.95
1600	3" diameter		190	.042		8.45	1.52		9.97	11.80
1800	4" diameter		145	.055		10.55	1.99		12.54	14.90
1900	5" diameter		130	.062		18.20	2.22		20.42	23.50
2100	Rectangular, corrugated copper, stock, 2" x 3"		190	.042		8.80	1.52		10.32	12.20
2200	3" x 4"		145	.055		12.20	1.99		14.19	16.75
2400	Rectangular, plain copper, stock, 2" x 3"		190	.042		13.30	1.52		14.82	17.20
2500	3" x 4"		145	.055		16.90	1.99		18.89	22
2700	Wire strainers, rectangular, 2" x 3"		145	.055	Ea.	13.50	1.99		15.49	18.15
2800	3" x 4"		145	.055		14.65	1.99		16.64	19.45
3000	Round, 2" diameter		145	.055		5.95	1.99		7.94	9.80
3100	3" diameter		145	.055		5.95	1.99		7.94	9.80
3300	4" diameter		145	.055		8	1.99		9.99	12.10
3400	5" diameter		115	.070		19.80	2.51		22.31	26
3600	Lead-coated copper, round, stock, 2" diameter		190	.042	L.F.	25	1.52		26.52	30
3700	3" diameter		190	.042		21.50	1.52		23.02	26
3900	4" diameter		145	.055		22.50	1.99		24.49	28
4000	5" diameter, corrugated		130	.062		24	2.22		26.22	30
4200	6" diameter, corrugated		105	.076		30	2.75		32.75	37.50
4300	Rectangular, corrugated, stock, 2" x 3"		190	.042		15	1.52		16.52	19.05
4500	Plain, stock, 2" x 3"		190	.042		24	1.52		25.52	29
4600	3" x 4"		145	.055		33	1.99		34.99	40
4800	Steel, galvanized, round, corrugated, 2" or 3" diameter, 28 ga.		190	.042		2.08	1.52		3.60	4.83
4900	4" diameter, 28 ga.		145	.055		2.61	1.99		4.60	6.20
5700	Rectangular, corrugated, 28 ga., 2" x 3"		190	.042		1.94	1.52		3.46	4.67
5800	3" x 4"		145	.055		1.82	1.99		3.81	5.30
6000	Rectangular, plain, 28 ga., galvanized, 2" x 3"		190	.042		3.03	1.52		4.55	5.85
6100	3" x 4"		145	.055		3.06	1.99		5.05	6.70
6300	Epoxy painted, 24 ga., corrugated, 2" x 3"		190	.042		2.20	1.52		3.72	4.96
6400	3" x 4"		145	.055		2.75	1.99		4.74	6.35
6600	Wire strainers, rectangular, 2" x 3"		145	.055	Ea.	15.90	1.99		17.89	21
6700	3" x 4"		145	.055		16.60	1.99		18.59	21.50
6900	Round strainers, 2" or 3" diameter		145	.055		3.86	1.99		5.85	7.55
7000	4" diameter		145	.055		5.80	1.99		7.79	9.65
8200	Vinyl, rectangular, 2" x 3"		210	.038	L.F.	2.08	1.38		3.46	4.58
8300	Round, 2-1/2"		220	.036	"	1.31	1.31		2.62	3.63

07 71 Roof Specialties

07 71 23 – Manufactured Gutters and Downspouts

07 71 23.20 Downspout Elbows	Crew	Daily Output	Labor-Hours	Unit	Material	2014 Bare Costs Labor	Equipment	Total	Total Incl O&P
0010 **DOWNSPOUT ELBOWS**									
0020 Aluminum, 2" x 3", embossed	1 Shee	100	.080	Ea.	.95	2.89		3.84	5.85
0100 Enameled		100	.080		1.75	2.89		4.64	6.75
0200 3" x 4", .025" thick, embossed		100	.080		3.50	2.89		6.39	8.65
0300 Enameled		100	.080		3.75	2.89		6.64	8.95
0400 Round corrugated, 3", embossed, .020" thick		100	.080		2.74	2.89		5.63	7.85
0500 4", .025" thick		100	.080		5.80	2.89		8.69	11.15
0600 Copper, 16 oz. round, 2" diameter		100	.080		9.45	2.89		12.34	15.20
0700 3" diameter		100	.080		9	2.89		11.89	14.70
0800 4" diameter		100	.080		13.15	2.89		16.04	19.30
1000 2" x 3" corrugated		100	.080		9	2.89		11.89	14.70
1100 3" x 4" corrugated		100	.080		13.65	2.89		16.54	19.80
1300 Vinyl, 2-1/2" diameter, 45° or 75°		100	.080		3.88	2.89		6.77	9.10
1400 Tee Y junction	↓	75	.107	↓	12.90	3.85		16.75	20.50

07 71 23.30 Gutters

	Crew	Daily Output	Labor-Hours	Unit	Material	2014 Bare Costs Labor	Equipment	Total	Total Incl O&P
0010 **GUTTERS**									
0012 Aluminum, stock units, 5" K type, .027" thick, plain	1 Shee	125	.064	L.F.	2.61	2.31		4.92	6.70
0100 Enameled		125	.064		2.60	2.31		4.91	6.70
0300 5" K type type, .032" thick, plain		125	.064		3.20	2.31		5.51	7.35
0400 Enameled		125	.064		3	2.31		5.31	7.15
0700 Copper, half round, 16 oz., stock units, 4" wide		125	.064		10.50	2.31		12.81	15.40
0900 5" wide		125	.064		7.70	2.31		10.01	12.30
1000 6" wide		118	.068		14	2.45		16.45	19.50
1200 K type, 16 oz., stock, 5" wide		125	.064		12.60	2.31		14.91	17.70
1300 6" wide		125	.064		8.80	2.31		11.11	13.55
1500 Lead coated copper, half round, stock, 4" wide		125	.064		13.80	2.31		16.11	19.05
1600 6" wide		118	.068		22	2.45		24.45	28.50
1800 K type, stock, 5" wide		125	.064		18.90	2.31		21.21	25
1900 6" wide		125	.064		18.40	2.31		20.71	24
2100 Copper clad stainless steel, K type, 5" wide		125	.064		7	2.31		9.31	11.55
2200 6" wide		125	.064		8.90	2.31		11.21	13.65
2400 Steel, galv, half round or box, 28 ga., 5" wide, plain		125	.064		2.18	2.31		4.49	6.25
2500 Enameled		125	.064		2.13	2.31		4.44	6.20
2700 26 ga., stock, 5" wide		125	.064		2.18	2.31		4.49	6.25
2800 6" wide	↓	125	.064	↓	2.67	2.31		4.98	6.80
3000 Vinyl, O.G., 4" wide	1 Carp	115	.070		1.19	2.23		3.42	5.05
3100 5" wide		115	.070		1.55	2.23		3.78	5.45
3200 4" half round, stock units	↓	115	.070	↓	1.28	2.23		3.51	5.15
3250 Joint connectors				Ea.	2.88			2.88	3.17
3300 Wood, clear treated cedar, fir or hemlock, 3" x 4"	1 Carp	100	.080	L.F.	12.40	2.57		14.97	17.95
3400 4" x 5"	"	100	.080	"	19.45	2.57		22.02	26
5000 Accessories, end cap, K type, aluminum 5"	1 Shee	625	.013	Ea.	.66	.46		1.12	1.50
5010 6"		625	.013		1.44	.46		1.90	2.35
5020 Copper, 5"		625	.013		3.89	.46		4.35	5.05
5030 6"		625	.013		3.54	.46		4	4.66
5040 Lead coated copper, 5"		625	.013		12.50	.46		12.96	14.50
5050 6"		625	.013		13.35	.46		13.81	15.45
5060 Copper clad stainless steel, 5"		625	.013		3	.46		3.46	4.07
5070 6"		625	.013		3.60	.46		4.06	4.73
5080 Galvanized steel, 5"		625	.013		1.28	.46		1.74	2.18
5090 6"	↓	625	.013		2.18	.46		2.64	3.17
5100 Vinyl, 4"	1 Carp	625	.013	↓	5.80	.41		6.21	7.10

07 71 23 – Manufactured Gutters and Downspouts

07 71 23.30 Gutters

		Crew	Daily Output	Labor-Hours	Unit	Material	2014 Bare Costs Labor	Equipment	Total	Total Incl O&P
5110	5"	1 Carp	625	.013	Ea.	6.10	.41		6.51	7.40
5120	Half round, copper, 4"	1 Shee	625	.013		4.40	.46		4.86	5.60
5130	5"		625	.013		4.72	.46		5.18	5.95
5140	6"		625	.013		5.15	.46		5.61	6.40
5150	Lead coated copper, 5"		625	.013		14.15	.46		14.61	16.30
5160	6"		625	.013		21	.46		21.46	24.50
5170	Copper clad stainless steel, 5"		625	.013		4.50	.46		4.96	5.70
5180	6"		625	.013		4.50	.46		4.96	5.70
5190	Galvanized steel, 5"		625	.013		2.25	.46		2.71	3.25
5200	6"		625	.013		2.80	.46		3.26	3.85
5210	Outlet, aluminum, 2" x 3"		420	.019		.62	.69		1.31	1.83
5220	3" x 4"		420	.019		1.05	.69		1.74	2.31
5230	2-3/8" round		420	.019		.56	.69		1.25	1.77
5240	Copper, 2" x 3"		420	.019		6.50	.69		7.19	8.30
5250	3" x 4"		420	.019		7.85	.69		8.54	9.80
5260	2-3/8" round		420	.019		4.55	.69		5.24	6.15
5270	Lead coated copper, 2" x 3"		420	.019		25.50	.69		26.19	29
5280	3" x 4"		420	.019		28.50	.69		29.19	32.50
5290	2-3/8" round		420	.019		25.50	.69		26.19	29
5300	Copper clad stainless steel, 2" x 3"		420	.019		6.50	.69		7.19	8.30
5310	3" x 4"		420	.019		7.85	.69		8.54	9.80
5320	2-3/8" round		420	.019		4.55	.69		5.24	6.15
5330	Galvanized steel, 2" x 3"		420	.019		3.18	.69		3.87	4.65
5340	3" x 4"		420	.019		4.90	.69		5.59	6.55
5350	2-3/8" round		420	.019		3.98	.69		4.67	5.55
5360	K type mitres, aluminum		65	.123		3	4.44		7.44	10.70
5370	Copper		65	.123		17.40	4.44		21.84	26.50
5380	Lead coated copper		65	.123		54.50	4.44		58.94	67.50
5390	Copper clad stainless steel		65	.123		27.50	4.44		31.94	38
5400	Galvanized steel		65	.123		22.50	4.44		26.94	32.50
5420	Half round mitres, copper		65	.123		63.50	4.44		67.94	77.50
5430	Lead coated copper		65	.123		89.50	4.44		93.94	106
5440	Copper clad stainless steel		65	.123		56	4.44		60.44	69.50
5450	Galvanized steel		65	.123		25.50	4.44		29.94	35.50
5460	Vinyl mitres and outlets		65	.123		9.75	4.44		14.19	18.15
5470	Sealant		940	.009	L.F.	.01	.31		.32	.52
5480	Soldering		96	.083	"	.20	3.01		3.21	5.20

07 71 23.35 Gutter Guard

		Crew	Daily Output	Labor-Hours	Unit	Material	2014 Bare Costs Labor	Equipment	Total	Total Incl O&P
0010	**GUTTER GUARD**									
0020	6" wide strip, aluminum mesh	1 Carp	500	.016	L.F.	2.17	.51		2.68	3.25
0100	Vinyl mesh	"	500	.016	"	2.25	.51		2.76	3.34

07 71 43 – Drip Edge

07 71 43.10 Drip Edge, Rake Edge, Ice Belts

		Crew	Daily Output	Labor-Hours	Unit	Material	2014 Bare Costs Labor	Equipment	Total	Total Incl O&P
0010	**DRIP EDGE, RAKE EDGE, ICE BELTS**									
0020	Aluminum, .016" thick, 5" wide, mill finish	1 Carp	400	.020	L.F.	.40	.64		1.04	1.52
0100	White finish		400	.020		.41	.64		1.05	1.53
0200	8" wide, mill finish		400	.020		.69	.64		1.33	1.84
0300	Ice belt, 28" wide, mill finish		100	.080		3.85	2.57		6.42	8.55
0310	Vented, mill finish		400	.020		2.86	.64		3.50	4.23
0320	Painted finish		400	.020		2.90	.64		3.54	4.27
0400	Galvanized, 5" wide		400	.020		.53	.64		1.17	1.66
0500	8" wide, mill finish		400	.020		.69	.64		1.33	1.84

07 71 Roof Specialties

07 71 43 – Drip Edge

07 71 43.10 Drip Edge, Rake Edge, Ice Belts

		Crew	Daily Output	Labor-Hours	Unit	Material	2014 Bare Costs Labor	Equipment	Total	Total Incl O&P
0510	Rake edge, aluminum, 1-1/2" x 1-1/2"	1 Carp	400	.020	L.F.	.30	.64		.94	1.41
0520	3-1/2" x 1-1/2"	↓	400	.020	↓	.41	.64		1.05	1.53

07 72 Roof Accessories

07 72 23 – Relief Vents

07 72 23.20 Vents

		Crew	Daily Output	Labor-Hours	Unit	Material	2014 Bare Costs Labor	Equipment	Total	Total Incl O&P
0010	**VENTS**									
0100	Soffit or eave, aluminum, mill finish, strips, 2-1/2" wide	1 Carp	200	.040	L.F.	.42	1.28		1.70	2.62
0200	3" wide		200	.040		.39	1.28		1.67	2.59
0300	Enamel finish, 3" wide		200	.040	↓	.50	1.28		1.78	2.71
0400	Mill finish, rectangular, 4" x 16"		72	.111	Ea.	1.45	3.57		5.02	7.60
0500	8" x 16"	↓	72	.111		2.26	3.57		5.83	8.50
2420	Roof ventilator	Q-9	16	1		50.50	32.50		83	110
2500	Vent, roof vent	1 Rofc	24	.333	↓	25.50	9		34.50	44.50

07 72 26 – Ridge Vents

07 72 26.10 Ridge Vents and Accessories

		Crew	Daily Output	Labor-Hours	Unit	Material	2014 Bare Costs Labor	Equipment	Total	Total Incl O&P
0010	**RIDGE VENTS AND ACCESSORIES**									
0100	Aluminum strips, mill finish	1 Rofc	160	.050	L.F.	2.75	1.35		4.10	5.50
0150	Painted finish		160	.050	"	4.05	1.35		5.40	6.95
0200	Connectors		48	.167	Ea.	4.65	4.50		9.15	13.40
0300	End caps		48	.167	"	1.98	4.50		6.48	10.50
0400	Galvanized strips		160	.050	L.F.	3.58	1.35		4.93	6.45
0430	Molded polyethylene, shingles not included		160	.050	"	2.74	1.35		4.09	5.50
0440	End plugs		48	.167	Ea.	1.98	4.50		6.48	10.50
0450	Flexible roll, shingles not included	↓	160	.050	L.F.	2.38	1.35		3.73	5.10
2300	Ridge vent strip, mill finish	1 Shee	155	.052	"	2.98	1.86		4.84	6.40

07 72 53 – Snow Guards

07 72 53.10 Snow Guard Options

		Crew	Daily Output	Labor-Hours	Unit	Material	2014 Bare Costs Labor	Equipment	Total	Total Incl O&P
0010	**SNOW GUARD OPTIONS**									
0100	Slate & asphalt shingle roofs, fastened with nails	1 Rofc	160	.050	Ea.	12.55	1.35		13.90	16.30
0200	Standing seam metal roofs, fastened with set screws		48	.167		16.95	4.50		21.45	27
0300	Surface mount for metal roofs, fastened with solder		48	.167	↓	6.05	4.50		10.55	14.95
0400	Double rail pipe type, including pipe	↓	130	.062	L.F.	32	1.66		33.66	38

07 72 80 – Vents

07 72 80.30 Vent Options

		Crew	Daily Output	Labor-Hours	Unit	Material	2014 Bare Costs Labor	Equipment	Total	Total Incl O&P
0010	**VENT OPTIONS**									
0800	Polystyrene baffles, 12" wide for 16" O.C. rafter spacing	1 Carp	90	.089	Ea.	.40	2.85		3.25	5.25
0900	For 24" O.C. rafter spacing	"	110	.073	"	.75	2.33		3.08	4.76

07 76 Roof Pavers

07 76 16 – Roof Decking Pavers

07 76 16.10 Roof Pavers and Supports	Crew	Daily Output	Labor-Hours	Unit	Material	2014 Bare Costs Labor	Equipment	Total	Total Incl O&P
0010	**ROOF PAVERS AND SUPPORTS**									
1000	Roof decking pavers, concrete blocks, 2" thick, natural	1 Clab	115	.070	S.F.	3.37	1.66		5.03	6.50
1100	Colors		115	.070	"	3.73	1.66		5.39	6.90
1200	Support pedestal, bottom cap		960	.008	Ea.	2.99	.20		3.19	3.62
1300	Top cap		960	.008		4.79	.20		4.99	5.60
1400	Leveling shims, 1/16"		1920	.004		1.19	.10		1.29	1.48
1500	1/8"		1920	.004		1.19	.10		1.29	1.48
1600	Buffer pad		960	.008		2.49	.20		2.69	3.07
1700	PVC legs (4" SDR 35)		2880	.003	Inch	.12	.07		.19	.24
2000	Alternate pricing method, system in place		101	.079	S.F.	7	1.89		8.89	10.85

07 91 Preformed Joint Seals

07 91 13 – Compression Seals

07 91 13.10 Compression Seals

		Crew	Daily Output	Labor-Hours	Unit	Material	2014 Bare Costs Labor	Equipment	Total	Total Incl O&P
0010	**COMPRESSION SEALS**									
4900	O-ring type cord, 1/4"	1 Bric	472	.017	L.F.	.48	.54		1.02	1.43
4910	1/2"		440	.018		1.79	.58		2.37	2.94
4920	3/4"		424	.019		3.62	.60		4.22	4.98
4930	1"		408	.020		6.95	.63		7.58	8.70
4940	1-1/4"		384	.021		13.75	.66		14.41	16.20
4950	1-1/2"		368	.022		17.40	.69		18.09	20.50
4960	1-3/4"		352	.023		36.50	.73		37.23	41
4970	2"		344	.023		64.50	.74		65.24	71.50

07 91 16 – Joint Gaskets

07 91 16.10 Joint Gaskets

		Crew	Daily Output	Labor-Hours	Unit	Material	2014 Bare Costs Labor	Equipment	Total	Total Incl O&P
0010	**JOINT GASKETS**									
4400	Joint gaskets, neoprene, closed cell w/adh, 1/8" x 3/8"	1 Bric	240	.033	L.F.	.28	1.06		1.34	2.08
4500	1/4" x 3/4"		215	.037		.59	1.19		1.78	2.63
4700	1/2" x 1"		200	.040		1.30	1.28		2.58	3.55
4800	3/4" x 1-1/2"		165	.048		1.45	1.55		3	4.17

07 91 23 – Backer Rods

07 91 23.10 Backer Rods

		Crew	Daily Output	Labor-Hours	Unit	Material	2014 Bare Costs Labor	Equipment	Total	Total Incl O&P
0010	**BACKER RODS**									
0030	Backer rod, polyethylene, 1/4" diameter	1 Bric	4.60	1.739	C.L.F.	2.43	55.50		57.93	95
0050	1/2" diameter		4.60	1.739		3.66	55.50		59.16	96.50
0070	3/4" diameter		4.60	1.739		5.55	55.50		61.05	98.50
0090	1" diameter		4.60	1.739		8.80	55.50		64.30	102

07 91 26 – Joint Fillers

07 91 26.10 Joint Fillers

		Crew	Daily Output	Labor-Hours	Unit	Material	2014 Bare Costs Labor	Equipment	Total	Total Incl O&P
0010	**JOINT FILLERS**									
4360	Butyl rubber filler, 1/4" x 1/4"	1 Bric	290	.028	L.F.	.23	.88		1.11	1.72
4365	1/2" x 1/2"		250	.032		.92	1.02		1.94	2.71
4370	1/2" x 3/4"		210	.038		1.38	1.22		2.60	3.54
4375	3/4" x 3/4"		230	.035		2.08	1.11		3.19	4.13
4380	1" x 1"		180	.044		2.77	1.42		4.19	5.40
4390	For coloring, add					12%				
4980	Polyethylene joint backing, 1/4" x 2"	1 Bric	2.08	3.846	C.L.F.	12	123		135	217
4990	1/4" x 6"		1.28	6.250	"	28	199		227	360
5600	Silicone, room temp vulcanizing foam seal, 1/4" x 1/2"		1312	.006	L.F.	.33	.19		.52	.69

07 91 Preformed Joint Seals

07 91 26 – Joint Fillers

07 91 26.10 Joint Fillers	Crew	Daily Output	Labor-Hours	Unit	Material	2014 Bare Costs Labor	2014 Bare Costs Equipment	Total	Total Incl O&P
5610	1/2" x 1/2"	1 Bric	656	.012	L.F.	.67	.39		1.06	1.39
5620	1/2" x 3/4"		442	.018		1	.58		1.58	2.06
5630	3/4" x 3/4"		328	.024		1.50	.78		2.28	2.95
5640	1/8" x 1"		1312	.006		.33	.19		.52	.69
5650	1/8" x 3"		442	.018		1	.58		1.58	2.06
5670	1/4" x 3"		295	.027		2.01	.87		2.88	3.65
5680	1/4" x 6"		148	.054		4.01	1.72		5.73	7.30
5690	1/2" x 6"		82	.098		8	3.11		11.11	14
5700	1/2" x 9"		52.50	.152		12.05	4.86		16.91	21.50
5710	1/2" x 12"		33	.242		16.05	7.75		23.80	30.50

07 92 Joint Sealants

07 92 13 – Elastomeric Joint Sealants

07 92 13.20 Caulking and Sealant Options

		Crew	Daily Output	Labor-Hours	Unit	Material	2014 Bare Costs Labor	2014 Bare Costs Equipment	Total	Total Incl O&P
0010	**CAULKING AND SEALANT OPTIONS**									
0050	Latex acrylic based, bulk				Gal.	29.50			29.50	32.50
0055	Bulk in place 1/4" x 1/4" bead	1 Bric	300	.027	L.F.	.09	.85		.94	1.52
0060	1/4" x 3/8"		294	.027		.16	.87		1.03	1.61
0065	1/4" x 1/2"		288	.028		.21	.89		1.10	1.71
0075	3/8" x 3/8"		284	.028		.23	.90		1.13	1.75
0080	3/8" x 1/2"		280	.029		.31	.91		1.22	1.86
0085	3/8" x 5/8"		276	.029		.39	.92		1.31	1.97
0095	3/8" x 3/4"		272	.029		.46	.94		1.40	2.07
0100	1/2" x 1/2"		275	.029		.41	.93		1.34	2
0105	1/2" x 5/8"		269	.030		.52	.95		1.47	2.15
0110	1/2" x 3/4"		263	.030		.62	.97		1.59	2.30
0115	1/2" x 7/8"		256	.031		.72	1		1.72	2.46
0120	1/2" x 1"		250	.032		.83	1.02		1.85	2.61
0125	3/4" x 3/4"		244	.033		.93	1.05		1.98	2.77
0130	3/4" x 1"		225	.036		1.24	1.13		2.37	3.26
0135	1" x 1"		200	.040		1.66	1.28		2.94	3.94
0190	Cartridges				Gal.	26.50			26.50	29
0200	11 fl. oz. cartridge				Ea.	2.28			2.28	2.51
0500	1/4" x 1/2"	1 Bric	288	.028	L.F.	.19	.89		1.08	1.68
0600	1/2" x 1/2"		275	.029		.37	.93		1.30	1.95
0800	3/4" x 3/4"		244	.033		.84	1.05		1.89	2.66
0900	3/4" x 1"		225	.036		1.12	1.13		2.25	3.12
1000	1" x 1"		200	.040		1.40	1.28		2.68	3.66
1400	Butyl based, bulk				Gal.	34			34	37.50
1500	Cartridges				"	38.50			38.50	42.50
1700	1/4" x 1/2", 154 L.F./gal.	1 Bric	288	.028	L.F.	.22	.89		1.11	1.72
1800	1/2" x 1/2", 77 L.F./gal.	"	275	.029	"	.44	.93		1.37	2.03
2300	Polysulfide compounds, 1 component, bulk				Gal.	61			61	67
2400	Cartridges				"	59			59	65
2600	1 or 2 component, in place, 1/4" x 1/4", 308 L.F./gal.	1 Bric	300	.027	L.F.	.20	.85		1.05	1.64
2700	1/2" x 1/4", 154 L.F./gal.		288	.028		.40	.89		1.29	1.92
2900	3/4" x 3/8", 68 L.F./gal.		272	.029		.90	.94		1.84	2.55
3000	1" x 1/2", 38 L.F./gal.		250	.032		1.61	1.02		2.63	3.47
3200	Polyurethane, 1 or 2 component				Gal.	51			51	56
3300	Cartridges				"	64			64	70.50
3500	Bulk, in place, 1/4" x 1/4"	1 Bric	300	.027	L.F.	.17	.85		1.02	1.60

07 92 Joint Sealants

07 92 13 – Elastomeric Joint Sealants

07 92 13.20 Caulking and Sealant Options		Crew	Daily Output	Labor-Hours	Unit	Material	2014 Bare Costs Labor	Equipment	Total	Total Incl O&P
3655	1/2" x 1/4"	1 Bric	288	.028	L.F.	.33	.89		1.22	1.84
3800	3/4" x 3/8"		272	.029		.75	.94		1.69	2.39
3900	1" x 1/2"		250	.032		1.33	1.02		2.35	3.16
4100	Silicone rubber, bulk				Gal.	45.50			45.50	50
4200	Cartridges				"	45			45	49.50

07 92 19 – Acoustical Joint Sealants

07 92 19.10 Acoustical Sealant

		Crew	Daily Output	Labor-Hours	Unit	Material	2014 Bare Costs Labor	Equipment	Total	Total Incl O&P
0010	**ACOUSTICAL SEALANT**									
0020	Acoustical sealant, elastomeric, cartridges				Ea.	8.50			8.50	9.35
0025	In place, 1/4" x 1/4"	1 Bric	300	.027	L.F.	.35	.85		1.20	1.80
0030	1/4" x 1/2"		288	.028		.69	.89		1.58	2.24
0035	1/2" x 1/2"		275	.029		1.39	.93		2.32	3.06
0040	1/2" x 3/4"		263	.030		2.08	.97		3.05	3.91
0045	3/4" x 3/4"		244	.033		3.12	1.05		4.17	5.15
0050	1" x 1"		200	.040		5.55	1.28		6.83	8.20

Estimating Tips

08 10 00 Doors and Frames

All exterior doors should be addressed for their energy conservation (insulation and seals).

- Most metal doors and frames look alike, but there may be significant differences among them. When estimating these items, be sure to choose the line item that most closely compares to the specification or door schedule requirements regarding:
    — type of metal
    — metal gauge
    — door core material
    — fire rating
    — finish
- Wood and plastic doors vary considerably in price. The primary determinant is the veneer material. Lauan, birch, and oak are the most common veneers. Other variables include the following:
    — hollow or solid core
    — fire rating
    — flush or raised panel
    — finish
- Door pricing includes bore for cylindrical lockset and mortise for hinges.

08 30 00 Specialty Doors and Frames

- There are many varieties of special doors, and they are usually priced per each. Add frames, hardware, or operators required for a complete installation.

08 40 00 Entrances, Storefronts, and Curtain Walls

- Glazed curtain walls consist of the metal tube framing and the glazing material. The cost data in this subdivision is presented for the metal tube framing alone or the composite wall. If your estimate requires a detailed takeoff of the framing, be sure to add the glazing cost.

08 50 00 Windows

- Most metal windows are delivered preglazed. However, some metal windows are priced without glass. Refer to 08 80 00 Glazing for glass pricing. The grade C indicates commercial grade windows, usually ASTM C-35.
- All wood windows and vinyl are priced preglazed. The glazing is insulating glass. Some wood windows may have single pane float glass. Add the cost of screens and grills if required, and not already included.

08 70 00 Hardware

- Hardware costs add considerably to the cost of a door. The most efficient method to determine the hardware requirements for a project is to review the door and hardware schedule together.

- Door hinges are priced by the pair, with most doors requiring 1-1/2 pairs per door. The hinge prices do not include installation labor because it is included in door installation. Hinges are classified according to the frequency of use, base material, and finish.

08 80 00 Glazing

- Different openings require different types of glass. The most common types are:
    — float
    — tempered
    — insulating
    — impact-resistant
    — ballistic-resistant
- Most exterior windows are glazed with insulating glass. Entrance doors and window walls, where the glass is less than 18" from the floor, are generally glazed with tempered glass. Interior windows and some residential windows are glazed with float glass.
- Coastal communities require the use of impact-resistant glass, dependant on wind speed.
- The insulation or 'u' value is a strong consideration, along with solar heat gain, to determine total energy efficiency.

Reference Numbers

Reference numbers are shown in shaded boxes at the beginning of some major classifications. These numbers refer to related items in the Reference Section. The reference information may be an estimating procedure, an alternate pricing method, or technical information.

Note: Not all subdivisions listed here necessarily appear in this publication.

08 01 Operation and Maintenance of Openings

08 01 53 – Operation and Maintenance of Plastic Windows

08 01 53.81 Solid Vinyl Replacement Windows

		Crew	Daily Output	Labor-Hours	Unit	Material	2014 Bare Costs Labor	2014 Bare Costs Equipment	Total	Total Incl O&P
0010	**SOLID VINYL REPLACEMENT WINDOWS** R085313-20									
0020	Double hung, insulated glass, up to 83 united inches G	2 Carp	8	2	Ea.	340	64		404	485
0040	84 to 93 G		8	2		380	64		444	525
0060	94 to 101 G		6	2.667		380	85.50		465.50	560
0080	102 to 111 G		6	2.667		395	85.50		480.50	580
0100	112 to 120 G		6	2.667		430	85.50		515.50	620
0120	For each united inch over 120 , add G		800	.020	Inch	5.50	.64		6.14	7.15
0140	Casement windows, one operating sash , 42 to 60 united inches G		8	2	Ea.	222	64		286	350
0160	61 to 70 G		8	2		248	64		312	380
0180	71 to 80 G		8	2		269	64		333	405
0200	81 to 96 G		8	2		286	64		350	425
0220	Two operating sash, 58 to 78 united inches G		8	2		440	64		504	595
0240	79 to 88 G		8	2		470	64		534	630
0260	89 to 98 G		8	2		515	64		579	675
0280	99 to 108 G		6	2.667		535	85.50		620.50	735
0300	109 to 121 G		6	2.667		575	85.50		660.50	780
0320	Two operating.one fixed sash, 73 to 108 united inches G		8	2		700	64		764	880
0340	109 to 118 G		8	2		735	64		799	920
0360	119 to 128 G		6	2.667		755	85.50		840.50	975
0380	129 to 138 G		6	2.667		805	85.50		890.50	1,025
0400	139 to 156 G		6	2.667		850	85.50		935.50	1,075
0420	Four operating sash, 98 to 118 united inches G		8	2		1,000	64		1,064	1,200
0440	119 to 128 G		8	2		1,075	64		1,139	1,275
0460	129 to 138 G		6	2.667		1,125	85.50		1,210.50	1,400
0480	139 to 148 G		6	2.667		1,175	85.50		1,260.50	1,450
0500	149 to 168 G		6	2.667		1,250	85.50		1,335.50	1,550
0520	169 to 178 G		6	2.667		1,350	85.50		1,435.50	1,650
0560	Fixed picture window, up to 63 united inches G		8	2		180	64		244	305
0580	64 to 83 G		8	2		206	64		270	335
0600	84 to 101 G		8	2		257	64		321	390
0620	For each united inch over 101, add G		900	.018	Inch	3.10	.57		3.67	4.37
0780	Diamond shape, per full or partial diamond				Ea.	8.10			8.10	8.90
0800	Cellulose fiber insulation, poured into sash balance cavity G	1 Carp	36	.222	C.F.	.69	7.15		7.84	12.75
0820	Silicone caulking at perimeter G	"	800	.010	L.F.	.15	.32		.47	.70

08 05 Common Work Results for Openings

08 05 05 – Selective Windows and Doors Demolition

08 05 05.10 Selective Demolition Doors

		Crew	Daily Output	Labor-Hours	Unit	Material	2014 Bare Costs Labor	2014 Bare Costs Equipment	Total	Total Incl O&P
0010	**SELECTIVE DEMOLITION DOORS** R024119-10									
0200	Doors, exterior, 1-3/4" thick, single, 3' x 7' high	1 Clab	16	.500	Ea.		11.90		11.90	20
0210	3' x 8' high		10	.800			19.05		19.05	32
0215	Double, 3' x 8' high		6	1.333			31.50		31.50	53.50
0220	Double, 6' x 7' high		12	.667			15.85		15.85	26.50
0500	Interior, 1-3/8" thick, single, 3' x 7' high		20	.400			9.50		9.50	16
0520	Double, 6' x 7' high		16	.500			11.90		11.90	20
0700	Bi-folding, 3' x 6'-8" high		20	.400			9.50		9.50	16
0720	6' x 6'-8" high		18	.444			10.60		10.60	17.80
0900	Bi-passing, 3' x 6'-8" high		16	.500			11.90		11.90	20
0940	6' x 6'-8" high		14	.571			13.60		13.60	23
1500	Remove and reset, minimum	1 Carp	8	1			32		32	54
1520	Maximum		6	1.333			43		43	72

08 05 05 – Selective Windows and Doors Demolition

08 05 05.10 Selective Demolition Doors

		Crew	Daily Output	Labor-Hours	Unit	Material	2014 Bare Costs Labor	Equipment	Total	Total Incl O&P
2000	Frames, including trim, metal	1 Carp	8	1	Ea.		32		32	54
2200	Wood	2 Carp	32	.500	↓		16.05		16.05	27
2201	Alternate pricing method	1 Carp	200	.040	L.F.		1.28		1.28	2.16
3000	Special doors, counter doors	2 Carp	6	2.667	Ea.		85.50		85.50	144
3300	Glass, sliding, including frames		12	1.333			43		43	72
3400	Overhead, commercial, 12' x 12' high		4	4			128		128	216
3500	Residential, 9' x 7' high		8	2			64		64	108
3540	16' x 7' high		7	2.286			73.50		73.50	123
3600	Remove and reset, minimum		4	4			128		128	216
3620	Maximum	↓	2.50	6.400			205		205	345
3660	Remove and reset elec. garage door opener	1 Carp	8	1			32		32	54
4000	Residential lockset, exterior		28	.286			9.15		9.15	15.45
4010	Residential lockset, exterior w/deadbolt		26	.308			9.90		9.90	16.60
4020	Residential lockset, interior		30	.267			8.55		8.55	14.40
4200	Deadbolt lock		32	.250			8.05		8.05	13.50
4224	Pocket door	↓	8	1			32		32	54
5590	Remove mail slot	1 Clab	45	.178			4.23		4.23	7.10
5600	Remove door sidelight	1 Carp	6	1.333	↓		43		43	72

08 05 05.20 Selective Demolition of Windows

		Crew	Daily Output	Labor-Hours	Unit	Material	2014 Bare Costs Labor	Equipment	Total	Total Incl O&P
0010	**SELECTIVE DEMOLITION OF WINDOWS** R024119-10									
0200	Aluminum, including trim, to 12 S.F.	1 Clab	16	.500	Ea.		11.90		11.90	20
0240	To 25 S.F.		11	.727			17.30		17.30	29
0280	To 50 S.F.		5	1.600			38		38	64
0320	Storm windows/screens, to 12 S.F.		27	.296			7.05		7.05	11.85
0360	To 25 S.F.		21	.381			9.05		9.05	15.25
0400	To 50 S.F.		16	.500			11.90		11.90	20
0500	Screens, incl. aluminum frame, small		20	.400			9.50		9.50	16
0510	Large		16	.500	↓		11.90		11.90	20
0600	Glass, minimum		200	.040	S.F.		.95		.95	1.60
0620	Maximum		150	.053	"		1.27		1.27	2.14
2000	Wood, including trim, to 12 S.F.		22	.364	Ea.		8.65		8.65	14.55
2020	To 25 S.F.		18	.444			10.60		10.60	17.80
2060	To 50 S.F.		13	.615			14.65		14.65	24.50
2065	To 180 S.F.	↓	8	1			24		24	40
4300	Remove bay/bow window	2 Carp	6	2.667	↓		85.50		85.50	144
4410	Remove skylight, plstc domes, flush/curb mtd	G-3	395	.081	S.F.		2.43		2.43	4.06
5020	Remove and reset window, minimum	1 Carp	6	1.333	Ea.		43		43	72
5040	Average		4	2			64		64	108
5080	Maximum	↓	2	4	↓		128		128	216
6000	Screening only	1 Clab	4000	.002	S.F.		.05		.05	.08
9100	Window awning, residential	"	80	.100	L.F.		2.38		2.38	4.01

08 11 Metal Doors and Frames

08 11 63 – Metal Screen and Storm Doors and Frames

08 11 63.23 Aluminum Screen and Storm Doors and Frames	Crew	Daily Output	Labor-Hours	Unit	Material	2014 Bare Costs Labor	Equipment	Total	Total Incl O&P
0010 **ALUMINUM SCREEN AND STORM DOORS AND FRAMES**									
0020 Combination storm and screen									
0420 Clear anodic coating, 2'-8" wide	2 Carp	14	1.143	Ea.	165	36.50		201.50	244
0440 3'-0" wide	"	14	1.143	"	163	36.50		199.50	241
0500 For 7' door height, add					8%				
1020 Mill finish, 2'-8" wide	2 Carp	14	1.143	Ea.	235	36.50		271.50	320
1040 3'-0" wide	"	14	1.143		258	36.50		294.50	345
1100 For 7'-0" door, add					8%				
1520 White painted, 2'-8" wide	2 Carp	14	1.143		286	36.50		322.50	375
1540 3'-0" wide		14	1.143		305	36.50		341.50	395
1541 Storm door, painted, alum., insul., 6'-8" x 2'-6" wide		14	1.143		274	36.50		310.50	360
1545 2'-8" wide		14	1.143		274	36.50		310.50	360
1600 For 7'-0" door, add					8%				
1800 Aluminum screen door, minimum, 6'-8" x 2'-8" wide	2 Carp	14	1.143		148	36.50		184.50	225
1810 3'-0" wide		14	1.143		252	36.50		288.50	340
1820 Average, 6'-8" x 2'-8" wide		14	1.143		200	36.50		236.50	282
1830 3'-0" wide		14	1.143		252	36.50		288.50	340
1840 Maximum, 6'-8" x 2'-8" wide		14	1.143		405	36.50		441.50	505
1850 3'-0" wide		14	1.143		274	36.50		310.50	360
2000 Wood door & screen, see Section 08 14 33.20									

08 12 Metal Frames

08 12 13 – Hollow Metal Frames

08 12 13.13 Standard Hollow Metal Frames

		Crew	Daily Output	Labor-Hours	Unit	Material	2014 Bare Costs Labor	Equipment	Total	Total Incl O&P
0010 **STANDARD HOLLOW METAL FRAMES**										
0020 16 ga., up to 5-3/4" jamb depth										
0025 3'-0" x 6'-8" single	G	2 Carp	16	1	Ea.	145	32		177	214
0028 3'-6" wide, single	G		16	1		152	32		184	221
0030 4'-0" wide, single	G		16	1		151	32		183	220
0040 6'-0" wide, double	G		14	1.143		204	36.50		240.50	286
0045 8'-0" wide, double	G		14	1.143		213	36.50		249.50	296
0100 3'-0" x 7'-0" single	G		16	1		150	32		182	219
0110 3'-6" wide, single	G		16	1		157	32		189	227
0112 4'-0" wide, single	G		16	1		157	32		189	227
0140 6'-0" wide, double	G		14	1.143		194	36.50		230.50	276
0145 8'-0" wide, double	G		14	1.143		229	36.50		265.50	315
1000 16 ga., up to 4-7/8" deep, 3'-0" x 7'-0" single	G		16	1		166	32		198	237
1140 6'-0" wide, double	G		14	1.143		188	36.50		224.50	269
1200 16 ga., 8-3/4" deep, 3'-0" x 7'-0" single	G		16	1		199	32		231	273
1240 6'-0" wide, double	G		14	1.143		234	36.50		270.50	320
2800 14 ga., up to 3-7/8" deep, 3'-0" x 7'-0" single	G		16	1		181	32		213	253
2840 6'-0" wide, double	G		14	1.143		217	36.50		253.50	300
3000 14 ga., up to 5-3/4" deep, 3'-0" x 6'-8" single	G		16	1		155	32		187	225
3002 3'-6" wide, single	G		16	1		196	32		228	269
3005 4'-0" wide, single	G		16	1		196	32		228	269
3600 up to 5-3/4" jamb depth, 4'-0" x 7'-0" single	G		15	1.067		185	34		219	261
3620 6'-0" wide, double	G		12	1.333		235	43		278	330
3640 8'-0" wide, double	G		12	1.333		246	43		289	345
3700 8'-0" high, 4'-0" wide, single	G		15	1.067		235	34		269	315
3740 8'-0" wide, double	G		12	1.333		290	43		333	390
4000 6-3/4" deep, 4'-0" x 7'-0" single	G		15	1.067		220	34		254	300

08 12 Metal Frames

08 12 13 – Hollow Metal Frames

08 12 13.13 Standard Hollow Metal Frames		Crew	Daily Output	Labor-Hours	Unit	Material	2014 Bare Costs Labor	2014 Bare Costs Equipment	Total	Total Incl O&P
4020	6'-0" wide, double	G	2 Carp	12	1.333	Ea.	275	43		318	370
4040	8'-0", wide double	G		12	1.333		282	43		325	380
4100	8'-0" high, 4'-0" wide, single	G		15	1.067		276	34		310	365
4140	8'-0" wide, double	G		12	1.333		320	43		363	425
4400	8-3/4" deep, 4'-0" x 7'-0", single	G		15	1.067		252	34		286	335
4440	8'-0" wide, double	G		12	1.333		315	43		358	415
4500	4'-0" x 8'-0", single	G		15	1.067		283	34		317	370
4540	8'-0" wide, double	G		12	1.333		350	43		393	455
4900	For welded frames, add						63			63	69.50
5400	14 ga., "B" label, up to 5-3/4" deep, 4'-0" x 7'-0" single	G	2 Carp	15	1.067		208	34		242	287
5440	8'-0" wide, double	G		12	1.333		271	43		314	370
5800	6-3/4" deep, 7'-0" high, 4'-0" wide, single	G		15	1.067		218	34		252	298
5840	8'-0" wide, double	G		12	1.333		385	43		428	495
6200	8-3/4" deep, 4'-0" x 7'-0" single	G		15	1.067		289	34		323	380
6240	8'-0" wide, double	G		12	1.333		365	43		408	470
6300	For "A" label use same price as "B" label										
6400	For baked enamel finish, add						30%	15%			
6500	For galvanizing, add						20%				
6600	For hospital stop, add					Ea.	295			295	325
6620	For hospital stop, stainless steel add					"	380			380	420
7900	Transom lite frames, fixed, add		2 Carp	155	.103	S.F.	54	3.31		57.31	65
8000	Movable, add		"	130	.123	"	68	3.95		71.95	81.50

08 13 Metal Doors

08 13 13 – Hollow Metal Doors

08 13 13.15 Metal Fire Doors

		Crew	Daily Output	Labor-Hours	Unit	Material	2014 Bare Costs Labor	2014 Bare Costs Equipment	Total	Total Incl O&P
0010	**METAL FIRE DOORS** R081313-20									
0015	Steel, flush, "B" label, 90 minute									
0020	Full panel, 20 ga., 2'-0" x 6'-8"	2 Carp	20	.800	Ea.	420	25.50		445.50	505
0040	2'-8" x 6'-8"		18	.889		435	28.50		463.50	530
0060	3'-0" x 6'-8"		17	.941		435	30		465	530
0080	3'-0" x 7'-0"		17	.941		455	30		485	550
0140	18 ga., 3'-0" x 6'-8"		16	1		495	32		527	600
0160	2'-8" x 7'-0"		17	.941		520	30		550	620
0180	3'-0" x 7'-0"		16	1		505	32		537	610
0200	4'-0" x 7'-0"		15	1.067		650	34		684	775
0220	For "A" label, 3 hour, 18 ga., use same price as "B" label									
0240	For vision lite, add				Ea.	156			156	172
0520	Flush, "B" label 90 min., egress core, 20 ga., 2'-0" x 6'-8"	2 Carp	18	.889		655	28.50		683.50	770
0540	2'-8" x 6'-8"		17	.941		665	30		695	780
0560	3'-0" x 6'-8"		16	1		665	32		697	785
0580	3'-0" x 7'-0"		16	1		685	32		717	805
0640	Flush, "A" label 3 hour, egress core, 18 ga., 3'-0" x 6'-8"		15	1.067		720	34		754	855
0660	2'-8" x 7'-0"		16	1		750	32		782	875
0680	3'-0" x 7'-0"		15	1.067		740	34		774	875
0700	4'-0" x 7'-0"		14	1.143		885	36.50		921.50	1,025

08 13 13.20 Residential Steel Doors

		Crew	Daily Output	Labor-Hours	Unit	Material	2014 Bare Costs Labor	2014 Bare Costs Equipment	Total	Total Incl O&P
0010	**RESIDENTIAL STEEL DOORS**									
0020	Prehung, insulated, exterior									
0030	Embossed, full panel, 2'-8" x 6'-8" G	2 Carp	17	.941	Ea.	305	30		335	385
0040	3'-0" x 6'-8" G		15	1.067		247	34		281	330

445

08 13 Metal Doors

08 13 13 – Hollow Metal Doors

08 13 13.20 Residential Steel Doors

			Crew	Daily Output	Labor-Hours	Unit	Material	2014 Bare Costs Labor	Equipment	Total	Total Incl O&P
0060	3'-0" x 7'-0"	G	2 Carp	15	1.067	Ea.	330	34		364	425
0070	5'-4" x 6'-8", double	G		8	2		625	64		689	795
0220	Half glass, 2'-8" x 6'-8"	G		17	.941		320	30		350	400
0240	3'-0" x 6'-8"	G		16	1		320	32		352	405
0260	3'-0" x 7'-0"	G		16	1		370	32		402	460
0270	5'-4" x 6'-8", double	G		8	2		650	64		714	825
1320	Flush face, full panel, 2'-8" x 6'-8"	G		16	1		264	32		296	345
1340	3'-0" x 6'-8"	G		15	1.067		264	34		298	350
1360	3'-0" x 7'-0"	G		15	1.067		296	34		330	385
1380	5'-4" x 6'-8", double	G		8	2		560	64		624	725
1420	Half glass, 2'-8" x 6'-8"	G		17	.941		325	30		355	405
1440	3'-0" x 6'-8"	G		16	1		325	32		357	410
1460	3'-0" x 7'-0"	G		16	1		360	32		392	450
1480	5'-4" x 6'-8", double	G		8	2		640	64		704	815
1500	Sidelight, full lite, 1'-0" x 6'-8" with grille	G					252			252	277
1510	1'-0" x 6'-8", low e	G					268			268	295
1520	1'-0" x 6'-8", half lite	G					280			280	310
1530	1'-0" x 6'-8", half lite, low e	G					284			284	310
2300	Interior, residential, closet, bi-fold, 2'-0" x 6'-8"	G	2 Carp	16	1		161	32		193	231
2330	3'-0" wide	G		16	1		200	32		232	274
2360	4'-0" wide			15	1.067		260	34		294	345
2400	5'-0" wide	G		14	1.143		315	36.50		351.50	410
2420	6'-0" wide	G		13	1.231		335	39.50		374.50	435
2510	Bi-passing closet, incl. hardware, no frame or trim incl.										
2511	Mirrored, metal frame, 4'-0" x 6'-8"		2 Carp	10	1.600	Opng.	208	51.50		259.50	315
2512	5'-0" wide			10	1.600		238	51.50		289.50	350
2513	6'-0" wide			10	1.600		272	51.50		323.50	385
2514	7'-0" wide			9	1.778		269	57		326	390
2515	8'-0" wide			9	1.778		440	57		497	575
2611	Mirrored, metal, 4'-0" x 8'-0"			10	1.600		315	51.50		366.50	435
2612	5'-0" wide			10	1.600		330	51.50		381.50	445
2613	6'-0" wide			10	1.600		385	51.50		436.50	505
2614	7'-0" wide			9	1.778		400	57		457	535
2615	8'-0" wide			9	1.778		440	57		497	580

08 14 Wood Doors

08 14 13 – Carved Wood Doors

08 14 13.10 Types of Wood Doors, Carved

		Crew	Daily Output	Labor-Hours	Unit	Material	2014 Bare Costs Labor	Equipment	Total	Total Incl O&P
0010	**TYPES OF WOOD DOORS, CARVED**									
3000	Solid wood, 1-3/4" thick stile and rail									
3020	Mahogany, 3'-0" x 7'-0", minimum	2 Carp	14	1.143	Ea.	1,075	36.50		1,111.50	1,225
3030	Maximum		10	1.600		1,800	51.50		1,851.50	2,050
3040	3'-6" x 8'-0", minimum		10	1.600		1,500	51.50		1,551.50	1,725
3050	Maximum		8	2		2,500	64		2,564	2,850
3100	Pine, 3'-0" x 7'-0", minimum		14	1.143		490	36.50		526.50	595
3110	Maximum		10	1.600		825	51.50		876.50	995
3120	3'-6" x 8'-0", minimum		10	1.600		900	51.50		951.50	1,075
3130	Maximum		8	2		1,825	64		1,889	2,125
3200	Red oak, 3'-0" x 7'-0", minimum		14	1.143		1,725	36.50		1,761.50	1,950
3210	Maximum		10	1.600		2,300	51.50		2,351.50	2,600
3220	3'-6" x 8'-0", minimum		10	1.600		2,600	51.50		2,651.50	2,925

08 14 Wood Doors

08 14 13 – Carved Wood Doors

	08 14 13.10 Types of Wood Doors, Carved	Crew	Daily Output	Labor-Hours	Unit	Material	2014 Bare Costs Labor	Equipment	Total	Total Incl O&P
3230	Maximum	2 Carp	8	2	Ea.	3,300	64		3,364	3,725
4000	Hand carved door, mahogany									
4020	3'-0" x 7'-0", minimum	2 Carp	14	1.143	Ea.	1,750	36.50		1,786.50	1,975
4030	Maximum		11	1.455		3,700	46.50		3,746.50	4,150
4040	3'-6" x 8'-0", minimum		10	1.600		3,000	51.50		3,051.50	3,375
4050	Maximum		8	2		3,700	64		3,764	4,175
4200	Rose wood, 3'-0" x 7'-0", minimum		14	1.143		5,200	36.50		5,236.50	5,775
4210	Maximum		11	1.455		13,700	46.50		13,746.50	15,200
4220	3'-6" x 8'-0", minimum		10	1.600		5,900	51.50		5,951.50	6,575
4225	Maximum		10	1.600		8,900	51.50		8,951.50	9,875
4400	For custom finish, add					475			475	525
4600	Side light, mahogany, 7'-0" x 1'-6" wide, minimum	2 Carp	18	.889		1,100	28.50		1,128.50	1,250
4610	Maximum		14	1.143		2,625	36.50		2,661.50	2,950
4620	8'-0" x 1'-6" wide, minimum		14	1.143		1,800	36.50		1,836.50	2,025
4630	Maximum		10	1.600		2,100	51.50		2,151.50	2,375
4640	Side light, oak, 7'-0" x 1'-6" wide, minimum		18	.889		1,200	28.50		1,228.50	1,375
4650	Maximum		14	1.143		2,100	36.50		2,136.50	2,350
4660	8'-0" x 1'-6" wide, minimum		14	1.143		1,100	36.50		1,136.50	1,250
4670	Maximum		10	1.600		2,100	51.50		2,151.50	2,375

08 14 16 – Flush Wood Doors

08 14 16.09 Smooth Wood Doors

		Crew	Daily Output	Labor-Hours	Unit	Material	2014 Bare Costs Labor	Equipment	Total	Total Incl O&P
0010	**SMOOTH WOOD DOORS**									
0015	Flush, interior, hollow core									
0025	Lauan face, 1-3/8", 3'-0" x 6'-8"	2 Carp	17	.941	Ea.	54.50	30		84.50	111
0030	4'-0" x 6'-8"		16	1		126	32		158	193
0140	Birch face, 1-3/8", 2'-6" x 6'-8"		17	.941		85	30		115	144
0180	3'-0" x 6'-8"		17	.941		95.50	30		125.50	156
0200	4'-0" x 6'-8"		16	1		158	32		190	228
0202	1-3/4", 2'-0" x 6'-8"		17	.941		50.50	30		80.50	107
0204	2'-4" x 7'-0"		16	1		95.50	32		127.50	159
0206	2'-6" x 7'-0"		16	1		99	32		131	163
0208	2'-8" x 7'-0"		16	1		104	32		136	168
0210	3'-0" x 7'-0"		16	1		109	32		141	174
0212	3'-4" x 7'-0"		15	1.067		192	34		226	269
0214	Pair of 3'-0" x 7'-0"		9	1.778	Pr.	211	57		268	330
0480	For prefinishing, clear, add				Ea.	42			42	46
0500	For prefinishing, stain, add				"	52			52	57
0620	For dutch door with shelf, add					140%				
1320	M.D. overlay on hardboard, 1-3/8", 2'-0" x 6'-8"	2 Carp	17	.941	Ea.	115	30		145	178
1340	2'-6" x 6'-8"		17	.941		115	30		145	178
1380	3'-0" x 6'-8"		17	.941		126	30		156	190
1400	4'-0" x 6'-8"		16	1		178	32		210	250
1720	H.P. plastic laminate, 1-3/8", 2'-0" x 6'-8"		16	1		260	32		292	340
1740	2'-6" x 6'-8"		16	1		260	32		292	340
1780	3'-0" x 6'-8"		15	1.067		290	34		324	380
1785	Door, plastic laminate, 3'-0" x 6'-8"					290			290	320
1800	4'-0" x 6'-8"	2 Carp	14	1.143		385	36.50		421.50	480
2020	Particle core, lauan face, 1-3/8", 2'-6" x 6'-8"		15	1.067		92	34		126	159
2040	3'-0" x 6'-8"		14	1.143		94	36.50		130.50	165
2120	Birch face, 1-3/8", 2'-6" x 6'-8"		15	1.067		103	34		137	171
2140	3'-0" x 6'-8"		14	1.143		113	36.50		149.50	186
3320	M.D. overlay on hardboard, 1-3/8", 2'-6" x 6'-8"		14	1.143		106	36.50		142.50	179

08 14 Wood Doors

08 14 16 – Flush Wood Doors

08 14 16.09 Smooth Wood Doors

		Crew	Daily Output	Labor-Hours	Unit	Material	2014 Bare Costs Labor	Equipment	Total	Total Incl O&P
3340	3'-0" x 6'-8"	2 Carp	13	1.231	Ea.	115	39.50		154.50	194
4000	Exterior, flush, solid core, birch, 1-3/4" x 2'-6" x 7'-0"		15	1.067		173	34		207	248
4020	2'-8" wide		15	1.067		159	34		193	233
4040	3'-0" wide		14	1.143		209	36.50		245.50	292
4045	3'-0" x 8'-0"	1 Carp	8	1		430	32		462	530
4100	Oak faced 1-3/4" x 2'-6" x 7'-0"	2 Carp	15	1.067		215	34		249	295
4120	2'-8" wide		15	1.067		225	34		259	305
4140	3'-0" wide		14	1.143		230	36.50		266.50	315
4160	Walnut faced, 1-3/4" x 3'-0" x 6'-8"	1 Carp	17	.471		295	15.10		310.10	350
4180	3'-6" wide	"	17	.471		365	15.10		380.10	425
4200	Walnut faced, 1-3/4" x 2'-6" x 7'-0"	2 Carp	15	1.067		310	34		344	400
4220	2'-8" wide		15	1.067		315	34		349	405
4240	3'-0" wide		14	1.143		320	36.50		356.50	410
4250	3'-6" wide	1 Carp	14	.571		420	18.35		438.35	490
4260	3'-0" x 8'-0"		8	1		375	32		407	465
4270	3'-6" wide		8	1		450	32		482	550
4285	Cherry faced, flush, sc, 1-3/4" x 3'-0" x 8'-0" wide		8	1		465	32		497	565

08 14 16.10 Wood Doors Decorator

		Crew	Daily Output	Labor-Hours	Unit	Material	2014 Bare Costs Labor	Equipment	Total	Total Incl O&P
0010	**WOOD DOORS DECORATOR**									
1800	Exterior, flush, solid wood core, birch 1-3/4" x 2'-6" x 7'-0"	2 Carp	15	1.067	Ea.	320	34		354	410
1820	2'-8" wide		15	1.067		325	34		359	420
1840	3'-0" wide		14	1.143		335	36.50		371.50	430
1900	Oak faced, 1-3/4" x 2'-6" x 7'-0"		15	1.067		320	34		354	410
1920	2'-8" wide		15	1.067		330	34		364	425
1940	3'-0" wide		14	1.143		340	36.50		376.50	435
2100	Walnut faced, 1-3/4" x 2'-6" x 7'-0"		15	1.067		385	34		419	485
2120	2'-8" wide		15	1.067		400	34		434	500
2140	3'-0" wide		14	1.143		430	36.50		466.50	535

08 14 33 – Stile and Rail Wood Doors

08 14 33.10 Wood Doors Paneled

		Crew	Daily Output	Labor-Hours	Unit	Material	2014 Bare Costs Labor	Equipment	Total	Total Incl O&P
0010	**WOOD DOORS PANELED**									
0020	Interior, six panel, hollow core, 1-3/8" thick									
0040	Molded hardboard, 2'-0" x 6'-8"	2 Carp	17	.941	Ea.	62	30		92	119
0060	2'-6" x 6'-8"		17	.941		64	30		94	122
0070	2'-8" x 6'-8"		17	.941		67	30		97	125
0080	3'-0" x 6'-8"		17	.941		72	30		102	130
0140	Embossed print, molded hardboard, 2'-0" x 6'-8"		17	.941		64	30		94	122
0160	2'-6" x 6'-8"		17	.941		64	30		94	122
0180	3'-0" x 6'-8"		17	.941		72	30		102	130
0540	Six panel, solid, 1-3/8" thick, pine, 2'-0" x 6'-8"		15	1.067		155	34		189	229
0560	2'-6" x 6'-8"		14	1.143		170	36.50		206.50	249
0580	3'-0" x 6'-8"		13	1.231		145	39.50		184.50	227
1020	Two panel, bored rail, solid, 1-3/8" thick, pine, 1'-6" x 6'-8"		16	1		270	32		302	350
1040	2'-0" x 6'-8"		15	1.067		355	34		389	450
1060	2'-6" x 6'-8"		14	1.143		400	36.50		436.50	500
1340	Two panel, solid, 1-3/8" thick, fir, 2'-0" x 6'-8"		15	1.067		160	34		194	234
1360	2'-6" x 6'-8"		14	1.143		210	36.50		246.50	293
1380	3'-0" x 6'-8"		13	1.231		415	39.50		454.50	520
1740	Five panel, solid, 1-3/8" thick, fir, 2'-0" x 6'-8"		15	1.067		280	34		314	370
1760	2'-6" x 6'-8"		14	1.143		420	36.50		456.50	520
1780	3'-0" x 6'-8"		13	1.231		420	39.50		459.50	525
4190	Exterior, Knotty pine, paneled, 1-3/4", 3'-0" x 6'-8"		16	1		775	32		807	910

08 14 Wood Doors

08 14 33 – Stile and Rail Wood Doors

08 14 33.10 Wood Doors Paneled

		Crew	Daily Output	Labor-Hours	Unit	Material	2014 Bare Costs Labor	Equipment	Total	Total Incl O&P
4195	Double 1-3/4", 3'-0" x 6'-8"	2 Carp	16	1	Ea.	1,550	32		1,582	1,750
4200	Ash, paneled, 1-3/4", 3'-0" x 6'-8"		16	1		875	32		907	1,025
4205	Double 1-3/4", 3'-0" x 6'-8"		16	1		1,750	32		1,782	1,975
4210	Cherry, paneled, 1-3/4", 3'-0" x 6'-8"		16	1		875	32		907	1,025
4215	Double 1-3/4", 3'-0" x 6'-8"		16	1		1,750	32		1,782	1,975
4230	Ash, paneled, 1-3/4", 3'-0" x 8'-0"		16	1		950	32		982	1,100
4235	Double 1-3/4", 3'-0" x 8'-0"		16	1		1,900	32		1,932	2,150
4240	Hard Maple, paneled, 1-3/4", 3'-0" x 8'-0"		16	1		950	32		982	1,100
4245	Double 1-3/4", 3'-0" x 8'-0"		16	1		1,900	32		1,932	2,150
4250	Cherry, paneled, 1-3/4", 3'-0" x 8'-0"		16	1		950	32		982	1,100
4255	Double 1-3/4", 3'-0" x 8'-0"	▼	16	1	▼	1,900	32		1,932	2,150

08 14 33.20 Wood Doors Residential

		Crew	Daily Output	Labor-Hours	Unit	Material	2014 Bare Costs Labor	Equipment	Total	Total Incl O&P
0010	**WOOD DOORS RESIDENTIAL**									
0200	Exterior, combination storm & screen, pine									
0260	2'-8" wide	2 Carp	10	1.600	Ea.	300	51.50		351.50	415
0280	3'-0" wide		9	1.778		310	57		367	435
0300	7'-1" x 3'-0" wide		9	1.778		335	57		392	465
0400	Full lite, 6'-9" x 2'-6" wide		11	1.455		320	46.50		366.50	430
0420	2'-8" wide		10	1.600		320	51.50		371.50	435
0440	3'-0" wide		9	1.778		325	57		382	450
0500	7'-1" x 3'-0" wide		9	1.778		355	57		412	485
0604	Door, screen, plain full		12	1.333		325	43		368	430
0614	Divided		12	1.333		365	43		408	475
0634	Decor full		12	1.333		450	43		493	565
0700	Dutch door, pine, 1-3/4" x 2'-8" x 6'-8", minimum		12	1.333		790	43		833	935
0720	Maximum		10	1.600		900	51.50		951.50	1,075
0800	3'-0" wide, minimum		12	1.333		790	43		833	935
0820	Maximum		10	1.600		900	51.50		951.50	1,075
1000	Entrance door, colonial, 1-3/4" x 6'-8" x 2'-8" wide		16	1		500	32		532	600
1020	6 panel pine, 3'-0" wide		15	1.067		445	34		479	550
1100	8 panel pine, 2'-8" wide		16	1		575	32		607	690
1120	3'-0" wide	▼	15	1.067		570	34		604	685
1200	For tempered safety glass lites, (min of 2) add					76.50			76.50	84.50
1300	Flush, birch, solid core, 1-3/4" x 6'-8" x 2'-8" wide	2 Carp	16	1		113	32		145	179
1320	3'-0" wide		15	1.067		119	34		153	188
1350	7'-0" x 2'-8" wide		16	1		121	32		153	188
1360	3'-0" wide		15	1.067		143	34		177	215
1420	6'-8" x 3'-0" wide, fir		16	1		470	32		502	570
1720	Carved mahogany 3'-0" x 6'-8"		15	1.067		1,375	34		1,409	1,575
1760	Mahogany, 3'-0" x 6'-8"	▼	15	1.067	▼	750	34		784	885
2700	Interior, closet, bi-fold, w/hardware, no frame or trim incl.									
2720	Flush, birch, 6'-6" or 6'-8" x 2'-6" wide	2 Carp	13	1.231	Ea.	67.50	39.50		107	141
2740	3'-0" wide		13	1.231		71.50	39.50		111	145
2760	4'-0" wide		12	1.333		109	43		152	192
2780	5'-0" wide		11	1.455		105	46.50		151.50	195
2800	6'-0" wide		10	1.600		128	51.50		179.50	228
2804	Door bi-fold unit, flush lauan 2'-0" x 6'-8"		14	1.143		52.50	36.50		89	120
2810	8'-0" wide		9	1.778		195	57		252	310
2817	6'-0" wide		9	1.778		64	57		121	166
2820	Flush, hardboard, primed, 6'-8" x 2'-6" wide		13	1.231		56.50	39.50		96	129
2840	3'-0" wide		13	1.231		64	39.50		103.50	137
2860	4'-0" wide	▼	12	1.333	▼	94	43		137	175

08 14 33 – Stile and Rail Wood Doors

08 14 33.20 Wood Doors Residential	Crew	Daily Output	Labor-Hours	Unit	Material	2014 Bare Costs Labor	Equipment	Total	Total Incl O&P
2880	5'-0" wide	2 Carp	11	1.455	Ea.	101	46.50		147.50	190
2900	6'-0" wide		10	1.600		139	51.50		190.50	240
2920	Hardboard, primed 7'-0" x 4'-0", wide		12	1.333		182	43		225	272
2930	6'-0" wide		10	1.600		177	51.50		228.50	282
3000	Raised panel pine, 6'-6" or 6'-8" x 2'-6" wide		13	1.231		198	39.50		237.50	285
3020	3'-0" wide		13	1.231		278	39.50		317.50	370
3040	4'-0" wide		12	1.333		305	43		348	405
3060	5'-0" wide		11	1.455		365	46.50		411.50	480
3080	6'-0" wide		10	1.600		400	51.50		451.50	525
3180	Louvered, pine, 6'-6" or 6'-8" x 1'-6" wide		13	1.231		180	39.50		219.50	266
3190	2'-0" wide		14	1.143		158	36.50		194.50	235
3200	Louvered, pine 6'-6" or 6'-8" x 2'-6" wide		13	1.231		144	39.50		183.50	225
3220	3'-0" wide	↓	13	1.231		208	39.50		247.50	295
3225	Door, interior louvered bi-fold, pine, 3'-0" x 6'-8"					208			208	228
3240	4'-0" wide	2 Carp	12	1.333		235	43		278	330
3260	5'-0" wide		11	1.455		262	46.50		308.50	365
3280	6'-0" wide		10	1.600		289	51.50		340.50	405
3290	8'-0" wide		10	1.600		445	51.50		496.50	575
3300	7'-0" x 3'-0" wide		12	1.333		267	43		310	365
3320	6'-0" wide	↓	10	1.600	↓	305	51.50		356.50	420
4400	Bi-passing closet, incl. hardware and frame, no trim incl.									
4420	Flush, lauan, 6'-8" x 4'-0" wide	2 Carp	12	1.333	Opng.	176	43		219	266
4440	5'-0" wide		11	1.455		187	46.50		233.50	284
4460	6'-0" wide		10	1.600		209	51.50		260.50	315
4600	Flush, birch, 6'-8" x 4'-0" wide		12	1.333		223	43		266	315
4620	5'-0" wide		11	1.455		212	46.50		258.50	310
4640	6'-0" wide		10	1.600		260	51.50		311.50	375
4800	Louvered, pine, 6'-8" x 4'-0" wide		12	1.333		410	43		453	520
4820	5'-0" wide		11	1.455		395	46.50		441.50	515
4840	6'-0" wide		10	1.600	↓	530	51.50		581.50	670
4900	Mirrored, 6'-8" x 4'-0" wide		12	1.333	Ea.	300	43		343	400
5000	Paneled, pine, 6'-8" x 4'-0" wide		12	1.333	Opng.	510	43		553	635
5020	5'-0" wide		11	1.455		410	46.50		456.50	530
5040	6'-0" wide		10	1.600		610	51.50		661.50	755
5042	8'-0" wide		12	1.333		1,025	43		1,068	1,200
5061	Hardboard, 6'-8" x 4'-0" wide		10	1.600		190	51.50		241.50	296
5062	5'-0" wide		10	1.600		196	51.50		247.50	300
5063	6'-0" wide	↓	10	1.600	↓	217	51.50		268.50	325
6100	Folding accordion, closet, including track and frame									
6200	Rigid PVC	2 Carp	10	1.600	Ea.	55	51.50		106.50	147
7310	Passage doors, flush, no frame included									
7320	Hardboard, hollow core, 1-3/8" x 6'-8" x 1'-6" wide	2 Carp	18	.889	Ea.	40.50	28.50		69	92.50
7330	2'-0" wide		18	.889		43	28.50		71.50	95.50
7340	2'-6" wide		18	.889		47.50	28.50		76	101
7350	2'-8" wide		18	.889		49	28.50		77.50	102
7360	3'-0" wide		17	.941		52	30		82	109
7420	Lauan, hollow core, 1-3/8" x 6'-8" x 1'-6" wide		18	.889		34	28.50		62.50	85.50
7440	2'-0" wide		18	.889		35	28.50		63.50	86.50
7450	2'-4" wide		18	.889		38.50	28.50		67	90.50
7460	2'-6" wide		18	.889		38.50	28.50		67	90.50
7480	2'-8" wide		18	.889		40	28.50		68.50	92
7500	3'-0" wide		17	.941		42.50	30		72.50	97.50
7540	2'-6" wide	↓	16	1	↓	49	32		81	108

08 14 Wood Doors

08 14 33 – Stile and Rail Wood Doors

08 14 33.20 Wood Doors Residential		Crew	Daily Output	Labor-Hours	Unit	Material	2014 Bare Costs Labor	Equipment	Total	Total Incl O&P
7560	2'-8" wide	2 Carp	16	1	Ea.	50	32		82	109
7580	3'-0" wide		16	1	↓	52	32		84	112
7595	Pair of 3'-0" wide		9	1.778	Pr.	104	57		161	210
7700	Birch, hollow core, 1-3/8" x 6'-8" x 1'-6" wide		18	.889	Ea.	41	28.50		69.50	93
7720	2'-0" wide		18	.889		42.50	28.50		71	94.50
7740	2'-6" wide		18	.889		50	28.50		78.50	103
7760	2'-8" wide		18	.889		50.50	28.50		79	104
7780	3'-0" wide		17	.941		52	30		82	109
7790	2'-6" ash/oak door with hinges		18	.889		85	28.50		113.50	142
7910	2'-8" wide		16	1		63.50	32		95.50	124
7920	3'-0" wide		16	1	↓	68	32		100	129
7940	Pair of 3'-0" wide		9	1.778	Pr.	144	57		201	255
8000	Pine louvered, 1-3/8" x 6'-8" x 1'-6" wide		19	.842	Ea.	120	27		147	178
8020	2'-0" wide		18	.889		131	28.50		159.50	192
8040	2'-6" wide		18	.889		150	28.50		178.50	213
8060	2'-8" wide		18	.889		161	28.50		189.50	225
8080	3'-0" wide		17	.941		175	30		205	243
8300	Pine paneled, 1-3/8" x 6'-8" x 1'-6" wide		19	.842		128	27		155	187
8320	2'-0" wide		18	.889		153	28.50		181.50	216
8330	2'-4" wide		18	.889		182	28.50		210.50	248
8340	2'-6" wide		18	.889		182	28.50		210.50	248
8360	2'-8" wide		18	.889		185	28.50		213.50	252
8380	3'-0" wide		17	.941		204	30		234	275
8450	French door, pine, 15 lites, 1-3/8" x 6'-8" x 2'-6" wide		18	.889		195	28.50		223.50	263
8470	2'-8" wide		18	.889		251	28.50		279.50	325
8490	3'-0" wide		17	.941		276	30		306	355
8804	Pocket door, 6 panel pine, 2'-6" x 6'-8"		10.50	1.524		355	49		404	475
8814	2'-8" x 6'-8"		10.50	1.524		360	49		409	480
8824	3'-0" x 6'-8"		10.50	1.524		385	49		434	505
9000	Passage doors, flush, no frame, birch, solid core, 1-3/8" x 2'-4" x 7'-0"		16	1		117	32		149	183
9020	2'-8" wide		16	1		124	32		156	191
9040	3'-0" wide		16	1		134	32		166	201
9060	3'-4" wide		15	1.067	↓	155	34		189	229
9080	Pair of 3'-0" wide		9	1.778	Pr.	265	57		322	390
9100	Lauan, solid core, 1-3/8" x 7'-0" x 2'-4" wide		16	1	Ea.	108	32		140	172
9120	2'-8" wide		16	1		115	32		147	180
9140	3'-0" wide		16	1		122	32		154	188
9160	3'-4" wide		15	1.067	↓	128	34		162	199
9180	Pair of 3'-0" wide		9	1.778	Pr.	221	57		278	340
9200	Hardboard, solid core, 1-3/8" x 7'-0" x 2'-4" wide		16	1	Ea.	133	32		165	200
9220	2'-8" wide		16	1		138	32		170	206
9240	3'-0" wide		16	1		142	32		174	210
9260	3'-4" wide	↓	15	1.067	↓	157	34		191	230

08 14 40 – Interior Cafe Doors

08 14 40.10 Cafe Style Doors

		Crew	Daily Output	Labor-Hours	Unit	Material	2014 Bare Costs Labor	Equipment	Total	Total Incl O&P
0010	**CAFE STYLE DOORS**									
6520	Interior cafe doors, 2'-6" opening, stock, panel pine	2 Carp	16	1	Ea.	218	32		250	293
6540	3'-0" opening	"	16	1	"	240	32		272	320
6550	Louvered pine									
6560	2'-6" opening	2 Carp	16	1	Ea.	180	32		212	252
8000	3'-0" opening		16	1		193	32		225	266
8010	2'-6" opening, hardwood	↓	16	1	↓	264	32		296	345

08 14 Wood Doors

08 14 40 – Interior Cafe Doors

08 14 40.10 Cafe Style Doors		Crew	Daily Output	Labor-Hours	Unit	Material	2014 Bare Costs Labor	Equipment	Total	Total Incl O&P
8020	3'-0" opening	2 Carp	16	1	Ea.	281	32		313	365

08 16 Composite Doors

08 16 13 – Fiberglass Doors

08 16 13.10 Entrance Doors, Fiberous Glass

			Crew	Daily Output	Labor-Hours	Unit	Material	2014 Bare Costs Labor	Equipment	Total	Total Incl O&P
0010	**ENTRANCE DOORS, FIBEROUS GLASS**										
0020	Exterior, fiberglass, door, 2'-8" wide x 6'-8" high	G	2 Carp	15	1.067	Ea.	259	34		293	345
0040	3'-0" wide x 6'-8" high	G		15	1.067		259	34		293	345
0060	3'-0" wide x 7'-0" high	G		15	1.067		460	34		494	565
0080	3'-0" wide x 6'-8" high, with two lites	G		15	1.067		294	34		328	385
0100	3'-0" wide x 8'-0" high, with two lites	G		15	1.067		495	34		529	605
0110	Half glass, 3'-0" wide x 6'-8" high	G		15	1.067		435	34		469	540
0120	3'-0" wide x 6'-8" high, low e	G		15	1.067		465	34		499	570
0130	3'-0" wide x 8'-0" high	G		15	1.067		580	34		614	700
0140	3'-0" wide x 8'-0" high, low e	G		15	1.067		640	34		674	760
0150	Side lights, 1'-0" wide x 6'-8" high	G					251			251	276
0160	1'-0" wide x 6'-8" high, low e	G					256			256	281
0180	1'-0" wide x 6'-8" high, full glass	G					285			285	315
0190	1'-0" wide x 6'-8" high, low e	G					300			300	330

08 16 14 – French Doors

08 16 14.10 Exterior Doors With Glass Lites

		Crew	Daily Output	Labor-Hours	Unit	Material	2014 Bare Costs Labor	Equipment	Total	Total Incl O&P
0010	**EXTERIOR DOORS WITH GLASS LITES**									
0020	French, Fir, 1-3/4", 3'-0"wide x 6'-8" high	2 Carp	12	1.333	Ea.	600	43		643	730
0025	Double		12	1.333		1,200	43		1,243	1,400
0030	Maple, 1-3/4", 3'-0"wide x 6'-8" high		12	1.333		675	43		718	815
0035	Double		12	1.333		1,350	43		1,393	1,550
0040	Cherry, 1-3/4", 3'-0"wide x 6'-8" high		12	1.333		790	43		833	935
0045	Double		12	1.333		1,575	43		1,618	1,800
0100	Mahogany, 1-3/4", 3'-0"wide x 8'-0" high		10	1.600		800	51.50		851.50	965
0105	Double		10	1.600		1,600	51.50		1,651.50	1,825
0110	Fir, 1-3/4", 3'-0"wide x 8'-0" high		10	1.600		1,200	51.50		1,251.50	1,400
0115	Double		10	1.600		2,400	51.50		2,451.50	2,725
0120	Oak, 1-3/4", 3'-0"wide x 8'-0" high		10	1.600		1,825	51.50		1,876.50	2,075
0125	Double		10	1.600		3,650	51.50		3,701.50	4,075

08 17 Integrated Door Opening Assemblies

08 17 23 – Integrated Wood Door Opening Assemblies

08 17 23.10 Pre-Hung Doors

		Crew	Daily Output	Labor-Hours	Unit	Material	2014 Bare Costs Labor	Equipment	Total	Total Incl O&P
0010	**PRE-HUNG DOORS**									
0300	Exterior, wood, comb. storm & screen, 6'-9" x 2'-6" wide	2 Carp	15	1.067	Ea.	296	34		330	385
0320	2'-8" wide		15	1.067		296	34		330	385
0340	3'-0" wide		15	1.067		305	34		339	395
0360	For 7'-0" high door, add					30			30	33
1600	Entrance door, flush, birch, solid core									
1620	4-5/8" solid jamb, 1-3/4" x 6'-8" x 2'-8" wide	2 Carp	16	1	Ea.	289	32		321	375
1640	3'-0" wide		16	1		375	32		407	470
1642	5-5/8" jamb		16	1		325	32		357	415
1680	For 7'-0" high door, add					25			25	27.50
2000	Entrance door, colonial, 6 panel pine									

452

08 17 Integrated Door Opening Assemblies

08 17 23 – Integrated Wood Door Opening Assemblies

08 17 23.10 Pre-Hung Doors	Crew	Daily Output	Labor-Hours	Unit	Material	2014 Bare Costs Labor	Equipment	Total	Total Incl O&P
2020	4-5/8" solid jamb, 1-3/4" x 6'-8" x 2'-8" wide	2 Carp	16	1	Ea.	640	32		672	760
2040	3'-0" wide	"	16	1		675	32		707	795
2060	For 7'-0" high door, add					54			54	59
2200	For 5-5/8" solid jamb, add					41.50			41.50	46
2230	French style, exterior, 1 lite, 1-3/4" x 3'-0" x 6'-8"	1 Carp	14	.571		590	18.35		608.35	680
2235	9 lites	"	14	.571		660	18.35		678.35	755
2245	15 lites	2 Carp	14	1.143		640	36.50		676.50	765
2250	Double, 15 lites, 2'-0" x 6'-8", 4'-0" opening		7	2.286	Pr.	1,200	73.50		1,273.50	1,450
2260	2'-6" x 6'-8", 5'-0" opening		7	2.286		1,325	73.50		1,398.50	1,575
2280	3'-0" x 6'-8", 6'-0" opening		7	2.286		1,350	73.50		1,423.50	1,600
2430	3'-0" x 7'-0", 15 lites		14	1.143	Ea.	950	36.50		986.50	1,100
2432	Two 3'-0" x 7'-0"		7	2.286	Pr.	1,975	73.50		2,048.50	2,275
2435	3'-0" x 8'-0"		14	1.143	Ea.	1,000	36.50		1,036.50	1,150
2437	Two, 3'-0" x 8'-0"		7	2.286	Pr.	2,075	73.50		2,148.50	2,425
2500	Exterior, metal face, insulated, incl. jamb, brickmold and									
2520	Threshold, flush, 2'-8" x 6'-8"	2 Carp	16	1	Ea.	289	32		321	375
2550	3'-0" x 6'-8"		16	1		289	32		321	375
3500	Embossed, 6 panel, 2'-8" x 6'-8"		16	1		320	32		352	410
3550	3'-0" x 6'-8"		16	1		325	32		357	410
3600	2 narrow lites, 2'-8" x 6'-8"		16	1		292	32		324	375
3650	3'-0" x 6'-8"		16	1		296	32		328	380
3700	Half glass, 2'-8" x 6'-8"		16	1		315	32		347	405
3750	3'-0" x 6'-8"		16	1		340	32		372	425
3800	2 top lites, 2'-8" x 6'-8"		16	1		300	32		332	385
3850	3'-0" x 6'-8"		16	1		315	32		347	400
4000	Interior, passage door, 4-5/8" solid jamb									
4370	Pine, louvered, 2'-8" x 6'-8"	2 Carp	17	.941	Ea.	193	30		223	263
4380	3'-0"		17	.941		203	30		233	274
4400	Lauan, flush, solid core, 1-3/8" x 6'-8" x 2'-6" wide		17	.941		186	30		216	256
4420	2'-8" wide		17	.941		186	30		216	256
4440	3'-0" wide		16	1		201	32		233	275
4600	Hollow core, 1-3/8" x 6'-8" x 2'-6" wide		17	.941		125	30		155	189
4620	2'-8" wide		17	.941		125	30		155	188
4640	3'-0" wide		16	1		140	32		172	208
4700	For 7'-0" high door, add					35.50			35.50	39
5000	Birch, flush, solid core, 1-3/8" x 6'-8" x 2'-6" wide	2 Carp	17	.941		259	30		289	335
5020	2'-8" wide		17	.941		201	30		231	272
5040	3'-0" wide		16	1		288	32		320	370
5200	Hollow core, 1-3/8" x 6'-8" x 2'-6" wide		17	.941		210	30		240	282
5220	2'-8" wide		17	.941		252	30		282	330
5240	3'-0" wide		16	1		216	32		248	292
5280	For 7'-0" high door, add					30.50			30.50	33.50
5500	Hardboard paneled, 1-3/8" x 6'-8" x 2'-6" wide	2 Carp	17	.941		145	30		175	210
5520	2'-8" wide		17	.941		153	30		183	219
5540	3'-0" wide		16	1		150	32		182	219
6000	Pine paneled, 1-3/8" x 6'-8" x 2'-6" wide		17	.941		255	30		285	330
6020	2'-8" wide		17	.941		274	30		304	350
6040	3'-0" wide		16	1		282	32		314	365
6500	For 5-5/8" solid jamb, add					25			25	27.50
6520	For split jamb, deduct					24			24	26.50
7200	Prehung, bifold, mirrored, 6'-8" x 5'-0"	1 Carp	9	.889		410	28.50		438.50	500
7220	6'-8" x 6'-0"		9	.889		410	28.50		438.50	500
7240	6'-8" x 8'-0"		6	1.333		645	43		688	780

08 17 Integrated Door Opening Assemblies

08 17 23 – Integrated Wood Door Opening Assemblies

08 17 23.10 Pre-Hung Doors	Crew	Daily Output	Labor-Hours	Unit	Material	2014 Bare Costs Labor	Equipment	Total	Total Incl O&P
7600	Oak, 6 panel, 1-3/4" x 6'-8" x 3'-0"	1 Carp	17	.471	Ea.	880	15.10		895.10	990
8500	Pocket door frame with lauan, flush, hollow core, 1-3/8" x 3'-0" x 6'-8"		17	.471		224	15.10		239.10	273

08 31 Access Doors and Panels

08 31 13 – Access Doors and Frames

08 31 13.20 Bulkhead/Cellar Doors

		Crew	Daily Output	Labor-Hours	Unit	Material	2014 Bare Costs Labor	Equipment	Total	Total Incl O&P
0010	**BULKHEAD/CELLAR DOORS**									
0020	Steel, not incl. sides, 44" x 62"	1 Carp	5.50	1.455	Ea.	560	46.50		606.50	695
0100	52" x 73"		5.10	1.569		790	50.50		840.50	955
0500	With sides and foundation plates, 57" x 45" x 24"		4.70	1.702		810	54.50		864.50	980
0600	42" x 49" x 51"		4.30	1.860		915	59.50		974.50	1,100

08 31 13.40 Kennel Doors

		Crew	Daily Output	Labor-Hours	Unit	Material	2014 Bare Costs Labor	Equipment	Total	Total Incl O&P
0010	**KENNEL DOORS**									
0020	2 way, swinging type, 13" x 19" opening	2 Carp	11	1.455	Opng.	90	46.50		136.50	178
0100	17" x 29" opening		11	1.455		110	46.50		156.50	200
0200	9" x 9" opening, electronic with accessories		11	1.455		144	46.50		190.50	237

08 32 Sliding Glass Doors

08 32 13 – Sliding Aluminum-Framed Glass Doors

08 32 13.10 Sliding Aluminum Doors

		Crew	Daily Output	Labor-Hours	Unit	Material	2014 Bare Costs Labor	Equipment	Total	Total Incl O&P
0010	**SLIDING ALUMINUM DOORS**									
0350	Aluminum, 5/8" tempered insulated glass, 6' wide									
0400	Premium	2 Carp	4	4	Ea.	1,575	128		1,703	1,950
0450	Economy		4	4		905	128		1,033	1,200
0500	8' wide, premium		3	5.333		1,650	171		1,821	2,125
0550	Economy		3	5.333		1,425	171		1,596	1,850
0600	12' wide, premium		2.50	6.400		2,975	205		3,180	3,625
0650	Economy		2.50	6.400		1,525	205		1,730	2,025
4000	Aluminum, baked on enamel, temp glass, 6'-8" x 10'-0" wide		4	4		1,050	128		1,178	1,400
4020	Insulating glass, 6'-8" x 6'-0" wide		4	4		920	128		1,048	1,250
4040	8'-0" wide		3	5.333		1,075	171		1,246	1,475
4060	10'-0" wide		2	8		1,325	257		1,582	1,875
4080	Anodized, temp glass, 6'-8" x 6'-0" wide		4	4		455	128		583	715
4100	8'-0" wide		3	5.333		575	171		746	925
4120	10'-0" wide		2	8		645	257		902	1,150

08 32 19 – Sliding Wood-Framed Glass Doors

08 32 19.10 Sliding Wood Doors

		Crew	Daily Output	Labor-Hours	Unit	Material	2014 Bare Costs Labor	Equipment	Total	Total Incl O&P
0010	**SLIDING WOOD DOORS**									
0020	Wood, tempered insul. glass, 6' wide, premium	2 Carp	4	4	Ea.	1,425	128		1,553	1,800
0100	Economy		4	4		1,175	128		1,303	1,500
0150	8' wide, wood, premium		3	5.333		1,825	171		1,996	2,300
0200	Economy		3	5.333		1,500	171		1,671	1,950
0235	10' wide, wood, premium		2.50	6.400		2,600	205		2,805	3,200
0240	Economy		2.50	6.400		2,200	205		2,405	2,775
0250	12' wide, wood, premium		2.50	6.400		3,000	205		3,205	3,650
0300	Economy		2.50	6.400		2,450	205		2,655	3,050

08 32 Sliding Glass Doors

08 32 19 – Sliding Wood-Framed Glass Doors

08 32 19.15 Sliding Glass Vinyl-Clad Wood Doors		Crew	Daily Output	Labor-Hours	Unit	Material	2014 Bare Costs Labor	Equipment	Total	Total Incl O&P
0010	**SLIDING GLASS VINYL-CLAD WOOD DOORS**									
0020	Glass, sliding vinyl clad, insul. glass, 6'-0" x 6'-8"	G	2 Carp	4	4	Opng.	1,500	128		1,628	1,900
0025	6'-0" x 6'-10" high	G		4	4		1,650	128		1,778	2,050
0030	6'-0" x 8'-0" high	G		4	4		1,975	128		2,103	2,400
0050	5'-0" x 6'-8" high	G		4	4		1,500	128		1,628	1,875
0100	8'-0" x 6'-10" high	G		4	4		2,025	128		2,153	2,450
0104	8'-0" x 6'-8"	G		4	4		1,925	128		2,053	2,325
0150	8'-0" x 8'-0" high	G		4	4		2,225	128		2,353	2,675
0500	4 leaf, 9'-0" x 6'-10" high	G		3	5.333		3,250	171		3,421	3,875
0550	9'-0" x 8'-0" high	G		3	5.333		3,775	171		3,946	4,450
0600	12'-0" x 6'-10" high	G		3	5.333		3,875	171		4,046	4,575

08 36 Panel Doors

08 36 13 – Sectional Doors

08 36 13.20 Residential Garage Doors		Crew	Daily Output	Labor-Hours	Unit	Material	2014 Bare Costs Labor	Equipment	Total	Total Incl O&P
0010	**RESIDENTIAL GARAGE DOORS**									
0050	Hinged, wood, custom, double door, 9' x 7'	2 Carp	4	4	Ea.	715	128		843	1,000
0070	16' x 7'		3	5.333		1,100	171		1,271	1,500
0200	Overhead, sectional, incl. hardware, fiberglass, 9' x 7', standard		5.28	3.030		930	97.50		1,027.50	1,200
0220	Deluxe		5.28	3.030		1,150	97.50		1,247.50	1,425
0300	16' x 7', standard		6	2.667		1,575	85.50		1,660.50	1,875
0320	Deluxe		6	2.667		2,150	85.50		2,235.50	2,500
0500	Hardboard, 9' x 7', standard		8	2		590	64		654	760
0520	Deluxe		8	2		815	64		879	1,000
0600	16' x 7', standard		6	2.667		1,225	85.50		1,310.50	1,500
0620	Deluxe		6	2.667		1,425	85.50		1,510.50	1,725
0700	Metal, 9' x 7', standard		5.28	3.030		685	97.50		782.50	920
0720	Deluxe		8	2		910	64		974	1,100
0800	16' x 7', standard		3	5.333		870	171		1,041	1,250
0820	Deluxe		6	2.667		1,400	85.50		1,485.50	1,700
0900	Wood, 9' x 7', standard		8	2		920	64		984	1,100
0920	Deluxe		8	2		2,150	64		2,214	2,450
1000	16' x 7', standard		6	2.667		1,625	85.50		1,710.50	1,950
1020	Deluxe		6	2.667		3,025	85.50		3,110.50	3,475
1800	Door hardware, sectional	1 Carp	4	2		330	64		394	475
1810	Door tracks only		4	2		163	64		227	287
1820	One side only		7	1.143		112	36.50		148.50	185
3000	Swing-up, including hardware, fiberglass, 9' x 7', standard	2 Carp	8	2		1,000	64		1,064	1,200
3020	Deluxe		8	2		1,100	64		1,164	1,300
3100	16' x 7', standard		6	2.667		1,250	85.50		1,335.50	1,525
3120	Deluxe		6	2.667		1,600	85.50		1,685.50	1,900
3200	Hardboard, 9' x 7', standard		8	2		550	64		614	715
3220	Deluxe		8	2		650	64		714	825
3300	16' x 7', standard		6	2.667		670	85.50		755.50	880
3320	Deluxe		6	2.667		850	85.50		935.50	1,075
3400	Metal, 9' x 7', standard		8	2		600	64		664	770
3420	Deluxe		8	2		965	64		1,029	1,150
3500	16' x 7', standard		6	2.667		800	85.50		885.50	1,025
3520	Deluxe		6	2.667		1,100	85.50		1,185.50	1,350
3600	Wood, 9' x 7', standard		8	2		700	64		764	880

08 36 Panel Doors

08 36 13 – Sectional Doors

08 36 13.20 Residential Garage Doors

		Crew	Daily Output	Labor-Hours	Unit	Material	2014 Bare Costs Labor	Equipment	Total	Total Incl O&P
3620	Deluxe	2 Carp	8	2	Ea.	1,125	64		1,189	1,325
3700	16' x 7', standard		6	2.667		900	85.50		985.50	1,125
3720	Deluxe		6	2.667		2,100	85.50		2,185.50	2,450
3900	Door hardware only, swing up	1 Carp	4	2		168	64		232	293
3920	One side only		7	1.143		90	36.50		126.50	161
4000	For electric operator, economy, add		8	1		425	32		457	525
4100	Deluxe, including remote control		8	1		610	32		642	730
4500	For transmitter/receiver control , add to operator				Total	110			110	121
4600	Transmitters, additional				"	60			60	66
6000	Replace section, on sectional door, fiberglass, 9' x 7'	1 Carp	4	2	Ea.	590	64		654	755
6020	16' x 7'		3.50	2.286		710	73.50		783.50	905
6200	Hardboard, 9' x 7'		4	2		115	64		179	234
6220	16' x 7'		3.50	2.286		218	73.50		291.50	365
6300	Metal, 9' x 7'		4	2		184	64		248	310
6320	16' x 7'		3.50	2.286		300	73.50		373.50	455
6500	Wood, 9' x 7'		4	2		116	64		180	236
6520	16' x 7'		3.50	2.286		225	73.50		298.50	370
7010	Garage doors, row of lites					105			105	116

08 51 Metal Windows

08 51 13 – Aluminum Windows

08 51 13.20 Aluminum Windows

		Crew	Daily Output	Labor-Hours	Unit	Material	2014 Bare Costs Labor	Equipment	Total	Total Incl O&P
0010	**ALUMINUM WINDOWS**, incl. frame and glazing, commercial grade									
1000	Stock units, casement, 3'-1" x 3'-2" opening	2 Sswk	10	1.600	Ea.	370	55		425	510
1040	Insulating glass	"	10	1.600		505	55		560	660
1050	Add for storms					119			119	131
1600	Projected, with screen, 3'-1" x 3'-2" opening	2 Sswk	10	1.600		350	55		405	490
1650	Insulating glass	"	10	1.600		355	55		410	495
1700	Add for storms					116			116	128
2000	4'-5" x 5'-3" opening	2 Sswk	8	2		395	68.50		463.50	565
2050	Insulating glass	"	8	2		460	68.50		528.50	635
2100	Add for storms					124			124	136
2500	Enamel finish windows, 3'-1" x 3'-2"	2 Sswk	10	1.600		355	55		410	495
2550	Insulating glass		10	1.600		305	55		360	440
2600	4'-5" x 5'-3"		8	2		400	68.50		468.50	570
2700	Insulating glass		8	2		400	68.50		468.50	565
3000	Single hung, 2' x 3' opening, enameled, standard glazed		10	1.600		205	55		260	330
3100	Insulating glass		10	1.600		249	55		304	380
3300	2'-8" x 6'-8" opening, standard glazed		8	2		360	68.50		428.50	530
3400	Insulating glass		8	2		465	68.50		533.50	645
3700	3'-4" x 5'-0" opening, standard glazed		9	1.778		296	61		357	440
3800	Insulating glass		9	1.778		330	61		391	475
4000	Sliding aluminum, 3' x 2' opening, standard glazed		10	1.600		217	55		272	345
4100	Insulating glass		10	1.600		232	55		287	360
4300	5' x 3' opening, standard glazed		9	1.778		330	61		391	480
4400	Insulating glass		9	1.778		385	61		446	540
4600	8' x 4' opening, standard glazed		6	2.667		350	91.50		441.50	560
4700	Insulating glass		6	2.667		565	91.50		656.50	795
5000	9' x 5' opening, standard glazed		4	4		530	137		667	845
5100	Insulating glass		4	4		850	137		987	1,200
5500	Sliding, with thermal barrier and screen, 6' x 4', 2 track		8	2		725	68.50		793.50	925

08 51 Metal Windows

08 51 13 – Aluminum Windows

08 51 13.20 Aluminum Windows	Crew	Daily Output	Labor-Hours	Unit	Material	2014 Bare Costs Labor	Equipment	Total	Total Incl O&P
5700	4 track	2 Sswk	8	2	Ea.	910	68.50		978.50	1,125
6000	For above units with bronze finish, add					15%				
6200	For installation in concrete openings, add				↓	8%				

08 51 23 – Steel Windows

08 51 23.40 Basement Utility Windows

		Crew	Daily Output	Labor-Hours	Unit	Material	Labor	Equipment	Total	Total Incl O&P
0010	**BASEMENT UTILITY WINDOWS**									
0015	1'-3" x 2'-8"	1 Carp	16	.500	Ea.	128	16.05		144.05	167
1100	1'-7" x 2'-8"		16	.500		140	16.05		156.05	181
1200	1'-11" x 2'-8"	↓	14	.571	↓	143	18.35		161.35	189

08 51 66 – Metal Window Screens

08 51 66.10 Screens

		Crew	Daily Output	Labor-Hours	Unit	Material	Labor	Equipment	Total	Total Incl O&P
0010	**SCREENS**									
0020	For metal sash, aluminum or bronze mesh, flat screen	2 Sswk	1200	.013	S.F.	4.24	.46		4.70	5.55
0500	Wicket screen, inside window	"	1000	.016	"	6.55	.55		7.10	8.25
0600	Residential, aluminum mesh and frame, 2' x 3'	2 Carp	32	.500	Ea.	14.60	16.05		30.65	43
0610	Rescreen		50	.320		12.50	10.25		22.75	31
0620	3' x 5'		32	.500		52.50	16.05		68.55	85
0630	Rescreen		45	.356		31.50	11.40		42.90	54
0640	4' x 8'		25	.640		82.50	20.50		103	126
0650	Rescreen		40	.400		48	12.85		60.85	74
0660	Patio door		25	.640	↓	150	20.50		170.50	200
0680	Rescreening	↓	1600	.010	S.F.	2.20	.32		2.52	2.96
1000	Screens for solar louvers	2 Sswk	160	.100	"	24.50	3.43		27.93	33

08 52 Wood Windows

08 52 10 – Plain Wood Windows

08 52 10.10 Wood Windows

		Crew	Daily Output	Labor-Hours	Unit	Material	Labor	Equipment	Total	Total Incl O&P
0010	**WOOD WINDOWS**, including frame, screens and grilles									
0020	Residential, stock units									
0050	Awning type, double insulated glass, 2'-10" x 1'-9" opening	2 Carp	12	1.333	Opng.	228	43		271	325
0100	2'-10" x 6'-0" opening	1 Carp	8	1		545	32		577	655
0200	4'-0" x 3'-6" single pane		10	.800	↓	365	25.50		390.50	450
0300	6' x 5' single pane	↓	8	1	Ea.	500	32		532	605
1000	Casement, 2'-0" x 3'-4" high	2 Carp	20	.800		262	25.50		287.50	330
1020	2'-0" x 4'-0"		18	.889		279	28.50		307.50	355
1040	2'-0" x 5'-0"		17	.941		305	30		335	390
1060	2'-0" x 6'-0"		16	1		305	32		337	390
1080	4'-0" x 3'-4"		15	1.067		585	34		619	700
1100	4'-0" x 4'-0"		15	1.067		655	34		689	780
1120	4'-0" x 5'-0"		14	1.143		740	36.50		776.50	875
1140	4'-0" x 6'-0"		12	1.333	↓	835	43		878	985
1600	Casement units, 8' x 5', with screens, double insulated glass		2.50	6.400	Opng.	1,425	205		1,630	1,900
1700	Low E glass		2.50	6.400		1,600	205		1,805	2,100
2300	Casements, including screens, 2'-0" x 3'-4", dbl. insulated glass		11	1.455		269	46.50		315.50	375
2400	Low E glass		11	1.455		269	46.50		315.50	375
2600	2 lite, 4'-0" x 4'-0", double insulated glass		9	1.778		495	57		552	635
2700	Low E glass		9	1.778		505	57		562	650
2900	3 lite, 5'-2" x 5'-0", double insulated glass		7	2.286		750	73.50		823.50	950
3000	Low E glass		7	2.286		790	73.50		863.50	995
3200	4 lite, 7'-0" x 5'-0", double insulated glass	↓	6	2.667	↓	1,075	85.50		1,160.50	1,325

08 52 10.10 Wood Windows

		Crew	Daily Output	Labor-Hours	Unit	Material	2014 Bare Costs Labor	Equipment	Total	Total Incl O&P
3300	Low E glass	2 Carp	6	2.667	Opng.	1,125	85.50		1,210.50	1,400
3500	5 lite, 8'-6" x 5'-0", double insulated glass		5	3.200		1,425	103		1,528	1,725
3600	Low E glass		5	3.200		1,500	103		1,603	1,825
3800	For removable wood grilles, diamond pattern, add				Leaf	36.50			36.50	40.50
3900	Rectangular pattern, add				"	35.50			35.50	39.50
4000	Bow, fixed lites, 8' x 5', double insulated glass	2 Carp	3	5.333	Opng.	1,425	171		1,596	1,850
4100	Low E glass	"	3	5.333	"	1,875	171		2,046	2,375
4150	6'-0" x 5'-0"	1 Carp	8	1	Ea.	1,250	32		1,282	1,425
4300	Fixed lites, 9'-9" x 5'-0", double insulated glass	2 Carp	2	8	Opng.	975	257		1,232	1,500
4400	Low E glass	"	2	8	"	1,075	257		1,332	1,600
5000	Bow, casement, 8'-1" x 4'-8" high	3 Carp	8	3	Ea.	1,575	96.50		1,671.50	1,875
5020	9'-6" x 4'-8"		8	3		1,700	96.50		1,796.50	2,000
5040	8'-1" x 5'-1"		8	3		1,900	96.50		1,996.50	2,250
5060	9'-6" x 5'-1"		6	4		1,925	128		2,053	2,325
5080	8'-1" x 6'-0"		6	4		1,900	128		2,028	2,325
5100	9'-6" x 6'-0"		6	4		2,000	128		2,128	2,425
5800	Skylights, hatches, vents, and sky roofs, see Section 08 62 13.00									

08 52 10.20 Awning Window

		Crew	Daily Output	Labor-Hours	Unit	Material	2014 Bare Costs Labor	Equipment	Total	Total Incl O&P
0010	**AWNING WINDOW**, Including frame, screens and grilles									
0100	34" x 22", insulated glass	1 Carp	10	.800	Ea.	270	25.50		295.50	340
0200	Low E glass		10	.800		271	25.50		296.50	340
0300	40" x 28", insulated glass		9	.889		315	28.50		343.50	395
0400	Low E Glass		9	.889		340	28.50		368.50	425
0500	48" x 36", insulated glass		8	1		465	32		497	570
0600	Low E glass		8	1		490	32		522	595
4000	Impact windows, minimum, add					60%				
4010	Impact windows, maximum, add					160%				

08 52 10.30 Wood Windows

		Crew	Daily Output	Labor-Hours	Unit	Material	2014 Bare Costs Labor	Equipment	Total	Total Incl O&P
0010	**WOOD WINDOWS**, double hung									
0020	Including frame, double insulated glass, screens and grilles									
0040	Double hung, 2'-2" x 3'-4" high	2 Carp	15	1.067	Ea.	210	34		244	289
0060	2'-2" x 4'-4"		14	1.143		229	36.50		265.50	315
0080	2'-6" x 3'-4"		13	1.231		219	39.50		258.50	310
0100	2'-6" x 4'-0"		12	1.333		229	43		272	325
0120	2'-6" x 4'-8"		12	1.333		250	43		293	345
0140	2'-10" x 3'-4"		10	1.600		224	51.50		275.50	335
0160	2'-10" x 4'-0"		10	1.600		247	51.50		298.50	360
0180	3'-7" x 3'-4"		9	1.778		254	57		311	375
0200	3'-7" x 5'-4"		9	1.778		284	57		341	405
0220	3'-10" x 5'-4"		8	2		510	64		574	670
3800	Triple glazing for above, add					25%				

08 52 10.40 Casement Window

			Crew	Daily Output	Labor-Hours	Unit	Material	2014 Bare Costs Labor	Equipment	Total	Total Incl O&P
0010	**CASEMENT WINDOW**, including frame, screen and grilles	R085216-10									
0100	2'-0" x 3'-0" H, dbl. insulated glass	G	1 Carp	10	.800	Ea.	268	25.50		293.50	340
0150	Low E glass	G		10	.800		259	25.50		284.50	330
0200	2'-0" x 4'-6" high, double insulated glass	G		9	.889		360	28.50		388.50	445
0250	Low E glass	G		9	.889		370	28.50		398.50	455
0260	Casement 4'-2" x 4'-2" double insulated glass	G		11	.727		875	23.50		898.50	1,000
0270	4'-0" x 4'-0" Low E glass	G		11	.727		535	23.50		558.50	630
0290	6'-4" x 5'-7" Low E glass	G		9	.889		1,125	28.50		1,153.50	1,275
0300	2'-4" x 6'-0" high, double insulated glass	G		8	1		430	32		462	530
0350	Low E glass	G		8	1		475	32		507	580

08 52 10.40 Casement Window		Crew	Daily Output	Labor-Hours	Unit	Material	2014 Bare Costs Labor	Equipment	Total	Total Incl O&P
0522	Vinyl clad, premium, double insulated glass, 2'-0" x 3'-0"	G	1 Carp	10	.800	Ea.	271	25.50		296.50	340
0524	2'-0" x 4'-0"	G		9	.889		315	28.50		343.50	400
0525	2'-0" x 5'-0"	G		8	1		360	32		392	455
0528	2'-0" x 6'-0"	G		8	1		380	32		412	475
0600	3'-0" x 5'-0"	G		8	1		665	32		697	785
0700	4'-0" x 3'-0"	G		8	1		730	32		762	860
0710	4'-0" x 4'-0"	G		8	1		625	32		657	740
0720	4'-8" x 4'-0"	G		8	1		690	32		722	815
0730	4'-8" x 5'-0"	G		6	1.333		790	43		833	935
0740	4'-8" x 6'-0"	G		6	1.333		880	43		923	1,050
0750	6'-0" x 4'-0"	G		6	1.333		805	43		848	955
0800	6'-0" x 5'-0"	G		6	1.333		895	43		938	1,050
0900	5'-6" x 5'-6"	G	2 Carp	15	1.067		1,425	34		1,459	1,625
2000	Bay, casement units, 8' x 5', w/screens, dbl. insul. glass			2.50	6.400	Opng.	1,600	205		1,805	2,100
2100	Low E glass			2.50	6.400	"	1,675	205		1,880	2,200
3020	Vinyl clad, premium, double insulated glass, multiple leaf units										
3080	Single unit, 1'-6" x 5'-0"	G	2 Carp	20	.800	Ea.	315	25.50		340.50	390
3100	2'-0" x 2'-0"	G		20	.800		215	25.50		240.50	279
3140	2'-0" x 2'-6"	G		20	.800		271	25.50		296.50	340
3220	2'-0" x 3'-6"	G		20	.800		273	25.50		298.50	345
3260	2'-0" x 4'-0"	G		19	.842		315	27		342	395
3300	2'-0" x 4'-6"	G		19	.842		315	27		342	395
3340	2'-0" x 5'-0"	G		18	.889		360	28.50		388.50	450
3460	2'-4" x 3'-0"	G		20	.800		275	25.50		300.50	345
3500	2'-4" x 4'-0"	G		19	.842		340	27		367	420
3540	2'-4" x 5'-0"	G		18	.889		405	28.50		433.50	495
3700	Double unit, 2'-8" x 5'-0"	G		18	.889		570	28.50		598.50	675
3740	2'-8" x 6'-0"	G		17	.941		660	30		690	775
3840	3'-0" x 4'-6"	G		18	.889		515	28.50		543.50	620
3860	3'-0" x 5'-0"	G		17	.941		665	30		695	780
3880	3'-0" x 6'-0"	G		17	.941		715	30		745	835
3980	3'-4" x 2'-6"	G		19	.842		435	27		462	525
4000	3'-4" x 3'-0"	G		12	1.333		435	43		478	550
4030	3'-4" x 4'-0"	G		18	.889		530	28.50		558.50	635
4050	3'-4" x 5'-0"	G		12	1.333		660	43		703	795
4100	3'-4" x 6'-0"	G		11	1.455		715	46.50		761.50	865
4200	3'-6" x 3'-0"	G		18	.889		520	28.50		548.50	620
4340	4'-0" x 3'-0"	G		18	.889		490	28.50		518.50	585
4380	4'-0" x 3'-6"	G		17	.941		530	30		560	630
4420	4'-0" x 4'-0"	G		16	1		625	32		657	740
4460	4'-0" x 4'-4"	G		16	1		625	32		657	740
4540	4'-0" x 5'-0"	G		16	1		675	32		707	800
4580	4'-0" x 6'-0"	G		15	1.067		765	34		799	900
4740	4'-8" x 3'-0"	G		18	.889		555	28.50		583.50	660
4780	4'-8" x 3'-6"	G		17	.941		595	30		625	700
4820	4'-8" x 4'-0"	G		16	1		690	32		722	815
4860	4'-8" x 5'-0"	G		15	1.067		790	34		824	925
4900	4'-8" x 6'-0"	G		15	1.067		880	34		914	1,025
5060	5'-0" x 5'-0"	G		15	1.067		1,025	34		1,059	1,175
5100	Triple unit, 5'-6" x 3'-0"	G		17	.941		700	30		730	820
5140	5'-6" x 3'-6"	G		16	1		760	32		792	890
5180	5'-6" x 4'-6"	G		15	1.067		855	34		889	1,000
5220	5'-6" x 5'-6"	G		15	1.067		1,125	34		1,159	1,275

08 52 Wood Windows

08 52 10 – Plain Wood Windows

08 52 10.40 Casement Window

			Crew	Daily Output	Labor-Hours	Unit	Material	2014 Bare Costs Labor	Equipment	Total	Total Incl O&P
5300	6'-0" x 4'-6"	G	2 Carp	15	1.067	Ea.	835	34		869	975
5850	5'-0" x 3'-0"	G		12	1.333		590	43		633	720
5900	5'-0" x 4'-0"	G		11	1.455		910	46.50		956.50	1,075
6100	5'-0" x 5'-6"	G		10	1.600		1,050	51.50		1,101.50	1,225
6150	5'-0" x 6'-0"	G		10	1.600		1,175	51.50		1,226.50	1,375
6200	6'-0" x 3'-0"	G		12	1.333		1,150	43		1,193	1,350
6250	6'-0" x 3'-4"	G		12	1.333		740	43		783	885
6300	6'-0" x 4'-0"	G		11	1.455		825	46.50		871.50	990
6350	6'-0" x 5'-0"	G		10	1.600		900	51.50		951.50	1,075
6400	6'-0" x 6'-0"	G		10	1.600		1,150	51.50		1,201.50	1,325
6500	Quadruple unit, 7'-0" x 4'-0"	G		9	1.778		1,100	57		1,157	1,300
6700	8'-0" x 4'-6"	G		9	1.778		1,350	57		1,407	1,600
6950	6'-8" x 4'-0"	G		10	1.600		1,075	51.50		1,126.50	1,250
7000	6'-8" x 6'-0"	G		10	1.600		1,425	51.50		1,476.50	1,650
8190	For installation, add per leaf							15%			
8200	For multiple leaf units, deduct for stationary sash										
8220	2' high					Ea.	23			23	25.50
8240	4'-6" high						26			26	28.50
8260	6' high						34.50			34.50	38
8300	Impact windows, minimum, add						60%				
8310	Impact windows, maximum, add						160%				

08 52 10.50 Double Hung

			Crew	Daily Output	Labor-Hours	Unit	Material	2014 Bare Costs Labor	Equipment	Total	Total Incl O&P
0010	**DOUBLE HUNG**, Including frame, screens and grilles										
0100	2'-0" x 3'-0" high, low E insul. glass	G	1 Carp	10	.800	Ea.	210	25.50		235.50	274
0200	3'-0" x 4'-0" high, double insulated glass	G		9	.889		279	28.50		307.50	355
0300	4'-0" x 4'-6" high, low E insulated glass	G		8	1		320	32		352	410
8000	Impact windows, minimum, add						60%				
8010	Impact windows, maximum, add						160%				

08 52 10.55 Picture Window

			Crew	Daily Output	Labor-Hours	Unit	Material	2014 Bare Costs Labor	Equipment	Total	Total Incl O&P
0010	**PICTURE WINDOW**, Including frame and grilles										
0100	3'-6" x 4'-0" high, dbl. insulated glass		2 Carp	12	1.333	Ea.	420	43		463	535
0150	Low E glass			12	1.333		435	43		478	545
0200	4'-0" x 4'-6" high, double insulated glass			11	1.455		550	46.50		596.50	685
0250	Low E glass			11	1.455		530	46.50		576.50	665
0300	5'-0" x 4'-0" high, double insulated glass			11	1.455		580	46.50		626.50	720
0350	Low E glass			11	1.455		605	46.50		651.50	745
0400	6'-0" x 4'-6" high, double insulated glass			10	1.600		625	51.50		676.50	775
0450	Low E glass			10	1.600		635	51.50		686.50	785

08 52 10.65 Wood Sash

			Crew	Daily Output	Labor-Hours	Unit	Material	2014 Bare Costs Labor	Equipment	Total	Total Incl O&P
0010	**WOOD SASH**, Including glazing but not trim										
0050	Custom, 5'-0" x 4'-0", 1" dbl. glazed, 3/16" thick lites		2 Carp	3.20	5	Ea.	230	161		391	525
0100	1/4" thick lites			5	3.200		245	103		348	445
0200	1" thick, triple glazed			5	3.200		415	103		518	630
0300	7'-0" x 4'-6" high, 1" double glazed, 3/16" thick lites			4.30	3.721		420	119		539	660
0400	1/4" thick lites			4.30	3.721		475	119		594	720
0500	1" thick, triple glazed			4.30	3.721		540	119		659	795
0600	8'-6" x 5'-0" high, 1" double glazed, 3/16" thick lites			3.50	4.571		565	147		712	870
0700	1/4" thick lites			3.50	4.571		620	147		767	925
0800	1" thick, triple glazed			3.50	4.571		625	147		772	930
0900	Window frames only, based on perimeter length					L.F.	4.02			4.02	4.42

08 52 Wood Windows

08 52 10 – Plain Wood Windows

08 52 10.70 Sliding Windows

		Crew	Daily Output	Labor-Hours	Unit	Material	2014 Bare Costs Labor	2014 Bare Costs Equipment	Total	Total Incl O&P
0010	**SLIDING WINDOWS**									
0100	3'-0" x 3'-0" high, double insulated	G 1 Carp	10	.800	Ea.	284	25.50		309.50	355
0120	Low E glass	G	10	.800		310	25.50		335.50	385
0200	4'-0" x 3'-6" high, double insulated	G	9	.889		355	28.50		383.50	440
0220	Low E glass	G	9	.889		360	28.50		388.50	450
0300	6'-0" x 5'-0" high, double insulated	G	8	1		490	32		522	590
0320	Low E glass	G	8	1		530	32		562	635
6000	Sliding, insulating glass, including screens,									
6100	3'-0" x 3'-0"	2 Carp	6.50	2.462	Ea.	325	79		404	495
6200	4'-0" x 3'-6"		6.30	2.540		330	81.50		411.50	500
6300	5'-0" x 4'-0"		6	2.667		410	85.50		495.50	595

08 52 13 – Metal-Clad Wood Windows

08 52 13.10 Awning Windows, Metal-Clad

		Crew	Daily Output	Labor-Hours	Unit	Material	2014 Bare Costs Labor	2014 Bare Costs Equipment	Total	Total Incl O&P
0010	**AWNING WINDOWS, METAL-CLAD**									
2000	Metal clad, awning deluxe, double insulated glass, 34" x 22"	1 Carp	9	.889	Ea.	247	28.50		275.50	320
2050	36" x 25"		9	.889		272	28.50		300.50	345
2100	40" x 22"		9	.889		291	28.50		319.50	370
2150	40" x 30"		9	.889		340	28.50		368.50	425
2200	48" x 28"		8	1		345	32		377	435
2250	60" x 36"		8	1		370	32		402	465

08 52 13.20 Casement Windows, Metal-Clad

		Crew	Daily Output	Labor-Hours	Unit	Material	2014 Bare Costs Labor	2014 Bare Costs Equipment	Total	Total Incl O&P
0010	**CASEMENT WINDOWS, METAL-CLAD**									
0100	Metal clad, deluxe, dbl. insul. glass, 2'-0" x 3'-0" high	G 1 Carp	10	.800	Ea.	279	25.50		304.50	350
0120	2'-0" x 4'-0" high	G	9	.889		315	28.50		343.50	395
0130	2'-0" x 5'-0" high	G	8	1		325	32		357	415
0140	2'-0" x 6'-0" high	G	8	1		365	32		397	455
0150	Casement window, metal clad, double insul. glass, 3'-6" x 3'-6"	G	8.90	.899		480	29		509	580
0300	Metal clad, casement, bldrs mdl, 6'-0" x 4'-0", dbl. insltd gls, 3 panels	2 Carp	10	1.600		1,200	51.50		1,251.50	1,400
0310	9'-0" x 4'-0", 4 panels		8	2		1,550	64		1,614	1,800
0320	10'-0" x 5'-0", 5 panels		7	2.286		2,100	73.50		2,173.50	2,450
0330	12'-0" x 6'-0", 6 panels		6	2.667		2,700	85.50		2,785.50	3,100

08 52 13.30 Double-Hung Windows, Metal-clad

		Crew	Daily Output	Labor-Hours	Unit	Material	2014 Bare Costs Labor	2014 Bare Costs Equipment	Total	Total Incl O&P
0010	**DOUBLE-HUNG WINDOWS, METAL-CLAD**									
0100	Metal clad, deluxe, dbl. insul. glass, 2'-6" x 3'-0" high	G 1 Carp	10	.800	Ea.	272	25.50		297.50	340
0120	3'-0" x 3'-6" high	G	10	.800		315	25.50		340.50	390
0140	3'-0" x 4'-0" high	G	9	.889		325	28.50		353.50	410
0160	3'-0" x 4'-6" high	G	9	.889		345	28.50		373.50	430
0180	3'-0" x 5'-0" high	G	8	1		370	32		402	465
0200	3'-6" x 6'-0" high	G	8	1		450	32		482	550

08 52 13.35 Picture and Sliding Windows Metal-Clad

		Crew	Daily Output	Labor-Hours	Unit	Material	2014 Bare Costs Labor	2014 Bare Costs Equipment	Total	Total Incl O&P
0010	**PICTURE AND SLIDING WINDOWS METAL-CLAD**									
2000	Metal clad, dlx picture, dbl. insul. glass, 4'-0" x 4'-0" high	2 Carp	12	1.333	Ea.	375	43		418	480
2100	4'-0" x 6'-0" high		11	1.455		545	46.50		591.50	680
2200	5'-0" x 6'-0" high		10	1.600		610	51.50		661.50	755
2300	6'-0" x 6'-0" high		10	1.600		695	51.50		746.50	850
2400	Metal clad, dlx sliding, double insulated glass, 3'-0" x 3'-0" high	G 1 Carp	10	.800		330	25.50		355.50	405
2420	4'-0" x 3'-6" high	G	9	.889		400	28.50		428.50	490
2440	5'-0" x 4'-0" high	G	9	.889		480	28.50		508.50	575
2460	6'-0" x 5'-0" high	G	8	1		725	32		757	850

08 52 Wood Windows

08 52 13 – Metal-Clad Wood Windows

08 52 13.40 Bow and Bay Windows, Metal-Clad

		Crew	Daily Output	Labor-Hours	Unit	Material	2014 Bare Costs Labor	2014 Bare Costs Equipment	Total	Total Incl O&P
0010	**BOW AND BAY WINDOWS, METAL-CLAD**									
0100	Metal clad, deluxe, dbl. insul. glass, 8'-0" x 5'-0" high, 4 panels	2 Carp	10	1.600	Ea.	1,675	51.50		1,726.50	1,900
0120	10'-0" x 5'-0" high, 5 panels		8	2		1,800	64		1,864	2,075
0140	10'-0" x 6'-0" high, 5 panels		7	2.286		2,100	73.50		2,173.50	2,450
0160	12'-0" x 6'-0" high, 6 panels		6	2.667		2,925	85.50		3,010.50	3,375
0400	Double hung, bldrs. model, bay, 8' x 4' high, dbl. insulated glass		10	1.600		1,325	51.50		1,376.50	1,525
0440	Low E glass		10	1.600		1,425	51.50		1,476.50	1,650
0460	9'-0" x 5'-0" high, double insulated glass		6	2.667		1,425	85.50		1,510.50	1,725
0480	Low E glass		6	2.667		1,500	85.50		1,585.50	1,800
0500	Metal clad, deluxe, dbl. insul. glass, 7'-0" x 4'-0" high		10	1.600		1,275	51.50		1,326.50	1,475
0520	8'-0" x 4'-0" high		8	2		1,300	64		1,364	1,550
0540	8'-0" x 5'-0" high		7	2.286		1,350	73.50		1,423.50	1,625
0560	9'-0" x 5'-0" high		6	2.667		1,450	85.50		1,535.50	1,725

08 52 16 – Plastic-Clad Wood Windows

08 52 16.10 Bow Window

		Crew	Daily Output	Labor-Hours	Unit	Material	2014 Bare Costs Labor	2014 Bare Costs Equipment	Total	Total Incl O&P
0010	**BOW WINDOW** Including frames, screens, and grilles									
0020	End panels operable									
1000	Bow type, casement, wood, bldrs. mdl., 8' x 5' dbl. insltd glass, 4 panel	2 Carp	10	1.600	Ea.	1,500	51.50		1,551.50	1,725
1050	Low E glass		10	1.600		1,325	51.50		1,376.50	1,525
1100	10'-0" x 5'-0", double insulated glass, 6 panels		6	2.667		1,350	85.50		1,435.50	1,650
1200	Low E glass, 6 panels		6	2.667		1,450	85.50		1,535.50	1,750
1300	Vinyl clad, bldrs. model, double insulated glass, 6'-0" x 4'-0", 3 panel		10	1.600		1,025	51.50		1,076.50	1,200
1340	9'-0" x 4'-0", 4 panel		8	2		1,350	64		1,414	1,600
1380	10'-0" x 6'-0", 5 panels		7	2.286		2,250	73.50		2,323.50	2,600
1420	12'-0" x 6'-0", 6 panels		6	2.667		2,925	85.50		3,010.50	3,375
2000	Bay window, 8' x 5', dbl. insul glass		10	1.600		1,875	51.50		1,926.50	2,150
2050	Low E glass		10	1.600		2,275	51.50		2,326.50	2,575
2100	12'-0" x 6'-0", double insulated glass, 6 panels		6	2.667		2,350	85.50		2,435.50	2,725
2200	Low E glass		6	2.667		2,375	85.50		2,460.50	2,775
2280	6'-0" x 4'-0"		11	1.455		1,250	46.50		1,296.50	1,450
2300	Vinyl clad, premium, double insulated glass, 8'-0" x 5'-0"		10	1.600		1,750	51.50		1,801.50	2,000
2340	10'-0" x 5'-0"		8	2		2,300	64		2,364	2,625
2380	10'-0" x 6'-0"		7	2.286		2,625	73.50		2,698.50	3,000
2420	12'-0" x 6'-0"		6	2.667		3,200	85.50		3,285.50	3,675
2430	14'-0" x 3'-0"		7	2.286		2,950	73.50		3,023.50	3,375
2440	14'-0" x 6'-0"		5	3.200		5,000	103		5,103	5,675
3300	Vinyl clad, premium, double insulated glass, 7'-0" x 4'-6"		10	1.600		1,375	51.50		1,426.50	1,575
3340	8'-0" x 4'-6"		8	2		1,400	64		1,464	1,625
3380	8'-0" x 5'-0"		7	2.286		1,450	73.50		1,523.50	1,725
3420	9'-0" x 5'-0"		6	2.667		1,500	85.50		1,585.50	1,800

08 52 16.15 Awning Window Vinyl-Clad

		Crew	Daily Output	Labor-Hours	Unit	Material	2014 Bare Costs Labor	2014 Bare Costs Equipment	Total	Total Incl O&P
0010	**AWNING WINDOW VINYL-CLAD** Including frames, screens, and grilles									
0200	Vinyl clad, premium, double insulated glass, 24" x 17"	1 Carp	12	.667	Ea.	210	21.50		231.50	267
0210	24" x 28"		11	.727		254	23.50		277.50	320
0250	36" x 17"		9	.889		261	28.50		289.50	335
0280	36" x 28"		9	.889		305	28.50		333.50	385
0300	36" x 36"		9	.889		340	28.50		368.50	425
0320	36" x 40"		9	.889		395	28.50		423.50	480
0340	40" x 22"		10	.800		288	25.50		313.50	360
0360	48" x 28"		8	1		370	32		402	460
0380	60" x 36"		8	1		500	32		532	605

08 52 Wood Windows

08 52 16 – Plastic-Clad Wood Windows

08 52 16.20 Half Round, Vinyl Clad

		Crew	Daily Output	Labor-Hours	Unit	Material	2014 Bare Costs Labor	Equipment	Total	Total Incl O&P
0010	**HALF ROUND, VINYL CLAD**, double insulated glass, incl. grille									
0800	14" height x 24" base	2 Carp	9	1.778	Ea.	415	57		472	550
1040	15" height x 25" base		8	2		385	64		449	530
1060	16" height x 28" base		7	2.286		405	73.50		478.50	570
1080	17" height x 29" base		7	2.286		420	73.50		493.50	585
2000	19" height x 33" base	1 Carp	6	1.333		465	43		508	580
2100	20" height x 35" base		6	1.333		465	43		508	580
2200	21" height x 37" base		6	1.333		480	43		523	600
2250	23" height x 41" base	2 Carp	6	2.667		520	85.50		605.50	715
2300	26" height x 48" base		6	2.667		535	85.50		620.50	730
2350	30" height x 56" base		6	2.667		615	85.50		700.50	820
3000	36" height x 67"base	1 Carp	4	2		1,050	64		1,114	1,250
3040	38" height x 71" base	2 Carp	5	3.200		975	103		1,078	1,250
3050	40" height x 75" base	"	5	3.200		1,275	103		1,378	1,575
5000	Elliptical, 71" x 16"	1 Carp	11	.727		975	23.50		998.50	1,125
5100	95" x 21"	"	10	.800		1,375	25.50		1,400.50	1,575

08 52 16.30 Palladian Windows

		Crew	Daily Output	Labor-Hours	Unit	Material	2014 Bare Costs Labor	Equipment	Total	Total Incl O&P
0010	**PALLADIAN WINDOWS**									
0020	Vinyl clad, double insulated glass, including frame and grilles									
0040	3'-2" x 2'-6" high	2 Carp	11	1.455	Ea.	1,250	46.50		1,296.50	1,450
0060	3'-2" x 4'-10"		11	1.455		1,750	46.50		1,796.50	1,975
0080	3'-2" x 6'-4"		10	1.600		1,700	51.50		1,751.50	1,950
0100	4'-0" x 4'-0"		10	1.600		1,525	51.50		1,576.50	1,750
0120	4'-0" x 5'-4"	3 Carp	10	2.400		1,875	77		1,952	2,175
0140	4'-0" x 6'-0"		9	2.667		1,950	85.50		2,035.50	2,300
0160	4'-0" x 7'-4"		9	2.667		2,125	85.50		2,210.50	2,475
0180	5'-5" x 4'-10"		9	2.667		2,275	85.50		2,360.50	2,650
0200	5'-5" x 6'-10"		9	2.667		2,575	85.50		2,660.50	3,000
0220	5'-5" x 7'-9"		9	2.667		2,800	85.50		2,885.50	3,225
0240	6'-0" x 7'-11"		8	3		3,475	96.50		3,571.50	3,975
0260	8'-0" x 6'-0"		8	3		3,075	96.50		3,171.50	3,525

08 52 16.35 Double-Hung Window

			Crew	Daily Output	Labor-Hours	Unit	Material	2014 Bare Costs Labor	Equipment	Total	Total Incl O&P
0010	**DOUBLE-HUNG WINDOW** Including frames, screens, and grilles										
0300	Vinyl clad, premium, double insulated glass, 2'-6" x 3'-0"	G	1 Carp	10	.800	Ea.	310	25.50		335.50	385
0305	2'-6" x 4'-0"	G		10	.800		360	25.50		385.50	440
0400	3'-0" x 3'-6"	G		10	.800		335	25.50		360.50	415
0500	3'-0" x 4'-0"	G		9	.889		395	28.50		423.50	485
0600	3'-0" x 4'-6"	G		9	.889		410	28.50		438.50	500
0700	3'-0" x 5'-0"	G		8	1		445	32		477	540
0790	3'-4" x 5'-0"	G		8	1		455	32		487	555
0800	3'-6" x 6'-0"	G		8	1		490	32		522	595
0820	4'-0" x 5'-0"	G		7	1.143		560	36.50		596.50	675
0830	4'-0" x 6'-0"	G		7	1.143		700	36.50		736.50	825

08 52 16.40 Transom Windows

		Crew	Daily Output	Labor-Hours	Unit	Material	2014 Bare Costs Labor	Equipment	Total	Total Incl O&P
0010	**TRANSOM WINDOWS**									
0050	Vinyl clad, premium, double insulated glass, 32" x 8"	1 Carp	16	.500	Ea.	188	16.05		204.05	233
0100	36" x 8"		16	.500		199	16.05		215.05	246
0110	36" x 12"		16	.500		212	16.05		228.05	260
1000	Vinyl clad, premium, dbl. insul. glass, 4'-0" x 4'-0"	2 Carp	12	1.333		495	43		538	615
1100	4'-0" x 6'-0"		11	1.455		935	46.50		981.50	1,100
1200	5'-0" x 6'-0"		10	1.600		1,050	51.50		1,101.50	1,225

08 52 Wood Windows

08 52 16 – Plastic-Clad Wood Windows

08 52 16.40 Transom Windows		Crew	Daily Output	Labor-Hours	Unit	Material	2014 Bare Costs Labor	Equipment	Total	Total Incl O&P
1300	6'-0" x 6'-0"	2 Carp	10	1.600	Ea.	1,050	51.50		1,101.50	1,225

08 52 16.45 Trapezoid Windows

		Crew	Daily Output	Labor-Hours	Unit	Material	Labor	Equipment	Total	Total Incl O&P
0010	**TRAPEZOID WINDOWS**									
0100	Vinyl clad, including frame and exterior trim									
0900	20" base x 44" leg x 53" leg	2 Carp	13	1.231	Ea.	390	39.50		429.50	495
1000	24" base x 90" leg x 102" leg		8	2		670	64		734	850
3000	36" base x 40" leg x 22" leg		12	1.333		430	43		473	540
3010	36" base x 44" leg x 25" leg		13	1.231		450	39.50		489.50	560
3050	36" base x 26" leg x 48" leg		9	1.778		455	57		512	595
3100	36" base x 42" legs, 50" peak		9	1.778		545	57		602	695
3200	36" base x 60" leg x 81" leg		11	1.455		710	46.50		756.50	865
4320	44" base x 23" leg x 56" leg		11	1.455		560	46.50		606.50	700
4350	44" base x 59" leg x 92" leg		10	1.600		840	51.50		891.50	1,000
4500	46" base x 15" leg x 46" leg		8	2		425	64		489	575
4550	46" base x 16" leg x 48" leg		8	2		450	64		514	605
4600	46" base x 50" leg x 80" leg		7	2.286		680	73.50		753.50	875
6600	66" base x 12" leg x 42" leg		8	2		575	64		639	745
6650	66" base x 12" legs, 28" peak		9	1.778		455	57		512	595
6700	68" base x 23" legs, 31" peak		8	2		575	64		639	745

08 52 16.70 Vinyl Clad, Premium, Dbl. Insulated Glass

			Crew	Daily Output	Labor-Hours	Unit	Material	Labor	Equipment	Total	Total Incl O&P
0010	**VINYL CLAD, PREMIUM, DBL. INSULATED GLASS**										
1000	Sliding, 3'-0" x 3'-0"	G	1 Carp	10	.800	Ea.	605	25.50		630.50	710
1020	4'-0" x 1'-11"	G		11	.727		585	23.50		608.50	680
1040	4'-0" x 3'-0"	G		10	.800		700	25.50		725.50	810
1050	4'-0" x 3'-6"	G		9	.889		685	28.50		713.50	805
1090	4'-0" x 5'-0"	G		9	.889		915	28.50		943.50	1,050
1100	5'-0" x 4'-0"	G		9	.889		900	28.50		928.50	1,050
1120	5'-0" x 5'-0"	G		8	1		1,000	32		1,032	1,150
1140	6'-0" x 4'-0"	G		8	1		1,025	32		1,057	1,175
1150	6'-0" x 5'-0"	G		8	1		1,125	32		1,157	1,300

08 52 50 – Window Accessories

08 52 50.10 Window Grille or Muntin

		Crew	Daily Output	Labor-Hours	Unit	Material	Labor	Equipment	Total	Total Incl O&P
0010	**WINDOW GRILLE OR MUNTIN**, snap in type									
0020	Standard pattern interior grilles									
2000	Wood, awning window, glass size 28" x 16" high	1 Carp	30	.267	Ea.	28	8.55		36.55	45.50
2060	44" x 24" high		32	.250		40	8.05		48.05	57.50
2100	Casement, glass size, 20" x 36" high		30	.267		32	8.55		40.55	49.50
2180	20" x 56" high		32	.250		43	8.05		51.05	61
2200	Double hung, glass size, 16" x 24" high		24	.333	Set	51	10.70		61.70	74.50
2280	32" x 32" high		34	.235	"	131	7.55		138.55	157
2500	Picture, glass size, 48" x 48" high		30	.267	Ea.	120	8.55		128.55	146
2580	60" x 68" high		28	.286	"	183	9.15		192.15	217
2600	Sliding, glass size, 14" x 36" high		24	.333	Set	35.50	10.70		46.20	57
2680	36" x 36" high		22	.364	"	43.50	11.65		55.15	67

08 52 66 – Wood Window Screens

08 52 66.10 Wood Screens

		Crew	Daily Output	Labor-Hours	Unit	Material	Labor	Equipment	Total	Total Incl O&P
0010	**WOOD SCREENS**									
0020	Over 3 S.F., 3/4" frames	2 Carp	375	.043	S.F.	4.89	1.37		6.26	7.70
0100	1-1/8" frames	"	375	.043	"	8.15	1.37		9.52	11.30

08 52 Wood Windows

08 52 69 – Wood Storm Windows

08 52 69.10 Storm Windows		Crew	Daily Output	Labor-Hours	Unit	Material	2014 Bare Costs Labor	Equipment	Total	Total Incl O&P
0010	**STORM WINDOWS**, aluminum residential									
0300	Basement, mill finish, incl. fiberglass screen									
0320	1'-10" x 1'-0" high [G]	2 Carp	30	.533	Ea.	35	17.10		52.10	67.50
0340	2'-9" x 1'-6" high [G]		30	.533		38	17.10		55.10	71
0360	3'-4" x 2'-0" high [G]		30	.533		44	17.10		61.10	77.50
1600	Double-hung, combination, storm & screen									
1700	Custom, clear anodic coating, 2'-0" x 3'-5" high	2 Carp	30	.533	Ea.	90	17.10		107.10	128
1720	2'-6" x 5'-0" high		28	.571		110	18.35		128.35	152
1740	4'-0" x 6'-0" high		25	.640		226	20.50		246.50	284
1800	White painted, 2'-0" x 3'-5" high		30	.533		100	17.10		117.10	139
1820	2'-6" x 5'-0" high		28	.571		160	18.35		178.35	207
1840	4'-0" x 6'-0" high		25	.640		273	20.50		293.50	335
2000	Clear anodic coating, 2'-0" x 3'-5" high [G]		30	.533		86	17.10		103.10	124
2020	2'-6" x 5'-0" high [G]		28	.571		114	18.35		132.35	156
2040	4'-0" x 6'-0" high [G]		25	.640		126	20.50		146.50	174
2400	White painted, 2'-0" x 3'-5" high [G]		30	.533		85	17.10		102.10	123
2420	2'-6" x 5'-0" high [G]		28	.571		92	18.35		110.35	132
2440	4'-0" x 6'-0" high [G]		25	.640		100	20.50		120.50	145
2600	Mill finish, 2'-0" x 3'-5" high [G]		30	.533		77	17.10		94.10	114
2620	2'-6" x 5'-0" high [G]		28	.571		86	18.35		104.35	126
2640	4'-0" x 6'-8" high [G]		25	.640		100	20.50		120.50	145
4000	Picture window, storm, 1 lite, white or bronze finish									
4020	4'-6" x 4'-6" high	2 Carp	25	.640	Ea.	120	20.50		140.50	167
4040	5'-8" x 4'-6" high		20	.800		144	25.50		169.50	201
4400	Mill finish, 4'-6" x 4'-6" high		25	.640		126	20.50		146.50	174
4420	5'-8" x 4'-6" high		20	.800		144	25.50		169.50	201
4600	3 lite, white or bronze finish									
4620	4'-6" x 4'-6" high	2 Carp	25	.640	Ea.	152	20.50		172.50	202
4640	5'-8" x 4'-6" high		20	.800		166	25.50		191.50	226
4800	Mill finish, 4'-6" x 4'-6" high		25	.640		144	20.50		164.50	193
4820	5'-8" x 4'-6" high		20	.800		152	25.50		177.50	210
6000	Sliding window, storm, 2 lite, white or bronze finish									
6020	3'-4" x 2'-7" high	2 Carp	28	.571	Ea.	130	18.35		148.35	174
6040	4'-4" x 3'-3" high		25	.640		150	20.50		170.50	200
6060	5'-4" x 6'-0" high		20	.800		240	25.50		265.50	305
9000	Magnetic interior storm window									
9100	3/16" plate glass	1 Glaz	107	.075	S.F.	5.55	2.34		7.89	10

08 53 Plastic Windows

08 53 13 – Vinyl Windows

08 53 13.10 Solid Vinyl Windows

		Crew	Daily Output	Labor-Hours	Unit	Material	2014 Bare Costs Labor	Equipment	Total	Total Incl O&P
0010	**SOLID VINYL WINDOWS**									
0020	Double hung, including frame and screen, 2'-0" x 2'-6"	2 Carp	15	1.067	Ea.	199	34		233	277
0040	2'-0" x 3'-6"		14	1.143		212	36.50		248.50	295
0060	2'-6" x 4'-6"		13	1.231		250	39.50		289.50	340
0080	3'-0" x 4'-0"		10	1.600		216	51.50		267.50	325
0100	3'-0" x 4'-6"		9	1.778		278	57		335	400
0120	3'-6" x 4'-6"		8	2		292	64		356	430
0140	3'-6" x 6'-0"		7	2.286		340	73.50		413.50	500

08 53 Plastic Windows

08 53 13 – Vinyl Windows

08 53 13.20 Vinyl Single Hung Windows

		Crew	Daily Output	Labor-Hours	Unit	Material	2014 Bare Costs Labor	Equipment	Total	Total Incl O&P
0010	**VINYL SINGLE HUNG WINDOWS**, insulated glass									
0100	Grids, low E, J fin, ext. jambs, 21" x 53"	G	2 Carp	18	.889	Ea.	198	28.50		226.50	266
0110	21" x 57"	G		17	.941		200	30		230	271
0120	21" x 65"	G		16	1		205	32		237	280
0130	25" x 41"	G		20	.800		190	25.50		215.50	252
0140	25" x 49"	G		18	.889	*	200	28.50		228.50	268
0150	25" x 57"	G		17	.941		205	30		235	277
0160	25" x 65"	G		16	1		240	32		272	320
0170	29" x 41"	G		18	.889		195	28.50		223.50	263
0180	29" x 53"	G		18	.889		205	28.50		233.50	274
0190	29" x 57"	G		17	.941		210	30		240	282
0200	29" x 65"	G		16	1		215	32		247	291
0210	33" x 41"	G		20	.800		200	25.50		225.50	263
0220	33" x 53"	G		18	.889		215	28.50		243.50	285
0230	33" x 57"	G		17	.941		215	30		245	288
0240	33" x 65"	G		16	1		220	32		252	296
0250	37" x 41"	G		20	.800		225	25.50		250.50	291
0260	37" x 53"	G		18	.889		235	28.50		263.50	305
0270	37" x 57"	G		17	.941		240	30		270	315
0280	37" x 65"	G		16	1		256	32		288	335
0500	Vinyl clad, premium, double insulated glass, circle, 24" diameter		1 Carp	6	1.333		460	43		503	575
1000	2'-4" diameter			6	1.333		540	43		583	665
1500	2'-11" diameter			6	1.333		640	43		683	770

08 53 13.30 Vinyl Double Hung Windows

		Crew	Daily Output	Labor-Hours	Unit	Material	2014 Bare Costs Labor	Equipment	Total	Total Incl O&P
0010	**VINYL DOUBLE HUNG WINDOWS**, insulated glass									
0100	Grids, low E, J fin, ext. jambs, 21" x 53"	G	2 Carp	18	.889	Ea.	215	28.50		243.50	285
0102	21" x 37"	G		18	.889		200	28.50		228.50	268
0104	21" x 41"	G		18	.889		205	28.50		233.50	274
0106	21" x 49"	G		18	.889		221	28.50		249.50	291
0110	21" x 57"	G		17	.941		222	30		252	295
0120	21" x 65"	G		16	1		230	32		262	305
0128	25" x 37"	G		20	.800		210	25.50		235.50	274
0130	25" x 41"	G		20	.800		215	25.50		240.50	280
0140	25" x 49"	G		18	.889		220	28.50		248.50	290
0145	25" x 53"	G		18	.889		225	28.50		253.50	296
0150	25" x 57"	G		17	.941		225	30		255	299
0160	25" x 65"	G		16	1		235	32		267	315
0162	25" x 69"	G		16	1		242	32		274	320
0164	25" x 77"	G		16	1		260	32		292	340
0168	29" x 37"	G		18	.889		215	28.50		243.50	285
0170	29" x 41"	G		18	.889		218	28.50		246.50	288
0172	29" x 49"	G		18	.889		225	28.50		253.50	296
0180	29" x 53"	G		18	.889		230	28.50		258.50	300
0190	29" x 57"	G		17	.941		232	30		262	305
0200	29" x 65"	G		16	1		240	32		272	320
0202	29" x 69"	G		16	1		247	32		279	325
0205	29" x 77"	G		16	1		267	32		299	350
0208	33" x 37"	G		20	.800		220	25.50		245.50	285
0210	33" x 41"	G		20	.800		222	25.50		247.50	287
0215	33" x 49"	G		20	.800		230	25.50		255.50	296
0220	33" x 53"	G		18	.889		235	28.50		263.50	305
0230	33" x 57"	G		17	.941		238	30		268	315

08 53 13 – Vinyl Windows

08 53 13.30 Vinyl Double Hung Windows		Crew	Daily Output	Labor-Hours	Unit	Material	2014 Bare Costs Labor	Equipment	Total	Total Incl O&P
0240	33" x 65"	G	2 Carp	16	1	Ea.	242	32		274	320
0242	33" x 69"	G		16	1		257	32		289	335
0246	33" x 77"	G		16	1		263	32		295	345
0250	37" x 41"	G		20	.800		242	25.50		267.50	310
0255	37" x 49"	G		20	.800		250	25.50		275.50	320
0260	37" x 53"	G		18	.889		257	28.50		285.50	330
0270	37" x 57"	G		17	.941		262	30		292	340
0280	37" x 65"	G		16	1		280	32		312	365
0282	37" x 69"	G		16	1		287	32		319	370
0286	37" x 77"	G		16	1		295	32		327	380
0300	Solid vinyl, average quality, double insulated glass, 2'-0" x 3'-0"	G	1 Carp	10	.800		291	25.50		316.50	365
0310	3'-0" x 4'-0"	G		9	.889		205	28.50		233.50	273
0320	4'-0" x 4'-6"	G		8	1		335	32		367	420
0330	Premium, double insulated glass, 2'-6" x 3'-0"	G		10	.800		260	25.50		285.50	330
0340	3'-0" x 3'-6"	G		9	.889		283	28.50		311.50	360
0350	3'-0" x 4'-0"	G		9	.889		310	28.50		338.50	390
0360	3'-0" x 4'-6"	G		9	.889		320	28.50		348.50	400
0370	3'-0" x 5'-0"	G		8	1		340	32		372	425
0380	3'-6" x 6'-0"	G		8	1		360	32		392	455

08 53 13.40 Vinyl Casement Windows

		Crew	Daily Output	Labor-Hours	Unit	Material	2014 Bare Costs Labor	Equipment	Total	Total Incl O&P
0010	**VINYL CASEMENT WINDOWS**, insulated glass										
0015	Grids, low E, J fin, extension jambs, screens										
0100	One lite, 21" x 41"	G	2 Carp	20	.800	Ea.	271	25.50		296.50	340
0110	21" x 47"	G		20	.800		294	25.50		319.50	370
0120	21" x 53"	G		20	.800		315	25.50		340.50	395
0128	24" x 35"	G		19	.842		263	27		290	335
0130	24" x 41"	G		19	.842		283	27		310	355
0140	24" x 47"	G		19	.842		305	27		332	380
0150	24" x 53"	G		19	.842		325	27		352	405
0158	28" x 35"	G		19	.842		278	27		305	350
0160	28" x 41"	G		19	.842		298	27		325	375
0170	28" x 47"	G		19	.842		320	27		347	395
0180	28" x 53"	G		19	.842		350	27		377	430
0184	28" x 59"	G		19	.842		350	27		377	430
0188	Two lites, 33" x 35"	G		18	.889		435	28.50		463.50	530
0190	33" x 41"	G		18	.889		460	28.50		488.50	555
0200	33" x 47"	G		18	.889		495	28.50		523.50	595
0210	33" x 53"	G		18	.889		525	28.50		553.50	630
0212	33" x 59"	G		18	.889		555	28.50		583.50	660
0215	33" x 72"	G		18	.889		570	28.50		598.50	680
0220	41" x 41"	G		18	.889		455	28.50		483.50	550
0230	41" x 47"	G		18	.889		530	28.50		558.50	635
0240	41" x 53"	G		17	.941		565	30		595	670
0242	41" x 59"	G		17	.941		590	30		620	700
0246	41" x 72"	G		17	.941		615	30		645	730
0250	47" x 41"	G		17	.941		505	30		535	605
0260	47" x 47"	G		17	.941		535	30		565	640
0270	47" x 53"	G		17	.941		565	30		595	670
0272	47" x 59"	G		17	.941		615	30		645	730
0280	56" x 41"	G		15	1.067		540	34		574	655
0290	56" x 47"	G		15	1.067		565	34		599	680
0300	56" x 53"	G		15	1.067		615	34		649	735

08 53 Plastic Windows

08 53 13 – Vinyl Windows

08 53 13.40 Vinyl Casement Windows

		Crew	Daily Output	Labor-Hours	Unit	Material	2014 Bare Costs Labor	2014 Bare Costs Equipment	Total	Total Incl O&P
0302	56" x 59"	G	2 Carp	15	1.067	Ea.	640	34		674	765
0310	56" x 72"	G	↓	15	1.067		690	34		724	820
0340	Solid vinyl, premium, double insulated glass, 2'-0" x 3'-0" high	G	1 Carp	10	.800		263	25.50		288.50	330
0360	2'-0" x 4'-0" high	G		9	.889		293	28.50		321.50	370
0380	2'-0" x 5'-0" high	G	↓	8	1	↓	325	32		357	410

08 53 13.50 Vinyl Picture Windows

		Crew	Daily Output	Labor-Hours	Unit	Material	2014 Bare Costs Labor	2014 Bare Costs Equipment	Total	Total Incl O&P
0010	**VINYL PICTURE WINDOWS**, insulated glass									
0100	Grids, low E, J fin, ext. jambs, 33" x 47"	2 Carp	12	1.333	Ea.	250	43		293	345
0110	35" x 71"		12	1.333		335	43		378	440
0120	41" x 47"		12	1.333		270	43		313	370
0130	41" x 71"		12	1.333		350	43		393	455
0140	47" x 47"		12	1.333		305	43		348	405
0150	47" x 71"		11	1.455		380	46.50		426.50	500
0160	53" x 47"		11	1.455		330	46.50		376.50	445
0170	53" x 71"		11	1.455		345	46.50		391.50	460
0180	59" x 47"		11	1.455		370	46.50		416.50	485
0190	59" x 71"		11	1.455		380	46.50		426.50	500
0200	71" x 47"		10	1.600		390	51.50		441.50	515
0210	71" x 71"	↓	10	1.600	↓	405	51.50		456.50	530

08 53 13.60 Vinyl Half Round Windows

		Crew	Daily Output	Labor-Hours	Unit	Material	2014 Bare Costs Labor	2014 Bare Costs Equipment	Total	Total Incl O&P
0010	**VINYL HALF ROUND WINDOWS**, Including grille, j fin low E, ext. jambs									
0100	10" height x 20" base	2 Carp	8	2	Ea.	475	64		539	630
0110	15" height x 30" base		8	2		440	64		504	595
0120	17" height x 34" base		7	2.286		320	73.50		393.50	475
0130	19" height x 38" base		7	2.286		345	73.50		418.50	505
0140	19" height x 33" base		7	2.286		555	73.50		628.50	740
0150	24" height x 48" base	1 Carp	6	1.333		365	43		408	470
0160	25" height x 50" base	"	6	1.333		755	43		798	900
0170	30" height x 60" base	2 Carp	6	2.667	↓	660	85.50		745.50	870

08 54 Composite Windows

08 54 13 – Fiberglass Windows

08 54 13.10 Fiberglass Single Hung Windows

			Crew	Daily Output	Labor-Hours	Unit	Material	2014 Bare Costs Labor	2014 Bare Costs Equipment	Total	Total Incl O&P
0010	**FIBERGLASS SINGLE HUNG WINDOWS**										
0100	Grids, low E, 18" x 24"	G	2 Carp	18	.889	Ea.	335	28.50		363.50	420
0110	18" x 40"	G		17	.941		340	30		370	425
0130	24" x 40"	G		20	.800		360	25.50		385.50	440
0230	36" x 36"	G		17	.941		370	30		400	455
0250	36" x 48"	G		20	.800		405	25.50		430.50	490
0260	36" x 60"	G		18	.889		445	28.50		473.50	540
0280	36" x 72"	G		16	1		470	32		502	570
0290	48" x 40"	G	↓	16	1	↓	470	32		502	570

08 54 13.30 Fiberglass Slider Wind

			Crew	Daily Output	Labor-Hours	Unit	Material	2014 Bare Costs Labor	2014 Bare Costs Equipment	Total	Total Incl O&P
0010	**FIBERGLASS SLIDER WINDOWS**										
0100	Grids, low E, 36" x 24"	G	2 Carp	20	.800	Ea.	340	25.50		365.50	420
0110	36" x 36"	G	"	20	.800	"	390	25.50		415.50	475

08 54 13.50 Fiberglass Bay Window

			Crew	Daily Output	Labor-Hours	Unit	Material	2014 Bare Costs Labor	2014 Bare Costs Equipment	Total	Total Incl O&P
0010	**FIBERGLASS BAY WINDOWS**										
0150	48" x 36"	G	2 Carp	11	1.455	Ea.	1,100	46.50		1,146.50	1,275

08 61 Roof Windows

08 61 13 – Metal Roof Windows

08 61 13.10 Roof Windows		Crew	Daily Output	Labor-Hours	Unit	Material	2014 Bare Costs Labor	2014 Bare Costs Equipment	Total	Total Incl O&P
0010	**ROOF WINDOWS**, fixed high perf tmpd glazing, metallic framed									
0020	46" x 21-1/2", Flashed for shingled roof	1 Carp	8	1	Ea.	270	32		302	350
0100	46" x 28"		8	1		300	32		332	385
0125	57" x 44"		6	1.333		370	43		413	475
0130	72" x 28"		7	1.143		370	36.50		406.50	465
0150	Fixed, laminated tempered glazing, 46" x 21-1/2"		8	1		455	32		487	555
0175	46" x 28"		8	1		505	32		537	610
0200	57" x 44"		6	1.333		475	43		518	590
0500	Vented flashing set for shingled roof, 46" x 21-1/2"		7	1.143		455	36.50		491.50	560
0525	46" x 28"		6	1.333		505	43		548	625
0550	57" x 44"		5	1.600		635	51.50		686.50	780
0560	72" x 28"		5	1.600		635	51.50		686.50	780
0575	Flashing set for low pitched roof, 46" x 21-1/2"		7	1.143		525	36.50		561.50	640
0600	46" x 28"		7	1.143		575	36.50		611.50	695
0625	57" x 44"		5	1.600		715	51.50		766.50	870
0650	Flashing set for curb 46" x 21-1/2"		7	1.143		605	36.50		641.50	725
0675	46" x 28"		7	1.143		660	36.50		696.50	785
0700	57" x 44"		5	1.600		810	51.50		861.50	975

08 61 16 – Wood Roof Windows

08 61 16.16 Roof Windows, Wood Framed

		Crew	Daily Output	Labor-Hours	Unit	Material	2014 Bare Costs Labor	2014 Bare Costs Equipment	Total	Total Incl O&P
0010	**ROOF WINDOWS, WOOD FRAMED**									
5600	Roof window incl. frame, flashing, double insulated glass & screens,									
5610	complete unit, 22" x 38"	2 Carp	3	5.333	Ea.	605	171		776	955
5650	2'-5" x 3'-8"		3.20	5		735	161		896	1,075
5700	3'-5" x 4'-9"		3.40	4.706		845	151		996	1,175

08 62 Unit Skylights

08 62 13 – Domed Unit Skylights

08 62 13.10 Domed Skylights

			Crew	Daily Output	Labor-Hours	Unit	Material	2014 Bare Costs Labor	2014 Bare Costs Equipment	Total	Total Incl O&P
0010	**DOMED SKYLIGHTS**										
0020	Skylight, fixed dome type, 22" x 22"	G	G-3	12	2.667	Ea.	210	80		290	365
0030	22" x 46"	G		10	3.200		232	96		328	415
0040	30" x 30"	G		12	2.667		235	80		315	395
0050	30" x 46"	G		10	3.200		310	96		406	500
0110	Fixed, double glazed, 22" x 27"	G		12	2.667		230	80		310	385
0120	22" x 46"	G		10	3.200		282	96		378	470
0130	44" x 46"	G		10	3.200		430	96		526	635
0210	Operable, double glazed, 22" x 27"	G		12	2.667		325	80		405	495
0220	22" x 46"	G		10	3.200		390	96		486	590
0230	44" x 46"	G		10	3.200		830	96		926	1,075

08 62 13.20 Skylights

			Crew	Daily Output	Labor-Hours	Unit	Material	2014 Bare Costs Labor	2014 Bare Costs Equipment	Total	Total Incl O&P
0010	**SKYLIGHTS**, flush or curb mounted										
2120	Ventilating insulated plexiglass dome with										
2130	curb mounting, 36" x 36"	G	G-3	12	2.667	Ea.	480	80		560	665
2150	52" x 52"	G		12	2.667		660	80		740	860
2160	28" x 52"	G		10	3.200		485	96		581	695
2170	36" x 52"	G		10	3.200		540	96		636	755
2180	For electric opening system, add	G					310			310	340
2210	Operating skylight, with thermopane glass, 24" x 48"	G	G-3	10	3.200		575	96		671	795
2220	32" x 48"	G	"	9	3.556		600	106		706	840

08 62 Unit Skylights

08 62 13 – Domed Unit Skylights

08 62 13.20 Skylights

		Crew	Daily Output	Labor-Hours	Unit	Material	Labor	Equipment	Total	Total Incl O&P
							2014 Bare Costs			
2310	Non venting insulated plexiglass dome skylight with									
2320	Flush mount 22" x 46" [G]	G-3	15.23	2.101	Ea.	325	63		388	465
2330	30" x 30" [G]		16	2		300	60		360	430
2340	46" x 46" [G]		13.91	2.301		550	69		619	720
2350	Curb mount 22" x 46" [G]		15.23	2.101		360	63		423	500
2360	30" x 30" [G]		16	2		400	60		460	540
2370	46" x 46" [G]		13.91	2.301		610	69		679	785
2381	Non-insulated flush mount 22" x 46"		15.23	2.101		220	63		283	345
2382	30" x 30"		16	2		200	60		260	320
2383	46" x 46"		13.91	2.301		370	69		439	520
2384	Curb mount 22" x 46"		15.23	2.101		190	63		253	315
2385	30" x 30"		16	2		190	60		250	310
4000	Skylight, solar tube kit, incl dome, flashing, diffuser, 1 pipe, 10" dia. [G]	1 Carp	2	4		230	128		358	470
4010	14" diam. [G]		2	4		310	128		438	555
4020	21" diam. [G]		2	4		410	128		538	665
4030	Accessories for, 1' long x 9" dia pipe [G]		24	.333		30	10.70		40.70	51
4040	2' long x 9" dia pipe [G]		24	.333		45	10.70		55.70	67.50
4050	4' long x 9" dia pipe [G]		20	.400		72	12.85		84.85	101
4060	1' long x 13" dia pipe [G]		24	.333		45	10.70		55.70	67.50
4070	2' long x 13" dia pipe [G]		24	.333		60	10.70		70.70	84
4080	4' long x 13" dia pipe [G]		20	.400		100	12.85		112.85	132
4090	6.5" turret ext for 21" dia pipe [G]		16	.500		50	16.05		66.05	82
4100	12' long x 21" dia flexible pipe [G]		12	.667		90	21.50		111.50	135
4110	45 degree elbow, 10" [G]		16	.500		50	16.05		66.05	82
4120	14" [G]		16	.500		45	16.05		61.05	76.50
4130	Interior decorative ring, 9" [G]		20	.400		30	12.85		42.85	54.50
4140	13" [G]		20	.400		45	12.85		57.85	71

08 71 Door Hardware

08 71 20 – Hardware

08 71 20.15 Hardware

		Crew	Daily Output	Labor-Hours	Unit	Material	Labor	Equipment	Total	Total Incl O&P
0010	**HARDWARE**									
0020	Average percentage for hardware, total job cost									
0025	Minimum				Job					2%
0050	Maximum									5%
0500	Total hardware for building, average distribution					85%	15%			
1000	Door hardware, apartment, interior	1 Carp	4	2	Door	450	64		514	610
1300	Average, door hardware, motel/hotel interior, with access card		4	2	"	580	64		644	750
2100	Pocket door		6	1.333	Ea.	100	43		143	182
4000	Door knocker, bright brass		32	.250		45	8.05		53.05	63
4100	Mail slot, bright brass, 2" x 11"		25	.320		60	10.25		70.25	83.50
4200	Peep hole, add to price of door					11			11	12.10

08 71 20.40 Lockset

		Crew	Daily Output	Labor-Hours	Unit	Material	Labor	Equipment	Total	Total Incl O&P
0010	**LOCKSET**, Standard duty									
0020	Non-keyed, passage, w/sect.trim	1 Carp	12	.667	Ea.	63.50	21.50		85	106
0100	Privacy		12	.667		75	21.50		96.50	119
0400	Keyed, single cylinder function		10	.800		108	25.50		133.50	161
0500	Lever handled, keyed, single cylinder function		10	.800		128	25.50		153.50	184
1700	Residential, interior door, minimum		16	.500		30	16.05		46.05	60
1720	Maximum		8	1		120	32		152	186
1800	Exterior, minimum		14	.571		50	18.35		68.35	86

08 71 Door Hardware

08 71 20 – Hardware

08 71 20.40 Lockset		Crew	Daily Output	Labor-Hours	Unit	Material	2014 Bare Costs Labor	Equipment	Total	Total Incl O&P
1810	Average	1 Carp	8	1	Ea.	72.50	32		104.50	134
1820	Maximum	↓	8	1	↓	220	32		252	296
08 71 20.41 Dead Locks										
0010	**DEAD LOCKS**									
1203	Deadlock night latch	1 Carp	7.70	1.039	Ea.	45	33.50		78.50	106
1420	Deadbolt lock, single cylinder		10	.800		48.50	25.50		74	96.50
1440	Double cylinder	↓	10	.800	↓	63	25.50		88.50	113
08 71 20.50 Door Stops										
0010	**DOOR STOPS**									
0020	Holder & bumper, floor or wall	1 Carp	32	.250	Ea.	34.50	8.05		42.55	51
1300	Wall bumper, 4" diameter, with rubber pad, aluminum		32	.250		11.70	8.05		19.75	26.50
1600	Door bumper, floor type, aluminum		32	.250		8.10	8.05		16.15	22.50
1620	Brass		32	.250		9.65	8.05		17.70	24
1630	Bronze		32	.250		18.20	8.05		26.25	33.50
1900	Plunger type, door mounted		32	.250		28	8.05		36.05	44
2520	Wall type, aluminum		32	.250		35	8.05		43.05	52
2540	Plunger type, aluminum		32	.250		28	8.05		36.05	44
2560	Brass		32	.250		43	8.05		51.05	60.50
3020	Floor mounted, US3	↓	3	2.667	↓	315	85.50		400.50	495
08 71 20.60 Entrance Locks										
0010	**ENTRANCE LOCKS**									
0015	Cylinder, grip handle deadlocking latch	1 Carp	9	.889	Ea.	175	28.50		203.50	241
0020	Deadbolt		8	1		175	32		207	247
0100	Push and pull plate, dead bolt ♿	↓	8	1		225	32		257	300
0900	For handicapped lever, add				↓	150			150	165
08 71 20.65 Thresholds										
0010	**THRESHOLDS**									
0011	Threshold 3' long saddles aluminum	1 Carp	48	.167	L.F.	8.15	5.35		13.50	17.95
0100	Aluminum, 8" wide, 1/2" thick		12	.667	Ea.	49	21.50		70.50	89.50
0500	Bronze ♿		60	.133	L.F.	41.50	4.28		45.78	52.50
0600	Bronze, panic threshold, 5" wide, 1/2" thick		12	.667	Ea.	158	21.50		179.50	209
0700	Rubber, 1/2" thick, 5-1/2" wide		20	.400		40	12.85		52.85	65.50
0800	2-3/4" wide	↓	20	.400	↓	37.50	12.85		50.35	63
1950	ADA Compliant Thresholds ♿									
2000	Threshold, wood oak 3-1/2" wide x 24" long	1 Carp	12	.667	Ea.	9	21.50		30.50	46
2010	3-1/2" wide x 36" long		12	.667		13.50	21.50		35	51
2020	3-1/2" wide x 48" long		12	.667		18	21.50		39.50	56
2030	4-1/2" wide x 24" long		12	.667		12	21.50		33.50	49
2040	4-1/2" wide x 36" long		12	.667		17	21.50		38.50	54.50
2050	4-1/2" wide x 48" long		12	.667		23	21.50		44.50	61.50
2060	6-1/2" wide x 24" long		12	.667		16.50	21.50		38	54
2070	6-1/2" wide x 36" long		12	.667		25	21.50		46.50	63.50
2080	6-1/2" wide x 48" long		12	.667		33	21.50		54.50	72.50
2090	Threshold, wood cherry 3-1/2" wide x 24" long		12	.667		13.50	21.50		35	51
2100	3-1/2" wide x 36" long		12	.667		21	21.50		42.50	59
2110	3-1/2" wide x 48" long		12	.667		27	21.50		48.50	65.50
2120	4-1/2" wide x 24" long		12	.667		17.50	21.50		39	55.50
2130	4-1/2" wide x 36" long		12	.667		25.50	21.50		47	64
2140	4-1/2" wide x 48" long		12	.667		34	21.50		55.50	73.50
2150	6-1/2" wide x 24" long		12	.667		25.50	21.50		47	64
2160	6-1/2" wide x 36" long		12	.667		36.50	21.50		58	76
2170	6-1/2" wide x 48" long	↓	12	.667		48.50	21.50		70	89.50

08 71 20 – Hardware

08 71 20.65 Thresholds

	Crew	Daily Output	Labor-Hours	Unit	Material	2014 Bare Costs Labor	Equipment	Total	Total Incl O&P
2180	Threshold, wood walnut 3-1/2" wide x 24" long	1 Carp	12	.667	Ea.	15.50	21.50		37	53
2190	3-1/2" wide x 36" long		12	.667		22	21.50		43.50	60
2200	3-1/2" wide x 48" long		12	.667		30	21.50		51.50	69
2210	4-1/2" wide x 24" long		12	.667		19.50	21.50		41	57.50
2220	4-1/2" wide x 36" long		12	.667		28.50	21.50		50	67.50
2230	4-1/2" wide x 48" long		12	.667		38	21.50		59.50	78
2240	6-1/2" wide x 24" long		12	.667		28	21.50		49.50	67
2250	6-1/2" wide x 36" long		12	.667		41.50	21.50		63	81.50
2260	6-1/2" wide x 48" long		12	.667		55	21.50		76.50	96.50
2300	Threshold, aluminum 4" wide x 36" long		12	.667		33	21.50		54.50	72.50
2310	4" wide x 48" long		12	.667		41	21.50		62.50	81
2320	4" wide x 72" long		12	.667		66	21.50		87.50	109
2330	5" wide x 36" long		12	.667		45	21.50		66.50	85.50
2340	5" wide x 48" long		12	.667		56	21.50		77.50	97.50
2350	5" wide x 72" long		12	.667		89	21.50		110.50	134
2360	6" wide x 36" long		12	.667		53	21.50		74.50	94.50
2370	6" wide x 48" long		12	.667		68	21.50		89.50	111
2380	6" wide x 72" long		12	.667		106	21.50		127.50	153
2390	7" wide x 36" long		12	.667		69	21.50		90.50	112
2400	7" wide x 48" long		12	.667		90	21.50		111.50	135
2410	7" wide x 72" long		12	.667		137	21.50		158.50	187
2500	Threshold, ramp, aluminum or rubber 24" x 24"		12	.667		190	21.50		211.50	245

08 71 20.75 Door Hardware Accessories

	Crew	Daily Output	Labor-Hours	Unit	Material	Labor	Equipment	Total	Total Incl O&P
0010	**DOOR HARDWARE ACCESSORIES**									
1000	Knockers, brass, standard	1 Carp	16	.500	Ea.	44	16.05		60.05	75.50
1100	Deluxe		10	.800		121	25.50		146.50	176
4500	Rubber door silencers		540	.015		.36	.48		.84	1.20

08 71 20.90 Hinges

	Crew	Daily Output	Labor-Hours	Unit	Material	Labor	Equipment	Total	Total Incl O&P
0010	**HINGES** R087120-10									
0012	Full mortise, avg. freq., steel base, USP, 4-1/2" x 4-1/2"				Pr.	36			36	40
0100	5" x 5", USP					57.50			57.50	63
0200	6" x 6", USP					119			119	131
0400	Brass base, 4-1/2" x 4-1/2", US10					58.50			58.50	64.50
0500	5" x 5", US10					86			86	94.50
0600	6" x 6", US10					162			162	178
0800	Stainless steel base, 4-1/2" x 4-1/2", US32					74			74	81.50
0900	For non removable pin, add (security item)				Ea.	4.88			4.88	5.35
0910	For floating pin, driven tips, add					3.30			3.30	3.63
0930	For hospital type tip on pin, add					13.95			13.95	15.35
0940	For steeple type tip on pin, add					18.95			18.95	21
0950	Full mortise, high frequency, steel base, 3-1/2" x 3-1/2", US26D				Pr.	30			30	33
1000	4-1/2" x 4-1/2", USP					63			63	69
1100	5" x 5", USP					50			50	55
1200	6" x 6", USP					134			134	148
1400	Brass base, 3-1/2" x 3-1/2", US4					51			51	56
1430	4-1/2" x 4-1/2", US10					73.50			73.50	81
1500	5" x 5", US10					122			122	134
1600	6" x 6", US10					166			166	183
1800	Stainless steel base, 4-1/2" x 4-1/2", US32					103			103	114
1810	5" x 4-1/2", US32					137			137	151
1930	For hospital type tip on pin, add				Ea.	13.15			13.15	14.45
1950	Full mortise, low frequency, steel base, 3-1/2" x 3-1/2", US26D				Pr.	23			23	25.50

08 71 Door Hardware

08 71 20 – Hardware

08 71 20.90 Hinges

		Crew	Daily Output	Labor-Hours	Unit	Material	2014 Bare Costs Labor	2014 Bare Costs Equipment	Total	Total Incl O&P
2000	4-1/2" x 4-1/2", USP				Pr.	22			22	24.50
2100	5" x 5", USP					47.50			47.50	52
2200	6" x 6", USP					89			89	98
2300	4-1/2" x 4-1/2", US3					17.70			17.70	19.45
2310	5" x 5", US3					42.50			42.50	46.50
2400	Brass bass, 4-1/2" x 4-1/2", US10					53			53	58.50
2500	5" x 5", US10					76.50			76.50	84
2800	Stainless steel base, 4-1/2" x 4-1/2", US32					74.50			74.50	82
8000	Install hinge	1 Carp	34	.235			7.55		7.55	12.70

08 71 20.91 Special Hinges

		Crew	Daily Output	Labor-Hours	Unit	Material	2014 Bare Costs Labor	2014 Bare Costs Equipment	Total	Total Incl O&P
0010	**SPECIAL HINGES**									
8000	Continuous hinges									
8010	Steel, piano, 2" x 72"	1 Carp	20	.400	Ea.	22	12.85		34.85	45.50
8020	Brass, piano, 1-1/16" x 30"		30	.267		8	8.55		16.55	23
8030	Acrylic, piano, 1-3/4" x 12"		40	.200		15	6.40		21.40	27.50

08 71 20.92 Mortised Hinges

		Crew	Daily Output	Labor-Hours	Unit	Material	2014 Bare Costs Labor	2014 Bare Costs Equipment	Total	Total Incl O&P
0010	**MORTISED HINGES**									
0200	Average frequency, steel plated, ball bearing, 3-1/2" x 3-1/2"				Pr.	26			26	28.50
0300	Bronze, ball bearing					30			30	33
0900	High frequency, steel plated, ball bearing					73.50			73.50	81
1100	Bronze, ball bearing					73.50			73.50	81
1300	Average frequency, steel plated, ball bearing, 4-1/2" x 4-1/2"					33.50			33.50	37
1500	Bronze, ball bearing, to 36" wide					34.50			34.50	38
1700	Low frequency, steel, plated, plain bearing					19			19	21
1900	Bronze, plain bearing					26.50			26.50	29.50

08 71 20.95 Kick Plates

		Crew	Daily Output	Labor-Hours	Unit	Material	2014 Bare Costs Labor	2014 Bare Costs Equipment	Total	Total Incl O&P
0010	**KICK PLATES**									
0020	Stainless steel, .050, 16 ga., 8" x 28", US32	1 Carp	15	.533	Ea.	38	17.10		55.10	71
0080	Mop/Kick, 4" x 28"		15	.533		34	17.10		51.10	66.50
0090	4" x 30"		15	.533		36	17.10		53.10	68.50
0100	4" x 34"		15	.533		41	17.10		58.10	74
0110	6" x 28"		15	.533		43	17.10		60.10	76.50
0120	6" x 30"		15	.533		47	17.10		64.10	80.50
0130	6" x 34"		15	.533		53	17.10		70.10	87.50

08 71 21 – Astragals

08 71 21.10 Exterior Mouldings, Astragals

		Crew	Daily Output	Labor-Hours	Unit	Material	2014 Bare Costs Labor	2014 Bare Costs Equipment	Total	Total Incl O&P
0010	**EXTERIOR MOULDINGS, ASTRAGALS**									
4170	Astragal for double doors, aluminum	1 Carp	4	2	Opng.	30.50	64		94.50	142
4174	Bronze	"	4	2	"	46	64		110	159

08 71 25 – Weatherstripping

08 71 25.10 Mechanical Seals, Weatherstripping

		Crew	Daily Output	Labor-Hours	Unit	Material	2014 Bare Costs Labor	2014 Bare Costs Equipment	Total	Total Incl O&P
0010	**MECHANICAL SEALS, WEATHERSTRIPPING**									
1000	Doors, wood frame, interlocking, for 3' x 7' door, zinc	1 Carp	3	2.667	Opng.	44	85.50		129.50	193
1100	Bronze		3	2.667		56	85.50		141.50	206
1300	6' x 7' opening, zinc		2	4		54	128		182	276
1400	Bronze		2	4		65	128		193	288
1500	Vinyl V strip		6.40	1.250	Ea.	11.80	40		51.80	80.50
1700	Wood frame, spring type, bronze									
1800	3' x 7' door	1 Carp	7.60	1.053	Opng.	23	34		57	82.50
1900	6' x 7' door		7	1.143		29.50	36.50		66	94
1920	Felt, 3' x 7' door		14	.571		3.70	18.35		22.05	35

08 71 Door Hardware

08 71 25 – Weatherstripping

08 71 25.10 Mechanical Seals, Weatherstripping

	08 71 25.10 Mechanical Seals, Weatherstripping	Crew	Daily Output	Labor-Hours	Unit	Material	2014 Bare Costs Labor	Equipment	Total	Total Incl O&P
1930	6' x 7' door	1 Carp	13	.615	Opng.	4.33	19.75		24.08	38
1950	Rubber, 3' x 7' door		7.60	1.053		9.10	34		43.10	67
1960	6' x 7' door	↓	7	1.143	↓	11.10	36.50		47.60	73.50
2200	Metal frame, spring type, bronze									
2300	3' x 7' door	1 Carp	3	2.667	Opng.	46.50	85.50		132	195
2400	6' x 7' door	"	2.50	3.200	"	52	103		155	230
2500	For stainless steel, spring type, add					133%				
2700	Metal frame, extruded sections, 3' x 7' door, aluminum	1 Carp	3	2.667	Opng.	28	85.50		113.50	175
2800	Bronze		3	2.667		82	85.50		167.50	234
3100	6' x 7' door, aluminum		1.50	5.333		35	171		206	325
3200	Bronze	↓	1.50	5.333	↓	137	171		308	440
3500	Threshold weatherstripping									
3650	Door sweep, flush mounted, aluminum	1 Carp	25	.320	Ea.	19	10.25		29.25	38.50
3700	Vinyl		25	.320		18	10.25		28.25	37
5000	Garage door bottom weatherstrip, 12' aluminum, clear		14	.571		25	18.35		43.35	58.50
5010	Bronze		14	.571		90	18.35		108.35	130
5050	Bottom protection, Rubber		14	.571		37	18.35		55.35	71.50
5100	Threshold	↓	14	.571	↓	72	18.35		90.35	110

08 75 Window Hardware

08 75 10 – Window Handles and Latches

08 75 10.10 Handles and Latches

	08 75 10.10 Handles and Latches	Crew	Daily Output	Labor-Hours	Unit	Material	2014 Bare Costs Labor	Equipment	Total	Total Incl O&P
0010	**HANDLES AND LATCHES**									
1000	Handles, surface mounted, aluminum	1 Carp	24	.333	Ea.	4.30	10.70		15	22.50
1020	Brass		24	.333		5.55	10.70		16.25	24
1040	Chrome		24	.333		6.90	10.70		17.60	25.50
1500	Recessed, aluminum		12	.667		2.46	21.50		23.96	38.50
1520	Brass		12	.667		3.88	21.50		25.38	40.50
1540	Chrome		12	.667		3.43	21.50		24.93	40
2000	Latches, aluminum		20	.400		3.26	12.85		16.11	25
2020	Brass		20	.400		4.18	12.85		17.03	26
2040	Chrome	↓	20	.400	↓	3.04	12.85		15.89	25

08 75 30 – Weatherstripping

08 75 30.10 Mechanical Weather Seals

	08 75 30.10 Mechanical Weather Seals	Crew	Daily Output	Labor-Hours	Unit	Material	2014 Bare Costs Labor	Equipment	Total	Total Incl O&P
0010	**MECHANICAL WEATHER SEALS**, Window, double hung, 3' X 5'									
0020	Zinc	1 Carp	7.20	1.111	Opng.	20	35.50		55.50	82
0100	Bronze		7.20	1.111		39	35.50		74.50	103
0200	Vinyl V strip		7	1.143		9.25	36.50		45.75	71.50
0500	As above but heavy duty, zinc		4.60	1.739	↓	20	56		76	116
0600	Bronze	↓	4.60	1.739		70	56		126	171

08 79 Hardware Accessories

08 79 20 – Door Accessories

08 79 20.10 Door Hardware Accessories

		Crew	Daily Output	Labor-Hours	Unit	Material	2014 Bare Costs Labor	Equipment	Total	Total Incl O&P
0010	**DOOR HARDWARE ACCESSORIES**									
0140	Door bolt, surface, 4"	1 Carp	32	.250	Ea.	11.70	8.05		19.75	26.50
0160	Door latch	"	12	.667	"	8.55	21.50		30.05	45.50
0200	Sliding closet door									
0220	Track and hanger, single	1 Carp	10	.800	Ea.	56	25.50		81.50	105
0240	Double		8	1		80	32		112	142
0260	Door guide, single		48	.167		30	5.35		35.35	42
0280	Double		48	.167		40	5.35		45.35	53
0600	Deadbolt and lock cover plate, brass or stainless steel		30	.267		28	8.55		36.55	45.50
0620	Hole cover plate, brass or chrome		35	.229		8	7.35		15.35	21
2240	Mortise lockset, passage, lever handle		9	.889		170	28.50		198.50	235
4000	Security chain, standard		18	.444		10	14.25		24.25	35
4100	Deluxe		18	.444		45	14.25		59.25	73.50

08 81 Glass Glazing

08 81 10 – Float Glass

08 81 10.10 Various Types and Thickness of Float Glass

		Crew	Daily Output	Labor-Hours	Unit	Material	2014 Bare Costs Labor	Equipment	Total	Total Incl O&P
0010	**VARIOUS TYPES AND THICKNESS OF FLOAT GLASS**									
0020	3/16" Plain	2 Glaz	130	.123	S.F.	4.93	3.85		8.78	11.80
0200	Tempered, clear		130	.123		6.85	3.85		10.70	13.95
0300	Tinted		130	.123		7.80	3.85		11.65	15
0600	1/4" thick, clear, plain		120	.133		5.75	4.17		9.92	13.30
0700	Tinted		120	.133		9.10	4.17		13.27	16.95
0800	Tempered, clear		120	.133		8.70	4.17		12.87	16.50
0900	Tinted		120	.133		10.70	4.17		14.87	18.75
1600	3/8" thick, clear, plain		75	.213		10.05	6.70		16.75	22
1700	Tinted		75	.213		15.70	6.70		22.40	28.50
1800	Tempered, clear		75	.213		16.40	6.70		23.10	29
1900	Tinted		75	.213		18.55	6.70		25.25	31.50
2200	1/2" thick, clear, plain		55	.291		17	9.10		26.10	34
2300	Tinted		55	.291		27.50	9.10		36.60	45
2400	Tempered, clear		55	.291		24.50	9.10		33.60	41.50
2500	Tinted		55	.291		25.50	9.10		34.60	43
2800	5/8" thick, clear, plain		45	.356		27.50	11.15		38.65	48.50
2900	Tempered, clear		45	.356		31.50	11.15		42.65	53

08 81 25 – Glazing Variables

08 81 25.10 Applications of Glazing

		Crew	Daily Output	Labor-Hours	Unit	Material	2014 Bare Costs Labor	Equipment	Total	Total Incl O&P
0010	**APPLICATIONS OF GLAZING**									
0600	For glass replacement, add				S.F.		100%			
0700	For gasket settings, add				L.F.	5.75			5.75	6.35
0900	For sloped glazing, add				S.F.		26%			
2000	Fabrication, polished edges, 1/4" thick				Inch	.55			.55	.61
2100	1/2" thick					1.30			1.30	1.43
2500	Mitered edges, 1/4" thick					1.30			1.30	1.43
2600	1/2" thick					2.15			2.15	2.37

08 81 30 – Insulating Glass

08 81 30.10 Reduce Heat Transfer Glass

			Crew	Daily Output	Labor-Hours	Unit	Material	2014 Bare Costs Labor	Equipment	Total	Total Incl O&P
0010	**REDUCE HEAT TRANSFER GLASS**										
0015	2 lites 1/8" float, 1/2" thk under 15 S.F.										
0100	Tinted	G	2 Glaz	95	.168	S.F.	13.80	5.25		19.05	24

08 81 Glass Glazing

08 81 30 – Insulating Glass

08 81 30.10 Reduce Heat Transfer Glass

		Crew	Daily Output	Labor-Hours	Unit	Material	2014 Bare Costs Labor	Equipment	Total	Total Incl O&P
0280	Double glazed, 5/8" thk unit, 3/16" float, 15-30 S.F., clear	2 Glaz	90	.178	S.F.	13.70	5.55		19.25	24.50
0400	1" thk, dbl. glazed, 1/4" float, 30-70 S.F., clear G		75	.213		16.60	6.70		23.30	29.50
0500	Tinted G		75	.213		23.50	6.70		30.20	37
2000	Both lites, light & heat reflective G		85	.188		31.50	5.90		37.40	44.50
2500	Heat reflective, film inside, 1" thick unit, clear G		85	.188		27.50	5.90		33.40	40.50
2600	Tinted G		85	.188		28.50	5.90		34.40	41.50
3000	Film on weatherside, clear, 1/2" thick unit G		95	.168		19.60	5.25		24.85	30.50
3100	5/8" thick unit G		90	.178		19.90	5.55		25.45	31.50
3200	1" thick unit G		85	.188		27	5.90		32.90	40
5000	Spectrally selective film, on ext, blocks solar gain/allows 70% of light G	↓	95	.168	↓	12.50	5.25		17.75	22.50

08 81 40 – Plate Glass

08 81 40.10 Plate Glass

		Crew	Daily Output	Labor-Hours	Unit	Material	2014 Bare Costs Labor	Equipment	Total	Total Incl O&P
0010	**PLATE GLASS** Twin ground, polished,									
0015	3/16" thick, material				S.F.	5.15			5.15	5.65
0020	3/16" thick	2 Glaz	100	.160		5.15	5		10.15	13.95
0100	1/4" thick		94	.170		7.05	5.35		12.40	16.65
0200	3/8" thick		60	.267		12.25	8.35		20.60	27.50
0300	1/2" thick	↓	40	.400	↓	24	12.50		36.50	47

08 81 55 – Window Glass

08 81 55.10 Sheet Glass

		Crew	Daily Output	Labor-Hours	Unit	Material	2014 Bare Costs Labor	Equipment	Total	Total Incl O&P
0010	**SHEET GLASS** (window), clear float, stops, putty bed									
0015	1/8" thick, clear float	2 Glaz	480	.033	S.F.	3.60	1.04		4.64	5.70
0500	3/16" thick, clear		480	.033		5.80	1.04		6.84	8.15
0600	Tinted		480	.033		7.45	1.04		8.49	9.95
0700	Tempered	↓	480	.033	↓	9.20	1.04		10.24	11.85

08 83 Mirrors

08 83 13 – Mirrored Glass Glazing

08 83 13.10 Mirrors

		Crew	Daily Output	Labor-Hours	Unit	Material	2014 Bare Costs Labor	Equipment	Total	Total Incl O&P
0010	**MIRRORS**, No frames, wall type, 1/4" plate glass, polished edge									
0100	Up to 5 S.F.	2 Glaz	125	.128	S.F.	9.50	4.01		13.51	17.10
0200	Over 5 S.F.		160	.100		9.25	3.13		12.38	15.40
0500	Door type, 1/4" plate glass, up to 12 S.F.		160	.100		8.55	3.13		11.68	14.60
1000	Float glass, up to 10 S.F., 1/8" thick		160	.100		5.65	3.13		8.78	11.40
1100	3/16" thick		150	.107		6.95	3.34		10.29	13.20
1500	12" x 12" wall tiles, square edge, clear		195	.082		2.22	2.57		4.79	6.70
1600	Veined		195	.082		5.80	2.57		8.37	10.65
2010	Bathroom, unframed, laminated	↓	160	.100	↓	13.30	3.13		16.43	19.80

08 87 Glazing Surface Films

08 87 23 – Safety and Security Films

08 87 23.16 Security Films	Crew	Daily Output	Labor-Hours	Unit	Material	2014 Bare Costs Labor	Equipment	Total	Total Incl O&P
0010 **SECURITY FILMS**, clear, 32000 psi tensile strength, adhered to glass									
0100 .002" thick, daylight installation	H-2	950	.025	S.F.	2.70	.73		3.43	4.18
0150 .004" thick, daylight installation		800	.030		3.35	.86		4.21	5.15
0200 .006" thick, daylight installation		700	.034		3.60	.99		4.59	5.60
0210 Install for anchorage		600	.040		4	1.15		5.15	6.30
0400 .007" thick, daylight installation		600	.040		4.45	1.15		5.60	6.80
0410 Install for anchorage		500	.048		4.94	1.38		6.32	7.75
0500 .008" thick, daylight installation		500	.048		5	1.38		6.38	7.80
0510 Install for anchorage		500	.048		5.55	1.38		6.93	8.40
0600 .015" thick, daylight installation		400	.060		8.80	1.73		10.53	12.60
0610 Install for anchorage		400	.060		5.55	1.73		7.28	9
0900 Security film anchorage, mechanical attachment and cover plate	H-3	370	.043	L.F.	9.75	1.19		10.94	12.70
0950 Security film anchorage, wet glaze structural caulking	1 Glaz	225	.036	"	.92	1.11		2.03	2.86
1000 Adhered security film removal	1 Clab	275	.029	S.F.		.69		.69	1.17

08 91 Louvers

08 91 19 – Fixed Louvers

08 91 19.10 Aluminum Louvers

	Crew	Daily Output	Labor-Hours	Unit	Material	2014 Bare Costs Labor	Equipment	Total	Total Incl O&P
0010 **ALUMINUM LOUVERS**									
0020 Aluminum with screen, residential, 8" x 8"	1 Carp	38	.211	Ea.	17.50	6.75		24.25	30.50
0100 12" x 12"		38	.211		15	6.75		21.75	28
0200 12" x 18"		35	.229		19	7.35		26.35	33.50
0250 14" x 24"		30	.267		26	8.55		34.55	43
0300 18" x 24"		27	.296		29	9.50		38.50	48
0500 24" x 30"		24	.333		62.50	10.70		73.20	87
0700 Triangle, adjustable, small		20	.400		47.50	12.85		60.35	74
0800 Large		15	.533		59	17.10		76.10	94
2100 Midget, aluminum, 3/4" deep, 1" diameter		85	.094		.78	3.02		3.80	5.95
2150 3" diameter		60	.133		2.28	4.28		6.56	9.70
2200 4" diameter		50	.160		3.64	5.15		8.79	12.65
2250 6" diameter		30	.267		4.10	8.55		12.65	18.90

08 95 Vents

08 95 13 – Soffit Vents

08 95 13.10 Wall Louvers

	Crew	Daily Output	Labor-Hours	Unit	Material	2014 Bare Costs Labor	Equipment	Total	Total Incl O&P
0010 **WALL LOUVERS**									
2400 Under eaves vent, aluminum, mill finish, 16" x 4"	1 Carp	48	.167	Ea.	1.90	5.35		7.25	11.10
2500 16" x 8"	"	48	.167	"	2.18	5.35		7.53	11.40

08 95 16 – Wall Vents

08 95 16.10 Louvers

	Crew	Daily Output	Labor-Hours	Unit	Material	2014 Bare Costs Labor	Equipment	Total	Total Incl O&P
0010 **LOUVERS**									
0020 Redwood, 2'-0" diameter, full circle	1 Carp	16	.500	Ea.	190	16.05		206.05	236
0100 Half circle		16	.500		190	16.05		206.05	236
0200 Octagonal		16	.500		142	16.05		158.05	183
0300 Triangular, 5/12 pitch, 5'-0" at base		16	.500		200	16.05		216.05	247
1000 Rectangular, 1'-4" x 1'-3"		16	.500		19.50	16.05		35.55	48.50
1100 Rectangular, 1'-4" x 1'-8"		16	.500		28	16.05		44.05	58
1200 1'-4" x 2'-2"		15	.533		31	17.10		48.10	63.50
1300 1'-9" x 2'-2"		15	.533		37.50	17.10		54.60	70.50

08 95 Vents

08 95 16 – Wall Vents

08 95 16.10 Louvers		Crew	Daily Output	Labor-Hours	Unit	Material	2014 Bare Costs Labor	Equipment	Total	Total Incl O&P
1400	2'-3" x 2'-2"	1 Carp	14	.571	Ea.	49.50	18.35		67.85	85.50
1700	2'-4" x 2'-11"		13	.615		49.50	19.75		69.25	87.50
2000	Aluminum, 12" x 16"		25	.320		20	10.25		30.25	39.50
2010	16" x 20"		25	.320		27.50	10.25		37.75	48
2020	24" x 30"		25	.320		59	10.25		69.25	82.50
2100	6' triangle		12	.667		168	21.50		189.50	221
3100	Round, 2'-2" diameter		16	.500		124	16.05		140.05	163
7000	Vinyl gable vent, 8" x 8"		38	.211		14	6.75		20.75	27
7020	12" x 12"		38	.211		27	6.75		33.75	41
7080	12" x 18"		35	.229		35	7.35		42.35	51
7200	18" x 24"		30	.267		45	8.55		53.55	64

Estimating Tips

General

- Room Finish Schedule: A complete set of plans should contain a room finish schedule. If one is not available, it would be well worth the time and effort to obtain one.

09 20 00 Plaster and Gypsum Board

- Lath is estimated by the square yard plus a 5% allowance for waste. Furring, channels, and accessories are measured by the linear foot. An extra foot should be allowed for each accessory miter or stop.

- Plaster is also estimated by the square yard. Deductions for openings vary by preference, from zero deduction to 50% of all openings over 2 feet in width. The estimator should allow one extra square foot for each linear foot of horizontal interior or exterior angle located below the ceiling level. Also, double the areas of small radius work.

- Drywall accessories, studs, track, and acoustical caulking are all measured by the linear foot. Drywall taping is figured by the square foot. Gypsum wallboard is estimated by the square foot. No material deductions should be made for door or window openings under 32 S.F.

09 60 00 Flooring

- Tile and terrazzo areas are taken off on a square foot basis. Trim and base materials are measured by the linear foot. Accent tiles are listed per each. Two basic methods of installation are used. Mud set is approximately 30% more expensive than thin set. In terrazzo work, be sure to include the linear footage of embedded decorative strips, grounds, machine rubbing, and power cleanup.

- Wood flooring is available in strip, parquet, or block configuration. The latter two types are set in adhesives with quantities estimated by the square foot. The laying pattern will influence labor costs and material waste. In addition to the material and labor for laying wood floors, the estimator must make allowances for sanding and finishing these areas unless the flooring is prefinished.

- Sheet flooring is measured by the square yard. Roll widths vary, so consideration should be given to use the most economical width, as waste must be figured into the total quantity. Consider also the installation methods available, direct glue down or stretched.

09 70 00 Wall Finishes

- Wall coverings are estimated by the square foot. The area to be covered is measured, length by height of wall above baseboards, to calculate the square footage of each wall. This figure is divided by the number of square feet in the single roll which is being used. Deduct, in full, the areas of openings such as doors and windows. Where a pattern match is required allow 25%-30% waste.

09 80 00 Acoustic Treatment

- Acoustical systems fall into several categories. The takeoff of these materials should be by the square foot of area with a 5% allowance for waste. Do not forget about scaffolding, if applicable, when estimating these systems.

09 90 00 Painting and Coating

- A major portion of the work in painting involves surface preparation. Be sure to include cleaning, sanding, filling, and masking costs in the estimate.

- Protection of adjacent surfaces is not included in painting costs. When considering the method of paint application, an important factor is the amount of protection and masking required. These must be estimated separately and may be the determining factor in choosing the method of application.

Reference Numbers

Reference numbers are shown in shaded boxes at the beginning of some major classifications. These numbers refer to related items in the Reference Section. The reference information may be an estimating procedure, an alternate pricing method, or technical information.

Note: Not all subdivisions listed here necessarily appear in this publication.

09 01 Maintenance of Finishes

09 01 70 – Maintenance of Wall Finishes

09 01 70.10 Gypsum Wallboard Repairs

		Crew	Daily Output	Labor-Hours	Unit	Material	2014 Bare Costs Labor	Equipment	Total	Total Incl O&P
0010	**GYPSUM WALLBOARD REPAIRS**									
0100	Fill and sand, pin/nail holes	1 Carp	960	.008	Ea.		.27		.27	.45
0110	Screw head pops		480	.017			.54		.54	.90
0120	Dents, up to 2" square		48	.167		.01	5.35		5.36	9
0130	2" to 4" square		24	.333		.04	10.70		10.74	18.05
0140	Cut square, patch, sand and finish, holes, up to 2" square		12	.667		.04	21.50		21.54	36
0150	2" to 4" square		11	.727		.09	23.50		23.59	39.50
0160	4" to 8" square		10	.800		.24	25.50		25.74	43.50
0170	8" to 12" square		8	1		.47	32		32.47	54.50
0180	12" to 32" square		6	1.333		1.55	43		44.55	73.50
0210	16" by 48"		5	1.600		2.61	51.50		54.11	89.50
0220	32" by 48"		4	2		4.12	64		68.12	113
0230	48" square		3.50	2.286		5.80	73.50		79.30	129
0240	60" square		3.20	2.500		9.35	80.50		89.85	145
0500	Skim coat surface with joint compound		1600	.005	S.F.	.03	.16		.19	.31
0510	Prepare, retape and refinish joints		60	.133	L.F.	.67	4.28		4.95	7.95

09 05 Common Work Results for Finishes

09 05 05 – Selective Finishes Demolition

09 05 05.10 Selective Demolition, Ceilings

		Crew	Daily Output	Labor-Hours	Unit	Material	2014 Bare Costs Labor	Equipment	Total	Total Incl O&P
0010	**SELECTIVE DEMOLITION, CEILINGS** R024119-10									
0200	Ceiling, drywall, furred and nailed or screwed	2 Clab	800	.020	S.F.		.48		.48	.80
1000	Plaster, lime and horse hair, on wood lath, incl. lath		700	.023			.54		.54	.92
1200	Suspended ceiling, mineral fiber, 2' x 2' or 2' x 4'		1500	.011			.25		.25	.43
1250	On suspension system, incl. system		1200	.013			.32		.32	.53
1500	Tile, wood fiber, 12" x 12", glued		900	.018			.42		.42	.71
1540	Stapled		1500	.011			.25		.25	.43
2000	Wood, tongue and groove, 1" x 4"		1000	.016			.38		.38	.64
2040	1" x 8"		1100	.015			.35		.35	.58
2400	Plywood or wood fiberboard, 4' x 8' sheets		1200	.013			.32		.32	.53

09 05 05.20 Selective Demolition, Flooring

		Crew	Daily Output	Labor-Hours	Unit	Material	2014 Bare Costs Labor	Equipment	Total	Total Incl O&P
0010	**SELECTIVE DEMOLITION, FLOORING** R024119-10									
0200	Brick with mortar	2 Clab	475	.034	S.F.		.80		.80	1.35
0400	Carpet, bonded, including surface scraping		2000	.008			.19		.19	.32
0480	Tackless		9000	.002			.04		.04	.07
0550	Carpet tile, releasable adhesive		5000	.003			.08		.08	.13
0560	Permanent adhesive		1850	.009			.21		.21	.35
0800	Resilient, sheet goods		1400	.011			.27		.27	.46
0850	Vinyl or rubber cove base	1 Clab	1000	.008	L.F.		.19		.19	.32
0860	Vinyl or rubber cove base, molded corner	"	1000	.008	Ea.		.19		.19	.32
0870	For glued and caulked installation, add to labor						50%			
0900	Vinyl composition tile, 12" x 12"	2 Clab	1000	.016	S.F.		.38		.38	.64
2000	Tile, ceramic, thin set		675	.024			.56		.56	.95
2020	Mud set		625	.026			.61		.61	1.03
3000	Wood, block, on end	1 Carp	400	.020			.64		.64	1.08
3200	Parquet		450	.018			.57		.57	.96
3400	Strip flooring, interior, 2-1/4" x 25/32" thick		325	.025			.79		.79	1.33
3500	Exterior, porch flooring, 1" x 4"		220	.036			1.17		1.17	1.96
3800	Subfloor, tongue and groove, 1" x 6"		325	.025			.79		.79	1.33
3820	1" x 8"		430	.019			.60		.60	1
3840	1" x 10"		520	.015			.49		.49	.83

09 05 Common Work Results for Finishes

09 05 05 – Selective Finishes Demolition

09 05 05.20 Selective Demolition, Flooring

		Crew	Daily Output	Labor-Hours	Unit	Material	2014 Bare Costs Labor	Equipment	Total	Total Incl O&P
4000	Plywood, nailed	1 Carp	600	.013	S.F.		.43		.43	.72
4100	Glued and nailed		400	.020			.64		.64	1.08
4200	Hardboard, 1/4" thick	↓	760	.011	↓		.34		.34	.57

09 05 05.30 Selective Demolition, Walls and Partitions

		Crew	Daily Output	Labor-Hours	Unit	Material	2014 Bare Costs Labor	Equipment	Total	Total Incl O&P
0010	**SELECTIVE DEMOLITION, WALLS AND PARTITIONS** R024119-10									
0020	Walls, concrete, reinforced	B-39	120	.400	C.F.		9.65	1.95	11.60	18.40
0025	Plain	"	160	.300	"		7.25	1.46	8.71	13.80
1000	Drywall, nailed or screwed	1 Clab	1000	.008	S.F.		.19		.19	.32
1010	2 layers		400	.020			.48		.48	.80
1500	Fiberboard, nailed		900	.009			.21		.21	.36
1568	Plenum barrier, sheet lead	↓	300	.027			.63		.63	1.07
2200	Metal or wood studs, finish 2 sides, fiberboard	B-1	520	.046			1.13		1.13	1.90
2250	Lath and plaster		260	.092			2.26		2.26	3.80
2300	Plasterboard (drywall)		520	.046			1.13		1.13	1.90
2350	Plywood	↓	450	.053			1.31		1.31	2.20
2800	Paneling, 4' x 8' sheets	1 Clab	475	.017			.40		.40	.67
3000	Plaster, lime and horsehair, on wood lath		400	.020			.48		.48	.80
3020	On metal lath		335	.024	↓		.57		.57	.96
3450	Plaster, interior gypsum, acoustic, or cement		60	.133	S.Y.		3.17		3.17	5.35
3500	Stucco, on masonry		145	.055			1.31		1.31	2.21
3510	Commercial 3-coat		80	.100			2.38		2.38	4.01
3520	Interior stucco		25	.320	↓		7.60		7.60	12.80
3760	Tile, ceramic, on walls, thin set		300	.027	S.F.		.63		.63	1.07
3765	Mud set	↓	250	.032	"		.76		.76	1.28

09 22 Supports for Plaster and Gypsum Board

09 22 03 – Fastening Methods for Finishes

09 22 03.20 Drilling Plaster/Drywall

		Crew	Daily Output	Labor-Hours	Unit	Material	2014 Bare Costs Labor	Equipment	Total	Total Incl O&P
0010	**DRILLING PLASTER/DRYWALL**									
1100	Drilling & layout for drywall/plaster walls, up to 1" deep, no anchor									
1200	Holes, 1/4" diameter	1 Carp	150	.053	Ea.	.01	1.71		1.72	2.89
1300	3/8" diameter		140	.057		.01	1.83		1.84	3.10
1400	1/2" diameter		130	.062		.01	1.98		1.99	3.33
1500	3/4" diameter		120	.067		.01	2.14		2.15	3.62
1600	1" diameter		110	.073		.02	2.33		2.35	3.95
1700	1-1/4" diameter		100	.080		.03	2.57		2.60	4.35
1800	1-1/2" diameter	↓	90	.089		.04	2.85		2.89	4.84
1900	For ceiling installations, add				↓		40%			

09 22 13 – Metal Furring

09 22 13.13 Metal Channel Furring

		Crew	Daily Output	Labor-Hours	Unit	Material	2014 Bare Costs Labor	Equipment	Total	Total Incl O&P
0010	**METAL CHANNEL FURRING**									
0030	Beams and columns, 7/8" channels, galvanized, 12" O.C.	1 Lath	155	.052	S.F.	.37	1.47		1.84	2.77
0050	16" O.C.		170	.047		.31	1.34		1.65	2.49
0070	24" O.C.		185	.043		.20	1.23		1.43	2.20
0100	Ceilings, on steel, 7/8" channels, galvanized, 12" O.C.		210	.038		.34	1.08		1.42	2.11
0300	16" O.C.		290	.028		.31	.78		1.09	1.60
0400	24" O.C.		420	.019		.20	.54		.74	1.09
0600	1-5/8" channels, galvanized, 12" O.C.		190	.042		.46	1.20		1.66	2.43
0700	16" O.C.		260	.031		.41	.87		1.28	1.87
0900	24" O.C.	↓	390	.021	↓	.28	.58		.86	1.24

09 22 Supports for Plaster and Gypsum Board

09 22 13 – Metal Furring

09 22 13.13 Metal Channel Furring

		Crew	Daily Output	Labor-Hours	Unit	Material	2014 Bare Costs Labor	Equipment	Total	Total Incl O&P
0930	7/8" channels with sound isolation clips, 12" O.C.	1 Lath	120	.067	S.F.	1.72	1.89		3.61	4.94
0940	16" O.C.		100	.080		1.29	2.27		3.56	5.10
0950	24" O.C.		165	.048		.86	1.38		2.24	3.16
0960	1-5/8" channels, galvanized, 12" O.C.		110	.073		1.83	2.07		3.90	5.35
0970	16" O.C.		100	.080		1.38	2.27		3.65	5.15
0980	24" O.C.		155	.052		.92	1.47		2.39	3.37
1000	Walls, 7/8" channels, galvanized, 12" O.C.		235	.034		.34	.97		1.31	1.93
1200	16" O.C.		265	.030		.31	.86		1.17	1.72
1300	24" O.C.		350	.023		.20	.65		.85	1.26
1500	1-5/8" channels, galvanized, 12" O.C.		210	.038		.46	1.08		1.54	2.25
1600	16" O.C.		240	.033		.41	.95		1.36	1.98
1800	24" O.C.		305	.026		.28	.74		1.02	1.50
1920	7/8" channels with sound isolation clips, 12" O.C.		125	.064		1.72	1.82		3.54	4.81
1940	16" O.C.		100	.080		1.29	2.27		3.56	5.10
1950	24" O.C.		150	.053		.86	1.51		2.37	3.38
1960	1-5/8" channels, galvanized, 12" O.C.		115	.070		1.83	1.98		3.81	5.20
1970	16" O.C.		95	.084		1.38	2.39		3.77	5.35
1980	24" O.C.		140	.057		.92	1.62		2.54	3.62

09 22 16 – Non-Structural Metal Framing

09 22 16.13 Non-Structural Metal Stud Framing

		Crew	Daily Output	Labor-Hours	Unit	Material	2014 Bare Costs Labor	Equipment	Total	Total Incl O&P
0010	**NON-STRUCTURAL METAL STUD FRAMING**									
1600	Non-load bearing, galv., 8' high, 25 ga. 1-5/8" wide, 16" O.C.	1 Carp	619	.013	S.F.	.27	.41		.68	1
1610	24" O.C.		950	.008		.20	.27		.47	.68
1620	2-1/2" wide, 16" O.C.		613	.013		.32	.42		.74	1.05
1630	24" O.C.		938	.009		.24	.27		.51	.73
1640	3-5/8" wide, 16" O.C.		600	.013		.39	.43		.82	1.14
1650	24" O.C.		925	.009		.29	.28		.57	.79
1660	4" wide, 16" O.C.		594	.013		.42	.43		.85	1.20
1670	24" O.C.		925	.009		.32	.28		.60	.82
1680	6" wide, 16" O.C.		588	.014		.53	.44		.97	1.31
1690	24" O.C.		906	.009		.40	.28		.68	.92
1700	20 ga. studs, 1-5/8" wide, 16" O.C.		494	.016		.38	.52		.90	1.28
1710	24" O.C.		763	.010		.28	.34		.62	.88
1720	2-1/2" wide, 16" O.C.		488	.016		.46	.53		.99	1.39
1730	24" O.C.		750	.011		.35	.34		.69	.96
1740	3-5/8" wide, 16" O.C.		481	.017		.50	.53		1.03	1.45
1750	24" O.C.		738	.011		.37	.35		.72	1
1760	4" wide, 16" O.C.		475	.017		.60	.54		1.14	1.57
1770	24" O.C.		738	.011		.45	.35		.80	1.09
1780	6" wide, 16" O.C.		469	.017		.76	.55		1.31	1.75
1790	24" O.C.		725	.011		.57	.35		.92	1.23
2000	Non-load bearing, galv., 10' high, 25 ga. 1-5/8" wide, 16" O.C.		495	.016		.26	.52		.78	1.15
2100	24" O.C.		760	.011		.19	.34		.53	.78
2200	2-1/2" wide, 16" O.C.		490	.016		.30	.52		.82	1.21
2250	24" O.C.		750	.011		.22	.34		.56	.83
2300	3-5/8" wide, 16" O.C.		480	.017		.36	.54		.90	1.30
2350	24" O.C.		740	.011		.27	.35		.62	.88
2400	4" wide, 16" O.C.		475	.017		.40	.54		.94	1.35
2450	24" O.C.		740	.011		.30	.35		.65	.90
2500	6" wide, 16" O.C.		470	.017		.50	.55		1.05	1.47
2550	24" O.C.		725	.011		.37	.35		.72	1.01
2600	20 ga. studs, 1-5/8" wide, 16" O.C.		395	.020		.36	.65		1.01	1.48

09 22 Supports for Plaster and Gypsum Board

09 22 16 – Non-Structural Metal Framing

09 22 16.13 Non-Structural Metal Stud Framing

		Crew	Daily Output	Labor-Hours	Unit	Material	2014 Bare Costs Labor	Equipment	Total	Total Incl O&P
2650	24" O.C.	1 Carp	610	.013	S.F.	.26	.42		.68	1
2700	2-1/2" wide, 16" O.C.		390	.021		.43	.66		1.09	1.59
2750	24" O.C.		600	.013		.32	.43		.75	1.07
2800	3-5/8" wide, 16" OC		385	.021		.47	.67		1.14	1.64
2850	24" O.C.		590	.014		.35	.44		.79	1.11
2900	4" wide, 16" O.C.		380	.021		.57	.68		1.25	1.77
2950	24" O.C.		590	.014		.42	.44		.86	1.19
3000	6" wide, 16" O.C.		375	.021		.72	.68		1.40	1.94
3050	24" O.C.		580	.014		.53	.44		.97	1.32
3060	Non-load bearing, galv., 12' high, 25 ga. 1-5/8" wide, 16" O.C.		413	.019		.25	.62		.87	1.32
3070	24" O.C.		633	.013		.18	.41		.59	.88
3080	2-1/2" wide, 16" O.C.		408	.020		.29	.63		.92	1.38
3090	24" O.C.		625	.013		.21	.41		.62	.92
3100	3-5/8" wide, 16" O.C.		400	.020		.35	.64		.99	1.46
3110	24" O.C.		617	.013		.25	.42		.67	.98
3120	4" wide, 16" O.C.		396	.020		.38	.65		1.03	1.51
3130	24" O.C.		617	.013		.28	.42		.70	1.01
3140	6" wide, 16" O.C.		392	.020		.48	.66		1.14	1.63
3150	24" O.C.		604	.013		.35	.43		.78	1.10
3160	20 ga. studs, 1-5/8" wide, 16" O.C.		329	.024		.34	.78		1.12	1.68
3170	24" O.C.		508	.016		.25	.51		.76	1.12
3180	2-1/2" wide, 16" O.C.		325	.025		.41	.79		1.20	1.78
3190	24" O.C.		500	.016		.30	.51		.81	1.19
3200	3-5/8" wide, 16" O.C.		321	.025		.45	.80		1.25	1.85
3210	24" O.C.		492	.016		.33	.52		.85	1.24
3220	4" wide, 16" O.C.		317	.025		.55	.81		1.36	1.96
3230	24" O.C.		492	.016		.40	.52		.92	1.32
3240	6" wide, 16" O.C.		313	.026		.69	.82		1.51	2.14
3250	24" O.C.	↓	483	.017	↓	.50	.53		1.03	1.44
5000	Load bearing studs, see Section 05 41 13.30									

09 22 26 – Suspension Systems

09 22 26.13 Ceiling Suspension Systems

		Crew	Daily Output	Labor-Hours	Unit	Material	2014 Bare Costs Labor	Equipment	Total	Total Incl O&P
0010	**CEILING SUSPENSION SYSTEMS** for gypsum board or plaster									
8000	Suspended ceilings, including carriers									
8200	1-1/2" carriers, 24" O.C. with:									
8300	7/8" channels, 16" O.C.	1 Lath	275	.029	S.F.	.51	.83		1.34	1.89
8320	24" O.C.		310	.026		.41	.73		1.14	1.63
8400	1-5/8" channels, 16" O.C.		205	.039		.62	1.11		1.73	2.46
8420	24" O.C.	↓	250	.032	↓	.48	.91		1.39	1.99
8600	2" carriers, 24" O.C. with:									
8700	7/8" channels, 16" O.C.	1 Lath	250	.032	S.F.	.56	.91		1.47	2.07
8720	24" O.C.		285	.028		.45	.80		1.25	1.78
8800	1-5/8" channels, 16" O.C.		190	.042		.66	1.20		1.86	2.65
8820	24" O.C.	↓	225	.036	↓	.53	1.01		1.54	2.21

09 22 36 – Lath

09 22 36.13 Gypsum Lath

		Crew	Daily Output	Labor-Hours	Unit	Material	2014 Bare Costs Labor	Equipment	Total	Total Incl O&P
0011	**GYPSUM LATH** Plain or perforated, nailed, 3/8" thick	1 Lath	765	.010	S.F.	.30	.30		.60	.81
0101	1/2" thick, nailed		720	.011		.27	.32		.59	.81
0301	Clipped to steel studs, 3/8" thick		675	.012		.30	.34		.64	.87
0401	1/2" thick		630	.013		.27	.36		.63	.88
0601	Firestop gypsum base, to steel studs, 3/8" thick		630	.013		.27	.36		.63	.88
0701	1/2" thick	↓	585	.014	↓	.30	.39		.69	.96

09 22 Supports for Plaster and Gypsum Board

09 22 36 – Lath

09 22 36.13 Gypsum Lath

		Crew	Daily Output	Labor-Hours	Unit	Material	2014 Bare Costs Labor	Equipment	Total	Total Incl O&P
0901	Foil back, to steel studs, 3/8" thick	1 Lath	675	.012	S.F.	.36	.34		.70	.94
1001	1/2" thick		630	.013		.39	.36		.75	1.01
1501	For ceiling installations, add		1950	.004			.12		.12	.19
1601	For columns and beams, add		1550	.005			.15		.15	.24

09 22 36.23 Metal Lath

		Crew	Daily Output	Labor-Hours	Unit	Material	2014 Bare Costs Labor	Equipment	Total	Total Incl O&P
0010	**METAL LATH** R092000-50									
3601	2.5 lb. diamond painted, on wood framing, on walls	1 Lath	765	.010	S.F.	.42	.30		.72	.95
3701	On ceilings		675	.012		.42	.34		.76	1.01
4201	3.4 lb. diamond painted, wired to steel framing, on walls		675	.012		.43	.34		.77	1.01
4301	On ceilings		540	.015		.43	.42		.85	1.15
5101	Rib lath, painted, wired to steel, on walls, 2.75 lb.		675	.012		.33	.34		.67	.90
5201	3.4 lb.		630	.013		.44	.36		.80	1.06
5701	Suspended ceiling system, incl. 3.4 lb. diamond lath, painted		135	.059		.49	1.68		2.17	3.25
5801	Galvanized		135	.059		.49	1.68		2.17	3.25

09 22 36.83 Accessories, Plaster

		Crew	Daily Output	Labor-Hours	Unit	Material	2014 Bare Costs Labor	Equipment	Total	Total Incl O&P
0010	**ACCESSORIES, PLASTER**									
0020	Casing bead, expanded flange, galvanized	1 Lath	2.70	2.963	C.L.F.	50.50	84		134.50	191
0200	Foundation weep screed, galvanized	"	2.70	2.963		52	84		136	192
0900	Channels, cold rolled, 16 ga., 3/4" deep, galvanized					34			34	37.50
1620	Corner bead, expanded bullnose, 3/4" radius, #10, galvanized	1 Lath	2.60	3.077		25	87.50		112.50	169
1650	#1, galvanized		2.55	3.137		44	89		133	192
1670	Expanded wing, 2-3/4" wide, #1, galvanized		2.65	3.019		37	85.50		122.50	179
1700	Inside corner (corner rite), 3" x 3", painted		2.60	3.077		21	87.50		108.50	165
1750	Strip-ex, 4" wide, painted		2.55	3.137		37	89		126	184
1800	Expansion joint, 3/4" grounds, limited expansion, galv., 1 piece		2.70	2.963		81.50	84		165.50	225
2100	Extreme expansion, galvanized, 2 piece		2.60	3.077		149	87.50		236.50	305

09 23 Gypsum Plastering

09 23 13 – Acoustical Gypsum Plastering

09 23 13.10 Perlite or Vermiculite Plaster

		Crew	Daily Output	Labor-Hours	Unit	Material	2014 Bare Costs Labor	Equipment	Total	Total Incl O&P
0010	**PERLITE OR VERMICULITE PLASTER** R092000-50									
0020	In 100 lb. bags, under 200 bags				Bag	16.65			16.65	18.30
0301	2 coats, no lath included, on walls	J-1	830	.048	S.F.	.42	1.35	.17	1.94	2.87
0401	On ceilings		710	.056		.42	1.58	.20	2.20	3.28
0901	3 coats, no lath included, on walls		665	.060		.70	1.69	.22	2.61	3.78
1001	On ceilings		565	.071		.70	1.98	.25	2.93	4.32
1700	For irregular or curved surfaces, add to above				S.Y.		30%			
1800	For columns and beams, add to above						50%			
1900	For soffits, add to ceiling prices						40%			

09 23 20 – Gypsum Plaster

09 23 20.10 Gypsum Plaster On Walls and Ceilings

		Crew	Daily Output	Labor-Hours	Unit	Material	2014 Bare Costs Labor	Equipment	Total	Total Incl O&P
0010	**GYPSUM PLASTER ON WALLS AND CEILINGS** R092000-50									
0020	80# bag, less than 1 ton				Bag	14.45			14.45	15.85
0302	2 coats, no lath included, on walls	J-1	750	.053	S.F.	.37	1.49	.19	2.05	3.08
0402	On ceilings		660	.061		.37	1.70	.22	2.29	3.45
0903	3 coats, no lath included, on walls		620	.065		.54	1.81	.23	2.58	3.82
1002	On ceilings		560	.071		1.01	2	.26	3.27	4.68
1600	For irregular or curved surfaces, add						30%			
1800	For columns & beams, add						50%			

09 24 Cement Plastering

09 24 23 – Cement Stucco

09 24 23.40 Stucco

		Crew	Daily Output	Labor-Hours	Unit	Material	2014 Bare Costs Labor	Equipment	Total	Total Incl O&P
0010	**STUCCO** R092000-50									
0011	3 coats 1" thick, float finish, with mesh, on wood frame	J-2	470	.102	S.F.	.94	2.87	.31	4.12	6.05
0101	On masonry construction	J-1	495	.081		.25	2.27	.29	2.81	4.33
0151	2 coats, 3/4" thick, float finish, no lath incl.	"	980	.041		.25	1.14	.15	1.54	2.32
0301	For trowel finish, add	1 Plas	1530	.005	↓		.15		.15	.25
0600	For coloring and special finish, add, minimum	J-1	685	.058	S.Y.	.39	1.64	.21	2.24	3.35
0700	Maximum		200	.200	"	1.38	5.60	.72	7.70	11.50
1001	Exterior stucco, with bonding agent, 3 coats, on walls		1800	.022	S.F.	.36	.62	.08	1.06	1.50
1201	Ceilings		1620	.025		.36	.69	.09	1.14	1.63
1301	Beams		720	.056		.36	1.56	.20	2.12	3.17
1501	Columns	↓	900	.044		.36	1.25	.16	1.77	2.62
1601	Mesh, painted, nailed to wood, 1.8 lb.	1 Lath	540	.015		.69	.42		1.11	1.44
1801	3.6 lb.		495	.016		.45	.46		.91	1.23
1901	Wired to steel, painted, 1.8 lb.		477	.017		.69	.48		1.17	1.53
2101	3.6 lb.	↓	450	.018	↓	.45	.51		.96	1.30

09 25 Other Plastering

09 25 23 – Lime Based Plastering

09 25 23.10 Venetian Plaster

		Crew	Daily Output	Labor-Hours	Unit	Material	2014 Bare Costs Labor	Equipment	Total	Total Incl O&P
0010	**VENETIAN PLASTER**									
0100	Walls, 1 coat primer, roller applied	1 Plas	950	.008	S.F.	.16	.25		.41	.59
0220	For pigment, dark colors add				Gal.	50			50	55
0300	For sealer/wax coat incl. burnishing, add	1 Plas	300	.027	S.F.	.41	.78		1.19	1.74

09 26 Veneer Plastering

09 26 13 – Gypsum Veneer Plastering

09 26 13.20 Blueboard

		Crew	Daily Output	Labor-Hours	Unit	Material	2014 Bare Costs Labor	Equipment	Total	Total Incl O&P
0010	**BLUEBOARD** For use with thin coat									
0100	plaster application see Section 09 26 13.80									
1000	3/8" thick, on walls or ceilings, standard, no finish included	2 Carp	1900	.008	S.F.	.31	.27		.58	.79
1100	With thin coat plaster finish		875	.018		.41	.59		1	1.44
1400	On beams, columns, or soffits, standard, no finish included		675	.024		.36	.76		1.12	1.67
1450	With thin coat plaster finish		475	.034		.46	1.08		1.54	2.32
3000	1/2" thick, on walls or ceilings, standard, no finish included		1900	.008		.31	.27		.58	.79
3100	With thin coat plaster finish		875	.018		.41	.59		1	1.44
3300	Fire resistant, no finish included		1900	.008		.31	.27		.58	.79
3400	With thin coat plaster finish		875	.018		.41	.59		1	1.44
3450	On beams, columns, or soffits, standard, no finish included		675	.024		.36	.76		1.12	1.67
3500	With thin coat plaster finish		475	.034		.46	1.08		1.54	2.32
3700	Fire resistant, no finish included		675	.024		.36	.76		1.12	1.67
3800	With thin coat plaster finish		475	.034		.46	1.08		1.54	2.32
5000	5/8" thick, on walls or ceilings, fire resistant, no finish included		1900	.008		.33	.27		.60	.81
5100	With thin coat plaster finish		875	.018		.43	.59		1.02	1.46
5500	On beams, columns, or soffits, no finish included		675	.024		.38	.76		1.14	1.70
5600	With thin coat plaster finish		475	.034		.48	1.08		1.56	2.35
6000	For high ceilings, over 8' high, add		3060	.005			.17		.17	.28
6500	For over 3 stories high, add per story		6100	.003	↓		.08		.08	.14

09 26 13.80 Thin Coat Plaster

		Crew	Daily Output	Labor-Hours	Unit	Material	2014 Bare Costs Labor	Equipment	Total	Total Incl O&P
0010	**THIN COAT PLASTER** R092000-50									

09 26 Veneer Plastering

09 26 13 – Gypsum Veneer Plastering

09 26 13.80 Thin Coat Plaster	Crew	Daily Output	Labor-Hours	Unit	Material	2014 Bare Costs Labor	Equipment	Total	Total Incl O&P
0012	1 coat veneer, not incl. lath	J-1	3600	.011	S.F.	.10	.31	.04	.45	.66
1000	In 50 lb. bags				Bag	13.70			13.70	15.10

09 28 Backing Boards and Underlayments

09 28 13 – Cementitious Backing Boards

09 28 13.10 Cementitious Backerboard

		Crew	Daily Output	Labor-Hours	Unit	Material	Labor	Equipment	Total	Total Incl O&P
0010	**CEMENTITIOUS BACKERBOARD**									
0070	Cementitious backerboard, on floor, 3' x 4' x 1/2" sheets	2 Carp	525	.030	S.F.	.80	.98		1.78	2.53
0080	3' x 5' x 1/2" sheets		525	.030		.74	.98		1.72	2.47
0090	3' x 6' x 1/2" sheets		525	.030		.74	.98		1.72	2.46
0100	3' x 4' x 5/8" sheets		525	.030		1.02	.98		2	2.77
0110	3' x 5' x 5/8" sheets		525	.030		.99	.98		1.97	2.73
0120	3' x 6' x 5/8" sheets		525	.030		.96	.98		1.94	2.71
0150	On wall, 3' x 4' x 1/2" sheets		350	.046		.80	1.47		2.27	3.35
0160	3' x 5' x 1/2" sheets		350	.046		.74	1.47		2.21	3.29
0170	3' x 6' x 1/2" sheets		350	.046		.74	1.47		2.21	3.28
0180	3' x 4' x 5/8" sheets		350	.046		1.02	1.47		2.49	3.59
0190	3' x 5' x 5/8" sheets		350	.046		.99	1.47		2.46	3.55
0200	3' x 6' x 5/8" sheets		350	.046		.96	1.47		2.43	3.53
0250	On counter, 3' x 4' x 1/2" sheets		180	.089		.80	2.85		3.65	5.70
0260	3' x 5' x 1/2" sheets		180	.089		.74	2.85		3.59	5.60
0270	3' x 6' x 1/2" sheets		180	.089		.74	2.85		3.59	5.60
0300	3' x 4' x 5/8" sheets		180	.089		1.02	2.85		3.87	5.90
0310	3' x 5' x 5/8" sheets		180	.089		.99	2.85		3.84	5.90
0320	3' x 6' x 5/8" sheets		180	.089		.96	2.85		3.81	5.85

09 29 Gypsum Board

09 29 10 – Gypsum Board Panels

09 29 10.20 Taping and Finishing

		Crew	Daily Output	Labor-Hours	Unit	Material	Labor	Equipment	Total	Total Incl O&P
0010	**TAPING AND FINISHING**									
3600	For taping and finishing joints, add	2 Carp	2000	.008	S.F.	.05	.26		.31	.48
4500	For thin coat plaster instead of taping, add	J-1	3600	.011	"	.10	.31	.04	.45	.66

09 29 10.30 Gypsum Board

		Crew	Daily Output	Labor-Hours	Unit	Material	Labor	Equipment	Total	Total Incl O&P
0010	**GYPSUM BOARD** on walls & ceilings R092910-10									
0100	Nailed or screwed to studs unless otherwise noted									
0110	1/4" thick, on walls or ceilings, standard, no finish included	2 Carp	1330	.012	S.F.	.31	.39		.70	.99
0115	1/4" thick, on walls or ceilings, flexible, no finish included		1050	.015		.47	.49		.96	1.34
0117	1/4" thick, on columns or soffits, flexible, no finish included		1050	.015		.47	.49		.96	1.34
0130	1/4" thick, standard, no finish included, less than 800 S.F.		510	.031		.31	1.01		1.32	2.03
0150	3/8" thick, on walls, standard, no finish included		2000	.008		.31	.26		.57	.77
0200	On ceilings, standard, no finish included		1800	.009		.31	.29		.60	.82
0250	On beams, columns, or soffits, no finish included		675	.024		.31	.76		1.07	1.62
0300	1/2" thick, on walls, standard, no finish included		2000	.008		.30	.26		.56	.76
0350	Taped and finished (level 4 finish)		965	.017		.35	.53		.88	1.28
0390	With compound skim coat (level 5 finish)		775	.021		.41	.66		1.07	1.57
0400	Fire resistant, no finish included		2000	.008		.32	.26		.58	.78
0450	Taped and finished (level 4 finish)		965	.017		.37	.53		.90	1.31
0490	With compound skim coat (level 5 finish)		775	.021		.43	.66		1.09	1.59
0500	Water resistant, no finish included		2000	.008		.38	.26		.64	.85

09 29 Gypsum Board

09 29 10 – Gypsum Board Panels

09 29 10.30 Gypsum Board	Crew	Daily Output	Labor-Hours	Unit	Material	2014 Bare Costs Labor	Equipment	Total	Total Incl O&P
0550	Taped and finished (level 4 finish)	2 Carp	965	.017	S.F.	.43	.53		.96	1.37
0590	With compound skim coat (level 5 finish)		775	.021		.49	.66		1.15	1.65
0600	Prefinished, vinyl, clipped to studs		900	.018		.48	.57		1.05	1.49
0700	Mold resistant, no finish included		2000	.008		.40	.26		.66	.87
0710	Taped and finished (level 4 finish)		965	.017		.45	.53		.98	1.39
0720	With compound skim coat (level 5 finish)		775	.021		.51	.66		1.17	1.68
1000	On ceilings, standard, no finish included		1800	.009		.30	.29		.59	.81
1050	Taped and finished (level 4 finish)		765	.021		.35	.67		1.02	1.51
1090	With compound skim coat (level 5 finish)		610	.026		.41	.84		1.25	1.87
1100	Fire resistant, no finish included		1800	.009		.32	.29		.61	.83
1150	Taped and finished (level 4 finish)		765	.021		.37	.67		1.04	1.54
1195	With compound skim coat (level 5 finish)		610	.026		.43	.84		1.27	1.89
1200	Water resistant, no finish included		1800	.009		.38	.29		.67	.90
1250	Taped and finished (level 4 finish)		765	.021		.43	.67		1.10	1.60
1290	With compound skim coat (level 5 finish)		610	.026		.49	.84		1.33	1.95
1310	Mold resistant, no finish included		1800	.009		.40	.29		.69	.92
1320	Taped and finished (level 4 finish)		765	.021		.45	.67		1.12	1.62
1330	With compound skim coat (level 5 finish)		610	.026		.51	.84		1.35	1.98
1350	Sag resistant, no finish included		1600	.010		.32	.32		.64	.89
1360	Taped and finished (level 4 finish)		765	.021		.37	.67		1.04	1.54
1370	With compound skim coat (level 5 finish)		610	.026		.43	.84		1.27	1.89
1500	On beams, columns, or soffits, standard, no finish included		675	.024		.35	.76		1.11	1.66
1550	Taped and finished (level 4 finish)		540	.030		.35	.95		1.30	1.98
1590	With compound skim coat (level 5 finish)		475	.034		.41	1.08		1.49	2.27
1600	Fire resistant, no finish included		675	.024		.32	.76		1.08	1.63
1650	Taped and finished (level 4 finish)		540	.030		.37	.95		1.32	2.01
1690	With compound skim coat (level 5 finish)		475	.034		.43	1.08		1.51	2.29
1700	Water resistant, no finish included		675	.024		.44	.76		1.20	1.76
1750	Taped and finished (level 4 finish)		540	.030		.43	.95		1.38	2.07
1790	With compound skim coat (level 5 finish)		475	.034		.49	1.08		1.57	2.35
1800	Mold resistant, no finish included		675	.024		.46	.76		1.22	1.79
1810	Taped and finished (level 4 finish)		540	.030		.45	.95		1.40	2.09
1820	With compound skim coat (level 5 finish)		475	.034		.51	1.08		1.59	2.38
1850	Sag resistant, no finish included		675	.024		.37	.76		1.13	1.68
1860	Taped and finished (level 4 finish)		540	.030		.37	.95		1.32	2.01
1870	With compound skim coat (level 5 finish)		475	.034		.43	1.08		1.51	2.29
2000	5/8" thick, on walls, standard, no finish included		2000	.008		.32	.26		.58	.78
2050	Taped and finished (level 4 finish)		965	.017		.37	.53		.90	1.31
2090	With compound skim coat (level 5 finish)		775	.021		.43	.66		1.09	1.59
2100	Fire resistant, no finish included		2000	.008		.34	.26		.60	.80
2150	Taped and finished (level 4 finish)		965	.017		.39	.53		.92	1.33
2195	With compound skim coat (level 5 finish)		775	.021		.45	.66		1.11	1.61
2200	Water resistant, no finish included		2000	.008		.45	.26		.71	.93
2250	Taped and finished (level 4 finish)		965	.017		.50	.53		1.03	1.45
2290	With compound skim coat (level 5 finish)		775	.021		.56	.66		1.22	1.73
2300	Prefinished, vinyl, clipped to studs		900	.018		.89	.57		1.46	1.94
2510	Mold resistant, no finish included		2000	.008		.45	.26		.71	.93
2520	Taped and finished (level 4 finish)		965	.017		.50	.53		1.03	1.45
2530	With compound skim coat (level 5 finish)		775	.021		.56	.66		1.22	1.73
3000	On ceilings, standard, no finish included		1800	.009		.32	.29		.61	.83
3050	Taped and finished (level 4 finish)		765	.021		.37	.67		1.04	1.54
3090	With compound skim coat (level 5 finish)		615	.026		.43	.84		1.27	1.88
3100	Fire resistant, no finish included		1800	.009		.34	.29		.63	.85

09 29 10.30 Gypsum Board		Crew	Daily Output	Labor-Hours	Unit	Material	2014 Bare Costs Labor	Equipment	Total	Total Incl O&P
3150	Taped and finished (level 4 finish)	2 Carp	765	.021	S.F.	.39	.67		1.06	1.56
3190	With compound skim coat (level 5 finish)		615	.026		.45	.84		1.29	1.90
3200	Water resistant, no finish included		1800	.009		.45	.29		.74	.98
3250	Taped and finished (level 4 finish)		765	.021		.50	.67		1.17	1.68
3290	With compound skim coat (level 5 finish)		615	.026		.56	.84		1.40	2.02
3300	Mold resistant, no finish included		1800	.009		.45	.29		.74	.98
3310	Taped and finished (level 4 finish)		765	.021		.50	.67		1.17	1.68
3320	With compound skim coat (level 5 finish)		615	.026		.56	.84		1.40	2.02
3500	On beams, columns, or soffits, no finish included		675	.024		.37	.76		1.13	1.68
3550	Taped and finished (level 4 finish)		475	.034		.43	1.08		1.51	2.29
3590	With compound skim coat (level 5 finish)		380	.042		.49	1.35		1.84	2.81
3600	Fire resistant, no finish included		675	.024		.39	.76		1.15	1.71
3650	Taped and finished (level 4 finish)		475	.034		.45	1.08		1.53	2.31
3690	With compound skim coat (level 5 finish)		380	.042		.45	1.35		1.80	2.76
3700	Water resistant, no finish included		675	.024		.52	.76		1.28	1.85
3750	Taped and finished (level 4 finish)		475	.034		.56	1.08		1.64	2.43
3790	With compound skim coat (level 5 finish)		380	.042		.57	1.35		1.92	2.90
3800	Mold resistant, no finish included		675	.024		.52	.76		1.28	1.85
3810	Taped and finished (level 4 finish)		475	.034		.56	1.08		1.64	2.43
3820	With compound skim coat (level 5 finish)		380	.042		.57	1.35		1.92	2.90
4000	Fireproofing, beams or columns, 2 layers, 1/2" thick, incl finish		330	.048		.74	1.56		2.30	3.43
4010	Mold resistant		330	.048		.90	1.56		2.46	3.61
4050	5/8" thick		300	.053		.78	1.71		2.49	3.74
4060	Mold resistant		300	.053		1	1.71		2.71	3.98
4100	3 layers, 1/2" thick		225	.071		1.11	2.28		3.39	5.05
4110	Mold resistant		225	.071		1.35	2.28		3.63	5.30
4150	5/8" thick		210	.076		1.17	2.45		3.62	5.40
4160	Mold resistant		210	.076		1.50	2.45		3.95	5.75
5200	For work over 8' high, add	▼	3060	.005			.17		.17	.28
5270	For textured spray, add	2 Lath	1600	.010		.04	.28		.32	.50
5350	For finishing inner corners, add	2 Carp	950	.017	L.F.	.11	.54		.65	1.03
5355	For finishing outer corners, add	"	1250	.013		.23	.41		.64	.95
5500	For acoustical sealant, add per bead	1 Carp	500	.016	▼	.04	.51		.55	.91
5550	Sealant, 1 quart tube				Ea.	7.05			7.05	7.80
6000	Gypsum sound dampening panels									
6010	1/2" thick on walls, multi-layer, light weight, no finish included	2 Carp	1500	.011	S.F.	1.87	.34		2.21	2.64
6015	Taped and finished (level 4 finish)		725	.022		1.92	.71		2.63	3.30
6020	With compound skim coat (level 5 finish)		580	.028		1.98	.89		2.87	3.66
6025	5/8" thick on walls, for wood studs, no finish included		1500	.011		2.70	.34		3.04	3.55
6030	Taped and finished (level 4 finish)		725	.022		2.75	.71		3.46	4.21
6035	With compound skim coat (level 5 finish)		580	.028		2.81	.89		3.70	4.58
6040	For metal stud, no finish included		1500	.011		2.06	.34		2.40	2.85
6045	Taped and finished (level 4 finish)		725	.022		2.11	.71		2.82	3.51
6050	With compound skim coat (level 5 finish)		580	.028		2.17	.89		3.06	3.87
6055	Abuse resist, no finish included		1500	.011		3.75	.34		4.09	4.71
6060	Taped and finished (level 4 finish)		725	.022		3.80	.71		4.51	5.35
6065	With compound skim coat (level 5 finish)		580	.028		3.86	.89		4.75	5.75
6070	Shear rated, no finish included		1500	.011		4.30	.34		4.64	5.30
6075	Taped and finished (level 4 finish)		725	.022		4.35	.71		5.06	5.95
6080	With compound skim coat (level 5 finish)		580	.028		4.41	.89		5.30	6.35
6085	For SCIF applications, no finish included		1500	.011		4.72	.34		5.06	5.80
6090	Taped and finished (level 4 finish)		725	.022		4.77	.71		5.48	6.45
6095	With compound skim coat (level 5 finish)	▼	580	.028	▼	4.83	.89		5.72	6.80

09 29 Gypsum Board

09 29 10 – Gypsum Board Panels

09 29 10.30 Gypsum Board

		Crew	Daily Output	Labor-Hours	Unit	Material	2014 Bare Costs Labor	Equipment	Total	Total Incl O&P
6100	1-3/8" thick on walls, THX Certified, no finish included	2 Carp	1500	.011	S.F.	8.40	.34		8.74	9.85
6105	Taped and finished (level 4 finish)		725	.022		8.45	.71		9.16	10.50
6110	With compound skim coat (level 5 finish)		580	.028		8.50	.89		9.39	10.85
6115	5/8" thick on walls, score & snap installation, no finish included		2000	.008		1.78	.26		2.04	2.39
6120	Taped and finished (level 4 finish)		965	.017		1.83	.53		2.36	2.91
6125	With compound skim coat (level 5 finish)		775	.021		1.89	.66		2.55	3.19
7020	5/8" thick on ceilings, for wood joists, no finish included		1200	.013		2.70	.43		3.13	3.69
7025	Taped and finished (level 4 finish)		510	.031		2.75	1.01		3.76	4.71
7030	With compound skim coat (level 5 finish)		410	.039		2.81	1.25		4.06	5.20
7035	For metal joists, no finish included		1200	.013		2.06	.43		2.49	2.99
7040	Taped and finished (level 4 finish)		510	.031		2.11	1.01		3.12	4.01
7045	With compound skim coat (level 5 finish)		410	.039		2.17	1.25		3.42	4.49
7050	Abuse resist, no finish included		1200	.013		3.75	.43		4.18	4.85
7055	Taped and finished (level 4 finish)		510	.031		3.80	1.01		4.81	5.85
7060	With compound skim coat (level 5 finish)		410	.039		3.86	1.25		5.11	6.35
7065	Shear rated, no finish included		1200	.013		4.30	.43		4.73	5.45
7070	Taped and finished (level 4 finish)		510	.031		4.35	1.01		5.36	6.45
7075	With compound skim coat (level 5 finish)		410	.039		4.41	1.25		5.66	6.95
7080	For SCIF applications, no finish included		1200	.013		4.72	.43		5.15	5.90
7085	Taped and finished (level 4 finish)		510	.031		4.77	1.01		5.78	6.95
7090	With compound skim coat (level 5 finish)		410	.039		4.83	1.25		6.08	7.40
8010	5/8" thick on ceilings, score & snap installation, no finish included		1600	.010		1.78	.32		2.10	2.50
8015	Taped and finished (level 4 finish)		680	.024		1.83	.76		2.59	3.28
8020	With compound skim coat (level 5 finish)	▼	545	.029	▼	1.89	.94		2.83	3.66

09 29 15 – Gypsum Board Accessories

09 29 15.10 Accessories, Drywall

		Crew	Daily Output	Labor-Hours	Unit	Material	2014 Bare Costs Labor	Equipment	Total	Total Incl O&P
0011	**ACCESSORIES, DRYWALL** Casing bead, galvanized steel	1 Carp	290	.028	L.F.	.25	.89		1.14	1.76
0101	Vinyl		290	.028		.22	.89		1.11	1.73
0401	Corner bead, galvanized steel, 1-1/4" x 1-1/4"		350	.023	▼	.16	.73		.89	1.41
0411	1-1/4" x 1-1/4", 10' long		35	.229	Ea.	1.60	7.35		8.95	14.10
0601	Vinyl corner bead		400	.020	L.F.	.16	.64		.80	1.26
0901	Furring channel, galv. steel, 7/8" deep, standard		260	.031		.33	.99		1.32	2.02
1001	Resilient		260	.031		.29	.99		1.28	1.98
1101	J trim, galvanized steel, 1/2" wide		300	.027			.86		.86	1.44
1121	5/8" wide	▼	300	.027	▼	.27	.86		1.13	1.74
1160	Screws #6 x 1" A				M	9.45			9.45	10.40
1170	#6 x 1-5/8" A				"	13.65			13.65	15
1501	Z stud, galvanized steel, 1-1/2" wide	1 Carp	260	.031	L.F.	.36	.99		1.35	2.06

09 30 Tiling

09 30 13 – Ceramic Tiling

09 30 13.10 Ceramic Tile

		Crew	Daily Output	Labor-Hours	Unit	Material	2014 Bare Costs Labor	Equipment	Total	Total Incl O&P
0010	**CERAMIC TILE**									
0020	Backsplash, thinset, average grade tiles	1 Tilf	50	.160	S.F.	2.45	4.70		7.15	10.30
0022	Custom grade tiles		50	.160		4.90	4.70		9.60	13
0024	Luxury grade tiles		50	.160		9.80	4.70		14.50	18.35
0026	Economy grade tiles	▼	50	.160	▼	2.24	4.70		6.94	10.05
0050	Base, using 1' x 4" high pc. with 1" x 1" tiles, mud set	D-7	82	.195	L.F.	5.15	5.15		10.30	13.95
0100	Thin set	"	128	.125		4.77	3.29		8.06	10.55
0300	For 6" high base, 1" x 1" tile face, add				▼	.76			.76	.84

489

09 30 13 – Ceramic Tiling

09 30 13.10 Ceramic Tile	Crew	Daily Output	Labor-Hours	Unit	Material	2014 Bare Costs Labor	Equipment	Total	Total Incl O&P
0400	For 2" x 2" tile face, add to above				L.F.	.41			.41	.45
0600	Cove base, 4-1/4" x 4-1/4" high, mud set	D-7	91	.176		3.88	4.63		8.51	11.70
0700	Thin set		128	.125		3.95	3.29		7.24	9.65
0900	6" x 4-1/4" high, mud set		100	.160		4.05	4.21		8.26	11.25
1000	Thin set		137	.117		3.93	3.08		7.01	9.30
1200	Sanitary cove base, 6" x 4-1/4" high, mud set		93	.172		4.11	4.53		8.64	11.85
1300	Thin set		124	.129		3.99	3.40		7.39	9.90
1500	6" x 6" high, mud set		84	.190		5.10	5		10.10	13.70
1600	Thin set		117	.137		4.96	3.60		8.56	11.25
1800	Bathroom accessories, average (soap dish, tooth brush holder)		82	.195	Ea.	12	5.15		17.15	21.50
1900	Bathtub, 5', rec. 4-1/4" x 4-1/4" tile wainscot, adhesive set 6' high		2.90	5.517		156	145		301	405
2100	7' high wainscot		2.50	6.400		179	169		348	470
2200	8' high wainscot		2.20	7.273		190	191		381	520
2400	Bullnose trim, 4-1/4" x 4-1/4", mud set		82	.195	L.F.	3.81	5.15		8.96	12.50
2500	Thin set		128	.125		3.73	3.29		7.02	9.40
2700	2" x 6" bullnose trim, mud set		84	.190		4.27	5		9.27	12.80
2800	Thin set		124	.129		4.21	3.40		7.61	10.15
3000	Floors, natural clay, random or uniform, thin set, color group 1		183	.087	S.F.	4.15	2.30		6.45	8.25
3100	Color group 2		183	.087		5.85	2.30		8.15	10.15
3255	Floors, glazed, thin set, 6" x 6", color group 1		300	.053		4.45	1.40		5.85	7.15
3260	8" x 8" tile		300	.053		4.45	1.40		5.85	7.15
3270	12" x 12" tile		290	.055		5.85	1.45		7.30	8.80
3280	16" x 16" tile		280	.057		6.70	1.50		8.20	9.85
3281	18" x 18" tile		270	.059		8.15	1.56		9.71	11.50
3282	20" x 20" tile		260	.062		9.30	1.62		10.92	12.80
3283	24" x 24" tile		250	.064		10.60	1.69		12.29	14.35
3285	Border, 6" x 12" tile		200	.080		15.25	2.11		17.36	20
3290	3" x 12" tile		200	.080		38.50	2.11		40.61	45.50
3300	Porcelain type, 1 color, color group 2, 1" x 1"		183	.087		5.20	2.30		7.50	9.40
3310	2" x 2" or 2" x 1", thin set		190	.084		5.95	2.22		8.17	10.15
3350	For random blend, 2 colors, add					1			1	1.10
3360	4 colors, add					1.50			1.50	1.65
4300	Specialty tile, 4-1/4" x 4-1/4" x 1/2", decorator finish	D-7	183	.087		10.40	2.30		12.70	15.15
4500	Add for epoxy grout, 1/16" joint, 1" x 1" tile		800	.020		.66	.53		1.19	1.58
4600	2" x 2" tile		820	.020		.61	.51		1.12	1.50
4800	Pregrouted sheets, walls, 4-1/4" x 4-1/4", 6" x 4-1/4"									
4810	and 8-1/2" x 4-1/4", 4 S.F. sheets, silicone grout	D-7	240	.067	S.F.	5.05	1.76		6.81	8.40
5100	Floors, unglazed, 2 S.F. sheets,									
5110	Urethane adhesive	D-7	180	.089	S.F.	5.05	2.34		7.39	9.35
5400	Walls, interior, thin set, 4-1/4" x 4-1/4" tile		190	.084		2.26	2.22		4.48	6.05
5500	6" x 4-1/4" tile		190	.084		2.92	2.22		5.14	6.80
5700	8-1/2" x 4-1/4" tile		190	.084		4.86	2.22		7.08	8.95
5800	6" x 6" tile		175	.091		3.12	2.41		5.53	7.30
5810	8" x 8" tile		170	.094		4.27	2.48		6.75	8.70
5820	12" x 12" tile		160	.100		4.35	2.63		6.98	9.05
5830	16" x 16" tile		150	.107		4.77	2.81		7.58	9.80
6000	Decorated wall tile, 4-1/4" x 4-1/4", minimum		270	.059		3.18	1.56		4.74	6
6100	Maximum		180	.089		49.50	2.34		51.84	58.50
6600	Crystalline glazed, 4-1/4" x 4-1/4", mud set, plain		100	.160		4.27	4.21		8.48	11.50
6700	4-1/4" x 4-1/4", scored tile		100	.160		5.80	4.21		10.01	13.20
6900	6" x 6" plain		93	.172		6.50	4.53		11.03	14.45
7000	For epoxy grout, 1/16" joints, 4-1/4" tile, add		800	.020		.41	.53		.94	1.30
7200	For tile set in dry mortar, add		1735	.009			.24		.24	.39

09 30 Tiling

09 30 13 – Ceramic Tiling

09 30 13.10 Ceramic Tile

		Crew	Daily Output	Labor-Hours	Unit	Material	2014 Bare Costs Labor	Equipment	Total	Total Incl O&P
7300	For tile set in Portland cement mortar, add	D-7	290	.055	S.F.	.16	1.45		1.61	2.52
9300	Ceramic tiles, recycled glass, standard colors, 2" x 2" thru 6" x 6" G		190	.084		20	2.22		22.22	25.50
9310	6" x 6" G		175	.091		20	2.41		22.41	26
9320	8" x 8" G		170	.094		22	2.48		24.48	28.50
9330	12" x 12" G		160	.100		22	2.63		24.63	29
9340	Earthtones, 2" x 2" to 4" x 8" G		190	.084		25	2.22		27.22	31
9350	6" x 6" G		175	.091		25	2.41		27.41	31.50
9360	8" x 8" G		170	.094		26	2.48		28.48	32.50
9370	12" x 12" G		160	.100		26	2.63		28.63	33
9380	Deep colors, 2" x 2" to 4" x 8" G		190	.084		29.50	2.22		31.72	36
9390	6" x 6" G		175	.091		29.50	2.41		31.91	36.50
9400	8" x 8" G		170	.094		31	2.48		33.48	38
9410	12" x 12" G		160	.100		31	2.63		33.63	38.50

09 30 16 – Quarry Tiling

09 30 16.10 Quarry Tile

		Crew	Daily Output	Labor-Hours	Unit	Material	Labor	Equipment	Total	Total Incl O&P
0010	**QUARRY TILE**									
0100	Base, cove or sanitary, mud set, to 5" high, 1/2" thick	D-7	110	.145	L.F.	5.35	3.83		9.18	12.10
0300	Bullnose trim, red, mud set, 6" x 6" x 1/2" thick		120	.133		4.39	3.51		7.90	10.50
0400	4" x 4" x 1/2" thick		110	.145		4.50	3.83		8.33	11.15
0600	4" x 8" x 1/2" thick, using 8" as edge		130	.123		4.50	3.24		7.74	10.20
0700	Floors, mud set, 1,000 S.F. lots, red, 4" x 4" x 1/2" thick		120	.133	S.F.	7.05	3.51		10.56	13.40
0900	6" x 6" x 1/2" thick		140	.114		7.30	3.01		10.31	12.90
1000	4" x 8" x 1/2" thick		130	.123		6.05	3.24		9.29	11.90
1300	For waxed coating, add					.74			.74	.81
1500	For non-standard colors, add					.45			.45	.50
1600	For abrasive surface, add					.51			.51	.56
1800	Brown tile, imported, 6" x 6" x 3/4"	D-7	120	.133		7.85	3.51		11.36	14.25
1900	8" x 8" x 1"		110	.145		8.55	3.83		12.38	15.60
2100	For thin set mortar application, deduct		700	.023			.60		.60	.97
2700	Stair tread, 6" x 6" x 3/4", plain		50	.320		6.95	8.45		15.40	21.50
2800	Abrasive		47	.340		5.95	8.95		14.90	21
3000	Wainscot, 6" x 6" x 1/2", thin set, red		105	.152		4.63	4.01		8.64	11.55
3100	Non-standard colors		105	.152		5.15	4.01		9.16	12.10
3300	Window sill, 6" wide, 3/4" thick		90	.178	L.F.	6.20	4.68		10.88	14.35
3400	Corners		80	.200	Ea.	6.65	5.25		11.90	15.80

09 30 23 – Glass Mosaic Tiling

09 30 23.10 Glass Mosaics

		Crew	Daily Output	Labor-Hours	Unit	Material	Labor	Equipment	Total	Total Incl O&P
0010	**GLASS MOSAICS** 3/4" tile on 12" sheets, standard grout									
1020	1" tile on 12" sheets, opalescent finish	D-7	73	.219	S.F.	17.55	5.75		23.30	28.50
1040	1" x 2" tile on 12" sheet, blend		73	.219		17.30	5.75		23.05	28.50
1060	2" tile on 12" sheet, blend		73	.219		17.10	5.75		22.85	28
1080	5/8" x random tile, linear, on 12" sheet, blend		73	.219		28	5.75		33.75	40.50
1600	Dots on 12" sheet		73	.219		28	5.75		33.75	40.50
1700	For glass mosaic tiles set in dry mortar, add		290	.055		.45	1.45		1.90	2.84
1720	For glass mosaic tile set in Portland cement mortar, add		290	.055		.01	1.45		1.46	2.35
1730	For polyblend sanded tile grout		96.15	.166	Lb.	2.19	4.38		6.57	9.45

09 30 29 – Metal Tiling

09 30 29.10 Metal Tile

		Crew	Daily Output	Labor-Hours	Unit	Material	Labor	Equipment	Total	Total Incl O&P
0010	**METAL TILE** 4' x 4' sheet, 24 ga., tile pattern, nailed									
0200	Stainless steel	2 Carp	512	.031	S.F.	27.50	1		28.50	31.50
0400	Aluminized steel	"	512	.031	"	14.80	1		15.80	17.95

09 34 Waterproofing-Membrane Tiling

09 34 13 – Waterproofing-Membrane Ceramic Tiling

09 34 13.10 Ceramic Tile Waterproofing Membrane	Crew	Daily Output	Labor-Hours	Unit	Material	2014 Bare Costs Labor	Equipment	Total	Total Incl O&P
0010 **CERAMIC TILE WATERPROOFING MEMBRANE**									
0020 On floors, including thinset									
0030 Fleece laminated polyethylene grid, 1/8" thick	D-7	250	.064	S.F.	2.23	1.69		3.92	5.15
0040 5/16" thick	"	250	.064	"	2.55	1.69		4.24	5.50
0050 On walls, including thinset									
0060 Fleece laminated polyethylene sheet, 8 mil thick	D-7	480	.033	S.F.	2.23	.88		3.11	3.87
0070 Accessories, including thinset									
0080 Joint and corner sheet, 4 mils thick, 5" wide	1 Tilf	240	.033	L.F.	1.32	.98		2.30	3.03
0090 7-1/4" wide		180	.044		1.68	1.30		2.98	3.95
0100 10" wide		120	.067	▼	2.05	1.96		4.01	5.40
0110 Pre-formed corners, inside		32	.250	Ea.	6.20	7.35		13.55	18.65
0120 Outside		32	.250		7.35	7.35		14.70	19.95
0130 2" flanged floor drain with 6" stainless steel grate		16	.500	▼	380	14.70		394.70	440
0140 EPS, sloped shower floor		480	.017	S.F.	4.77	.49		5.26	6.05
0150 Curb	▼	32	.250	L.F.	13.50	7.35		20.85	26.50

09 51 Acoustical Ceilings

09 51 23 – Acoustical Tile Ceilings

09 51 23.10 Suspended Acoustic Ceiling Tiles

	Crew	Daily Output	Labor-Hours	Unit	Material	2014 Bare Costs Labor	Equipment	Total	Total Incl O&P
0010 **SUSPENDED ACOUSTIC CEILING TILES**, not including									
0100 suspension system									
0300 Fiberglass boards, film faced, 2' x 2' or 2' x 4', 5/8" thick	1 Carp	625	.013	S.F.	1.02	.41		1.43	1.81
0400 3/4" thick		600	.013		1.67	.43		2.10	2.56
0500 3" thick, thermal, R11		450	.018		1.90	.57		2.47	3.05
0600 Glass cloth faced fiberglass, 3/4" thick		500	.016		2.01	.51		2.52	3.07
0700 1" thick		485	.016		2.74	.53		3.27	3.90
0820 1-1/2" thick, nubby face		475	.017		2.50	.54		3.04	3.66
1110 Mineral fiber tile, lay-in, 2' x 2' or 2' x 4', 5/8" thick, fine texture		625	.013		1.25	.41		1.66	2.07
1115 Rough textured		625	.013		1.21	.41		1.62	2.02
1125 3/4" thick, fine textured		600	.013		1.66	.43		2.09	2.55
1130 Rough textured		600	.013		1.65	.43		2.08	2.54
1135 Fissured		600	.013		2.70	.43		3.13	3.69
1150 Tegular, 5/8" thick, fine textured		470	.017		1.64	.55		2.19	2.72
1155 Rough textured		470	.017		1.18	.55		1.73	2.22
1165 3/4" thick, fine textured		450	.018		2.70	.57		3.27	3.93
1170 Rough textured		450	.018		1.54	.57		2.11	2.65
1175 Fissured	▼	450	.018		2.70	.57		3.27	3.93
1185 For plastic film face, add					.84			.84	.92
1190 For fire rating, add					.45			.45	.50
1900 Eggcrate, acrylic, 1/2" x 1/2" x 1/2" cubes	1 Carp	500	.016		1.86	.51		2.37	2.91
2100 Polystyrene eggcrate, 3/8" x 3/8" x 1/2" cubes		510	.016		1.56	.50		2.06	2.57
2200 1/2" x 1/2" x 1/2" cubes		500	.016		1.74	.51		2.25	2.77
2400 Luminous panels, prismatic, acrylic		400	.020		2.26	.64		2.90	3.57
2500 Polystyrene		400	.020		1.16	.64		1.80	2.36
2700 Flat white acrylic		400	.020		3.94	.64		4.58	5.40
2800 Polystyrene		400	.020		2.70	.64		3.34	4.05
3000 Drop pan, white, acrylic		400	.020		5.75	.64		6.39	7.45
3100 Polystyrene		400	.020		4.82	.64		5.46	6.40
3600 Perforated aluminum sheets, .024" thick, corrugated, painted		490	.016		2.34	.52		2.86	3.45
3700 Plain		500	.016		3.92	.51		4.43	5.15
3750 Wood fiber in cementitious binder, 2' x 2' or 4', painted, 1" thick		600	.013		1.54	.43		1.97	2.41

09 51 Acoustical Ceilings

09 51 23 – Acoustical Tile Ceilings

09 51 23.10 Suspended Acoustic Ceiling Tiles		Crew	Daily Output	Labor-Hours	Unit	Material	2014 Bare Costs Labor	Equipment	Total	Total Incl O&P
3760	2" thick	1 Carp	550	.015	S.F.	2.53	.47		3	3.57
3770	2-1/2" thick		500	.016		3.47	.51		3.98	4.68
3780	3" thick	↓	450	.018	↓	3.90	.57		4.47	5.25

09 51 23.30 Suspended Ceilings, Complete

		Crew	Daily Output	Labor-Hours	Unit	Material	Labor	Equipment	Total	Total Incl O&P
0010	**SUSPENDED CEILINGS, COMPLETE**, including standard									
0100	suspension system but not incl. 1-1/2" carrier channels									
0600	Fiberglass ceiling board, 2' x 4' x 5/8", plain faced	1 Carp	500	.016	S.F.	1.72	.51		2.23	2.75
0700	Offices, 2' x 4' x 3/4"		380	.021		2.37	.68		3.05	3.75
1800	Tile, Z bar suspension, 5/8" mineral fiber tile		150	.053		2.32	1.71		4.03	5.45
1900	3/4" mineral fiber tile	↓	150	.053	↓	2.48	1.71		4.19	5.60

09 51 53 – Direct-Applied Acoustical Ceilings

09 51 53.10 Ceiling Tile

		Crew	Daily Output	Labor-Hours	Unit	Material	Labor	Equipment	Total	Total Incl O&P
0010	**CEILING TILE**, stapled or cemented									
0100	12" x 12" or 12" x 24", not including furring									
0600	Mineral fiber, vinyl coated, 5/8" thick	1 Carp	300	.027	S.F.	1.87	.86		2.73	3.50
0700	3/4" thick		300	.027		1.78	.86		2.64	3.40
0900	Fire rated, 3/4" thick, plain faced		300	.027		1.29	.86		2.15	2.86
1000	Plastic coated face		300	.027		1.29	.86		2.15	2.86
1200	Aluminum faced, 5/8" thick, plain	↓	300	.027		1.61	.86		2.47	3.21
3300	For flameproofing, add					.10			.10	.11
3400	For sculptured 3 dimensional, add					.30			.30	.33
3900	For ceiling primer, add					.13			.13	.14
4000	For ceiling cement, add				↓	.38			.38	.42

09 53 Acoustical Ceiling Suspension Assemblies

09 53 23 – Metal Acoustical Ceiling Suspension Assemblies

09 53 23.30 Ceiling Suspension Systems

		Crew	Daily Output	Labor-Hours	Unit	Material	Labor	Equipment	Total	Total Incl O&P
0010	**CEILING SUSPENSION SYSTEMS** for boards and tile									
0050	Class A suspension system, 15/16" T bar, 2' x 4' grid	1 Carp	800	.010	S.F.	.70	.32		1.02	1.31
0300	2' x 2' grid	"	650	.012		.91	.40		1.31	1.66
0350	For 9/16" grid, add					.16			.16	.18
0360	For fire rated grid, add					.09			.09	.10
0370	For colored grid, add					.21			.21	.23
0400	Concealed Z bar suspension system, 12" module	1 Carp	520	.015		.78	.49		1.27	1.69
0600	1-1/2" carrier channels, 4' O.C., add		470	.017		.11	.55		.66	1.04
0650	1-1/2" x 3-1/2" channels	↓	470	.017	↓	.30	.55		.85	1.25
0700	Carrier channels for ceilings with									
0900	recessed lighting fixtures, add	1 Carp	460	.017	S.F.	.20	.56		.76	1.16
5000	Wire hangers, #12 wire	"	300	.027	Ea.	.05	.86		.91	1.50

09 62 Specialty Flooring

09 62 19 – Laminate Flooring

09 62 19.10 Floating Floor		Crew	Daily Output	Labor-Hours	Unit	Material	2014 Bare Costs Labor	Equipment	Total	Total Incl O&P
0010	**FLOATING FLOOR**									
8300	Floating floor, laminate, wood pattern strip, complete	1 Clab	133	.060	S.F.	5.05	1.43		6.48	7.95
8310	Components, T & G wood composite strips					4.02			4.02	4.42
8320	Film					.14			.14	.15
8330	Foam					.25			.25	.28
8340	Adhesive					.65			.65	.72
8350	Installation kit					.17			.17	.19
8360	Trim, 2" wide x 3' long				L.F.	3.85			3.85	4.24
8370	Reducer moulding				"	5.20			5.20	5.70

09 62 23 – Bamboo Flooring

09 62 23.10 Flooring, Bamboo			Crew	Daily Output	Labor-Hours	Unit	Material	2014 Bare Costs Labor	Equipment	Total	Total Incl O&P
0010	**FLOORING, BAMBOO**										
8600	Flooring, wood, bamboo strips, unfinished, 5/8" x 4" x 3'	G	1 Carp	255	.031	S.F.	4.53	1.01		5.54	6.65
8610	5/8" x 4" x 4'	G		275	.029		4.70	.93		5.63	6.70
8620	5/8" x 4" x 6'	G		295	.027		5.15	.87		6.02	7.15
8630	Finished, 5/8" x 4" x 3'	G		255	.031		4.99	1.01		6	7.20
8640	5/8" x 4" x 4'	G		275	.029		5.20	.93		6.13	7.30
8650	5/8" x 4" x 6'	G		295	.027		4.54	.87		5.41	6.45
8660	Stair treads, unfinished, 1-1/16" x 11-1/2" x 4'	G		18	.444	Ea.	43.50	14.25		57.75	72
8670	Finished, 1-1/16" x 11-1/2" x 4'	G		18	.444		77	14.25		91.25	109
8680	Stair risers, unfinished, 5/8" x 7-1/2" x 4'	G		18	.444		16.05	14.25		30.30	41.50
8690	Finished, 5/8" x 7-1/2" x 4'	G		18	.444		30.50	14.25		44.75	57.50
8700	Stair nosing, unfinished, 6' long	G		16	.500		35.50	16.05		51.55	66
8710	Finished, 6' long	G		16	.500		42	16.05		58.05	73

09 63 Masonry Flooring

09 63 13 – Brick Flooring

09 63 13.10 Miscellaneous Brick Flooring			Crew	Daily Output	Labor-Hours	Unit	Material	2014 Bare Costs Labor	Equipment	Total	Total Incl O&P
0010	**MISCELLANEOUS BRICK FLOORING**										
0020	Acid-proof shales, red, 8" x 3-3/4" x 1-1/4" thick		D-7	.43	37.209	M	685	980		1,665	2,325
0050	2-1/4" thick		D-1	.40	40		950	1,150		2,100	2,975
0200	Acid-proof clay brick, 8" x 3-3/4" x 2-1/4" thick	G	"	.40	40		930	1,150		2,080	2,950
0260	Cast ceramic, pressed, 4" x 8" x 1/2", unglazed		D-7	100	.160	S.F.	6.25	4.21		10.46	13.70
0270	Glazed			100	.160		8.35	4.21		12.56	15.95
0280	Hand molded flooring, 4" x 8" x 3/4", unglazed			95	.168		8.25	4.43		12.68	16.25
0290	Glazed			95	.168		10.35	4.43		14.78	18.55
0300	8" hexagonal, 3/4" thick, unglazed			85	.188		9.05	4.96		14.01	17.95
0310	Glazed			85	.188		16.35	4.96		21.31	26
0450	Acid-proof joints, 1/4" wide		D-1	65	.246		1.44	7.10		8.54	13.45
0500	Pavers, 8" x 4", 1" to 1-1/4" thick, red		D-7	95	.168		3.64	4.43		8.07	11.15
0510	Ironspot		"	95	.168		5.15	4.43		9.58	12.80
0540	1-3/8" to 1-3/4" thick, red		D-1	95	.168		3.51	4.87		8.38	11.95
0560	Ironspot			95	.168		5.10	4.87		9.97	13.70
0580	2-1/4" thick, red			90	.178		3.57	5.15		8.72	12.50
0590	Ironspot			90	.178		5.55	5.15		10.70	14.65
0700	Paver, adobe brick, 6" x 12", 1/2" joint	G		42	.381		1.38	11		12.38	19.80
0710	Mexican red, 12" x 12"	G	1 Tilf	48	.167		1.66	4.89		6.55	9.75
0720	Saltillo, 12" x 12"	G	"	48	.167		1.40	4.89		6.29	9.45
0800	For sidewalks and patios with pavers, see Section 32 14 16.10										
0870	For epoxy joints, add		D-1	600	.027	S.F.	2.77	.77		3.54	4.33

09 63 Masonry Flooring

09 63 13 – Brick Flooring

09 63 13.10 Miscellaneous Brick Flooring

	09 63 13.10 Miscellaneous Brick Flooring	Crew	Daily Output	Labor-Hours	Unit	Material	2014 Bare Costs Labor	Equipment	Total	Total Incl O&P
0880	For Furan underlayment, add	D-1	600	.027	S.F.	2.30	.77		3.07	3.81
0890	For waxed surface, steam cleaned, add	A-1H	1000	.008	↓	.20	.19	.08	.47	.62

09 63 40 – Stone Flooring

09 63 40.10 Marble

		Crew	Daily Output	Labor-Hours	Unit	Material	2014 Bare Costs Labor	Equipment	Total	Total Incl O&P
0010	**MARBLE**									
0020	Thin gauge tile, 12" x 6", 3/8", white Carara	D-7	60	.267	S.F.	14.90	7		21.90	28
0100	Travertine		60	.267		13.30	7		20.30	26
0200	12" x 12" x 3/8", thin set, floors		60	.267		9	7		16	21.50
0300	On walls		52	.308	↓	9.85	8.10		17.95	24
1000	Marble threshold, 4" wide x 36" long x 5/8" thick, white	↓	60	.267	Ea.	9	7		16	21.50

09 63 40.20 Slate Tile

		Crew	Daily Output	Labor-Hours	Unit	Material	2014 Bare Costs Labor	Equipment	Total	Total Incl O&P
0010	**SLATE TILE**									
0020	Vermont, 6" x 6" x 1/4" thick, thin set	D-7	180	.089	S.F.	7	2.34		9.34	11.50

09 64 Wood Flooring

09 64 23 – Wood Parquet Flooring

09 64 23.10 Wood Parquet

		Crew	Daily Output	Labor-Hours	Unit	Material	2014 Bare Costs Labor	Equipment	Total	Total Incl O&P
0010	**WOOD PARQUET** flooring									
5200	Parquetry, standard, 5/16" thick, not incl. finish, oak, minimum	1 Carp	160	.050	S.F.	4.14	1.61		5.75	7.25
5300	Maximum		100	.080		7	2.57		9.57	12
5500	Teak, minimum		160	.050		4.86	1.61		6.47	8.05
5600	Maximum		100	.080		8.50	2.57		11.07	13.65
5650	13/16" thick, select grade oak, minimum		160	.050		9.50	1.61		11.11	13.15
5700	Maximum		100	.080		14.40	2.57		16.97	20
5800	Custom parquetry, including finish, minimum		100	.080		15.65	2.57		18.22	21.50
5900	Maximum		50	.160		21	5.15		26.15	31.50
6700	Parquetry, prefinished white oak, 5/16" thick, minimum		160	.050		4.27	1.61		5.88	7.40
6800	Maximum		100	.080		4.69	2.57		7.26	9.45
7000	Walnut or teak, parquetry, minimum		160	.050		5.35	1.61		6.96	8.60
7100	Maximum	▼	100	.080	▼	9.35	2.57		11.92	14.60
7200	Acrylic wood parquet blocks, 12" x 12" x 5/16",									
7210	Irradiated, set in epoxy	1 Carp	160	.050	S.F.	7.80	1.61		9.41	11.25

09 64 29 – Wood Strip and Plank Flooring

09 64 29.10 Wood

		Crew	Daily Output	Labor-Hours	Unit	Material	2014 Bare Costs Labor	Equipment	Total	Total Incl O&P
0010	**WOOD**									
0020	Fir, vertical grain, 1" x 4", not incl. finish, grade B & better	1 Carp	255	.031	S.F.	2.74	1.01		3.75	4.70
0100	C grade & better		255	.031		2.58	1.01		3.59	4.53
0300	Flat grain, 1" x 4", not incl. finish, B & better		255	.031		3.13	1.01		4.14	5.15
0400	C & better		255	.031		3.01	1.01		4.02	5
4000	Maple, strip, 25/32" x 2-1/4", not incl. finish, select		170	.047		5.75	1.51		7.26	8.90
4100	#2 & better		170	.047		4.29	1.51		5.80	7.25
4300	33/32" x 3-1/4", not incl. finish, #1 grade		170	.047		4.49	1.51		6	7.50
4400	#2 & better	▼	170	.047	▼	4	1.51		5.51	6.95
4600	Oak, white or red, 25/32" x 2-1/4", not incl. finish									
4700	#1 common	1 Carp	170	.047	S.F.	2.98	1.51		4.49	5.80
4900	Select quartered, 2-1/4" wide		170	.047		4.24	1.51		5.75	7.20
5000	Clear		170	.047		4.12	1.51		5.63	7.05
6100	Prefinished, white oak, prime grade, 2-1/4" wide		170	.047		4.69	1.51		6.20	7.70
6200	3-1/4" wide		185	.043		5.10	1.39		6.49	7.95
6400	Ranch plank	↓	145	.055	↓	7.15	1.77		8.92	10.85

09 64 Wood Flooring

09 64 29 – Wood Strip and Plank Flooring

09 64 29.10 Wood		Crew	Daily Output	Labor-Hours	Unit	Material	2014 Bare Costs Labor	Equipment	Total	Total Incl O&P
6500	Hardwood blocks, 9" x 9", 25/32" thick	1 Carp	160	.050	S.F.	5.90	1.61		7.51	9.20
7400	Yellow pine, 3/4" x 3-1/8", T & G, C & better, not incl. finish	↓	200	.040		1.49	1.28		2.77	3.80
7500	Refinish wood floor, sand, 2 coats poly, wax, soft wood, min.	1 Clab	400	.020		.88	.48		1.36	1.77
7600	Hard wood, max.		130	.062		1.31	1.46		2.77	3.90
7800	Sanding and finishing, 2 coats polyurethane	↓	295	.027	↓	.88	.65		1.53	2.06
7900	Subfloor and underlayment, see Section 06 16									
8015	Transition molding, 2 1/4" wide, 5' long	1 Carp	19.20	.417	Ea.	10.70	13.40		24.10	34.50

09 65 Resilient Flooring

09 65 10 – Resilient Tile Underlayment

09 65 10.10 Latex Underlayment

		Crew	Daily Output	Labor-Hours	Unit	Material	2014 Bare Costs Labor	Equipment	Total	Total Incl O&P
0010	**LATEX UNDERLAYMENT**									
3600	Latex underlayment, 1/8" thk., cementitious for resilient flooring	1 Tilf	160	.050	S.F.	1.16	1.47		2.63	3.65
4000	Liquid, fortified				Gal.	34			34	37.50

09 65 13 – Resilient Base and Accessories

09 65 13.13 Resilient Base

		Crew	Daily Output	Labor-Hours	Unit	Material	2014 Bare Costs Labor	Equipment	Total	Total Incl O&P
0010	**RESILIENT BASE**									
0690	1/8" vinyl base, 2 1/2" H, straight or cove, standard colors	1 Tilf	315	.025	L.F.	1.34	.75		2.09	2.67
0700	4" high		315	.025		1.26	.75		2.01	2.59
0710	6" high		315	.025	↓	1.52	.75		2.27	2.87
0720	Corners, 2 1/2" high		315	.025	Ea.	2.02	.75		2.77	3.42
0730	4" high		315	.025	↓	2.56	.75		3.31	4.02
0740	6" high		315	.025	↓	2.99	.75		3.74	4.49
0800	1/8" rubber base, 2 1/2" H, straight or cove, standard colors		315	.025	L.F.	1.13	.75		1.88	2.44
1100	4" high		315	.025		1.26	.75		2.01	2.59
1110	6" high		315	.025	↓	1.65	.75		2.40	3.02
1150	Corners, 2 1/2" high		315	.025	Ea.	1.70	.75		2.45	3.07
1153	4" high		315	.025		2.51	.75		3.26	3.96
1155	6" high	↓	315	.025	↓	3.15	.75		3.90	4.67
1450	For premium color/finish add					50%				
1500	Millwork profile	1 Tilf	315	.025	L.F.	5.85	.75		6.60	7.65

09 65 16 – Resilient Sheet Flooring

09 65 16.10 Rubber and Vinyl Sheet Flooring

			Crew	Daily Output	Labor-Hours	Unit	Material	2014 Bare Costs Labor	Equipment	Total	Total Incl O&P
0010	**RUBBER AND VINYL SHEET FLOORING**										
5500	Linoleum, sheet goods	G	1 Tilf	360	.022	S.F.	3.59	.65		4.24	5
5900	Rubber, sheet goods, 36" wide, 1/8" thick			120	.067		7.65	1.96		9.61	11.55
5950	3/16" thick			100	.080		10.35	2.35		12.70	15.20
6000	1/4" thick			90	.089		12.25	2.61		14.86	17.70
8000	Vinyl sheet goods, backed, .065" thick, minimum			250	.032		4.10	.94		5.04	6.05
8050	Maximum			200	.040		5	1.17		6.17	7.40
8100	.080" thick, minimum			230	.035		4.10	1.02		5.12	6.15
8150	Maximum			200	.040		5.90	1.17		7.07	8.40
8200	.125" thick, minimum			230	.035		4.25	1.02		5.27	6.35
8250	Maximum			200	.040	↓	7.50	1.17		8.67	10.15
8400	For welding seams, add	↓		100	.080	L.F.	.20	2.35		2.55	4.01
8700	Adhesive cement, 1 gallon per 200 to 300 S.F.					Gal.	27			27	29.50
8800	Asphalt primer, 1 gallon per 300 S.F.						14			14	15.40
8900	Emulsion, 1 gallon per 140 S.F.					↓	18			18	19.80

09 65 Resilient Flooring

09 65 19 – Resilient Tile Flooring

09 65 19.10 Miscellaneous Resilient Tile Flooring

		Crew	Daily Output	Labor-Hours	Unit	Material	2014 Bare Costs Labor	Equipment	Total	Total Incl O&P
0010	**MISCELLANEOUS RESILIENT TILE FLOORING**									
2200	Cork tile, standard finish, 1/8" thick G	1 Tilf	315	.025	S.F.	7	.75		7.75	8.90
2250	3/16" thick G		315	.025		7.75	.75		8.50	9.75
2300	5/16" thick G		315	.025		8.45	.75		9.20	10.45
2350	1/2" thick G		315	.025		10.70	.75		11.45	12.95
2500	Urethane finish, 1/8" thick G		315	.025		9.50	.75		10.25	11.65
2550	3/16" thick G		315	.025		10.30	.75		11.05	12.55
2600	5/16" thick G		315	.025		11.70	.75		12.45	14.05
2650	1/2" thick G		315	.025		15.75	.75		16.50	18.55
6050	Rubber tile, marbleized colors, 12" x 12", 1/8" thick		400	.020		7.25	.59		7.84	8.90
6100	3/16" thick		400	.020		9.25	.59		9.84	11.15
6300	Special tile, plain colors, 1/8" thick		400	.020		10	.59		10.59	11.95
6350	3/16" thick		400	.020		10.25	.59		10.84	12.25
7000	Vinyl composition tile, 12" x 12", 1/16" thick		500	.016		.86	.47		1.33	1.71
7050	Embossed		500	.016		2.21	.47		2.68	3.19
7100	Marbleized		500	.016		2.21	.47		2.68	3.19
7150	Solid		500	.016		2.85	.47		3.32	3.90
7200	3/32" thick, embossed		500	.016		1.46	.47		1.93	2.37
7250	Marbleized		500	.016		2.54	.47		3.01	3.55
7300	Solid		500	.016		2.36	.47		2.83	3.36
7350	1/8" thick, marbleized		500	.016		2.22	.47		2.69	3.20
7400	Solid		500	.016		2.26	.47		2.73	3.25
7450	Conductive		500	.016		6.70	.47		7.17	8.10
7500	Vinyl tile, 12" x 12", .050" thick, minimum		500	.016		3.42	.47		3.89	4.52
7550	Maximum		500	.016		7	.47		7.47	8.45
7600	1/8" thick, minimum		500	.016		4.99	.47		5.46	6.25
7650	Solid colors		500	.016		3.65	.47		4.12	4.78
7700	Marbleized or Travertine pattern		500	.016		5.90	.47		6.37	7.25
7750	Florentine pattern		500	.016		6.30	.47		6.77	7.70
7800	Maximum		500	.016		13	.47		13.47	15.05

09 65 33 – Conductive Resilient Flooring

09 65 33.10 Conductive Rubber and Vinyl Flooring

		Crew	Daily Output	Labor-Hours	Unit	Material	Labor	Equipment	Total	Total Incl O&P
0010	**CONDUCTIVE RUBBER AND VINYL FLOORING**									
1700	Conductive flooring, rubber tile, 1/8" thick	1 Tilf	315	.025	S.F.	6.60	.75		7.35	8.45
1800	Homogeneous vinyl tile, 1/8" thick	"	315	.025	"	8.75	.75		9.50	10.85

09 66 Terrazzo Flooring

09 66 13 – Portland Cement Terrazzo Flooring

09 66 13.10 Portland Cement Terrazzo

		Crew	Daily Output	Labor-Hours	Unit	Material	Labor	Equipment	Total	Total Incl O&P
0010	**PORTLAND CEMENT TERRAZZO**, cast-in-place									
4300	Stone chips, onyx gemstone, per 50 lb. bag				Bag	16.50			16.50	18.15

09 66 16 – Terrazzo Floor Tile

09 66 16.13 Portland Cement Terrazzo Floor Tile

		Crew	Daily Output	Labor-Hours	Unit	Material	Labor	Equipment	Total	Total Incl O&P
0010	**PORTLAND CEMENT TERRAZZO FLOOR TILE**									
1200	Floor tiles, non-slip, 1" thick, 12" x 12"	D-1	60	.267	S.F.	19.70	7.70		27.40	34.50
1300	1-1/4" thick, 12" x 12"		60	.267		20.50	7.70		28.20	35.50
1500	16" x 16"		50	.320		22	9.25		31.25	40
1600	1-1/2" thick, 16" x 16"		45	.356		20.50	10.30		30.80	39.50

09 66 Terrazzo Flooring

09 66 16 – Terrazzo Floor Tile

09 66 16.30 Terrazzo, Precast

	Crew	Daily Output	Labor-Hours	Unit	Material	2014 Bare Costs Labor	Equipment	Total	Total Incl O&P
0010 **TERRAZZO, PRECAST**									
0020 Base, 6" high, straight	1 Mstz	70	.114	L.F.	11.85	3.33		15.18	18.40
0100 Cove		60	.133		12.80	3.89		16.69	20.50
0300 8" high, straight		60	.133		11.45	3.89		15.34	18.85
0400 Cove		50	.160		16.85	4.66		21.51	26
0600 For white cement, add					.45			.45	.50
0700 For 16 ga. zinc toe strip, add					1.72			1.72	1.89
0900 Curbs, 4" x 4" high	1 Mstz	40	.200		32.50	5.85		38.35	45
1000 8" x 8" high		30	.267		37.50	7.75		45.25	53.50
4800 Wainscot, 12" x 12" x 1" tiles		12	.667	S.F.	6.85	19.45		26.30	39
4900 16" x 16" x 1-1/2" tiles		8	1	"	14.25	29		43.25	62.50

09 68 Carpeting

09 68 05 – Carpet Accessories

09 68 05.11 Flooring Transition Strip

	Crew	Daily Output	Labor-Hours	Unit	Material	2014 Bare Costs Labor	Equipment	Total	Total Incl O&P
0010 **FLOORING TRANSITION STRIP**									
0107 Clamp down brass divider, 12' strip, vinyl to carpet	1 Tilf	31.25	.256	Ea.	11.05	7.50		18.55	24.50
0117 Vinyl to hard surface	"	31.25	.256	"	11.05	7.50		18.55	24.50

09 68 10 – Carpet Pad

09 68 10.10 Commercial Grade Carpet Pad

	Crew	Daily Output	Labor-Hours	Unit	Material	2014 Bare Costs Labor	Equipment	Total	Total Incl O&P
0010 **COMMERCIAL GRADE CARPET PAD**									
9001 Sponge rubber pad, minimum	1 Tilf	1350	.006	S.F.	.48	.17		.65	.81
9101 Maximum		1350	.006		1.13	.17		1.30	1.53
9201 Felt pad, minimum		1350	.006		.57	.17		.74	.90
9301 Maximum		1350	.006		.85	.17		1.02	1.21
9401 Bonded urethane pad, minimum		1350	.006		.56	.17		.73	.90
9501 Maximum		1350	.006		1.02	.17		1.19	1.40
9601 Prime urethane pad, minimum		1350	.006		.36	.17		.53	.67
9701 Maximum		1350	.006		.61	.17		.78	.95

09 68 13 – Tile Carpeting

09 68 13.10 Carpet Tile

	Crew	Daily Output	Labor-Hours	Unit	Material	2014 Bare Costs Labor	Equipment	Total	Total Incl O&P
0010 **CARPET TILE**									
0100 Tufted nylon, 18" x 18", hard back, 20 oz.	1 Tilf	80	.100	S.Y.	22.50	2.94		25.44	29.50
0110 26 oz.		80	.100		38.50	2.94		41.44	47
0200 Cushion back, 20 oz.		80	.100		28.50	2.94		31.44	35.50
0210 26 oz.		80	.100		44.50	2.94		47.44	53.50

09 68 16 – Sheet Carpeting

09 68 16.10 Sheet Carpet

	Crew	Daily Output	Labor-Hours	Unit	Material	2014 Bare Costs Labor	Equipment	Total	Total Incl O&P
0010 **SHEET CARPET**									
0701 Nylon, level loop, 26 oz., light to medium traffic	1 Tilf	445	.018	S.F.	3.33	.53		3.86	4.52
0901 32 oz., medium traffic		445	.018		4.23	.53		4.76	5.50
1101 40 oz., medium to heavy traffic		445	.018		6.20	.53		6.73	7.70
2101 Nylon, plush, 20 oz., light traffic		445	.018		2.19	.53		2.72	3.26
2801 24 oz., light to medium traffic		445	.018		2.19	.53		2.72	3.26
2901 30 oz., medium traffic		445	.018		3.29	.53		3.82	4.47
3001 36 oz., medium traffic		445	.018		4.37	.53		4.90	5.65
3101 42 oz., medium to heavy traffic		370	.022		4.92	.63		5.55	6.40
3201 46 oz., medium to heavy traffic		370	.022		5.75	.63		6.38	7.35
3301 54 oz., heavy traffic		370	.022		6.25	.63		6.88	7.90

09 68 Carpeting

09 68 16 – Sheet Carpeting

09 68 16.10 Sheet Carpet

		Crew	Daily Output	Labor-Hours	Unit	Material	2014 Bare Costs Labor	2014 Bare Costs Equipment	Total	Total Incl O&P
3501	Olefin, 15 oz., light traffic	1 Tilf	445	.018	S.F.	1.16	.53		1.69	2.13
3651	22 oz., light traffic		445	.018		1.39	.53		1.92	2.38
4501	50 oz., medium to heavy traffic, level loop		445	.018		14.65	.53		15.18	17
4701	32 oz., medium to heavy traffic, patterned		400	.020		14.55	.59		15.14	16.95
4901	48 oz., heavy traffic, patterned	↓	400	.020	↓	15	.59		15.59	17.45
5000	For less than full roll (approx. 1500 S.F.), add					25%				
5100	For small rooms, less than 12' wide, add						25%			
5200	For large open areas (no cuts), deduct						25%			
5600	For bound carpet baseboard, add	1 Tilf	300	.027	L.F.	3	.78		3.78	4.56
5610	For stairs, not incl. price of carpet, add	"	30	.267	Riser		7.85		7.85	12.65
8950	For tackless, stretched installation, add padding from 09 68 10.10 to above									
9850	For brand-named specific fiber, add				S.Y.	25%				

09 68 20 – Athletic Carpet

09 68 20.10 Indoor Athletic Carpet

		Crew	Daily Output	Labor-Hours	Unit	Material	2014 Bare Costs Labor	2014 Bare Costs Equipment	Total	Total Incl O&P
0010	**INDOOR ATHLETIC CARPET**									
3700	Polyethylene, in rolls, no base incl., landscape surfaces	1 Tilf	275	.029	S.F.	4.07	.85		4.92	5.85
3800	Nylon action surface, 1/8" thick		275	.029		3.76	.85		4.61	5.50
3900	1/4" thick		275	.029		5.45	.85		6.30	7.35
4000	3/8" thick	↓	275	.029	↓	6.80	.85		7.65	8.90

09 72 Wall Coverings

09 72 19 – Textile Wall Covering

09 72 19.10 Textile Wall Covering

		Crew	Daily Output	Labor-Hours	Unit	Material	2014 Bare Costs Labor	2014 Bare Costs Equipment	Total	Total Incl O&P
0010	**TEXTILE WALL COVERING**, including sizing; add 10-30% waste @ takeoff									
0020	Silk	1 Pape	640	.013	S.F.	4.09	.35		4.44	5.10
0030	Cotton		640	.013		6.55	.35		6.90	7.80
0040	Linen		640	.013		1.82	.35		2.17	2.58
0050	Blend	↓	640	.013	↓	2.93	.35		3.28	3.80

09 72 20 – Natural Fiber Wall Covering

09 72 20.10 Natural Fiber Wall Covering

		Crew	Daily Output	Labor-Hours	Unit	Material	2014 Bare Costs Labor	2014 Bare Costs Equipment	Total	Total Incl O&P
0010	**NATURAL FIBER WALL COVERING**, including sizing; add 10-30% waste @ takeoff									
0015	Bamboo	1 Pape	640	.013	S.F.	2.23	.35		2.58	3.03
0030	Burlap		640	.013		2	.35		2.35	2.78
0045	Jute		640	.013		1.27	.35		1.62	1.98
0060	Sisal	↓	640	.013	↓	1.44	.35		1.79	2.16

09 72 23 – Wallpapering

09 72 23.10 Wallpaper

		Crew	Daily Output	Labor-Hours	Unit	Material	2014 Bare Costs Labor	2014 Bare Costs Equipment	Total	Total Incl O&P
0010	**WALLPAPER** including sizing; add 10-30 percent waste @ takeoff R097223-10									
0050	Aluminum foil	1 Pape	275	.029	S.F.	1.04	.82		1.86	2.49
0100	Copper sheets, .025" thick, vinyl backing		240	.033		5.55	.94		6.49	7.65
0300	Phenolic backing		240	.033		7.20	.94		8.14	9.50
0600	Cork tiles, light or dark, 12" x 12" x 3/16"		240	.033		5.05	.94		5.99	7.10
0700	5/16" thick		235	.034		2.95	.96		3.91	4.83
0900	1/4" basketweave		240	.033		3.50	.94		4.44	5.40
1000	1/2" natural, non-directional pattern		240	.033		7.60	.94		8.54	9.95
1100	3/4" natural, non-directional pattern		240	.033		11.65	.94		12.59	14.35
1200	Granular surface, 12" x 36", 1/2" thick		385	.021		1.29	.59		1.88	2.39
1300	1" thick		370	.022		1.66	.61		2.27	2.83
1500	Polyurethane coated, 12" x 12" x 3/16" thick	↓	240	.033	↓	4.03	.94		4.97	6

09 72 Wall Coverings

09 72 23 – Wallpapering

09 72 23.10 Wallpaper		Crew	Daily Output	Labor-Hours	Unit	Material	2014 Bare Costs Labor	Equipment	Total	Total Incl O&P
1600	5/16" thick	1 Pape	235	.034	S.F.	6.30	.96		7.26	8.50
1800	Cork wallpaper, paperbacked, natural		480	.017		2.04	.47		2.51	3.01
1900	Colors		480	.017		2.84	.47		3.31	3.89
2100	Flexible wood veneer, 1/32" thick, plain woods		100	.080		2.41	2.26		4.67	6.35
2200	Exotic woods		95	.084		3.65	2.38		6.03	7.95
2400	Gypsum-based, fabric-backed, fire resistant									
2500	for masonry walls, minimum, 21 oz./S.Y.	1 Pape	800	.010	S.F.	.89	.28		1.17	1.44
2600	Average		720	.011		1.25	.31		1.56	1.90
2700	Maximum (small quantities)		640	.013		1.40	.35		1.75	2.12
2750	Acrylic, modified, semi-rigid PVC, .028" thick	2 Carp	330	.048		1.21	1.56		2.77	3.95
2800	.040" thick	"	320	.050		1.78	1.61		3.39	4.66
3000	Vinyl wall covering, fabric-backed, lightweight, type 1 (12-15 oz./S.Y.)	1 Pape	640	.013		.93	.35		1.28	1.60
3300	Medium weight, type 2 (20-24 oz./S.Y.)		480	.017		.90	.47		1.37	1.76
3400	Heavy weight, type 3 (28 oz./S.Y.)		435	.018		1.48	.52		2	2.48
3600	Adhesive, 5 gal. lots (18 S.Y./gal.)				Gal.	14.20			14.20	15.60
3700	Wallpaper, average workmanship, solid pattern, low cost paper	1 Pape	640	.013	S.F.	.43	.35		.78	1.05
3900	basic patterns (matching required), avg. cost paper		535	.015		.98	.42		1.40	1.77
4000	Paper at $85 per double roll, quality workmanship		435	.018		1.94	.52		2.46	2.98
4100	Linen wall covering, paper backed									
4150	Flame treatment, minimum				S.F.	1.01			1.01	1.11
4180	Maximum					1.65			1.65	1.82
4200	Grass cloths with lining paper, minimum [G]	1 Pape	400	.020		.66	.57		1.23	1.66
4300	Maximum [G]	"	350	.023		2.66	.65		3.31	3.99

09 91 Painting

09 91 03 – Paint Restoration

09 91 03.20 Sanding

		Crew	Daily Output	Labor-Hours	Unit	Material	2014 Bare Costs Labor	Equipment	Total	Total Incl O&P
0010	**SANDING** and puttying interior trim, compared to									
0100	Painting 1 coat, on quality work				L.F.		100%			
0300	Medium work						50%			
0400	Industrial grade						25%			
0500	Surface protection, placement and removal									
0510	Basic drop cloths	1 Pord	6400	.001	S.F.		.04		.04	.06
0520	Masking with paper		800	.010		.04	.28		.32	.50
0530	Volume cover up (using plastic sheathing, or building paper)		16000	.001			.01		.01	.02

09 91 03.30 Exterior Surface Preparation

		Crew	Daily Output	Labor-Hours	Unit	Material	2014 Bare Costs Labor	Equipment	Total	Total Incl O&P
0010	**EXTERIOR SURFACE PREPARATION**									
0015	Doors, per side, not incl. frames or trim									
0020	Scrape & sand									
0030	Wood, flush	1 Pord	616	.013	S.F.		.37		.37	.60
0040	Wood, detail		496	.016			.45		.45	.75
0050	Wood, louvered		280	.029			.80		.80	1.32
0060	Wood, overhead		616	.013			.37		.37	.60
0070	Wire brush									
0080	Metal, flush	1 Pord	640	.013	S.F.		.35		.35	.58
0090	Metal, detail		520	.015			.43		.43	.71
0100	Metal, louvered		360	.022			.62		.62	1.03
0110	Metal or fibr., overhead		640	.013			.35		.35	.58
0120	Metal, roll up		560	.014			.40		.40	.66
0130	Metal, bulkhead		640	.013			.35		.35	.58
0140	Power wash, based on 2500 lb. operating pressure									

09 91 Painting

09 91 03 – Paint Restoration

09 91 03.30 Exterior Surface Preparation

	Crew	Daily Output	Labor-Hours	Unit	Material	2014 Bare Costs Labor	Equipment	Total	Total Incl O&P
0150	Metal, flush	A-1H	2240	.004	S.F.		.09	.03	.12	.18
0160	Metal, detail		2120	.004			.09	.04	.13	.19
0170	Metal, louvered		2000	.004			.10	.04	.14	.20
0180	Metal or fibr., overhead		2400	.003			.08	.03	.11	.16
0190	Metal, roll up		2400	.003			.08	.03	.11	.16
0200	Metal, bulkhead	↓	2200	.004	↓		.09	.03	.12	.19
0400	Windows, per side, not incl. trim									
0410	Scrape & sand									
0420	Wood, 1-2 lite	1 Pord	320	.025	S.F.		.70		.70	1.16
0430	Wood, 3-6 lite		280	.029			.80		.80	1.32
0440	Wood, 7-10 lite		240	.033			.94		.94	1.54
0450	Wood, 12 lite		200	.040			1.12		1.12	1.85
0460	Wood, Bay/Bow	↓	320	.025	↓		.70		.70	1.16
0470	Wire brush									
0480	Metal, 1-2 lite	1 Pord	480	.017	S.F.		.47		.47	.77
0490	Metal, 3-6 lite		400	.020			.56		.56	.92
0500	Metal, Bay/Bow	↓	480	.017	↓		.47		.47	.77
0510	Power wash, based on 2500 lb. operating pressure									
0520	1-2 lite	A-1H	4400	.002	S.F.		.04	.02	.06	.09
0530	3-6 lite		4320	.002			.04	.02	.06	.09
0540	7-10 lite		4240	.002			.05	.02	.07	.10
0550	12 lite		4160	.002			.05	.02	.07	.10
0560	Bay/Bow	↓	4400	.002	↓		.04	.02	.06	.09
0600	Siding, scrape and sand, light=10-30%, med.=30-70%									
0610	Heavy=70-100% of surface to sand									
0650	Texture 1-11, light	1 Pord	480	.017	S.F.		.47		.47	.77
0660	Med.		440	.018			.51		.51	.84
0670	Heavy		360	.022			.62		.62	1.03
0680	Wood shingles, shakes, light		440	.018			.51		.51	.84
0690	Med.		360	.022			.62		.62	1.03
0700	Heavy		280	.029			.80		.80	1.32
0710	Clapboard, light		520	.015			.43		.43	.71
0720	Med.		480	.017			.47		.47	.77
0730	Heavy	↓	400	.020	↓		.56		.56	.92
0740	Wire brush									
0750	Aluminum, light	1 Pord	600	.013	S.F.		.37		.37	.62
0760	Med.		520	.015			.43		.43	.71
0770	Heavy	↓	440	.018	↓		.51		.51	.84
0780	Pressure wash, based on 2500 lb. operating pressure									
0790	Stucco	A-1H	3080	.003	S.F.		.06	.02	.08	.13
0800	Aluminum or vinyl		3200	.003			.06	.02	.08	.13
0810	Siding, masonry, brick & block	↓	2400	.003	↓		.08	.03	.11	.16
1300	Miscellaneous, wire brush									
1310	Metal, pedestrian gate	1 Pord	100	.080	S.F.		2.25		2.25	3.70

09 91 03.40 Interior Surface Preparation

	Crew	Daily Output	Labor-Hours	Unit	Material	2014 Bare Costs Labor	Equipment	Total	Total Incl O&P
0010	**INTERIOR SURFACE PREPARATION**									
0020	Doors, per side, not incl. frames or trim									
0030	Scrape & sand									
0040	Wood, flush	1 Pord	616	.013	S.F.		.37		.37	.60
0050	Wood, detail		496	.016			.45		.45	.75
0060	Wood, louvered	↓	280	.029	↓		.80		.80	1.32
0070	Wire brush									

09 91 Painting

09 91 03 – Paint Restoration

09 91 03.40 Interior Surface Preparation

		Crew	Daily Output	Labor-Hours	Unit	Material	2014 Bare Costs Labor	Equipment	Total	Total Incl O&P
0080	Metal, flush	1 Pord	640	.013	S.F.		.35		.35	.58
0090	Metal, detail		520	.015			.43		.43	.71
0100	Metal, louvered	↓	360	.022	↓		.62		.62	1.03
0110	Hand wash									
0120	Wood, flush	1 Pord	2160	.004	S.F.		.10		.10	.17
0130	Wood, detailed		2000	.004			.11		.11	.18
0140	Wood, louvered		1360	.006			.17		.17	.27
0150	Metal, flush		2160	.004			.10		.10	.17
0160	Metal, detail		2000	.004			.11		.11	.18
0170	Metal, louvered	↓	1360	.006	↓		.17		.17	.27
0400	Windows, per side, not incl. trim									
0410	Scrape & sand									
0420	Wood, 1-2 lite	1 Pord	360	.022	S.F.		.62		.62	1.03
0430	Wood, 3-6 lite		320	.025			.70		.70	1.16
0440	Wood, 7-10 lite		280	.029			.80		.80	1.32
0450	Wood, 12 lite		240	.033			.94		.94	1.54
0460	Wood, Bay/Bow	↓	360	.022	↓		.62		.62	1.03
0470	Wire brush									
0480	Metal, 1-2 lite	1 Pord	520	.015	S.F.		.43		.43	.71
0490	Metal, 3-6 lite		440	.018			.51		.51	.84
0500	Metal, Bay/Bow	↓	520	.015	↓		.43		.43	.71
0600	Walls, sanding, light=10-30%, medium - 30-70%,									
0610	heavy=70-100% of surface to sand									
0650	Walls, sand									
0660	Gypsum board or plaster, light	1 Pord	3077	.003	S.F.		.07		.07	.12
0670	Gypsum board or plaster, medium		2160	.004			.10		.10	.17
0680	Gypsum board or plaster, heavy		923	.009			.24		.24	.40
0690	Wood, T&G, light		2400	.003			.09		.09	.15
0700	Wood, T&G, med.		1600	.005			.14		.14	.23
0710	Wood, T&G, heavy	↓	800	.010	↓		.28		.28	.46
0720	Walls, wash									
0730	Gypsum board or plaster	1 Pord	3200	.003	S.F.		.07		.07	.12
0740	Wood, T&G		3200	.003			.07		.07	.12
0750	Masonry, brick & block, smooth		2800	.003			.08		.08	.13
0760	Masonry, brick & block, coarse	↓	2000	.004	↓		.11		.11	.18
8000	For chemical washing, see Section 04 01 30									

09 91 03.41 Scrape After Fire Damage

		Crew	Daily Output	Labor-Hours	Unit	Material	2014 Bare Costs Labor	Equipment	Total	Total Incl O&P
0010	**SCRAPE AFTER FIRE DAMAGE**									
0050	Boards, 1" x 4"	1 Pord	336	.024	L.F.		.67		.67	1.10
0060	1" x 6"		260	.031			.86		.86	1.42
0070	1" x 8"		207	.039			1.09		1.09	1.79
0080	1" x 10"		174	.046			1.29		1.29	2.12
0500	Framing, 2" x 4"		265	.030			.85		.85	1.39
0510	2" x 6"		221	.036			1.02		1.02	1.67
0520	2" x 8"		190	.042			1.18		1.18	1.95
0530	2" x 10"		165	.048			1.36		1.36	2.24
0540	2" x 12"		144	.056			1.56		1.56	2.57
1000	Heavy framing, 3" x 4"		226	.035			.99		.99	1.64
1010	4" x 4"		210	.038			1.07		1.07	1.76
1020	4" x 6"		191	.042			1.18		1.18	1.93
1030	4" x 8"		165	.048			1.36		1.36	2.24
1040	4" x 10"	↓	144	.056	↓		1.56		1.56	2.57

09 91 Painting

09 91 03 – Paint Restoration

09 91 03.41 Scrape After Fire Damage

		Crew	Daily Output	Labor-Hours	Unit	Material	2014 Bare Costs Labor	Equipment	Total	Total Incl O&P
1060	4" x 12"	1 Pord	131	.061	L.F.		1.72		1.72	2.82
2900	For sealing, minimum		825	.010	S.F.	.14	.27		.41	.60
2920	Maximum		460	.017	"	.30	.49		.79	1.13

09 91 13 – Exterior Painting

09 91 13.30 Fences

		Crew	Daily Output	Labor-Hours	Unit	Material	2014 Bare Costs Labor	Equipment	Total	Total Incl O&P
0010	**FENCES** R099100-20									
0100	Chain link or wire metal, one side, water base									
0110	Roll & brush, first coat	1 Pord	960	.008	S.F.	.08	.23		.31	.46
0120	Second coat		1280	.006		.07	.18		.25	.37
0130	Spray, first coat		2275	.004		.08	.10		.18	.24
0140	Second coat		2600	.003		.08	.09		.17	.22
0150	Picket, water base									
0160	Roll & brush, first coat	1 Pord	865	.009	S.F.	.08	.26		.34	.52
0170	Second coat		1050	.008		.08	.21		.29	.44
0180	Spray, first coat		2275	.004		.08	.10		.18	.25
0190	Second coat		2600	.003		.08	.09		.17	.23
0200	Stockade, water base									
0210	Roll & brush, first coat	1 Pord	1040	.008	S.F.	.08	.22		.30	.45
0220	Second coat		1200	.007		.08	.19		.27	.40
0230	Spray, first coat		2275	.004		.08	.10		.18	.25
0240	Second coat		2600	.003		.08	.09		.17	.23

09 91 13.42 Miscellaneous, Exterior

		Crew	Daily Output	Labor-Hours	Unit	Material	2014 Bare Costs Labor	Equipment	Total	Total Incl O&P
0010	**MISCELLANEOUS, EXTERIOR** R099100-20									
0100	Railing, ext., decorative wood, incl. cap & baluster									
0110	Newels & spindles @ 12" O.C.									
0120	Brushwork, stain, sand, seal & varnish									
0130	First coat	1 Pord	90	.089	L.F.	.75	2.50		3.25	4.93
0140	Second coat	"	120	.067	"	.75	1.87		2.62	3.90
0150	Rough sawn wood, 42" high, 2" x 2" verticals, 6" O.C.									
0160	Brushwork, stain, each coat	1 Pord	90	.089	L.F.	.24	2.50		2.74	4.38
0170	Wrought iron, 1" rail, 1/2" sq. verticals									
0180	Brushwork, zinc chromate, 60" high, bars 6" O.C.									
0190	Primer	1 Pord	130	.062	L.F.	.86	1.73		2.59	3.79
0200	Finish coat		130	.062		1.13	1.73		2.86	4.08
0210	Additional coat		190	.042		1.32	1.18		2.50	3.40
0220	Shutters or blinds, single panel, 2' x 4', paint all sides									
0230	Brushwork, primer	1 Pord	20	.400	Ea.	.69	11.25		11.94	19.25
0240	Finish coat, exterior latex		20	.400		.61	11.25		11.86	19.20
0250	Primer & 1 coat, exterior latex		13	.615		1.15	17.30		18.45	30
0260	Spray, primer		35	.229		1	6.40		7.40	11.65
0270	Finish coat, exterior latex		35	.229		1.30	6.40		7.70	12
0280	Primer & 1 coat, exterior latex		20	.400		1.08	11.25		12.33	19.70
0290	For louvered shutters, add				S.F.	10%				
0300	Stair stringers, exterior, metal									
0310	Roll & brush, zinc chromate, to 14", each coat	1 Pord	320	.025	L.F.	.38	.70		1.08	1.57
0320	Rough sawn wood, 4" x 12"									
0330	Roll & brush, exterior latex, each coat	1 Pord	215	.037	L.F.	.09	1.05		1.14	1.82
0340	Trellis/lattice, 2" x 2" @ 3" O.C. with 2" x 8" supports									
0350	Spray, latex, per side, each coat	1 Pord	475	.017	S.F.	.09	.47		.56	.88
0450	Decking, ext., sealer, alkyd, brushwork, sealer coat		1140	.007		.09	.20		.29	.42
0460	1st coat		1140	.007		.09	.20		.29	.42
0470	2nd coat		1300	.006		.07	.17		.24	.36

09 91 Painting

09 91 13 – Exterior Painting

09 91 13.42 Miscellaneous, Exterior

		Crew	Daily Output	Labor-Hours	Unit	Material	2014 Bare Costs Labor	2014 Bare Costs Equipment	Total	Total Incl O&P
0500	Paint, alkyd, brushwork, primer coat	1 Pord	1140	.007	S.F.	.10	.20		.30	.43
0510	1st coat		1140	.007		.16	.20		.36	.49
0520	2nd coat		1300	.006		.12	.17		.29	.41
0600	Sand paint, alkyd, brushwork, 1 coat		150	.053		.13	1.50		1.63	2.60

09 91 13.60 Siding Exterior

		Crew	Daily Output	Labor-Hours	Unit	Material	2014 Bare Costs Labor	2014 Bare Costs Equipment	Total	Total Incl O&P
0010	**SIDING EXTERIOR**, Alkyd (oil base)									
0450	Steel siding, oil base, paint 1 coat, brushwork	2 Pord	2015	.008	S.F.	.13	.22		.35	.51
0500	Spray		4550	.004		.19	.10		.29	.37
0800	Paint 2 coats, brushwork		1300	.012		.25	.35		.60	.85
1000	Spray		2750	.006		.17	.16		.33	.46
1200	Stucco, rough, oil base, paint 2 coats, brushwork		1300	.012		.25	.35		.60	.85
1400	Roller		1625	.010		.27	.28		.55	.75
1600	Spray		2925	.005		.28	.15		.43	.56
1800	Texture 1-11 or clapboard, oil base, primer coat, brushwork		1300	.012		.13	.35		.48	.72
2000	Spray		4550	.004		.13	.10		.23	.31
2100	Paint 1 coat, brushwork		1300	.012		.18	.35		.53	.77
2200	Spray		4550	.004		.18	.10		.28	.36
2400	Paint 2 coats, brushwork		810	.020		.37	.56		.93	1.31
2600	Spray		2600	.006		.41	.17		.58	.73
3000	Stain 1 coat, brushwork		1520	.011		.08	.30		.38	.58
3200	Spray		5320	.003		.09	.08		.17	.24
3400	Stain 2 coats, brushwork		950	.017		.16	.47		.63	.96
4000	Spray		3050	.005		.18	.15		.33	.44
4200	Wood shingles, oil base primer coat, brushwork		1300	.012		.12	.35		.47	.71
4400	Spray		3900	.004		.12	.12		.24	.32
4600	Paint 1 coat, brushwork		1300	.012		.15	.35		.50	.74
4800	Spray		3900	.004		.19	.12		.31	.40
5000	Paint 2 coats, brushwork		810	.020		.31	.56		.87	1.25
5200	Spray		2275	.007		.29	.20		.49	.64
5800	Stain 1 coat, brushwork		1500	.011		.08	.30		.38	.58
6000	Spray		3900	.004		.08	.12		.20	.28
6500	Stain 2 coats, brushwork		950	.017		.16	.47		.63	.96
7000	Spray		2660	.006		.22	.17		.39	.53
8000	For latex paint, deduct					10%				
8100	For work over 12' H, from pipe scaffolding, add						15%			
8200	For work over 12' H, from extension ladder, add						25%			
8300	For work over 12' H, from swing staging, add						35%			

09 91 13.62 Siding, Misc.

		Crew	Daily Output	Labor-Hours	Unit	Material	2014 Bare Costs Labor	2014 Bare Costs Equipment	Total	Total Incl O&P
0010	**SIDING, MISC.**, latex paint R099100-10									
0100	Aluminum siding									
0110	Brushwork, primer	2 Pord	2275	.007	S.F.	.06	.20		.26	.39
0120	Finish coat, exterior latex		2275	.007		.05	.20		.25	.38
0130	Primer & 1 coat exterior latex		1300	.012		.13	.35		.48	.71
0140	Primer & 2 coats exterior latex		975	.016		.18	.46		.64	.96
0150	Mineral fiber shingles									
0160	Brushwork, primer	2 Pord	1495	.011	S.F.	.13	.30		.43	.64
0170	Finish coat, industrial enamel		1495	.011		.18	.30		.48	.69
0180	Primer & 1 coat enamel		810	.020		.32	.56		.88	1.26
0190	Primer & 2 coats enamel		540	.030		.50	.83		1.33	1.92
0200	Roll, primer		1625	.010		.15	.28		.43	.62
0210	Finish coat, industrial enamel		1625	.010		.20	.28		.48	.68
0220	Primer & 1 coat enamel		975	.016		.35	.46		.81	1.14

09 91 13.62 Siding, Misc.

	Crew	Daily Output	Labor-Hours	Unit	Material	2014 Bare Costs Labor	Equipment	Total	Total Incl O&P
0230 Primer & 2 coats enamel	2 Pord	650	.025	S.F.	.54	.69		1.23	1.74
0240 Spray, primer		3900	.004		.12	.12		.24	.32
0250 Finish coat, industrial enamel		3900	.004		.16	.12		.28	.37
0260 Primer & 1 coat enamel		2275	.007		.28	.20		.48	.63
0270 Primer & 2 coats enamel		1625	.010		.44	.28		.72	.95
0280 Waterproof sealer, first coat		4485	.004		.08	.10		.18	.24
0290 Second coat	▼	5235	.003	▼	.07	.09		.16	.22
0300 Rough wood incl. shingles, shakes or rough sawn siding									
0310 Brushwork, primer	2 Pord	1280	.013	S.F.	.14	.35		.49	.73
0320 Finish coat, exterior latex		1280	.013		.10	.35		.45	.69
0330 Primer & 1 coat exterior latex		960	.017		.23	.47		.70	1.03
0340 Primer & 2 coats exterior latex		700	.023		.33	.64		.97	1.42
0350 Roll, primer		2925	.005		.18	.15		.33	.45
0360 Finish coat, exterior latex		2925	.005		.12	.15		.27	.38
0370 Primer & 1 coat exterior latex		1790	.009		.30	.25		.55	.74
0380 Primer & 2 coats exterior latex		1300	.012		.42	.35		.77	1.03
0390 Spray, primer		3900	.004		.16	.12		.28	.36
0400 Finish coat, exterior latex		3900	.004		.09	.12		.21	.29
0410 Primer & 1 coat exterior latex		2600	.006		.25	.17		.42	.55
0420 Primer & 2 coats exterior latex		2080	.008		.33	.22		.55	.73
0430 Waterproof sealer, first coat		4485	.004		.14	.10		.24	.31
0440 Second coat	▼	4485	.004	▼	.08	.10		.18	.24
0450 Smooth wood incl. butt, T&G, beveled, drop or B&B siding									
0460 Brushwork, primer	2 Pord	2325	.007	S.F.	.10	.19		.29	.43
0470 Finish coat, exterior latex		1280	.013		.10	.35		.45	.69
0480 Primer & 1 coat exterior latex		800	.020		.20	.56		.76	1.14
0490 Primer & 2 coats exterior latex		630	.025		.29	.71		1	1.49
0500 Roll, primer		2275	.007		.11	.20		.31	.44
0510 Finish coat, exterior latex		2275	.007		.10	.20		.30	.43
0520 Primer & 1 coat exterior latex		1300	.012		.21	.35		.56	.81
0530 Primer & 2 coats exterior latex		975	.016		.32	.46		.78	1.11
0540 Spray, primer		4550	.004		.09	.10		.19	.25
0550 Finish coat, exterior latex		4550	.004		.09	.10		.19	.26
0560 Primer & 1 coat exterior latex		2600	.006		.18	.17		.35	.47
0570 Primer & 2 coats exterior latex		1950	.008		.26	.23		.49	.67
0580 Waterproof sealer, first coat		5230	.003		.08	.09		.17	.22
0590 Second coat	▼	5980	.003		.08	.08		.16	.20
0600 For oil base paint, add				▼	10%				

09 91 13.70 Doors and Windows, Exterior

	Crew	Daily Output	Labor-Hours	Unit	Material	2014 Bare Costs Labor	Equipment	Total	Total Incl O&P
0010 **DOORS AND WINDOWS, EXTERIOR** R099100-10									
0100 Door frames & trim, only									
0110 Brushwork, primer R099100-20	1 Pord	512	.016	L.F.	.06	.44		.50	.79
0120 Finish coat, exterior latex		512	.016		.08	.44		.52	.80
0130 Primer & 1 coat, exterior latex		300	.027		.14	.75		.89	1.38
0140 Primer & 2 coats, exterior latex	▼	265	.030	▼	.22	.85		1.07	1.63
0150 Doors, flush, both sides, incl. frame & trim									
0160 Roll & brush, primer	1 Pord	10	.800	Ea.	4.74	22.50		27.24	42
0170 Finish coat, exterior latex		10	.800		5.85	22.50		28.35	43.50
0180 Primer & 1 coat, exterior latex		7	1.143		10.55	32		42.55	64.50
0190 Primer & 2 coats, exterior latex		5	1.600		16.40	45		61.40	92
0200 Brushwork, stain, sealer & 2 coats polyurethane	▼	4	2	▼	26	56		82	121
0210 Doors, French, both sides, 10-15 lite, incl. frame & trim									

09 91 Painting

09 91 13 – Exterior Painting

09 91 13.70 Doors and Windows, Exterior

		Crew	Daily Output	Labor-Hours	Unit	Material	2014 Bare Costs Labor	Equipment	Total	Total Incl O&P
0220	Brushwork, primer	1 Pord	6	1.333	Ea.	2.37	37.50		39.87	64
0230	Finish coat, exterior latex		6	1.333		2.92	37.50		40.42	64.50
0240	Primer & 1 coat, exterior latex		3	2.667		5.30	75		80.30	129
0250	Primer & 2 coats, exterior latex		2	4		8.05	112		120.05	194
0260	Brushwork, stain, sealer & 2 coats polyurethane		2.50	3.200		9.45	90		99.45	158
0270	Doors, louvered, both sides, incl. frame & trim									
0280	Brushwork, primer	1 Pord	7	1.143	Ea.	4.74	32		36.74	58
0290	Finish coat, exterior latex		7	1.143		5.85	32		37.85	59.50
0300	Primer & 1 coat, exterior latex		4	2		10.55	56		66.55	104
0310	Primer & 2 coats, exterior latex		3	2.667		16.05	75		91.05	141
0320	Brushwork, stain, sealer & 2 coats polyurethane		4.50	1.778		26	50		76	111
0330	Doors, panel, both sides, incl. frame & trim									
0340	Roll & brush, primer	1 Pord	6	1.333	Ea.	4.74	37.50		42.24	66.50
0350	Finish coat, exterior latex		6	1.333		5.85	37.50		43.35	68
0360	Primer & 1 coat, exterior latex		3	2.667		10.55	75		85.55	135
0370	Primer & 2 coats, exterior latex		2.50	3.200		16.05	90		106.05	166
0380	Brushwork, stain, sealer & 2 coats polyurethane		3	2.667		26	75		101	152
0400	Windows, per ext. side, based on 15 S.F.									
0410	1 to 6 lite									
0420	Brushwork, primer	1 Pord	13	.615	Ea.	.94	17.30		18.24	29.50
0430	Finish coat, exterior latex		13	.615		1.15	17.30		18.45	30
0440	Primer & 1 coat, exterior latex		8	1		2.09	28		30.09	48.50
0450	Primer & 2 coats, exterior latex		6	1.333		3.17	37.50		40.67	65
0460	Stain, sealer & 1 coat varnish		7	1.143		3.73	32		35.73	57
0470	7 to 10 lite									
0480	Brushwork, primer	1 Pord	11	.727	Ea.	.94	20.50		21.44	34.50
0490	Finish coat, exterior latex		11	.727		1.15	20.50		21.65	35
0500	Primer & 1 coat, exterior latex		7	1.143		2.09	32		34.09	55.50
0510	Primer & 2 coats, exterior latex		5	1.600		3.17	45		48.17	77.50
0520	Stain, sealer & 1 coat varnish		6	1.333		3.73	37.50		41.23	65.50
0530	12 lite									
0540	Brushwork, primer	1 Pord	10	.800	Ea.	.94	22.50		23.44	38
0550	Finish coat, exterior latex		10	.800		1.15	22.50		23.65	38.50
0560	Primer & 1 coat, exterior latex		6	1.333		2.09	37.50		39.59	64
0570	Primer & 2 coats, exterior latex		5	1.600		3.17	45		48.17	77.50
0580	Stain, sealer & 1 coat varnish		6	1.333		3.87	37.50		41.37	66
0590	For oil base paint, add					10%				

09 91 13.80 Trim, Exterior

		Crew	Daily Output	Labor-Hours	Unit	Material	2014 Bare Costs Labor	Equipment	Total	Total Incl O&P
0010	**TRIM, EXTERIOR** R099100-10									
0100	Door frames & trim (see Doors, interior or exterior)									
0110	Fascia, latex paint, one coat coverage									
0120	1" x 4", brushwork	1 Pord	640	.013	L.F.	.02	.35		.37	.60
0130	Roll		1280	.006		.03	.18		.21	.32
0140	Spray		2080	.004		.02	.11		.13	.20
0150	1" x 6" to 1" x 10", brushwork		640	.013		.08	.35		.43	.67
0160	Roll		1230	.007		.09	.18		.27	.39
0170	Spray		2100	.004		.07	.11		.18	.25
0180	1" x 12", brushwork		640	.013		.08	.35		.43	.67
0190	Roll		1050	.008		.09	.21		.30	.44
0200	Spray		2200	.004		.07	.10		.17	.24
0210	Gutters & downspouts, metal, zinc chromate paint									
0220	Brushwork, gutters, 5", first coat	1 Pord	640	.013	L.F.	.40	.35		.75	1.02

09 91 Painting

09 91 13 – Exterior Painting

09 91 13.80 Trim, Exterior

		Crew	Daily Output	Labor-Hours	Unit	Material	2014 Bare Costs Labor	2014 Bare Costs Equipment	Total	Total Incl O&P
0230	Second coat	1 Pord	960	.008	L.F.	.38	.23		.61	.79
0240	Third coat		1280	.006		.30	.18		.48	.63
0250	Downspouts, 4", first coat		640	.013		.40	.35		.75	1.02
0260	Second coat		960	.008		.38	.23		.61	.79
0270	Third coat		1280	.006		.30	.18		.48	.63
0280	Gutters & downspouts, wood									
0290	Brushwork, gutters, 5", primer	1 Pord	640	.013	L.F.	.06	.35		.41	.65
0300	Finish coat, exterior latex		640	.013		.07	.35		.42	.66
0310	Primer & 1 coat exterior latex		400	.020		.14	.56		.70	1.07
0320	Primer & 2 coats exterior latex		325	.025		.22	.69		.91	1.38
0330	Downspouts, 4", primer		640	.013		.06	.35		.41	.65
0340	Finish coat, exterior latex		640	.013		.07	.35		.42	.66
0350	Primer & 1 coat exterior latex		400	.020		.14	.56		.70	1.07
0360	Primer & 2 coats exterior latex		325	.025		.11	.69		.80	1.26
0370	Molding, exterior, up to 14" wide									
0380	Brushwork, primer	1 Pord	640	.013	L.F.	.07	.35		.42	.66
0390	Finish coat, exterior latex		640	.013		.08	.35		.43	.67
0400	Primer & 1 coat exterior latex		400	.020		.17	.56		.73	1.10
0410	Primer & 2 coats exterior latex		315	.025		.17	.71		.88	1.35
0420	Stain & fill		1050	.008		.10	.21		.31	.46
0430	Shellac		1850	.004		.13	.12		.25	.34
0440	Varnish		1275	.006		.11	.18		.29	.41

09 91 13.90 Walls, Masonry (CMU), Exterior

		Crew	Daily Output	Labor-Hours	Unit	Material	2014 Bare Costs Labor	2014 Bare Costs Equipment	Total	Total Incl O&P
0010	**WALLS, MASONRY (CMU), EXTERIOR**									
0360	Concrete masonry units (CMU), smooth surface									
0370	Brushwork, latex, first coat	1 Pord	640	.013	S.F.	.07	.35		.42	.66
0380	Second coat		960	.008		.06	.23		.29	.44
0390	Waterproof sealer, first coat		736	.011		.25	.31		.56	.77
0400	Second coat		1104	.007		.25	.20		.45	.61
0410	Roll, latex, paint, first coat		1465	.005		.09	.15		.24	.34
0420	Second coat		1790	.004		.07	.13		.20	.28
0430	Waterproof sealer, first coat		1680	.005		.25	.13		.38	.49
0440	Second coat		2060	.004		.25	.11		.36	.45
0450	Spray, latex, paint, first coat		1950	.004		.07	.12		.19	.26
0460	Second coat		2600	.003		.05	.09		.14	.20
0470	Waterproof sealer, first coat		2245	.004		.25	.10		.35	.43
0480	Second coat		2990	.003		.25	.08		.33	.39
0490	Concrete masonry unit (CMU), porous									
0500	Brushwork, latex, first coat	1 Pord	640	.013	S.F.	.14	.35		.49	.74
0510	Second coat		960	.008		.07	.23		.30	.46
0520	Waterproof sealer, first coat		736	.011		.25	.31		.56	.77
0530	Second coat		1104	.007		.25	.20		.45	.61
0540	Roll latex, first coat		1465	.005		.11	.15		.26	.37
0550	Second coat		1790	.004		.07	.13		.20	.29
0560	Waterproof sealer, first coat		1680	.005		.25	.13		.38	.49
0570	Second coat		2060	.004		.25	.11		.36	.45
0580	Spray latex, first coat		1950	.004		.08	.12		.20	.28
0590	Second coat		2600	.003		.05	.09		.14	.20
0600	Waterproof sealer, first coat		2245	.004		.25	.10		.35	.43
0610	Second coat		2990	.003		.25	.08		.33	.39

09 91 23.20 Cabinets and Casework

	09 91 23.20 Cabinets and Casework	Crew	Daily Output	Labor-Hours	Unit	Material	2014 Bare Costs Labor	Equipment	Total	Total Incl O&P
0010	**CABINETS AND CASEWORK**									
1000	Primer coat, oil base, brushwork	1 Pord	650	.012	S.F.	.06	.35		.41	.64
2000	Paint, oil base, brushwork, 1 coat		650	.012		.11	.35		.46	.69
2500	2 coats		400	.020		.22	.56		.78	1.16
3000	Stain, brushwork, wipe off		650	.012		.08	.35		.43	.66
4000	Shellac, 1 coat, brushwork		650	.012		.10	.35		.45	.69
4500	Varnish, 3 coats, brushwork, sand after 1st coat		325	.025		.28	.69		.97	1.45
5000	For latex paint, deduct					10%				

09 91 23.33 Doors and Windows, Interior Alkyd (Oil Base)

	09 91 23.33 Doors and Windows, Interior Alkyd (Oil Base)	Crew	Daily Output	Labor-Hours	Unit	Material	2014 Bare Costs Labor	Equipment	Total	Total Incl O&P
0010	**DOORS AND WINDOWS, INTERIOR ALKYD (OIL BASE)**									
0500	Flush door & frame, 3' x 7', oil, primer, brushwork	1 Pord	10	.800	Ea.	3.32	22.50		25.82	40.50
1000	Paint, 1 coat		10	.800		4.11	22.50		26.61	41.50
1200	2 coats		6	1.333		4.59	37.50		42.09	66.50
1400	Stain, brushwork, wipe off		18	.444		1.71	12.50		14.21	22.50
1600	Shellac, 1 coat, brushwork		25	.320		2.20	9		11.20	17.20
1800	Varnish, 3 coats, brushwork, sand after 1st coat		9	.889		5.95	25		30.95	47.50
2000	Panel door & frame, 3' x 7', oil, primer, brushwork		6	1.333		2.44	37.50		39.94	64
2200	Paint, 1 coat		6	1.333		4.11	37.50		41.61	66
2400	2 coats		3	2.667		10.65	75		85.65	135
2600	Stain, brushwork, panel door, 3' x 7', not incl. frame		16	.500		1.71	14.05		15.76	25
2800	Shellac, 1 coat, brushwork		22	.364		2.20	10.20		12.40	19.20
3000	Varnish, 3 coats, brushwork, sand after 1st coat		7.50	1.067		5.95	30		35.95	56
3020	French door, incl. 3' x 7', 6 lites, frame & trim									
3022	Paint, 1 coat, over existing paint	1 Pord	5	1.600	Ea.	8.25	45		53.25	83
3024	2 coats, over existing paint		5	1.600		16	45		61	91.50
3026	Primer & 1 coat		3.50	2.286		13.10	64		77.10	120
3028	Primer & 2 coats		3	2.667		21.50	75		96.50	147
3032	Varnish or polyurethane, 1 coat		5	1.600		7.05	45		52.05	82
3034	2 coats, sanding between		3	2.667		14.15	75		89.15	139
4400	Windows, including frame and trim, per side									
4600	Colonial type, 6/6 lites, 2' x 3', oil, primer, brushwork	1 Pord	14	.571	Ea.	.38	16.05		16.43	27
5800	Paint, 1 coat		14	.571		.65	16.05		16.70	27
6000	2 coats		9	.889		1.26	25		26.26	42.50
6200	3' x 5' opening, 6/6 lites, primer coat, brushwork		12	.667		.96	18.75		19.71	32
6400	Paint, 1 coat		12	.667		1.62	18.75		20.37	33
6600	2 coats		7	1.143		3.15	32		35.15	56.50
6800	4' x 8' opening, 6/6 lites, primer coat, brushwork		8	1		2.05	28		30.05	48.50
7000	Paint, 1 coat		8	1		3.46	28		31.46	50
7200	2 coats		5	1.600		6.75	45		51.75	81.50
8000	Single lite type, 2' x 3', oil base, primer coat, brushwork		33	.242		.38	6.80		7.18	11.60
8200	Paint, 1 coat		33	.242		.65	6.80		7.45	11.90
8400	2 coats		20	.400		1.26	11.25		12.51	19.90
8600	3' x 5' opening, primer coat, brushwork		20	.400		.96	11.25		12.21	19.55
8800	Paint, 1 coat		20	.400		1.62	11.25		12.87	20.50
8900	2 coats		13	.615		3.15	17.30		20.45	32
9200	4' x 8' opening, primer coat, brushwork		14	.571		2.05	16.05		18.10	29
9400	Paint, 1 coat		14	.571		3.46	16.05		19.51	30.50
9600	2 coats		8	1		6.75	28		34.75	53.50

09 91 23.35 Doors and Windows, Interior Latex

	09 91 23.35 Doors and Windows, Interior Latex	Crew	Daily Output	Labor-Hours	Unit	Material	2014 Bare Costs Labor	Equipment	Total	Total Incl O&P
0010	**DOORS & WINDOWS, INTERIOR LATEX** R099100-10									
0100	Doors, flush, both sides, incl. frame & trim									
0110	Roll & brush, primer	1 Pord	10	.800	Ea.	3.97	22.50		26.47	41.50

09 91 Painting

09 91 23 – Interior Painting

09 91 23.35 Doors and Windows, Interior Latex

09 91 23.35 Doors and Windows, Interior Latex	Crew	Daily Output	Labor-Hours	Unit	Material	2014 Bare Costs Labor	Equipment	Total	Total Incl O&P
0120	Finish coat, latex	1 Pord	10	.800	Ea.	5.35	22.50		27.85	43
0130	Primer & 1 coat latex		7	1.143		9.35	32		41.35	63.50
0140	Primer & 2 coats latex		5	1.600		14.40	45		59.40	90
0160	Spray, both sides, primer		20	.400		4.18	11.25		15.43	23
0170	Finish coat, latex		20	.400		5.65	11.25		16.90	24.50
0180	Primer & 1 coat latex		11	.727		9.90	20.50		30.40	44.50
0190	Primer & 2 coats latex		8	1		15.25	28		43.25	63
0200	Doors, French, both sides, 10-15 lite, incl. frame & trim									
0210	Roll & brush, primer	1 Pord	6	1.333	Ea.	1.99	37.50		39.49	63.50
0220	Finish coat, latex		6	1.333		2.68	37.50		40.18	64.50
0230	Primer & 1 coat latex		3	2.667		4.67	75		79.67	128
0240	Primer & 2 coats latex		2	4		7.20	112		119.20	193
0260	Doors, louvered, both sides, incl. frame & trim									
0270	Roll & brush, primer	1 Pord	7	1.143	Ea.	3.97	32		35.97	57.50
0280	Finish coat, latex		7	1.143		5.35	32		37.35	59
0290	Primer & 1 coat, latex		4	2		9.10	56		65.10	103
0300	Primer & 2 coats, latex		3	2.667		14.70	75		89.70	139
0320	Spray, both sides, primer		20	.400		4.18	11.25		15.43	23
0330	Finish coat, latex		20	.400		5.65	11.25		16.90	24.50
0340	Primer & 1 coat, latex		11	.727		9.90	20.50		30.40	44.50
0350	Primer & 2 coats, latex		8	1		15.55	28		43.55	63
0360	Doors, panel, both sides, incl. frame & trim									
0370	Roll & brush, primer	1 Pord	6	1.333	Ea.	4.18	37.50		41.68	66
0380	Finish coat, latex		6	1.333		5.35	37.50		42.85	67.50
0390	Primer & 1 coat, latex		3	2.667		9.35	75		84.35	133
0400	Primer & 2 coats, latex		2.50	3.200		14.70	90		104.70	164
0420	Spray, both sides, primer		10	.800		4.18	22.50		26.68	41.50
0430	Finish coat, latex		10	.800		5.65	22.50		28.15	43
0440	Primer & 1 coat, latex		5	1.600		9.90	45		54.90	85
0450	Primer & 2 coats, latex		4	2		15.55	56		71.55	110
0460	Windows, per interior side, based on 15 S.F.									
0470	1 to 6 lite									
0480	Brushwork, primer	1 Pord	13	.615	Ea.	.78	17.30		18.08	29.50
0490	Finish coat, enamel		13	.615		1.06	17.30		18.36	29.50
0500	Primer & 1 coat enamel		8	1		1.84	28		29.84	48
0510	Primer & 2 coats enamel		6	1.333		2.90	37.50		40.40	64.50
0530	7 to 10 lite									
0540	Brushwork, primer	1 Pord	11	.727	Ea.	.78	20.50		21.28	34.50
0550	Finish coat, enamel		11	.727		1.06	20.50		21.56	34.50
0560	Primer & 1 coat enamel		7	1.143		1.84	32		33.84	55
0570	Primer & 2 coats enamel		5	1.600		2.90	45		47.90	77
0590	12 lite									
0600	Brushwork, primer	1 Pord	10	.800	Ea.	.78	22.50		23.28	38
0610	Finish coat, enamel		10	.800		1.06	22.50		23.56	38
0620	Primer & 1 coat enamel		6	1.333		1.84	37.50		39.34	63.50
0630	Primer & 2 coats enamel		5	1.600		2.90	45		47.90	77
0650	For oil base paint, add					10%				

09 91 23.39 Doors and Windows, Interior Latex, Zero Voc

09 91 23.39 Doors and Windows, Interior Latex, Zero Voc		Crew	Daily Output	Labor-Hours	Unit	Material	2014 Bare Costs Labor	Equipment	Total	Total Incl O&P
0010	**DOORS & WINDOWS, INTERIOR LATEX, ZERO VOC**									
0100	Doors flush, both sides, incl. frame & trim									
0110	Roll & brush, primer	G	1 Pord	10	.800	Ea.	4.84	22.50		27.34	42.50
0120	Finish coat, latex	G		10	.800		5.65	22.50		28.15	43

09 91 Painting

09 91 23 – Interior Painting

09 91 23.39 Doors and Windows, Interior Latex, Zero Voc

			Crew	Daily Output	Labor-Hours	Unit	Material	2014 Bare Costs Labor	Equipment	Total	Total Incl O&P
0130	Primer & 1 coat latex	G	1 Pord	7	1.143	Ea.	10.45	32		42.45	64.50
0140	Primer & 2 coats latex	G		5	1.600		15.80	45		60.80	91.50
0160	Spray, both sides, primer	G		20	.400		5.10	11.25		16.35	24
0170	Finish coat, latex	G		20	.400		5.90	11.25		17.15	25
0180	Primer & 1 coat latex	G		11	.727		11.10	20.50		31.60	45.50
0190	Primer & 2 coats latex	G		8	1		16.70	28		44.70	64.50
0200	Doors, French, both sides, 10-15 lite, incl. frame & trim										
0210	Roll & brush, primer	G	1 Pord	6	1.333	Ea.	2.42	37.50		39.92	64
0220	Finish coat, latex	G		6	1.333		2.81	37.50		40.31	64.50
0230	Primer & 1 coat latex	G		3	2.667		5.25	75		80.25	129
0240	Primer & 2 coats latex	G		2	4		7.90	112		119.90	194
0360	Doors, panel, both sides, incl. frame & trim										
0370	Roll & brush, primer	G	1 Pord	6	1.333	Ea.	5.10	37.50		42.60	67
0380	Finish coat, latex	G		6	1.333		5.65	37.50		43.15	67.50
0390	Primer & 1 coat, latex	G		3	2.667		10.45	75		85.45	135
0400	Primer & 2 coats, latex	G		2.50	3.200		16.10	90		106.10	166
0420	Spray, both sides, primer	G		10	.800		5.10	22.50		27.60	42.50
0430	Finish coat, latex	G		10	.800		5.90	22.50		28.40	43.50
0440	Primer & 1 coat, latex	G		5	1.600		11.10	45		56.10	86
0450	Primer & 2 coats, latex	G		4	2		17.05	56		73.05	111
0460	Windows, per interior side, based on 15 S.F.										
0470	1 to 6 lite										
0480	Brushwork, primer	G	1 Pord	13	.615	Ea.	.96	17.30		18.26	29.50
0490	Finish coat, enamel	G		13	.615		1.11	17.30		18.41	29.50
0500	Primer & 1 coat enamel	G		8	1		2.07	28		30.07	48.50
0510	Primer & 2 coats enamel	G		6	1.333		3.18	37.50		40.68	65

09 91 23.40 Floors, Interior

		Crew	Daily Output	Labor-Hours	Unit	Material	2014 Bare Costs Labor	Equipment	Total	Total Incl O&P
0010	**FLOORS, INTERIOR**									
0100	Concrete paint, latex									
0110	Brushwork									
0120	1st coat	1 Pord	975	.008	S.F.	.15	.23		.38	.55
0130	2nd coat		1150	.007		.10	.20		.30	.43
0140	3rd coat		1300	.006		.08	.17		.25	.37
0150	Roll									
0160	1st coat	1 Pord	2600	.003	S.F.	.20	.09		.29	.36
0170	2nd coat		3250	.002		.12	.07		.19	.24
0180	3rd coat		3900	.002		.09	.06		.15	.19
0190	Spray									
0200	1st coat	1 Pord	2600	.003	S.F.	.18	.09		.27	.33
0210	2nd coat		3250	.002		.10	.07		.17	.22
0220	3rd coat		3900	.002		.08	.06		.14	.17
0300	Acid stain and sealer									
0310	Stain, one coat	1 Pord	650	.012	S.F.	.11	.35		.46	.69
0320	Two coats		570	.014		.22	.39		.61	.89
0330	Acrylic sealer, one coat		2600	.003		.18	.09		.27	.34
0340	Two coats		1400	.006		.37	.16		.53	.67

09 91 23.52 Miscellaneous, Interior

		Crew	Daily Output	Labor-Hours	Unit	Material	2014 Bare Costs Labor	Equipment	Total	Total Incl O&P
0010	**MISCELLANEOUS, INTERIOR**									
2400	Floors, conc./wood, oil base, primer/sealer coat, brushwork	2 Pord	1950	.008	S.F.	.08	.23		.31	.47
2450	Roller		5200	.003		.09	.09		.18	.24
2600	Spray		6000	.003		.09	.08		.17	.22
2650	Paint 1 coat, brushwork		1950	.008		.08	.23		.31	.47

09 91 23.52 Miscellaneous, Interior		Crew	Daily Output	Labor-Hours	Unit	Material	2014 Bare Costs Labor	Equipment	Total	Total Incl O&P
2800	Roller	2 Pord	5200	.003	S.F.	.08	.09		.17	.23
2850	Spray		6000	.003		.09	.08		.17	.22
3000	Stain, wood floor, brushwork, 1 coat		4550	.004		.08	.10		.18	.25
3200	Roller		5200	.003		.09	.09		.18	.23
3250	Spray		6000	.003		.09	.08		.17	.21
3400	Varnish, wood floor, brushwork		4550	.004		.09	.10		.19	.26
3450	Roller		5200	.003		.10	.09		.19	.25
3600	Spray		6000	.003		.11	.08		.19	.24
3800	Grilles, per side, oil base, primer coat, brushwork	1 Pord	520	.015		.13	.43		.56	.85
3850	Spray		1140	.007		.13	.20		.33	.47
3880	Paint 1 coat, brushwork		520	.015		.22	.43		.65	.95
3900	Spray		1140	.007		.24	.20		.44	.58
3920	Paint 2 coats, brushwork		325	.025		.42	.69		1.11	1.60
3940	Spray		650	.012		.48	.35		.83	1.10
4500	Louvers, one side, primer, brushwork		524	.015		.08	.43		.51	.80
4520	Paint one coat, brushwork		520	.015		.10	.43		.53	.81
4530	Spray		1140	.007		.11	.20		.31	.44
4540	Paint two coats, brushwork		325	.025		.19	.69		.88	1.34
4550	Spray		650	.012		.21	.35		.56	.80
4560	Paint three coats, brushwork		270	.030		.27	.83		1.10	1.67
4570	Spray		500	.016		.31	.45		.76	1.08
5000	Pipe, 1" - 4" diameter, primer or sealer coat, oil base, brushwork	2 Pord	1250	.013	L.F.	.09	.36		.45	.69
5100	Spray		2165	.007		.08	.21		.29	.43
5200	Paint 1 coat, brushwork		1250	.013		.11	.36		.47	.71
5300	Spray		2165	.007		.10	.21		.31	.45
5350	Paint 2 coats, brushwork		775	.021		.19	.58		.77	1.16
5400	Spray		1240	.013		.22	.36		.58	.84
5450	5" - 8" diameter, primer or sealer coat, brushwork		620	.026		.18	.73		.91	1.38
5500	Spray		1085	.015		.29	.41		.70	1
5550	Paint 1 coat, brushwork		620	.026		.30	.73		1.03	1.51
5600	Spray		1085	.015		.33	.41		.74	1.04
5650	Paint 2 coats, brushwork		385	.042		.39	1.17		1.56	2.35
5700	Spray		620	.026		.43	.73		1.16	1.66
6600	Radiators, per side, primer, brushwork	1 Pord	520	.015	S.F.	.08	.43		.51	.80
6620	Paint, one coat		520	.015		.08	.43		.51	.80
6640	Two coats		340	.024		.19	.66		.85	1.29
6660	Three coats		283	.028		.27	.79		1.06	1.61
7000	Trim, wood, incl. puttying, under 6" wide									
7200	Primer coat, oil base, brushwork	1 Pord	650	.012	L.F.	.03	.35		.38	.61
7250	Paint, 1 coat, brushwork		650	.012		.05	.35		.40	.63
7400	2 coats		400	.020		.11	.56		.67	1.04
7450	3 coats		325	.025		.16	.69		.85	1.31
7500	Over 6" wide, primer coat, brushwork		650	.012		.06	.35		.41	.64
7550	Paint, 1 coat, brushwork		650	.012		.11	.35		.46	.69
7600	2 coats		400	.020		.21	.56		.77	1.15
7650	3 coats		325	.025		.31	.69		1	1.48
8000	Cornice, simple design, primer coat, oil base, brushwork		650	.012	S.F.	.06	.35		.41	.64
8250	Paint, 1 coat		650	.012		.11	.35		.46	.69
8300	2 coats		400	.020		.21	.56		.77	1.15
8350	Ornate design, primer coat		350	.023		.06	.64		.70	1.13
8400	Paint, 1 coat		350	.023		.11	.64		.75	1.18
8450	2 coats		400	.020		.21	.56		.77	1.15
8600	Balustrades, primer coat, oil base, brushwork		520	.015		.06	.43		.49	.78

09 91 Painting

09 91 23 – Interior Painting

09 91 23.52 Miscellaneous, Interior

		Crew	Daily Output	Labor-Hours	Unit	Material	2014 Bare Costs Labor	Equipment	Total	Total Incl O&P
8650	Paint, 1 coat	1 Pord	520	.015	S.F.	.11	.43		.54	.83
8700	2 coats		325	.025		.21	.69		.90	1.37
8900	Trusses and wood frames, primer coat, oil base, brushwork		800	.010		.06	.28		.34	.53
8950	Spray		1200	.007		.07	.19		.26	.38
9000	Paint 1 coat, brushwork		750	.011		.11	.30		.41	.61
9200	Spray		1200	.007		.12	.19		.31	.44
9220	Paint 2 coats, brushwork		500	.016		.21	.45		.66	.97
9240	Spray		600	.013		.23	.37		.60	.88
9260	Stain, brushwork, wipe off		600	.013		.08	.37		.45	.71
9280	Varnish, 3 coats, brushwork		275	.029		.28	.82		1.10	1.65
9350	For latex paint, deduct					10%				

09 91 23.72 Walls and Ceilings, Interior

		Crew	Daily Output	Labor-Hours	Unit	Material	2014 Bare Costs Labor	Equipment	Total	Total Incl O&P
0010	**WALLS AND CEILINGS, INTERIOR**									
0100	Concrete, drywall or plaster, latex , primer or sealer coat									
0200	Smooth finish, brushwork	1 Pord	1150	.007	S.F.	.06	.20		.26	.39
0240	Roller		1350	.006		.06	.17		.23	.34
0280	Spray		2750	.003		.05	.08		.13	.19
0300	Sand finish, brushwork		975	.008		.06	.23		.29	.45
0340	Roller		1150	.007		.06	.20		.26	.39
0380	Spray		2275	.004		.05	.10		.15	.22
0400	Paint 1 coat, smooth finish, brushwork		1200	.007		.06	.19		.25	.38
0440	Roller		1300	.006		.06	.17		.23	.35
0480	Spray		2275	.004		.05	.10		.15	.22
0500	Sand finish, brushwork		1050	.008		.06	.21		.27	.42
0540	Roller		1600	.005		.06	.14		.20	.30
0580	Spray		2100	.004		.02	.11		.13	.20
0800	Paint 2 coats, smooth finish, brushwork		680	.012		.13	.33		.46	.68
0840	Roller		800	.010		.13	.28		.41	.60
0880	Spray		1625	.005		.12	.14		.26	.36
0900	Sand finish, brushwork		605	.013		.13	.37		.50	.75
0940	Roller		1020	.008		.13	.22		.35	.50
0980	Spray		1700	.005		.12	.13		.25	.35
1200	Paint 3 coats, smooth finish, brushwork		510	.016		.19	.44		.63	.93
1240	Roller		650	.012		.19	.35		.54	.78
1280	Spray		1625	.005		.18	.14		.32	.43
1300	Sand finish, brushwork		454	.018		.37	.50		.87	1.21
1340	Roller		680	.012		.39	.33		.72	.97
1380	Spray		1133	.007		.33	.20		.53	.70
1600	Glaze coating, 2 coats, spray, clear		1200	.007		.49	.19		.68	.85
1640	Multicolor		1200	.007		.98	.19		1.17	1.39
1660	Painting walls, complete, including surface prep, primer &									
1670	2 coats finish, on drywall or plaster, with roller	1 Pord	325	.025	S.F.	.20	.69		.89	1.35
1700	For oil base paint, add					10%				
1800	For ceiling installations, add						25%			
2000	Masonry or concrete block, primer/sealer, latex paint									
2100	Primer, smooth finish, brushwork	1 Pord	1000	.008	S.F.	.10	.22		.32	.48
2110	Roller		1150	.007		.10	.20		.30	.43
2180	Spray		2400	.003		.09	.09		.18	.25
2200	Sand finish, brushwork		850	.009		.10	.26		.36	.54
2210	Roller		975	.008		.10	.23		.33	.49
2280	Spray		2050	.004		.09	.11		.20	.28
2400	Finish coat, smooth finish, brush		1100	.007		.08	.20		.28	.43

09 91 23 – Interior Painting

09 91 23.72 Walls and Ceilings, Interior

		Crew	Daily Output	Labor-Hours	Unit	Material	2014 Bare Costs Labor	2014 Bare Costs Equipment	Total	Total Incl O&P
2410	Roller	1 Pord	1300	.006	S.F.	.08	.17		.25	.37
2480	Spray		2400	.003		.07	.09		.16	.23
2500	Sand finish, brushwork		950	.008		.08	.24		.32	.48
2510	Roller		1090	.007		.08	.21		.29	.43
2580	Spray		2040	.004		.07	.11		.18	.26
2800	Primer plus one finish coat, smooth brush		525	.015		.29	.43		.72	1.02
2810	Roller		615	.013		.18	.37		.55	.80
2880	Spray		1200	.007		.16	.19		.35	.49
2900	Sand finish, brushwork		450	.018		.18	.50		.68	1.02
2910	Roller		515	.016		.18	.44		.62	.92
2980	Spray		1025	.008		.16	.22		.38	.54
3200	Primer plus 2 finish coats, smooth, brush		355	.023		.26	.63		.89	1.33
3210	Roller		415	.019		.26	.54		.80	1.18
3280	Spray		800	.010		.23	.28		.51	.71
3300	Sand finish, brushwork		305	.026		.26	.74		1	1.50
3310	Roller		350	.023		.26	.64		.90	1.35
3380	Spray		675	.012		.23	.33		.56	.80
3600	Glaze coating, 3 coats, spray, clear		900	.009		.70	.25		.95	1.18
3620	Multicolor		900	.009		1.13	.25		1.38	1.66
4000	Block filler, 1 coat, brushwork		425	.019		.12	.53		.65	1
4100	Silicone, water repellent, 2 coats, spray	↓	2000	.004		.29	.11		.40	.50
4120	For oil base paint, add					10%				
8200	For work 8' - 15' H, add						10%			
8300	For work over 15' H, add						20%			
8400	For light textured surfaces, add						10%			
8410	Heavy textured, add						25%			

09 91 23.74 Walls and Ceilings, Interior, Zero VOC Latex

			Crew	Daily Output	Labor-Hours	Unit	Material	2014 Bare Costs Labor	2014 Bare Costs Equipment	Total	Total Incl O&P
0010	**WALLS AND CEILINGS, INTERIOR, ZERO VOC LATEX**										
0100	Concrete, dry wall or plaster, latex, primer or sealer coat										
0200	Smooth finish, brushwork	G	1 Pord	1150	.007	S.F.	.06	.20		.26	.39
0240	Roller	G		1350	.006		.06	.17		.23	.34
0280	Spray	G		2750	.003		.05	.08		.13	.18
0300	Sand finish, brushwork	G		975	.008		.06	.23		.29	.45
0340	Roller	G		1150	.007		.07	.20		.27	.39
0380	Spray	G		2275	.004		.05	.10		.15	.22
0400	Paint 1 coat, smooth finish, brushwork	G		1200	.007		.07	.19		.26	.39
0440	Roller	G		1300	.006		.07	.17		.24	.36
0480	Spray	G		2275	.004		.06	.10		.16	.23
0500	Sand finish, brushwork	G		1050	.008		.07	.21		.28	.43
0540	Roller	G		1600	.005		.07	.14		.21	.31
0580	Spray	G		2100	.004		.06	.11		.17	.25
0800	Paint 2 coats, smooth finish, brushwork	G		680	.012		.14	.33		.47	.70
0840	Roller	G		800	.010		.15	.28		.43	.62
0880	Spray	G		1625	.005		.13	.14		.27	.37
0900	Sand finish, brushwork	G		605	.013		.14	.37		.51	.76
0940	Roller	G		1020	.008		.15	.22		.37	.52
0980	Spray	G		1700	.005		.13	.13		.26	.36
1200	Paint 3 coats, smooth finish, brushwork	G		510	.016		.21	.44		.65	.95
1240	Roller	G		650	.012		.22	.35		.57	.81
1280	Spray	G	↓	1625	.005		.19	.14		.33	.44
1800	For ceiling installations, add	G						25%			
8200	For work 8' - 15' H, add							10%			

09 91 Painting

09 91 23 – Interior Painting

09 91 23.74 Walls and Ceilings, Interior, Zero VOC Latex	Crew	Daily Output	Labor-Hours	Unit	Material	2014 Bare Costs Labor	Equipment	Total	Total Incl O&P
8300 For work over 15' H, add				S.F.		20%			

09 91 23.75 Dry Fall Painting

	Crew	Daily Output	Labor-Hours	Unit	Material	2014 Bare Costs Labor	Equipment	Total	Total Incl O&P
0010 **DRY FALL PAINTING**									
0100 Sprayed on walls, gypsum board or plaster									
0220 One coat	1 Pord	2600	.003	S.F.	.06	.09		.15	.20
0250 Two coats		1560	.005		.11	.14		.25	.36
0280 Concrete or textured plaster, one coat		1560	.005		.06	.14		.20	.30
0310 Two coats		1300	.006		.11	.17		.28	.40
0340 Concrete block, one coat		1560	.005		.06	.14		.20	.30
0370 Two coats		1300	.006		.11	.17		.28	.40
0400 Wood, one coat		877	.009		.06	.26		.32	.48
0430 Two coats	▼	650	.012	▼	.11	.35		.46	.69
0440 On ceilings, gypsum board or plaster									
0470 One coat	1 Pord	1560	.005	S.F.	.06	.14		.20	.30
0500 Two coats		1300	.006		.11	.17		.28	.40
0530 Concrete or textured plaster, one coat		1560	.005		.06	.14		.20	.30
0560 Two coats		1300	.006		.11	.17		.28	.40
0570 Structural steel, bar joists or metal deck, one coat		1560	.005		.06	.14		.20	.30
0580 Two coats	▼	1040	.008	▼	.11	.22		.33	.48

09 93 Staining and Transparent Finishing

09 93 23 – Interior Staining and Finishing

09 93 23.10 Varnish

	Crew	Daily Output	Labor-Hours	Unit	Material	2014 Bare Costs Labor	Equipment	Total	Total Incl O&P
0010 **VARNISH**									
0012 1 coat + sealer, on wood trim, brush, no sanding included	1 Pord	400	.020	S.F.	.07	.56		.63	1
0020 1 coat + sealer, on wood trim, brush, no sanding included, no VOC		400	.020		.18	.56		.74	1.12
0100 Hardwood floors, 2 coats, no sanding included, roller	▼	1890	.004	▼	.15	.12		.27	.37

09 96 High-Performance Coatings

09 96 56 – Epoxy Coatings

09 96 56.20 Wall Coatings

	Crew	Daily Output	Labor-Hours	Unit	Material	2014 Bare Costs Labor	Equipment	Total	Total Incl O&P
0010 **WALL COATINGS**									
0100 Acrylic glazed coatings, minimum	1 Pord	525	.015	S.F.	.31	.43		.74	1.04
0200 Maximum		305	.026		.65	.74		1.39	1.93
0300 Epoxy coatings, minimum		525	.015		.40	.43		.83	1.14
0400 Maximum		170	.047		1.20	1.32		2.52	3.49
0600 Exposed aggregate, troweled on, 1/16" to 1/4", minimum		235	.034		.61	.96		1.57	2.24
0700 Maximum (epoxy or polyacrylate)		130	.062		1.31	1.73		3.04	4.28
0900 1/2" to 5/8" aggregate, minimum		130	.062		1.19	1.73		2.92	4.15
1000 Maximum		80	.100		2.06	2.81		4.87	6.90
1200 1" aggregate size, minimum		90	.089		2.09	2.50		4.59	6.40
1300 Maximum		55	.145		3.19	4.09		7.28	10.20
1500 Exposed aggregate, sprayed on, 1/8" aggregate, minimum		295	.027		.56	.76		1.32	1.87
1600 Maximum	▼	145	.055	▼	1.04	1.55		2.59	3.69

Estimating Tips

General

- The items in this division are usually priced per square foot or each.

- Many items in Division 10 require some type of support system or special anchors that are not usually furnished with the item. The required anchors must be added to the estimate in the appropriate division.

- Some items in Division 10, such as lockers, may require assembly before installation. Verify the amount of assembly required. Assembly can often exceed installation time.

10 20 00 Interior Specialties

- Support angles and blocking are not included in the installation of toilet compartments, shower/dressing compartments, or cubicles. Appropriate line items from Divisions 5 or 6 may need to be added to support the installations.

- Toilet partitions are priced by the stall. A stall consists of a side wall, pilaster, and door with hardware. Toilet tissue holders and grab bars are extra.

- The required acoustical rating of a folding partition can have a significant impact on costs. Verify the sound transmission coefficient rating of the panel priced to the specification requirements.

- Grab bar installation does not include supplemental blocking or backing to support the required load. When grab bars are installed at an existing facility, provisions must be made to attach the grab bars to solid structure.

Reference Numbers

Reference numbers are shown in shaded boxes at the beginning of some major classifications. These numbers refer to related items in the Reference Section. The reference information may be an estimating procedure, an alternate pricing method, or technical information.

Note: Not all subdivisions listed here necessarily appear in this publication.

10 21 Compartments and Cubicles

10 21 16 – Shower and Dressing Compartments

10 21 16.10 Partitions, Shower

		Crew	Daily Output	Labor-Hours	Unit	Material	2014 Bare Costs Labor	Equipment	Total	Total Incl O&P
0010	**PARTITIONS, SHOWER** floor mounted, no plumbing									
0400	Cabinet, one piece, fiberglass, 32" x 32"	2 Carp	5	3.200	Ea.	510	103		613	735
0420	36" x 36"		5	3.200		610	103		713	845
0440	36" x 48"		5	3.200		1,300	103		1,403	1,600
0460	Acrylic, 32" x 32"		5	3.200		299	103		402	505
0480	36" x 36"		5	3.200		1,000	103		1,103	1,275
0500	36" x 48"		5	3.200		1,500	103		1,603	1,825
0520	Shower door for above, clear plastic, 24" wide	1 Carp	8	1		177	32		209	249
0540	28" wide		8	1		201	32		233	276
0560	Tempered glass, 24" wide		8	1		191	32		223	264
0580	28" wide		8	1		216	32		248	291
2400	Glass stalls, with doors, no receptors, chrome on brass	2 Shee	3	5.333		1,650	193		1,843	2,150
2700	Anodized aluminum	"	4	4		1,150	144		1,294	1,525
3200	Receptors, precast terrazzo, 32" x 32"	2 Marb	14	1.143		330	34		364	420
3300	48" x 34"		9.50	1.684		440	50		490	570
3500	Plastic, simulated terrazzo receptor, 32" x 32"		14	1.143		148	34		182	220
3600	32" x 48"		12	1.333		215	39.50		254.50	305
3800	Precast concrete, colors, 32" x 32"		14	1.143		186	34		220	262
3900	48" x 48"		8	2		251	59		310	375
4100	Shower doors, economy plastic, 24" wide	1 Shee	9	.889		144	32		176	212
4200	Tempered glass door, economy		8	1		260	36		296	345
4400	Folding, tempered glass, aluminum frame		6	1.333		390	48		438	510
4700	Deluxe, tempered glass, chrome on brass frame, minimum		8	1		385	36		421	480
4800	Maximum		1	8		625	289		914	1,175
4850	On anodized aluminum frame, minimum		2	4		540	144		684	830
4900	Maximum		1	8		625	289		914	1,175
5100	Shower enclosure, tempered glass, anodized alum. frame									
5120	2 panel & door, corner unit, 32" x 32"	1 Shee	2	4	Ea.	1,025	144		1,169	1,400
5140	Neo-angle corner unit, 16" x 24" x 16"	"	2	4		1,075	144		1,219	1,450
5200	Shower surround, 3 wall, polypropylene, 32" x 32"	1 Carp	4	2		455	64		519	610
5220	PVC, 32" x 32"		4	2		380	64		444	530
5240	Fiberglass		4	2		420	64		484	570
5250	2 wall, polypropylene, 32" x 32"		4	2		315	64		379	460
5270	PVC		4	2		395	64		459	545
5290	Fiberglass		4	2		400	64		464	550
5300	Tub doors, tempered glass & frame, minimum	1 Shee	8	1		229	36		265	310
5400	Maximum		6	1.333		535	48		583	670
5600	Chrome plated, brass frame, minimum		8	1		305	36		341	395
5700	Maximum		6	1.333		745	48		793	895
5900	Tub/shower enclosure, temp. glass, alum. frame, minimum		2	4		410	144		554	690
6200	Maximum		1.50	5.333		855	193		1,048	1,250
6500	On chrome-plated brass frame, minimum		2	4		565	144		709	865
6600	Maximum		1.50	5.333		1,200	193		1,393	1,650
6800	Tub surround, 3 wall, polypropylene	1 Carp	4	2		256	64		320	390
6900	PVC		4	2		390	64		454	540
7000	Fiberglass, minimum		4	2		400	64		464	550
7100	Maximum		3	2.667		680	85.50		765.50	895

10 28 Toilet, Bath, and Laundry Accessories

10 28 13 – Toilet Accessories

10 28 13.13 Commercial Toilet Accessories

10 28 13.13 Commercial Toilet Accessories	Crew	Daily Output	Labor-Hours	Unit	Material	2014 Bare Costs Labor	Equipment	Total	Total Incl O&P
0010 **COMMERCIAL TOILET ACCESSORIES**									
0200 Curtain rod, stainless steel, 5' long, 1" diameter	1 Carp	13	.615	Ea.	26.50	19.75		46.25	62
0300 1-1/4" diameter		13	.615		30.50	19.75		50.25	66.50
0800 Grab bar, straight, 1-1/4" diameter, stainless steel, 18" long		24	.333		29	10.70		39.70	50
1100 36" long		20	.400		38.50	12.85		51.35	64
1105 42" long		20	.400		46	12.85		58.85	72
1120 Corner, 36" long		20	.400		85.50	12.85		98.35	116
3000 Mirror, with stainless steel 3/4" square frame, 18" x 24"		20	.400		47	12.85		59.85	73
3100 36" x 24"		15	.533		103	17.10		120.10	142
3300 72" x 24"		6	1.333		256	43		299	355
4300 Robe hook, single, regular		36	.222		18.10	7.15		25.25	32
4400 Heavy duty, concealed mounting		36	.222		21	7.15		28.15	35
6400 Towel bar, stainless steel, 18" long		23	.348		41.50	11.15		52.65	65
6500 30" long		21	.381		111	12.25		123.25	144
7400 Tumbler holder, tumbler only		30	.267		15.90	8.55		24.45	32
7410 Tumbler holder		20	.400		9.10	12.85		21.95	31.50
7500 Soap, tumbler & toothbrush		30	.267		19.60	8.55		28.15	36
7510 Tumbler & toothbrush holder		20	.400		12.60	12.85		25.45	35.50

10 28 16 – Bath Accessories

10 28 16.20 Medicine Cabinets

	Crew	Daily Output	Labor-Hours	Unit	Material	2014 Bare Costs Labor	Equipment	Total	Total Incl O&P
0010 **MEDICINE CABINETS**									
0020 With mirror, sst frame, 16" x 22", unlighted	1 Carp	14	.571	Ea.	95	18.35		113.35	136
0100 Wood frame		14	.571		136	18.35		154.35	181
0300 Sliding mirror doors, 20" x 16" x 4-3/4", unlighted		7	1.143		125	36.50		161.50	199
0400 24" x 19" x 8-1/2", lighted		5	1.600		179	51.50		230.50	284
0600 Triple door, 30" x 32", unlighted, plywood body		7	1.143		320	36.50		356.50	410
0700 Steel body		7	1.143		350	36.50		386.50	445
0900 Oak door, wood body, beveled mirror, single door		7	1.143		195	36.50		231.50	276
1000 Double door		6	1.333		390	43		433	500

10 28 23 – Laundry Accessories

10 28 23.13 Built-In Ironing Boards

	Crew	Daily Output	Labor-Hours	Unit	Material	2014 Bare Costs Labor	Equipment	Total	Total Incl O&P
0010 **BUILT-IN IRONING BOARDS**									
0020 Including cabinet, board & light, minimum	1 Carp	2	4	Ea.	365	128		493	615

10 31 Manufactured Fireplaces

10 31 13 – Manufactured Fireplace Chimneys

10 31 13.10 Fireplace Chimneys

	Crew	Daily Output	Labor-Hours	Unit	Material	2014 Bare Costs Labor	Equipment	Total	Total Incl O&P
0010 **FIREPLACE CHIMNEYS**									
0500 Chimney dbl. wall, all stainless, over 8'-6", 7" diam., add to fireplace	1 Carp	33	.242	V.L.F.	83.50	7.80		91.30	105
0600 10" diameter, add to fireplace		32	.250		112	8.05		120.05	138
0700 12" diameter, add to fireplace		31	.258		159	8.30		167.30	189
0800 14" diameter, add to fireplace		30	.267		243	8.55		251.55	281
1000 Simulated brick chimney top, 4' high, 16" x 16"		10	.800	Ea.	425	25.50		450.50	515
1100 24" x 24"		7	1.143	"	540	36.50		576.50	655

10 31 13.20 Chimney Accessories

	Crew	Daily Output	Labor-Hours	Unit	Material	2014 Bare Costs Labor	Equipment	Total	Total Incl O&P
0010 **CHIMNEY ACCESSORIES**									
0020 Chimney screens, galv., 13" x 13" flue	1 Bric	8	1	Ea.	58.50	32		90.50	117
0050 24" x 24" flue		5	1.600		124	51		175	222
0200 Stainless steel, 13" x 13" flue		8	1		97.50	32		129.50	160
0250 20" x 20" flue		5	1.600		152	51		203	252

10 31 Manufactured Fireplaces

10 31 13 – Manufactured Fireplace Chimneys

10 31 13.20 Chimney Accessories	Crew	Daily Output	Labor-Hours	Unit	Material	2014 Bare Costs Labor	Equipment	Total	Total Incl O&P
2400 Squirrel and bird screens, galvanized, 8" x 8" flue	1 Bric	16	.500	Ea.	53	15.95		68.95	85
2450 13" x 13" flue		12	.667		55	21.50		76.50	96

10 31 16 – Manufactured Fireplace Forms

10 31 16.10 Fireplace Forms

	Crew	Daily Output	Labor-Hours	Unit	Material	2014 Bare Costs Labor	Equipment	Total	Total Incl O&P
0010 **FIREPLACE FORMS**									
1800 Fireplace forms, no accessories, 32" opening	1 Bric	3	2.667	Ea.	670	85		755	880
1900 36" opening		2.50	3.200		855	102		957	1,100
2000 40" opening		2	4		1,125	128		1,253	1,450
2100 78" opening		1.50	5.333		1,650	170		1,820	2,100

10 31 23 – Prefabricated Fireplaces

10 31 23.10 Fireplace, Prefabricated

	Crew	Daily Output	Labor-Hours	Unit	Material	2014 Bare Costs Labor	Equipment	Total	Total Incl O&P
0010 **FIREPLACE, PREFABRICATED**, free standing or wall hung									
0100 With hood & screen, minimum	1 Carp	1.30	6.154	Ea.	1,200	198		1,398	1,650
0150 Average		1	8		1,450	257		1,707	2,025
0200 Maximum		.90	8.889		2,725	285		3,010	3,475
1500 Simulated logs, gas fired, 40,000 BTU, 2' long, minimum		7	1.143	Set	485	36.50		521.50	595
1600 Maximum		6	1.333		1,125	43		1,168	1,325
1700 Electric, 1,500 BTU, 1'-6" long, minimum		7	1.143		200	36.50		236.50	282
1800 11,500 BTU, maximum		6	1.333		300	43		343	405
2000 Fireplace, built-in, 36" hearth, radiant		1.30	6.154	Ea.	660	198		858	1,050
2100 Recirculating, small fan		1	8		945	257		1,202	1,475
2150 Large fan		.90	8.889		1,900	285		2,185	2,575
2200 42" hearth, radiant		1.20	6.667		890	214		1,104	1,350
2300 Recirculating, small fan		.90	8.889		1,175	285		1,460	1,775
2350 Large fan		.80	10		1,300	320		1,620	1,975
2400 48" hearth, radiant		1.10	7.273		2,075	233		2,308	2,675
2500 Recirculating, small fan		.80	10		2,350	320		2,670	3,150
2550 Large fan		.70	11.429		2,375	365		2,740	3,225
3000 See through, including doors		.80	10		2,525	320		2,845	3,350
3200 Corner (2 wall)		1	8		3,250	257		3,507	4,000

10 32 Fireplace Specialties

10 32 13 – Fireplace Dampers

10 32 13.10 Dampers

	Crew	Daily Output	Labor-Hours	Unit	Material	2014 Bare Costs Labor	Equipment	Total	Total Incl O&P
0010 **DAMPERS**									
0800 Damper, rotary control, steel, 30" opening	1 Bric	6	1.333	Ea.	119	42.50		161.50	202
0850 Cast iron, 30" opening		6	1.333		125	42.50		167.50	208
1200 Steel plate, poker control, 60" opening		8	1		320	32		352	410
1250 84" opening, special order		5	1.600		585	51		636	730
1400 "Universal" type, chain operated, 32" x 20" opening		8	1		250	32		282	330
1450 48" x 24" opening		5	1.600		375	51		426	495

10 32 23 – Fireplace Doors

10 32 23.10 Doors

	Crew	Daily Output	Labor-Hours	Unit	Material	2014 Bare Costs Labor	Equipment	Total	Total Incl O&P
0010 **DOORS**									
0400 Cleanout doors and frames, cast iron, 8" x 8"	1 Bric	12	.667	Ea.	41	21.50		62.50	80.50
0450 12" x 12"		10	.800		108	25.50		133.50	162
0500 18" x 24"		8	1		150	32		182	218
0550 Cast iron frame, steel door, 24" x 30"		5	1.600		315	51		366	430
1600 Dutch Oven door and frame, cast iron, 12" x 15" opening		13	.615		131	19.65		150.65	178

10 32 Fireplace Specialties

10 32 23 – Fireplace Doors

10 32 23.10 Doors	Crew	Daily Output	Labor-Hours	Unit	Material	2014 Bare Costs Labor	Equipment	Total	Total Incl O&P
1650 Copper plated, 12" x 15" opening	1 Bric	13	.615	Ea.	257	19.65		276.65	315

10 35 Stoves

10 35 13 – Heating Stoves

10 35 13.10 Woodburning Stoves

		Crew	Daily Output	Labor-Hours	Unit	Material	Labor	Equipment	Total	Total Incl O&P
0010	**WOODBURNING STOVES**									
0015	Cast iron, minimum	2 Carp	1.30	12.308	Ea.	980	395		1,375	1,750
0020	Average		1	16		1,825	515		2,340	2,900
0030	Maximum	↓	.80	20		2,525	640		3,165	3,850
0050	For gas log lighter, add				↓	45			45	49.50

10 44 Fire Protection Specialties

10 44 16 – Fire Extinguishers

10 44 16.13 Portable Fire Extinguishers

		Crew	Daily Output	Labor-Hours	Unit	Material	Labor	Equipment	Total	Total Incl O&P
0010	**PORTABLE FIRE EXTINGUISHERS**									
0140	CO_2, with hose and "H" horn, 10 lb.				Ea.	268			268	295
1000	Dry chemical, pressurized									
1040	Standard type, portable, painted, 2-1/2 lb.				Ea.	36.50			36.50	40
1080	10 lb.					79.50			79.50	87.50
1100	20 lb.					134			134	148
1120	30 lb.					395			395	435
2000	ABC all purpose type, portable, 2-1/2 lb.					21			21	23.50
2080	9-1/2 lb.				↓	44			44	48

10 55 Postal Specialties

10 55 23 – Mail Boxes

10 55 23.10 Mail Boxes

		Crew	Daily Output	Labor-Hours	Unit	Material	Labor	Equipment	Total	Total Incl O&P
0011	**MAIL BOXES**									
1900	Letter slot, residential	1 Carp	20	.400	Ea.	80	12.85		92.85	110
2400	Residential, galv. steel, small 20" x 7" x 9"	1 Clab	16	.500		175	11.90		186.90	213
2410	With galv. steel post, 54" long		6	1.333		225	31.50		256.50	300
2420	Large, 24" x 12" x 15"		16	.500		180	11.90		191.90	218
2430	With galv. steel post, 54" long		6	1.333		225	31.50		256.50	300
2440	Decorative, polyethylene, 22" x 10" x 10"		16	.500		60	11.90		71.90	86
2450	With alum. post, decorative, 54" long	↓	6	1.333	↓	180	31.50		211.50	252

10 56 Storage Assemblies

10 56 13 – Metal Storage Shelving

10 56 13.10 Shelving		Crew	Daily Output	Labor-Hours	Unit	Material	2014 Bare Costs Labor	2014 Bare Costs Equipment	Total	Total Incl O&P
0010	**SHELVING**									
0020	Metal, industrial, cross-braced, 3' wide, 12" deep	1 Sswk	175	.046	SF Shlf	7.45	1.57		9.02	11.20
0100	24" deep		330	.024		4.95	.83		5.78	7.05
2200	Wide span, 1600 lb. capacity per shelf, 6' wide, 24" deep		380	.021		6.30	.72		7.02	8.30
2400	36" deep		440	.018		6.75	.62		7.37	8.65
3000	Residential, vinyl covered wire, wardrobe, 12" deep	1 Carp	195	.041	L.F.	11.95	1.32		13.27	15.35
3100	16" deep		195	.041		10.30	1.32		11.62	13.50
3200	Standard, 6" deep		195	.041		3.85	1.32		5.17	6.45
3300	9" deep		195	.041		5.80	1.32		7.12	8.55
3400	12" deep		195	.041		7.70	1.32		9.02	10.65
3500	16" deep		195	.041		17.40	1.32		18.72	21.50
3600	20" deep		195	.041		19.55	1.32		20.87	23.50
3700	Support bracket		80	.100	Ea.	6.40	3.21		9.61	12.45

10 57 Wardrobe and Closet Specialties

10 57 23 – Closet and Utility Shelving

10 57 23.19 Wood Closet and Utility Shelving

		Crew	Daily Output	Labor-Hours	Unit	Material	2014 Bare Costs Labor	2014 Bare Costs Equipment	Total	Total Incl O&P
0010	**WOOD CLOSET AND UTILITY SHELVING**									
0020	Pine, clear grade, no edge band, 1" x 8"	1 Carp	115	.070	L.F.	3.04	2.23		5.27	7.10
0100	1" x 10"		110	.073		3.78	2.33		6.11	8.10
0200	1" x 12"		105	.076		4.56	2.45		7.01	9.10
0450	1" x 18"		95	.084		6.85	2.70		9.55	12.05
0460	1" x 24"		85	.094		9.10	3.02		12.12	15.15
0600	Plywood, 3/4" thick with lumber edge, 12" wide		75	.107		1.78	3.42		5.20	7.70
0700	24" wide		70	.114		3.18	3.67		6.85	9.65
0900	Bookcase, clear grade pine, shelves 12" O.C., 8" deep, per S.F. shelf		70	.114	S.F.	9.90	3.67		13.57	17
1000	12" deep shelves		65	.123	"	14.80	3.95		18.75	23
1200	Adjustable closet rod and shelf, 12" wide, 3' long		20	.400	Ea.	10.95	12.85		23.80	33.50
1300	8' long		15	.533	"	20	17.10		37.10	51
1500	Prefinished shelves with supports, stock, 8" wide		75	.107	L.F.	3.38	3.42		6.80	9.45
1600	10" wide		70	.114	"	4.75	3.67		8.42	11.40

10 73 Protective Covers

10 73 16 – Canopies

10 73 16.10 Canopies, Residential

		Crew	Daily Output	Labor-Hours	Unit	Material	2014 Bare Costs Labor	2014 Bare Costs Equipment	Total	Total Incl O&P
0010	**CANOPIES, RESIDENTIAL** Prefabricated									
0500	Carport, free standing, baked enamel, alum., .032", 40 psf									
0520	16' x 8', 4 posts	2 Carp	3	5.333	Ea.	4,475	171		4,646	5,225
0600	20' x 10', 6 posts		2	8		4,600	257		4,857	5,475
0605	30' x 10', 8 posts		2	8		6,900	257		7,157	8,025
1000	Door canopies, extruded alum., .032", 42" projection, 4' wide	1 Carp	8	1		201	32		233	275
1020	6' wide	"	6	1.333		284	43		327	380
1040	8' wide	2 Carp	9	1.778		370	57		427	505
1060	10' wide		7	2.286		345	73.50		418.50	500
1080	12' wide		5	3.200		560	103		663	790
1200	54" projection, 4' wide	1 Carp	8	1		248	32		280	325
1220	6' wide	"	6	1.333		290	43		333	390
1240	8' wide	2 Carp	9	1.778		350	57		407	480
1260	10' wide		7	2.286		515	73.50		588.50	695

10 73 Protective Covers

10 73 16 – Canopies

10 73 16.10 Canopies, Residential	Crew	Daily Output	Labor-Hours	Unit	Material	2014 Bare Costs Labor	Equipment	Total	Total Incl O&P
1280	12' wide	2 Carp	5	3.200	Ea.	555	103		658	790
1300	Painted, add					20%				
1310	Bronze anodized, add					50%				
3000	Window awnings, aluminum, window 3' high, 4' wide	1 Carp	10	.800		126	25.50		151.50	182
3020	6' wide	"	8	1		180	32		212	252
3040	9' wide	2 Carp	9	1.778		305	57		362	430
3060	12' wide	"	5	3.200		305	103		408	510
3100	Window, 4' high, 4' wide	1 Carp	10	.800		159	25.50		184.50	218
3120	6' wide	"	8	1		229	32		261	305
3140	9' wide	2 Carp	9	1.778		375	57		432	505
3160	12' wide	"	5	3.200		375	103		478	585
3200	Window, 6' high, 4' wide	1 Carp	10	.800		295	25.50		320.50	370
3220	6' wide	"	8	1		340	32		372	430
3240	9' wide	2 Carp	9	1.778		900	57		957	1,075
3260	12' wide	"	5	3.200		1,375	103		1,478	1,700
3400	Roll-up aluminum, 2'-6" wide	1 Carp	14	.571		190	18.35		208.35	240
3420	3' wide		12	.667		195	21.50		216.50	250
3440	4' wide		10	.800		244	25.50		269.50	310
3460	6' wide		8	1		290	32		322	375
3480	9' wide	2 Carp	9	1.778		400	57		457	535
3500	12' wide	"	5	3.200		535	103		638	765
3600	Window awnings, canvas, 24" drop, 3' wide	1 Carp	30	.267	L.F.	50	8.55		58.55	69.50
3620	4' wide		40	.200		43	6.40		49.40	58.50
3700	30" drop, 3' wide		30	.267		51.50	8.55		60.05	71.50
3720	4' wide		40	.200		44.50	6.40		50.90	60
3740	5' wide		45	.178		40	5.70		45.70	53.50
3760	6' wide		48	.167		37	5.35		42.35	49.50
3780	8' wide		48	.167		34.50	5.35		39.85	47
3800	10' wide		50	.160		42	5.15		47.15	54.50

10 74 Manufactured Exterior Specialties

10 74 23 – Cupolas

10 74 23.10 Wood Cupolas

		Crew	Daily Output	Labor-Hours	Unit	Material	2014 Bare Costs Labor	Equipment	Total	Total Incl O&P
0010	**WOOD CUPOLAS**									
0020	Stock units, pine, painted, 18" sq., 28" high, alum. roof	1 Carp	4.10	1.951	Ea.	184	62.50		246.50	305
0100	Copper roof		3.80	2.105		255	67.50		322.50	395
0300	23" square, 33" high, aluminum roof		3.70	2.162		360	69.50		429.50	510
0400	Copper roof		3.30	2.424		470	78		548	645
0600	30" square, 37" high, aluminum roof		3.70	2.162		560	69.50		629.50	730
0700	Copper roof		3.30	2.424		670	78		748	865
0900	Hexagonal, 31" wide, 46" high, copper roof		4	2		860	64		924	1,050
1000	36" wide, 50" high, copper roof		3.50	2.286		1,400	73.50		1,473.50	1,675
1200	For deluxe stock units, add to above					25%				
1400	For custom built units, add to above					50%	50%			

10 74 33 – Weathervanes

10 74 33.10 Residential Weathervanes

		Crew	Daily Output	Labor-Hours	Unit	Material	2014 Bare Costs Labor	Equipment	Total	Total Incl O&P
0010	**RESIDENTIAL WEATHERVANES**									
0020	Residential types, minimum	1 Carp	8	1	Ea.	151	32		183	220
0100	Maximum	"	2	4	"	1,700	128		1,828	2,100

10 74 Manufactured Exterior Specialties

10 74 46 – Window Wells

10 74 46.10 Area Window Wells	Crew	Daily Output	Labor-Hours	Unit	Material	2014 Bare Costs Labor	2014 Bare Costs Equipment	Total	Total Incl O&P
0010 **AREA WINDOW WELLS**, Galvanized steel									
0020 20 ga., 3'-2" wide, 1' deep	1 Sswk	29	.276	Ea.	16.95	9.45		26.40	36.50
0100 2' deep		23	.348		27.50	11.90		39.40	52.50
0300 16 ga., 3'-2" wide, 1' deep		29	.276		23	9.45		32.45	43.50
0400 3' deep		23	.348		47	11.90		58.90	74
0600 Welded grating for above, 15 lb., painted		45	.178		87.50	6.10		93.60	108
0700 Galvanized		45	.178		118	6.10		124.10	142
0900 Translucent plastic cap for above		60	.133		17.65	4.57		22.22	28

10 75 Flagpoles

10 75 16 – Ground-Set Flagpoles

10 75 16.10 Flagpoles

10 75 16.10 Flagpoles	Crew	Daily Output	Labor-Hours	Unit	Material	2014 Bare Costs Labor	2014 Bare Costs Equipment	Total	Total Incl O&P
0010 **FLAGPOLES**, ground set									
0050 Not including base or foundation									
0100 Aluminum, tapered, ground set 20' high	K-1	2	8	Ea.	980	232	166	1,378	1,650
0200 25' high		1.70	9.412		1,150	273	196	1,619	1,925
0300 30' high		1.50	10.667		1,275	310	222	1,807	2,175
0500 40' high		1.20	13.333		2,525	385	277	3,187	3,725

Estimating Tips

General

- The items in this division are usually priced per square foot or each. Many of these items are purchased by the owner for installation by the contractor. Check the specifications for responsibilities and include time for receiving, storage, installation, and mechanical and electrical hookups in the appropriate divisions.

- Many items in Division 11 require some type of support system that is not usually furnished with the item. Examples of these systems include blocking for the attachment of casework and support angles for ceiling-hung projection screens. The required blocking or supports must be added to the estimate in the appropriate division.

- Some items in Division 11 may require assembly or electrical hookups. Verify the amount of assembly required or the need for a hard electrical connection and add the appropriate costs.

Reference Numbers

Reference numbers are shown in shaded boxes at the beginning of some major classifications. These numbers refer to related items in the Reference Section. The reference information may be an estimating procedure, an alternate pricing method, or technical information.

Note: Not all subdivisions listed here necessarily appear in this publication.

Division 11 - Equipment

11 24 Maintenance Equipment

11 24 19 – Vacuum Cleaning Systems

11 24 19.10 Vacuum Cleaning		Crew	Daily Output	Labor-Hours	Unit	Material	2014 Bare Costs Labor	2014 Bare Costs Equipment	Total	Total Incl O&P
0010	**VACUUM CLEANING**									
0020	Central, 3-inlet, residential	1 Skwk	.90	8.889	Total	1,050	288		1,338	1,650
0400	5 inlet system, residential		.50	16		1,475	520		1,995	2,500
0600	7 inlet system, commercial		.40	20		1,675	650		2,325	2,950
0800	9 inlet system, residential	▼	.30	26.667		3,700	865		4,565	5,525
4010	Rule of thumb: First 1200 S.F., installed				▼				1,425	1,575
4020	For each additional S.F., add				S.F.					.26

11 26 Unit Kitchens

11 26 13 – Metal Unit Kitchens

11 26 13.10 Commercial Unit Kitchens

		Crew	Daily Output	Labor-Hours	Unit	Material	Labor	Equipment	Total	Total Incl O&P
0010	**COMMERCIAL UNIT KITCHENS**									
1500	Combination range, refrigerator and sink, 30" wide, minimum	L-1	2	5	Ea.	1,100	188		1,288	1,500
1550	Maximum		1	10		1,450	375		1,825	2,225
1570	60" wide, average		1.40	7.143		1,525	268		1,793	2,125
1590	72" wide, average	▼	1.20	8.333	▼	1,600	315		1,915	2,275

11 31 Residential Appliances

11 31 13 – Residential Kitchen Appliances

11 31 13.13 Cooking Equipment

		Crew	Daily Output	Labor-Hours	Unit	Material	Labor	Equipment	Total	Total Incl O&P
0010	**COOKING EQUIPMENT**									
0020	Cooking range, 30" free standing, 1 oven, minimum	2 Clab	10	1.600	Ea.	435	38		473	545
0050	Maximum		4	4		2,000	95		2,095	2,350
0150	2 oven, minimum		10	1.600		1,200	38		1,238	1,400
0200	Maximum	▼	10	1.600		2,525	38		2,563	2,850
0350	Built-in, 30" wide, 1 oven, minimum	1 Elec	6	1.333		675	47.50		722.50	820
0400	Maximum	2 Carp	2	8		1,350	257		1,607	1,900
0500	2 oven, conventional, minimum		4	4		1,300	128		1,428	1,650
0550	1 conventional, 1 microwave, maximum	▼	2	8		1,775	257		2,032	2,375
0700	Free-standing, 1 oven, 21" wide range, minimum	2 Clab	10	1.600		450	38		488	560
0750	21" wide, maximum	"	4	4		445	95		540	650
0900	Countertop cooktops, 4 burner, standard, minimum	1 Elec	6	1.333		293	47.50		340.50	400
0950	Maximum		3	2.667		1,300	95.50		1,395.50	1,575
1050	As above, but with grill and griddle attachment, minimum		6	1.333		1,225	47.50		1,272.50	1,425
1100	Maximum		3	2.667		3,650	95.50		3,745.50	4,175
1250	Microwave oven, minimum		4	2		119	71.50		190.50	248
1300	Maximum		2	4		460	143		603	740
5380	Oven, built in, standard		4	2		625	71.50		696.50	805
5390	Deluxe	▼	2	4	▼	2,250	143		2,393	2,675

11 31 13.23 Refrigeration Equipment

		Crew	Daily Output	Labor-Hours	Unit	Material	Labor	Equipment	Total	Total Incl O&P
0010	**REFRIGERATION EQUIPMENT**									
2000	Deep freeze, 15 to 23 C.F., minimum	2 Clab	10	1.600	Ea.	605	38		643	730
2050	Maximum		5	3.200		810	76		886	1,025
2200	30 C.F., minimum		8	2		695	47.50		742.50	845
2250	Maximum	▼	3	5.333		900	127		1,027	1,200
5200	Icemaker, automatic, 20 lb. per day	1 Plum	7	1.143		885	43.50		928.50	1,050
5350	51 lb. per day	"	2	4		1,575	152		1,727	1,975
5450	Refrigerator, no frost, 6 C.F.	2 Clab	15	1.067		241	25.50		266.50	310
5500	Refrigerator, no frost, 10 C.F. to 12 C.F., minimum	▼	10	1.600	▼	420	38		458	525

11 31 Residential Appliances

11 31 13 – Residential Kitchen Appliances

11 31 13.23 Refrigeration Equipment

		Crew	Daily Output	Labor-Hours	Unit	Material	2014 Bare Costs Labor	2014 Bare Costs Equipment	Total	Total Incl O&P
5600	Maximum	2 Clab	6	2.667	Ea.	445	63.50		508.50	590
5750	14 C.F. to 16 C.F., minimum		9	1.778		500	42.50		542.50	620
5800	Maximum		5	3.200		615	76		691	805
5950	18 C.F. to 20 C.F., minimum		8	2		620	47.50		667.50	765
6000	Maximum		4	4		1,400	95		1,495	1,700
6150	21 C.F. to 29 C.F., minimum		7	2.286		955	54.50		1,009.50	1,150
6200	Maximum		3	5.333		3,325	127		3,452	3,900
6790	Energy-star qualified, 18 C.F., minimum [G]	2 Carp	4	4		505	128		633	770
6795	Maximum [G]		2	8		1,150	257		1,407	1,700
6797	21.7 C.F., minimum [G]		4	4		1,025	128		1,153	1,350
6799	Maximum [G]		4	4		2,075	128		2,203	2,525

11 31 13.33 Kitchen Cleaning Equipment

		Crew	Daily Output	Labor-Hours	Unit	Material	2014 Bare Costs Labor	2014 Bare Costs Equipment	Total	Total Incl O&P
0010	**KITCHEN CLEANING EQUIPMENT**									
2750	Dishwasher, built-in, 2 cycles, minimum	L-1	4	2.500	Ea.	235	94		329	415
2800	Maximum		2	5		430	188		618	780
2950	4 or more cycles, minimum		4	2.500		370	94		464	565
2960	Average		4	2.500		495	94		589	700
3000	Maximum		2	5		1,075	188		1,263	1,500
3100	Energy-star qualified, minimum [G]		4	2.500		365	94		459	555
3110	Maximum [G]		2	5		1,500	188		1,688	1,950

11 31 13.43 Waste Disposal Equipment

		Crew	Daily Output	Labor-Hours	Unit	Material	2014 Bare Costs Labor	2014 Bare Costs Equipment	Total	Total Incl O&P
0010	**WASTE DISPOSAL EQUIPMENT**									
1750	Compactor, residential size, 4 to 1 compaction, minimum	1 Carp	5	1.600	Ea.	640	51.50		691.50	790
1800	Maximum	"	3	2.667		1,000	85.50		1,085.50	1,250
3300	Garbage disposal, sink type, minimum	L-1	10	1		86.50	37.50		124	157
3350	Maximum	"	10	1		217	37.50		254.50	300

11 31 13.53 Kitchen Ventilation Equipment

		Crew	Daily Output	Labor-Hours	Unit	Material	2014 Bare Costs Labor	2014 Bare Costs Equipment	Total	Total Incl O&P
0010	**KITCHEN VENTILATION EQUIPMENT**									
4150	Hood for range, 2 speed, vented, 30" wide, minimum	L-3	5	2	Ea.	69.50	65.50		135	187
4200	Maximum		3	3.333		770	109		879	1,025
4300	42" wide, minimum		5	2		166	65.50		231.50	293
4330	Custom		5	2		1,650	65.50		1,715.50	1,900
4350	Maximum		3	3.333		2,000	109		2,109	2,375
4500	For ventless hood, 2 speed, add					18.45			18.45	20.50
4650	For vented 1 speed, deduct from maximum					49.50			49.50	54.50

11 31 23 – Residential Laundry Appliances

11 31 23.13 Washers

		Crew	Daily Output	Labor-Hours	Unit	Material	2014 Bare Costs Labor	2014 Bare Costs Equipment	Total	Total Incl O&P
0010	**WASHERS**									
6650	Washing machine, automatic, minimum	1 Plum	3	2.667	Ea.	480	101		581	690
6700	Maximum		1	8		1,500	305		1,805	2,150
6750	Energy star qualified, front loading, minimum [G]		3	2.667		645	101		746	875
6760	Maximum [G]		1	8		1,575	305		1,880	2,225
6764	Top loading, minimum [G]		3	2.667		445	101		546	655
6766	Maximum [G]		3	2.667		1,225	101		1,326	1,525

11 31 23.23 Dryers

		Crew	Daily Output	Labor-Hours	Unit	Material	2014 Bare Costs Labor	2014 Bare Costs Equipment	Total	Total Incl O&P
0010	**DRYERS**									
6770	Electric, front loading, energy-star qualified, minimum [G]	L-2	3	5.333	Ea.	380	149		529	670
6780	Maximum [G]	"	2	8		1,900	224		2,124	2,450
7450	Vent kits for dryers	1 Carp	10	.800		38.50	25.50		64	85

11 31 Residential Appliances

11 31 33 – Miscellaneous Residential Appliances

11 31 33.13 Sump Pumps

11 31 33.13 Sump Pumps	Crew	Daily Output	Labor-Hours	Unit	Material	2014 Bare Costs Labor	Equipment	Total	Total Incl O&P
0010 **SUMP PUMPS**									
6400 Cellar drainer, pedestal, 1/3 H.P., molded PVC base	1 Plum	3	2.667	Ea.	135	101		236	315
6450 Solid brass	"	2	4	"	289	152		441	570
6460 Sump pump, see also Section 22 14 29.16									

11 31 33.23 Water Heaters

11 31 33.23 Water Heaters	Crew	Daily Output	Labor-Hours	Unit	Material	2014 Bare Costs Labor	Equipment	Total	Total Incl O&P
0010 **WATER HEATERS**									
6900 Electric, glass lined, 30 gallon, minimum	L-1	5	2	Ea.	430	75		505	595
6950 Maximum		3	3.333		595	125		720	860
7100 80 gallon, minimum		2	5		1,225	188		1,413	1,650
7150 Maximum		1	10		1,700	375		2,075	2,475
7180 Gas, glass lined, 30 gallon, minimum	2 Plum	5	3.200		805	122		927	1,075
7220 Maximum		3	5.333		1,125	203		1,328	1,550
7260 50 gallon, minimum		2.50	6.400		845	243		1,088	1,325
7300 Maximum		1.50	10.667		1,175	405		1,580	1,950
7310 Water heater, see also Section 22 33 30.13									

11 31 33.43 Air Quality

11 31 33.43 Air Quality	Crew	Daily Output	Labor-Hours	Unit	Material	2014 Bare Costs Labor	Equipment	Total	Total Incl O&P
0010 **AIR QUALITY**									
2450 Dehumidifier, portable, automatic, 15 pint	1 Elec	4	2	Ea.	150	71.50		221.50	282
2550 40 pint					207			207	228
3550 Heater, electric, built-in, 1250 watt, ceiling type, minimum	1 Elec	4	2		106	71.50		177.50	233
3600 Maximum		3	2.667		172	95.50		267.50	345
3700 Wall type, minimum		4	2		170	71.50		241.50	305
3750 Maximum		3	2.667		183	95.50		278.50	355
3900 1500 watt wall type, with blower		4	2		170	71.50		241.50	305
3950 3000 watt		3	2.667		350	95.50		445.50	540
4850 Humidifier, portable, 8 gallons per day					131			131	144
5000 15 gallons per day					208			208	229

11 33 Retractable Stairs

11 33 10 – Disappearing Stairs

11 33 10.10 Disappearing Stairway

11 33 10.10 Disappearing Stairway	Crew	Daily Output	Labor-Hours	Unit	Material	2014 Bare Costs Labor	Equipment	Total	Total Incl O&P
0010 **DISAPPEARING STAIRWAY** No trim included									
0020 One piece, yellow pine, 8'-0" ceiling	2 Carp	4	4	Ea.	254	128		382	495
0030 9'-0" ceiling		4	4		259	128		387	500
0040 10'-0" ceiling		3	5.333		270	171		441	585
0050 11'-0" ceiling		3	5.333		425	171		596	760
0060 12'-0" ceiling		3	5.333		490	171		661	830
0100 Custom grade, pine, 8'-6" ceiling, minimum	1 Carp	4	2		175	64		239	300
0150 Average		3.50	2.286		250	73.50		323.50	400
0200 Maximum		3	2.667		320	85.50		405.50	500
0500 Heavy duty, pivoted, from 7'-7" to 12'-10" floor to floor		3	2.667		735	85.50		820.50	950
0600 16'-0" ceiling		2	4		1,500	128		1,628	1,875
0800 Economy folding, pine, 8'-6" ceiling		4	2		174	64		238	299
0900 9'-6" ceiling		4	2		194	64		258	320
1100 Automatic electric, aluminum, floor to floor height, 8' to 9'	2 Carp	1	16		8,425	515		8,940	10,100

11 41 Foodservice Storage Equipment

11 41 13 – Refrigerated Food Storage Cases

11 41 13.30 Wine Cellar	Crew	Daily Output	Labor-Hours	Unit	Material	2014 Bare Costs Labor	Equipment	Total	Total Incl O&P
0010 **WINE CELLAR**, refrigerated, Redwood interior, carpeted, walk-in type									
0020 6'-8" high, including racks									
0200 80" W x 48" D for 900 bottles	2 Carp	1.50	10.667	Ea.	4,250	340		4,590	5,250
0250 80" W x 72" D for 1300 bottles		1.33	12.030		5,175	385		5,560	6,350
0300 80" W x 94" D for 1900 bottles		1.17	13.675		6,275	440		6,715	7,650

Division Notes

	CREW	DAILY OUTPUT	LABOR-HOURS	UNIT	BARE COSTS				TOTAL INCL O&P
					MAT.	LABOR	EQUIP.	TOTAL	

Estimating Tips

General

- The items in this division are usually priced per square foot or each. Most of these items are purchased by the owner and installed by the contractor. Do not assume the items in Division 12 will be purchased and installed by the contractor. Check the specifications for responsibilities and include receiving, storage, installation, and mechanical and electrical hookups in the appropriate divisions.

- Some items in this division require some type of support system that is not usually furnished with the item. Examples of these systems include blocking for the attachment of casework and heavy drapery rods. The required blocking must be added to the estimate in the appropriate division.

Reference Numbers

Reference numbers are shown in shaded boxes at the beginning of some major classifications. These numbers refer to related items in the Reference Section. The reference information may be an estimating procedure, an alternate pricing method, or technical information.

Note: Not all subdivisions listed here necessarily appear in this publication.

12 21 Window Blinds

12 21 13 – Horizontal Louver Blinds

12 21 13.13 Metal Horizontal Louver Blinds	Crew	Daily Output	Labor-Hours	Unit	Material	2014 Bare Costs Labor	Equipment	Total	Total Incl O&P
0010 **METAL HORIZONTAL LOUVER BLINDS**									
0020　Horizontal, 1" aluminum slats, solid color, stock	1 Carp	590	.014	S.F.	4.80	.44		5.24	6.05
0070　Horizontal, 1" aluminum slats, custom color	"	590	.014	"	5.30	.44		5.74	6.55

12 22 Curtains and Drapes

12 22 16 – Drapery Track and Accessories

12 22 16.10 Drapery Hardware

	Crew	Daily Output	Labor-Hours	Unit	Material	2014 Bare Costs Labor	Equipment	Total	Total Incl O&P
0010 **DRAPERY HARDWARE**									
0030　Standard traverse, per foot, minimum	1 Carp	59	.136	L.F.	6.85	4.35		11.20	14.80
0100　　Maximum		51	.157	"	10	5.05		15.05	19.45
0200　Decorative traverse, 28"-48", minimum		22	.364	Ea.	24	11.65		35.65	46
0220　　Maximum		21	.381		49	12.25		61.25	74.50
0300　　48"-84", minimum		20	.400		22	12.85		34.85	45.50
0320　　Maximum		19	.421		62.50	13.50		76	91.50
0400　　66"-120", minimum		18	.444		42	14.25		56.25	70
0420　　Maximum		17	.471		95.50	15.10		110.60	131
0500　　84"-156", minimum		16	.500		61.50	16.05		77.55	94.50
0520　　Maximum		15	.533		130	17.10		147.10	172
0600　　130"-240", minimum		14	.571		33	18.35		51.35	67.50
0620　　Maximum	▼	13	.615		180	19.75		199.75	231
0700　Slide rings, each, minimum					1.04			1.04	1.14
0720　　Maximum					2.01			2.01	2.21
4000　Traverse rods, adjustable, 28" to 48"	1 Carp	22	.364		22.50	11.65		34.15	44
4020　　48" to 84"		20	.400		28.50	12.85		41.35	52.50
4040　　66" to 120"		18	.444		34.50	14.25		48.75	61.50
4060　　84" to 156"		16	.500		39	16.05		55.05	70
4080　　100" to 180"		14	.571		45.50	18.35		63.85	81
4100　　228" to 312"		13	.615		63	19.75		82.75	103
4500　Curtain rod, 28" to 48", single		22	.364		5.40	11.65		17.05	25.50
4510　　Double		22	.364		9.15	11.65		20.80	30
4520　　48" to 86", single		20	.400		9.20	12.85		22.05	31.50
4530　　Double		20	.400		15.35	12.85		28.20	38.50
4540　　66" to 120", single		18	.444		15.40	14.25		29.65	41
4550　　Double	▼	18	.444		24	14.25		38.25	50.50
4600　Valance, pinch pleated fabric, 12" deep, up to 54" long, minimum					38.50			38.50	42.50
4610　　Maximum					96			96	106
4620　　Up to 77" long, minimum					59			59	65
4630　　Maximum					155			155	171
5000　Stationary rods, first 2'				▼	8.10			8.10	8.90

12 23 Interior Shutters

12 23 10 – Wood Interior Shutters

12 23 10.10 Wood Interior Shutters

		Crew	Daily Output	Labor-Hours	Unit	Material	2014 Bare Costs Labor	2014 Bare Costs Equipment	Total	Total Incl O&P
0010	**WOOD INTERIOR SHUTTERS**, louvered									
0200	Two panel, 27" wide, 36" high	1 Carp	5	1.600	Set	147	51.50		198.50	249
0300	33" wide, 36" high		5	1.600		190	51.50		241.50	296
0500	47" wide, 36" high		5	1.600		255	51.50		306.50	365
1000	Four panel, 27" wide, 36" high		5	1.600		216	51.50		267.50	325
1100	33" wide, 36" high		5	1.600		276	51.50		327.50	390
1300	47" wide, 36" high		5	1.600		370	51.50		421.50	490

12 23 10.13 Wood Panels

		Crew	Daily Output	Labor-Hours	Unit	Material	2014 Bare Costs Labor	2014 Bare Costs Equipment	Total	Total Incl O&P
0010	**WOOD PANELS**									
3000	Wood folding panels with movable louvers, 7" x 20" each	1 Carp	17	.471	Pr.	78	15.10		93.10	112
3300	8" x 28" each		17	.471		78	15.10		93.10	112
3450	9" x 36" each		17	.471		90	15.10		105.10	125
3600	10" x 40" each		17	.471		98	15.10		113.10	134
4000	Fixed louver type, stock units, 8" x 20" each		17	.471		92	15.10		107.10	127
4150	10" x 28" each		17	.471		78	15.10		93.10	111
4300	12" x 36" each		17	.471		92	15.10		107.10	127
4450	18" x 40" each		17	.471		132	15.10		147.10	171
5000	Insert panel type, stock, 7" x 20" each		17	.471		20.50	15.10		35.60	48
5150	8" x 28" each		17	.471		37.50	15.10		52.60	66.50
5300	9" x 36" each		17	.471		47.50	15.10		62.60	77.50
5450	10" x 40" each		17	.471		51	15.10		66.10	81.50
5600	Raised panel type, stock, 10" x 24" each		17	.471		243	15.10		258.10	293
5650	12" x 26" each		17	.471		243	15.10		258.10	293
5700	14" x 30" each		17	.471		268	15.10		283.10	320
5750	16" x 36" each		17	.471		296	15.10		311.10	350
6000	For custom built pine, add					22%				
6500	For custom built hardwood blinds, add					42%				

12 24 Window Shades

12 24 13 – Roller Window Shades

12 24 13.10 Shades

			Crew	Daily Output	Labor-Hours	Unit	Material	2014 Bare Costs Labor	2014 Bare Costs Equipment	Total	Total Incl O&P
0010	**SHADES**										
0020	Basswood, roll-up, stain finish, 3/8" slats		1 Carp	300	.027	S.F.	14.65	.86		15.51	17.55
5011	Insulative shades	G		125	.064		11.55	2.05		13.60	16.15
6011	Solar screening, fiberglass	G		85	.094		6.60	3.02		9.62	12.35
8011	Interior insulative shutter										
8111	Stock unit, 15" x 60"	G	1 Carp	17	.471	Pr.	11.65	15.10		26.75	38.50

12 32 Manufactured Wood Casework

12 32 16 – Manufactured Plastic-Laminate-Clad Casework

12 32 16.20 Plastic Laminate Casework Doors

		Crew	Daily Output	Labor-Hours	Unit	Material	2014 Bare Costs Labor	2014 Bare Costs Equipment	Total	Total Incl O&P
0010	**PLASTIC LAMINATE CASEWORK DOORS**									
1000	For casework frames, see Section 12 32 23.15									
1100	For casework hardware, see Section 12 32 23.35									
6000	Plastic laminate on particle board									
6100	12" wide, 18" high	1 Carp	25	.320	Ea.	24	10.25		34.25	44
6120	24" high		24	.333		32	10.70		42.70	53
6140	30" high		23	.348		40	11.15		51.15	63
6160	36" high		21	.381		48	12.25		60.25	73

12 32 16 – Manufactured Plastic-Laminate-Clad Casework

12 32 16.20 Plastic Laminate Casework Doors

		Crew	Daily Output	Labor-Hours	Unit	Material	2014 Bare Costs Labor	2014 Bare Costs Equipment	Total	Total Incl O&P
6200	48" high	1 Carp	16	.500	Ea.	64	16.05		80.05	97
6250	60" high		13	.615		79.50	19.75		99.25	121
6300	72" high		12	.667		95.50	21.50		117	141
6320	15" wide, 18" high		24.50	.327		32	10.50		42.50	52.50
6340	24" high		23.50	.340		42.50	10.95		53.45	65.50
6360	30" high		22.50	.356		53	11.40		64.40	77.50
6380	36" high		20.50	.390		64	12.55		76.55	91
6400	48" high		15.50	.516		85	16.55		101.55	122
6450	60" high		12.50	.640		106	20.50		126.50	152
6480	72" high		11.50	.696		128	22.50		150.50	178
6500	18" wide, 18" high		24	.333		36	10.70		46.70	57.50
6550	24" high		23	.348		48	11.15		59.15	71.50
6600	30" high		22	.364		60	11.65		71.65	85.50
6650	36" high		20	.400		71.50	12.85		84.35	101
6700	48" high		15	.533		95.50	17.10		112.60	134
6750	60" high		12	.667		120	21.50		141.50	168
6800	72" high		11	.727		143	23.50		166.50	198

12 32 16.25 Plastic Laminate Drawer Fronts

		Crew	Daily Output	Labor-Hours	Unit	Material	2014 Bare Costs Labor	2014 Bare Costs Equipment	Total	Total Incl O&P
0010	**PLASTIC LAMINATE DRAWER FRONTS**									
2800	Plastic laminate on particle board front									
3000	4" high, 12" wide	1 Carp	17	.471	Ea.	3.93	15.10		19.03	30
3200	18" wide		16	.500		5.90	16.05		21.95	33.50
3600	24" wide		15	.533		7.85	17.10		24.95	37.50
3800	6" high, 12" wide		16	.500		5.90	16.05		21.95	33.50
4000	18" wide		15	.533		8.85	17.10		25.95	39
4500	24" wide		14	.571		11.80	18.35		30.15	44
4800	9" high, 12" wide		15	.533		8.85	17.10		25.95	39
5000	18" wide		14	.571		13.30	18.35		31.65	45.50
5200	24" wide		13	.615		17.70	19.75		37.45	52.50

12 32 23 – Hardwood Casework

12 32 23.10 Manufactured Wood Casework, Stock Units

		Crew	Daily Output	Labor-Hours	Unit	Material	2014 Bare Costs Labor	2014 Bare Costs Equipment	Total	Total Incl O&P
0010	**MANUFACTURED WOOD CASEWORK, STOCK UNITS**									
0700	Kitchen base cabinets, hardwood, not incl. counter tops,									
0710	24" deep, 35" high, prefinished									
0800	One top drawer, one door below, 12" wide	2 Carp	24.80	.645	Ea.	254	20.50		274.50	315
0820	15" wide		24	.667		264	21.50		285.50	325
0840	18" wide		23.30	.687		287	22		309	350
0860	21" wide		22.70	.705		294	22.50		316.50	365
0880	24" wide		22.30	.717		350	23		373	425
1000	Four drawers, 12" wide		24.80	.645		267	20.50		287.50	330
1020	15" wide		24	.667		271	21.50		292.50	335
1040	18" wide		23.30	.687		298	22		320	365
1060	24" wide		22.30	.717		330	23		353	400
1200	Two top drawers, two doors below, 27" wide		22	.727		375	23.50		398.50	455
1220	30" wide		21.40	.748		405	24		429	490
1240	33" wide		20.90	.766		420	24.50		444.50	505
1260	36" wide		20.30	.788		435	25.50		460.50	525
1280	42" wide		19.80	.808		460	26		486	555
1300	48" wide		18.90	.847		495	27		522	590
1500	Range or sink base, two doors below, 30" wide		21.40	.748		335	24		359	410
1520	33" wide		20.90	.766		360	24.50		384.50	440
1540	36" wide		20.30	.788		380	25.50		405.50	460

12 32 Manufactured Wood Casework

12 32 23 – Hardwood Casework

12 32 23.10 Manufactured Wood Casework, Stock Units

		Crew	Daily Output	Labor-Hours	Unit	Material	2014 Bare Costs Labor	2014 Bare Costs Equipment	Total	Total Incl O&P
1560	42" wide	2 Carp	19.80	.808	Ea.	400	26		426	485
1580	48" wide	↓	18.90	.847		415	27		442	505
1800	For sink front units, deduct					154			154	169
2000	Corner base cabinets, 36" wide, standard	2 Carp	18	.889		600	28.50		628.50	710
2100	Lazy Susan with revolving door	"	16.50	.970	↓	805	31		836	940
4000	Kitchen wall cabinets, hardwood, 12" deep with two doors									
4050	12" high, 30" wide	2 Carp	24.80	.645	Ea.	227	20.50		247.50	285
4100	36" wide		24	.667		270	21.50		291.50	335
4400	15" high, 30" wide		24	.667		231	21.50		252.50	290
4420	33" wide		23.30	.687		285	22		307	350
4440	36" wide		22.70	.705		277	22.50		299.50	345
4450	42" wide		22.70	.705		315	22.50		337.50	385
4700	24" high, 30" wide		23.30	.687		310	22		332	375
4720	36" wide		22.70	.705		340	22.50		362.50	415
4740	42" wide		22.30	.717		390	23		413	470
5000	30" high, one door, 12" wide		22	.727		207	23.50		230.50	267
5020	15" wide		21.40	.748		231	24		255	295
5040	18" wide		20.90	.766		254	24.50		278.50	320
5060	24" wide		20.30	.788		296	25.50		321.50	370
5300	Two doors, 27" wide		19.80	.808		325	26		351	400
5320	30" wide		19.30	.829		345	26.50		371.50	425
5340	36" wide		18.80	.851		395	27.50		422.50	475
5360	42" wide		18.50	.865		425	28		453	510
5380	48" wide		18.40	.870		480	28		508	575
6000	Corner wall, 30" high, 24" wide		18	.889		340	28.50		368.50	425
6050	30" wide		17.20	.930		360	30		390	450
6100	36" wide		16.50	.970		410	31		441	505
6500	Revolving Lazy Susan		15.20	1.053		460	34		494	560
7000	Broom cabinet, 84" high, 24" deep, 18" wide		10	1.600		625	51.50		676.50	770
7500	Oven cabinets, 84" high, 24" deep, 27" wide		8	2	↓	960	64		1,024	1,150
7750	Valance board trim	↓	396	.040	L.F.	13	1.30		14.30	16.50
7780	Toe kick trim	1 Carp	256	.031	"	2.79	1		3.79	4.76
7790	Base cabinet corner filler		16	.500	Ea.	41.50	16.05		57.55	72.50
7800	Cabinet filler, 3" x 24"		20	.400		18.05	12.85		30.90	41.50
7810	3" x 30"		20	.400		22.50	12.85		35.35	46.50
7820	3" x 42"		18	.444		31.50	14.25		45.75	58.50
7830	3" x 80"		16	.500	↓	60	16.05		76.05	93
7850	Cabinet panel	↓	50	.160	S.F.	8.35	5.15		13.50	17.80
9000	For deluxe models of all cabinets, add					40%				
9500	For custom built in place, add					25%	10%			
9558	Rule of thumb, kitchen cabinets not including									
9560	appliances & counter top, minimum	2 Carp	30	.533	L.F.	168	17.10		185.10	214
9600	Maximum	"	25	.640	"	380	20.50		400.50	450

12 32 23.15 Manufactured Wood Casework Frames

		Crew	Daily Output	Labor-Hours	Unit	Material	2014 Bare Costs Labor	2014 Bare Costs Equipment	Total	Total Incl O&P
0010	**MANUFACTURED WOOD CASEWORK FRAMES**									
0050	Base cabinets, counter storage, 36" high									
0100	One bay, 18" wide	1 Carp	2.70	2.963	Ea.	164	95		259	340
0400	Two bay, 36" wide		2.20	3.636		250	117		367	470
1100	Three bay, 54" wide		1.50	5.333		298	171		469	615
2800	Bookcases, one bay, 7' high, 18" wide		2.40	3.333		193	107		300	390
3500	Two bay, 36" wide		1.60	5		280	161		441	580
4100	Three bay, 54" wide	↓	1.20	6.667		465	214		679	870

12 32 Manufactured Wood Casework

12 32 23 – Hardwood Casework

12 32 23.15 Manufactured Wood Casework Frames

		Crew	Daily Output	Labor-Hours	Unit	Material	2014 Bare Costs Labor	Equipment	Total	Total Incl O&P
6100	Wall mounted cabinet, one bay, 24" high, 18" wide	1 Carp	3.60	2.222	Ea.	106	71.50		177.50	236
6800	Two bay, 36" wide		2.20	3.636		154	117		271	365
7400	Three bay, 54" wide		1.70	4.706		192	151		343	465
8400	30" high, one bay, 18" wide		3.60	2.222		115	71.50		186.50	246
9000	Two bay, 36" wide		2.15	3.721		153	119		272	370
9400	Three bay, 54" wide		1.60	5		191	161		352	480
9800	Wardrobe, 7' high, single, 24" wide		2.70	2.963		212	95		307	395
9950	Partition, adjustable shelves & drawers, 48" wide		1.40	5.714		405	183		588	755

12 32 23.20 Manufactured Hardwood Casework Doors

		Crew	Daily Output	Labor-Hours	Unit	Material	2014 Bare Costs Labor	Equipment	Total	Total Incl O&P
0010	**MANUFACTURED HARDWOOD CASEWORK DOORS**									
2000	Glass panel, hardwood frame									
2200	12" wide, 18" high	1 Carp	34	.235	Ea.	25.50	7.55		33.05	40.50
2400	24" high		33	.242		34	7.80		41.80	50.50
2600	30" high		32	.250		42.50	8.05		50.55	60.50
2800	36" high		30	.267		51	8.55		59.55	70.50
3000	48" high		23	.348		68	11.15		79.15	94
3200	60" high		17	.471		85	15.10		100.10	119
3400	72" high		15	.533		102	17.10		119.10	141
3600	15" wide, 18" high		33	.242		32	7.80		39.80	48
3800	24" high		32	.250		42.50	8.05		50.55	60.50
4000	30" high		30	.267		53	8.55		61.55	73
4250	36" high		28	.286		64	9.15		73.15	85.50
4300	48" high		22	.364		85	11.65		96.65	113
4350	60" high		16	.500		106	16.05		122.05	144
4400	72" high		14	.571		128	18.35		146.35	171
4450	18" wide, 18" high		32	.250		38.50	8.05		46.55	55.50
4500	24" high		30	.267		51	8.55		59.55	70.50
4550	30" high		29	.276		64	8.85		72.85	85
4600	36" high		27	.296		76.50	9.50		86	100
4650	48" high		21	.381		102	12.25		114.25	133
4700	60" high		15	.533		128	17.10		145.10	169
4750	72" high		13	.615		153	19.75		172.75	201
5000	Hardwood, raised panel									
5100	12" wide, 18" high	1 Carp	16	.500	Ea.	28.50	16.05		44.55	58.50
5150	24" high		15.50	.516		38	16.55		54.55	70
5200	30" high		15	.533		47.50	17.10		64.60	81.50
5250	36" high		14	.571		57	18.35		75.35	93.50
5300	48" high		11	.727		76	23.50		99.50	123
5320	60" high		8	1		95	32		127	159
5340	72" high		7	1.143		114	36.50		150.50	187
5360	15" wide, 18" high		15.50	.516		35.50	16.55		52.05	67
5380	24" high		15	.533		47.50	17.10		64.60	81.50
5400	30" high		14.50	.552		59.50	17.70		77.20	95.50
5420	36" high		13.50	.593		71.50	19		90.50	111
5440	48" high		10.50	.762		95	24.50		119.50	146
5460	60" high		7.50	1.067		119	34		153	189
5480	72" high		6.50	1.231		143	39.50		182.50	224
5500	18" wide, 18" high		15	.533		43	17.10		60.10	76
5550	24" high		14.50	.552		57	17.70		74.70	92.50
5600	30" high		14	.571		71.50	18.35		89.85	110
5650	36" high		13	.615		85.50	19.75		105.25	127
5700	48" high		10	.800		114	25.50		139.50	168

12 32 Manufactured Wood Casework

12 32 23 – Hardwood Casework

12 32 23.20 Manufactured Hardwood Casework Doors		Crew	Daily Output	Labor-Hours	Unit	Material	2014 Bare Costs Labor	Equipment	Total	Total Incl O&P
5750	60" high	1 Carp	7	1.143	Ea.	143	36.50		179.50	219
5800	72" high	↓	6	1.333	↓	171	43		214	260

12 32 23.25 Manufactured Wood Casework Drawer Fronts

		Crew	Daily Output	Labor-Hours	Unit	Material	2014 Bare Costs Labor	Equipment	Total	Total Incl O&P
0010	**MANUFACTURED WOOD CASEWORK DRAWER FRONTS**									
0100	Solid hardwood front									
1000	4" high, 12" wide	1 Carp	17	.471	Ea.	4.33	15.10		19.43	30.50
1200	18" wide		16	.500		6.50	16.05		22.55	34
1400	24" wide		15	.533		8.65	17.10		25.75	38.50
1600	6" high, 12" wide		16	.500		6.50	16.05		22.55	34
1800	18" wide		15	.533		9.75	17.10		26.85	40
2000	24" wide		14	.571		13	18.35		31.35	45.50
2200	9" high, 12" wide		15	.533		9.75	17.10		26.85	40
2400	18" wide		14	.571		14.60	18.35		32.95	47
2600	24" wide	↓	13	.615	↓	19.50	19.75		39.25	54.50

12 32 23.30 Manufactured Wood Casework Vanities

		Crew	Daily Output	Labor-Hours	Unit	Material	2014 Bare Costs Labor	Equipment	Total	Total Incl O&P
0010	**MANUFACTURED WOOD CASEWORK VANITIES**									
8000	Vanity bases, 2 doors, 30" high, 21" deep, 24" wide	2 Carp	20	.800	Ea.	297	25.50		322.50	370
8050	30" wide		16	1		355	32		387	445
8100	36" wide		13.33	1.200		345	38.50		383.50	445
8150	48" wide	↓	11.43	1.400		450	45		495	570
9000	For deluxe models of all vanities, add to above					40%				
9500	For custom built in place, add to above				↓	25%	10%			

12 32 23.35 Manufactured Wood Casework Hardware

		Crew	Daily Output	Labor-Hours	Unit	Material	2014 Bare Costs Labor	Equipment	Total	Total Incl O&P
0010	**MANUFACTURED WOOD CASEWORK HARDWARE**									
1000	Catches, minimum	1 Carp	235	.034	Ea.	1.17	1.09		2.26	3.13
1020	Average		119.40	.067		3.80	2.15		5.95	7.80
1040	Maximum	↓	80	.100	↓	7.20	3.21		10.41	13.35
2000	Door/drawer pulls, handles									
2200	Handles and pulls, projecting, metal, minimum	1 Carp	48	.167	Ea.	4.80	5.35		10.15	14.30
2220	Average		42	.190		7.45	6.10		13.55	18.50
2240	Maximum		36	.222		10.15	7.15		17.30	23
2300	Wood, minimum		48	.167		5.05	5.35		10.40	14.55
2320	Average		42	.190		6.75	6.10		12.85	17.70
2340	Maximum		36	.222		9.25	7.15		16.40	22
2600	Flush, metal, minimum		48	.167		5.05	5.35		10.40	14.55
2620	Average		42	.190		6.75	6.10		12.85	17.70
2640	Maximum		36	.222	↓	9.25	7.15		16.40	22
3000	Drawer tracks/glides, minimum		48	.167	Pr.	8.55	5.35		13.90	18.40
3020	Average		32	.250		14.50	8.05		22.55	29.50
3040	Maximum		24	.333		25	10.70		35.70	45.50
4000	Cabinet hinges, minimum		160	.050		2.90	1.61		4.51	5.90
4020	Average		95.24	.084		6.50	2.70		9.20	11.70
4040	Maximum	↓	68	.118	↓	11	3.78		14.78	18.45

12 34 Manufactured Plastic Casework

12 34 16 – Manufactured Solid-Plastic Casework

12 34 16.10 Outdoor Casework	Crew	Daily Output	Labor-Hours	Unit	Material	2014 Bare Costs Labor	Equipment	Total	Total Incl O&P
0010 **OUTDOOR CASEWORK**									
0020 Cabinet, base, sink/range, 36"	2 Carp	20.30	.788	Ea.	1,775	25.50		1,800.50	2,025
0100 Base, 36"		20.30	.788		2,000	25.50		2,025.50	2,250
0200 Filler strip, 1" x 30"		158	.101		31	3.25		34.25	39.50

12 36 Countertops

12 36 16 – Metal Countertops

12 36 16.10 Stainless Steel Countertops

	Crew	Daily Output	Labor-Hours	Unit	Material	Labor	Equipment	Total	Total Incl O&P
0010 **STAINLESS STEEL COUNTERTOPS**									
3200 Stainless steel, custom	1 Carp	24	.333	S.F.	150	10.70		160.70	183

12 36 19 – Wood Countertops

12 36 19.10 Maple Countertops

	Crew	Daily Output	Labor-Hours	Unit	Material	Labor	Equipment	Total	Total Incl O&P
0010 **MAPLE COUNTERTOPS**									
2900 Solid, laminated, 1-1/2" thick, no splash	1 Carp	28	.286	L.F.	74	9.15		83.15	97
3000 With square splash		28	.286	"	88	9.15		97.15	112
3400 Recessed cutting block with trim, 16" x 20" x 1"		8	1	Ea.	90	32		122	153
3411 Replace cutting block only		16	.500	"	67.50	16.05		83.55	102

12 36 23 – Plastic Countertops

12 36 23.13 Plastic-Laminate-Clad Countertops

	Crew	Daily Output	Labor-Hours	Unit	Material	Labor	Equipment	Total	Total Incl O&P
0010 **PLASTIC-LAMINATE-CLAD COUNTERTOPS**									
0020 Stock, 24" wide w/backsplash, minimum	1 Carp	30	.267	L.F.	16.65	8.55		25.20	33
0100 Maximum		25	.320		34	10.25		44.25	54.50
0300 Custom plastic, 7/8" thick, aluminum molding, no splash		30	.267		29.50	8.55		38.05	47
0400 Cove splash		30	.267		28.50	8.55		37.05	46
0600 1-1/4" thick, no splash		28	.286		34.50	9.15		43.65	53.50
0700 Square splash		28	.286		41.50	9.15		50.65	61
0900 Square edge, plastic face, 7/8" thick, no splash		30	.267		32.50	8.55		41.05	50.50
1000 With splash		30	.267		38.50	8.55		47.05	57
1200 For stainless channel edge, 7/8" thick, add					3.06			3.06	3.37
1300 1-1/4" thick, add					3.65			3.65	4.02
1500 For solid color suede finish, add					4			4	4.40
1700 For end splash, add				Ea.	18			18	19.80
1901 For cut outs, standard, add, minimum	1 Carp	32	.250			8.05		8.05	13.50
2000 Maximum		8	1		6	32		38	60.50
2010 Cut out in backsplash for elec. wall outlet		38	.211			6.75		6.75	11.35
2020 Cut out for sink		20	.400			12.85		12.85	21.50
2030 Cut out for stove top		18	.444			14.25		14.25	24
2100 Postformed, including backsplash and front edge		30	.267	L.F.	10	8.55		18.55	25.50
2110 Mitred, add		12	.667	Ea.		21.50		21.50	36
2200 Built-in place, 25" wide, plastic laminate		25	.320	L.F.	40.50	10.25		50.75	62

12 36 33 – Tile Countertops

12 36 33.10 Ceramic Tile Countertops

	Crew	Daily Output	Labor-Hours	Unit	Material	Labor	Equipment	Total	Total Incl O&P
0010 **CERAMIC TILE COUNTERTOPS**									
2300 Ceramic tile mosaic	1 Carp	25	.320	L.F.	33	10.25		43.25	54

12 36 40 – Stone Countertops

12 36 40.10 Natural Stone Countertops

	Crew	Daily Output	Labor-Hours	Unit	Material	Labor	Equipment	Total	Total Incl O&P
0010 **NATURAL STONE COUNTERTOPS**									
2500 Marble, stock, with splash, 1/2" thick, minimum	1 Bric	17	.471	L.F.	41	15		56	70
2700 3/4" thick, maximum		13	.615		103	19.65		122.65	146

12 36 Countertops

12 36 40 – Stone Countertops

12 36 40.10 Natural Stone Countertops	Crew	Daily Output	Labor-Hours	Unit	Material	2014 Bare Costs Labor	2014 Bare Costs Equipment	Total	Total Incl O&P
2800	Granite, average, 1-1/4" thick, 24" wide, no splash	1 Bric	13.01	.615	L.F.	135	19.60		154.60	182

12 36 61 – Simulated Stone Countertops

12 36 61.16 Solid Surface Countertops

		Crew	Daily Output	Labor-Hours	Unit	Material	Labor	Equipment	Total	Total Incl O&P
0010	**SOLID SURFACE COUNTERTOPS**, Acrylic polymer									
2000	Pricing for order of 1 – 50 L.F.									
2100	25" wide, solid colors	2 Carp	20	.800	L.F.	72.50	25.50		98	123
2200	Patterned colors		20	.800		91.50	25.50		117	144
2300	Premium patterned colors		20	.800		115	25.50		140.50	169
2400	With silicone attached 4" backsplash, solid colors		19	.842		79.50	27		106.50	133
2500	Patterned colors		19	.842		100	27		127	156
2600	Premium patterned colors		19	.842		125	27		152	184
2700	With hard seam attached 4" backsplash, solid colors		15	1.067		79.50	34		113.50	145
2800	Patterned colors		15	1.067		100	34		134	168
2900	Premium patterned colors		15	1.067		125	34		159	196
3800	Sinks, pricing for order of 1 – 50 units									
3900	Single bowl, hard seamed, solid colors, 13" x 17"	1 Carp	2	4	Ea.	490	128		618	750
4000	10" x 15"		4.55	1.758		226	56.50		282.50	345
4100	Cutouts for sinks		5.25	1.524			49		49	82.50

12 36 61.17 Solid Surface Vanity Tops

		Crew	Daily Output	Labor-Hours	Unit	Material	Labor	Equipment	Total	Total Incl O&P
0010	**SOLID SURFACE VANITY TOPS**									
0015	Solid surface, center bowl, 17" x 19"	1 Carp	12	.667	Ea.	186	21.50		207.50	241
0020	19" x 25"		12	.667		190	21.50		211.50	245
0030	19" x 31"		12	.667		223	21.50		244.50	281
0040	19" x 37"		12	.667		259	21.50		280.50	320
0050	22" x 25"		10	.800		340	25.50		365.50	420
0060	22" x 31"		10	.800		395	25.50		420.50	480
0070	22" x 37"		10	.800		460	25.50		485.50	555
0080	22" x 43"		10	.800		525	25.50		550.50	625
0090	22" x 49"		10	.800		585	25.50		610.50	685
0110	22" x 55"		8	1		660	32		692	785
0120	22" x 61"		8	1		755	32		787	885
0220	Double bowl, 22" x 61"		8	1		855	32		887	995
0230	Double bowl, 22" x 73"		8	1		930	32		962	1,075
0240	For aggregate colors, add					35%				
0250	For faucets and fittings, see Section 22 41 39.10									

12 36 61.19 Quartz Agglomerate Countertops

		Crew	Daily Output	Labor-Hours	Unit	Material	Labor	Equipment	Total	Total Incl O&P
0010	**QUARTZ AGGLOMERATE COUNTERTOPS**									
0100	25" wide, 4" backsplash, color group A, minimum	2 Carp	15	1.067	L.F.	63	34		97	127
0110	Maximum		15	1.067		88.50	34		122.50	155
0120	Color group B, minimum		15	1.067		65.50	34		99.50	130
0130	Maximum		15	1.067		92.50	34		126.50	160
0140	Color group C, minimum		15	1.067		76.50	34		110.50	142
0150	Maximum		15	1.067		105	34		139	173
0160	Color group D, minimum		15	1.067		83	34		117	149
0170	Maximum		15	1.067		112	34		146	182

12 93 Site Furnishings

12 93 33 – Manufactured Planters

12 93 33.10 Planters	Crew	Daily Output	Labor-Hours	Unit	Material	2014 Bare Costs Labor	Equipment	Total	Total Incl O&P
0010 **PLANTERS**									
0012 Concrete, sandblasted, precast, 48" diameter, 24" high	2 Clab	15	1.067	Ea.	620	25.50		645.50	725
0300 Fiberglass, circular, 36" diameter, 24" high		15	1.067		710	25.50		735.50	825
1200 Wood, square, 48" side, 24" high		15	1.067		1,375	25.50		1,400.50	1,575
1300 Circular, 48" diameter, 30" high		10	1.600		965	38		1,003	1,125
1600 Planter/bench, 72"		5	3.200		3,225	76		3,301	3,650

12 93 43 – Site Seating and Tables

12 93 43.13 Site Seating	Crew	Daily Output	Labor-Hours	Unit	Material	2014 Bare Costs Labor	Equipment	Total	Total Incl O&P
0010 **SITE SEATING**									
0012 Seating, benches, park, precast conc., w/backs, wood rails, 4' long	2 Clab	5	3.200	Ea.	580	76		656	765
0100 8' long		4	4		935	95		1,030	1,175
0500 Steel barstock pedestals w/backs, 2" x 3" wood rails, 4' long		10	1.600		1,100	38		1,138	1,275
0510 8' long		7	2.286		1,400	54.50		1,454.50	1,650
0800 Cast iron pedestals, back & arms, wood slats, 4' long		8	2		415	47.50		462.50	540
0820 8' long		5	3.200		920	76		996	1,150
1700 Steel frame, fir seat, 10' long		10	1.600		345	38		383	440

Estimating Tips

General

- The items and systems in this division are usually estimated, purchased, supplied, and installed as a unit by one or more subcontractors. The estimator must ensure that all parties are operating from the same set of specifications and assumptions, and that all necessary items are estimated and will be provided. Many times the complex items and systems are covered, but the more common ones, such as excavation or a crane, are overlooked for the very reason that everyone assumes nobody could miss them. The estimator should be the central focus and be able to ensure that all systems are complete.

- Another area where problems can develop in this division is at the interface between systems. The estimator must ensure, for instance, that anchor bolts, nuts, and washers are estimated and included for the air-supported structures and pre-engineered buildings to be bolted to their foundations. Utility supply is a common area where essential items or pieces of equipment can be missed or overlooked due to the fact that each subcontractor may feel it is another's responsibility. The estimator should also be aware of certain items which may be supplied as part of a package but installed by others, and ensure that the installing contractor's estimate includes the cost of installation. Conversely, the estimator must also ensure that items are not costed by two different subcontractors, resulting in an inflated overall estimate.

13 30 00 Special Structures

- The foundations and floor slab, as well as rough mechanical and electrical, should be estimated, as this work is required for the assembly and erection of the structure. Generally, as noted in the book, the pre-engineered building comes as a shell. Pricing is based on the size and structural design parameters stated in the reference section. Additional features, such as windows and doors with their related structural framing, must also be included by the estimator. Here again, the estimator must have a clear understanding of the scope of each portion of the work and all the necessary interfaces.

Reference Numbers

Reference numbers are shown in shaded boxes at the beginning of some major classifications. These numbers refer to related items in the Reference Section. The reference information may be an estimating procedure, an alternate pricing method, or technical information.

Note: Not all subdivisions listed here necessarily appear in this publication.

13 11 Swimming Pools

13 11 13 – Below-Grade Swimming Pools

13 11 13.50 Swimming Pools

		Crew	Daily Output	Labor-Hours	Unit	Material	2014 Bare Costs Labor	Equipment	Total	Total Incl O&P
0010	**SWIMMING POOLS** Residential in-ground, vinyl lined, concrete									
0020	Sides including equipment, sand bottom	B-52	300	.187	SF Surf	21.50	4.99	1.98	28.47	34
0100	Metal or polystyrene sides R131113-20	B-14	410	.117		17.75	2.99	.89	21.63	25.50
0200	Add for vermiculite bottom				▼	1.35			1.35	1.49
0500	Gunite bottom and sides, white plaster finish									
0600	12' x 30' pool	B-52	145	.386	SF Surf	39.50	10.30	4.11	53.91	65.50
0720	16' x 32' pool		155	.361		35.50	9.65	3.84	48.99	59.50
0750	20' x 40' pool	▼	250	.224	▼	32	6	2.38	40.38	47.50
0810	Concrete bottom and sides, tile finish									
0820	12' x 30' pool	B-52	80	.700	SF Surf	40	18.70	7.45	66.15	83.50
0830	16' x 32' pool		95	.589		33	15.75	6.25	55	70
0840	20' x 40' pool	▼	130	.431	▼	26.50	11.50	4.58	42.58	53.50
1600	For water heating system, see Section 23 52 28.10									
1700	Filtration and deck equipment only, as % of total				Total				20%	20%
1800	Deck equipment, rule of thumb, 20' x 40' pool				SF Pool				1.18	1.30
3000	Painting pools, preparation + 3 coats, 20' x 40' pool, epoxy	2 Pord	.33	48.485	Total	1,775	1,350		3,125	4,200
3100	Rubber base paint, 18 gallons	"	.33	48.485	"	1,325	1,350		2,675	3,700

13 11 46 – Swimming Pool Accessories

13 11 46.50 Swimming Pool Equipment

		Crew	Daily Output	Labor-Hours	Unit	Material	2014 Bare Costs Labor	Equipment	Total	Total Incl O&P
0010	**SWIMMING POOL EQUIPMENT**									
0020	Diving stand, stainless steel, 3 meter	2 Carp	.40	40	Ea.	14,500	1,275		15,775	18,100
0300	1 meter		2.70	5.926		8,825	190		9,015	10,000
0600	Diving boards, 16' long, aluminum		2.70	5.926		3,975	190		4,165	4,675
0700	Fiberglass		2.70	5.926		3,200	190		3,390	3,850
0800	14' long, aluminum		2.70	5.926		3,900	190		4,090	4,625
0850	Fiberglass		2.70	5.926		3,100	190		3,290	3,725
1200	Ladders, heavy duty, stainless steel, 2 tread		7	2.286		775	73.50		848.50	980
1500	4 tread	▼	6	2.667		1,050	85.50		1,135.50	1,300
2100	Lights, underwater, 12 volt, with transformer, 300 watt	1 Elec	1	8		335	286		621	840
2200	110 volt, 500 watt, standard	"	1	8	▼	293	286		579	790
3000	Pool covers, reinforced vinyl	3 Clab	1800	.013	S.F.	.35	.32		.67	.92
3100	Vinyl water tube		3200	.008		.21	.18		.39	.53
3200	Maximum	▼	3000	.008	▼	.41	.19		.60	.77
3300	Slides, tubular, fiberglass, aluminum handrails & ladder, 5'-0", straight	2 Carp	1.60	10	Ea.	3,400	320		3,720	4,300
3320	8'-0", curved	"	3	5.333	"	6,750	171		6,921	7,725

13 12 Fountains

13 12 13 – Exterior Fountains

13 12 13.10 Yard Fountains

		Crew	Daily Output	Labor-Hours	Unit	Material	2014 Bare Costs Labor	Equipment	Total	Total Incl O&P
0010	**YARD FOUNTAINS**									
0100	Outdoor fountain, 48" high with bowl and figures	2 Clab	2	8	Ea.	550	190		740	925

13 17 Tubs and Pools

13 17 13 – Hot Tubs

13 17 13.10 Redwood Hot Tub System

		Crew	Daily Output	Labor-Hours	Unit	Material	2014 Bare Costs Labor	Equipment	Total	Total Incl O&P
0010	**REDWOOD HOT TUB SYSTEM**									
7050	4' diameter x 4' deep	Q-1	1	16	Ea.	3,225	545		3,770	4,450
7150	6' diameter x 4' deep		.80	20		4,950	685		5,635	6,550
7200	8' diameter x 4' deep		.80	20		7,250	685		7,935	9,100

13 17 33 – Whirlpool Tubs

13 17 33.10 Whirlpool Bath

		Crew	Daily Output	Labor-Hours	Unit	Material	2014 Bare Costs Labor	Equipment	Total	Total Incl O&P
0010	**WHIRLPOOL BATH**									
6000	Whirlpool, bath with vented overflow, molded fiberglass									
6100	66" x 36" x 24"	Q-1	1	16	Ea.	3,325	545		3,870	4,550
6400	72" x 36" x 21"		1	16		1,800	545		2,345	2,900
6500	60" x 34" x 21"		1	16		1,700	545		2,245	2,775
6600	72" x 42" x 23"		1	16		2,175	545		2,720	3,300

13 24 Special Activity Rooms

13 24 16 – Saunas

13 24 16.50 Saunas and Heaters

		Crew	Daily Output	Labor-Hours	Unit	Material	2014 Bare Costs Labor	Equipment	Total	Total Incl O&P
0010	**SAUNAS AND HEATERS**									
0020	Prefabricated, incl. heater & controls, 7' high, 6' x 4', C/C	L-7	2.20	11.818	Ea.	5,375	325		5,700	6,475
0050	6' x 4', C/P		2	13		4,875	355		5,230	5,975
0400	6' x 5', C/C		2	13		5,675	355		6,030	6,850
0450	6' x 5', C/P		2	13		5,150	355		5,505	6,250
0600	6' x 6', C/C		1.80	14.444		6,275	395		6,670	7,575
0650	6' x 6', C/P		1.80	14.444		5,725	395		6,120	6,975
0800	6' x 9', C/C		1.60	16.250		7,750	445		8,195	9,275
0850	6' x 9', C/P		1.60	16.250		7,000	445		7,445	8,450
1000	8' x 12', C/C		1.10	23.636		11,600	645		12,245	13,900
1050	8' x 12', C/P		1.10	23.636		10,500	645		11,145	12,600
1200	8' x 8', C/C		1.40	18.571		9,150	505		9,655	11,000
1250	8' x 8', C/P		1.40	18.571		8,450	505		8,955	10,100
1400	8' x 10', C/C		1.20	21.667		10,100	590		10,690	12,200
1450	8' x 10', C/P		1.20	21.667		9,225	590		9,815	11,200
1600	10' x 12', C/C		1	26		12,300	710		13,010	14,700
1650	10' x 12', C/P		1	26		10,900	710		11,610	13,200
1700	Door only, cedar, 2'x6', with 1'x4' tempered insulated glass window	2 Carp	3.40	4.706		735	151		886	1,050
1800	Prehung, incl. jambs, pulls & hardware	"	12	1.333		730	43		773	870
2500	Heaters only (incl. above), wall mounted, to 200 C.F.					675			675	745
2750	To 300 C.F.					910			910	1,000
3000	Floor standing, to 720 C.F., 10,000 watts, w/controls	1 Elec	3	2.667		2,900	95.50		2,995.50	3,350
3250	To 1,000 C.F., 16,000 watts	"	3	2.667		3,700	95.50		3,795.50	4,225

13 24 26 – Steam Baths

13 24 26.50 Steam Baths and Components

		Crew	Daily Output	Labor-Hours	Unit	Material	2014 Bare Costs Labor	Equipment	Total	Total Incl O&P
0010	**STEAM BATHS AND COMPONENTS**									
0020	Heater, timer & head, single, to 140 C.F.	1 Plum	1.20	6.667	Ea.	1,450	253		1,703	2,025
0500	To 300 C.F.	"	1.10	7.273		1,550	276		1,826	2,150
2700	Conversion unit for residential tub, including door					3,600			3,600	3,950

13 34 Fabricated Engineered Structures

13 34 13 – Glazed Structures

13 34 13.13 Greenhouses

		Crew	Daily Output	Labor-Hours	Unit	Material	2014 Bare Costs Labor	Equipment	Total	Total Incl O&P
0010	**GREENHOUSES**, Shell only, stock units, not incl. 2' stub walls,									
0020	foundation, floors, heat or compartments									
0300	Residential type, free standing, 8'-6" long x 7'-6" wide	2 Carp	59	.271	SF Flr.	31.50	8.70		40.20	49.50
0400	10'-6" wide		85	.188		24	6.05		30.05	36.50
0600	13'-6" wide		108	.148		23.50	4.76		28.26	34
0700	17'-0" wide		160	.100		19.20	3.21		22.41	26.50
0900	Lean-to type, 3'-10" wide		34	.471		36.50	15.10		51.60	66
1000	6'-10" wide		58	.276		44.50	8.85		53.35	64
1100	Wall mounted to existing window, 3' x 3'	1 Carp	4	2	Ea.	1,550	64		1,614	1,800
1120	4' x 5'	"	3	2.667	"	1,900	85.50		1,985.50	2,250
1200	Deluxe quality, free standing, 7'-6" wide	2 Carp	55	.291	SF Flr.	59	9.35		68.35	80.50
1220	10'-6" wide		81	.198		53	6.35		59.35	68.50
1240	13'-6" wide		104	.154		51.50	4.94		56.44	65
1260	17'-0" wide		150	.107		48	3.42		51.42	58.50
1400	Lean-to type, 3'-10" wide		31	.516		105	16.55		121.55	144
1420	6'-10" wide		55	.291		63.50	9.35		72.85	85.50
1440	8'-0" wide		97	.165		55	5.30		60.30	69.50

13 34 13.19 Swimming Pool Enclosures

		Crew	Daily Output	Labor-Hours	Unit	Material	2014 Bare Costs Labor	Equipment	Total	Total Incl O&P
0010	**SWIMMING POOL ENCLOSURES** Translucent, free standing									
0020	not including foundations, heat or light									
0200	Economy, minimum	2 Carp	200	.080	SF Hor.	60	2.57		62.57	70.50
0300	Maximum		100	.160		65	5.15		70.15	80
0400	Deluxe, minimum		100	.160		72	5.15		77.15	87.50
0600	Maximum		70	.229		93	7.35		100.35	114

13 34 63 – Natural Fiber Construction

13 34 63.50 Straw Bale Construction

			Crew	Daily Output	Labor-Hours	Unit	Material	2014 Bare Costs Labor	Equipment	Total	Total Incl O&P
0010	**STRAW BALE CONSTRUCTION**										
2000	Straw bales wall, incl. labor & material complete, minimum	G				SF Flr.					130
2010	Maximum	G				"					160
2020	Straw bales in walls w/modified post and beam frame	G	2 Carp	320	.050	S.F.	6.05	1.61		7.66	9.35

Estimating Tips

General

- Many products in Division 14 will require some type of support or blocking for installation not included with the item itself. Examples are supports for conveyors or tube systems, attachment points for lifts, and footings for hoists or cranes. Add these supports in the appropriate division.

14 10 00 Dumbwaiters
14 20 00 Elevators

- Dumbwaiters and elevators are estimated and purchased in a method similar to buying a car. The manufacturer has a base unit with standard features. Added to this base unit price will be whatever options the owner or specifications require. Increased load capacity, additional vertical travel, additional stops, higher speed, and cab finish options are items to be considered. When developing an estimate for dumbwaiters and elevators, remember that some items needed by the installers may have to be included as part of the general contract.

Examples are:
- — shaftway
- — rail support brackets
- — machine room
- — electrical supply
- — sill angles
- — electrical connections
- — pits
- — roof penthouses
- — pit ladders

Check the job specifications and drawings before pricing.

- Installation of elevators and handicapped lifts in historic structures can require significant additional costs. The associated structural requirements may involve cutting into and repairing finishes, mouldings, flooring, etc. The estimator must account for these special conditions.

14 30 00 Escalators and Moving Walks

- Escalators and moving walks are specialty items installed by specialty contractors. There are numerous options associated with these items. For specific options, contact a manufacturer or contractor. In a method similar to estimating dumbwaiters and elevators, you should verify the extent of general contract work and add items as necessary.

14 40 00 Lifts
14 90 00 Other Conveying Equipment

- Products such as correspondence lifts, chutes, and pneumatic tube systems, as well as other items specified in this subdivision, may require trained installers. The general contractor might not have any choice as to who will perform the installation or when it will be performed. Long lead times are often required for these products, making early decisions in scheduling necessary.

Reference Numbers

Reference numbers are shown in shaded boxes at the beginning of some major classifications. These numbers refer to related items in the Reference Section. The reference information may be an estimating procedure, an alternate pricing method, or technical information.

Note: Not all subdivisions listed here necessarily appear in this publication.

Division 14 - Conveying Equipment

14 21 Electric Traction Elevators

14 21 33 – Electric Traction Residential Elevators

14 21 33.20 Residential Elevators	Crew	Daily Output	Labor- Hours	Unit	Material	2014 Bare Costs Labor	Equipment	Total	Total Incl O&P
0010 **RESIDENTIAL ELEVATORS**									
7000 Residential, cab type, 1 floor, 2 stop, minimum	2 Elev	.20	80	Ea.	11,200	3,975		15,175	18,900
7100 Maximum		.10	160		19,000	7,950		26,950	33,900
7200 2 floor, 3 stop, minimum		.12	133		16,700	6,625		23,325	29,200
7300 Maximum	↓	.06	266	↓	27,200	13,300		40,500	51,500

14 42 Wheelchair Lifts

14 42 13 – Inclined Wheelchair Lifts

14 42 13.10 Inclined Wheelchair Lifts and Stairclimbers

	Crew	Daily Output	Labor- Hours	Unit	Material	2014 Bare Costs Labor	Equipment	Total	Total Incl O&P
0010 **INCLINED WHEELCHAIR LIFTS AND STAIRCLIMBERS**									
7700 Stair climber (chair lift), single seat, minimum	2 Elev	1	16	Ea.	5,325	795		6,120	7,175
7800 Maximum	"	.20	80	"	7,350	3,975		11,325	14,600

Estimating Tips

Pipe for fire protection and all uses is located in Subdivisions 21 11 13 and 22 11 13.

The labor adjustment factors listed in Subdivision 22 01 02.20 also apply to Division 21.

Many, but not all, areas in the U.S. require backflow protection in the fire system. It is advisable to check local building codes for specific requirements.

For your reference, the following is a list of the most applicable Fire Codes and Standards which may be purchased from the NFPA, 1 Batterymarch Park, Quincy, MA 02169-7471.

NFPA 1: Uniform Fire Code

NFPA 10: Portable Fire Extinguishers

NFPA 11: Low-, Medium-, and High-Expansion Foam

NFPA 12: Carbon Dioxide Extinguishing Systems (Also companion 12A)

NFPA 13: Installation of Sprinkler Systems (Also companion 13D, 13E, and 13R)

NFPA 14: Installation of Standpipe and Hose Systems

NFPA 15: Water Spray Fixed Systems for Fire Protection

NFPA 16: Installation of Foam-Water Sprinkler and Foam-Water Spray Systems

NFPA 17: Dry Chemical Extinguishing Systems (Also companion 17A)

NFPA 18: Wetting Agents

NFPA 20: Installation of Stationary Pumps for Fire Protection

NFPA 22: Water Tanks for Private Fire Protection

NFPA 24: Installation of Private Fire Service Mains and their Appurtenances

NFPA 25: Inspection, Testing and Maintenance of Water-Based Fire Protection

Reference Numbers

Reference numbers are shown in shaded boxes at the beginning of some major classifications. These numbers refer to related items in the Reference Section. The reference information may be an estimating procedure, an alternate pricing method, or technical information.

Note: Not all subdivisions listed here necessarily appear in this publication.

Note: **Trade Service,** *in part, has been used as a reference source for some of the material prices used in Division 21.*

21 05 Common Work Results for Fire Suppression

21 05 23 – General-Duty Valves for Water-Based Fire-Suppression Piping

21 05 23.50 General-Duty Valves	Crew	Daily Output	Labor-Hours	Unit	Material	2014 Bare Costs Labor	Equipment	Total	Total Incl O&P
0010 **GENERAL-DUTY VALVES**, for water-based fire suppression									
6200 Valves and components									
6210 Alarm, includes									
6220 retard chamber, trim, gauges, alarm line strainer									
6260 3" size	Q-12	3	5.333	Ea.	1,550	175		1,725	2,000
6280 4" size	"	2	8		1,625	263		1,888	2,200
6300 6" size	Q-13	4	8	↓	1,800	263		2,063	2,425
6500 Check, swing, C.I. body, brass fittings, auto. ball drip									
6520 4" size	Q-12	3	5.333	Ea.	335	175		510	655
6800 Check, wafer, butterfly type, C.I. body, bronze fittings									
6820 4" size	Q-12	4	4	Ea.	460	132		592	720
8800 Flow control valve, includes trim and gauges, 2" size		2	8		4,475	263		4,738	5,350
8820 3" size	↓	1.50	10.667		4,925	350		5,275	6,000
8840 4" size	Q-13	2.80	11.429		5,450	375		5,825	6,625
8860 6" size	"	2	16		6,300	525		6,825	7,825
9200 Pressure operated relief valve, brass body	1 Spri	18	.444	↓	550	16.25		566.25	630
9600 Waterflow indicator, with recycling retard and									
9610 two single pole retard switches, 2" thru 6" pipe size	1 Spri	8	1	Ea.	129	36.50		165.50	203

21 11 Facility Fire-Suppression Water-Service Piping

21 11 13 – Facility Water Distribution Piping

21 11 13.16 Pipe, Plastic

	Crew	Daily Output	Labor-Hours	Unit	Material	2014 Bare Costs Labor	Equipment	Total	Total Incl O&P
0010 **PIPE, PLASTIC**									
0020 CPVC, fire suppression, (C-UL-S. FM, NFPA 13, 13D & 13R)									
0030 Socket joint, no couplings or hangers									
0100 SDR 13.5, (ASTM F442)									
0120 3/4" diameter	Q-12	420	.038	L.F.	1.62	1.25		2.87	3.85
0130 1" diameter		340	.047		2.50	1.55		4.05	5.30
0140 1-1/4" diameter		260	.062		3.90	2.02		5.92	7.65
0150 1-1/2" diameter		190	.084		5.40	2.77		8.17	10.50
0160 2" diameter		140	.114		8.60	3.76		12.36	15.65
0170 2-1/2" diameter		130	.123		15.85	4.05		19.90	24
0180 3" diameter	↓	120	.133	↓	24	4.39		28.39	34

21 11 13.18 Pipe Fittings, Plastic

	Crew	Daily Output	Labor-Hours	Unit	Material	2014 Bare Costs Labor	Equipment	Total	Total Incl O&P
0010 **PIPE FITTINGS, PLASTIC**									
0020 CPVC, fire suppression, (C-UL-S. FM, NFPA 13, 13D & 13R)									
0030 Socket joint									
0100 90° Elbow									
0120 3/4"	1 Plum	26	.308	Ea.	2.30	11.70		14	22
0130 1"		22.70	.352		5.05	13.40		18.45	27.50
0140 1-1/4"		20.20	.396		6.40	15.05		21.45	32
0150 1-1/2"	↓	18.20	.440		9.10	16.70		25.80	37.50
0160 2"	Q-1	33.10	.483		11.30	16.55		27.85	40
0170 2-1/2"		24.20	.661		21.50	22.50		44	61.50
0180 3"	↓	20.80	.769	↓	29.50	26.50		56	76
0200 45° Elbow									
0210 3/4"	1 Plum	26	.308	Ea.	3.17	11.70		14.87	23
0220 1"		22.70	.352		3.71	13.40		17.11	26
0230 1-1/4"		20.20	.396		5.35	15.05		20.40	31
0240 1-1/2"	↓	18.20	.440		7.50	16.70		24.20	36
0250 2"	Q-1	33.10	.483	↓	9.30	16.55		25.85	38

21 11 13.18 Pipe Fittings, Plastic		Crew	Daily Output	Labor-Hours	Unit	Material	2014 Bare Costs Labor	Equipment	Total	Total Incl O&P
0260	2-1/2"	Q-1	24.20	.661	Ea.	16.75	22.50		39.25	56
0270	3"	↓	20.80	.769	↓	24	26.50		50.50	70
0300	Tee									
0310	3/4"	1 Plum	17.30	.462	Ea.	3.17	17.55		20.72	32.50
0320	1"		15.20	.526		6.25	20		26.25	40
0330	1-1/4"		13.50	.593		9.40	22.50		31.90	47.50
0340	1-1/2"	↓	12.10	.661		13.80	25		38.80	56.50
0350	2"	Q-1	20	.800		20.50	27.50		48	67.50
0360	2-1/2"		16.20	.988		33	34		67	92
0370	3"	↓	13.90	1.151	↓	52	39.50		91.50	122
0400	Tee, reducing x any size									
0420	1"	1 Plum	15.20	.526	Ea.	5.25	20		25.25	39
0430	1-1/4"		13.50	.593		9.70	22.50		32.20	47.50
0440	1-1/2"	↓	12.10	.661		11.75	25		36.75	54.50
0450	2"	Q-1	20	.800		18.80	27.50		46.30	65.50
0460	2-1/2"		16.20	.988		26	34		60	84
0470	3"	↓	13.90	1.151	↓	30	39.50		69.50	98
0500	Coupling									
0510	3/4"	1 Plum	26	.308	Ea.	2.21	11.70		13.91	21.50
0520	1"		22.70	.352		2.93	13.40		16.33	25
0530	1-1/4"		20.20	.396		4.27	15.05		19.32	29.50
0540	1-1/2"	↓	18.20	.440		6.10	16.70		22.80	34
0550	2"	Q-1	33.10	.483		8.20	16.55		24.75	36.50
0560	2-1/2"		24.20	.661		12.55	22.50		35.05	51.50
0570	3"	↓	20.80	.769	↓	16.35	26.50		42.85	61.50
0600	Coupling, reducing									
0610	1" x 3/4"	1 Plum	22.70	.352	Ea.	2.93	13.40		16.33	25
0620	1-1/4" x 1"		20.20	.396		4.43	15.05		19.48	30
0630	1-1/2" x 3/4"		18.20	.440		6.65	16.70		23.35	35
0640	1-1/2" x 1"		18.20	.440		6.40	16.70		23.10	34.50
0650	1-1/2" x 1-1/4"	↓	18.20	.440		6.10	16.70		22.80	34
0660	2" x 1"	Q-1	33.10	.483		8.55	16.55		25.10	37
0670	2" x 1-1/2"	"	33.10	.483	↓	8.20	16.55		24.75	36.50
0700	Cross									
0720	3/4"	1 Plum	13	.615	Ea.	4.98	23.50		28.48	44
0730	1"		11.30	.708		6.25	27		33.25	51.50
0740	1-1/4"		10.10	.792		8.60	30		38.60	59
0750	1-1/2"	↓	9.10	.879		11.35	33.50		44.85	67.50
0760	2"	Q-1	16.60	.964		19.45	33		52.45	76
0770	2-1/2"	"	12.10	1.322	↓	42.50	45		87.50	122
0800	Cap									
0820	3/4"	1 Plum	52	.154	Ea.	1.28	5.85		7.13	11.05
0830	1"		45	.178		1.90	6.75		8.65	13.25
0840	1-1/4"		40	.200		3.30	7.60		10.90	16.20
0850	1-1/2"	↓	36.40	.220		4.27	8.35		12.62	18.50
0860	2"	Q-1	66	.242		6.40	8.30		14.70	21
0870	2-1/2"		48.40	.331		9.25	11.30		20.55	29
0880	3"	↓	41.60	.385	↓	14.95	13.15		28.10	38
0900	Adapter, sprinkler head, female w/metal thd. insert, (s x FNPT)									
0920	3/4" x 1/2"	1 Plum	52	.154	Ea.	5.85	5.85		11.70	16.05
0930	1" x 1/2"		45	.178		6.15	6.75		12.90	17.95
0940	1" x 3/4"	↓	45	.178	↓	9.70	6.75		16.45	22

21 11 16 – Facility Fire Hydrants

21 11 16.50 Fire Hydrants for Buildings	Crew	Daily Output	Labor-Hours	Unit	Material	2014 Bare Costs Labor	Equipment	Total	Total Incl O&P
0010 **FIRE HYDRANTS FOR BUILDINGS**									
3750 Hydrants, wall, w/caps, single, flush, polished brass									
3800 2-1/2" x 2-1/2"	Q-12	5	3.200	Ea.	193	105		298	385
3840 2-1/2" x 3"		5	3.200		410	105		515	625
3860 3" x 3"		4.80	3.333		330	110		440	545
3900 For polished chrome, add					20%				
3950 Double, flush, polished brass									
4000 2-1/2" x 2-1/2" x 4"	Q-12	5	3.200	Ea.	545	105		650	775
4040 2-1/2" x 2-1/2" x 6"		4.60	3.478		785	114		899	1,050
4080 3" x 3" x 4"		4.90	3.265		1,175	107		1,282	1,450
4120 3" x 3" x 6"		4.50	3.556		1,175	117		1,292	1,475
4200 For polished chrome, add					10%				
4350 Double, projecting, polished brass									
4400 2-1/2" x 2-1/2" x 4"	Q-12	5	3.200	Ea.	242	105		347	440
4450 2-1/2" x 2-1/2" x 6"	"	4.60	3.478	"	495	114		609	735
4460 Valve control, dbl. flush/projecting hydrant, cap &									
4470 chain, extension rod & cplg., escutcheon, polished brass	Q-12	8	2	Ea.	288	66		354	425
4480 Four-way square, flush, polished brass									
4540 2-1/2"(4) x 6"	Q-12	3.60	4.444	Ea.	2,925	146		3,071	3,475

21 11 19 – Fire-Department Connections

21 11 19.50 Connections for the Fire-Department	Crew	Daily Output	Labor-Hours	Unit	Material	2014 Bare Costs Labor	Equipment	Total	Total Incl O&P
0010 **CONNECTIONS FOR THE FIRE-DEPARTMENT**									
6000 Roof manifold, horiz., brass, without valves & caps									
6040 2-1/2" x 2-1/2" x 4"	Q-12	4.80	3.333	Ea.	160	110		270	355
6060 2-1/2" x 2-1/2" x 6"		4.60	3.478		173	114		287	380
6080 2-1/2" x 2-1/2" x 2-1/2" x 4"		4.60	3.478		256	114		370	470
6090 2-1/2" x 2-1/2" x 2-1/2" x 6"		4.60	3.478		263	114		377	480
7000 Sprinkler line tester, cast brass					23.50			23.50	25.50
7140 Standpipe connections, wall, w/plugs & chains									
7160 Single, flush, brass, 2-1/2" x 2-1/2"	Q-12	5	3.200	Ea.	151	105		256	340
7180 2-1/2" x 3"	"	5	3.200	"	156	105		261	345
7240 For polished chrome, add					15%				
7280 Double, flush, polished brass									
7300 2-1/2" x 2-1/2" x 4"	Q-12	5	3.200	Ea.	495	105		600	720
7330 2-1/2" x 2-1/2" x 6"		4.60	3.478		690	114		804	945
7340 3" x 3" x 4"		4.90	3.265		900	107		1,007	1,175
7370 3" x 3" x 6"		4.50	3.556		1,075	117		1,192	1,375
7400 For polished chrome, add					15%				
7440 For sill cock combination, add				Ea.	86			86	94.50
7580 Double projecting, polished brass									
7600 2-1/2" x 2-1/2" x 4"	Q-12	5	3.200	Ea.	450	105		555	670
7630 2-1/2" x 2-1/2" x 6"	"	4.60	3.478	"	765	114		879	1,025
7680 For polished chrome, add					15%				
7900 Three way, flush, polished brass									
7920 2-1/2" (3) x 4"	Q-12	4.80	3.333	Ea.	1,575	110		1,685	1,925
7930 2-1/2" (3) x 6"	"	4.80	3.333		1,575	110		1,685	1,925
8000 For polished chrome, add					9%				
8020 Three way, projecting, polished brass									
8040 2-1/2"(3) x 4"	Q-12	4.80	3.333	Ea.	1,400	110		1,510	1,725
8070 2-1/2" (3) x 6"	"	4.60	3.478		1,400	114		1,514	1,750
8100 For polished chrome, add					12%				
8200 Four way, square, flush, polished brass,									

21 11 Facility Fire-Suppression Water-Service Piping

21 11 19 – Fire-Department Connections

21 11 19.50 Connections for the Fire-Department

		Crew	Daily Output	Labor-Hours	Unit	Material	2014 Bare Costs Labor	Equipment	Total	Total Incl O&P
8240	2-1/2"(4) x 6"	Q-12	3.60	4.444	Ea.	1,250	146		1,396	1,625
8300	For polished chrome, add				"	10%				
8550	Wall, vertical, flush, cast brass									
8600	Two way, 2-1/2" x 2-1/2" x 4"	Q-12	5	3.200	Ea.	395	105		500	610
8660	Four way, 2-1/2"(4) x 6"	↓	3.80	4.211		1,300	139		1,439	1,650
8680	Six way, 2-1/2"(6) x 6"	↓	3.40	4.706		1,550	155		1,705	1,975
8700	For polished chrome, add				↓	10%				
8800	Sidewalk siamese unit, polished brass, two way									
8820	2-1/2" x 2-1/2" x 4"	Q-12	2.50	6.400	Ea.	605	211		816	1,025
8850	2-1/2" x 2-1/2" x 6"		2	8		740	263		1,003	1,250
8860	3" x 3" x 4"		2.50	6.400		860	211		1,071	1,300
8890	3" x 3" x 6"	↓	2	8	↓	1,150	263		1,413	1,700
8940	For polished chrome, add					12%				
9100	Sidewalk siamese unit, polished brass, three way									
9120	2-1/2" x 2-1/2" x 2-1/2" x 6"	Q-12	2	8	Ea.	960	263		1,223	1,475
9160	For polished chrome, add				"	15%				

21 12 Fire-Suppression Standpipes

21 12 19 – Fire-Suppression Hose Racks

21 12 19.50 Fire Hose Racks

		Crew	Daily Output	Labor-Hours	Unit	Material	2014 Bare Costs Labor	Equipment	Total	Total Incl O&P
0010	**FIRE HOSE RACKS**									
2600	Hose rack, swinging, for 1-1/2" diameter hose,									
2620	Enameled steel, 50' & 75' lengths of hose	Q-12	20	.800	Ea.	58	26.50		84.50	108
2640	100' and 125' lengths of hose		20	.800		58	26.50		84.50	108
2680	Chrome plated, 50' and 75' lengths of hose		20	.800		93.50	26.50		120	147
2700	100' and 125' lengths of hose	↓	20	.800		99.50	26.50		126	153
2780	For hose rack nipple, 1-1/2" polished brass, add					26.50			26.50	29
2820	2-1/2" polished brass, add					49			49	54
2840	1-1/2" polished chrome, add					37			37	41
2860	2-1/2" polished chrome, add					52			52	57.50

21 12 23 – Fire-Suppression Hose Valves

21 12 23.70 Fire Hose Valves

		Crew	Daily Output	Labor-Hours	Unit	Material	2014 Bare Costs Labor	Equipment	Total	Total Incl O&P
0010	**FIRE HOSE VALVES**									
0020	Angle, combination pressure adjust/restricting, rough brass									
0030	1-1/2"	1 Spri	12	.667	Ea.	81	24.50		105.50	130
0040	2-1/2"	"	7	1.143	"	167	42		209	252
0042	Nonpressure adjustable/restricting, rough brass									
0044	1-1/2"	1 Spri	12	.667	Ea.	50.50	24.50		75	96
0046	2-1/2"	"	7	1.143	"	85.50	42		127.50	163
0050	For polished brass, add					30%				
0060	For polished chrome, add					40%				
1000	Ball drip, automatic, rough brass, 1/2"	1 Spri	20	.400	Ea.	15.45	14.60		30.05	41
1010	3/4"	"	20	.400	"	17.30	14.60		31.90	43
1100	Ball, 175 lb., sprinkler system, FM/UL, threaded, bronze									
1120	Slow close									
1150	1" size	1 Spri	19	.421	Ea.	234	15.40		249.40	284
1160	1-1/4" size		15	.533		253	19.50		272.50	310
1170	1-1/2" size		13	.615		335	22.50		357.50	400
1180	2" size	↓	11	.727		405	26.50		431.50	490
1190	2-1/2" size	Q-12	15	1.067	↓	545	35		580	660

21 12 Fire-Suppression Standpipes

21 12 23 – Fire-Suppression Hose Valves

21 12 23.70 Fire Hose Valves	Crew	Daily Output	Labor-Hours	Unit	Material	2014 Bare Costs Labor	Equipment	Total	Total Incl O&P
1230	For supervisory switch kit, all sizes									
1240	One circuit, add	1 Spri	48	.167	Ea.	177	6.10		183.10	205
1280	Quarter turn for trim									
1300	1/2" size	1 Spri	22	.364	Ea.	31	13.30		44.30	56
1310	3/4" size		20	.400		33.50	14.60		48.10	60.50
1320	1" size		19	.421		37	15.40		52.40	66
1330	1-1/4" size		15	.533		60.50	19.50		80	99
1340	1-1/2" size		13	.615		76	22.50		98.50	121
1350	2" size	↓	11	.727		90.50	26.50		117	144
1400	Caps, polished brass with chain, 3/4"					40			40	44
1420	1"					51			51	56
1440	1-1/2"					13.60			13.60	14.95
1460	2-1/2"					20.50			20.50	22.50
1480	3"					32			32	35
1900	Escutcheon plate, for angle valves, polished brass, 1-1/2"					15.20			15.20	16.70
1920	2-1/2"					24.50			24.50	27
1940	3"					31			31	34
1980	For polished chrome, add					15%				
3000	Gate, hose, wheel handle, N.R.S., rough brass, 1-1/2"	1 Spri	12	.667		128	24.50		152.50	181
3040	2-1/2", 300 lb.	"	7	1.143		180	42		222	267
3080	For polished brass, add					40%				
3090	For polished chrome, add					50%				
5000	Pressure restricting, adjustable rough brass, 1-1/2"	1 Spri	12	.667		114	24.50		138.50	165
5020	2-1/2"	"	7	1.143		160	42		202	245
5080	For polished brass, add					30%				
5090	For polished chrome, add			↓		45%				

21 13 Fire-Suppression Sprinkler Systems

21 13 13 – Wet-Pipe Sprinkler Systems

21 13 13.50 Wet-Pipe Sprinkler System Components

		Crew	Daily Output	Labor-Hours	Unit	Material	2014 Bare Costs Labor	Equipment	Total	Total Incl O&P
0010	**WET-PIPE SPRINKLER SYSTEM COMPONENTS**									
1100	Alarm, electric pressure switch (circuit closer)	1 Spri	26	.308	Ea.	84	11.25		95.25	111
1140	For explosion proof, max 20 PSI, contacts close or open		26	.308		505	11.25		516.25	575
1220	Water motor, complete with gong	↓	4	2	↓	390	73		463	550
1900	Flexible sprinkler head connectors									
1910	Braided stainless steel hose with mounting bracket									
1920	1/2" and 3/4" outlet size									
1940	36" length	1 Spri	30	.267	Ea.	70.50	9.75		80.25	93.50
1960	60" length	"	22	.364	"	81	13.30		94.30	111
1982	May replace hard-pipe armovers									
1984	For wet, pre-action, deluge or dry pipe systems									
2000	Release, emergency, manual, for hydraulic or pneumatic system	1 Spri	12	.667	Ea.	205	24.50		229.50	266
2060	Release, thermostatic, for hydraulic or pneumatic release line		20	.400		635	14.60		649.60	725
2200	Sprinkler cabinets, 6 head capacity		16	.500		74.50	18.30		92.80	112
2260	12 head capacity		16	.500		79	18.30		97.30	117
2340	Sprinkler head escutcheons, standard, brass tone, 1" size		40	.200		2.69	7.30		9.99	15
2360	Chrome, 1" size		40	.200		2.87	7.30		10.17	15.20
2400	Recessed type, brass tone		40	.200		3.16	7.30		10.46	15.55
2440	Chrome or white enamel		40	.200		3.52	7.30		10.82	15.90
2600	Sprinkler heads, not including supply piping									
3700	Standard spray, pendent or upright, brass, 135°F to 286°F									

21 13 13 – Wet-Pipe Sprinkler Systems

21 13 13.50 Wet-Pipe Sprinkler System Components

21 13 13.50 Wet-Pipe Sprinkler System Components	Crew	Daily Output	Labor-Hours	Unit	Material	2014 Bare Costs Labor	Equipment	Total	Total Incl O&P
3720	1/2" NPT, 3/8" orifice	1 Spri	16	.500	Ea.	13.85	18.30		32.15	45
3730	1/2" NPT, 7/16" orifice		16	.500		14.35	18.30		32.65	46
3732	1/2" NPT, 7/16" orifice, chrome		16	.500		15.10	18.30		33.40	46.50
3740	1/2" NPT, 1/2" orifice		16	.500		9.35	18.30		27.65	40.50
3760	1/2" NPT, 17/32" orifice		16	.500		12.20	18.30		30.50	43.50
3780	3/4" NPT, 17/32" orifice		16	.500		11.20	18.30		29.50	42.50
3840	For chrome, add					3.13			3.13	3.44
4200	Sidewall, vertical brass, 135°F to 286°F									
4240	1/2" NPT, 1/2" orifice	1 Spri	16	.500	Ea.	23.50	18.30		41.80	56
4280	3/4" NPT, 17/32" orifice	"	16	.500		66	18.30		84.30	103
4360	For satin chrome, add					2.63			2.63	2.89
4500	Sidewall, horizontal, brass, 135°F to 286°F									
4520	1/2" NPT, 1/2" orifice	1 Spri	16	.500	Ea.	23.50	18.30		41.80	56
5600	Concealed, complete with cover plate									
5620	1/2" NPT, 1/2" orifice, 135°F to 212°F	1 Spri	9	.889	Ea.	22.50	32.50		55	78
6025	Residential sprinkler components, (one and two family)									
6026	Water motor alarm, with strainer	1 Spri	4	2	Ea.	390	73		463	550
6027	Fast response, glass bulb, 135°F to 155°F									
6028	1/2" NPT, pendent, brass	1 Spri	16	.500	Ea.	25.50	18.30		43.80	58
6029	1/2" NPT, sidewall, brass		16	.500		25.50	18.30		43.80	58
6030	1/2" NPT, pendent, brass, extended coverage		16	.500		22.50	18.30		40.80	54.50
6031	1/2" NPT, sidewall, brass, extended coverage		16	.500		20.50	18.30		38.80	52.50
6032	3/4" NPT sidewall, brass, extended coverage		16	.500		23	18.30		41.30	55
6033	For chrome, add					15%				
6034	For polyester/teflon coating add					20%				
6100	Sprinkler head wrenches, standard head				Ea.	23			23	25
6120	Recessed head					35.50			35.50	39
6160	Tamper switch, (valve supervisory switch)	1 Spri	16	.500		99.50	18.30		117.80	139

21 13 16 – Dry-Pipe Sprinkler Systems

21 13 16.50 Dry-Pipe Sprinkler System Components

		Crew	Daily Output	Labor-Hours	Unit	Material	2014 Bare Costs Labor	Equipment	Total	Total Incl O&P
0010	**DRY-PIPE SPRINKLER SYSTEM COMPONENTS**									
0600	Accelerator	1 Spri	8	1	Ea.	715	36.50		751.50	845
0800	Air compressor for dry pipe system, automatic, complete									
0820	30 gal. system capacity, 3/4 HP	1 Spri	1.30	6.154	Ea.	735	225		960	1,175
0860	30 gal. system capacity, 1 HP		1.30	6.154		760	225		985	1,200
0960	Air pressure maintenance control		24	.333		325	12.20		337.20	380
1600	Dehydrator package, incl. valves and nipples		12	.667		670	24.50		694.50	780
2600	Sprinkler heads, not including supply piping									
2640	Dry, pendent, 1/2" orifice, 3/4" or 1" NPT									
2660	1/2" to 6" length	1 Spri	14	.571	Ea.	117	21		138	163
2670	6-1/4" to 8" length		14	.571		122	21		143	169
2680	8-1/4" to 12" length		14	.571		127	21		148	174
2800	For each inch or fraction, add					2.84			2.84	3.12
6330	Valves and components									
6340	Alarm test/shut off valve, 1/2"	1 Spri	20	.400	Ea.	20.50	14.60		35.10	46.50
8000	Dry pipe air check valve, 3" size	Q-12	2	8		1,700	263		1,963	2,275
8200	Dry pipe valve, incl. trim and gauges, 3" size		2	8		2,500	263		2,763	3,175
8220	4" size		1	16		2,725	525		3,250	3,875
8240	6" size	Q-13	2	16		3,200	525		3,725	4,375
8280	For accelerator trim with gauges, add	1 Spri	8	1		228	36.50		264.50	310

Division Notes

		CREW	DAILY OUTPUT	LABOR-HOURS	UNIT	BARE COSTS				TOTAL INCL O&P
						MAT.	LABOR	EQUIP.	TOTAL	

Estimating Tips

22 10 00 Plumbing Piping and Pumps

This subdivision is primarily basic pipe and related materials. The pipe may be used by any of the mechanical disciplines, i.e., plumbing, fire protection, heating, and air conditioning.

Note: CPVC plastic piping approved for fire protection is located in 21 11 13.

- The labor adjustment factors listed in Subdivision 22 01 02.20 apply throughout Divisions 21, 22, and 23. CAUTION: the correct percentage may vary for the same items. For example, the percentage add for the basic pipe installation should be based on the maximum height that the craftsman must install for that particular section. If the pipe is to be located 14' above the floor but it is suspended on threaded rod from beams, the bottom flange of which is 18' high (4' rods), then the height is actually 18' and the add is 20%. The pipe coverer, however, does not have to go above the 14', and so his or her add should be 10%.

- Most pipe is priced first as straight pipe with a joint (coupling, weld, etc.) every 10' and a hanger usually every 10'.

There are exceptions with hanger spacing such as for cast iron pipe (5') and plastic pipe (3 per 10'). Following each type of pipe there are several lines listing sizes and the amount to be subtracted to delete couplings and hangers. This is for pipe that is to be buried or supported together on trapeze hangers. The reason that the couplings are deleted is that these runs are usually long, and frequently longer lengths of pipe are used. By deleting the couplings, the estimator is expected to look up and add back the correct reduced number of couplings.

- When preparing an estimate, it may be necessary to approximate the fittings. Fittings usually run between 25% and 50% of the cost of the pipe. The lower percentage is for simpler runs, and the higher number is for complex areas, such as mechanical rooms.

- For historic restoration projects, the systems must be as invisible as possible, and pathways must be sought for pipes, conduit, and ductwork. While installations in accessible spaces (such as basements and attics) are relatively straightforward to estimate, labor costs may be more difficult to determine when delivery systems must be concealed.

22 40 00 Plumbing Fixtures

- Plumbing fixture costs usually require two lines: the fixture itself and its "rough-in, supply, and waste."

- In the Assemblies Section (Plumbing D2010) for the desired fixture, the System Components Group at the center of the page shows the fixture on the first line. The rest of the list (fittings, pipe, tubing, etc.) will total up to what we refer to in the Unit Price section as "Rough-in, supply, waste, and vent." Note that for most fixtures we allow a nominal 5' of tubing to reach from the fixture to a main or riser.

- Remember that gas- and oil-fired units need venting.

Reference Numbers

Reference numbers are shown in shaded boxes at the beginning of some major classifications. These numbers refer to related items in the Reference Section. The reference information may be an estimating procedure, an alternate pricing method, or technical information.

Note: Not all subdivisions listed here necessarily appear in this publication.

Note: **Trade Service,** *in part, has been used as a reference source for some of the material prices used in Division 22.*

22 05 05 – Selective Plumbing Demolition

22 05 05.10 Plumbing Demolition

		Crew	Daily Output	Labor-Hours	Unit	Material	2014 Bare Costs Labor	Equipment	Total	Total Incl O&P
0010	**PLUMBING DEMOLITION**									
1020	Fixtures, including 10' piping									
1101	Bathtubs, cast iron	1 Clab	4	2	Ea.		47.50		47.50	80
1121	Fiberglass		6	1.333			31.50		31.50	53.50
1141	Steel		5	1.600			38		38	64
1200	Lavatory, wall hung	1 Plum	10	.800			30.50		30.50	50
1221	Counter top	1 Clab	16	.500			11.90		11.90	20
1301	Sink, single compartment		16	.500			11.90		11.90	20
1321	Double		10	.800			19.05		19.05	32
1400	Water closet, floor mounted	1 Plum	8	1			38		38	62.50
1421	Wall mounted	1 Clab	7	1.143			27		27	46
2001	Piping, metal, to 1-1/2" diameter		200	.040	L.F.		.95		.95	1.60
2051	2" thru 3-1/2" diameter		150	.053			1.27		1.27	2.14
2101	4" thru 6" diameter		100	.080			1.90		1.90	3.20
2160	Plastic pipe with fittings, up thru 1-1/2" diameter	1 Plum	250	.032			1.22		1.22	2.01
2162	2" thru 3" diameter	"	200	.040			1.52		1.52	2.51
2164	4" thru 6" diameter	Q-1	200	.080			2.74		2.74	4.51
2166	8" thru 14" diameter		150	.107			3.65		3.65	6
2168	16" diameter		100	.160			5.45		5.45	9.05
3000	Submersible sump pump	1 Plum	24	.333	Ea.		12.65		12.65	21
6000	Remove and reset fixtures, minimum		6	1.333			50.50		50.50	83.50
6100	Maximum		4	2			76		76	125

22 05 23 – General-Duty Valves for Plumbing Piping

22 05 23.20 Valves, Bronze

		Crew	Daily Output	Labor-Hours	Unit	Material	2014 Bare Costs Labor	Equipment	Total	Total Incl O&P
0010	**VALVES, BRONZE**									
1750	Check, swing, class 150, regrinding disc, threaded									
1860	3/4"	1 Plum	20	.400	Ea.	95	15.20		110.20	129
1870	1"	"	19	.421	"	137	16		153	177
2850	Gate, N.R.S., soldered, 125 psi									
2940	3/4"	1 Plum	20	.400	Ea.	53	15.20		68.20	83
2950	1"	"	19	.421	"	75	16		91	109
5600	Relief, pressure & temperature, self-closing, ASME, threaded									
5640	3/4"	1 Plum	28	.286	Ea.	253	10.85		263.85	296
5650	1"		24	.333		405	12.65		417.65	465
5660	1-1/4"		20	.400		895	15.20		910.20	1,000
6400	Pressure, water, ASME, threaded									
6440	3/4"	1 Plum	28	.286	Ea.	116	10.85		126.85	145
6450	1"	"	24	.333	"	260	12.65		272.65	305
6900	Reducing, water pressure									
6920	300 psi to 25-75 psi, threaded or sweat									
6940	1/2"	1 Plum	24	.333	Ea.	395	12.65		407.65	455
6950	3/4"		20	.400		395	15.20		410.20	460
6960	1"		19	.421		615	16		631	700
8350	Tempering, water, sweat connections									
8400	1/2"	1 Plum	24	.333	Ea.	109	12.65		121.65	141
8440	3/4"	"	20	.400	"	126	15.20		141.20	164
8650	Threaded connections									
8700	1/2"	1 Plum	24	.333	Ea.	126	12.65		138.65	160
8740	3/4"	"	20	.400	"	770	15.20		785.20	870

22 05 Common Work Results for Plumbing

22 05 29 – Hangers and Supports for Plumbing Piping and Equipment

22 05 29.10 Hangers & Supp. for Plumb'g/HVAC Pipe/Equip.

		Crew	Daily Output	Labor-Hours	Unit	Material	2014 Bare Costs Labor	2014 Bare Costs Equipment	Total	Total Incl O&P
0010	**HANGERS AND SUPPORTS FOR PLUMB'G/HVAC PIPE/EQUIP.**									
8000	Pipe clamp, plastic, 1/2" CTS	1 Plum	80	.100	Ea.	.23	3.80		4.03	6.50
8010	3/4" CTS		73	.110		.24	4.16		4.40	7.10
8020	1" CTS		68	.118		.54	4.47		5.01	8
8080	Economy clamp, 1/4" CTS		175	.046		.05	1.74		1.79	2.93
8090	3/8" CTS		168	.048		.07	1.81		1.88	3.07
8100	1/2" CTS		160	.050		.07	1.90		1.97	3.22
8110	3/4" CTS		145	.055		.14	2.10		2.24	3.61
8200	Half clamp, 1/2" CTS		80	.100		.08	3.80		3.88	6.35
8210	3/4" CTS		73	.110		.12	4.16		4.28	7
8300	Suspension clamp, 1/2" CTS		80	.100		.23	3.80		4.03	6.50
8310	3/4" CTS		73	.110		.24	4.16		4.40	7.10
8320	1" CTS		68	.118		.54	4.47		5.01	8
8400	Insulator, 1/2" CTS		80	.100		.37	3.80		4.17	6.65
8410	3/4" CTS		73	.110		.39	4.16		4.55	7.30
8420	1" CTS		68	.118		.40	4.47		4.87	7.85
8500	J hook clamp with nail 1/2" CTS		240	.033		.13	1.27		1.40	2.23
8501	3/4" CTS	▼	240	.033	▼	.13	1.27		1.40	2.23

22 05 48 – Vibration and Seismic Controls for Plumbing Piping and Equipment

22 05 48.10 Seismic Bracing Supports

		Crew	Daily Output	Labor-Hours	Unit	Material	2014 Bare Costs Labor	2014 Bare Costs Equipment	Total	Total Incl O&P
0010	**SEISMIC BRACING SUPPORTS**									
0020	Clamps									
0030	C-clamp, for mounting on steel beam									
0040	3/8" threaded rod	1 Skwk	160	.050	Ea.	1.95	1.62		3.57	4.89
0050	1/2" threaded rod		160	.050		2.09	1.62		3.71	5.05
0060	5/8" threaded rod		160	.050		3.52	1.62		5.14	6.60
0070	3/4" threaded rod	▼	160	.050	▼	4.34	1.62		5.96	7.50
0100	Brackets									
0110	Beam side or wall mallable iron									
0120	3/8" threaded rod	1 Skwk	48	.167	Ea.	2.96	5.40		8.36	12.40
0130	1/2" threaded rod		48	.167		4.18	5.40		9.58	13.75
0140	5/8" threaded rod		48	.167		7.85	5.40		13.25	17.75
0150	3/4" threaded rod		48	.167		10.75	5.40		16.15	21
0160	7/8" threaded rod	▼	48	.167	▼	11.10	5.40		16.50	21.50
0170	For concrete installation, add						30%			
0180	Wall, welded steel									
0190	0 size 12" wide 18" deep	1 Skwk	34	.235	Ea.	164	7.65		171.65	193
0200	1 size 18" wide 24" deep		34	.235		201	7.65		208.65	234
0210	2 size 24" wide 30" deep	▼	34	.235	▼	276	7.65		283.65	320
0300	Rod, carbon steel									
0310	Continuous thread									
0320	1/4" thread	1 Skwk	144	.056	L.F.	1.62	1.80		3.42	4.82
0330	3/8" thread		144	.056		1.72	1.80		3.52	4.93
0340	1/2" thread		144	.056		2.72	1.80		4.52	6.05
0350	5/8" thread		144	.056		3.86	1.80		5.66	7.30
0360	3/4" thread		144	.056		6.80	1.80		8.60	10.55
0370	7/8" thread	▼	144	.056	▼	8.55	1.80		10.35	12.45
0380	For galvanized, add						30%			
0400	Channel, steel									
0410	3/4" x 1-1/2"	1 Skwk	80	.100	L.F.	4.83	3.25		8.08	10.80
0420	1-1/2" x 1-1/2"		70	.114		6.35	3.71		10.06	13.25
0430	1-7/8" x 1-1/2"	▼	60	.133		22.50	4.33		26.83	32

22 05 48 – Vibration and Seismic Controls for Plumbing Piping and Equipment

22 05 48.10 Seismic Bracing Supports	Crew	Daily Output	Labor-Hours	Unit	Material	2014 Bare Costs Labor	2014 Bare Costs Equipment	Total	Total Incl O&P
0440	3" x 1-1/2"	1 Skwk	50	.160	L.F.	38	5.20		43.20	50.50
0450	Spring nuts									
0460	3/8"	1 Skwk	100	.080	Ea.	1.40	2.60		4	5.90
0470	1/2"	"	80	.100	"	1.67	3.25		4.92	7.35
0500	Welding, field									
0510	Cleaning and welding plates, bars, or rods									
0520	To existing beams, columns, or trusses									
0530	1" weld	1 Skwk	144	.056	Ea.	.22	1.80		2.02	3.28
0540	2" weld		72	.111		.38	3.61		3.99	6.50
0550	3" weld		54	.148		.59	4.81		5.40	8.75
0560	4" weld		36	.222		.81	7.20		8.01	13.10
0570	5" weld		30	.267		1.02	8.65		9.67	15.70
0580	6" weld		24	.333		1.15	10.80		11.95	19.50
0600	Vibration absorbers									
0610	Hangers, neoprene flex									
0620	10-120 lb. capacity	1 Skwk	8	1	Ea.	25.50	32.50		58	83.50
0630	75-550 lb. capacity		8	1		36	32.50		68.50	94.50
0640	250-1100 lb. capacity		6	1.333		66.50	43.50		110	146
0650	1000-4000 lb. capacity		6	1.333		124	43.50		167.50	210

22 05 76 – Facility Drainage Piping Cleanouts

22 05 76.10 Cleanouts

		Crew	Daily Output	Labor-Hours	Unit	Material	Labor	Equipment	Total	Total Incl O&P
0010	**CLEANOUTS**									
0060	Floor type									
0080	Round or square, scoriated nickel bronze top									
0100	2" pipe size	1 Plum	10	.800	Ea.	183	30.50		213.50	251
0120	3" pipe size		8	1		274	38		312	365
0140	4" pipe size		6	1.333		274	50.50		324.50	385

22 05 76.20 Cleanout Tees

		Crew	Daily Output	Labor-Hours	Unit	Material	Labor	Equipment	Total	Total Incl O&P
0010	**CLEANOUT TEES**									
0100	Cast iron, B&S, with countersunk plug									
0220	3" pipe size	1 Plum	3.60	2.222	Ea.	270	84.50		354.50	435
0240	4" pipe size	"	3.30	2.424	"	335	92		427	520
0500	For round smooth access cover, same price									
4000	Plastic, tees and adapters. Add plugs									
4010	ABS, DWV									
4020	Cleanout tee, 1-1/2" pipe size	1 Plum	15	.533	Ea.	20	20.50		40.50	55.50

22 07 Plumbing Insulation

22 07 16 – Plumbing Equipment Insulation

22 07 16.10 Insulation for Plumbing Equipment

		Crew	Daily Output	Labor-Hours	Unit	Material	Labor	Equipment	Total	Total Incl O&P
0010	**INSULATION FOR PLUMBING EQUIPMENT**									
2900	Domestic water heater wrap kit									
2920	1-1/2" with vinyl jacket, 20-60 gal. G	1 Plum	8	1	Ea.	18.60	38		56.60	83

22 07 19 – Plumbing Piping Insulation

22 07 19.10 Piping Insulation

		Crew	Daily Output	Labor-Hours	Unit	Material	Labor	Equipment	Total	Total Incl O&P
0010	**PIPING INSULATION**									
0230	Insulated protectors, (ADA)									
0235	For exposed piping under sinks or lavatories									
0240	Vinyl coated foam, velcro tabs									
0245	P Trap, 1-1/4" or 1-1/2"	1 Plum	32	.250	Ea.	44.50	9.50		54	64.50

22 07 Plumbing Insulation

22 07 19 – Plumbing Piping Insulation

22 07 19.10 Piping Insulation		Crew	Daily Output	Labor-Hours	Unit	Material	2014 Bare Costs Labor	Equipment	Total	Total Incl O&P
0260	Valve and supply cover									
0265	1/2", 3/8", and 7/16" pipe size	1 Plum	32	.250	Ea.	22	9.50		31.50	39.50
0285	1-1/4" pipe size	"	32	.250	"	18.20	9.50		27.70	35.50
0600	Pipe covering (price copper tube one size less than IPS)									
6600	Fiberglass, with all service jacket									
6840	1" wall, 1/2" iron pipe size **G**	Q-14	240	.067	L.F.	.89	2.03		2.92	4.42
6860	3/4" iron pipe size **G**		230	.070		.97	2.11		3.08	4.65
6870	1" iron pipe size **G**		220	.073		1.04	2.21		3.25	4.89
6900	2" iron pipe size **G**		200	.080		1.32	2.43		3.75	5.55
7879	Rubber tubing, flexible closed cell foam									
8100	1/2" wall, 1/4" iron pipe size **G**	1 Asbe	90	.089	L.F.	.54	3		3.54	5.70
8130	1/2" iron pipe size **G**		89	.090		.67	3.03		3.70	5.90
8140	3/4" iron pipe size **G**		89	.090		.75	3.03		3.78	6
8150	1" iron pipe size **G**		88	.091		.82	3.07		3.89	6.10
8170	1-1/2" iron pipe size **G**		87	.092		1.15	3.10		4.25	6.50
8180	2" iron pipe size **G**		86	.093		1.47	3.14		4.61	6.95
8300	3/4" wall, 1/4" iron pipe size **G**		90	.089		.85	3		3.85	6.05
8330	1/2" iron pipe size **G**		89	.090		1.10	3.03		4.13	6.35
8340	3/4" iron pipe size **G**		89	.090		1.35	3.03		4.38	6.65
8350	1" iron pipe size **G**		88	.091		1.54	3.07		4.61	6.90
8380	2" iron pipe size **G**		86	.093		2.68	3.14		5.82	8.30
8444	1" wall, 1/2" iron pipe size **G**		86	.093		2.05	3.14		5.19	7.60
8445	3/4" iron pipe size **G**		84	.095		2.48	3.21		5.69	8.20
8446	1" iron pipe size **G**		84	.095		2.89	3.21		6.10	8.65
8447	1-1/4" iron pipe size **G**		82	.098		3.23	3.29		6.52	9.15
8448	1-1/2" iron pipe size **G**		82	.098		3.76	3.29		7.05	9.75
8449	2" iron pipe size **G**		80	.100		4.95	3.38		8.33	11.20
8450	2-1/2" iron pipe size **G**		80	.100		6.45	3.38		9.83	12.85
8456	Rubber insulation tape, 1/8" x 2" x 30' **G**				Ea.	12.05			12.05	13.25

22 11 Facility Water Distribution

22 11 13 – Facility Water Distribution Piping

22 11 13.23 Pipe/Tube, Copper

		Crew	Daily Output	Labor-Hours	Unit	Material	2014 Bare Costs Labor	Equipment	Total	Total Incl O&P
0010	**PIPE/TUBE, COPPER**, Solder joints									
1000	Type K tubing, couplings & clevis hanger assemblies 10' O.C.									
1180	3/4" diameter	1 Plum	74	.108	L.F.	7.80	4.11		11.91	15.40
1200	1" diameter	"	66	.121	"	10.60	4.61		15.21	19.25
2000	Type L tubing, couplings & clevis hanger assemblies 10' O.C.									
2140	1/2" diameter	1 Plum	81	.099	L.F.	3.37	3.75		7.12	9.90
2160	5/8" diameter		79	.101		5.35	3.85		9.20	12.20
2180	3/4" diameter		76	.105		5.15	4		9.15	12.25
2200	1" diameter		68	.118		7.85	4.47		12.32	16.05
2220	1-1/4" diameter		58	.138		11.25	5.25		16.50	21
3000	Type M tubing, couplings & clevis hanger assemblies 10' O.C.									
3140	1/2" diameter	1 Plum	84	.095	L.F.	2.65	3.62		6.27	8.85
3180	3/4" diameter		78	.103		3.99	3.90		7.89	10.85
3200	1" diameter		70	.114		6.50	4.34		10.84	14.30
3220	1-1/4" diameter		60	.133		9.55	5.05		14.60	18.85
3240	1-1/2" diameter		54	.148		12.85	5.65		18.50	23.50
3260	2" diameter		44	.182		20	6.90		26.90	33.50
4000	Type DWV tubing, couplings & clevis hanger assemblies 10' O.C.									

22 11 13 – Facility Water Distribution Piping

22 11 13.23 Pipe/Tube, Copper	Crew	Daily Output	Labor-Hours	Unit	Material	2014 Bare Costs Labor	Equipment	Total	Total Incl O&P
4100	1-1/4" diameter	1 Plum	60	.133	L.F.	9.95	5.05		15	19.25
4120	1-1/2" diameter		54	.148		12.45	5.65		18.10	23
4140	2" diameter		44	.182		17.05	6.90		23.95	30
4160	3" diameter	Q-1	58	.276		35	9.45		44.45	54
4180	4" diameter	"	40	.400		62	13.70		75.70	90.50

22 11 13.25 Pipe/Tube Fittings, Copper	Crew	Daily Output	Labor-Hours	Unit	Material	2014 Bare Costs Labor	Equipment	Total	Total Incl O&P
0010	**PIPE/TUBE FITTINGS, COPPER**, Wrought unless otherwise noted									
0040	Solder joints, copper x copper									
0070	90° elbow, 1/4"	1 Plum	22	.364	Ea.	9.70	13.80		23.50	33.50
0100	1/2"		20	.400		3.08	15.20		18.28	28.50
0120	3/4"		19	.421		6.95	16		22.95	34
0250	45° elbow, 1/4"		22	.364		17.30	13.80		31.10	42
0280	1/2"		20	.400		5.65	15.20		20.85	31.50
0290	5/8"		19	.421		27	16		43	56
0300	3/4"		19	.421		9.90	16		25.90	37.50
0310	1"		16	.500		25	19		44	59
0320	1-1/4"		15	.533		33.50	20.50		54	70.50
0450	Tee, 1/4"		14	.571		19.40	21.50		40.90	57.50
0480	1/2"		13	.615		5.25	23.50		28.75	44.50
0490	5/8"		12	.667		34	25.50		59.50	79.50
0500	3/4"		12	.667		12.70	25.50		38.20	56
0510	1"		10	.800		39.50	30.50		70	93
0520	1-1/4"		9	.889		53.50	34		87.50	115
0612	Tee, reducing on the outlet, 1/4"		15	.533		33	20.50		53.50	69.50
0613	3/8"		15	.533		31	20.50		51.50	67.50
0614	1/2"		14	.571		27	21.50		48.50	66
0615	5/8"		13	.615		54.50	23.50		78	98.50
0616	3/4"		12	.667		15	25.50		40.50	58.50
0617	1"		11	.727		39.50	27.50		67	89
0618	1-1/4"		10	.800		58	30.50		88.50	114
0619	1-1/2"		9	.889		61.50	34		95.50	123
0620	2"		8	1		97.50	38		135.50	170
0621	2-1/2"	Q-1	9	1.778		305	61		366	435
0622	3"		8	2		365	68.50		433.50	520
0623	4"		6	2.667		685	91		776	900
0624	5"		5	3.200		3,150	109		3,259	3,625
0625	6"	Q-2	7	3.429		4,075	113		4,188	4,675
0626	8"	"	6	4		16,600	132		16,732	18,400
0630	Tee, reducing on the run, 1/4"	1 Plum	15	.533		41	20.50		61.50	79
0631	3/8"		15	.533		47	20.50		67.50	85
0632	1/2"		14	.571		37.50	21.50		59	77
0633	5/8"		13	.615		55	23.50		78.50	99
0634	3/4"		12	.667		15	25.50		40.50	58.50
0635	1"		11	.727		47	27.50		74.50	97
0636	1-1/4"		10	.800		74.50	30.50		105	132
0637	1-1/2"		9	.889		123	34		157	191
0638	2"		8	1		168	38		206	247
0639	2-1/2"	Q-1	9	1.778		415	61		476	560
0640	3"		8	2		560	68.50		628.50	730
0641	4"		6	2.667		1,275	91		1,366	1,550
0642	5"		5	3.200		2,975	109		3,084	3,450
0643	6"	Q-2	7	3.429		4,550	113		4,663	5,175

22 11 13 – Facility Water Distribution Piping

22 11 13.25 Pipe/Tube Fittings, Copper

		Crew	Daily Output	Labor-Hours	Unit	Material	2014 Bare Costs Labor	Equipment	Total	Total Incl O&P
0644	8"	Q-2	6	4	Ea.	16,100	132		16,232	17,900
0650	Coupling, 1/4"	1 Plum	24	.333		2.25	12.65		14.90	23.50
0680	1/2"		22	.364		2.34	13.80		16.14	25.50
0690	5/8"		21	.381		7.05	14.50		21.55	32
0700	3/4"		21	.381		4.70	14.50		19.20	29
0710	1"		18	.444		9.60	16.90		26.50	38.50
0715	1-1/4"		17	.471		16.60	17.90		34.50	48
2000	DWV, solder joints, copper x copper									
2030	90° Elbow, 1-1/4"	1 Plum	13	.615	Ea.	29.50	23.50		53	71
2050	1-1/2"		12	.667		44.50	25.50		70	91
2070	2"		10	.800		58.50	30.50		89	114
2090	3"	Q-1	10	1.600		144	54.50		198.50	250
2100	4"	"	9	1.778		1,000	61		1,061	1,200
2250	Tee, Sanitary, 1-1/4"	1 Plum	9	.889		59	34		93	121
2270	1-1/2"		8	1		73.50	38		111.50	143
2290	2"		7	1.143		85.50	43.50		129	166
2310	3"	Q-1	7	2.286		370	78		448	540
2330	4"	"	6	2.667		945	91		1,036	1,200
2400	Coupling, 1-1/4"	1 Plum	14	.571		13.95	21.50		35.45	51.50
2420	1-1/2"		13	.615		17.35	23.50		40.85	57.50
2440	2"		11	.727		24	27.50		51.50	72
2460	3"	Q-1	11	1.455		49	50		99	136
2480	4"	"	10	1.600		149	54.50		203.50	254

22 11 13.44 Pipe, Steel

		Crew	Daily Output	Labor-Hours	Unit	Material	2014 Bare Costs Labor	Equipment	Total	Total Incl O&P
0010	**PIPE, STEEL**									
0050	Schedule 40, threaded, with couplings, and clevis hanger									
0060	assemblies sized for covering, 10' O.C.									
0540	Black, 1/4" diameter	1 Plum	66	.121	L.F.	4.51	4.61		9.12	12.55
0560	1/2" diameter		63	.127		2.73	4.83		7.56	10.95
0570	3/4" diameter		61	.131		3.17	4.98		8.15	11.70
0580	1" diameter		53	.151		4.64	5.75		10.39	14.55
0590	1-1/4" diameter	Q-1	89	.180		5.75	6.15		11.90	16.45
0600	1-1/2" diameter		80	.200		6.70	6.85		13.55	18.65
0610	2" diameter		64	.250		8.95	8.55		17.50	24

22 11 13.45 Pipe Fittings, Steel, Threaded

		Crew	Daily Output	Labor-Hours	Unit	Material	2014 Bare Costs Labor	Equipment	Total	Total Incl O&P
0010	**PIPE FITTINGS, STEEL, THREADED**									
5000	Malleable iron, 150 lb.									
5020	Black									
5040	90° elbow, straight									
5090	3/4"	1 Plum	14	.571	Ea.	3.70	21.50		25.20	40
5100	1"	"	13	.615		6.40	23.50		29.90	45.50
5120	1-1/2"	Q-1	20	.800		13.95	27.50		41.45	60.50
5130	2"	"	18	.889		24	30.50		54.50	76.50
5450	Tee, straight									
5500	3/4"	1 Plum	9	.889	Ea.	5.85	34		39.85	62
5510	1"	"	8	1		10.05	38		48.05	73.50
5520	1-1/4"	Q-1	14	1.143		16.30	39		55.30	82.50
5530	1-1/2"		13	1.231		20.50	42		62.50	92
5540	2"		11	1.455		34.50	50		84.50	120
5650	Coupling									
5700	3/4"	1 Plum	18	.444	Ea.	4.97	16.90		21.87	33.50
5710	1"	"	15	.533		7.45	20.50		27.95	41.50

22 11 13.45 Pipe Fittings, Steel, Threaded	Crew	Daily Output	Labor-Hours	Unit	Material	2014 Bare Costs Labor	Equipment	Total	Total Incl O&P
5720	1-1/4"	Q-1	26	.615	Ea.	9.65	21		30.65	45
5730	1-1/2"		24	.667		13	23		36	52
5740	2"	↓	21	.762	↓	19.25	26		45.25	64

22 11 13.74 Pipe, Plastic

		Crew	Daily Output	Labor-Hours	Unit	Material	2014 Bare Costs Labor	Equipment	Total	Total Incl O&P
0010	**PIPE, PLASTIC**									
1800	PVC, couplings 10' O.C., clevis hanger assemblies, 3 per 10'									
1820	Schedule 40									
1860	1/2" diameter	1 Plum	54	.148	L.F.	3.02	5.65		8.67	12.65
1870	3/4" diameter		51	.157		3.33	5.95		9.28	13.50
1880	1" diameter		46	.174		3.96	6.60		10.56	15.25
1890	1-1/4" diameter		42	.190		4.94	7.25		12.19	17.40
1900	1-1/2" diameter	↓	36	.222		4.76	8.45		13.21	19.20
1910	2" diameter	Q-1	59	.271		5.95	9.25		15.20	22
1920	2-1/2" diameter		56	.286		9.15	9.75		18.90	26
1930	3" diameter		53	.302		11.05	10.30		21.35	29
1940	4" diameter	↓	48	.333	↓	14.20	11.40		25.60	34.50
4100	DWV type, schedule 40, couplings 10' O.C., clevis hanger assy's, 3 per 10'									
4210	ABS, schedule 40, foam core type									
4212	Plain end black									
4214	1-1/2" diameter	1 Plum	39	.205	L.F.	2.96	7.80		10.76	16.10
4216	2" diameter	Q-1	62	.258		3.40	8.85		12.25	18.30
4218	3" diameter		56	.286		6.10	9.75		15.85	23
4220	4" diameter		51	.314		8.70	10.75		19.45	27.50
4222	6" diameter	↓	42	.381	↓	20.50	13.05		33.55	44
4240	To delete coupling & hangers, subtract									
4244	1-1/2" diam. to 6" diam.					43%	48%			
4400	PVC									
4410	1-1/4" diameter	1 Plum	42	.190	L.F.	3.41	7.25		10.66	15.70
4420	1-1/2" diameter	"	36	.222		2.98	8.45		11.43	17.25
4460	2" diameter	Q-1	59	.271		3.39	9.25		12.64	19.05
4470	3" diameter		53	.302		6.05	10.30		16.35	23.50
4480	4" diameter	↓	48	.333	↓	8.35	11.40		19.75	28
5300	CPVC, socket joint, couplings 10' O.C., clevis hanger assemblies, 3 per 10'									
5302	Schedule 40									
5304	1/2" diameter	1 Plum	54	.148	L.F.	3.65	5.65		9.30	13.30
5305	3/4" diameter		51	.157		4.30	5.95		10.25	14.60
5306	1" diameter		46	.174		5.50	6.60		12.10	16.95
5307	1-1/4" diameter		42	.190		6.90	7.25		14.15	19.55
5308	1-1/2" diameter	↓	36	.222		8.05	8.45		16.50	23
5309	2" diameter	Q-1	59	.271	↓	9.90	9.25		19.15	26
5360	CPVC, threaded, couplings 10' O.C., clevis hanger assemblies, 3 per 10'									
5380	Schedule 40									
5460	1/2" diameter	1 Plum	54	.148	L.F.	4.45	5.65		10.10	14.20
5470	3/4" diameter		51	.157		5.70	5.95		11.65	16.10
5480	1" diameter		46	.174		6.95	6.60		13.55	18.50
5490	1-1/4" diameter		42	.190		8	7.25		15.25	21
5500	1-1/2" diameter	↓	36	.222		9	8.45		17.45	24
5510	2" diameter	Q-1	59	.271	↓	11.10	9.25		20.35	27.50
6500	Residential installation, plastic pipe									
6510	Couplings 10' O.C., strap hangers 3 per 10'									
6520	PVC, Schedule 40									
6530	1/2" diameter	1 Plum	138	.058	L.F.	1.29	2.20		3.49	5.05

22 11 Facility Water Distribution

22 11 13 – Facility Water Distribution Piping

22 11 13.74 Pipe, Plastic

		Crew	Daily Output	Labor-Hours	Unit	Material	2014 Bare Costs Labor	2014 Bare Costs Equipment	Total	Total Incl O&P
6540	3/4" diameter	1 Plum	128	.063	L.F.	1.48	2.38		3.86	5.55
6550	1" diameter		119	.067		2.28	2.55		4.83	6.70
6560	1-1/4" diameter		111	.072		2.94	2.74		5.68	7.75
6570	1-1/2" diameter		104	.077		2.70	2.92		5.62	7.80
6580	2" diameter	Q-1	197	.081		3.35	2.78		6.13	8.25
6590	2-1/2" diameter		162	.099		6.25	3.38		9.63	12.40
6600	4" diameter		123	.130		9.10	4.45		13.55	17.40
6700	PVC, DWV, Schedule 40									
6720	1-1/4" diameter	1 Plum	100	.080	L.F.	2.25	3.04		5.29	7.50
6730	1-1/2" diameter	"	94	.085		1.83	3.23		5.06	7.35
6740	2" diameter	Q-1	178	.090		2.19	3.07		5.26	7.45
6760	4" diameter	"	110	.145		6.45	4.97		11.42	15.30
7280	PEX, flexible, no couplings or hangers									
7282	Note: For labor costs add 25% to the couplings and fittings labor total.									
7285	For fittings see section 23 83 16.10 7000									
7300	Non-barrier type, hot/cold tubing rolls									
7310	1/4" diameter x 100'				L.F.	.47			.47	.52
7350	3/8" diameter x 100'					.52			.52	.57
7360	1/2" diameter x 100'					.58			.58	.64
7370	1/2" diameter x 500'					.58			.58	.64
7380	1/2" diameter x 1000'					.58			.58	.64
7400	3/4" diameter x 100'					1.05			1.05	1.16
7410	3/4" diameter x 500'					1.05			1.05	1.16
7420	3/4" diameter x 1000'					1.05			1.05	1.16
7460	1" diameter x 100'					1.82			1.82	2
7470	1" diameter x 300'					1.82			1.82	2
7480	1" diameter x 500'					1.82			1.82	2
7500	1-1/4" diameter x 100'					3.08			3.08	3.39
7510	1-1/4" diameter x 300'					3.08			3.08	3.39
7540	1-1/2" diameter x 100'					4.19			4.19	4.61
7550	1-1/2" diameter x 300'					4.19			4.19	4.61
7596	Most sizes available in red or blue									
7700	Non-barrier type, hot/cold tubing straight lengths									
7710	1/2" diameter x 20'				L.F.	.58			.58	.64
7750	3/4" diameter x 20'					1.06			1.06	1.17
7760	1" diameter x 20'					1.82			1.82	2
7770	1-1/4" diameter x 20'					3.08			3.08	3.39
7780	1-1/2" diameter x 20'					4.19			4.19	4.61
7790	2" diameter					8.20			8.20	9
7796	Most sizes available in red or blue									

22 11 13.76 Pipe Fittings, Plastic

		Crew	Daily Output	Labor-Hours	Unit	Material	2014 Bare Costs Labor	2014 Bare Costs Equipment	Total	Total Incl O&P
0010	**PIPE FITTINGS, PLASTIC**									
2700	PVC (white), schedule 40, socket joints									
2760	90° elbow, 1/2"	1 Plum	33.30	.240	Ea.	.48	9.15		9.63	15.60
2770	3/4"		28.60	.280		.54	10.65		11.19	18.15
2780	1"		25	.320		.97	12.15		13.12	21
2790	1-1/4"		22.20	.360		1.71	13.70		15.41	24.50
2800	1-1/2"		20	.400		1.85	15.20		17.05	27
2810	2"	Q-1	36.40	.440		2.89	15.05		17.94	28
2820	2-1/2"		26.70	.599		8.80	20.50		29.30	43.50
2830	3"		22.90	.699		10.50	24		34.50	51
2840	4"		18.20	.879		18.80	30		48.80	70

22 11 13.76 Pipe Fittings, Plastic		Crew	Daily Output	Labor-Hours	Unit	Material	2014 Bare Costs Labor	Equipment	Total	Total Incl O&P
3180	Tee, 1/2"	1 Plum	22.20	.360	Ea.	.60	13.70		14.30	23
3190	3/4"		19	.421		.69	16		16.69	27.50
3200	1"		16.70	.479		1.29	18.20		19.49	31.50
3210	1-1/4"		14.80	.541		2.01	20.50		22.51	36
3220	1-1/2"		13.30	.602		2.45	23		25.45	40
3230	2"	Q-1	24.20	.661		3.56	22.50		26.06	41.50
3240	2-1/2"		17.80	.899		11.75	30.50		42.25	63.50
3250	3"		15.20	1.053		15.45	36		51.45	76.50
3260	4"		12.10	1.322		28	45		73	105
3380	Coupling, 1/2"	1 Plum	33.30	.240		.32	9.15		9.47	15.40
3390	3/4"		28.60	.280		.44	10.65		11.09	18.05
3400	1"		25	.320		.77	12.15		12.92	21
3410	1-1/4"		22.20	.360		1.06	13.70		14.76	23.50
3420	1-1/2"		20	.400		1.13	15.20		16.33	26
3430	2"	Q-1	36.40	.440		1.72	15.05		16.77	27
3440	2-1/2"		26.70	.599		3.81	20.50		24.31	38
3450	3"		22.90	.699		5.95	24		29.95	46
3460	4"		18.20	.879		8.65	30		38.65	59
4500	DWV, ABS, non pressure, socket joints									
4540	1/4 Bend, 1-1/4"	1 Plum	20.20	.396	Ea.	6.15	15.05		21.20	32
4560	1-1/2"	"	18.20	.440		4.69	16.70		21.39	32.50
4570	2"	Q-1	33.10	.483		7.45	16.55		24	35.50
4650	1/8 Bend, same as 1/4 Bend									
4800	Tee, sanitary									
4820	1-1/4"	1 Plum	13.50	.593	Ea.	8.15	22.50		30.65	46
4830	1-1/2"	"	12.10	.661		7.15	25		32.15	49.50
4840	2"	Q-1	20	.800		11	27.50		38.50	57
5000	DWV, PVC, schedule 40, socket joints									
5040	1/4 bend, 1-1/4"	1 Plum	20.20	.396	Ea.	12.55	15.05		27.60	39
5060	1-1/2"	"	18.20	.440		3.45	16.70		20.15	31.50
5070	2"	Q-1	33.10	.483		5.45	16.55		22	33.50
5080	3"		20.80	.769		16	26.50		42.50	61
5090	4"		16.50	.970		31.50	33		64.50	89
5110	1/4 bend, long sweep, 1-1/2"	1 Plum	18.20	.440		8.30	16.70		25	36.50
5112	2"	Q-1	33.10	.483		8.95	16.55		25.50	37.50
5114	3"		20.80	.769		21	26.50		47.50	67
5116	4"		16.50	.970		40	33		73	99
5250	Tee, sanitary 1-1/4"	1 Plum	13.50	.593		12.30	22.50		34.80	50.50
5254	1-1/2"	"	12.10	.661		6.25	25		31.25	48.50
5255	2"	Q-1	20	.800		9.20	27.50		36.70	55
5256	3"		13.90	1.151		23	39.50		62.50	90
5257	4"		11	1.455		43	50		93	129
5259	6"		6.70	2.388		179	81.50		260.50	330
5261	8"	Q-2	6.20	3.871		535	127		662	800
5264	2" x 1-1/2"	Q-1	22	.727		8.10	25		33.10	50
5266	3" x 1-1/2"		15.50	1.032		17.05	35.50		52.55	77.50
5268	4" x 3"		12.10	1.322		52	45		97	132
5271	6" x 4"		6.90	2.319		173	79.50		252.50	320
5314	Combination Y & 1/8 bend, 1-1/2"	1 Plum	12.10	.661		15.10	25		40.10	58
5315	2"	Q-1	20	.800		16.15	27.50		43.65	63
5317	3"		13.90	1.151		40	39.50		79.50	109
5318	4"		11	1.455		79.50	50		129.50	170
5324	Combination Y & 1/8 bend, reducing									

22 11 13.76 Pipe Fittings, Plastic	Crew	Daily Output	Labor-Hours	Unit	Material	2014 Bare Costs Labor	2014 Bare Costs Equipment	Total	Total Incl O&P
5325	2" x 2" x 1-1/2"	Q-1	22	.727	Ea.	21	25		46	64.50
5327	3" x 3" x 1-1/2"		15.50	1.032		38	35.50		73.50	100
5328	3" x 3" x 2"		15.30	1.046		26.50	36		62.50	88
5329	4" x 4" x 2"		12.20	1.311		43	45		88	122
5331	Wye, 1-1/4"	1 Plum	13.50	.593		16.10	22.50		38.60	54.50
5332	1-1/2"	"	12.10	.661		11.80	25		36.80	54.50
5333	2"	Q-1	20	.800		11.20	27.50		38.70	57.50
5334	3"		13.90	1.151		30	39.50		69.50	98
5335	4"		11	1.455		55	50		105	143
5336	6"		6.70	2.388		165	81.50		246.50	315
5337	8"	Q-2	6.20	3.871		385	127		512	635
5341	2" x 1-1/2"	Q-1	22	.727		13.85	25		38.85	56.50
5342	3" x 1-1/2"		15.50	1.032		19.85	35.50		55.35	80.50
5343	4" x 3"		12.10	1.322		44.50	45		89.50	124
5344	6" x 4"		6.90	2.319		122	79.50		201.50	265
5345	8" x 6"	Q-2	6.40	3.750		291	123		414	525
5347	Double wye, 1-1/2"	1 Plum	9.10	.879		25.50	33.50		59	83
5348	2"	Q-1	16.60	.964		29.50	33		62.50	87
5349	3"		10.40	1.538		60	52.50		112.50	153
5350	4"		8.25	1.939		122	66.50		188.50	243
5353	Double wye, reducing									
5354	2" x 2" x 1-1/2" x 1-1/2"	Q-1	16.80	.952	Ea.	26	32.50		58.50	82
5355	3" x 3" x 2" x 2"		10.60	1.509		44.50	51.50		96	134
5356	4" x 4" x 3" x 3"		8.45	1.893		96.50	65		161.50	213
5357	6" x 6" x 4" x 4"		7.25	2.207		325	75.50		400.50	480
5374	Coupling, 1-1/4"	1 Plum	20.20	.396		7.60	15.05		22.65	33.50
5376	1-1/2"	"	18.20	.440		1.72	16.70		18.42	29.50
5378	2"	Q-1	33.10	.483		2.24	16.55		18.79	30
5380	3"		20.80	.769		7.70	26.50		34.20	52
5390	4"		16.50	.970		13.65	33		46.65	69.50
5410	Reducer bushing, 2" x 1-1/4"		36.50	.438		7.05	15		22.05	32.50
5412	3" x 1-1/2"		27.30	.586		14.15	20		34.15	48.50
5414	4" x 2"		18.20	.879		24.50	30		54.50	76.50
5416	6" x 4"		11.10	1.441		65.50	49.50		115	154
5418	8" x 6"	Q-2	10.20	2.353		142	77.50		219.50	284
5500	CPVC, Schedule 80, threaded joints									
5540	90° Elbow, 1/4"	1 Plum	32	.250	Ea.	12.15	9.50		21.65	29
5560	1/2"		30.30	.264		7.05	10.05		17.10	24.50
5570	3/4"		26	.308		10.55	11.70		22.25	31
5580	1"		22.70	.352		14.80	13.40		28.20	38.50
5590	1-1/4"		20.20	.396		28.50	15.05		43.55	56.50
5600	1-1/2"		18.20	.440		30.50	16.70		47.20	61.50
5610	2"	Q-1	33.10	.483		41	16.55		57.55	72.50
5730	Coupling, 1/4"	1 Plum	32	.250		15.45	9.50		24.95	32.50
5732	1/2"		30.30	.264		12.75	10.05		22.80	30.50
5734	3/4"		26	.308		20.50	11.70		32.20	42
5736	1"		22.70	.352		23.50	13.40		36.90	48
5738	1-1/4"		20.20	.396		25	15.05		40.05	52
5740	1-1/2"		18.20	.440		26.50	16.70		43.20	57
5742	2"	Q-1	33.10	.483		31.50	16.55		48.05	62
5900	CPVC, Schedule 80, socket joints									
5904	90° Elbow, 1/4"	1 Plum	32	.250	Ea.	11.55	9.50		21.05	28.50
5906	1/2"		30.30	.264		4.53	10.05		14.58	21.50

22 11 13 – Facility Water Distribution Piping

22 11 13.76 Pipe Fittings, Plastic	Crew	Daily Output	Labor-Hours	Unit	Material	2014 Bare Costs Labor	Equipment	Total	Total Incl O&P
5908	3/4"	1 Plum	26	.308	Ea.	5.80	11.70		17.50	25.50
5910	1"		22.70	.352		9.20	13.40		22.60	32
5912	1-1/4"		20.20	.396		19.85	15.05		34.90	47
5914	1-1/2"		18.20	.440		22	16.70		38.70	52
5916	2"	Q-1	33.10	.483		26.50	16.55		43.05	57
5930	45° Elbow, 1/4"	1 Plum	32	.250		17.20	9.50		26.70	34.50
5932	1/2"		30.30	.264		5.55	10.05		15.60	22.50
5934	3/4"		26	.308		7.95	11.70		19.65	28
5936	1"		22.70	.352		12.75	13.40		26.15	36
5938	1-1/4"		20.20	.396		25	15.05		40.05	52.50
5940	1-1/2"		18.20	.440		25.50	16.70		42.20	55.50
5942	2"	Q-1	33.10	.483		29	16.55		45.55	59.50
5990	Coupling, 1/4"	1 Plum	32	.250		12.30	9.50		21.80	29.50
5992	1/2"		30.30	.264		4.79	10.05		14.84	22
5994	3/4"		26	.308		6.70	11.70		18.40	26.50
5996	1"		22.70	.352		9	13.40		22.40	32
5998	1-1/4"		20.20	.396		13.50	15.05		28.55	40
6000	1-1/2"		18.20	.440		17	16.70		33.70	46
6002	2"	Q-1	33.10	.483		19.75	16.55		36.30	49

22 11 19 – Domestic Water Piping Specialties

22 11 19.38 Water Supply Meters

0010	**WATER SUPPLY METERS**								
2000	Domestic/commercial, bronze								
2020	Threaded								
2060	5/8" diameter, to 20 GPM	1 Plum	16	.500	Ea.	48.50	19		67.50	85
2080	3/4" diameter, to 30 GPM		14	.571		88.50	21.50		110	134
2100	1" diameter, to 50 GPM		12	.667		134	25.50		159.50	190

22 11 19.42 Backflow Preventers

0010	**BACKFLOW PREVENTERS**, Includes valves								
0020	and four test cocks, corrosion resistant, automatic operation								
4000	Reduced pressure principle								
4100	Threaded, bronze, valves are ball								
4120	3/4" pipe size	1 Plum	16	.500	Ea.	445	19		464	520

22 11 19.50 Vacuum Breakers

0010	**VACUUM BREAKERS**								
0013	See also backflow preventers Section 22 11 19.42								
1000	Anti-siphon continuous pressure type								
1010	Max. 150 PSI - 210°F								
1020	Bronze body								
1030	1/2" size	1 Stpi	24	.333	Ea.	187	12.85		199.85	227
1040	3/4" size		20	.400		187	15.45		202.45	232
1050	1" size		19	.421		194	16.25		210.25	240
1060	1-1/4" size		15	.533		380	20.50		400.50	455
1070	1-1/2" size		13	.615		470	24		494	555
1080	2" size		11	.727		485	28		513	575
1200	Max. 125 PSI with atmospheric vent								
1210	Brass, in-line construction								
1220	1/4" size	1 Stpi	24	.333	Ea.	117	12.85		129.85	150
1230	3/8" size	"	24	.333		117	12.85		129.85	150
1260	For polished chrome finish, add					13%				
2000	Anti-siphon, non-continuous pressure type								
2010	Hot or cold water 125 PSI - 210°F								

22 11 Facility Water Distribution

22 11 19 – Domestic Water Piping Specialties

22 11 19.50 Vacuum Breakers

		Crew	Daily Output	Labor-Hours	Unit	Material	2014 Bare Costs Labor	2014 Bare Costs Equipment	Total	Total Incl O&P
2020	Bronze body									
2030	1/4" size	1 Stpi	24	.333	Ea.	64	12.85		76.85	91.50
2040	3/8" size		24	.333		64	12.85		76.85	91.50
2050	1/2" size		24	.333		72.50	12.85		85.35	101
2060	3/4" size		20	.400		86.50	15.45		101.95	121
2070	1" size		19	.421		134	16.25		150.25	174
2080	1-1/4" size		15	.533		235	20.50		255.50	292
2090	1-1/2" size		13	.615		276	24		300	345
2100	2" size		11	.727		430	28		458	515
2110	2-1/2" size		8	1		1,225	38.50		1,263.50	1,425
2120	3" size	▼	6	1.333	▼	1,625	51.50		1,676.50	1,875
2150	For polished chrome finish, add					50%				

22 11 19.54 Water Hammer Arresters/Shock Absorbers

		Crew	Daily Output	Labor-Hours	Unit	Material	2014 Bare Costs Labor	2014 Bare Costs Equipment	Total	Total Incl O&P
0010	**WATER HAMMER ARRESTERS/SHOCK ABSORBERS**									
0490	Copper									
0500	3/4" male I.P.S. For 1 to 11 fixtures	1 Plum	12	.667	Ea.	28	25.50		53.50	73

22 13 Facility Sanitary Sewerage

22 13 16 – Sanitary Waste and Vent Piping

22 13 16.20 Pipe, Cast Iron

		Crew	Daily Output	Labor-Hours	Unit	Material	2014 Bare Costs Labor	2014 Bare Costs Equipment	Total	Total Incl O&P
0010	**PIPE, CAST IRON**, Soil, on clevis hanger assemblies, 5' O.C. R221113-50									
0020	Single hub, service wt., lead & oakum joints 10' O.C.									
2120	2" diameter	Q-1	63	.254	L.F.	9.30	8.70		18	24.50
2140	3" diameter		60	.267		12.95	9.10		22.05	29.50
2160	4" diameter	▼	55	.291	▼	16.85	9.95		26.80	35
4000	No hub, couplings 10' O.C.									
4100	1-1/2" diameter	Q-1	71	.225	L.F.	9.15	7.70		16.85	23
4120	2" diameter		67	.239		9.40	8.15		17.55	24
4140	3" diameter		64	.250		13.35	8.55		21.90	29
4160	4" diameter	▼	58	.276		16.95	9.45		26.40	34

22 13 16.30 Pipe Fittings, Cast Iron

		Crew	Daily Output	Labor-Hours	Unit	Material	2014 Bare Costs Labor	2014 Bare Costs Equipment	Total	Total Incl O&P
0010	**PIPE FITTINGS, CAST IRON**, Soil									
0040	Hub and spigot, service weight, lead & oakum joints									
0080	1/4 bend, 2"	Q-1	16	1	Ea.	19.25	34		53.25	77.50
0120	3"		14	1.143		25.50	39		64.50	92.50
0140	4"		13	1.231		40	42		82	114
0340	1/8 bend, 2"		16	1		13.65	34		47.65	71.50
0350	3"		14	1.143		21.50	39		60.50	88
0360	4"		13	1.231		31.50	42		73.50	104
0500	Sanitary tee, 2"		10	1.600		26.50	54.50		81	120
0540	3"		9	1.778		43.50	61		104.50	148
0620	4"	▼	8	2	▼	53	68.50		121.50	171
5990	No hub									
6000	Cplg. & labor required at joints not incl. in fitting									
6010	price. Add 1 coupling per joint for installed price									
6020	1/4 Bend, 1-1/2"				Ea.	9.85			9.85	10.85
6060	2"					10.70			10.70	11.80
6080	3"					15			15	16.50
6120	4"					22			22	24.50
6184	1/4 Bend, long sweep, 1-1/2"	▼			▼	24.50			24.50	27

22 13 Facility Sanitary Sewerage

22 13 16 – Sanitary Waste and Vent Piping

22 13 16.30 Pipe Fittings, Cast Iron		Crew	Daily Output	Labor-Hours	Unit	Material	2014 Bare Costs Labor	Equipment	Total	Total Incl O&P
6186	2"				Ea.	23.50			23.50	26
6188	3"					28.50			28.50	31.50
6189	4"					45			45	49.50
6190	5"					87.50			87.50	96.50
6191	6"					99.50			99.50	110
6192	8"					269			269	296
6193	10"					550			550	605
6200	1/8 Bend, 1-1/2"					8.35			8.35	9.15
6210	2"					9.25			9.25	10.15
6212	3"					12.40			12.40	13.65
6214	4"					16.25			16.25	17.85
6380	Sanitary Tee, tapped, 1-1/2"					19.60			19.60	21.50
6382	2" x 1-1/2"					17.35			17.35	19.05
6384	2"					18.55			18.55	20.50
6386	3" x 2"					27.50			27.50	30.50
6388	3"					47.50			47.50	52.50
6390	4" x 1-1/2"					24.50			24.50	27
6392	4" x 2"					28			28	30.50
6393	4"					28			28	30.50
6394	6" x 1-1/2"					64			64	70.50
6396	6" x 2"					65			65	71.50
6459	Sanitary Tee, 1-1/2"					13.85			13.85	15.25
6460	2"					14.75			14.75	16.25
6470	3"					18.25			18.25	20
6472	4"					34.50			34.50	38
8000	Coupling, standard (by CISPI Mfrs.)									
8020	1-1/2"	Q-1	48	.333	Ea.	13.95	11.40		25.35	34
8040	2"		44	.364		15.25	12.45		27.70	37.50
8080	3"		38	.421		17.10	14.40		31.50	43
8120	4"		33	.485		20	16.60		36.60	49.50

22 13 16.50 Shower Drains

		Crew	Daily Output	Labor-Hours	Unit	Material	Labor	Equipment	Total	Total Incl O&P
0010	**SHOWER DRAINS**									
2780	Shower, with strainer, uniform diam. trap, bronze top									
2800	2" and 3" pipe size	Q-1	8	2	Ea.	395	68.50		463.50	550
2820	4" pipe size	"	7	2.286		435	78		513	605
2840	For galvanized body, add					175			175	193

22 13 16.60 Traps

		Crew	Daily Output	Labor-Hours	Unit	Material	Labor	Equipment	Total	Total Incl O&P
0010	**TRAPS**									
0030	Cast iron, service weight									
0050	Running P trap, without vent									
1100	2"	Q-1	16	1	Ea.	164	34		198	237
1150	4"	"	13	1.231		164	42		206	250
1160	6"	Q-2	17	1.412		605	46.50		651.50	740
3000	P trap, B&S, 2" pipe size	Q-1	16	1		32.50	34		66.50	92.50
3040	3" pipe size	"	14	1.143		49	39		88	118
4700	Copper, drainage, drum trap									
4840	3" x 6" swivel, 1-1/2" pipe size	1 Plum	16	.500	Ea.	455	19		474	530
5100	P trap, standard pattern									
5200	1-1/4" pipe size	1 Plum	18	.444	Ea.	211	16.90		227.90	260
5240	1-1/2" pipe size		17	.471		204	17.90		221.90	255
5260	2" pipe size		15	.533		315	20.50		335.50	380
5280	3" pipe size		11	.727		760	27.50		787.50	880

22 13 16 – Sanitary Waste and Vent Piping

22 13 16.60 Traps

	Crew	Daily Output	Labor-Hours	Unit	Material	2014 Bare Costs Labor	Equipment	Total	Total Incl O&P
6710	ABS DWV P trap, solvent weld joint								
6720	1-1/2" pipe size	1 Plum	18	.444	Ea.	12.65	16.90		29.55	42
6722	2" pipe size		17	.471		19.80	17.90		37.70	51.50
6724	3" pipe size		15	.533		78	20.50		98.50	120
6726	4" pipe size		14	.571		161	21.50		182.50	213
6732	PVC DWV P trap, solvent weld joint								
6733	1-1/2" pipe size	1 Plum	18	.444	Ea.	11.95	16.90		28.85	41
6734	2" pipe size		17	.471		16.15	17.90		34.05	47.50
6735	3" pipe size		15	.533		54.50	20.50		75	93.50
6736	4" pipe size		14	.571		125	21.50		146.50	173
6860	PVC DWV hub x hub, basin trap, 1-1/4" pipe size		18	.444		14.60	16.90		31.50	44
6870	Sink P trap, 1-1/2" pipe size		18	.444		12.25	16.90		29.15	41.50
6880	Tubular S trap, 1-1/2" pipe size		17	.471		22.50	17.90		40.40	54.50
6890	PVC sch. 40 DWV, drum trap								
6900	1-1/2" pipe size	1 Plum	16	.500	Ea.	49.50	19		68.50	86
6910	P trap, 1-1/2" pipe size		18	.444		12.25	16.90		29.15	41.50
6920	2" pipe size		17	.471		16.45	17.90		34.35	47.50
6930	3" pipe size		15	.533		35.50	20.50		56	72.50
6940	4" pipe size		14	.571		128	21.50		149.50	176
6950	P trap w/clean out, 1-1/2" pipe size		18	.444		20	16.90		36.90	50
6960	2" pipe size		17	.471		34	17.90		51.90	67

22 13 16.80 Vent Flashing and Caps

	Crew	Daily Output	Labor-Hours	Unit	Material	2014 Bare Costs Labor	Equipment	Total	Total Incl O&P
0010	**VENT FLASHING AND CAPS**								
0120	Vent caps								
0140	Cast iron								
0160	1-1/4" - 1-1/2" pipe	1 Plum	23	.348	Ea.	34	13.20		47.20	59.50
0170	2" - 2-1/8" pipe		22	.364		39.50	13.80		53.30	66.50
0180	2-1/2" - 3-5/8" pipe		21	.381		45	14.50		59.50	73.50
0190	4" - 4-1/8" pipe		19	.421		55	16		71	87
0200	5" - 6" pipe		17	.471		83.50	17.90		101.40	122
0300	PVC								
0320	1-1/4" - 1-1/2" pipe	1 Plum	24	.333	Ea.	9.20	12.65		21.85	31
0330	2" - 2-1/8" pipe	"	23	.348	"	9.30	13.20		22.50	32
0900	Vent flashing								
1350	Copper with neoprene ring								
1400	1-1/4" pipe	1 Plum	20	.400	Ea.	20.50	15.20		35.70	47.50
1430	1-1/2" pipe		20	.400		20.50	15.20		35.70	47.50
1440	2" pipe		18	.444		21.50	16.90		38.40	51.50
1450	3" pipe		17	.471		25.50	17.90		43.40	57.50
1460	4" pipe		16	.500		28	19		47	62
2980	Neoprene, one piece								
3000	1-1/4" pipe	1 Plum	24	.333	Ea.	7.45	12.65		20.10	29
3030	1-1/2" pipe		24	.333		7.50	12.65		20.15	29.50
3040	2" pipe		23	.348		7.50	13.20		20.70	30.50
3050	3" pipe		21	.381		8.65	14.50		23.15	33.50
3060	4" pipe		20	.400		12.85	15.20		28.05	39

22 13 19 – Sanitary Waste Piping Specialties

22 13 19.13 Sanitary Drains

	Crew	Daily Output	Labor-Hours	Unit	Material	2014 Bare Costs Labor	Equipment	Total	Total Incl O&P
0010	**SANITARY DRAINS**								
2000	Floor, medium duty, C.I., deep flange, 7" diam. top								
2040	2" and 3" pipe size	Q-1	12	1.333	Ea.	186	45.50		231.50	280
2080	For galvanized body, add					89.50			89.50	98.50

22 13 Facility Sanitary Sewerage

22 13 19 – Sanitary Waste Piping Specialties

22 13 19.13 Sanitary Drains	Crew	Daily Output	Labor-Hours	Unit	Material	2014 Bare Costs Labor	Equipment	Total	Total Incl O&P
2120	With polished bronze top				Ea.	291			291	320

22 14 Facility Storm Drainage

22 14 26 – Facility Storm Drains

22 14 26.13 Roof Drains

0010	ROOF DRAINS									
3860	Roof, flat metal deck, C.I. body, 12" C.I. dome								
3890	3" pipe size	Q-1	14	1.143	Ea.	365	39		404	465

22 14 29 – Sump Pumps

22 14 29.16 Submersible Sump Pumps

0010	SUBMERSIBLE SUMP PUMPS									
7000	Sump pump, automatic								
7100	Plastic, 1-1/4" discharge, 1/4 HP	1 Plum	6	1.333	Ea.	134	50.50		184.50	231
7500	Cast iron, 1-1/4" discharge, 1/4 HP	"	6	1.333	"	189	50.50		239.50	292

22 31 Domestic Water Softeners

22 31 13 – Residential Domestic Water Softeners

22 31 13.10 Residential Water Softeners

0010	RESIDENTIAL WATER SOFTENERS									
7350	Water softener, automatic, to 30 grains per gallon	2 Plum	5	3.200	Ea.	400	122		522	640
7400	To 100 grains per gallon	"	4	4	"	650	152		802	965

22 33 Electric Domestic Water Heaters

22 33 30 – Residential, Electric Domestic Water Heaters

22 33 30.13 Residential, Small-Capacity Elec. Water Heaters

0010	RESIDENTIAL, SMALL-CAPACITY ELECTRIC DOMESTIC WATER HEATERS									
1000	Residential, electric, glass lined tank, 5 yr., 10 gal., single element	1 Plum	2.30	3.478	Ea.	330	132		462	580
1060	30 gallon, double element		2.20	3.636		475	138		613	755
1080	40 gallon, double element		2	4		800	152		952	1,125
1100	52 gallon, double element		2	4		895	152		1,047	1,225
1120	66 gallon, double element		1.80	4.444		1,200	169		1,369	1,600
1140	80 gallon, double element		1.60	5		1,350	190		1,540	1,800

22 34 Fuel-Fired Domestic Water Heaters

22 34 13 – Instantaneous, Tankless, Gas Domestic Water Heaters

22 34 13.10 Instantaneous, Tankless, Gas Water Heaters

0010	INSTANTANEOUS, TANKLESS, GAS WATER HEATERS										
9410	Natural gas/propane, 3.2 GPM	G	1 Plum	2	4	Ea.	365	152		517	650
9420	6.4 GPM	G		1.90	4.211		745	160		905	1,075
9430	8.4 GPM	G		1.80	4.444		890	169		1,059	1,250
9440	9.5 GPM	G		1.60	5		1,150	190		1,340	1,575

22 34 Fuel-Fired Domestic Water Heaters

22 34 30 – Residential Gas Domestic Water Heaters

22 34 30.13 Residential, Atmos, Gas Domestic Wtr Heaters	Crew	Daily Output	Labor-Hours	Unit	Material	2014 Bare Costs Labor	Equipment	Total	Total Incl O&P
0010 **RESIDENTIAL, ATMOSPHERIC, GAS DOMESTIC WATER HEATERS**									
2000 Gas fired, foam lined tank, 10 yr., vent not incl.									
2040 30 gallon	1 Plum	2	4	Ea.	895	152		1,047	1,225
2100 75 gallon	"	1.50	5.333	"	1,350	203		1,553	1,825

22 34 46 – Oil-Fired Domestic Water Heaters

22 34 46.10 Residential Oil-Fired Water Heaters

	Crew	Daily Output	Labor-Hours	Unit	Material	Labor	Equipment	Total	Total Incl O&P
0010 **RESIDENTIAL OIL-FIRED WATER HEATERS**									
3000 Oil fired, glass lined tank, 5 yr., vent not included, 30 gallon	1 Plum	2	4	Ea.	1,175	152		1,327	1,525
3040 50 gallon	"	1.80	4.444	"	1,375	169		1,544	1,800

22 41 Residential Plumbing Fixtures

22 41 13 – Residential Water Closets, Urinals, and Bidets

22 41 13.40 Water Closets

	Crew	Daily Output	Labor-Hours	Unit	Material	Labor	Equipment	Total	Total Incl O&P
0010 **WATER CLOSETS**									
0150 Tank type, vitreous china, incl. seat, supply pipe w/stop, 1.6 gpf or noted									
0200 Wall hung									
0400 Two piece, close coupled	Q-1	5.30	3.019	Ea.	630	103		733	860
0960 For rough-in, supply, waste, vent and carrier	"	2.73	5.861	"	810	200		1,010	1,225
0999 Floor mounted									
1020 One piece, low profile	Q-1	5.30	3.019	Ea.	1,100	103		1,203	1,375
1100 Two piece, close coupled		5.30	3.019		233	103		336	425
1102 Economy		5.30	3.019		130	103		233	315
1110 Two piece, close coupled, dual flush		5.30	3.019		299	103		402	500
1140 Two piece, close coupled, 1.28 gpf, ADA G		5.30	3.019		305	103		408	505
1960 For color, add					30%				
1980 For rough-in, supply, waste and vent	Q-1	3.05	5.246	Ea.	330	179		509	660

22 41 16 – Residential Lavatories and Sinks

22 41 16.10 Lavatories

	Crew	Daily Output	Labor-Hours	Unit	Material	Labor	Equipment	Total	Total Incl O&P
0010 **LAVATORIES**, With trim, white unless noted otherwise									
0500 Vanity top, porcelain enamel on cast iron									
0600 20" x 18"	Q-1	6.40	2.500	Ea.	330	85.50		415.50	500
0640 33" x 19" oval		6.40	2.500		690	85.50		775.50	900
0720 19" round		6.40	2.500		425	85.50		510.50	610
0860 For color, add					25%				
1000 Cultured marble, 19" x 17", single bowl	Q-1	6.40	2.500	Ea.	175	85.50		260.50	335
1120 25" x 22", single bowl		6.40	2.500		215	85.50		300.50	375
1160 37" x 22", single bowl		6.40	2.500		245	85.50		330.50	410
1580 For color, same price									
1900 Stainless steel, self-rimming, 25" x 22", single bowl, ledge	Q-1	6.40	2.500	Ea.	365	85.50		450.50	545
1960 17" x 22", single bowl		6.40	2.500		355	85.50		440.50	530
2600 Steel, enameled, 20" x 17", single bowl		5.80	2.759		197	94.50		291.50	375
2900 Vitreous china, 20" x 16", single bowl		5.40	2.963		260	101		361	455
3200 22" x 13", single bowl		5.40	2.963		267	101		368	460
3580 Rough-in, supply, waste and vent for all above lavatories		2.30	6.957		415	238		653	850
4000 Wall hung									
4040 Porcelain enamel on cast iron, 16" x 14", single bowl	Q-1	8	2	Ea.	510	68.50		578.50	675
4180 20" x 18", single bowl	"	8	2	"	277	68.50		345.50	420
4580 For color, add					30%				
6000 Vitreous china, 18" x 15", single bowl with backsplash	Q-1	7	2.286	Ea.	231	78		309	385

22 41 16 – Residential Lavatories and Sinks

22 41 16.10 Lavatories

		Crew	Daily Output	Labor-Hours	Unit	Material	2014 Bare Costs Labor	2014 Bare Costs Equipment	Total	Total Incl O&P
6060	19" x 17", single bowl	Q-1	7	2.286	Ea.	190	78		268	340
6960	Rough-in, supply, waste and vent for above lavatories	↓	1.66	9.639	↓	470	330		800	1,075
7000	Pedestal type									
7600	Vitreous china, 27" x 21", white	Q-1	6.60	2.424	Ea.	690	83		773	895
7610	27" x 21", colored		6.60	2.424		865	83		948	1,075
7620	27" x 21", premium color		6.60	2.424		970	83		1,053	1,200
7660	26" x 20", white		6.60	2.424		770	83		853	980
7670	26" x 20", colored		6.60	2.424		770	83		853	980
7680	26" x 20", premium color		6.60	2.424		970	83		1,053	1,200
7700	24" x 20", white		6.60	2.424		395	83		478	570
7710	24" x 20", colored		6.60	2.424		480	83		563	660
7720	24" x 20", premium color		6.60	2.424		535	83		618	725
7760	21" x 18", white		6.60	2.424		284	83		367	450
7770	21" x 18", colored		6.60	2.424		300	83		383	465
7990	Rough-in, supply, waste and vent for pedestal lavatories	↓	1.66	9.639	↓	470	330		800	1,075

22 41 16.30 Sinks

		Crew	Daily Output	Labor-Hours	Unit	Material	2014 Bare Costs Labor	2014 Bare Costs Equipment	Total	Total Incl O&P
0010	**SINKS**, With faucets and drain									
2000	Kitchen, counter top style, P.E. on C.I., 24" x 21" single bowl	Q-1	5.60	2.857	Ea.	275	97.50		372.50	460
2100	31" x 22" single bowl		5.60	2.857		575	97.50		672.50	790
2200	32" x 21" double bowl		4.80	3.333		340	114		454	565
3000	Stainless steel, self rimming, 19" x 18" single bowl		5.60	2.857		590	97.50		687.50	810
3100	25" x 22" single bowl		5.60	2.857		660	97.50		757.50	885
3200	33" x 22" double bowl		4.80	3.333		960	114		1,074	1,250
3300	43" x 22" double bowl		4.80	3.333		1,125	114		1,239	1,425
4000	Steel, enameled, with ledge, 24" x 21" single bowl		5.60	2.857		505	97.50		602.50	715
4100	32" x 21" double bowl	↓	4.80	3.333		495	114		609	735
4960	For color sinks except stainless steel, add					10%				
4980	For rough-in, supply, waste and vent, counter top sinks	Q-1	2.14	7.477	↓	460	256		716	925
5000	Kitchen, raised deck, P.E. on C.I.									
5100	32" x 21", dual level, double bowl	Q-1	2.60	6.154	Ea.	410	210		620	795
5790	For rough-in, supply, waste & vent, sinks	"	1.85	8.649	"	460	296		756	995

22 41 19 – Residential Bathtubs

22 41 19.10 Baths

		Crew	Daily Output	Labor-Hours	Unit	Material	2014 Bare Costs Labor	2014 Bare Costs Equipment	Total	Total Incl O&P
0010	**BATHS** R224000-40									
0100	Tubs, recessed porcelain enamel on cast iron, with trim									
0180	48" x 42"	Q-1	4	4	Ea.	2,625	137		2,762	3,125
0220	72" x 36"	"	3	5.333	"	2,725	182		2,907	3,300
0300	Mat bottom									
0380	5' long	Q-1	4.40	3.636	Ea.	1,100	124		1,224	1,425
0480	Above floor drain, 5' long		4	4		785	137		922	1,100
0560	Corner 48" x 44"		4.40	3.636		2,625	124		2,749	3,100
2000	Enameled formed steel, 4'-6" long	↓	5.80	2.759	↓	495	94.50		589.50	700
4600	Module tub & showerwall surround, molded fiberglass									
4610	5' long x 34" wide x 76" high	Q-1	4	4	Ea.	815	137		952	1,125
9600	Rough-in, supply, waste and vent, for all above tubs, add	"	2.07	7.729	"	485	264		749	970

22 41 23 – Residential Showers

22 41 23.20 Showers

		Crew	Daily Output	Labor-Hours	Unit	Material	2014 Bare Costs Labor	2014 Bare Costs Equipment	Total	Total Incl O&P
0010	**SHOWERS**									
1500	Stall, with drain only. Add for valve and door/curtain									
1520	32" square	Q-1	5	3.200	Ea.	1,175	109		1,284	1,450
1530	36" square	↓	4.80	3.333	↓	2,925	114		3,039	3,400

22 41 Residential Plumbing Fixtures

22 41 23 – Residential Showers

22 41 23.20 Showers

		Crew	Daily Output	Labor-Hours	Unit	Material	2014 Bare Costs Labor	Equipment	Total	Total Incl O&P
1540	Terrazzo receptor, 32" square	Q-1	5	3.200	Ea.	1,350	109		1,459	1,650
1560	36" square		4.80	3.333		1,475	114		1,589	1,825
1580	36" corner angle		4.80	3.333		1,725	114		1,839	2,100
3000	Fiberglass, one piece, with 3 walls, 32" x 32" square		5.50	2.909		490	99.50		589.50	705
3100	36" x 36" square		5.50	2.909		505	99.50		604.50	720
4200	Rough-in, supply, waste and vent for above showers		2.05	7.805		540	267		807	1,025

22 41 36 – Residential Laundry Trays

22 41 36.10 Laundry Sinks

		Crew	Daily Output	Labor-Hours	Unit	Material	2014 Bare Costs Labor	Equipment	Total	Total Incl O&P
0010	**LAUNDRY SINKS**, With trim									
0020	Porcelain enamel on cast iron, black iron frame									
0050	24" x 21", single compartment	Q-1	6	2.667	Ea.	580	91		671	785
0100	26" x 21", single compartment	"	6	2.667	"	610	91		701	820
3000	Plastic, on wall hanger or legs									
3020	18" x 23", single compartment	Q-1	6.50	2.462	Ea.	135	84		219	288
3100	20" x 24", single compartment		6.50	2.462		154	84		238	310
3200	36" x 23", double compartment		5.50	2.909		185	99.50		284.50	365
3300	40" x 24", double compartment		5.50	2.909		278	99.50		377.50	470
5000	Stainless steel, counter top, 22" x 17" single compartment		6	2.667		64	91		155	221
5200	33" x 22", double compartment		5	3.200		79	109		188	268
9600	Rough-in, supply, waste and vent, for all laundry sinks		2.14	7.477		460	256		716	925

22 41 39 – Residential Faucets, Supplies and Trim

22 41 39.10 Faucets and Fittings

		Crew	Daily Output	Labor-Hours	Unit	Material	2014 Bare Costs Labor	Equipment	Total	Total Incl O&P
0010	**FAUCETS AND FITTINGS**									
0150	Bath, faucets, diverter spout combination, sweat	1 Plum	8	1	Ea.	86.50	38		124.50	158
0200	For integral stops, IPS unions, add					109			109	120
0420	Bath, press-bal mix valve w/diverter, spout, shower head, arm/flange	1 Plum	8	1		168	38		206	248
0500	Drain, central lift, 1-1/2" IPS male		20	.400		71	15.20		86.20	104
0600	Trip lever, 1-1/2" IPS male		20	.400		45	15.20		60.20	74.50
1000	Kitchen sink faucets, top mount, cast spout		10	.800		61.50	30.50		92	118
1100	For spray, add		24	.333		16.15	12.65		28.80	39
1300	Single control lever handle									
1310	With pull out spray									
1320	Polished chrome	1 Plum	10	.800	Ea.	196	30.50		226.50	265
2000	Laundry faucets, shelf type, IPS or copper unions		12	.667		49.50	25.50		75	96.50
2100	Lavatory faucet, centerset, without drain		10	.800		44.50	30.50		75	99
2120	With pop-up drain		6.66	1.201		62.50	45.50		108	144
2210	Porcelain cross handles and pop-up drain									
2220	Polished chrome	1 Plum	6.66	1.201	Ea.	189	45.50		234.50	284
2230	Polished brass	"	6.66	1.201	"	284	45.50		329.50	385
2260	Single lever handle and pop-up drain									
2280	Satin nickel	1 Plum	6.66	1.201	Ea.	277	45.50		322.50	380
2290	Polished chrome		6.66	1.201		198	45.50		243.50	294
2800	Self-closing, center set		10	.800		131	30.50		161.50	194
4000	Shower by-pass valve with union		18	.444		68.50	16.90		85.40	103
4200	Shower thermostatic mixing valve, concealed, with shower head trim kit		8	1		330	38		368	425
4220	Shower pressure balancing mixing valve,									
4230	With shower head, arm, flange and diverter tub spout									
4240	Chrome	1 Plum	6.14	1.303	Ea.	350	49.50		399.50	465
4250	Satin nickel		6.14	1.303		475	49.50		524.50	600
4260	Polished graphite		6.14	1.303		475	49.50		524.50	600
5000	Sillcock, compact, brass, IPS or copper to hose		24	.333		9.70	12.65		22.35	31.50

22 41 Residential Plumbing Fixtures

22 41 39 – Residential Faucets, Supplies and Trim

22 41 39.70 Washer/Dryer Accessories

		Daily Output	Labor-Hours	Unit	Material	2014 Bare Costs Labor	2014 Bare Costs Equipment	Total	Total Incl O&P
		Crew							
0010	**WASHER/DRYER ACCESSORIES**								
1020	Valves ball type single lever								
1030	1/2" diam., IPS	1 Plum	21	.381	Ea.	54.50	14.50		69	84
1040	1/2" diam., solder	"	21	.381	"	54.50	14.50		69	84
1050	Recessed box, 16 ga., two hose valves and drain								
1060	1/2" size, 1-1/2" drain	1 Plum	18	.444	Ea.	116	16.90		132.90	156
1070	1/2" size, 2" drain	"	17	.471	"	108	17.90		125.90	149
1080	With grounding electric receptacle								
1090	1/2" size, 1-1/2" drain	1 Plum	18	.444	Ea.	127	16.90		143.90	168
1100	1/2" size, 2" drain	"	17	.471	"	138	17.90		155.90	181
1110	With grounding and dryer receptacle								
1120	1/2" size, 1-1/2" drain	1 Plum	18	.444	Ea.	157	16.90		173.90	201
1130	1/2" size, 2" drain	"	17	.471	"	159	17.90		176.90	205
1140	Recessed box 16 ga., ball valves with single lever and drain								
1150	1/2" size, 1-1/2" drain	1 Plum	19	.421	Ea.	219	16		235	268
1160	1/2" size, 2" drain	"	18	.444	"	197	16.90		213.90	245
1170	With grounding electric receptacle								
1180	1/2" size, 1-1/2" drain	1 Plum	19	.421	Ea.	190	16		206	236
1190	1/2" size, 2" drain	"	18	.444	"	211	16.90		227.90	260
1200	With grounding and dryer receptacles								
1210	1/2" size, 1-1/2" drain	1 Plum	19	.421	Ea.	208	16		224	255
1220	1/2" size, 2" drain	"	18	.444	"	230	16.90		246.90	282
1300	Recessed box, 20 ga., two hose valves and drain (economy type)								
1310	1/2" size, 1-1/2" drain	1 Plum	19	.421	Ea.	90.50	16		106.50	126
1320	1/2" size, 2" drain		18	.444		86	16.90		102.90	123
1330	Box with drain only		24	.333		52.50	12.65		65.15	78.50
1340	1/2" size, 1-1/2" ABS/PVC drain		19	.421		100	16		116	137
1350	1/2" size, 2" ABS/PVC drain		18	.444		108	16.90		124.90	146
1352	Box with drain and 15 A receptacle		24	.333		90.50	12.65		103.15	121
1360	1/2" size, 2" drain ABS/PVC, 15 A receptacle		24	.333		127	12.65		139.65	161
1400	Wall mounted								
1410	1/2" size, 1-1/2" plastic drain	1 Plum	19	.421	Ea.	24.50	16		40.50	53.50
1420	1/2" size, 2" plastic drain	"	18	.444	"	21	16.90		37.90	51
1500	Dryer vent kit								
1510	8' flex duct, clamps and outside hood	1 Plum	20	.400	Ea.	15.30	15.20		30.50	42
1980	Rough-in, supply, waste, and vent for washer boxes		3.46	2.310		520	88		608	715
9605	Washing machine valve assembly, hot & cold water supply, recessed		8	1		70	38		108	140
9610	Washing machine valve assembly, hot & cold water supply, mounted		8	1		54.50	38		92.50	123

22 42 Commercial Plumbing Fixtures

22 42 13 – Commercial Water Closets, Urinals, and Bidets

22 42 13.40 Water Closets

		Daily Output	Labor-Hours	Unit	Material	2014 Bare Costs Labor	2014 Bare Costs Equipment	Total	Total Incl O&P
		Crew							
0010	**WATER CLOSETS**								
3000	Bowl only, with flush valve, seat, 1.6 gpf unless noted								
3100	Wall hung	Q-1	5.80	2.759	Ea.	755	94.50		849.50	985
3200	For rough-in, supply, waste and vent, single WC		2.56	6.250		890	214		1,104	1,325
3300	Floor mounted		5.80	2.759		355	94.50		449.50	545
3370	For rough-in, supply, waste and vent, single WC		2.84	5.634		410	193		603	775
3390	Floor mounted children's size, 10-3/4" high								
3392	With automatic flush sensor, 1.6 gpf	Q-1	6.20	2.581	Ea.	610	88.50		698.50	815

22 42 Commercial Plumbing Fixtures

22 42 13 – Commercial Water Closets, Urinals, and Bidets

22 42 13.40 Water Closets		Crew	Daily Output	Labor-Hours	Unit	Material	2014 Bare Costs Labor	Equipment	Total	Total Incl O&P
3396	With automatic flush sensor, 1.28 gpf	Q-1	6.20	2.581	Ea.	610	88.50		698.50	815
3400	For rough-in, supply, waste and vent, single WC	↓	2.84	5.634	↓	410	193		603	775

22 42 16 – Commercial Lavatories and Sinks

22 42 16.14 Lavatories

0010	**LAVATORIES**, With trim, white unless noted otherwise									
0020	Commercial lavatories same as residential. See Section 22 41 16.10									

22 42 16.40 Service Sinks

		Crew	Daily Output	Labor-Hours	Unit	Material	Labor	Equipment	Total	Total Incl O&P
0010	**SERVICE SINKS**									
6650	Service, floor, corner, P.E. on C.I., 28" x 28"	Q-1	4.40	3.636	Ea.	990	124		1,114	1,300
6750	Vinyl coated rim guard, add					67.50			67.50	74
6760	Mop sink, molded stone, 24" x 36"	1 Plum	3.33	2.402		273	91.50		364.50	450
6770	Mop sink, molded stone, 24" x 36", w/rim 3 sides	"	3.33	2.402		278	91.50		369.50	455
6790	For rough-in, supply, waste & vent, floor service sinks	Q-1	1.64	9.756	↓	1,475	335		1,810	2,175

22 42 39 – Commercial Faucets, Supplies, and Trim

22 42 39.10 Faucets and Fittings

		Crew	Daily Output	Labor-Hours	Unit	Material	Labor	Equipment	Total	Total Incl O&P
0010	**FAUCETS AND FITTINGS**									
2790	Faucets for lavatories									
2800	Self-closing, center set	1 Plum	10	.800	Ea.	131	30.50		161.50	194
2810	Automatic sensor and operator, with faucet head		6.15	1.301		450	49.50		499.50	575
3000	Service sink faucet, cast spout, pail hook, hose end	↓	14	.571	↓	80	21.50		101.50	124

22 42 39.30 Carriers and Supports

		Crew	Daily Output	Labor-Hours	Unit	Material	Labor	Equipment	Total	Total Incl O&P
0010	**CARRIERS AND SUPPORTS**, For plumbing fixtures									
0600	Plate type with studs, top back plate	1 Plum	7	1.143	Ea.	83.50	43.50		127	163
3000	Lavatory, concealed arm									
3050	Floor mounted, single									
3100	High back fixture	1 Plum	6	1.333	Ea.	465	50.50		515.50	595
3200	Flat slab fixture	"	6	1.333	"	400	50.50		450.50	525
8200	Water closet, residential									
8220	Vertical centerline, floor mount									
8240	Single, 3" caulk, 2" or 3" vent	1 Plum	6	1.333	Ea.	535	50.50		585.50	670
8260	4" caulk, 2" or 4" vent	"	6	1.333	"	690	50.50		740.50	840

22 51 Swimming Pool Plumbing Systems

22 51 19 – Swimming Pool Water Treatment Equipment

22 51 19.50 Swimming Pool Filtration Equipment

		Crew	Daily Output	Labor-Hours	Unit	Material	Labor	Equipment	Total	Total Incl O&P
0010	**SWIMMING POOL FILTRATION EQUIPMENT**									
0900	Filter system, sand or diatomite type, incl. pump, 6,000 gal./hr.	2 Plum	1.80	8.889	Total	1,925	340		2,265	2,675
1020	Add for chlorination system, 800 S.F. pool	"	3	5.333	Ea.	177	203		380	530

Division Notes

	CREW	DAILY OUTPUT	LABOR-HOURS	UNIT	BARE COSTS				TOTAL INCL O&P
					MAT.	LABOR	EQUIP.	TOTAL	

Estimating Tips

The labor adjustment factors listed in Subdivision 22 01 02.20 also apply to Division 23.

23 10 00 Facility Fuel Systems

- The prices in this subdivision for above- and below-ground storage tanks do not include foundations or hold-down slabs, unless noted. The estimator should refer to Divisions 3 and 31 for foundation system pricing. In addition to the foundations, required tank accessories, such as tank gauges, leak detection devices, and additional manholes and piping, must be added to the tank prices.

23 50 00 Central Heating Equipment

- When estimating the cost of an HVAC system, check to see who is responsible for providing and installing the temperature control system. It is possible to overlook controls, assuming that they would be included in the electrical estimate.

- When looking up a boiler, be careful on specified capacity. Some manufacturers rate their products on output while others use input.

- Include HVAC insulation for pipe, boiler, and duct (wrap and liner).

- Be careful when looking up mechanical items to get the correct pressure rating and connection type (thread, weld, flange).

23 70 00 Central HVAC Equipment

- Combination heating and cooling units are sized by the air conditioning requirements. (See Reference No. R236000-20 for preliminary sizing guide.)

- A ton of air conditioning is nominally 400 CFM.

- Rectangular duct is taken off by the linear foot for each size, but its cost is usually estimated by the pound. Remember that SMACNA standards now base duct on internal pressure.

- Prefabricated duct is estimated and purchased like pipe: straight sections and fittings.

- Note that cranes or other lifting equipment are not included on any lines in Division 23. For example, if a crane is required to lift a heavy piece of pipe into place high above a gym floor, or to put a rooftop unit on the roof of a four-story building, etc., it must be added. Due to the potential for extreme variation—from nothing additional required to a major crane or helicopter—we feel that including a nominal amount for "lifting contingency" would be useless and detract from the accuracy of the estimate. When using equipment rental cost data from RSMeans, do not forget to include the cost of the operator(s).

Reference Numbers

Reference numbers are shown in shaded boxes at the beginning of some major classifications. These numbers refer to related items in the Reference Section. The reference information may be an estimating procedure, an alternate pricing method, or technical information.

Note: Not all subdivisions listed here necessarily appear in this publication.

Note: **Trade Service**, *in part, has been used as a reference source for some of the material prices used in Division 23.*

23 05 Common Work Results for HVAC

23 05 05 – Selective HVAC Demolition

23 05 05.10 HVAC Demolition

		Crew	Daily Output	Labor-Hours	Unit	Material	2014 Bare Costs Labor	Equipment	Total	Total Incl O&P
0010	**HVAC DEMOLITION**									
0100	Air conditioner, split unit, 3 ton	Q-5	2	8	Ea.		278		278	460
0150	Package unit, 3 ton	Q-6	3	8	"		268		268	440
0260	Baseboard, hydronic fin tube, 1/2"	Q-5	117	.137	L.F.		4.75		4.75	7.85
0298	Boilers									
0300	Electric, up thru 148 kW	Q-19	2	12	Ea.		420		420	695
0310	150 thru 518 kW	"	1	24			840		840	1,375
0320	550 thru 2000 kW	Q-21	.40	80			2,875		2,875	4,750
0330	2070 kW and up	"	.30	106			3,825		3,825	6,325
0340	Gas and/or oil, up thru 150 MBH	Q-7	2.20	14.545			505		505	835
0350	160 thru 2000 MBH		.80	40			1,400		1,400	2,300
0360	2100 thru 4500 MBH		.50	64			2,225		2,225	3,675
0370	4600 thru 7000 MBH		.30	106			3,700		3,700	6,125
0390	12,200 thru 25,000 MBH		.12	266			9,275		9,275	15,300
1000	Ductwork, 4" high, 8" wide	1 Clab	200	.040	L.F.		.95		.95	1.60
1100	6" high, 8" wide		165	.048			1.15		1.15	1.94
1200	10" high, 12" wide		125	.064			1.52		1.52	2.56
1300	12"-14" high, 16"-18" wide		85	.094			2.24		2.24	3.77
1500	30" high, 36" wide		56	.143			3.40		3.40	5.70
2200	Furnace, electric	Q-20	2	10	Ea.		330		330	550
2300	Gas or oil, under 120 MBH	Q-9	4	4			130		130	217
2340	Over 120 MBH	"	3	5.333			173		173	289
2800	Heat pump, package unit, 3 ton	Q-5	2.40	6.667			232		232	380
2840	Split unit, 3 ton		2	8			278		278	460
2950	Tank, steel, oil, 275 gal., above ground		10	1.600			55.50		55.50	92
2960	Remove and reset		3	5.333			185		185	305
5090	Remove refrigerant from system	1 Stpi	40	.200	Lb.		7.70		7.70	12.75

23 07 HVAC Insulation

23 07 13 – Duct Insulation

23 07 13.10 Duct Thermal Insulation

			Crew	Daily Output	Labor-Hours	Unit	Material	2014 Bare Costs Labor	Equipment	Total	Total Incl O&P
0010	**DUCT THERMAL INSULATION**										
3000	Ductwork										
3020	Blanket type, fiberglass, flexible										
3140	FSK vapor barrier wrap, .75 lb. density										
3160	1" thick	G	Q-14	350	.046	S.F.	.19	1.39		1.58	2.57
3170	1-1/2" thick	G	"	320	.050	"	.23	1.52		1.75	2.83
3210	Vinyl jacket, same as FSK										

23 09 Instrumentation and Control for HVAC

23 09 53 – Pneumatic and Electric Control System for HVAC

23 09 53.10 Control Components

			Crew	Daily Output	Labor-Hours	Unit	Material	2014 Bare Costs Labor	Equipment	Total	Total Incl O&P
0010	**CONTROL COMPONENTS**										
5000	Thermostats										
5030	Manual		1 Stpi	8	1	Ea.	46.50	38.50		85	115
5040	1 set back, electric, timed	G		8	1		35.50	38.50		74	103
5050	2 set back, electric, timed	G		8	1		179	38.50		217.50	261

23 13 Facility Fuel-Storage Tanks

23 13 13 – Facility Underground Fuel-Oil, Storage Tanks

23 13 13.09 Single-Wall Steel Fuel-Oil Tanks

		Crew	Daily Output	Labor-Hours	Unit	Material	2014 Bare Costs Labor	Equipment	Total	Total Incl O&P
0010	**SINGLE-WALL STEEL FUEL-OIL TANKS**									
5000	Tanks, steel ugnd., sti-p3, not incl. hold-down bars									
5500	Excavation, pad, pumps and piping not included									
5510	Single wall, 500 gallon capacity, 7 ga. shell	Q-5	2.70	5.926	Ea.	2,050	206		2,256	2,600
5520	1,000 gallon capacity, 7 ga. shell	"	2.50	6.400		3,825	222		4,047	4,575
5530	2,000 gallon capacity, 1/4" thick shell	Q-7	4.60	6.957		6,200	242		6,442	7,225
5535	2,500 gallon capacity, 7 ga. shell	Q-5	3	5.333		6,850	185		7,035	7,825
5610	25,000 gallon capacity, 3/8" thick shell	Q-7	1.30	24.615		37,900	855		38,755	43,100
5630	40,000 gallon capacity, 3/8" thick shell		.90	35.556		42,000	1,225		43,225	48,300
5640	50,000 gallon capacity, 3/8" thick shell	↓	.80	40	↓	46,600	1,400		48,000	54,000

23 13 13.23 Glass-Fiber-Reinfcd-Plastic, Fuel-Oil, Storage

		Crew	Daily Output	Labor-Hours	Unit	Material	2014 Bare Costs Labor	Equipment	Total	Total Incl O&P
0010	**GLASS-FIBER-REINFCD-PLASTIC, UNDERGRND. FUEL-OIL, STORAGE**									
0210	Fiberglass, underground, single wall, U.L. listed, not including									
0220	manway or hold-down strap									
0230	1,000 gallon capacity	Q-5	2.46	6.504	Ea.	3,925	226		4,151	4,675
0240	2,000 gallon capacity	Q-7	4.57	7.002		5,675	243		5,918	6,625
0245	3,000 gallon capacity		3.90	8.205		6,800	285		7,085	7,950
0255	5,000 gallon capacity	↓	3.20	10		8,750	350		9,100	10,200
0500	For manway, fittings and hold-downs, add				↓	20%	15%			
2210	Fiberglass, underground, single wall, U.L. listed, including									
2220	hold-down straps, no manways									
2230	1,000 gallon capacity	Q-5	1.88	8.511	Ea.	4,350	296		4,646	5,275
2240	2,000 gallon capacity	Q-7	3.55	9.014	"	6,100	315		6,415	7,225

23 13 23 – Facility Aboveground Fuel-Oil, Storage Tanks

23 13 23.16 Steel

		Crew	Daily Output	Labor-Hours	Unit	Material	2014 Bare Costs Labor	Equipment	Total	Total Incl O&P
3001	**STEEL**, storage, above ground, including supports, coating									
3020	fittings, not including foundation, pumps or piping									
3040	Single wall, 275 gallon	Q-5	5	3.200	Ea.	490	111		601	725
3060	550 gallon	"	2.70	5.926		3,400	206		3,606	4,100
3080	1,000 gallon	Q-7	5	6.400		5,600	222		5,822	6,525
3320	Double wall, 500 gallon capacity	Q-5	2.40	6.667		2,625	232		2,857	3,250
3330	2000 gallon capacity	Q-7	4.15	7.711		9,975	268		10,243	11,400
3340	4000 gallon capacity		3.60	8.889		17,800	310		18,110	20,100
3350	6000 gallon capacity		2.40	13.333		21,000	465		21,465	23,900
3360	8000 gallon capacity		2	16		27,000	555		27,555	30,600
3370	10000 gallon capacity		1.80	17.778		30,200	620		30,820	34,200
3380	15000 gallon capacity		1.50	21.333		45,900	740		46,640	51,500
3390	20000 gallon capacity		1.30	24.615		52,500	855		53,355	59,000
3400	25000 gallon capacity		1.15	27.826		63,500	965		64,465	71,500
3410	30000 gallon capacity	↓	1	32	↓	69,500	1,100		70,600	78,500

23 13 23.26 Horizontal, Conc., Abvgrd Fuel-Oil, Stor. Tanks

		Crew	Daily Output	Labor-Hours	Unit	Material	2014 Bare Costs Labor	Equipment	Total	Total Incl O&P
0010	**HORIZONTAL, CONCRETE, ABOVEGROUND FUEL-OIL, STORAGE TANKS**									
0050	Concrete, storage, above ground, including pad & pump									
0100	500 gallon	F-3	2	20	Ea.	10,000	585	330	10,915	12,400
0200	1,000 gallon	"	2	20	"	14,000	585	330	14,915	16,800

23 21 Hydronic Piping and Pumps

23 21 20 – Hydronic HVAC Piping Specialties

23 21 20.46 Expansion Tanks

23 21 20.46 Expansion Tanks	Crew	Daily Output	Labor-Hours	Unit	Material	2014 Bare Costs Labor	Equipment	Total	Total Incl O&P
0010 **EXPANSION TANKS**									
1507 Underground fuel-oil storage tanks, see Section 23 13 13									
2000 Steel, liquid expansion, ASME, painted, 15 gallon capacity	Q-5	17	.941	Ea.	640	32.50		672.50	755
2040 30 gallon capacity		12	1.333		715	46.50		761.50	860
3000 Steel ASME expansion, rubber diaphragm, 19 gal. cap. accept.		12	1.333		2,425	46.50		2,471.50	2,750
3020 31 gallon capacity		8	2		2,700	69.50		2,769.50	3,100

23 21 23 – Hydronic Pumps

23 21 23.13 In-Line Centrifugal Hydronic Pumps

	Crew	Daily Output	Labor-Hours	Unit	Material	2014 Bare Costs Labor	Equipment	Total	Total Incl O&P
0010 **IN-LINE CENTRIFUGAL HYDRONIC PUMPS**									
0600 Bronze, sweat connections, 1/40 HP, in line									
0640 3/4" size	Q-1	16	1	Ea.	212	34		246	290
1000 Flange connection, 3/4" to 1-1/2" size									
1040 1/12 HP	Q-1	6	2.667	Ea.	545	91		636	750
1060 1/8 HP		6	2.667		940	91		1,031	1,175
2101 Pumps, circulating, 3/4" to 1-1/2" size, 1/3 HP		6	2.667		765	91		856	995

23 31 HVAC Ducts and Casings

23 31 13 – Metal Ducts

23 31 13.13 Rectangular Metal Ducts

	Crew	Daily Output	Labor-Hours	Unit	Material	2014 Bare Costs Labor	Equipment	Total	Total Incl O&P
0010 **RECTANGULAR METAL DUCTS**									
0020 Fabricated rectangular, includes fittings, joints, supports,									
0021 allowance for flexible connections and field sketches.									
0030 Does not include "as-built dwgs." or insulation.									
0031 NOTE: Fabrication and installation are combined									
0040 as LABOR cost. Approx. 25% fittings assumed.									
0042 Fabrication/Inst. is to commercial quality standards									
0043 (SMACNA or equiv.) for structure, sealing, leak testing, etc.									
0100 Aluminum, alloy 3003-H14, under 100 lb.	Q-10	75	.320	Lb.	3.66	10.80		14.46	22
0110 100 to 500 lb.		80	.300		2.38	10.10		12.48	19.45
0120 500 to 1,000 lb.		95	.253		2.25	8.50		10.75	16.70
0140 1,000 to 2,000 lb.		120	.200		2.16	6.75		8.91	13.65
0500 Galvanized steel, under 200 lb.		235	.102		.66	3.44		4.10	6.50
0520 200 to 500 lb.		245	.098		.62	3.30		3.92	6.20
0540 500 to 1,000 lb.		255	.094		.61	3.17		3.78	5.95

23 33 Air Duct Accessories

23 33 13 – Dampers

23 33 13.13 Volume-Control Dampers

	Crew	Daily Output	Labor-Hours	Unit	Material	2014 Bare Costs Labor	Equipment	Total	Total Incl O&P
0010 **VOLUME-CONTROL DAMPERS**									
6000 12" x 12"	1 Shee	21	.381	Ea.	29.50	13.75		43.25	55.50
8000 Multi-blade dampers, parallel blade									
8100 8" x 8"	1 Shee	24	.333	Ea.	82	12.05		94.05	110

23 33 13.16 Fire Dampers

	Crew	Daily Output	Labor-Hours	Unit	Material	2014 Bare Costs Labor	Equipment	Total	Total Incl O&P
0010 **FIRE DAMPERS**									
3000 Fire damper, curtain type, 1-1/2 hr. rated, vertical, 6" x 6"	1 Shee	24	.333	Ea.	24	12.05		36.05	46.50
3020 8" x 6"	"	22	.364	"	24	13.15		37.15	48.50

23 33 Air Duct Accessories

23 33 46 – Flexible Ducts

23 33 46.10 Flexible Air Ducts		Crew	Daily Output	Labor-Hours	Unit	Material	2014 Bare Costs Labor	Equipment	Total	Total Incl O&P
0010	**FLEXIBLE AIR DUCTS**									
1300	Flexible, coated fiberglass fabric on corr. resist. metal helix									
1400	pressure to 12" (WG) UL-181									
1500	Noninsulated, 3" diameter	Q-9	400	.040	L.F.	1.12	1.30		2.42	3.40
1540	5" diameter		320	.050		1.30	1.63		2.93	4.14
1561	Ductwork, flexible, non-insulated, 6" diameter		280	.057		1.50	1.86		3.36	4.75
1580	7" diameter		240	.067		1.53	2.17		3.70	5.30
1900	Insulated, 1" thick, PE jacket, 3" diameter **G**		380	.042		2.60	1.37		3.97	5.15
1910	4" diameter **G**		340	.047		2.60	1.53		4.13	5.40
1920	5" diameter **G**		300	.053		2.60	1.73		4.33	5.75
1940	6" diameter **G**		260	.062		2.94	2		4.94	6.55
1960	7" diameter **G**		220	.073		3.20	2.36		5.56	7.45
1980	8" diameter **G**		180	.089		3.49	2.89		6.38	8.65
2040	12" diameter **G**		100	.160		4.90	5.20		10.10	14.05

23 33 53 – Duct Liners

23 33 53.10 Duct Liner Board

		Crew	Daily Output	Labor-Hours	Unit	Material	Labor	Equipment	Total	Total Incl O&P
0010	**DUCT LINER BOARD**									
3490	Board type, fiberglass liner, 3 lb. density									
3940	Board type, non-fibrous foam									
3950	Temperature, bacteria and fungi resistant									
3960	1" thick **G**	Q-14	150	.107	S.F.	2.38	3.24		5.62	8.10
3970	1-1/2" thick **G**		130	.123		3.28	3.74		7.02	9.95
3980	2" thick **G**		120	.133		3.98	4.05		8.03	11.25

23 34 HVAC Fans

23 34 23 – HVAC Power Ventilators

23 34 23.10 HVAC Power Circulators and Ventilators

		Crew	Daily Output	Labor-Hours	Unit	Material	Labor	Equipment	Total	Total Incl O&P
0010	**HVAC POWER CIRCULATORS AND VENTILATORS**									
6650	Residential, bath exhaust, grille, back draft damper									
6660	50 CFM	Q-20	24	.833	Ea.	61	27.50		88.50	114
6670	110 CFM		22	.909		94.50	30		124.50	154
6900	Kitchen exhaust, grille, complete, 160 CFM		22	.909		104	30		134	164
6910	180 CFM		20	1		87	33		120	151
6920	270 CFM		18	1.111		164	37		201	242
6930	350 CFM		16	1.250		124	41.50		165.50	205
6940	Residential roof jacks and wall caps									
6944	Wall cap with back draft damper									
6946	3" & 4" diam. round duct	1 Shee	11	.727	Ea.	24.50	26.50		51	71
6948	6" diam. round duct	"	11	.727	"	61.50	26.50		88	112
6958	Roof jack with bird screen and back draft damper									
6960	3" & 4" diam. round duct	1 Shee	11	.727	Ea.	25	26.50		51.50	71.50
6962	3-1/4" x 10" rectangular duct	"	10	.800	"	46.50	29		75.50	99
8020	Attic, roof type									
8030	Aluminum dome, damper & curb									
8080	12" diameter, 1000 CFM (gravity)	1 Elec	10	.800	Ea.	545	28.50		573.50	645
8090	16" diameter, 1500 CFM (gravity)		9	.889		660	32		692	775
8100	20" diameter, 2500 CFM (gravity)		8	1		805	36		841	950
8160	Plastic, ABS dome									
8180	1050 CFM	1 Elec	14	.571	Ea.	160	20.50		180.50	210
8200	1600 CFM	"	12	.667	"	240	24		264	305

23 34 HVAC Fans

23 34 23 – HVAC Power Ventilators

23 34 23.10 HVAC Power Circulators and Ventilators	Crew	Daily Output	Labor-Hours	Unit	Material	2014 Bare Costs Labor	Equipment	Total	Total Incl O&P
8240	Attic, wall type, with shutter, one speed									
8250	12" diameter, 1000 CFM	1 Elec	14	.571	Ea.	385	20.50		405.50	460
8260	14" diameter, 1500 CFM		12	.667		420	24		444	500
8270	16" diameter, 2000 CFM		9	.889		475	32		507	570
8290	Whole house, wall type, with shutter, one speed									
8300	30" diameter, 4800 CFM	1 Elec	7	1.143	Ea.	1,025	41		1,066	1,200
8310	36" diameter, 7000 CFM		6	1.333		1,100	47.50		1,147.50	1,300
8320	42" diameter, 10,000 CFM		5	1.600		1,225	57		1,282	1,450
8330	48" diameter, 16,000 CFM		4	2		1,525	71.50		1,596.50	1,825
8340	For two speed, add					92.50			92.50	102
8350	Whole house, lay-down type, with shutter, one speed									
8360	30" diameter, 4500 CFM	1 Elec	8	1	Ea.	1,075	36		1,111	1,250
8370	36" diameter, 6500 CFM		7	1.143		1,150	41		1,191	1,350
8380	42" diameter, 9000 CFM		6	1.333		1,275	47.50		1,322.50	1,475
8390	48" diameter, 12,000 CFM		5	1.600		1,450	57		1,507	1,700
8440	For two speed, add					69.50			69.50	76.50
8450	For 12 hour timer switch, add	1 Elec	32	.250		69.50	8.95		78.45	91

23 37 Air Outlets and Inlets

23 37 13 – Diffusers, Registers, and Grilles

23 37 13.10 Diffusers

		Crew	Daily Output	Labor-Hours	Unit	Material	2014 Bare Costs Labor	Equipment	Total	Total Incl O&P
0010	**DIFFUSERS**, Aluminum, opposed blade damper unless noted									
0100	Ceiling, linear, also for sidewall									
0120	2" wide	1 Shee	32	.250	L.F.	16.20	9.05		25.25	33
0160	4" wide		26	.308	"	21.50	11.10		32.60	42
0500	Perforated, 24" x 24" lay-in panel size, 6" x 6"		16	.500	Ea.	151	18.05		169.05	196
0520	8" x 8"		15	.533		159	19.25		178.25	207
0530	9" x 9"		14	.571		161	20.50		181.50	212
0590	16" x 16"		11	.727		189	26.50		215.50	251
1000	Rectangular, 1 to 4 way blow, 6" x 6"		16	.500		50	18.05		68.05	85
1010	8" x 8"		15	.533		58	19.25		77.25	95.50
1014	9" x 9"		15	.533		66	19.25		85.25	105
1016	10" x 10"		15	.533		80	19.25		99.25	120
1020	12" x 6"		15	.533		71.50	19.25		90.75	111
1040	12" x 9"		14	.571		75.50	20.50		96	118
1060	12" x 12"		12	.667		84.50	24		108.50	133
1070	14" x 6"		13	.615		77.50	22		99.50	123
1074	14" x 14"		12	.667		128	24		152	180
1150	18" x 18"		9	.889		138	32		170	205
1170	24" x 12"		10	.800		163	29		192	228
1180	24" x 24"		7	1.143		270	41.50		311.50	365
1500	Round, butterfly damper, steel, diffuser size, 6" diameter		18	.444		9	16.05		25.05	37
1520	8" diameter		16	.500		9.55	18.05		27.60	40.50
2000	T bar mounting, 24" x 24" lay-in frame, 6" x 6"		16	.500		49	18.05		67.05	84
2020	8" x 8"		14	.571		51	20.50		71.50	91
2040	12" x 12"		12	.667		60.50	24		84.50	107
2060	16" x 16"		11	.727		81	26.50		107.50	133
2080	18" x 18"		10	.800		90	29		119	147
6000	For steel diffusers instead of aluminum, deduct					10%				

23 37 Air Outlets and Inlets

23 37 13 – Diffusers, Registers, and Grilles

23 37 13.30 Grilles

23 37 13.30 Grilles	Crew	Daily Output	Labor-Hours	Unit	Material	2014 Bare Costs Labor	Equipment	Total	Total Incl O&P
0010 **GRILLES**									
0020 Aluminum, unless noted otherwise									
1000 Air return, steel, 6" x 6"	1 Shee	26	.308	Ea.	18.70	11.10		29.80	39
1020 10" x 6"		24	.333		18.70	12.05		30.75	40.50
1080 16" x 8"		22	.364		26.50	13.15		39.65	51
1100 12" x 12"		22	.364		26.50	13.15		39.65	51
1120 24" x 12"		18	.444		36	16.05		52.05	66.50
1180 16" x 16"		22	.364		34	13.15		47.15	59.50

23 37 13.60 Registers

23 37 13.60 Registers	Crew	Daily Output	Labor-Hours	Unit	Material	2014 Bare Costs Labor	Equipment	Total	Total Incl O&P
0010 **REGISTERS**									
0980 Air supply									
3000 Baseboard, hand adj. damper, enameled steel									
3012 8" x 6"	1 Shee	26	.308	Ea.	4.85	11.10		15.95	24
3020 10" x 6"		24	.333		5.30	12.05		17.35	26
3040 12" x 5"		23	.348		5.60	12.55		18.15	27
3060 12" x 6"		23	.348		5.75	12.55		18.30	27.50
4000 Floor, toe operated damper, enameled steel									
4020 4" x 8"	1 Shee	32	.250	Ea.	9	9.05		18.05	25
4040 4" x 12"	"	26	.308	"	10.55	11.10		21.65	30
4300 Spiral pipe supply register									
4310 Aluminum, double deflection, w/damper extractor									
4320 4" x 12", for 6" thru 10" diameter duct	1 Shee	25	.320	Ea.	66	11.55		77.55	92
4330 4" x 18", for 6" thru 10" diameter duct		18	.444		82	16.05		98.05	117
4340 6" x 12", for 8" thru 12" diameter duct		19	.421		72	15.20		87.20	105
4350 6" x 18", for 8" thru 12" diameter duct		18	.444		93.50	16.05		109.55	130
4360 6" x 24", for 8" thru 12" diameter duct		16	.500		116	18.05		134.05	157
4370 6" x 30", for 8" thru 12" diameter duct		15	.533		147	19.25		166.25	194
4380 8" x 18", for 10" thru 14" diameter duct		18	.444		100	16.05		116.05	137
4390 8" x 24", for 10" thru 14" diameter duct		15	.533		125	19.25		144.25	169
4400 8" x 30", for 10" thru 14" diameter duct		14	.571		166	20.50		186.50	217
4410 10" x 24", for 12" thru 18" diameter duct		13	.615		137	22		159	188
4420 10" x 30", for 12" thru 18" diameter duct		12	.667		181	24		205	239
4430 10" x 36", for 12" thru 18" diameter duct		11	.727		225	26.50		251.50	291

23 41 Particulate Air Filtration

23 41 13 – Panel Air Filters

23 41 13.10 Panel Type Air Filters

23 41 13.10 Panel Type Air Filters	Crew	Daily Output	Labor-Hours	Unit	Material	2014 Bare Costs Labor	Equipment	Total	Total Incl O&P
0010 **PANEL TYPE AIR FILTERS**									
2950 Mechanical media filtration units									
3000 High efficiency type, with frame, non-supported [G]				MCFM	65			65	71.50
3100 Supported type [G]				"	60			60	66
5500 Throwaway glass or paper media type				Ea.	3.35			3.35	3.69

23 41 16 – Renewable-Media Air Filters

23 41 16.10 Disposable Media Air Filters

23 41 16.10 Disposable Media Air Filters	Crew	Daily Output	Labor-Hours	Unit	Material	2014 Bare Costs Labor	Equipment	Total	Total Incl O&P
0010 **DISPOSABLE MEDIA AIR FILTERS**									
5000 Renewable disposable roll				MCFM	19.35			19.35	21.50

23 41 Particulate Air Filtration

23 41 19 – Washable Air Filters

23 41 19.10 Permanent Air Filters		Crew	Daily Output	Labor-Hours	Unit	Material	2014 Bare Costs Labor	Equipment	Total	Total Incl O&P
0010	**PERMANENT AIR FILTERS**									
4500	Permanent washable	G			MCFM	20			20	22

23 41 23 – Extended Surface Filters

23 41 23.10 Expanded Surface Filters

		Crew	Daily Output	Labor-Hours	Unit	Material	Labor	Equipment	Total	Total Incl O&P
0010	**EXPANDED SURFACE FILTERS**									
4000	Medium efficiency, extended surface	G			MCFM	5.50			5.50	6.05

23 42 Gas-Phase Air Filtration

23 42 13 – Activated-Carbon Air Filtration

23 42 13.10 Charcoal Type Air Filtration

		Crew	Daily Output	Labor-Hours	Unit	Material	Labor	Equipment	Total	Total Incl O&P
0010	**CHARCOAL TYPE AIR FILTRATION**									
0050	Activated charcoal type, full flow				MCFM	600			600	660
0060	Full flow, impregnated media 12" deep					225			225	248
0070	HEPA filter & frame for field erection					350			350	385
0080	HEPA filter-diffuser, ceiling install.				↓	300			300	330

23 43 Electronic Air Cleaners

23 43 13 – Washable Electronic Air Cleaners

23 43 13.10 Electronic Air Cleaners

		Crew	Daily Output	Labor-Hours	Unit	Material	Labor	Equipment	Total	Total Incl O&P
0010	**ELECTRONIC AIR CLEANERS**									
2000	Electronic air cleaner, duct mounted									
2150	1000 CFM	1 Shee	4	2	Ea.	420	72		492	585
2200	1200 CFM		3.80	2.105		505	76		581	680
2250	1400 CFM	↓	3.60	2.222	↓	520	80		600	710

23 51 Breechings, Chimneys, and Stacks

23 51 23 – Gas Vents

23 51 23.10 Gas Chimney Vents

		Crew	Daily Output	Labor-Hours	Unit	Material	Labor	Equipment	Total	Total Incl O&P
0010	**GAS CHIMNEY VENTS**, Prefab metal, U.L. listed									
0020	Gas, double wall, galvanized steel									
0080	3" diameter	Q-9	72	.222	V.L.F.	5.55	7.20		12.75	18.15
0100	4" diameter	"	68	.235	"	7.20	7.65		14.85	20.50

23 52 Heating Boilers

23 52 13 – Electric Boilers

23 52 13.10 Electric Boilers, ASME

		Crew	Daily Output	Labor-Hours	Unit	Material	Labor	Equipment	Total	Total Incl O&P
0010	**ELECTRIC BOILERS, ASME**, Standard controls and trim									
1000	Steam, 6 KW, 20.5 MBH	Q-19	1.20	20	Ea.	3,950	700		4,650	5,500
1160	60 KW, 205 MBH		1	24		6,650	840		7,490	8,700
2000	Hot water, 7.5 KW, 25.6 MBH		1.30	18.462		4,975	650		5,625	6,550
2040	30 KW, 102 MBH		1.20	20		5,325	700		6,025	7,000
2060	45 KW, 164 MBH	↓	1.20	20	↓	5,425	700		6,125	7,100

23 52 Heating Boilers

23 52 23 – Cast-Iron Boilers

23 52 23.20 Gas-Fired Boilers

		Crew	Daily Output	Labor-Hours	Unit	Material	2014 Bare Costs Labor	Equipment	Total	Total Incl O&P
0010	**GAS-FIRED BOILERS**, Natural or propane, standard controls, packaged									
1000	Cast iron, with insulated jacket									
3000	Hot water, gross output, 80 MBH	Q-7	1.46	21.918	Ea.	2,150	760		2,910	3,625
3020	100 MBH	"	1.35	23.704		2,300	825		3,125	3,875
7000	For tankless water heater, add					10%				
7050	For additional zone valves up to 312 MBH add					188			188	207

23 52 23.30 Gas/Oil Fired Boilers

		Crew	Daily Output	Labor-Hours	Unit	Material	2014 Bare Costs Labor	Equipment	Total	Total Incl O&P
0010	**GAS/OIL FIRED BOILERS**, Combination with burners and controls, packaged									
1000	Cast iron with insulated jacket									
2000	Steam, gross output, 720 MBH	Q-7	.43	74.074	Ea.	14,400	2,575		16,975	20,100
2900	Hot water, gross output									
2910	200 MBH	Q-6	.62	39.024	Ea.	10,400	1,300		11,700	13,600
2920	300 MBH		.49	49.080		10,400	1,650		12,050	14,100
2930	400 MBH		.41	57.971		12,200	1,950		14,150	16,600
2940	500 MBH		.36	67.039		13,100	2,250		15,350	18,100
3000	584 MBH	Q-7	.44	72.072		14,500	2,500		17,000	20,100

23 52 23.40 Oil-Fired Boilers

		Crew	Daily Output	Labor-Hours	Unit	Material	2014 Bare Costs Labor	Equipment	Total	Total Incl O&P
0010	**OIL-FIRED BOILERS**, Standard controls, flame retention burner, packaged									
1000	Cast iron, with insulated flush jacket									
2000	Steam, gross output, 109 MBH	Q-7	1.20	26.667	Ea.	2,175	925		3,100	3,925
2060	207 MBH	"	.90	35.556	"	3,000	1,225		4,225	5,350
3000	Hot water, same price as steam									

23 52 26 – Steel Boilers

23 52 26.40 Oil-Fired Boilers

		Crew	Daily Output	Labor-Hours	Unit	Material	2014 Bare Costs Labor	Equipment	Total	Total Incl O&P
0010	**OIL-FIRED BOILERS**, Standard controls, flame retention burner									
5000	Steel, with insulated flush jacket									
7000	Hot water, gross output, 103 MBH	Q-6	1.60	15	Ea.	1,775	500		2,275	2,775
7020	122 MBH		1.45	16.506		1,875	550		2,425	2,975
7060	168 MBH		1.30	18.405		2,100	615		2,715	3,350
7080	225 MBH		1.22	19.704		2,575	660		3,235	3,925

23 52 28 – Swimming Pool Boilers

23 52 28.10 Swimming Pool Heaters

		Crew	Daily Output	Labor-Hours	Unit	Material	2014 Bare Costs Labor	Equipment	Total	Total Incl O&P
0010	**SWIMMING POOL HEATERS**, Not including wiring, external									
0020	piping, base or pad,									
0160	Gas fired, input, 155 MBH	Q-6	1.50	16	Ea.	1,900	535		2,435	2,975
0200	199 MBH		1	24		2,025	805		2,830	3,550
0280	500 MBH		.40	60		8,475	2,000		10,475	12,600
2000	Electric, 12 KW, 4,800 gallon pool	Q-19	3	8		2,075	281		2,356	2,725
2020	15 KW, 7,200 gallon pool		2.80	8.571		2,100	300		2,400	2,825
2040	24 KW, 9,600 gallon pool		2.40	10		2,425	350		2,775	3,250
2100	57 KW, 24,000 gallon pool		1.20	20		3,575	700		4,275	5,075

23 52 88 – Burners

23 52 88.10 Replacement Type Burners

		Crew	Daily Output	Labor-Hours	Unit	Material	2014 Bare Costs Labor	Equipment	Total	Total Incl O&P
0010	**REPLACEMENT TYPE BURNERS**									
0990	Residential, conversion, gas fired, LP or natural									
1000	Gun type, atmospheric input 50 to 225 MBH	Q-1	2.50	6.400	Ea.	720	219		939	1,150
1020	100 to 400 MBH	"	2	8		1,200	274		1,474	1,775
1025	Burner, gas, 100 – 400 MBH [G]					1,200			1,200	1,325
1040	300 to 1000 MBH	Q-1	1.70	9.412		3,625	320		3,945	4,500

23 54 Furnaces

23 54 13 – Electric-Resistance Furnaces

23 54 13.10 Electric Furnaces

		Crew	Daily Output	Labor-Hours	Unit	Material	2014 Bare Costs Labor	Equipment	Total	Total Incl O&P
0010	**ELECTRIC FURNACES**, Hot air, blowers, std. controls									
0011	not including gas, oil or flue piping									
1000	Electric, UL listed									
1100	34.1 MBH	Q-20	4.40	4.545	Ea.	560	151		711	865

23 54 16 – Fuel-Fired Furnaces

23 54 16.13 Gas-Fired Furnaces

		Crew	Daily Output	Labor-Hours	Unit	Material	Labor	Equipment	Total	Total Incl O&P
0010	**GAS-FIRED FURNACES**									
3000	Gas, AGA certified, upflow, direct drive models									
3020	45 MBH input	Q-9	4	4	Ea.	535	130		665	805
3040	60 MBH input		3.80	4.211		535	137		672	820
3060	75 MBH input		3.60	4.444		575	144		719	875
3100	100 MBH input		3.20	5		625	163		788	960
3120	125 MBH input		3	5.333		655	173		828	1,000
3130	150 MBH input		2.80	5.714		670	186		856	1,050
3140	200 MBH input		2.60	6.154		2,800	200		3,000	3,400
4000	For starter plenum, add		16	1		87.50	32.50		120	150

23 54 16.16 Oil-Fired Furnaces

		Crew	Daily Output	Labor-Hours	Unit	Material	Labor	Equipment	Total	Total Incl O&P
0010	**OIL-FIRED FURNACES**									
6000	Oil, UL listed, atomizing gun type burner									
6020	56 MBH output	Q-9	3.60	4.444	Ea.	1,550	144		1,694	1,950
6030	84 MBH output		3.50	4.571		1,850	149		1,999	2,300
6040	95 MBH output		3.40	4.706		1,875	153		2,028	2,325
6060	134 MBH output		3.20	5		2,175	163		2,338	2,675
6080	151 MBH output		3	5.333		2,250	173		2,423	2,775
6100	200 MBH input		2.60	6.154		2,450	200		2,650	3,025

23 54 16.21 Solid Fuel-Fired Furnaces

			Crew	Daily Output	Labor-Hours	Unit	Material	Labor	Equipment	Total	Total Incl O&P
0010	**SOLID FUEL-FIRED FURNACES**										
6020	Wood fired furnaces										
6030	Includes hot water coil, thermostat, and auto draft control										
6040	24" long firebox	G	Q-9	4	4	Ea.	4,300	130		4,430	4,950
6050	30" long firebox	G		3.60	4.444		5,025	144		5,169	5,775
6060	With fireplace glass doors	G		3.20	5		6,350	163		6,513	7,275
6200	Wood/oil fired furnaces, includes two thermostats										
6210	Includes hot water coil and auto draft control										
6240	24" long firebox	G	Q-9	3.40	4.706	Ea.	5,150	153		5,303	5,925
6250	30" long firebox	G		3	5.333		5,775	173		5,948	6,650
6260	With fireplace glass doors	G		2.80	5.714		7,075	186		7,261	8,075
6400	Wood/gas fired furnaces, includes two thermostats										
6410	Includes hot water coil and auto draft control										
6440	24" long firebox	G	Q-9	2.80	5.714	Ea.	5,925	186		6,111	6,825
6450	30" long firebox	G		2.40	6.667		6,625	217		6,842	7,650
6460	With fireplace glass doors	G		2	8		7,900	260		8,160	9,125
6600	Wood/oil/gas fired furnaces, optional accessories										
6610	Hot air plenum		Q-9	16	1	Ea.	108	32.50		140.50	173
6620	Safety heat dump			24	.667		94	21.50		115.50	139
6630	Auto air intake			18	.889		148	29		177	211
6640	Cold air return package			14	1.143		159	37		196	237
6650	Wood fork						51			51	56
6700	Wood fired outdoor furnace										
6740	24" long firebox	G	Q-9	3.80	4.211	Ea.	4,500	137		4,637	5,175
6760	Wood fired outdoor furnace, optional accessories										
6770	Chimney section, stainless steel, 6" ID x 3' lg.	G	Q-9	36	.444	Ea.	165	14.45		179.45	206

23 54 Furnaces

23 54 16 – Fuel-Fired Furnaces

23 54 16.21 Solid Fuel-Fired Furnaces

		Crew	Daily Output	Labor-Hours	Unit	Material	2014 Bare Costs Labor	Equipment	Total	Total Incl O&P
6780	Chimney cap, stainless steel **G**	Q-9	40	.400	Ea.	95	13		108	127
6800	Wood fired hot water furnace									
6820	Includes 200 gal. hot water storage, thermostat, and auto draft control									
6840	30" long firebox **G**	Q-9	2.10	7.619	Ea.	8,275	248		8,523	9,525
6850	Water to air heat exchanger									
6870	Includes mounting kit and blower relay									
6880	140 MBH, 18.75" W x 18.75" L	Q-9	7.50	2.133	Ea.	370	69.50		439.50	520
6890	200 MBH, 24" W x 24" L	"	7	2.286	"	525	74.50		599.50	705
6900	Water to water heat exchanger									
6940	100 MBH	Q-9	6.50	2.462	Ea.	370	80		450	545
6960	290 MBH	"	6	2.667	"	535	86.50		621.50	735
7000	Optional accessories									
7010	Large volume circulation pump, (2 Included)	Q-9	14	1.143	Ea.	242	37		279	330
7020	Air bleed fittings, (package)		24	.667		50.50	21.50		72	91.50
7030	Domestic water preheater		6	2.667		219	86.50		305.50	385
7040	Smoke pipe kit	↓	4	4	↓	88	130		218	315

23 54 24 – Furnace Components for Cooling

23 54 24.10 Furnace Components and Combinations

		Crew	Daily Output	Labor-Hours	Unit	Material	2014 Bare Costs Labor	Equipment	Total	Total Incl O&P
0010	**FURNACE COMPONENTS AND COMBINATIONS**									
0080	Coils, A.C. evaporator, for gas or oil furnaces									
0090	Add-on, with holding charge									
0100	Upflow									
0120	1-1/2 ton cooling	Q-5	4	4	Ea.	220	139		359	470
0130	2 ton cooling		3.70	4.324		241	150		391	515
0140	3 ton cooling		3.30	4.848		375	168		543	695
0150	4 ton cooling		3	5.333		465	185		650	820
0160	5 ton cooling	↓	2.70	5.926	↓	505	206		711	895
0300	Downflow									
0330	2-1/2 ton cooling	Q-5	3	5.333	Ea.	295	185		480	630
0340	3-1/2 ton cooling		2.60	6.154		435	214		649	830
0350	5 ton cooling	↓	2.20	7.273	↓	505	253		758	970
0600	Horizontal									
0630	2 ton cooling	Q-5	3.90	4.103	Ea.	320	143		463	590
0640	3 ton cooling		3.50	4.571		370	159		529	665
0650	4 ton cooling		3.20	5		460	174		634	790
0660	5 ton cooling	↓	2.90	5.517	↓	460	192		652	820
2000	Cased evaporator coils for air handlers									
2100	1-1/2 ton cooling	Q-5	4.40	3.636	Ea.	267	126		393	505
2110	2 ton cooling		4.10	3.902		300	136		436	555
2120	2-1/2 ton cooling		3.90	4.103		320	143		463	585
2130	3 ton cooling		3.70	4.324		360	150		510	645
2140	3-1/2 ton cooling		3.50	4.571		485	159		644	795
2150	4 ton cooling		3.20	5		515	174		689	855
2160	5 ton cooling	↓	2.90	5.517	↓	525	192		717	895
3010	Air handler, modular									
3100	With cased evaporator cooling coil									
3120	1-1/2 ton cooling	Q-5	3.80	4.211	Ea.	1,300	146		1,446	1,675
3130	2 ton cooling		3.50	4.571		1,350	159		1,509	1,725
3140	2-1/2 ton cooling		3.30	4.848		1,450	168		1,618	1,875
3150	3 ton cooling		3.10	5.161		1,550	179		1,729	2,025
3160	3-1/2 ton cooling		2.90	5.517		1,600	192		1,792	2,100
3170	4 ton cooling	↓	2.50	6.400	↓	1,800	222		2,022	2,375

23 54 Furnaces

23 54 24 - Furnace Components for Cooling

23 54 24.10 Furnace Components and Combinations	Crew	Daily Output	Labor-Hours	Unit	Material	2014 Bare Costs Labor	Equipment	Total	Total Incl O&P
3180	5 ton cooling	Q-5	2.10	7.619	Ea.	2,050	265		2,315	2,675
3500	With no cooling coil									
3520	1-1/2 ton coil size	Q-5	12	1.333	Ea.	620	46.50		666.50	755
3530	2 ton coil size		10	1.600		620	55.50		675.50	775
3540	2-1/2 ton coil size		10	1.600		725	55.50		780.50	885
3554	3 ton coil size		9	1.778		825	62		887	1,000
3560	3-1/2 ton coil size		9	1.778		845	62		907	1,025
3570	4 ton coil size		8.50	1.882		1,050	65.50		1,115.50	1,275
3580	5 ton coil size		8	2		1,075	69.50		1,144.50	1,300
4000	With heater									
4120	5 kW, 17.1 MBH	Q-5	16	1	Ea.	670	35		705	795
4130	7.5 kW, 25.6 MBH		15.60	1.026		680	35.50		715.50	805
4140	10 kW, 34.2 MBH		15.20	1.053		845	36.50		881.50	990
4150	12.5 KW, 42.7 MBH		14.80	1.081		950	37.50		987.50	1,100
4160	15 KW, 51.2 MBH		14.40	1.111		1,025	38.50		1,063.50	1,200
4170	25 KW, 85.4 MBH		14	1.143		1,375	39.50		1,414.50	1,575
4180	30 KW, 102 MBH		13	1.231		1,600	43		1,643	1,825

23 62 Packaged Compressor and Condenser Units

23 62 13 - Packaged Air-Cooled Refrigerant Compressor and Condenser Units

23 62 13.10 Packaged Air-Cooled Refrig. Condensing Units

0010	PACKAGED AIR-COOLED REFRIGERANT CONDENSING UNITS									
0020	Condensing unit									
0030	Air cooled, compressor, standard controls									
0050	1.5 ton	Q-5	2.50	6.400	Ea.	1,300	222		1,522	1,800
0100	2 ton		2.10	7.619		1,450	265		1,715	2,025
0200	2.5 ton		1.70	9.412		1,525	325		1,850	2,225
0300	3 ton		1.30	12.308		1,525	430		1,955	2,375
0350	3.5 ton		1.10	14.545		1,775	505		2,280	2,775
0400	4 ton		.90	17.778		1,975	620		2,595	3,200
0500	5 ton		.60	26.667		2,475	925		3,400	4,225

23 74 Packaged Outdoor HVAC Equipment

23 74 33 - Dedicated Outdoor-Air Units

23 74 33.10 Rooftop Air Conditioners

0010	ROOFTOP AIR CONDITIONERS, Standard controls, curb, economizer									
1000	Single zone, electric cool, gas heat									
1140	5 ton cooling, 112 MBH heating	Q-5	.56	28.521	Ea.	5,275	990		6,265	7,425
1150	7.5 ton cooling, 170 MBH heating		.50	32.258		8,125	1,125		9,250	10,800
1156	8.5 ton cooling, 170 MBH heating		.46	34.783		8,800	1,200		10,000	11,700
1160	10 ton cooling, 200 MBH heating	Q-6	.67	35.982		11,600	1,200		12,800	14,800

23 81 Decentralized Unitary HVAC Equipment

23 81 13 – Packaged Terminal Air-Conditioners

23 81 13.10 Packaged Cabinet Type Air-Conditioners	Crew	Daily Output	Labor-Hours	Unit	Material	2014 Bare Costs Labor	Equipment	Total	Total Incl O&P
0010 **PACKAGED CABINET TYPE AIR-CONDITIONERS**, Cabinet, wall sleeve,									
0100 louver, electric heat, thermostat, manual changeover, 208 V									
0200 6,000 BTUH cooling, 8800 BTU heat	Q-5	6	2.667	Ea.	775	92.50		867.50	1,000
0220 9,000 BTUH cooling, 13,900 BTU heat		5	3.200		850	111		961	1,125
0240 12,000 BTUH cooling, 13,900 BTU heat		4	4		920	139		1,059	1,225
0260 15,000 BTUH cooling, 13,900 BTU heat	↓	3	5.333	↓	1,150	185		1,335	1,575

23 81 19 – Self-Contained Air-Conditioners

23 81 19.10 Window Unit Air Conditioners

	Crew	Daily Output	Labor-Hours	Unit	Material	2014 Bare Costs Labor	Equipment	Total	Total Incl O&P
0010 **WINDOW UNIT AIR CONDITIONERS**									
4000 Portable/window, 15 amp 125 V grounded receptacle required									
4060 5000 BTUH	1 Carp	8	1	Ea.	284	32		316	365
4340 6000 BTUH		8	1		325	32		357	415
4480 8000 BTUH		6	1.333		445	43		488	560
4500 10,000 BTUH		6	1.333		570	43		613	695
4520 12,000 BTUH	L-2	8	2	↓	695	56		751	860
4600 Window/thru-the-wall, 15 amp 230 V grounded receptacle required									
4780 18,000 BTUH	L-2	6	2.667	Ea.	930	74.50		1,004.50	1,150
4940 25,000 BTUH		4	4		1,175	112		1,287	1,500
4960 29,000 BTUH	↓	4	4	↓	1,300	112		1,412	1,625

23 81 19.20 Self-Contained Single Package

	Crew	Daily Output	Labor-Hours	Unit	Material	2014 Bare Costs Labor	Equipment	Total	Total Incl O&P
0010 **SELF-CONTAINED SINGLE PACKAGE**									
0100 Air cooled, for free blow or duct, not incl. remote condenser									
0110 Constant volume									
0200 3 ton cooling	Q-5	1	16	Ea.	3,750	555		4,305	5,025
0210 4 ton cooling	"	.80	20	"	4,075	695		4,770	5,625
1000 Water cooled for free blow or duct, not including tower									
1010 Constant volume									
1100 3 ton cooling	Q-6	1	24	Ea.	3,725	805		4,530	5,400
1300 For hot water or steam heat coils, add				"	12%	10%			

23 81 26 – Split-System Air-Conditioners

23 81 26.10 Split Ductless Systems

	Crew	Daily Output	Labor-Hours	Unit	Material	2014 Bare Costs Labor	Equipment	Total	Total Incl O&P
0010 **SPLIT DUCTLESS SYSTEMS**									
0100 Cooling only, single zone									
0110 Wall mount									
0120 3/4 ton cooling	Q-5	2	8	Ea.	690	278		968	1,225
0130 1 ton cooling		1.80	8.889		765	310		1,075	1,350
0140 1-1/2 ton cooling		1.60	10		1,225	350		1,575	1,925
0150 2 ton cooling	↓	1.40	11.429	↓	1,400	395		1,795	2,200
1000 Ceiling mount									
1020 2 ton cooling	Q-5	1.40	11.429	Ea.	1,250	395		1,645	2,025
1030 3 ton cooling	"	1.20	13.333	"	1,600	465		2,065	2,525
3000 Multizone									
3010 Wall mount									
3020 2 @ 3/4 ton cooling	Q-5	1.80	8.889	Ea.	2,100	310		2,410	2,825
5000 Cooling/Heating									
5010 Wall mount									
5110 1 ton cooling	Q-5	1.70	9.412	Ea.	765	325		1,090	1,375
5120 1-1/2 ton cooling	"	1.50	10.667	"	1,225	370		1,595	1,950
7000 Accessories for all split ductless systems									
7010 Add for ambient frost control	Q-5	8	2	Ea.	79	69.50		148.50	202
7020 Add for tube/wiring kit, (Line sets)									

23 81 Decentralized Unitary HVAC Equipment

23 81 26 – Split-System Air-Conditioners

23 81 26.10 Split Ductless Systems	Crew	Daily Output	Labor-Hours	Unit	Material	2014 Bare Costs Labor	Equipment	Total	Total Incl O&P
7030	15' kit	Q-5	32	.500	Ea.	103	17.40		120.40	142
7036	25' kit		28	.571		116	19.85		135.85	161
7040	35' kit		24	.667		174	23		197	229
7050	50' kit	↓	20	.800	↓	191	28		219	256

23 81 43 – Air-Source Unitary Heat Pumps

23 81 43.10 Air-Source Heat Pumps

		Crew	Daily Output	Labor-Hours	Unit	Material	Labor	Equipment	Total	Total Incl O&P
0010	**AIR-SOURCE HEAT PUMPS**, Not including interconnecting tubing									
1000	Air to air, split system, not including curbs, pads, fan coil and ductwork									
1012	Outside condensing unit only, for fan coil see Section 23 82 19.10									
1020	2 ton cooling, 8.5 MBH heat @ 0°F	Q-5	2	8	Ea.	2,300	278		2,578	3,000
1054	4 ton cooling, 24 MBH heat @ 0°F	"	.80	20	"	3,300	695		3,995	4,800
1500	Single package, not including curbs, pads, or plenums									
1520	2 ton cooling, 6.5 MBH heat @ 0°F	Q-5	1.50	10.667	Ea.	2,950	370		3,320	3,850
1580	4 ton cooling, 13 MBH heat @ 0°F	"	.96	16.667	"	4,125	580		4,705	5,500

23 81 46 – Water-Source Unitary Heat Pumps

23 81 46.10 Water Source Heat Pumps

		Crew	Daily Output	Labor-Hours	Unit	Material	Labor	Equipment	Total	Total Incl O&P
0010	**WATER SOURCE HEAT PUMPS**, Not incl. connecting tubing or water source									
2000	Water source to air, single package									
2100	1 ton cooling, 13 MBH heat @ 75°F	Q-5	2	8	Ea.	1,825	278		2,103	2,450
2200	4 ton cooling, 31 MBH heat @ 75°F	"	1.20	13.333	"	2,700	465		3,165	3,750

23 82 Convection Heating and Cooling Units

23 82 19 – Fan Coil Units

23 82 19.10 Fan Coil Air Conditioning

		Crew	Daily Output	Labor-Hours	Unit	Material	Labor	Equipment	Total	Total Incl O&P
0010	**FAN COIL AIR CONDITIONING**									
0030	Fan coil AC, cabinet mounted, filters and controls									
0100	Chilled water, 1/2 ton cooling	Q-5	8	2	Ea.	810	69.50		879.50	1,000
0110	3/4 ton cooling		7	2.286		840	79.50		919.50	1,050
0120	1 ton cooling	↓	6	2.667	↓	935	92.50		1,027.50	1,175

23 82 29 – Radiators

23 82 29.10 Hydronic Heating

		Crew	Daily Output	Labor-Hours	Unit	Material	Labor	Equipment	Total	Total Incl O&P
0010	**HYDRONIC HEATING**, Terminal units, not incl. main supply pipe									
1000	Radiation									
1100	Panel, baseboard, C.I., including supports, no covers	Q-5	46	.348	L.F.	36.50	12.10		48.60	60
3000	Radiators, cast iron									
3100	Free standing or wall hung, 6 tube, 25" high	Q-5	96	.167	Section	44	5.80		49.80	58
3200	4 tube, 19" high	"	96	.167	"	30.50	5.80		36.30	43
3250	Adj. brackets, 2 per wall radiator up to 30 sections	1 Stpi	32	.250	Ea.	34	9.65		43.65	53.50

23 82 36 – Finned-Tube Radiation Heaters

23 82 36.10 Finned Tube Radiation

		Crew	Daily Output	Labor-Hours	Unit	Material	Labor	Equipment	Total	Total Incl O&P
0010	**FINNED TUBE RADIATION**, Terminal units, not incl. main supply pipe									
1310	Baseboard, pkgd, 1/2" copper tube, alum. fin, 7" high	Q-5	60	.267	L.F.	11.20	9.25		20.45	27.50
1320	3/4" copper tube, alum. fin, 7" high		58	.276		7.35	9.60		16.95	24
1340	1" copper tube, alum. fin, 8-7/8" high		56	.286		18.85	9.95		28.80	37
1360	1-1/4" copper tube, alum. fin, 8-7/8" high	↓	54	.296	↓	28	10.30		38.30	47.50
1500	Note: fin tube may also require corners, caps, etc.									

23 83 Radiant Heating Units

23 83 16 – Radiant-Heating Hydronic Piping

23 83 16.10 Radiant Floor Heating	Crew	Daily Output	Labor-Hours	Unit	Material	2014 Bare Costs Labor	Equipment	Total	Total Incl O&P
0010 **RADIANT FLOOR HEATING**									
0100 Tubing, PEX (cross-linked polyethylene)									
0110 Oxygen barrier type for systems with ferrous materials									
0120 1/2"	Q-5	800	.020	L.F.	1.02	.70		1.72	2.27
0130 3/4"		535	.030		1.44	1.04		2.48	3.30
0140 1"	↓	400	.040	↓	2.25	1.39		3.64	4.77
0200 Non barrier type for ferrous free systems									
0210 1/2"	Q-5	800	.020	L.F.	.58	.70		1.28	1.79
0220 3/4"		535	.030		1.05	1.04		2.09	2.88
0230 1"	↓	400	.040	↓	1.46	1.39		2.85	3.90
1000 Manifolds									
1110 Brass									
1120 With supply and return valves, flow meter, thermometer,									
1122 auto air vent and drain/fill valve.									
1130 1", 2 circuit	Q-5	14	1.143	Ea.	245	39.50		284.50	335
1140 1", 3 circuit		13.50	1.185		280	41		321	380
1150 1", 4 circuit		13	1.231		305	43		348	405
1154 1", 5 circuit		12.50	1.280		365	44.50		409.50	475
1158 1", 6 circuit		12	1.333		395	46.50		441.50	510
1162 1", 7 circuit		11.50	1.391		430	48.50		478.50	555
1166 1", 8 circuit		11	1.455		480	50.50		530.50	610
1172 1", 9 circuit		10.50	1.524		515	53		568	655
1174 1", 10 circuit		10	1.600		555	55.50		610.50	700
1178 1", 11 circuit		9.50	1.684		575	58.50		633.50	730
1182 1", 12 circuit	↓	9	1.778	↓	635	62		697	800
1610 Copper manifold header, (cut to size)									
1620 1" header, 12 – 1/2" sweat outlets	Q-5	3.33	4.805	Ea.	91	167		258	375
1630 1-1/4" header, 12 – 1/2" sweat outlets		3.20	5		106	174		280	405
1640 1-1/4" header, 12 – 3/4" sweat outlets		3	5.333		114	185		299	430
1650 1-1/2" header, 12 – 3/4" sweat outlets		3.10	5.161		139	179		318	450
1660 2" header, 12 – 3/4" sweat outlets	↓	2.90	5.517	↓	201	192		393	535
3000 Valves									
3110 Thermostatic zone valve actuator with end switch	Q-5	40	.400	Ea.	38.50	13.90		52.40	65.50
3114 Thermostatic zone valve actuator	"	36	.444	"	81	15.45		96.45	115
3120 Motorized straight zone valve with operator complete									
3130 3/4"	Q-5	35	.457	Ea.	130	15.90		145.90	169
3140 1"		32	.500		141	17.40		158.40	184
3150 1-1/4"	↓	29.60	.541	↓	179	18.80		197.80	228
3500 4 Way mixing valve, manual, brass									
3530 1"	Q-5	13.30	1.203	Ea.	180	42		222	267
3540 1-1/4"		11.40	1.404		195	49		244	295
3550 1-1/2"		11	1.455		249	50.50		299.50	360
3560 2"		10.60	1.509		350	52.50		402.50	475
3800 Mixing valve motor, 4 way for valves, 1" and 1-1/4"		34	.471		310	16.35		326.35	365
3810 Mixing valve motor, 4 way for valves, 1-1/2" and 2"	↓	30	.533	↓	355	18.55		373.55	420
5000 Radiant floor heating, zone control panel									
5120 4 Zone actuator valve control, expandable	Q-5	20	.800	Ea.	163	28		191	225
5130 6 Zone actuator valve control, expandable		18	.889		226	31		257	299
6070 Thermal track, straight panel for long continuous runs, 5.333 S.F.		40	.400		26.50	13.90		40.40	52.50
6080 Thermal track, utility panel, for direction reverse at run end, 5.333 S.F.		40	.400		26.50	13.90		40.40	52.50
6090 Combination panel, for direction reverse plus straight run, 5.333 S.F.	↓	40	.400	↓	26.50	13.90		40.40	52.50
7000 PEX tubing fittings									
7100 Compression type									

23 83 Radiant Heating Units

23 83 16 – Radiant-Heating Hydronic Piping

23 83 16.10 Radiant Floor Heating

		Crew	Daily Output	Labor-Hours	Unit	Material	2014 Bare Costs Labor	Equipment	Total	Total Incl O&P
7116	Coupling									
7120	1/2" x 1/2"	1 Stpi	27	.296	Ea.	6.70	11.45		18.15	26.50
7124	3/4" x 3/4"	"	23	.348	"	10.60	13.45		24.05	33.50
7130	Adapter									
7132	1/2" x female sweat 1/2"	1 Stpi	27	.296	Ea.	4.36	11.45		15.81	23.50
7134	1/2" x female sweat 3/4"		26	.308		4.88	11.90		16.78	25
7136	5/8" x female sweat 3/4"	↓	24	.333	↓	7	12.85		19.85	28.50
7140	Elbow									
7142	1/2" x female sweat 1/2"	1 Stpi	27	.296	Ea.	6.65	11.45		18.10	26
7144	1/2" x female sweat 3/4"		26	.308		7.80	11.90		19.70	28
7146	5/8" x female sweat 3/4"	↓	24	.333	↓	8.75	12.85		21.60	30.50
7200	Insert type									
7206	PEX x male NPT									
7210	1/2" x 1/2"	1 Stpi	29	.276	Ea.	2.59	10.65		13.24	20.50
7220	3/4" x 3/4"		27	.296		3.81	11.45		15.26	23
7230	1" x 1"	↓	26	.308	↓	6.45	11.90		18.35	26.50
7300	PEX coupling									
7310	1/2" x 1/2"	1 Stpi	30	.267	Ea.	1.76	10.30		12.06	18.95
7320	3/4" x 3/4"		29	.276		2.15	10.65		12.80	19.90
7330	1" x 1"	↓	28	.286	↓	5.85	11.05		16.90	24.50
7400	PEX stainless crimp ring									
7410	1/2" x 1/2"	1 Stpi	86	.093	Ea.	.34	3.59		3.93	6.30
7420	3/4" x 3/4"		84	.095		.47	3.68		4.15	6.55
7430	1" x 1"	↓	82	.098	↓	.68	3.77		4.45	6.95

23 83 33 – Electric Radiant Heaters

23 83 33.10 Electric Heating

		Crew	Daily Output	Labor-Hours	Unit	Material	2014 Bare Costs Labor	Equipment	Total	Total Incl O&P
0010	**ELECTRIC HEATING**, not incl. conduit or feed wiring									
1100	Rule of thumb: Baseboard units, including control	1 Elec	4.40	1.818	kW	101	65		166	217
1300	Baseboard heaters, 2' long, 350 watt		8	1	Ea.	30	36		66	91.50
1400	3' long, 750 watt		8	1		34.50	36		70.50	96.50
1600	4' long, 1000 watt		6.70	1.194		41	42.50		83.50	115
1800	5' long, 935 watt		5.70	1.404		51	50		101	138
2000	6' long, 1500 watt		5	1.600		56	57		113	155
2400	8' long, 2000 watt		4	2		69.50	71.50		141	193
2800	10' long, 1875 watt	↓	3.30	2.424	↓	193	86.50		279.50	355
2950	Wall heaters with fan, 120 to 277 volt									
3160	Recessed, residential, 750 watt	1 Elec	6	1.333	Ea.	134	47.50		181.50	225
3170	1000 watt		6	1.333		134	47.50		181.50	225
3180	1250 watt		5	1.600		134	57		191	241
3190	1500 watt		4	2		134	71.50		205.50	264
3600	Thermostats, integral		16	.500		30	17.90		47.90	62.50
3800	Line voltage, 1 pole		8	1		20.50	36		56.50	81
5000	Radiant heating ceiling panels, 2' x 4', 500 watt		16	.500		291	17.90		308.90	350
5050	750 watt		16	.500		310	17.90		327.90	375
5300	Infrared quartz heaters, 120 volts, 1000 watts		6.70	1.194		230	42.50		272.50	325
5350	1500 watt		5	1.600		230	57		287	345
5400	240 volts, 1500 watt		5	1.600		230	57		287	345
5450	2000 watt		4	2		230	71.50		301.50	370
5500	3000 watt	↓	3	2.667	↓	255	95.50		350.50	435

Estimating Tips

26 05 00 Common Work Results for Electrical

- Conduit should be taken off in three main categories—power distribution, branch power, and branch lighting—so the estimator can concentrate on systems and components, therefore making it easier to ensure all items have been accounted for.
- For cost modifications for elevated conduit installation, add the percentages to labor according to the height of installation, and only to the quantities exceeding the different height levels, not to the total conduit quantities.
- Remember that aluminum wiring of equal ampacity is larger in diameter than copper and may require larger conduit.
- If more than three wires at a time are being pulled, deduct percentages from the labor hours of that grouping of wires.
- When taking off grounding systems, identify separately the type and size of wire, and list each unique type of ground connection.

- The estimator should take the weights of materials into consideration when completing a takeoff. Topics to consider include: How will the materials be supported? What methods of support are available? How high will the support structure have to reach? Will the final support structure be able to withstand the total burden? Is the support material included or separate from the fixture, equipment, and material specified?
- Do not overlook the costs for equipment used in the installation. If scaffolding or highlifts are available in the field, contractors may use them in lieu of the proposed ladders and rolling staging.

26 20 00 Low-Voltage Electrical Transmission

- Supports and concrete pads may be shown on drawings for the larger equipment, or the support system may be only a piece of plywood for the back of a panelboard. In either case, it must be included in the costs.

26 40 00 Electrical and Cathodic Protection

- When taking off cathodic protections systems, identify the type and size of cable, and list each unique type of anode connection.

26 50 00 Lighting

- Fixtures should be taken off room by room, using the fixture schedule, specifications, and the ceiling plan. For large concentrations of lighting fixtures in the same area, deduct the percentages from labor hours.

Reference Numbers

Reference numbers are shown in shaded boxes at the beginning of some major classifications. These numbers refer to related items in the Reference Section. The reference information may be an estimating procedure, an alternate pricing method, or technical information.

Note: Not all subdivisions listed here necessarily appear in this publication.

Note: **Trade Service,** *in part, has been used as a reference source for some of the material prices used in Division 26.*

26 05 05 – Selective Electrical Demolition

26 05 05.10 Electrical Demolition	Crew	Daily Output	Labor-Hours	Unit	Material	2014 Bare Costs Labor	Equipment	Total	Total Incl O&P
0010 **ELECTRICAL DEMOLITION**									
0020 Conduit to 15' high, including fittings & hangers									
0100 Rigid galvanized steel, 1/2" to 1" diameter	1 Elec	242	.033	L.F.		1.18		1.18	1.93
0120 1-1/4" to 2"	"	200	.040	"		1.43		1.43	2.34
0270 Armored cable, (BX) avg. 50' runs									
0280 #14, 2 wire	1 Elec	690	.012	L.F.		.41		.41	.68
0290 #14, 3 wire		571	.014			.50		.50	.82
0300 #12, 2 wire		605	.013			.47		.47	.77
0310 #12, 3 wire		514	.016			.56		.56	.91
0320 #10, 2 wire		514	.016			.56		.56	.91
0330 #10, 3 wire		425	.019			.67		.67	1.10
0340 #8, 3 wire		342	.023			.84		.84	1.37
0350 Non metallic sheathed cable (Romex)									
0360 #14, 2 wire	1 Elec	720	.011	L.F.		.40		.40	.65
0370 #14, 3 wire		657	.012			.44		.44	.71
0380 #12, 2 wire		629	.013			.45		.45	.74
0390 #10, 3 wire		450	.018			.64		.64	1.04
0400 Wiremold raceway, including fittings & hangers									
0420 No. 3000	1 Elec	250	.032	L.F.		1.14		1.14	1.87
0440 No. 4000		217	.037			1.32		1.32	2.16
0460 No. 6000		166	.048			1.72		1.72	2.82
0462 Plugmold with receptacle		114	.070			2.51		2.51	4.11
0465 Telephone/power pole		12	.667	Ea.		24		24	39
0470 Non-metallic, straight section		480	.017	L.F.		.60		.60	.98
0500 Channels, steel, including fittings & hangers									
0520 3/4" x 1-1/2"	1 Elec	308	.026	L.F.		.93		.93	1.52
0540 1-1/2" x 1-1/2"		269	.030			1.06		1.06	1.74
0560 1-1/2" x 1-7/8"		229	.035			1.25		1.25	2.04
1210 Panel boards, incl. removal of all breakers,									
1220 conduit terminations & wire connections									
1230 3 wire, 120/240 V, 100A, to 20 circuits	1 Elec	2.60	3.077	Ea.		110		110	180
1240 200 amps, to 42 circuits	2 Elec	2.60	6.154			220		220	360
1260 4 wire, 120/208 V, 125A, to 20 circuits	1 Elec	2.40	3.333			119		119	195
1270 200 amps, to 42 circuits	2 Elec	2.40	6.667			238		238	390
1720 Junction boxes, 4" sq. & oct.	1 Elec	80	.100			3.58		3.58	5.85
1740 Handy box		107	.075			2.67		2.67	4.37
1760 Switch box		107	.075			2.67		2.67	4.37
1780 Receptacle & switch plates		257	.031			1.11		1.11	1.82
1800 Wire, THW-THWN-THHN, removed from									
1810 in place conduit, to 15' high									
1830 #14	1 Elec	65	.123	C.L.F.		4.40		4.40	7.20
1840 #12		55	.145			5.20		5.20	8.50
1850 #10		45.50	.176			6.30		6.30	10.30
2000 Interior fluorescent fixtures, incl. supports									
2010 & whips, to 15' high									
2100 Recessed drop-in 2' x 2', 2 lamp	2 Elec	35	.457	Ea.		16.35		16.35	26.50
2140 2' x 4', 4 lamp	"	30	.533	"		19.05		19.05	31
2180 Surface mount, acrylic lens & hinged frame									
2220 2' x 2', 2 lamp	2 Elec	44	.364	Ea.		13		13	21.50
2260 2' x 4', 4 lamp	"	33	.485	"		17.35		17.35	28.50
2300 Strip fixtures, surface mount									
2320 4' long, 1 lamp	2 Elec	53	.302	Ea.		10.80		10.80	17.65
2380 8' long, 2 lamp	"	40	.400	"		14.30		14.30	23.50

26 05 Common Work Results for Electrical

26 05 05 – Selective Electrical Demolition

26 05 05.10 Electrical Demolition

		Crew	Daily Output	Labor-Hours	Unit	Material	2014 Bare Costs Labor	2014 Bare Costs Equipment	Total	Total Incl O&P
2460	Interior incandescent, surface, ceiling									
2470	or wall mount, to 12' high									
2480	Metal cylinder type, 75 Watt	2 Elec	62	.258	Ea.		9.25		9.25	15.10
2600	Exterior fixtures, incandescent, wall mount									
2620	100 Watt	2 Elec	50	.320	Ea.		11.45		11.45	18.70
3000	Ceiling fan, tear out and remove	1 Elec	24	.333	"		11.90		11.90	19.50

26 05 19 – Low-Voltage Electrical Power Conductors and Cables

26 05 19.20 Armored Cable

		Crew	Daily Output	Labor-Hours	Unit	Material	2014 Bare Costs Labor	2014 Bare Costs Equipment	Total	Total Incl O&P
0010	**ARMORED CABLE**									
0051	600 volt, copper (BX), #14, 2 conductor, solid	1 Elec	240	.033	L.F.	.54	1.19		1.73	2.54
0101	3 conductor, solid		200	.040		.83	1.43		2.26	3.26
0151	#12, 2 conductor, solid		210	.038		.54	1.36		1.90	2.83
0201	3 conductor, solid		180	.044		.89	1.59		2.48	3.58
0251	#10, 2 conductor, solid		180	.044		1	1.59		2.59	3.70
0301	3 conductor, solid		150	.053		1.39	1.91		3.30	4.65
0351	3 conductor, stranded	↓	120	.067	↓	2.62	2.38		5	6.80

26 05 19.55 Non-Metallic Sheathed Cable

		Crew	Daily Output	Labor-Hours	Unit	Material	2014 Bare Costs Labor	2014 Bare Costs Equipment	Total	Total Incl O&P
0010	**NON-METALLIC SHEATHED CABLE** 600 volt									
0100	Copper with ground wire, (Romex)									
0151	#14, 2 wire	1 Elec	250	.032	L.F.	.25	1.14		1.39	2.15
0201	3 wire		230	.035		.35	1.24		1.59	2.42
0251	#12, 2 wire		220	.036		.39	1.30		1.69	2.56
0301	3 wire		200	.040		.54	1.43		1.97	2.94
0351	#10, 2 wire		200	.040		.60	1.43		2.03	3
0401	3 wire		140	.057		.86	2.04		2.90	4.28
0451	#8, 3 conductor		130	.062		1.38	2.20		3.58	5.10
0501	#6, 3 wire	↓	120	.067	↓	2.24	2.38		4.62	6.35
0550	SE type SER aluminum cable, 3 RHW and									
0601	1 bare neutral, 3 #8 & 1 #8	1 Elec	150	.053	L.F.	1.37	1.91		3.28	4.63
0651	3 #6 & 1 #6	"	130	.062		1.56	2.20		3.76	5.30
0701	3 #4 & 1 #6	2 Elec	220	.073		1.44	2.60		4.04	5.85
0751	3 #2 & 1 #4		200	.080		2.57	2.86		5.43	7.50
0801	3 #1/0 & 1 #2		180	.089		3.89	3.18		7.07	9.50
0851	3 #2/0 & 1 #1		160	.100		4.58	3.58		8.16	10.90
0901	3 #4/0 & 1 #2/0	↓	140	.114		6.55	4.09		10.64	13.90
2401	SEU service entrance cable, copper 2 conductors, #8 + #8 neutral	1 Elec	150	.053		1.19	1.91		3.10	4.43
2601	#6 + #8 neutral		130	.062		1.76	2.20		3.96	5.55
2801	#6 + #6 neutral	↓	130	.062		2	2.20		4.20	5.80
3001	#4 + #6 neutral	2 Elec	220	.073		2.77	2.60		5.37	7.30
3201	#4 + #4 neutral		220	.073		3.12	2.60		5.72	7.70
3401	#3 + #5 neutral	↓	210	.076	↓	3.65	2.72		6.37	8.50
6500	Service entrance cap for copper SEU									
6600	100 amp	1 Elec	12	.667	Ea.	10.35	24		34.35	50.50
6700	150 amp		10	.800		18.90	28.50		47.40	68
6800	200 amp	↓	8	1	↓	29	36		65	90

26 05 19.90 Wire

		Crew	Daily Output	Labor-Hours	Unit	Material	2014 Bare Costs Labor	2014 Bare Costs Equipment	Total	Total Incl O&P
0010	**WIRE**									
0021	600 volt, copper type THW, solid, #14	1 Elec	1300	.006	L.F.	.08	.22		.30	.45
0031	#12		1100	.007		.13	.26		.39	.57
0041	#10		1000	.008		.20	.29		.49	.69
0161	#6	↓	650	.012		.64	.44		1.08	1.42
0181	#4	2 Elec	1060	.015	↓	1.01	.54		1.55	1.99

26 05 Common Work Results for Electrical

26 05 19 – Low-Voltage Electrical Power Conductors and Cables

26 05 19.90 Wire		Crew	Daily Output	Labor-Hours	Unit	Material	2014 Bare Costs Labor	Equipment	Total	Total Incl O&P
0201	#3	2 Elec	1000	.016	L.F.	1.26	.57		1.83	2.33
0221	#2		900	.018		1.60	.64		2.24	2.80
0241	#1		800	.020		2.02	.72		2.74	3.39
0261	1/0		660	.024		2.51	.87		3.38	4.19
0281	2/0		580	.028		3.16	.99		4.15	5.10
0301	3/0		500	.032		3.96	1.14		5.10	6.25
0351	4/0		440	.036		5.05	1.30		6.35	7.70

26 05 26 – Grounding and Bonding for Electrical Systems

26 05 26.80 Grounding

		Crew	Daily Output	Labor-Hours	Unit	Material	2014 Bare Costs Labor	Equipment	Total	Total Incl O&P
0010	**GROUNDING**									
0030	Rod, copper clad, 8' long, 1/2" diameter	1 Elec	5.50	1.455	Ea.	20.50	52		72.50	108
0050	3/4" diameter		5.30	1.509		34	54		88	126
0080	10' long, 1/2" diameter		4.80	1.667		22.50	59.50		82	123
0100	3/4" diameter		4.40	1.818		39	65		104	149
0261	Wire, ground bare armored, #8-1 conductor		200	.040	L.F.	.90	1.43		2.33	3.33
0271	#6-1 conductor		180	.044	"	1.07	1.59		2.66	3.78
0390	Bare copper wire, stranded, #8		11	.727	C.L.F.	35	26		61	81
0401	Bare copper, #6 wire		1000	.008	L.F.	.61	.29		.90	1.14
0601	#2 stranded	2 Elec	1000	.016	"	1.62	.57		2.19	2.73
1800	Water pipe ground clamps, heavy duty									
2000	Bronze, 1/2" to 1" diameter	1 Elec	8	1	Ea.	23.50	36		59.50	84

26 05 33 – Raceway and Boxes for Electrical Systems

26 05 33.13 Conduit

		Crew	Daily Output	Labor-Hours	Unit	Material	2014 Bare Costs Labor	Equipment	Total	Total Incl O&P
0010	**CONDUIT** To 15' high, includes 2 terminations, 2 elbows,									
0020	11 beam clamps, and 11 couplings per 100 L.F.									
1750	Rigid galvanized steel, 1/2" diameter	1 Elec	90	.089	L.F.	2.40	3.18		5.58	7.85
1770	3/4" diameter		80	.100		2.56	3.58		6.14	8.65
1800	1" diameter		65	.123		3.69	4.40		8.09	11.25
1830	1-1/4" diameter		60	.133		4.84	4.77		9.61	13.15
1850	1-1/2" diameter		55	.145		5.75	5.20		10.95	14.80
1870	2" diameter		45	.178		7.45	6.35		13.80	18.60
5000	Electric metallic tubing (EMT), 1/2" diameter		170	.047		.56	1.68		2.24	3.37
5020	3/4" diameter		130	.062		.86	2.20		3.06	4.54
5040	1" diameter		115	.070		1.48	2.49		3.97	5.70
5060	1-1/4" diameter		100	.080		2.45	2.86		5.31	7.35
5080	1-1/2" diameter		90	.089		3.16	3.18		6.34	8.70
9100	PVC, schedule 40, 1/2" diameter		190	.042		.97	1.51		2.48	3.53
9110	3/4" diameter		145	.055		1.07	1.97		3.04	4.40
9120	1" diameter		125	.064		2.09	2.29		4.38	6.05
9130	1-1/4" diameter		110	.073		2.76	2.60		5.36	7.30
9140	1-1/2" diameter		100	.080		3.14	2.86		6	8.15
9150	2" diameter		90	.089		4.09	3.18		7.27	9.70

26 05 33.16 Outlet Boxes

		Crew	Daily Output	Labor-Hours	Unit	Material	2014 Bare Costs Labor	Equipment	Total	Total Incl O&P
0010	**OUTLET BOXES**									
0021	Pressed steel, octagon, 4"	1 Elec	18	.444	Ea.	3.07	15.90		18.97	29.50
0060	Covers, blank		64	.125		1.29	4.47		5.76	8.70
0100	Extension rings		40	.200		5.10	7.15		12.25	17.30
0151	Square 4"		18	.444		2.10	15.90		18	28.50
0200	Extension rings		40	.200		5.15	7.15		12.30	17.35
0250	Covers, blank		64	.125		1.39	4.47		5.86	8.85
0300	Plaster rings		64	.125		2.83	4.47		7.30	10.40

26 05 Common Work Results for Electrical

26 05 33 – Raceway and Boxes for Electrical Systems

26 05 33.16 Outlet Boxes

		Crew	Daily Output	Labor-Hours	Unit	Material	2014 Bare Costs Labor	Equipment	Total	Total Incl O&P
0651	Switchbox	1 Elec	24	.333	Ea.	4.91	11.90		16.81	25
1100	Concrete, floor, 1 gang	↓	5.30	1.509	↓	89	54		143	186

26 05 33.17 Outlet Boxes, Plastic

		Crew	Daily Output	Labor-Hours	Unit	Material	2014 Bare Costs Labor	Equipment	Total	Total Incl O&P
0010	**OUTLET BOXES, PLASTIC**									
0051	4" diameter, round, with 2 mounting nails	1 Elec	23	.348	Ea.	2.57	12.45		15.02	23.50
0101	Bar hanger mounted		23	.348		5.30	12.45		17.75	26.50
0201	Square with 2 mounting nails		23	.348		4.54	12.45		16.99	25.50
0300	Plaster ring		64	.125		2.02	4.47		6.49	9.50
0401	Switch box with 2 mounting nails, 1 gang		27	.296		4.31	10.60		14.91	22
0501	2 gang		23	.348		3.68	12.45		16.13	24.50
0601	3 gang	↓	18	.444		5.80	15.90		21.70	32.50

26 05 33.18 Pull Boxes

		Crew	Daily Output	Labor-Hours	Unit	Material	2014 Bare Costs Labor	Equipment	Total	Total Incl O&P
0010	**PULL BOXES**									
0100	Sheet metal, pull box, NEMA 1, type SC, 6" W x 6" H x 4" D	1 Elec	8	1	Ea.	10.75	36		46.75	70.50
0200	8" W x 8" H x 4" D		8	1		15.30	36		51.30	75.50
0300	10" W x 12" H x 6" D	↓	5.30	1.509		29	54		83	121

26 05 33.25 Conduit Fittings for Rigid Galvanized Steel

		Crew	Daily Output	Labor-Hours	Unit	Material	2014 Bare Costs Labor	Equipment	Total	Total Incl O&P
0010	**CONDUIT FITTINGS FOR RIGID GALVANIZED STEEL**									
2280	LB, LR or LL fittings & covers, 1/2" diameter	1 Elec	16	.500	Ea.	8.35	17.90		26.25	38.50
2290	3/4" diameter		13	.615		10.35	22		32.35	47.50
2300	1" diameter		11	.727		15.10	26		41.10	59
2330	1-1/4" diameter		8	1		23.50	36		59.50	84.50
2350	1-1/2" diameter		6	1.333		31	47.50		78.50	113
2370	2" diameter		5	1.600		51	57		108	150
5280	Service entrance cap, 1/2" diameter		16	.500		6.65	17.90		24.55	37
5300	3/4" diameter		13	.615		7.60	22		29.60	44.50
5320	1" diameter		10	.800		9.25	28.50		37.75	57
5340	1-1/4" diameter		8	1		12.40	36		48.40	72
5360	1-1/2" diameter		6.50	1.231		37	44		81	113
5380	2" diameter	↓	5.50	1.455		37	52		89	126

26 05 33.35 Flexible Metallic Conduit

		Crew	Daily Output	Labor-Hours	Unit	Material	2014 Bare Costs Labor	Equipment	Total	Total Incl O&P
0010	**FLEXIBLE METALLIC CONDUIT**									
0050	Steel, 3/8" diameter	1 Elec	200	.040	L.F.	.51	1.43		1.94	2.90
0100	1/2" diameter		200	.040		.57	1.43		2	2.97
0200	3/4" diameter		160	.050		.78	1.79		2.57	3.79
0250	1" diameter		100	.080		1.42	2.86		4.28	6.25
0300	1-1/4" diameter		70	.114		1.84	4.09		5.93	8.70
0350	1-1/2" diameter		50	.160		3	5.70		8.70	12.65
0370	2" diameter	↓	40	.200	↓	3.66	7.15		10.81	15.75

26 05 39 – Underfloor Raceways for Electrical Systems

26 05 39.30 Conduit In Concrete Slab

		Crew	Daily Output	Labor-Hours	Unit	Material	2014 Bare Costs Labor	Equipment	Total	Total Incl O&P
0010	**CONDUIT IN CONCRETE SLAB** Including terminations,									
0020	fittings and supports									
3230	PVC, schedule 40, 1/2" diameter	1 Elec	270	.030	L.F.	.64	1.06		1.70	2.43
3250	3/4" diameter		230	.035		.75	1.24		1.99	2.85
3270	1" diameter		200	.040		.94	1.43		2.37	3.38
3300	1-1/4" diameter		170	.047		1.36	1.68		3.04	4.24
3330	1-1/2" diameter		140	.057		1.63	2.04		3.67	5.15
3350	2" diameter		120	.067		2.07	2.38		4.45	6.15
4350	Rigid galvanized steel, 1/2" diameter		200	.040		2.31	1.43		3.74	4.88
4400	3/4" diameter		170	.047		2.44	1.68		4.12	5.45

26 05 39 – Underfloor Raceways for Electrical Systems

26 05 39.30 Conduit In Concrete Slab

		Crew	Daily Output	Labor-Hours	Unit	Material	2014 Bare Costs Labor	Equipment	Total	Total Incl O&P
4450	1" diameter	1 Elec	130	.062	L.F.	3.36	2.20		5.56	7.30
4500	1-1/4" diameter		110	.073		4.59	2.60		7.19	9.30
4600	1-1/2" diameter		100	.080		5.15	2.86		8.01	10.35
4800	2" diameter		90	.089		6.40	3.18		9.58	12.25

26 05 39.40 Conduit In Trench

		Crew	Daily Output	Labor-Hours	Unit	Material	2014 Bare Costs Labor	Equipment	Total	Total Incl O&P
0010	**CONDUIT IN TRENCH** Includes terminations and fittings									
0020	Does not include excavation or backfill, see Section 31 23 16.00									
0200	Rigid galvanized steel, 2" diameter	1 Elec	150	.053	L.F.	6	1.91		7.91	9.70
0400	2-1/2" diameter	"	100	.080		11.75	2.86		14.61	17.65
0600	3" diameter	2 Elec	160	.100		13.90	3.58		17.48	21
0800	3-1/2" diameter	"	140	.114		18.35	4.09		22.44	26.50

26 05 80 – Wiring Connections

26 05 80.10 Motor Connections

		Crew	Daily Output	Labor-Hours	Unit	Material	2014 Bare Costs Labor	Equipment	Total	Total Incl O&P
0010	**MOTOR CONNECTIONS**									
0020	Flexible conduit and fittings, 115 volt, 1 phase, up to 1 HP motor	1 Elec	8	1	Ea.	7.25	36		43.25	66.50

26 05 90 – Residential Applications

26 05 90.10 Residential Wiring

		Crew	Daily Output	Labor-Hours	Unit	Material	2014 Bare Costs Labor	Equipment	Total	Total Incl O&P
0010	**RESIDENTIAL WIRING**									
0020	20' avg. runs and #14/2 wiring incl. unless otherwise noted									
1000	Service & panel, includes 24' SE-AL cable, service eye, meter,									
1010	Socket, panel board, main bkr., ground rod, 15 or 20 amp									
1020	1-pole circuit breakers, and misc. hardware									
1100	100 amp, with 10 branch breakers	1 Elec	1.19	6.723	Ea.	540	240		780	990
1110	With PVC conduit and wire		.92	8.696		595	310		905	1,175
1120	With RGS conduit and wire		.73	10.959		740	390		1,130	1,450
1150	150 amp, with 14 branch breakers		1.03	7.767		840	278		1,118	1,375
1170	With PVC conduit and wire		.82	9.756		955	350		1,305	1,625
1180	With RGS conduit and wire		.67	11.940		1,225	425		1,650	2,050
1200	200 amp, with 18 branch breakers	2 Elec	1.80	8.889		1,125	320		1,445	1,750
1220	With PVC conduit and wire		1.46	10.959		1,225	390		1,615	2,000
1230	With RGS conduit and wire		1.24	12.903		1,600	460		2,060	2,500
1800	Lightning surge suppressor	1 Elec	32	.250		50.50	8.95		59.45	70.50
2000	Switch devices									
2100	Single pole, 15 amp, Ivory, with a 1-gang box, cover plate,									
2110	Type NM (Romex) cable	1 Elec	17.10	.468	Ea.	12.30	16.75		29.05	41
2120	Type MC (BX) cable		14.30	.559		23.50	20		43.50	58.50
2130	EMT & wire		5.71	1.401		29.50	50		79.50	115
2150	3-way, #14/3, type NM cable		14.55	.550		15.60	19.65		35.25	49
2170	Type MC cable		12.31	.650		31	23		54	72
2180	EMT & wire		5	1.600		32.50	57		89.50	129
2200	4-way, #14/3, type NM cable		14.55	.550		22.50	19.65		42.15	56.50
2220	Type MC cable		12.31	.650		37.50	23		60.50	79.50
2230	EMT & wire		5	1.600		39.50	57		96.50	137
2250	S.P., 20 amp, #12/2, type NM cable		13.33	.600		21	21.50		42.50	58.50
2270	Type MC cable		11.43	.700		30	25		55	74
2280	EMT & wire		4.85	1.649		40	59		99	141
2290	S.P. rotary dimmer, 600W, no wiring		17	.471		27	16.80		43.80	57
2300	S.P. rotary dimmer, 600W, type NM cable		14.55	.550		32	19.65		51.65	67
2320	Type MC cable		12.31	.650		43.50	23		66.50	85.50
2330	EMT & wire		5	1.600		51	57		108	150
2350	3-way rotary dimmer, type NM cable		13.33	.600		31.50	21.50		53	69.50

26 05 90.10 Residential Wiring		Crew	Daily Output	Labor-Hours	Unit	Material	2014 Bare Costs Labor	2014 Bare Costs Equipment	Total	Total Incl O&P
2370	Type MC cable	1 Elec	11.43	.700	Ea.	42.50	25		67.50	88
2380	EMT & wire	↓	4.85	1.649	↓	50	59		109	152
2400	Interval timer wall switch, 20 amp, 1-30 min., #12/2									
2410	Type NM cable	1 Elec	14.55	.550	Ea.	54	19.65		73.65	91.50
2420	Type MC cable		12.31	.650		59	23		82	103
2430	EMT & wire	↓	5	1.600	↓	73	57		130	174
2500	Decorator style									
2510	S.P., 15 amp, type NM cable	1 Elec	17.10	.468	Ea.	16.15	16.75		32.90	45.50
2520	Type MC cable		14.30	.559		27.50	20		47.50	62.50
2530	EMT & wire		5.71	1.401		33.50	50		83.50	119
2550	3-way, #14/3, type NM cable		14.55	.550		19.40	19.65		39.05	53.50
2570	Type MC cable		12.31	.650		34.50	23		57.50	76
2580	EMT & wire		5	1.600		36.50	57		93.50	134
2600	4-way, #14/3, type NM cable		14.55	.550		26.50	19.65		46.15	61
2620	Type MC cable		12.31	.650		41.50	23		64.50	83.50
2630	EMT & wire		5	1.600		43	57		100	141
2650	S.P., 20 amp, #12/2, type NM cable		13.33	.600		25	21.50		46.50	62.50
2670	Type MC cable		11.43	.700		34	25		59	78
2680	EMT & wire		4.85	1.649		44	59		103	145
2700	S.P., slide dimmer, type NM cable		17.10	.468		32	16.75		48.75	63
2720	Type MC cable		14.30	.559		43.50	20		63.50	80.50
2730	EMT & wire		5.71	1.401		51	50		101	138
2750	S.P., touch dimmer, type NM cable		17.10	.468		29.50	16.75		46.25	59.50
2770	Type MC cable		14.30	.559		40.50	20		60.50	77
2780	EMT & wire		5.71	1.401		48	50		98	135
2800	3-way touch dimmer, type NM cable		13.33	.600		51.50	21.50		73	91.50
2820	Type MC cable		11.43	.700		63	25		88	110
2830	EMT & wire	↓	4.85	1.649	↓	70.50	.59		129.50	174
3000	Combination devices									
3100	S.P. switch/15 amp recpt., Ivory, 1-gang box, plate									
3110	Type NM cable	1 Elec	11.43	.700	Ea.	24	25		49	67.50
3120	Type MC cable		10	.800		35.50	28.50		64	86
3130	EMT & wire		4.40	1.818		43	65		108	153
3150	S.P. switch/pilot light, type NM cable		11.43	.700		24	25		49	67.50
3170	Type MC cable		10	.800		35.50	28.50		64	86
3180	EMT & wire		4.43	1.806		43	64.50		107.50	154
3190	2-S.P. switches, 2-#14/2, no wiring		14	.571		6.95	20.50		27.45	41
3200	2-S.P. switches, 2-#14/2, type NM cables		10	.800		27.50	28.50		56	77.50
3220	Type MC cable		8.89	.900		44.50	32		76.50	102
3230	EMT & wire		4.10	1.951		46.50	70		116.50	165
3250	3-way switch/15 amp recpt., #14/3, type NM cable		10	.800		31.50	28.50		60	81.50
3270	Type MC cable		8.89	.900		46.50	32		78.50	104
3280	EMT & wire		4.10	1.951		48	70		118	167
3300	2-3 way switches, 2-#14/3, type NM cables		8.89	.900		41	32		73	97.50
3320	Type MC cable		8	1		66	36		102	131
3330	EMT & wire		4	2		56	71.50		127.50	179
3350	S.P. switch/20 amp recpt., #12/2, type NM cable		10	.800		32	28.50		60.50	82.50
3370	Type MC cable		8.89	.900		37	32		69	93.50
3380	EMT & wire	↓	4.10	1.951	↓	51	70		121	170
3400	Decorator style									
3410	S.P. switch/15 amp recpt., type NM cable	1 Elec	11.43	.700	Ea.	28	25		53	71.50
3420	Type MC cable		10	.800		39	28.50		67.50	90
3430	EMT & wire	↓	4.40	1.818	↓	46.50	65		111.50	158

26 05 90.10 Residential Wiring	Crew	Daily Output	Labor-Hours	Unit	Material	2014 Bare Costs Labor	2014 Bare Costs Equipment	Total	Total Incl O&P
3450 S.P. switch/pilot light, type NM cable	1 Elec	11.43	.700	Ea.	28	25		53	72
3470 Type MC cable		10	.800		39.50	28.50		68	90.50
3480 EMT & wire		4.40	1.818		47	65		112	158
3500 2-S.P. switches, 2-#14/2, type NM cables		10	.800		31.50	28.50		60	81.50
3520 Type MC cable		8.89	.900		48.50	32		80.50	106
3530 EMT & wire		4.10	1.951		50	70		120	169
3550 3-way/15 amp recpt., #14/3, type NM cable		10	.800		35	28.50		63.50	85.50
3570 Type MC cable		8.89	.900		50.50	32		82.50	108
3580 EMT & wire		4.10	1.951		52	70		122	171
3650 2-3 way switches, 2-#14/3, type NM cables		8.89	.900		45	32		77	102
3670 Type MC cable		8	1		69.50	36		105.50	135
3680 EMT & wire		4	2		59.50	71.50		131	183
3700 S.P. switch/20 amp recpt., #12/2, type NM cable		10	.800		36	28.50		64.50	86.50
3720 Type MC cable		8.89	.900		41	32		73	97.50
3730 EMT & wire	▼	4.10	1.951	▼	55	70		125	174
4000 Receptacle devices									
4010 Duplex outlet, 15 amp recpt., Ivory, 1-gang box, plate									
4015 Type NM cable	1 Elec	14.55	.550	Ea.	11	19.65		30.65	44
4020 Type MC cable		12.31	.650		22.50	23		45.50	62.50
4030 EMT & wire		5.33	1.501		28	53.50		81.50	119
4050 With #12/2, type NM cable		12.31	.650		13.65	23		36.65	53
4070 Type MC cable		10.67	.750		22.50	27		49.50	68.50
4080 EMT & wire		4.71	1.699		32.50	60.50		93	135
4100 20 amp recpt., #12/2, type NM cable		12.31	.650		21	23		44	61
4120 Type MC cable		10.67	.750		29.50	27		56.50	76.50
4130 EMT & wire	▼	4.71	1.699	▼	39.50	60.50		100	143
4140 For GFI see Section 26 05 90.10 line 4300 below									
4150 Decorator style, 15 amp recpt., type NM cable	1 Elec	14.55	.550	Ea.	14.80	19.65		34.45	48.50
4170 Type MC cable		12.31	.650		26	23		49	66.50
4180 EMT & wire		5.33	1.501		32	53.50		85.50	123
4200 With #12/2, type NM cable		12.31	.650		17.45	23		40.45	57
4220 Type MC cable		10.67	.750		26	27		53	73
4230 EMT & wire		4.71	1.699		36	60.50		96.50	140
4250 20 amp recpt. #12/2, type NM cable		12.31	.650		24.50	23		47.50	65
4270 Type MC cable		10.67	.750		33.50	27		60.50	80.50
4280 EMT & wire		4.71	1.699		43.50	60.50		104	147
4300 GFI, 15 amp recpt., type NM cable		12.31	.650		47.50	23		70.50	90
4320 Type MC cable		10.67	.750		58.50	27		85.50	109
4330 EMT & wire		4.71	1.699		64.50	60.50		125	171
4350 GFI with #12/2, type NM cable		10.67	.750		50	27		77	99
4370 Type MC cable		9.20	.870		58.50	31		89.50	116
4380 EMT & wire		4.21	1.900		68.50	68		136.50	187
4400 20 amp recpt., #12/2 type NM cable		10.67	.750		52	27		79	102
4420 Type MC cable		9.20	.870		61	31		92	118
4430 EMT & wire		4.21	1.900		71	68		139	189
4500 Weather-proof cover for above receptacles, add	▼	32	.250	▼	4.08	8.95		13.03	19.15
4550 Air conditioner outlet, 20 amp-240 volt recpt.									
4560 30' of #12/2, 2 pole circuit breaker									
4570 Type NM cable	1 Elec	10	.800	Ea.	63	28.50		91.50	116
4580 Type MC cable		9	.889		73	32		105	133
4590 EMT & wire		4	2		81.50	71.50		153	207
4600 Decorator style, type NM cable		10	.800		67.50	28.50		96	122
4620 Type MC cable		9	.889		78	32		110	138

26 05 90.10 Residential Wiring	Crew	Daily Output	Labor-Hours	Unit	Material	2014 Bare Costs Labor	Equipment	Total	Total Incl O&P
4630 EMT & wire	1 Elec	4	2	Ea.	86.50	71.50		158	212
4650 Dryer outlet, 30 amp-240 volt recpt., 20' of #10/3									
4660 2 pole circuit breaker									
4670 Type NM cable	1 Elec	6.41	1.248	Ea.	64	44.50		108.50	144
4680 Type MC cable		5.71	1.401		69	50		119	158
4690 EMT & wire	↓	3.48	2.299	↓	75.50	82		157.50	217
4700 Range outlet, 50 amp-240 volt recpt., 30' of #8/3									
4710 Type NM cable	1 Elec	4.21	1.900	Ea.	92	68		160	212
4720 Type MC cable		4	2		136	71.50		207.50	267
4730 EMT & wire		2.96	2.703		106	96.50		202.50	275
4750 Central vacuum outlet, Type NM cable		6.40	1.250		60	44.50		104.50	139
4770 Type MC cable		5.71	1.401		75.50	50		125.50	165
4780 EMT & wire	↓	3.48	2.299	↓	81.50	82		163.50	224
4800 30 amp-110 volt locking recpt., #10/2 circ. bkr.									
4810 Type NM cable	1 Elec	6.20	1.290	Ea.	69	46		115	152
4820 Type MC cable		5.40	1.481		86.50	53		139.50	182
4830 EMT & wire	↓	3.20	2.500	↓	92	89.50		181.50	247
4900 Low voltage outlets									
4910 Telephone recpt., 20' of 4/C phone wire	1 Elec	26	.308	Ea.	10.95	11		21.95	30
4920 TV recpt., 20' of RG59U coax wire, F type connector	"	16	.500	"	19.20	17.90		37.10	50.50
4950 Door bell chime, transformer, 2 buttons, 60' of bellwire									
4970 Economy model	1 Elec	11.50	.696	Ea.	58	25		83	105
4980 Custom model		11.50	.696		123	25		148	176
4990 Luxury model, 3 buttons	↓	9.50	.842	↓	305	30		335	385
6000 Lighting outlets									
6050 Wire only (for fixture), type NM cable	1 Elec	32	.250	Ea.	7.20	8.95		16.15	22.50
6070 Type MC cable		24	.333		13.85	11.90		25.75	34.50
6080 EMT & wire		10	.800		18.65	28.50		47.15	67.50
6100 Box (4"), and wire (for fixture), type NM cable		25	.320		16.10	11.45		27.55	36.50
6120 Type MC cable		20	.400		23	14.30		37.30	48.50
6130 EMT & wire	↓	11	.727	↓	27.50	26		53.50	73
6200 Fixtures (use with lines 6050 or 6100 above)									
6210 Canopy style, economy grade	1 Elec	40	.200	Ea.	37.50	7.15		44.65	52.50
6220 Custom grade		40	.200		57.50	7.15		64.65	74.50
6250 Dining room chandelier, economy grade		19	.421		93.50	15.05		108.55	128
6260 Custom grade		19	.421		274	15.05		289.05	325
6270 Luxury grade		15	.533		620	19.05		639.05	710
6310 Kitchen fixture (fluorescent), economy grade		30	.267		69.50	9.55		79.05	92
6320 Custom grade		25	.320		190	11.45		201.45	228
6350 Outdoor, wall mounted, economy grade		30	.267		35.50	9.55		45.05	54.50
6360 Custom grade		30	.267		121	9.55		130.55	150
6370 Luxury grade		25	.320		274	11.45		285.45	320
6410 Outdoor PAR floodlights, 1 lamp, 150 watt		20	.400		38	14.30		52.30	65.50
6420 2 lamp, 150 watt each		20	.400		63	14.30		77.30	92.50
6425 Motion sensing, 2 lamp, 150 watt each		20	.400		76	14.30		90.30	107
6430 For infrared security sensor, add		32	.250		127	8.95		135.95	155
6450 Outdoor, quartz-halogen, 300 watt flood		20	.400		46	14.30		60.30	74
6600 Recessed downlight, round, pre-wired, 50 or 75 watt trim		30	.267		47	9.55		56.55	67
6610 With shower light trim		30	.267		58	9.55		67.55	79.50
6620 With wall washer trim		28	.286		70	10.20		80.20	93.50
6630 With eye-ball trim	↓	28	.286		70	10.20		80.20	93.50
6640 For direct contact with insulation, add					2.49			2.49	2.74
6700 Porcelain lamp holder	1 Elec	40	.200	↓	3.50	7.15		10.65	15.55

26 05 90 – Residential Applications

26 05 90.10 Residential Wiring	Crew	Daily Output	Labor-Hours	Unit	Material	2014 Bare Costs Labor	Equipment	Total	Total Incl O&P
6710	With pull switch	1 Elec	40	.200	Ea.	5.70	7.15		12.85	18
6750	Fluorescent strip, 1-20 watt tube, wrap around diffuser, 24"		24	.333		58.50	11.90		70.40	84
6760	1-34 watt tube, 48"		24	.333		75.50	11.90		87.40	103
6770	2-34 watt tubes, 48"		20	.400		89.50	14.30		103.80	122
6780	With residential ballast		20	.400		100	14.30		114.30	134
6800	Bathroom heat lamp, 1-250 watt		28	.286		51.50	10.20		61.70	73
6810	2-250 watt lamps		28	.286		82	10.20		92.20	107
6820	For timer switch, see Section 26 05 90.10 line 2400									
6900	Outdoor post lamp, incl. post, fixture, 35' of #14/2									
6910	Type NMC cable	1 Elec	3.50	2.286	Ea.	226	81.50		307.50	380
6920	Photo-eye, add		27	.296		38	10.60		48.60	59.50
6950	Clock dial time switch, 24 hr., w/enclosure, type NM cable		11.43	.700		70.50	25		95.50	119
6970	Type MC cable		11	.727		82	26		108	133
6980	EMT & wire		4.85	1.649		88	59		147	193
7000	Alarm systems									
7050	Smoke detectors, box, #14/3, type NM cable	1 Elec	14.55	.550	Ea.	35	19.65		54.65	71
7070	Type MC cable		12.31	.650		46.50	23		69.50	89
7080	EMT & wire		5	1.600		48.50	57		105.50	147
7090	For relay output to security system, add					14.10			14.10	15.55
8000	Residential equipment									
8050	Disposal hook-up, incl. switch, outlet box, 3' of flex									
8060	20 amp-1 pole circ. bkr., and 25' of #12/2									
8070	Type NM cable	1 Elec	10	.800	Ea.	32.50	28.50		61	83
8080	Type MC cable		8	1		42	36		78	105
8090	EMT & wire		5	1.600		53.50	57		110.50	153
8100	Trash compactor or dishwasher hook-up, incl. outlet box,									
8110	3' of flex, 15 amp-1 pole circ. bkr., and 25' of #14/2									
8130	Type MC cable	1 Elec	8	1	Ea.	37	36		73	99
8140	EMT & wire	"	5	1.600	"	45	57		102	143
8150	Hot water sink dispensor hook-up, use line 8100									
8200	Vent/exhaust fan hook-up, type NM cable	1 Elec	32	.250	Ea.	7.20	8.95		16.15	22.50
8220	Type MC cable		24	.333		13.85	11.90		25.75	34.50
8230	EMT & wire		10	.800		18.65	28.50		47.15	67.50
8250	Bathroom vent fan, 50 CFM (use with above hook-up)									
8260	Economy model	1 Elec	15	.533	Ea.	27	19.05		46.05	61
8270	Low noise model		15	.533		37	19.05		56.05	71.50
8280	Custom model		12	.667		127	24		151	179
8300	Bathroom or kitchen vent fan, 110 CFM									
8310	Economy model	1 Elec	15	.533	Ea.	75.50	19.05		94.55	114
8320	Low noise model	"	15	.533	"	93.50	19.05		112.55	134
8350	Paddle fan, variable speed (w/o lights)									
8360	Economy model (AC motor)	1 Elec	10	.800	Ea.	125	28.50		153.50	184
8362	With light kit		10	.800		166	28.50		194.50	229
8370	Custom model (AC motor)		10	.800		197	28.50		225.50	264
8372	With light kit		10	.800		238	28.50		266.50	310
8380	Luxury model (DC motor)		8	1		390	36		426	490
8382	With light kit		8	1		430	36		466	535
8390	Remote speed switch for above, add		12	.667		32.50	24		56.50	74.50
8500	Whole house exhaust fan, ceiling mount, 36", variable speed									
8510	Remote switch, incl. shutters, 20 amp-1 pole circ. bkr.									
8520	30' of #12/2, type NM cable	1 Elec	4	2	Ea.	1,250	71.50		1,321.50	1,500
8530	Type MC cable		3.50	2.286		1,275	81.50		1,356.50	1,525
8540	EMT & wire		3	2.667		1,275	95.50		1,370.50	1,550

26 05 90 – Residential Applications

26 05 90.10 Residential Wiring

		Crew	Daily Output	Labor-Hours	Unit	Material	2014 Bare Costs Labor	Equipment	Total	Total Incl O&P
8600	Whirlpool tub hook-up, incl. timer switch, outlet box									
8610	3' of flex, 20 amp-1 pole GFI circ. bkr.									
8620	30' of #12/2, type NM cable	1 Elec	5	1.600	Ea.	127	57		184	233
8630	Type MC cable		4.20	1.905		131	68		199	256
8640	EMT & wire		3.40	2.353		141	84		225	294
8650	Hot water heater hook-up, incl. 1-2 pole circ. bkr., box;									
8660	3' of flex, 20' of #10/2, type NM cable	1 Elec	5	1.600	Ea.	34	57		91	131
8670	Type MC cable		4.20	1.905		47.50	68		115.50	163
8680	EMT & wire		3.40	2.353		48.50	84		132.50	191
9000	Heating/air conditioning									
9050	Furnace/boiler hook-up, incl. firestat, local on-off switch									
9060	Emergency switch, and 40' of type NM cable	1 Elec	4	2	Ea.	52.50	71.50		124	175
9070	Type MC cable		3.50	2.286		69.50	81.50		151	211
9080	EMT & wire		1.50	5.333		81	191		272	400
9100	Air conditioner hook-up, incl. local 60 amp disc. switch									
9110	3' sealtite, 40 amp, 2 pole circuit breaker									
9130	40' of #8/2, type NM cable	1 Elec	3.50	2.286	Ea.	182	81.50		263.50	335
9140	Type MC cable		3	2.667		249	95.50		344.50	430
9150	EMT & wire		1.30	6.154		218	220		438	600
9200	Heat pump hook-up, 1-40 & 1-100 amp 2 pole circ. bkr.									
9210	Local disconnect switch, 3' sealtite									
9220	40' of #8/2 & 30' of #3/2									
9230	Type NM cable	1 Elec	1.30	6.154	Ea.	525	220		745	940
9240	Type MC cable		1.08	7.407		600	265		865	1,100
9250	EMT & wire		.94	8.511		590	305		895	1,150
9500	Thermostat hook-up, using low voltage wire									
9520	Heating only, 25' of #18-3	1 Elec	24	.333	Ea.	9.60	11.90		21.50	30
9530	Heating/cooling, 25' of #18-4	"	20	.400	"	11.75	14.30		26.05	36.50

26 24 Switchboards and Panelboards

26 24 16 – Panelboards

26 24 16.10 Load Centers

		Crew	Daily Output	Labor-Hours	Unit	Material	2014 Bare Costs Labor	Equipment	Total	Total Incl O&P
0010	**LOAD CENTERS** (residential type)									
0100	3 wire, 120/240 V, 1 phase, including 1 pole plug-in breakers									
0200	100 amp main lugs, indoor, 8 circuits	1 Elec	1.40	5.714	Ea.	174	204		378	525
0300	12 circuits		1.20	6.667		243	238		481	655
0400	Rainproof, 8 circuits		1.40	5.714		209	204		413	565
0500	12 circuits		1.20	6.667		294	238		532	715
0600	200 amp main lugs, indoor, 16 circuits	R-1A	1.80	8.889		325	265		590	795
0700	20 circuits		1.50	10.667		405	320		725	970
0800	24 circuits		1.30	12.308		530	365		895	1,200
1200	Rainproof, 16 circuits		1.80	8.889		385	265		650	865
1300	20 circuits		1.50	10.667		460	320		780	1,025
1400	24 circuits		1.30	12.308		690	365		1,055	1,375

26 24 16.20 Panelboard and Load Center Circuit Breakers

		Crew	Daily Output	Labor-Hours	Unit	Material	2014 Bare Costs Labor	Equipment	Total	Total Incl O&P
0010	**PANELBOARD AND LOAD CENTER CIRCUIT BREAKERS**									
2000	Plug-in panel or load center, 120/240 volt, to 60 amp, 1 pole	1 Elec	12	.667	Ea.	11.15	24		35.15	51.50
2004	Circuit breaker, 20 A, 1 pole with NM cable		6.50	1.231		18.90	44		62.90	93
2006	30 A, 1 pole with NM cable		6.50	1.231		18.90	44		62.90	93
2010	2 pole		9	.889		25	32		57	79.50
2014	50 A, 2 pole with NM cable		5.50	1.455		33	52		85	121

26 24 Switchboards and Panelboards

26 24 16 – Panelboards

26 24 16.20 Panelboard and Load Center Circuit Breakers

		Crew	Daily Output	Labor-Hours	Unit	Material	2014 Bare Costs Labor	Equipment	Total	Total Incl O&P
2020	3 pole	1 Elec	7.50	1.067	Ea.	87	38		125	159
2030	100 amp, 2 pole		6	1.333		117	47.50		164.50	206
2040	3 pole		4.50	1.778		130	63.50		193.50	247
2050	150 to 200 amp, 2 pole		3	2.667		213	95.50		308.50	390
2060	Plug-in tandem, 120/240 V, 2-15 A, 1 pole		11	.727		24.50	26		50.50	69.50
2070	1-15 A & 1-20 A		11	.727		24.50	26		50.50	69.50
2080	2-20 A		11	.727		24.50	26		50.50	69.50
2300	Ground fault, 240 volt, 30 amp, 1 pole		7	1.143		86.50	41		127.50	162
2310	2 pole		6	1.333		155	47.50		202.50	248

26 27 Low-Voltage Distribution Equipment

26 27 13 – Electricity Metering

26 27 13.10 Meter Centers and Sockets

		Crew	Daily Output	Labor-Hours	Unit	Material	2014 Bare Costs Labor	Equipment	Total	Total Incl O&P
0010	**METER CENTERS AND SOCKETS**									
0100	Sockets, single position, 4 terminal, 100 amp	1 Elec	3.20	2.500	Ea.	42	89.50		131.50	192
0200	150 amp		2.30	3.478		54.50	124		178.50	263
0300	200 amp		1.90	4.211		89.50	151		240.50	345
0500	Double position, 4 terminal, 100 amp		2.80	2.857		198	102		300	385
0600	150 amp		2.10	3.810		233	136		369	480
0700	200 amp		1.70	4.706		440	168		608	755
1100	Meter centers and sockets, three phase, single pos, 7 terminal, 100 amp		2.80	2.857		144	102		246	325
1200	200 amp		2.10	3.810		278	136		414	530
1400	400 amp		1.70	4.706		715	168		883	1,050
2590	Basic meter device									
2600	1P 3W 120/240 V 4 jaw 125A sockets, 3 meter	2 Elec	1	16	Ea.	615	570		1,185	1,600
2620	5 meter		.80	20		925	715		1,640	2,200
2640	7 meter		.56	28.571		1,350	1,025		2,375	3,175
2660	10 meter		.48	33.333		1,850	1,200		3,050	3,975
2680	Rainproof 1P 3W 120/240 V 4 jaw 125A sockets									
2690	3 meter	2 Elec	1	16	Ea.	615	570		1,185	1,600
2710	6 meter		.60	26.667		1,050	955		2,005	2,725
2730	8 meter		.52	30.769		1,475	1,100		2,575	3,425
2750	1P 3W 120/240 V 4 jaw sockets									
2760	with 125A circuit breaker, 3 meter	2 Elec	1	16	Ea.	1,150	570		1,720	2,200
2780	5 meter		.80	20		1,825	715		2,540	3,175
2800	7 meter		.56	28.571		2,600	1,025		3,625	4,550
2820	10 meter		.48	33.333		3,625	1,200		4,825	5,950
2830	Rainproof 1P 3W 120/240 V 4 jaw sockets									
2840	with 125A circuit breaker, 3 meter	2 Elec	1	16	Ea.	1,150	570		1,720	2,200
2870	6 meter		.60	26.667		2,125	955		3,080	3,900
2890	8 meter		.52	30.769		2,900	1,100		4,000	5,000
3250	1P 3W 120/240 V 4 jaw sockets									
3260	with 200A circuit breaker, 3 meter	2 Elec	1	16	Ea.	1,725	570		2,295	2,825
3290	6 meter		.60	26.667		3,450	955		4,405	5,350
3310	8 meter		.56	28.571		4,675	1,025		5,700	6,800
3330	Rainproof 1P 3W 120/240 V 4 jaw sockets									
3350	with 200A circuit breaker, 3 meter	2 Elec	1	16	Ea.	1,725	570		2,295	2,825
3380	6 meter		.60	26.667		3,450	955		4,405	5,350
3400	8 meter		.52	30.769		4,675	1,100		5,775	6,925

26 27 Low-Voltage Distribution Equipment

26 27 23 – Indoor Service Poles

26 27 23.40 Surface Raceway

		Crew	Daily Output	Labor-Hours	Unit	Material	2014 Bare Costs Labor	Equipment	Total	Total Incl O&P
0010	**SURFACE RACEWAY**									
0090	Metal, straight section									
0100	No. 500	1 Elec	100	.080	L.F.	1.04	2.86		3.90	5.80
0110	No. 700		100	.080		1.17	2.86		4.03	5.95
0200	No. 1000		90	.089		1.66	3.18		4.84	7.05
0400	No. 1500, small pancake		90	.089		2.15	3.18		5.33	7.55
0600	No. 2000, base & cover, blank		90	.089		2.19	3.18		5.37	7.60
0800	No. 3000, base & cover, blank		75	.107		4.40	3.81		8.21	11.10
2400	Fittings, elbows, No. 500		40	.200	Ea.	1.90	7.15		9.05	13.80
2800	Elbow cover, No. 2000		40	.200		3.57	7.15		10.72	15.65
2880	Tee, No. 500		42	.190		3.66	6.80		10.46	15.20
2900	No. 2000		27	.296		11.85	10.60		22.45	30.50
3000	Switch box, No. 500		16	.500		11	17.90		28.90	41.50
3400	Telephone outlet, No. 1500		16	.500		14.10	17.90		32	45
3600	Junction box, No. 1500		16	.500		9.65	17.90		27.55	40
3800	Plugmold wired sections, No. 2000									
4000	1 circuit, 6 outlets, 3 ft. long	1 Elec	8	1	Ea.	36	36		72	98
4100	2 circuits, 8 outlets, 6 ft. long	"	5.30	1.509	"	53	54		107	147

26 27 26 – Wiring Devices

26 27 26.10 Low Voltage Switching

		Crew	Daily Output	Labor-Hours	Unit	Material	2014 Bare Costs Labor	Equipment	Total	Total Incl O&P
0010	**LOW VOLTAGE SWITCHING**									
3600	Relays, 120 V or 277 V standard	1 Elec	12	.667	Ea.	41	24		65	84.50
3800	Flush switch, standard		40	.200		11.40	7.15		18.55	24.50
4000	Interchangeable		40	.200		14.90	7.15		22.05	28
4100	Surface switch, standard		40	.200		8.05	7.15		15.20	20.50
4200	Transformer 115 V to 25 V		12	.667		129	24		153	181
4400	Master control, 12 circuit, manual		4	2		125	71.50		196.50	254
4500	25 circuit, motorized		4	2		139	71.50		210.50	269
4600	Rectifier, silicon		12	.667		45	24		69	88.50
4800	Switchplates, 1 gang, 1, 2 or 3 switch, plastic		80	.100		4.95	3.58		8.53	11.30
5000	Stainless steel		80	.100		11.25	3.58		14.83	18.25
5400	2 gang, 3 switch, stainless steel		53	.151		22.50	5.40		27.90	34
5500	4 switch, plastic		53	.151		10.25	5.40		15.65	20
5600	2 gang, 4 switch, stainless steel		53	.151		21.50	5.40		26.90	32.50
5700	6 switch, stainless steel		53	.151		42.50	5.40		47.90	56
5800	3 gang, 9 switch, stainless steel		32	.250		64	8.95		72.95	85

26 27 26.20 Wiring Devices Elements

		Crew	Daily Output	Labor-Hours	Unit	Material	2014 Bare Costs Labor	Equipment	Total	Total Incl O&P
0010	**WIRING DEVICES ELEMENTS**									
0200	Toggle switch, quiet type, single pole, 15 amp	1 Elec	40	.200	Ea.	5.70	7.15		12.85	18
0600	3 way, 15 amp		23	.348		5.95	12.45		18.40	27
0900	4 way, 15 amp		15	.533		10.75	19.05		29.80	43
1650	Dimmer switch, 120 volt, incandescent, 600 watt, 1 pole **G**		16	.500		18.40	17.90		36.30	49.50
2460	Receptacle, duplex, 120 volt, grounded, 15 amp		40	.200		1.22	7.15		8.37	13.05
2470	20 amp		27	.296		8.35	10.60		18.95	26.50
2490	Dryer, 30 amp		15	.533		5.20	19.05		24.25	36.50
2500	Range, 50 amp		11	.727		11.85	26		37.85	55.50
2600	Wall plates, stainless steel, 1 gang		80	.100		2.53	3.58		6.11	8.65
2800	2 gang		53	.151		4.29	5.40		9.69	13.55
3200	Lampholder, keyless		26	.308		11	11		22	30
3400	Pullchain with receptacle		22	.364		20.50	13		33.50	44

26 27 Low-Voltage Distribution Equipment

26 27 73 – Door Chimes

26 27 73.10 Doorbell System	Crew	Daily Output	Labor-Hours	Unit	Material	2014 Bare Costs Labor	Equipment	Total	Total Incl O&P
0010 **DOORBELL SYSTEM**, incl. transformer, button & signal									
1000 Door chimes, 2 notes, minimum	1 Elec	16	.500	Ea.	24.50	17.90		42.40	56.50
1020 Maximum		12	.667		115	24		139	165
1100 Tube type, 3 tube system		12	.667		187	24		211	245
1180 4 tube system		10	.800		385	28.50		413.50	470
1900 For transformer & button, minimum add		5	1.600		16.30	57		73.30	111
1960 Maximum, add		4.50	1.778		78	63.50		141.50	190
3000 For push button only, minimum		24	.333		3.03	11.90		14.93	23
3100 Maximum		20	.400		21.50	14.30		35.80	47

26 28 Low-Voltage Circuit Protective Devices

26 28 16 – Enclosed Switches and Circuit Breakers

26 28 16.10 Circuit Breakers

	Crew	Daily Output	Labor-Hours	Unit	Material	2014 Bare Costs Labor	Equipment	Total	Total Incl O&P
0010 **CIRCUIT BREAKERS** (in enclosure)									
0100 Enclosed (NEMA 1), 600 volt, 3 pole, 30 amp	1 Elec	3.20	2.500	Ea.	495	89.50		584.50	690
0200 60 amp		2.80	2.857		610	102		712	835
0400 100 amp		2.30	3.478		700	124		824	975

26 28 16.20 Safety Switches

	Crew	Daily Output	Labor-Hours	Unit	Material	2014 Bare Costs Labor	Equipment	Total	Total Incl O&P
0010 **SAFETY SWITCHES**									
0100 General duty 240 volt, 3 pole NEMA 1, fusible, 30 amp	1 Elec	3.20	2.500	Ea.	86	89.50		175.50	241
0200 60 amp		2.30	3.478		146	124		270	365
0300 100 amp		1.90	4.211		250	151		401	520
0400 200 amp		1.30	6.154		535	220		755	950
0500 400 amp	2 Elec	1.80	8.889		1,350	320		1,670	2,025
9010 Disc. switch, 600 V 3 pole fusible, 30 amp, to 10 HP motor	1 Elec	3.20	2.500		350	89.50		439.50	530
9050 60 amp, to 30 HP motor		2.30	3.478		805	124		929	1,100
9070 100 amp, to 60 HP motor		1.90	4.211		805	151		956	1,125

26 28 16.40 Time Switches

	Crew	Daily Output	Labor-Hours	Unit	Material	2014 Bare Costs Labor	Equipment	Total	Total Incl O&P
0010 **TIME SWITCHES**									
0100 Single pole, single throw, 24 hour dial	1 Elec	4	2	Ea.	138	71.50		209.50	269
0200 24 hour dial with reserve power		3.60	2.222		585	79.50		664.50	775
0300 Astronomic dial		3.60	2.222		180	79.50		259.50	330
0400 Astronomic dial with reserve power		3.30	2.424		665	86.50		751.50	870
0500 7 day calendar dial		3.30	2.424		158	86.50		244.50	315
0600 7 day calendar dial with reserve power		3.20	2.500		395	89.50		484.50	580
0700 Photo cell 2000 watt		8	1		27	36		63	88.50

26 32 Packaged Generator Assemblies

26 32 13 – Engine Generators

26 32 13.16 Gas-Engine-Driven Generator Sets

	Crew	Daily Output	Labor-Hours	Unit	Material	2014 Bare Costs Labor	Equipment	Total	Total Incl O&P
0010 **GAS-ENGINE-DRIVEN GENERATOR SETS**									
0020 Gas or gasoline operated, includes battery,									
0050 charger, & muffler									
0200 3 phase 4 wire, 277/480 volt, 7.5 kW	R-3	.83	24.096	Ea.	7,275	860	169	8,304	9,600
0300 11.5 kW		.71	28.169		10,300	1,000	197	11,497	13,200
0400 20 kW		.63	31.746		12,200	1,125	222	13,547	15,500
0500 35 kW		.55	36.364		14,500	1,300	255	16,055	18,300

26 33 Battery Equipment

26 33 43 – Battery Chargers

26 33 43.55 Electric Vehicle Charging		Crew	Daily Output	Labor-Hours	Unit	Material	2014 Bare Costs Labor	Equipment	Total	Total Incl O&P
0010	**ELECTRIC VEHICLE CHARGING**									
0020	Level 2, wall mounted									
2100	Light duty, hard wired G	1 Elec	20.48	.391	Ea.	1,000	13.95		1,013.95	1,125
2110	plug in G	"	30.72	.260	"	1,000	9.30		1,009.30	1,125

26 36 Transfer Switches

26 36 23 – Automatic Transfer Switches

26 36 23.10 Automatic Transfer Switch Devices

		Crew	Daily Output	Labor-Hours	Unit	Material	2014 Bare Costs Labor	Equipment	Total	Total Incl O&P
0010	**AUTOMATIC TRANSFER SWITCH DEVICES**									
0100	Switches, enclosed 480 volt, 3 pole, 30 amp	1 Elec	2.30	3.478	Ea.	2,625	124		2,749	3,075
0200	60 amp	"	1.90	4.211	"	2,625	151		2,776	3,125

26 41 Facility Lightning Protection

26 41 13 – Lightning Protection for Structures

26 41 13.13 Lightning Protection for Buildings

		Crew	Daily Output	Labor-Hours	Unit	Material	2014 Bare Costs Labor	Equipment	Total	Total Incl O&P
0010	**LIGHTNING PROTECTION FOR BUILDINGS**									
0200	Air terminals & base, copper									
0400	3/8" diameter x 10" (to 75' high)	1 Elec	8	1	Ea.	24.50	36		60.50	85.50
1000	Aluminum, 1/2" diameter x 12" (to 75' high)		8	1		15.70	36		51.70	76
1020	1/2" diameter x 24"		7.30	1.096		18.20	39		57.20	84
1040	1/2" diameter x 60"		6.70	1.194		25.50	42.50		68	98
2000	Cable, copper, 220 lb. per thousand ft. (to 75' high)		320	.025	L.F.	3	.89		3.89	4.76
2500	Aluminum, 101 lb. per thousand ft. (to 75' high)		280	.029	"	.93	1.02		1.95	2.69
3000	Arrester, 175 volt AC to ground		8	1	Ea.	88	36		124	156

26 51 Interior Lighting

26 51 13 – Interior Lighting Fixtures, Lamps, and Ballasts

26 51 13.50 Interior Lighting Fixtures

		Crew	Daily Output	Labor-Hours	Unit	Material	2014 Bare Costs Labor	Equipment	Total	Total Incl O&P
0010	**INTERIOR LIGHTING FIXTURES** Including lamps, mounting									
0030	hardware and connections									
0100	Fluorescent, C.W. lamps, troffer, recess mounted in grid, RS									
0130	Grid ceiling mount									
0200	Acrylic lens, 1'W x 4'L, two 40 watt	1 Elec	5.70	1.404	Ea.	47.50	50		97.50	134
0300	2'W x 2'L, two U40 watt		5.70	1.404		51	50		101	139
0600	2'W x 4'L, four 40 watt		4.70	1.702		57.50	61		118.50	163
1000	Surface mounted, RS									
1030	Acrylic lens with hinged & latched door frame									
1100	1'W x 4'L, two 40 watt	1 Elec	7	1.143	Ea.	63.50	41		104.50	137
1200	2'W x 2'L, two U40 watt		7	1.143		68	41		109	142
1500	2'W x 4'L, four 40 watt		5.30	1.509		81	54		135	178
2100	Strip fixture									
2200	4' long, one 40 watt, RS	1 Elec	8.50	.941	Ea.	27.50	33.50		61	85
2300	4' long, two 40 watt, RS	"	8	1		38.50	36		74.50	101
2600	8' long, one 75 watt, SL	2 Elec	13.40	1.194		47.50	42.50		90	123
2700	8' long, two 75 watt, SL	"	12.40	1.290		57.50	46		103.50	139
4450	Incandescent, high hat can, round alzak reflector, prewired									
4470	100 watt	1 Elec	8	1	Ea.	70.50	36		106.50	137

26 51 Interior Lighting

26 51 13 – Interior Lighting Fixtures, Lamps, and Ballasts

26 51 13.50 Interior Lighting Fixtures

		Crew	Daily Output	Labor-Hours	Unit	Material	2014 Bare Costs Labor	Equipment	Total	Total Incl O&P
4480	150 watt	1 Elec	8	1	Ea.	103	36		139	172
5200	Ceiling, surface mounted, opal glass drum									
5300	8", one 60 watt lamp	1 Elec	10	.800	Ea.	44	28.50		72.50	95.50
5400	10", two 60 watt lamps		8	1		49.50	36		85.50	113
5500	12", four 60 watt lamps		6.70	1.194		69.50	42.50		112	147
6900	Mirror light, fluorescent, RS, acrylic enclosure, two 40 watt		8	1		126	36		162	198
6910	One 40 watt		8	1		105	36		141	174
6920	One 20 watt		12	.667		81	24		105	128

26 51 13.55 Interior LED Fixtures

			Crew	Daily Output	Labor-Hours	Unit	Material	2014 Bare Costs Labor	Equipment	Total	Total Incl O&P
0010	**INTERIOR LED FIXTURES** Incl. lamps, and mounting hardware										
0100	Downlight, recess mounted, 7.5" diameter, 25 watt	G	1 Elec	8	1	Ea.	770	36		806	910
0120	10" diameter, 36 watt	G		8	1		815	36		851	955
0140	12" x 12", 40 watt	G		6.70	1.194		855	42.50		897.50	1,000
0160	cylinder, 7.8 watts	G		8	1		440	36		476	545
0180	13.3 watts	G		8	1		585	36		621	705
1000	Troffer, recess mounted, 2' x 4', 3750 Lumens	G		5.30	1.509		194	54		248	305
1010	4000 Lumens	G		5	1.600		239	57		296	355
1020	4500 Lumens	G		4.70	1.702		325	61		386	460
1100	Troffer retrofit kit, 46", 37 watt	G		21	.381		405	13.60		418.60	470
1110	55 watt	G		20	.400		560	14.30		574.30	640
1120	74 watt	G		18	.444		560	15.90		575.90	640
1200	Troffer, volumetric recess mounted, 2' x 2'	G		5.70	1.404		555	50		605	690
2000	Strip, surface mounted, one light bar 4' long, 40 watt	G		8.50	.941		720	33.50		753.50	845
2010	60 watt	G		8	1		745	36		781	880
2020	Two light bar 4' long, 80 watt	G		7	1.143		985	41		1,026	1,150
3000	Linear, suspended mounted, one light bar 4' long, 37 watt	G		6.70	1.194		330	42.50		372.50	435
3010	One light bar 8' long, 74 watt	G	2 Elec	12.20	1.311		615	47		662	750
3020	Two light bar 4' long, 74 watt	G	1 Elec	5.70	1.404		660	50		710	805
3030	Two light bar 8' long, 148 watt	G	2 Elec	8.80	1.818		1,225	65		1,290	1,450
4000	High bay, surface mounted, round, 150 watts	G		5.41	2.959		1,375	106		1,481	1,675
4010	2 bars,164 watts	G		5.41	2.959		970	106		1,076	1,250
4020	3 bars, 246 watts	G		5.01	3.197		1,250	114		1,364	1,550
4030	4 bars, 328 watts	G		4.60	3.478		1,525	124		1,649	1,875
4040	5 bars, 410 watts	G	3 Elec	4.20	5.716		1,775	204		1,979	2,300
4050	6 bars, 492 watts	G		3.80	6.324		2,025	226		2,251	2,600
4060	7 bars, 574 watts	G		3.39	7.075		2,300	253		2,553	2,950
4070	8 bars, 656 watts	G		2.99	8.029		2,550	287		2,837	3,275
5000	track, lighthead, 6 watt	G	1 Elec	32	.250		65.50	8.95		74.45	86.50
5010	9 watt	G	"	32	.250		85.50	8.95		94.45	109
6000	Garage, surface mount, 103 watts	G	2 Elec	6.50	2.462		1,150	88		1,238	1,425
6100	pendent mount, 80 watts	G		6.50	2.462		830	88		918	1,050
6200	95 watts	G		6.50	2.462		940	88		1,028	1,175
6300	125 watts	G		6.50	2.462		1,050	88		1,138	1,300

26 51 13.70 Residential Fixtures

		Crew	Daily Output	Labor-Hours	Unit	Material	2014 Bare Costs Labor	Equipment	Total	Total Incl O&P
0010	**RESIDENTIAL FIXTURES**									
0400	Fluorescent, interior, surface, circline, 32 watt & 40 watt	1 Elec	20	.400	Ea.	118	14.30		132.30	153
0700	Shallow under cabinet, two 20 watt		16	.500		54.50	17.90		72.40	89
0900	Wall mounted, 4'L, two 32 watt T8, with baffle		10	.800		137	28.50		165.50	198
2000	Incandescent, exterior lantern, wall mounted, 60 watt		16	.500		48	17.90		65.90	82.50
2100	Post light, 150W, with 7' post		4	2		238	71.50		309.50	380
2500	Lamp holder, weatherproof with 150W PAR		16	.500		32	17.90		49.90	64.50
2550	With reflector and guard		12	.667		56	24		80	101

26 51 Interior Lighting

26 51 13 – Interior Lighting Fixtures, Lamps, and Ballasts

26 51 13.70 Residential Fixtures		Crew	Daily Output	Labor-Hours	Unit	Material	2014 Bare Costs Labor	Equipment	Total	Total Incl O&P
2600	Interior pendent, globe with shade, 150 watt	1 Elec	20	.400	Ea.	191	14.30		205.30	234

26 55 Special Purpose Lighting

26 55 59 – Display Lighting

26 55 59.10 Track Lighting

		Crew	Daily Output	Labor-Hours	Unit	Material	2014 Bare Costs Labor	Equipment	Total	Total Incl O&P
0010	**TRACK LIGHTING**									
0100	8' section	2 Elec	10.60	1.509	Ea.	74.50	54		128.50	171
0300	3 circuits, 4' section	1 Elec	6.70	1.194		87	42.50		129.50	166
0400	8' section	2 Elec	10.60	1.509		109	54		163	209
0500	12' section	"	8.80	1.818		157	65		222	279
1000	Feed kit, surface mounting	1 Elec	16	.500		13	17.90		30.90	44
1100	End cover		24	.333		5.55	11.90		17.45	25.50
1200	Feed kit, stem mounting, 1 circuit		16	.500		42	17.90		59.90	75.50
1300	3 circuit		16	.500		42	17.90		59.90	75.50
2000	Electrical joiner, for continuous runs, 1 circuit		32	.250		18.05	8.95		27	34.50
2100	3 circuit		32	.250		51	8.95		59.95	71
2200	Fixtures, spotlight, 75W PAR halogen		16	.500		77	17.90		94.90	115
2210	50W MR16 halogen		16	.500		171	17.90		188.90	218
3000	Wall washer, 250 watt tungsten halogen		16	.500		130	17.90		147.90	173
3100	Low voltage, 25/50 watt, 1 circuit		16	.500		131	17.90		148.90	175
3120	3 circuit		16	.500		172	17.90		189.90	219

26 56 Exterior Lighting

26 56 13 – Lighting Poles and Standards

26 56 13.10 Lighting Poles

		Crew	Daily Output	Labor-Hours	Unit	Material	2014 Bare Costs Labor	Equipment	Total	Total Incl O&P
0010	**LIGHTING POLES**									
6420	Wood pole, 4-1/2" x 5-1/8", 8' high	1 Elec	6	1.333	Ea.	325	47.50		372.50	440
6440	12' high		5.70	1.404		470	50		520	600
6460	20' high		4	2		665	71.50		736.50	845

26 56 23 – Area Lighting

26 56 23.10 Exterior Fixtures

		Crew	Daily Output	Labor-Hours	Unit	Material	2014 Bare Costs Labor	Equipment	Total	Total Incl O&P
0010	**EXTERIOR FIXTURES** With lamps									
0400	Quartz, 500 watt	1 Elec	5.30	1.509	Ea.	49.50	54		103.50	143
1100	Wall pack, low pressure sodium, 35 watt		4	2		225	71.50		296.50	365
1150	55 watt		4	2		268	71.50		339.50	410

26 56 26 – Landscape Lighting

26 56 26.20 Landscape Fixtures

		Crew	Daily Output	Labor-Hours	Unit	Material	2014 Bare Costs Labor	Equipment	Total	Total Incl O&P
0010	**LANDSCAPE FIXTURES**									
7380	Landscape recessed uplight, incl. housing, ballast, transformer									
7390	& reflector, not incl. conduit, wire, trench									
7420	Incandescent, 250 watt	1 Elec	5	1.600	Ea.	585	57		642	740
7440	Quartz, 250 watt	"	5	1.600	"	555	57		612	705

26 56 33 – Walkway Lighting

26 56 33.10 Walkway Luminaire

		Crew	Daily Output	Labor-Hours	Unit	Material	2014 Bare Costs Labor	Equipment	Total	Total Incl O&P
0010	**WALKWAY LUMINAIRE**									
6500	Bollard light, lamp & ballast, 42" high with polycarbonate lens									
7200	Incandescent, 150 watt	1 Elec	3	2.667	Ea.	590	95.50		685.50	800

26 61 23 – Lamps Applications

26 61 23.10 Lamps		Crew	Daily Output	Labor-Hours	Unit	Material	2014 Bare Costs Labor	Equipment	Total	Total Incl O&P
0010	**LAMPS**									
0081	Fluorescent, rapid start, cool white, 2' long, 20 watt	1 Elec	100	.080	Ea.	3.09	2.86		5.95	8.10
0101	4' long, 40 watt		90	.089		2.36	3.18		5.54	7.80
1351	High pressure sodium, 70 watt		30	.267		36.50	9.55		46.05	56
1371	150 watt	↓	30	.267	↓	39	9.55		48.55	58.50

26 61 23.55 LED Lamps

26 61 23.55 LED Lamps			Crew	Daily Output	Labor-Hours	Unit	Material	2014 Bare Costs Labor	Equipment	Total	Total Incl O&P
0010	**LED LAMPS**										
0100	LED lamp, interior, shape A60, equal to 60 watt	G	1 Elec	160	.050	Ea.	22	1.79		23.79	27.50
0200	Globe frosted A60, equal to 60 watt	G		160	.050		22	1.79		23.79	27.50
0300	Globe earth, equal to 100 watt	G		160	.050		73.50	1.79		75.29	83.50
1100	MR16, 3 watt, replacement of halogen lamp 25 watt	G		130	.062		21	2.20		23.20	27
1200	6 watt replacement of halogen lamp 45 watt	G		130	.062		46.50	2.20		48.70	54.50
2100	10 watt, PAR20, equal to 60 watt	G		130	.062		47.50	2.20		49.70	55.50
2200	15 watt, PAR30, equal to 100 watt	G	↓	130	.062	↓	91.50	2.20		93.70	105

Estimating Tips

27 20 00 Data Communications
27 30 00 Voice Communications
27 40 00 Audio-Video Communications

When estimating material costs for special systems, it is always prudent to obtain manufacturers' quotations for equipment prices and special installation requirements which will affect the total costs.

Reference Numbers

Reference numbers are shown in shaded boxes at the beginning of some major classifications. These numbers refer to related items in the Reference Section. The reference information may be an estimating procedure, an alternate pricing method, or technical information.

Note: Not all subdivisions listed here necessarily appear in this publication.

Note: **Trade Service,** *in part, has been used as a reference source for some of the material prices used in Division 27.*

27 41 33 – Master Antenna Television Systems

27 41 33.10 T.V. Systems	Crew	Daily Output	Labor-Hours	Unit	Material	2014 Bare Costs Labor	Equipment	Total	Total Incl O&P
0010 **T.V. SYSTEMS**, not including rough-in wires, cables & conduits									
0100 Master TV antenna system									
0200 VHF reception & distribution, 12 outlets	1 Elec	6	1.333	Outlet	158	47.50		205.50	252
0800 VHF & UHF reception & distribution, 12 outlets		6	1.333	"	211	47.50		258.50	310
5000 T.V. Antenna, minimum		6	1.333	Ea.	46.50	47.50		94	129
5100 Maximum		4	2		196	71.50		267.50	335
5110 Rotor unit		8	1		76.50	36		112.50	143
5120 Single booster		8	1		37.50	36		73.50	100
5130 Antenna pole, 10'		3.20	2.500		27.50	89.50		117	177
6100 Satellite TV system	2 Elec	1	16		2,125	570		2,695	3,250
6110 Dish, mesh, 10' diam.	"	2.40	6.667		1,150	238		1,388	1,675
6111 Two way RF/IF tapeoff	1 Elec	36	.222		3.52	7.95		11.47	16.85
6112 Two way RF/IF splitter		24	.333		14.60	11.90		26.50	35.50
6113 Line amplifier		24	.333		14.60	11.90		26.50	35.50
6114 Line splitters		36	.222		4.64	7.95		12.59	18.10
6115 Line multi switches		8	1		675	36		711	800
6120 Motor unit		2.40	3.333		365	119		484	600
7000 Home theater, widescreen, 42", high definition, TV		10.24	.781		505	28		533	600
7050 Flat wall mount bracket		10.24	.781		127	28		155	186
7100 7 channel home theater receiver		10.24	.781		375	28		403	460
7200 Home theater speakers		10.24	.781	Set	189	28		217	254
7300 Home theater programmable remote		10.24	.781	Ea.	256	28		284	330
8000 Main video splitter		4	2		2,425	71.50		2,496.50	2,800
8010 Video distribution units		4	2		122	71.50		193.50	252

Estimating Tips

- When estimating material costs for electronic safety and security systems, it is always prudent to obtain manufacturers' quotations for equipment prices and special installation requirements that affect the total cost.

- Fire alarm systems consist of control panels, annunciator panels, battery with rack, charger, and fire alarm actuating and indicating devices. Some fire alarm systems include speakers, telephone lines, door closer controls, and other components. Be careful not to overlook the costs related to installation for these items.

Also be aware of costs for integrated automation instrumentation and terminal devices, control equipment, control wiring, and programming.

- Security equipment includes items such as CCTV, access control, and other detection and identification systems to perform alert and alarm functions. Be sure to consider the costs related to installation for this security equipment, such as for integrated automation instrumentation and terminal devices, control equipment, control wiring, and programming.

Reference Numbers

Reference numbers are shown in shaded boxes at the beginning of some major classifications. These numbers refer to related items in the Reference Section. The reference information may be an estimating procedure, an alternate pricing method, or technical information.

Note: Not all subdivisions listed here necessarily appear in this publication.

28 16 Intrusion Detection

28 16 16 – Intrusion Detection Systems Infrastructure

28 16 16.50 Intrusion Detection	Crew	Daily Output	Labor-Hours	Unit	Material	2014 Bare Costs Labor	2014 Bare Costs Equipment	Total	Total Incl O&P
0010 **INTRUSION DETECTION**, not including wires & conduits									
0100 Burglar alarm, battery operated, mechanical trigger	1 Elec	4	2	Ea.	275	71.50		346.50	415
0200 Electrical trigger		4	2		330	71.50		401.50	475
0400 For outside key control, add		8	1		83	36		119	150
0600 For remote signaling circuitry, add		8	1		124	36		160	195
0800 Card reader, flush type, standard		2.70	2.963		920	106		1,026	1,200
1000 Multi-code		2.70	2.963		1,175	106		1,281	1,475
1200 Door switches, hinge switch		5.30	1.509		58	54		112	152
1400 Magnetic switch		5.30	1.509		68.50	54		122.50	164
2800 Ultrasonic motion detector, 12 volt		2.30	3.478		227	124		351	455
3000 Infrared photoelectric detector		4	2		188	71.50		259.50	325
3200 Passive infrared detector		4	2		280	71.50		351.50	425
3420 Switchmats, 30" x 5'		5.30	1.509		84	54		138	181
3440 30" x 25'		4	2		201	71.50		272.50	340
3460 Police connect panel		4	2		242	71.50		313.50	385
3480 Telephone dialer		5.30	1.509		380	54		434	510
3500 Alarm bell		4	2		103	71.50		174.50	231
3520 Siren		4	2		145	71.50		216.50	276

28 31 Fire Detection and Alarm

28 31 23 – Fire Detection and Alarm Annunciation Panels and Fire Stations

28 31 23.50 Alarm Panels and Devices

28 31 23.50 Alarm Panels and Devices	Crew	Daily Output	Labor-Hours	Unit	Material	2014 Bare Costs Labor	2014 Bare Costs Equipment	Total	Total Incl O&P
0010 **ALARM PANELS AND DEVICES**, not including wires & conduits									
5600 Strobe and horn	1 Elec	5.30	1.509	Ea.	151	54		205	255
5800 Fire alarm horn		6.70	1.194		60.50	42.50		103	137
6600 Drill switch		8	1		365	36		401	465
6800 Master box		2.70	2.963		6,350	106		6,456	7,150
7800 Remote annunciator, 8 zone lamp		1.80	4.444		207	159		366	485
8000 12 zone lamp	2 Elec	2.60	6.154		330	220		550	725
8200 16 zone lamp	"	2.20	7.273		415	260		675	880

28 31 46 – Smoke Detection Sensors

28 31 46.50 Smoke Detectors

	Crew	Daily Output	Labor-Hours	Unit	Material	2014 Bare Costs Labor	2014 Bare Costs Equipment	Total	Total Incl O&P
0010 **SMOKE DETECTORS**									
5200 Smoke detector, ceiling type	1 Elec	6.20	1.290	Ea.	109	46		155	196

Estimating Tips

31 05 00 Common Work Results for Earthwork

- Estimating the actual cost of performing earthwork requires careful consideration of the variables involved. This includes items such as type of soil, whether water will be encountered, dewatering, whether banks need bracing, disposal of excavated earth, and length of haul to fill or spoil sites, etc. If the project has large quantities of cut or fill, consider raising or lowering the site to reduce costs, while paying close attention to the effect on site drainage and utilities.

- If the project has large quantities of fill, creating a borrow pit on the site can significantly lower the costs.

- It is very important to consider what time of year the project is scheduled for completion. Bad weather can create large cost overruns from dewatering, site repair, and lost productivity from cold weather.

Reference Numbers

Reference numbers are shown in shaded boxes at the beginning of some major classifications. These numbers refer to related items in the Reference Section. The reference information may be an estimating procedure, an alternate pricing method, or technical information.

Note: Not all subdivisions listed here necessarily appear in this publication.

Division 31 - Earthwork

31 05 Common Work Results for Earthwork

31 05 13 – Soils for Earthwork

31 05 13.10 Borrow	Crew	Daily Output	Labor-Hours	Unit	Material	2014 Bare Costs Labor	2014 Bare Costs Equipment	Total	Total Incl O&P
0010 **BORROW**									
0020 Spread, 200 H.P. dozer, no compaction, 2 mi. RT haul									
0200 Common borrow	B-15	600	.047	C.Y.	12.35	1.32	4.52	18.19	20.50

31 05 16 – Aggregates for Earthwork

31 05 16.10 Borrow	Crew	Daily Output	Labor-Hours	Unit	Material	2014 Bare Costs Labor	2014 Bare Costs Equipment	Total	Total Incl O&P
0010 **BORROW**									
0020 Spread, with 200 H.P. dozer, no compaction, 2 mi. RT haul									
0100 Bank run gravel	B-15	600	.047	L.C.Y.	22	1.32	4.52	27.84	31
0300 Crushed stone (1.40 tons per CY), 1-1/2"		600	.047		28.50	1.32	4.52	34.34	38
0320 3/4"		600	.047		28.50	1.32	4.52	34.34	38
0340 1/2"		600	.047		27	1.32	4.52	32.84	36.50
0360 3/8"		600	.047		25.50	1.32	4.52	31.34	35.50
0400 Sand, washed, concrete		600	.047		42	1.32	4.52	47.84	53
0500 Dead or bank sand		600	.047		17.55	1.32	4.52	23.39	26.50

31 11 Clearing and Grubbing

31 11 10 – Clearing and Grubbing Land

31 11 10.10 Clear and Grub Site	Crew	Daily Output	Labor-Hours	Unit	Material	2014 Bare Costs Labor	2014 Bare Costs Equipment	Total	Total Incl O&P
0010 **CLEAR AND GRUB SITE**									
0020 Cut & chip light trees to 6" diam.	B-7	1	48	Acre		1,250	1,675	2,925	3,925
0150 Grub stumps and remove	B-30	2	12			350	1,200	1,550	1,900
0200 Cut & chip medium, trees to 12" diam.	B-7	.70	68.571			1,775	2,400	4,175	5,600
0250 Grub stumps and remove	B-30	1	24			695	2,425	3,120	3,800
0300 Cut & chip heavy, trees to 24" diam.	B-7	.30	160			4,125	5,600	9,725	13,100
0350 Grub stumps and remove	B-30	.50	48			1,400	4,825	6,225	7,650
0400 If burning is allowed, deduct cut & chip								40%	40%

31 13 Selective Tree and Shrub Removal and Trimming

31 13 13 – Selective Tree and Shrub Removal

31 13 13.10 Selective Clearing	Crew	Daily Output	Labor-Hours	Unit	Material	2014 Bare Costs Labor	2014 Bare Costs Equipment	Total	Total Incl O&P
0010 **SELECTIVE CLEARING**									
0020 Clearing brush with brush saw	A-1C	.25	32	Acre		760	125	885	1,400
0100 By hand	1 Clab	.12	66.667			1,575		1,575	2,675
0300 With dozer, ball and chain, light clearing	B-11A	2	8			230	660	890	1,125
0400 Medium clearing	"	1.50	10.667			305	885	1,190	1,475

31 14 Earth Stripping and Stockpiling

31 14 13 – Soil Stripping and Stockpiling

31 14 13.23 Topsoil Stripping and Stockpiling	Crew	Daily Output	Labor-Hours	Unit	Material	2014 Bare Costs Labor	2014 Bare Costs Equipment	Total	Total Incl O&P
0010 **TOPSOIL STRIPPING AND STOCKPILING**									
1400 Loam or topsoil, remove and stockpile on site									
1420 6" deep, 200' haul	B-10B	865	.009	C.Y.		.31	1.53	1.84	2.21
1430 300' haul		520	.015			.52	2.55	3.07	3.66
1440 500' haul		225	.036			1.20	5.90	7.10	8.50
1450 Alternate method: 6" deep, 200' haul		5090	.002	S.Y.		.05	.26	.31	.38
1460 500' haul		1325	.006	"		.20	1	1.20	1.44
1500 Loam or topsoil, remove/stockpile on site									

31 14 Earth Stripping and Stockpiling

31 14 13 – Soil Stripping and Stockpiling

31 14 13.23 Topsoil Stripping and Stockpiling	Crew	Daily Output	Labor-Hours	Unit	Material	2014 Bare Costs Labor	Equipment	Total	Total Incl O&P
1510	By hand, 6" deep, 50' haul, less than 100 S.Y.	B-1	100	.240	S.Y.		5.85		5.85	9.90
1520	By skid steer, 6" deep, 100' haul, 101-500 S.Y.	B-62	500	.048			1.28	.35	1.63	2.52
1530	100' haul, 501-900 S.Y.	"	900	.027			.71	.19	.90	1.40
1540	200' haul, 901-1100 S.Y.	B-63	1000	.040			.95	.17	1.12	1.79
1550	By dozer, 200' haul, 1101-4000 S.Y.	B-10B	4000	.002			.07	.33	.40	.47

31 22 Grading

31 22 16 – Fine Grading

31 22 16.10 Finish Grading

		Crew	Daily Output	Labor-Hours	Unit	Material	Labor	Equipment	Total	Total Incl O&P
0010	**FINISH GRADING**									
0012	Finish grading area to be paved with grader, small area	B-11L	400	.040	S.Y.		1.15	1.77	2.92	3.86
0100	Large area		2000	.008			.23	.35	.58	.77
0200	Grade subgrade for base course, roadways		3500	.005			.13	.20	.33	.44
1020	For large parking lots	B-32C	5000	.010			.28	.45	.73	.97
1050	For small irregular areas	"	2000	.024			.70	1.14	1.84	2.41
1100	Fine grade for slab on grade, machine	B-11L	1040	.015			.44	.68	1.12	1.49
1150	Hand grading	B-18	700	.034			.84	.07	.91	1.48
1200	Fine grade granular base for sidewalks and bikeways	B-62	1200	.020			.53	.15	.68	1.05
2550	Hand grade select gravel	2 Clab	60	.267	C.S.F.		6.35		6.35	10.70
3000	Hand grade select gravel, including compaction, 4" deep	B-18	555	.043	S.Y.		1.06	.08	1.14	1.87
3100	6" deep		400	.060			1.47	.12	1.59	2.60
3120	8" deep		300	.080			1.96	.15	2.11	3.46
3300	Finishing grading slopes, gentle	B-11L	8900	.002			.05	.08	.13	.18
3310	Steep slopes	"	7100	.002			.06	.10	.16	.22

31 23 Excavation and Fill

31 23 16 – Excavation

31 23 16.13 Excavating, Trench

		Crew	Daily Output	Labor-Hours	Unit	Material	Labor	Equipment	Total	Total Incl O&P
0010	**EXCAVATING, TRENCH**									
0011	Or continuous footing									
0050	1' to 4' deep, 3/8 C.Y. excavator	B-11C	150	.107	B.C.Y.		3.07	2.44	5.51	7.80
0060	1/2 C.Y. excavator	B-11M	200	.080			2.30	1.99	4.29	6.05
0090	4' to 6' deep, 1/2 C.Y. excavator	"	200	.080			2.30	1.99	4.29	6.05
0100	5/8 C.Y. excavator	B-12Q	250	.064			1.87	2.38	4.25	5.75
0300	1/2 C.Y. excavator, truck mounted	B-12J	200	.080			2.34	4.41	6.75	8.75
1352	4' to 6' deep, 1/2 C.Y. excavator w/trench box	B-13H	188	.085			2.49	5.15	7.64	9.80
1354	5/8 C.Y. excavator	"	235	.068			1.99	4.11	6.10	7.85
1400	By hand with pick and shovel 2' to 6' deep, light soil	1 Clab	8	1			24		24	40
1500	Heavy soil	"	4	2			47.50		47.50	80
5020	Loam & Sandy clay with no sheeting or dewatering included									
5050	1' to 4' deep, 3/8 C.Y. tractor loader/backhoe	B-11C	162	.099	B.C.Y.		2.84	2.25	5.09	7.20
5060	1/2 C.Y. excavator	B-11M	216	.074			2.13	1.84	3.97	5.60
5080	4' to 6' deep, 1/2 C.Y. excavator	"	216	.074			2.13	1.84	3.97	5.60
5090	5/8 C.Y. excavator	B-12Q	276	.058			1.69	2.15	3.84	5.20
5130	1/2 C.Y. excavator, truck mounted	B-12J	216	.074			2.17	4.08	6.25	8.10
5352	4' to 6' deep, 1/2 C.Y. excavator w/trench box	B-13H	205	.078			2.28	4.71	6.99	9
5354	5/8 C.Y. excavator	"	257	.062			1.82	3.76	5.58	7.15
6020	Sand & gravel with no sheeting or dewatering included									
6050	1' to 4' deep, 3/8 C.Y. excavator	B-11C	165	.097	B.C.Y.		2.79	2.21	5	7.10

31 23 Excavation and Fill

31 23 16 – Excavation

31 23 16.13 Excavating, Trench

		Crew	Daily Output	Labor-Hours	Unit	Material	2014 Bare Costs Labor	2014 Bare Costs Equipment	Total	Total Incl O&P
6060	1/2 C.Y. excavator	B-11M	220	.073	B.C.Y.		2.09	1.81	3.90	5.50
6080	4' to 6' deep, 1/2 C.Y. excavator	"	220	.073			2.09	1.81	3.90	5.50
6090	5/8 C.Y. excavator	B-12Q	275	.058			1.70	2.16	3.86	5.20
6130	1/2 C.Y. excavator, truck mounted	B-12J	220	.073			2.13	4.01	6.14	7.95
6352	4' to 6' deep, 1/2 C.Y. excavator w/trench box	B-13H	209	.077			2.24	4.62	6.86	8.85
6354	5/8 C.Y. excavator	"	261	.061			1.79	3.70	5.49	7.05
7020	Dense hard clay with no sheeting or dewatering included									
7050	1' to 4' deep, 3/8 C.Y. excavator	B-11C	132	.121	B.C.Y.		3.49	2.77	6.26	8.85
7060	1/2 C.Y. excavator	B-11M	176	.091			2.62	2.26	4.88	6.85
7080	4' to 6' deep, 1/2 C.Y. excavator	"	176	.091			2.62	2.26	4.88	6.85
7090	5/8 C.Y. excavator	B-12Q	220	.073			2.13	2.70	4.83	6.50
7130	1/2 C.Y. excavator, truck mounted	B-12J	176	.091			2.66	5	7.66	9.95

31 23 16.14 Excavating, Utility Trench

		Crew	Daily Output	Labor-Hours	Unit	Material	Labor	Equipment	Total	Total Incl O&P
0010	**EXCAVATING, UTILITY TRENCH**									
0011	Common earth									
0050	Trenching with chain trencher, 12 H.P., operator walking									
0100	4" wide trench, 12" deep	B-53	800	.010	L.F.		.24	.09	.33	.50
1000	Backfill by hand including compaction, add									
1050	4" wide trench, 12" deep	A-1G	800	.010	L.F.		.24	.07	.31	.48

31 23 16.16 Structural Excavation for Minor Structures

		Crew	Daily Output	Labor-Hours	Unit	Material	Labor	Equipment	Total	Total Incl O&P
0010	**STRUCTURAL EXCAVATION FOR MINOR STRUCTURES**									
0015	Hand, pits to 6' deep, sandy soil	1 Clab	8	1	B.C.Y.		24		24	40
0100	Heavy soil or clay		4	2			47.50		47.50	80
1100	Hand loading trucks from stock pile, sandy soil		12	.667			15.85		15.85	26.50
1300	Heavy soil or clay		8	1			24		24	40
1500	For wet or muck hand excavation, add to above								50%	50%

31 23 16.42 Excavating, Bulk Bank Measure

		Crew	Daily Output	Labor-Hours	Unit	Material	Labor	Equipment	Total	Total Incl O&P
0010	**EXCAVATING, BULK BANK MEASURE**									
0011	Common earth piled									
0020	For loading onto trucks, add								15%	15%
0200	Excavator, hydraulic, crawler mtd., 1 C.Y. cap. = 100 C.Y./hr.	B-12A	800	.020	B.C.Y.		.58	1.02	1.60	2.09
0310	Wheel mounted, 1/2 C.Y. cap. = 40 C.Y./hr.	B-12E	320	.050			1.46	1.40	2.86	3.98
1200	Front end loader, track mtd., 1-1/2 C.Y. cap. = 70 C.Y./hr.	B-10N	560	.014			.48	.93	1.41	1.83
1500	Wheel mounted, 3/4 C.Y. cap. = 45 C.Y./hr.	B-10R	360	.022			.75	.82	1.57	2.14
5000	Excavating, bulk bank measure, sandy clay & loam piled									
5020	For loading onto trucks, add								15%	15%
5100	Excavator, hydraulic, crawler mtd., 1 C.Y. cap. = 120 C.Y./hr.	B-12A	960	.017	B.C.Y.		.49	.85	1.34	1.74
5610	Wheel mounted, 1/2 C.Y. cap. = 44 C.Y./hr.	B-12E	352	.045	"		1.33	1.27	2.60	3.61
8000	For hauling excavated material, see Section 31 23 23.20									

31 23 23 – Fill

31 23 23.13 Backfill

		Crew	Daily Output	Labor-Hours	Unit	Material	Labor	Equipment	Total	Total Incl O&P
0010	**BACKFILL**									
0015	By hand, no compaction, light soil	1 Clab	14	.571	L.C.Y.		13.60		13.60	23
0100	Heavy soil		11	.727	"		17.30		17.30	29
0300	Compaction in 6" layers, hand tamp, add to above		20.60	.388	E.C.Y.		9.25		9.25	15.55
0500	Air tamp, add	B-9D	190	.211			5.10	1.40	6.50	10.10
0600	Vibrating plate, add	A-1D	60	.133			3.17	.60	3.77	6
0800	Compaction in 12" layers, hand tamp, add to above	1 Clab	34	.235			5.60		5.60	9.40
1300	Dozer backfilling, bulk, up to 300' haul, no compaction	B-10B	1200	.007	L.C.Y.		.23	1.10	1.33	1.59
1400	Air tamped, add	B-11B	80	.200	E.C.Y.		5.65	3.78	9.43	13.55

31 23 Excavation and Fill

31 23 23 – Fill

31 23 23.16 Fill By Borrow and Utility Bedding

	Crew	Daily Output	Labor-Hours	Unit	Material	2014 Bare Costs Labor	2014 Bare Costs Equipment	Total	Total Incl O&P
0010 **FILL BY BORROW AND UTILITY BEDDING**									
0049 Utility bedding, for pipe & conduit, not incl. compaction									
0050 Crushed or screened bank run gravel	B-6	150	.160	L.C.Y.	25	4.27	2.44	31.71	37.50
0100 Crushed stone 3/4" to 1/2"		150	.160		28.50	4.27	2.44	35.21	41
0200 Sand, dead or bank	▼	150	.160	▼	17.55	4.27	2.44	24.26	29
0500 Compacting bedding in trench	A-1D	90	.089	E.C.Y.		2.12	.40	2.52	4
0600 If material source exceeds 2 miles, add for extra mileage.									
0610 See Section 31 23 23.20 for hauling mileage add.									

31 23 23.17 General Fill

	Crew	Daily Output	Labor-Hours	Unit	Material	2014 Bare Costs Labor	2014 Bare Costs Equipment	Total	Total Incl O&P
0010 **GENERAL FILL**									
0011 Spread dumped material, no compaction									
0020 By dozer, no compaction	B-10B	1000	.008	L.C.Y.		.27	1.33	1.60	1.91
0100 By hand	1 Clab	12	.667	"		15.85		15.85	26.50
0500 Gravel fill, compacted, under floor slabs, 4" deep	B-37	10000	.005	S.F.	.42	.12	.02	.56	.69
0600 6" deep		8600	.006		.63	.14	.02	.79	.96
0700 9" deep		7200	.007		1.05	.17	.02	1.24	1.47
0800 12" deep		6000	.008	▼	1.48	.20	.03	1.71	1.99
1000 Alternate pricing method, 4" deep		120	.400	E.C.Y.	31.50	10.25	1.32	43.07	53.50
1100 6" deep		160	.300		31.50	7.65	.99	40.14	49
1200 9" deep		200	.240		31.50	6.15	.79	38.44	46
1300 12" deep	▼	220	.218	▼	31.50	5.60	.72	37.82*	45

31 23 23.20 Hauling

	Crew	Daily Output	Labor-Hours	Unit	Material	2014 Bare Costs Labor	2014 Bare Costs Equipment	Total	Total Incl O&P
0010 **HAULING**									
0011 Excavated or borrow, loose cubic yards									
0012 no loading equipment, including hauling,waiting, loading/dumping									
0013 time per cycle (wait, load, travel, unload or dump & return)									
0014 8 C.Y. truck, 15 MPH ave, cycle 0.5 miles, 10 min. wait/Ld./Uld.	B-34A	320	.025	L.C.Y.		.67	1.30	1.97	2.54
0016 cycle 1 mile		272	.029			.78	1.53	2.31	3
0018 cycle 2 miles		208	.038			1.03	2.01	3.04	3.92
0020 cycle 4 miles		144	.056			1.48	2.90	4.38	5.65
0022 cycle 6 miles		112	.071			1.90	3.73	5.63	7.25
0024 cycle 8 miles		88	.091			2.42	4.74	7.16	9.25
0026 20 MPH ave,cycle 0.5 mile		336	.024			.63	1.24	1.87	2.43
0028 cycle 1 mile		296	.027			.72	1.41	2.13	2.75
0030 cycle 2 miles		240	.033			.89	1.74	2.63	3.39
0032 cycle 4 miles		176	.045			1.21	2.37	3.58	4.63
0034 cycle 6 miles		136	.059			1.57	3.07	4.64	6
0036 cycle 8 miles		112	.071			1.90	3.73	5.63	7.25
0044 25 MPH ave, cycle 4 miles		192	.042			1.11	2.17	3.28	4.24
0046 cycle 6 miles		160	.050			1.33	2.61	3.94	5.10
0048 cycle 8 miles		128	.063			1.67	3.26	4.93	6.35
0050 30 MPH ave, cycle 4 miles		216	.037			.99	1.93	2.92	3.77
0052 cycle 6 miles		176	.045			1.21	2.37	3.58	4.63
0054 cycle 8 miles		144	.056			1.48	2.90	4.38	5.65
0114 15 MPH ave, cycle 0.5 mile, 15 min. wait/Ld./Uld.		224	.036			.95	1.86	2.81	3.64
0116 cycle 1 mile		200	.040			1.07	2.09	3.16	4.07
0118 cycle 2 miles		168	.048			1.27	2.48	3.75	4.84
0120 cycle 4 miles		120	.067			1.78	3.48	5.26	6.80
0122 cycle 6 miles		96	.083			2.22	4.35	6.57	8.50
0124 cycle 8 miles		80	.100			2.67	5.20	7.87	10.20
0126 20 MPH ave, cycle 0.5 mile		232	.034			.92	1.80	2.72	3.51
0128 cycle 1 mile	▼	208	.038	▼		1.03	2.01	3.04	3.92

31 23 23 – Fill

31 23 23.20 Hauling	Crew	Daily Output	Labor-Hours	Unit	Material	2014 Bare Costs Labor	2014 Bare Costs Equipment	Total	Total Incl O&P
0130	cycle 2 miles	B-34A	184	.043	L.C.Y.		1.16	2.27	3.43	4.42
0132	cycle 4 miles		144	.056			1.48	2.90	4.38	5.65
0134	cycle 6 miles		112	.071			1.90	3.73	5.63	7.25
0136	cycle 8 miles		96	.083			2.22	4.35	6.57	8.50
0144	25 MPH ave, cycle 4 miles		152	.053			1.40	2.74	4.14	5.35
0146	cycle 6 miles		128	.063			1.67	3.26	4.93	6.35
0148	cycle 8 miles		112	.071			1.90	3.73	5.63	7.25
0150	30 MPH ave, cycle 4 miles		168	.048			1.27	2.48	3.75	4.84
0152	cycle 6 miles		144	.056			1.48	2.90	4.38	5.65
0154	cycle 8 miles		120	.067			1.78	3.48	5.26	6.80
0214	15 MPH ave, cycle 0.5 mile, 20 min wait/Ld./Uld.		176	.045			1.21	2.37	3.58	4.63
0216	cycle 1 mile		160	.050			1.33	2.61	3.94	5.10
0218	cycle 2 miles		136	.059			1.57	3.07	4.64	6
0220	cycle 4 miles		104	.077			2.05	4.01	6.06	7.85
0222	cycle 6 miles		88	.091			2.42	4.74	7.16	9.25
0224	cycle 8 miles		72	.111			2.96	5.80	8.76	11.30
0226	20 MPH ave, cycle 0.5 mile		176	.045			1.21	2.37	3.58	4.63
0228	cycle 1 mile		168	.048			1.27	2.48	3.75	4.84
0230	cycle 2 miles		144	.056			1.48	2.90	4.38	5.65
0232	cycle 4 miles		120	.067			1.78	3.48	5.26	6.80
0234	cycle 6 miles		96	.083			2.22	4.35	6.57	8.50
0236	cycle 8 miles		88	.091			2.42	4.74	7.16	9.25
0244	25 MPH ave, cycle 4 miles		128	.063			1.67	3.26	4.93	6.35
0246	cycle 6 miles		112	.071			1.90	3.73	5.63	7.25
0248	cycle 8 miles		96	.083			2.22	4.35	6.57	8.50
0250	30 MPH ave, cycle 4 miles		136	.059			1.57	3.07	4.64	6
0252	cycle 6 miles		120	.067			1.78	3.48	5.26	6.80
0254	cycle 8 miles		104	.077			2.05	4.01	6.06	7.85
0314	15 MPH ave, cycle 0.5 mile, 25 min wait/Ld./Uld.		144	.056			1.48	2.90	4.38	5.65
0316	cycle 1 mile		128	.063			1.67	3.26	4.93	6.35
0318	cycle 2 miles		112	.071			1.90	3.73	5.63	7.25
0320	cycle 4 miles		96	.083			2.22	4.35	6.57	8.50
0322	cycle 6 miles		80	.100			2.67	5.20	7.87	10.20
0324	cycle 8 miles		64	.125			3.33	6.50	9.83	12.70
0326	20 MPH ave, cycle 0.5 mile		144	.056			1.48	2.90	4.38	5.65
0328	cycle 1 mile		136	.059			1.57	3.07	4.64	6
0330	cycle 2 miles		120	.067			1.78	3.48	5.26	6.80
0332	cycle 4 miles		104	.077			2.05	4.01	6.06	7.85
0334	cycle 6 miles		88	.091			2.42	4.74	7.16	9.25
0336	cycle 8 miles		80	.100			2.67	5.20	7.87	10.20
0344	25 MPH ave, cycle 4 miles		112	.071			1.90	3.73	5.63	7.25
0346	cycle 6 miles		96	.083			2.22	4.35	6.57	8.50
0348	cycle 8 miles		88	.091			2.42	4.74	7.16	9.25
0350	30 MPH ave, cycle 4 miles		112	.071			1.90	3.73	5.63	7.25
0352	cycle 6 miles		104	.077			2.05	4.01	6.06	7.85
0354	cycle 8 miles		96	.083			2.22	4.35	6.57	8.50
0414	15 MPH ave, cycle 0.5 mile, 30 min wait/Ld./Uld.		120	.067			1.78	3.48	5.26	6.80
0416	cycle 1 mile		112	.071			1.90	3.73	5.63	7.25
0418	cycle 2 miles		96	.083			2.22	4.35	6.57	8.50
0420	cycle 4 miles		80	.100			2.67	5.20	7.87	10.20
0422	cycle 6 miles		72	.111			2.96	5.80	8.76	11.30
0424	cycle 8 miles		64	.125			3.33	6.50	9.83	12.70
0426	20 MPH ave, cycle 0.5 mile		120	.067			1.78	3.48	5.26	6.80

31 23 23 – Fill

31 23 23.20 Hauling		Crew	Daily Output	Labor-Hours	Unit	Material	2014 Bare Costs Labor	Equipment	Total	Total Incl O&P
0428	cycle 1 mile	B-34A	112	.071	L.C.Y.		1.90	3.73	5.63	7.25
0430	cycle 2 miles		104	.077			2.05	4.01	6.06	7.85
0432	cycle 4 miles		88	.091			2.42	4.74	7.16	9.25
0434	cycle 6 miles		80	.100			2.67	5.20	7.87	10.20
0436	cycle 8 miles		72	.111			2.96	5.80	8.76	11.30
0444	25 MPH ave, cycle 4 miles		96	.083			2.22	4.35	6.57	8.50
0446	cycle 6 miles		88	.091			2.42	4.74	7.16	9.25
0448	cycle 8 miles		80	.100			2.67	5.20	7.87	10.20
0450	30 MPH ave, cycle 4 miles		96	.083			2.22	4.35	6.57	8.50
0452	cycle 6 miles		88	.091			2.42	4.74	7.16	9.25
0454	cycle 8 miles		80	.100			2.67	5.20	7.87	10.20
0514	15 MPH ave, cycle 0.5 mile, 35 min wait/Ld./Uld.		104	.077			2.05	4.01	6.06	7.85
0516	cycle 1 mile		96	.083			2.22	4.35	6.57	8.50
0518	cycle 2 miles		88	.091			2.42	4.74	7.16	9.25
0520	cycle 4 miles		72	.111			2.96	5.80	8.76	11.30
0522	cycle 6 miles		64	.125			3.33	6.50	9.83	12.70
0524	cycle 8 miles		56	.143			3.81	7.45	11.26	14.55
0526	20 MPH ave, cycle 0.5 mile		104	.077			2.05	4.01	6.06	7.85
0528	cycle 1 mile		96	.083			2.22	4.35	6.57	8.50
0530	cycle 2 miles		96	.083			2.22	4.35	6.57	8.50
0532	cycle 4 miles		80	.100			2.67	5.20	7.87	10.20
0534	cycle 6 miles		72	.111			2.96	5.80	8.76	11.30
0536	cycle 8 miles		64	.125			3.33	6.50	9.83	12.70
0544	25 MPH ave, cycle 4 miles		88	.091			2.42	4.74	7.16	9.25
0546	cycle 6 miles		80	.100			2.67	5.20	7.87	10.20
0548	cycle 8 miles		72	.111			2.96	5.80	8.76	11.30
0550	30 MPH ave, cycle 4 miles		88	.091			2.42	4.74	7.16	9.25
0552	cycle 6 miles		80	.100			2.67	5.20	7.87	10.20
0554	cycle 8 miles		72	.111			2.96	5.80	8.76	11.30
1014	12 C.Y. truck, cycle 0.5 mile, 15 MPH ave, 15 min. wait/Ld./Uld.	B-34B	336	.024			.63	2.06	2.69	3.33
1016	cycle 1 mile		300	.027			.71	2.31	3.02	3.72
1018	cycle 2 miles		252	.032			.85	2.75	3.60	4.43
1020	cycle 4 miles		180	.044			1.18	3.85	5.03	6.20
1022	cycle 6 miles		144	.056			1.48	4.81	6.29	7.75
1024	cycle 8 miles		120	.067			1.78	5.75	7.53	9.30
1025	cycle 10 miles		96	.083			2.22	7.20	9.42	11.65
1026	20 MPH ave, cycle 0.5 mile		348	.023			.61	1.99	2.60	3.21
1028	cycle 1 mile		312	.026			.68	2.22	2.90	3.58
1030	cycle 2 miles		276	.029			.77	2.51	3.28	4.05
1032	cycle 4 miles		216	.037			.99	3.21	4.20	5.15
1034	cycle 6 miles		168	.048			1.27	4.12	5.39	6.65
1036	cycle 8 miles		144	.056			1.48	4.81	6.29	7.75
1038	cycle 10 miles		120	.067			1.78	5.75	7.53	9.30
1040	25 MPH ave, cycle 4 miles		228	.035			.94	3.04	3.98	4.90
1042	cycle 6 miles		192	.042			1.11	3.61	4.72	5.80
1044	cycle 8 miles		168	.048			1.27	4.12	5.39	6.65
1046	cycle 10 miles		144	.056			1.48	4.81	6.29	7.75
1050	30 MPH ave, cycle 4 miles		252	.032			.85	2.75	3.60	4.43
1052	cycle 6 miles		216	.037			.99	3.21	4.20	5.15
1054	cycle 8 miles		180	.044			1.18	3.85	5.03	6.20
1056	cycle 10 miles		156	.051			1.37	4.44	5.81	7.15
1060	35 MPH ave, cycle 4 miles		264	.030			.81	2.62	3.43	4.23
1062	cycle 6 miles		228	.035			.94	3.04	3.98	4.90

31 23 23 – Fill

31 23 23.20 Hauling	Crew	Daily Output	Labor-Hours	Unit	Material	2014 Bare Costs Labor	2014 Bare Costs Equipment	Total	Total Incl O&P
1064	cycle 8 miles	B-34B	204	.039	L.C.Y.		1.05	3.39	4.44	5.45
1066	cycle 10 miles		180	.044			1.18	3.85	5.03	6.20
1068	cycle 20 miles		120	.067			1.78	5.75	7.53	9.30
1069	cycle 30 miles		84	.095			2.54	8.25	10.79	13.30
1070	cycle 40 miles		72	.111			2.96	9.60	12.56	15.55
1072	40 MPH ave, cycle 6 miles		240	.033			.89	2.88	3.77	4.65
1074	cycle 8 miles		216	.037			.99	3.21	4.20	5.15
1076	cycle 10 miles		192	.042			1.11	3.61	4.72	5.80
1078	cycle 20 miles		120	.067			1.78	5.75	7.53	9.30
1080	cycle 30 miles		96	.083			2.22	7.20	9.42	11.65
1082	cycle 40 miles		72	.111			2.96	9.60	12.56	15.55
1084	cycle 50 miles		60	.133			3.55	11.55	15.10	18.60
1094	45 MPH ave, cycle 8 miles		216	.037			.99	3.21	4.20	5.15
1096	cycle 10 miles		204	.039			1.05	3.39	4.44	5.45
1098	cycle 20 miles		132	.061			1.62	5.25	6.87	8.45
1100	cycle 30 miles		108	.074			1.97	6.40	8.37	10.35
1102	cycle 40 miles		84	.095			2.54	8.25	10.79	13.30
1104	cycle 50 miles		72	.111			2.96	9.60	12.56	15.55
1106	50 MPH ave, cycle 10 miles		216	.037			.99	3.21	4.20	5.15
1108	cycle 20 miles		144	.056			1.48	4.81	6.29	7.75
1110	cycle 30 miles		108	.074			1.97	6.40	8.37	10.35
1112	cycle 40 miles		84	.095			2.54	8.25	10.79	13.30
1114	cycle 50 miles		72	.111			2.96	9.60	12.56	15.55
1214	15 MPH ave, cycle 0.5 mile, 20 min. wait/Ld./Uld.		264	.030			.81	2.62	3.43	4.23
1216	cycle 1 mile		240	.033			.89	2.88	3.77	4.65
1218	cycle 2 miles		204	.039			1.05	3.39	4.44	5.45
1220	cycle 4 miles		156	.051			1.37	4.44	5.81	7.15
1222	cycle 6 miles		132	.061			1.62	5.25	6.87	8.45
1224	cycle 8 miles		108	.074			1.97	6.40	8.37	10.35
1225	cycle 10 miles		96	.083			2.22	7.20	9.42	11.65
1226	20 MPH ave, cycle 0.5 mile		264	.030			.81	2.62	3.43	4.23
1228	cycle 1 mile		252	.032			.85	2.75	3.60	4.43
1230	cycle 2 miles		216	.037			.99	3.21	4.20	5.15
1232	cycle 4 miles		180	.044			1.18	3.85	5.03	6.20
1234	cycle 6 miles		144	.056			1.48	4.81	6.29	7.75
1236	cycle 8 miles		132	.061			1.62	5.25	6.87	8.45
1238	cycle 10 miles		108	.074			1.97	6.40	8.37	10.35
1240	25 MPH ave, cycle 4 miles		192	.042			1.11	3.61	4.72	5.80
1242	cycle 6 miles		168	.048			1.27	4.12	5.39	6.65
1244	cycle 8 miles		144	.056			1.48	4.81	6.29	7.75
1246	cycle 10 miles		132	.061			1.62	5.25	6.87	8.45
1250	30 MPH ave, cycle 4 miles		204	.039			1.05	3.39	4.44	5.45
1252	cycle 6 miles		180	.044			1.18	3.85	5.03	6.20
1254	cycle 8 miles		156	.051			1.37	4.44	5.81	7.15
1256	cycle 10 miles		144	.056			1.48	4.81	6.29	7.75
1260	35 MPH ave, cycle 4 miles		216	.037			.99	3.21	4.20	5.15
1262	cycle 6 miles		192	.042			1.11	3.61	4.72	5.80
1264	cycle 8 miles		168	.048			1.27	4.12	5.39	6.65
1266	cycle 10 miles		156	.051			1.37	4.44	5.81	7.15
1268	cycle 20 miles		108	.074			1.97	6.40	8.37	10.35
1269	cycle 30 miles		72	.111			2.96	9.60	12.56	15.55
1270	cycle 40 miles		60	.133			3.55	11.55	15.10	18.60
1272	40 MPH ave, cycle 6 miles		192	.042			1.11	3.61	4.72	5.80

31 23 23 — Fill

31 23 23.20 Hauling		Crew	Daily Output	Labor-Hours	Unit	Material	2014 Bare Costs		Total	Total Incl O&P
							Labor	Equipment		
1274	cycle 8 miles	B-34B	180	.044	L.C.Y.		1.18	3.85	5.03	6.20
1276	cycle 10 miles		156	.051			1.37	4.44	5.81	7.15
1278	cycle 20 miles		108	.074			1.97	6.40	8.37	10.35
1280	cycle 30 miles		84	.095			2.54	8.25	10.79	13.30
1282	cycle 40 miles		72	.111			2.96	9.60	12.56	15.55
1284	cycle 50 miles		60	.133			3.55	11.55	15.10	18.60
1294	45 MPH ave, cycle 8 miles		180	.044			1.18	3.85	5.03	6.20
1296	cycle 10 miles		168	.048			1.27	4.12	5.39	6.65
1298	cycle 20 miles		120	.067			1.78	5.75	7.53	9.30
1300	cycle 30 miles		96	.083			2.22	7.20	9.42	11.65
1302	cycle 40 miles		72	.111			2.96	9.60	12.56	15.55
1304	cycle 50 miles		60	.133			3.55	11.55	15.10	18.60
1306	50 MPH ave, cycle 10 miles		180	.044			1.18	3.85	5.03	6.20
1308	cycle 20 miles		132	.061			1.62	5.25	6.87	8.45
1310	cycle 30 miles		96	.083			2.22	7.20	9.42	11.65
1312	cycle 40 miles		84	.095			2.54	8.25	10.79	13.30
1314	cycle 50 miles		72	.111			2.96	9.60	12.56	15.55
1414	15 MPH ave, cycle 0.5 mile, 25 min. wait/Ld./Uld.		204	.039			1.05	3.39	4.44	5.45
1416	cycle 1 mile		192	.042			1.11	3.61	4.72	5.80
1418	cycle 2 miles		168	.048			1.27	4.12	5.39	6.65
1420	cycle 4 miles		132	.061			1.62	5.25	6.87	8.45
1422	cycle 6 miles		120	.067			1.78	5.75	7.53	9.30
1424	cycle 8 miles		96	.083			2.22	7.20	9.42	11.65
1425	cycle 10 miles		84	.095			2.54	8.25	10.79	13.30
1426	20 MPH ave, cycle 0.5 mile		216	.037			.99	3.21	4.20	5.15
1428	cycle 1 mile		204	.039			1.05	3.39	4.44	5.45
1430	cycle 2 miles		180	.044			1.18	3.85	5.03	6.20
1432	cycle 4 miles		156	.051			1.37	4.44	5.81	7.15
1434	cycle 6 miles		132	.061			1.62	5.25	6.87	8.45
1436	cycle 8 miles		120	.067			1.78	5.75	7.53	9.30
1438	cycle 10 miles		96	.083			2.22	7.20	9.42	11.65
1440	25 MPH ave, cycle 4 miles		168	.048			1.27	4.12	5.39	6.65
1442	cycle 6 miles		144	.056			1.48	4.81	6.29	7.75
1444	cycle 8 miles		132	.061			1.62	5.25	6.87	8.45
1446	cycle 10 miles		108	.074			1.97	6.40	8.37	10.35
1450	30 MPH ave, cycle 4 miles		168	.048			1.27	4.12	5.39	6.65
1452	cycle 6 miles		156	.051			1.37	4.44	5.81	7.15
1454	cycle 8 miles		132	.061			1.62	5.25	6.87	8.45
1456	cycle 10 miles		120	.067			1.78	5.75	7.53	9.30
1460	35 MPH ave, cycle 4 miles		180	.044			1.18	3.85	5.03	6.20
1462	cycle 6 miles		156	.051			1.37	4.44	5.81	7.15
1464	cycle 8 miles		144	.056			1.48	4.81	6.29	7.75
1466	cycle 10 miles		132	.061			1.62	5.25	6.87	8.45
1468	cycle 20 miles		96	.083			2.22	7.20	9.42	11.65
1469	cycle 30 miles		72	.111			2.96	9.60	12.56	15.55
1470	cycle 40 miles		60	.133			3.55	11.55	15.10	18.60
1472	40 MPH ave, cycle 6 miles		168	.048			1.27	4.12	5.39	6.65
1474	cycle 8 miles		156	.051			1.37	4.44	5.81	7.15
1476	cycle 10 miles		144	.056			1.48	4.81	6.29	7.75
1478	cycle 20 miles		96	.083			2.22	7.20	9.42	11.65
1480	cycle 30 miles		84	.095			2.54	8.25	10.79	13.30
1482	cycle 40 miles		60	.133			3.55	11.55	15.10	18.60
1484	cycle 50 miles		60	.133			3.55	11.55	15.10	18.60

31 23 23.20 Hauling		Crew	Daily Output	Labor-Hours	Unit	Material	2014 Bare Costs		Total	Total Incl O&P
							Labor	Equipment		
1494	45 MPH ave, cycle 8 miles	B-34B	156	.051	L.C.Y.		1.37	4.44	5.81	7.15
1496	cycle 10 miles		144	.056			1.48	4.81	6.29	7.75
1498	cycle 20 miles		108	.074			1.97	6.40	8.37	10.35
1500	cycle 30 miles		84	.095			2.54	8.25	10.79	13.30
1502	cycle 40 miles		72	.111			2.96	9.60	12.56	15.55
1504	cycle 50 miles		60	.133			3.55	11.55	15.10	18.60
1506	50 MPH ave, cycle 10 miles		156	.051			1.37	4.44	5.81	7.15
1508	cycle 20 miles		120	.067			1.78	5.75	7.53	9.30
1510	cycle 30 miles		96	.083			2.22	7.20	9.42	11.65
1512	cycle 40 miles		72	.111			2.96	9.60	12.56	15.55
1514	cycle 50 miles		60	.133			3.55	11.55	15.10	18.60
1614	15 MPH, cycle 0.5 mile, 30 min. wait/Ld./Uld.		180	.044			1.18	3.85	5.03	6.20
1616	cycle 1 mile		168	.048			1.27	4.12	5.39	6.65
1618	cycle 2 miles		144	.056			1.48	4.81	6.29	7.75
1620	cycle 4 miles		120	.067			1.78	5.75	7.53	9.30
1622	cycle 6 miles		108	.074			1.97	6.40	8.37	10.35
1624	cycle 8 miles		84	.095			2.54	8.25	10.79	13.30
1625	cycle 10 miles		84	.095			2.54	8.25	10.79	13.30
1626	20 MPH ave, cycle 0.5 mile		180	.044			1.18	3.85	5.03	6.20
1628	cycle 1 mile		168	.048			1.27	4.12	5.39	6.65
1630	cycle 2 miles		156	.051			1.37	4.44	5.81	7.15
1632	cycle 4 miles		132	.061			1.62	5.25	6.87	8.45
1634	cycle 6 miles		120	.067			1.78	5.75	7.53	9.30
1636	cycle 8 miles		108	.074			1.97	6.40	8.37	10.35
1638	cycle 10 miles		96	.083			2.22	7.20	9.42	11.65
1640	25 MPH ave, cycle 4 miles		144	.056			1.48	4.81	6.29	7.75
1642	cycle 6 miles		132	.061			1.62	5.25	6.87	8.45
1644	cycle 8 miles		108	.074			1.97	6.40	8.37	10.35
1646	cycle 10 miles		108	.074			1.97	6.40	8.37	10.35
1650	30 MPH ave, cycle 4 miles		144	.056			1.48	4.81	6.29	7.75
1652	cycle 6 miles		132	.061			1.62	5.25	6.87	8.45
1654	cycle 8 miles		120	.067			1.78	5.75	7.53	9.30
1656	cycle 10 miles		108	.074			1.97	6.40	8.37	10.35
1660	35 MPH ave, cycle 4 miles		156	.051			1.37	4.44	5.81	7.15
1662	cycle 6 miles		144	.056			1.48	4.81	6.29	7.75
1664	cycle 8 miles		132	.061			1.62	5.25	6.87	8.45
1666	cycle 10 miles		120	.067			1.78	5.75	7.53	9.30
1668	cycle 20 miles		84	.095			2.54	8.25	10.79	13.30
1669	cycle 30 miles		72	.111			2.96	9.60	12.56	15.55
1670	cycle 40 miles		60	.133			3.55	11.55	15.10	18.60
1672	40 MPH, cycle 6 miles		144	.056			1.48	4.81	6.29	7.75
1674	cycle 8 miles		132	.061			1.62	5.25	6.87	8.45
1676	cycle 10 miles		120	.067			1.78	5.75	7.53	9.30
1678	cycle 20 miles		96	.083			2.22	7.20	9.42	11.65
1680	cycle 30 miles		72	.111			2.96	9.60	12.56	15.55
1682	cycle 40 miles		60	.133			3.55	11.55	15.10	18.60
1684	cycle 50 miles		48	.167			4.44	14.40	18.84	23.50
1694	45 MPH ave, cycle 8 miles		144	.056			1.48	4.81	6.29	7.75
1696	cycle 10 miles		132	.061			1.62	5.25	6.87	8.45
1698	cycle 20 miles		96	.083			2.22	7.20	9.42	11.65
1700	cycle 30 miles		84	.095			2.54	8.25	10.79	13.30
1702	cycle 40 miles		60	.133			3.55	11.55	15.10	18.60
1704	cycle 50 miles		60	.133			3.55	11.55	15.10	18.60

31 23 23 – Fill

31 23 23.20 Hauling	Crew	Daily Output	Labor-Hours	Unit	Material	2014 Bare Costs Labor	2014 Bare Costs Equipment	Total	Total Incl O&P
1706	50 MPH ave, cycle 10 miles	B-34B	132	.061	L.C.Y.		1.62	5.25	6.87	8.45
1708	cycle 20 miles		108	.074			1.97	6.40	8.37	10.35
1710	cycle 30 miles		84	.095			2.54	8.25	10.79	13.30
1712	cycle 40 miles		72	.111			2.96	9.60	12.56	15.55
1714	cycle 50 miles		60	.133			3.55	11.55	15.10	18.60
2000	Hauling, 8 C.Y. truck, small project cost per hour	B-34A	8	1	Hr.		26.50	52	78.50	102
2100	12 C.Y. Truck	B-34B	8	1			26.50	86.50	113	140
2150	16.5 C.Y. Truck	B-34C	8	1			26.50	92.50	119	147
2175	18 C.Y. 8 wheel Truck	B-34I	8	1			26.50	108	134.50	164
2200	20 C.Y. Truck	B-34D	8	1			26.50	94	120.50	149
9014	18 C.Y. truck, 8 wheels,15 min. wait/Ld./Uld.,15 MPH, cycle 0.5 mi.	B-34I	504	.016	L.C.Y.		.42	1.72	2.14	2.59
9016	cycle 1 mile		450	.018			.47	1.93	2.40	2.91
9018	cycle 2 miles		378	.021			.56	2.29	2.85	3.46
9020	cycle 4 miles		270	.030			.79	3.21	4	4.85
9022	cycle 6 miles		216	.037			.99	4.02	5.01	6.05
9024	cycle 8 miles		180	.044			1.18	4.82	6	7.25
9025	cycle 10 miles		144	.056			1.48	6.05	7.53	9.10
9026	20 MPH ave, cycle 0.5 mile		522	.015			.41	1.66	2.07	2.51
9028	cycle 1 mile		468	.017			.46	1.85	2.31	2.80
9030	cycle 2 miles		414	.019			.51	2.10	2.61	3.16
9032	cycle 4 miles		324	.025			.66	2.68	3.34	4.05
9034	cycle 6 miles		252	.032			.85	3.44	4.29	5.20
9036	cycle 8 miles		216	.037			.99	4.02	5.01	6.05
9038	cycle 10 miles		180	.044			1.18	4.82	6	7.25
9040	25 MPH ave, cycle 4 miles		342	.023			.62	2.54	3.16	3.83
9042	cycle 6 miles		288	.028			.74	3.01	3.75	4.54
9044	cycle 8 miles		252	.032			.85	3.44	4.29	5.20
9046	cycle 10 miles		216	.037			.99	4.02	5.01	6.05
9050	30 MPH ave, cycle 4 miles		378	.021			.56	2.29	2.85	3.46
9052	cycle 6 miles		324	.025			.66	2.68	3.34	4.05
9054	cycle 8 miles		270	.030			.79	3.21	4	4.85
9056	cycle 10 miles		234	.034			.91	3.71	4.62	5.60
9060	35 MPH ave, cycle 4 miles		396	.020			.54	2.19	2.73	3.31
9062	cycle 6 miles		342	.023			.62	2.54	3.16	3.83
9064	cycle 8 miles		288	.028			.74	3.01	3.75	4.54
9066	cycle 10 miles		270	.030			.79	3.21	4	4.85
9068	cycle 20 miles		162	.049			1.32	5.35	6.67	8.10
9070	cycle 30 miles		126	.063			1.69	6.90	8.59	10.35
9072	cycle 40 miles		90	.089			2.37	9.65	12.02	14.55
9074	40 MPH ave, cycle 6 miles		360	.022			.59	2.41	3	3.64
9076	cycle 8 miles		324	.025			.66	2.68	3.34	4.05
9078	cycle 10 miles		288	.028			.74	3.01	3.75	4.54
9080	cycle 20 miles		180	.044			1.18	4.82	6	7.25
9082	cycle 30 miles		144	.056			1.48	6.05	7.53	9.10
9084	cycle 40 miles		108	.074			1.97	8.05	10.02	12.15
9086	cycle 50 miles		90	.089			2.37	9.65	12.02	14.55
9094	45 MPH ave, cycle 8 miles		324	.025			.66	2.68	3.34	4.05
9096	cycle 10 miles		306	.026			.70	2.83	3.53	4.28
9098	cycle 20 miles		198	.040			1.08	4.38	5.46	6.60
9100	cycle 30 miles		144	.056			1.48	6.05	7.53	9.10
9102	cycle 40 miles		126	.063			1.69	6.90	8.59	10.35
9104	cycle 50 miles		108	.074			1.97	8.05	10.02	12.15
9106	50 MPH ave, cycle 10 miles		324	.025			.66	2.68	3.34	4.05

31 23 Excavation and Fill

31 23 23 – Fill

31 23 23.20 Hauling		Crew	Daily Output	Labor-Hours	Unit	Material	2014 Bare Costs Labor	Equipment	Total	Total Incl O&P
9108	cycle 20 miles	B-34I	216	.037	L.C.Y.		.99	4.02	5.01	6.05
9110	cycle 30 miles		162	.049			1.32	5.35	6.67	8.10
9112	cycle 40 miles		126	.063			1.69	6.90	8.59	10.35
9114	cycle 50 miles		108	.074			1.97	8.05	10.02	12.15
9214	20 min. wait/Ld./Uld.,15 MPH, cycle 0.5 mi.		396	.020			.54	2.19	2.73	3.31
9216	cycle 1 mile		360	.022			.59	2.41	3	3.64
9218	cycle 2 miles		306	.026			.70	2.83	3.53	4.28
9220	cycle 4 miles		234	.034			.91	3.71	4.62	5.60
9222	cycle 6 miles		198	.040			1.08	4.38	5.46	6.60
9224	cycle 8 miles		162	.049			1.32	5.35	6.67	8.10
9225	cycle 10 miles		144	.056			1.48	6.05	7.53	9.10
9226	20 MPH ave, cycle 0.5 mile		396	.020			.54	2.19	2.73	3.31
9228	cycle 1 mile		378	.021			.56	2.29	2.85	3.46
9230	cycle 2 miles		324	.025			.66	2.68	3.34	4.05
9232	cycle 4 miles		270	.030			.79	3.21	4	4.85
9234	cycle 6 miles		216	.037			.99	4.02	5.01	6.05
9236	cycle 8 miles		198	.040			1.08	4.38	5.46	6.60
9238	cycle 10 miles		162	.049			1.32	5.35	6.67	8.10
9240	25 MPH ave, cycle 4 miles		288	.028			.74	3.01	3.75	4.54
9242	cycle 6 miles		252	.032			.85	3.44	4.29	5.20
9244	cycle 8 miles		216	.037			.99	4.02	5.01	6.05
9246	cycle 10 miles		198	.040			1.08	4.38	5.46	6.60
9250	30 MPH ave, cycle 4 miles		306	.026			.70	2.83	3.53	4.28
9252	cycle 6 miles		270	.030			.79	3.21	4	4.85
9254	cycle 8 miles		234	.034			.91	3.71	4.62	5.60
9256	cycle 10 miles		216	.037			.99	4.02	5.01	6.05
9260	35 MPH ave, cycle 4 miles		324	.025			.66	2.68	3.34	4.05
9262	cycle 6 miles		288	.028			.74	3.01	3.75	4.54
9264	cycle 8 miles		252	.032			.85	3.44	4.29	5.20
9266	cycle 10 miles		234	.034			.91	3.71	4.62	5.60
9268	cycle 20 miles		162	.049			1.32	5.35	6.67	8.10
9270	cycle 30 miles		108	.074			1.97	8.05	10.02	12.15
9272	cycle 40 miles		90	.089			2.37	9.65	12.02	14.55
9274	40 MPH ave, cycle 6 miles		288	.028			.74	3.01	3.75	4.54
9276	cycle 8 miles		270	.030			.79	3.21	4	4.85
9278	cycle 10 miles		234	.034			.91	3.71	4.62	5.60
9280	cycle 20 miles		162	.049			1.32	5.35	6.67	8.10
9282	cycle 30 miles		126	.063			1.69	6.90	8.59	10.35
9284	cycle 40 miles		108	.074			1.97	8.05	10.02	12.15
9286	cycle 50 miles		90	.089			2.37	9.65	12.02	14.55
9294	45 MPH ave, cycle 8 miles		270	.030			.79	3.21	4	4.85
9296	cycle 10 miles		252	.032			.85	3.44	4.29	5.20
9298	cycle 20 miles		180	.044			1.18	4.82	6	7.25
9300	cycle 30 miles		144	.056			1.48	6.05	7.53	9.10
9302	cycle 40 miles		108	.074			1.97	8.05	10.02	12.15
9304	cycle 50 miles		90	.089			2.37	9.65	12.02	14.55
9306	50 MPH ave, cycle 10 miles		270	.030			.79	3.21	4	4.85
9308	cycle 20 miles		198	.040			1.08	4.38	5.46	6.60
9310	cycle 30 miles		144	.056			1.48	6.05	7.53	9.10
9312	cycle 40 miles		126	.063			1.69	6.90	8.59	10.35
9314	cycle 50 miles		108	.074			1.97	8.05	10.02	12.15
9414	25 min. wait/Ld./Uld.,15 MPH, cycle 0.5 mi.		306	.026			.70	2.83	3.53	4.28
9416	cycle 1 mile		288	.028			.74	3.01	3.75	4.54

31 23 23 − Fill

31 23 23.20 Hauling		Crew	Daily Output	Labor-Hours	Unit	Material	2014 Bare Costs Labor	2014 Bare Costs Equipment	Total	Total Incl O&P
9418	cycle 2 miles	B-34I	252	.032	L.C.Y.		.85	3.44	4.29	5.20
9420	cycle 4 miles		198	.040			1.08	4.38	5.46	6.60
9422	cycle 6 miles		180	.044			1.18	4.82	6	7.25
9424	cycle 8 miles		144	.056			1.48	6.05	7.53	9.10
9425	cycle 10 miles		126	.063			1.69	6.90	8.59	10.35
9426	20 MPH ave, cycle 0.5 mile		324	.025			.66	2.68	3.34	4.05
9428	cycle 1 mile		306	.026			.70	2.83	3.53	4.28
9430	cycle 2 miles		270	.030			.79	3.21	4	4.85
9432	cycle 4 miles		234	.034			.91	3.71	4.62	5.60
9434	cycle 6 miles		198	.040			1.08	4.38	5.46	6.60
9436	cycle 8 miles		180	.044			1.18	4.82	6	7.25
9438	cycle 10 miles		144	.056			1.48	6.05	7.53	9.10
9440	25 MPH ave, cycle 4 miles		252	.032			.85	3.44	4.29	5.20
9442	cycle 6 miles		216	.037			.99	4.02	5.01	6.05
9444	cycle 8 miles		198	.040			1.08	4.38	5.46	6.60
9446	cycle 10 miles		180	.044			1.18	4.82	6	7.25
9450	30 MPH ave, cycle 4 miles		252	.032			.85	3.44	4.29	5.20
9452	cycle 6 miles		234	.034			.91	3.71	4.62	5.60
9454	cycle 8 miles		198	.040			1.08	4.38	5.46	6.60
9456	cycle 10 miles		180	.044			1.18	4.82	6	7.25
9460	35 MPH ave, cycle 4 miles		270	.030			.79	3.21	4	4.85
9462	cycle 6 miles		234	.034			.91	3.71	4.62	5.60
9464	cycle 8 miles		216	.037			.99	4.02	5.01	6.05
9466	cycle 10 miles		198	.040			1.08	4.38	5.46	6.60
9468	cycle 20 miles		144	.056			1.48	6.05	7.53	9.10
9470	cycle 30 miles		108	.074			1.97	8.05	10.02	12.15
9472	cycle 40 miles		90	.089			2.37	9.65	12.02	14.55
9474	40 MPH ave, cycle 6 miles		252	.032			.85	3.44	4.29	5.20
9476	cycle 8 miles		234	.034			.91	3.71	4.62	5.60
9478	cycle 10 miles		216	.037			.99	4.02	5.01	6.05
9480	cycle 20 miles		144	.056			1.48	6.05	7.53	9.10
9482	cycle 30 miles		126	.063			1.69	6.90	8.59	10.35
9484	cycle 40 miles		90	.089			2.37	9.65	12.02	14.55
9486	cycle 50 miles		90	.089			2.37	9.65	12.02	14.55
9494	45 MPH ave, cycle 8 miles		234	.034			.91	3.71	4.62	5.60
9496	cycle 10 miles		216	.037			.99	4.02	5.01	6.05
9498	cycle 20 miles		162	.049			1.32	5.35	6.67	8.10
9500	cycle 30 miles		126	.063			1.69	6.90	8.59	10.35
9502	cycle 40 miles		108	.074			1.97	8.05	10.02	12.15
9504	cycle 50 miles		90	.089			2.37	9.65	12.02	14.55
9506	50 MPH ave, cycle 10 miles		234	.034			.91	3.71	4.62	5.60
9508	cycle 20 miles		180	.044			1.18	4.82	6	7.25
9510	cycle 30 miles		144	.056			1.48	6.05	7.53	9.10
9512	cycle 40 miles		108	.074			1.97	8.05	10.02	12.15
9514	cycle 50 miles		90	.089			2.37	9.65	12.02	14.55
9614	30 min. wait/Ld./Uld.,15 MPH, cycle 0.5 mi.		270	.030			.79	3.21	4	4.85
9616	cycle 1 mile		252	.032			.85	3.44	4.29	5.20
9618	cycle 2 miles		216	.037			.99	4.02	5.01	6.05
9620	cycle 4 miles		180	.044			1.18	4.82	6	7.25
9622	cycle 6 miles		162	.049			1.32	5.35	6.67	8.10
9624	cycle 8 miles		126	.063			1.69	6.90	8.59	10.35
9625	cycle 10 miles		126	.063			1.69	6.90	8.59	10.35
9626	20 MPH ave, cycle 0.5 mile		270	.030			.79	3.21	4	4.85

31 23 23 – Fill

31 23 23.20 Hauling

		Crew	Daily Output	Labor-Hours	Unit	Material	2014 Bare Costs Labor	Equipment	Total	Total Incl O&P
9628	cycle 1 mile	B-34I	252	.032	L.C.Y.		.85	3.44	4.29	5.20
9630	cycle 2 miles		234	.034			.91	3.71	4.62	5.60
9632	cycle 4 miles		198	.040			1.08	4.38	5.46	6.60
9634	cycle 6 miles		180	.044			1.18	4.82	6	7.25
9636	cycle 8 miles		162	.049			1.32	5.35	6.67	8.10
9638	cycle 10 miles		144	.056			1.48	6.05	7.53	9.10
9640	25 MPH ave, cycle 4 miles		216	.037			.99	4.02	5.01	6.05
9642	cycle 6 miles		198	.040			1.08	4.38	5.46	6.60
9644	cycle 8 miles		180	.044			1.18	4.82	6	7.25
9646	cycle 10 miles		162	.049			1.32	5.35	6.67	8.10
9650	30 MPH ave, cycle 4 miles		216	.037			.99	4.02	5.01	6.05
9652	cycle 6 miles		198	.040			1.08	4.38	5.46	6.60
9654	cycle 8 miles		180	.044			1.18	4.82	6	7.25
9656	cycle 10 miles		162	.049			1.32	5.35	6.67	8.10
9660	35 MPH ave, cycle 4 miles		234	.034			.91	3.71	4.62	5.60
9662	cycle 6 miles		216	.037			.99	4.02	5.01	6.05
9664	cycle 8 miles		198	.040			1.08	4.38	5.46	6.60
9666	cycle 10 miles		180	.044			1.18	4.82	6	7.25
9668	cycle 20 miles		126	.063			1.69	6.90	8.59	10.35
9670	cycle 30 miles		108	.074			1.97	8.05	10.02	12.15
9672	cycle 40 miles		90	.089			2.37	9.65	12.02	14.55
9674	40 MPH ave, cycle 6 miles		216	.037			.99	4.02	5.01	6.05
9676	cycle 8 miles		198	.040			1.08	4.38	5.46	6.60
9678	cycle 10 miles		180	.044			1.18	4.82	6	7.25
9680	cycle 20 miles		144	.056			1.48	6.05	7.53	9.10
9682	cycle 30 miles		108	.074			1.97	8.05	10.02	12.15
9684	cycle 40 miles		90	.089			2.37	9.65	12.02	14.55
9686	cycle 50 miles		72	.111			2.96	12.05	15.01	18.20
9694	45 MPH ave, cycle 8 miles		216	.037			.99	4.02	5.01	6.05
9696	cycle 10 miles		198	.040			1.08	4.38	5.46	6.60
9698	cycle 20 miles		144	.056			1.48	6.05	7.53	9.10
9700	cycle 30 miles		126	.063			1.69	6.90	8.59	10.35
9702	cycle 40 miles		108	.074			1.97	8.05	10.02	12.15
9704	cycle 50 miles		90	.089			2.37	9.65	12.02	14.55
9706	50 MPH ave, cycle 10 miles		198	.040			1.08	4.38	5.46	6.60
9708	cycle 20 miles		162	.049			1.32	5.35	6.67	8.10
9710	cycle 30 miles		126	.063			1.69	6.90	8.59	10.35
9712	cycle 40 miles		108	.074			1.97	8.05	10.02	12.15
9714	cycle 50 miles		90	.089			2.37	9.65	12.02	14.55

31 23 23.24 Compaction, Structural

		Crew	Daily Output	Labor-Hours	Unit	Material	2014 Bare Costs Labor	Equipment	Total	Total Incl O&P
0010	**COMPACTION, STRUCTURAL**									
0020	Steel wheel tandem roller, 5 tons	B-10E	8	1	Hr.		34	19.90	53.90	78
0050	Air tamp, 6" to 8" lifts, common fill	B-9	250	.160	E.C.Y.		3.87	.93	4.80	7.55
0060	Select fill	"	300	.133			3.23	.78	4.01	6.30
0600	Vibratory plate, 8" lifts, common fill	A-1D	200	.040			.95	.18	1.13	1.80
0700	Select fill	"	216	.037			.88	.17	1.05	1.66

31 25 Erosion and Sedimentation Controls

31 25 14 – Stabilization Measures for Erosion and Sedimentation Control

31 25 14.16 Rolled Erosion Control Mats and Blankets

31 25 14.16 Rolled Erosion Control Mats and Blankets		Crew	Daily Output	Labor-Hours	Unit	Material	2014 Bare Costs Labor	2014 Bare Costs Equipment	Total	Total Incl O&P
0010	**ROLLED EROSION CONTROL MATS AND BLANKETS**									
0020	Jute mesh, 100 S.Y. per roll, 4' wide, stapled	G	B-80A	2400	.010	S.Y.	1.11	.24	.14	1.49	1.77
0100	Plastic netting, stapled, 2" x 1" mesh, 20 mil	G	B-1	2500	.010		.23	.23		.46	.65
0200	Polypropylene mesh, stapled, 6.5 oz./S.Y.	G		2500	.010		2.33	.23		2.56	2.96
0300	Tobacco netting, or jute mesh #2, stapled	G		2500	.010		.18	.23		.41	.60
1000	Silt fence, polypropylene, 3' high, ideal conditions	G	2 Clab	1600	.010	L.F.	.24	.24		.48	.66
1100	Adverse conditions	G	"	950	.017	"	.24	.40		.64	.93

31 31 Soil Treatment

31 31 16 – Termite Control

31 31 16.13 Chemical Termite Control

31 31 16.13 Chemical Termite Control		Crew	Daily Output	Labor-Hours	Unit	Material	2014 Bare Costs Labor	2014 Bare Costs Equipment	Total	Total Incl O&P
0010	**CHEMICAL TERMITE CONTROL**									
0020	Slab and walls, residential	1 Skwk	1200	.007	SF Flr.	.37	.22		.59	.78
0400	Insecticides for termite control, minimum		14.20	.563	Gal.	63	18.30		81.30	101
0500	Maximum		11	.727	"	108	23.50		131.50	159

Division Notes

		CREW	DAILY OUTPUT	LABOR-HOURS	UNIT	BARE COSTS				TOTAL INCL O&P
						MAT.	LABOR	EQUIP.	TOTAL	

Estimating Tips

32 01 00 Operations and Maintenance of Exterior Improvements

• Recycling of asphalt pavement is becoming very popular and is an alternative to removal and replacement. It can be a good value engineering proposal if removed pavement can be recycled, either at the project site or at another site that is reasonably close to the project site. Sections on repair of flexible and rigid pavement are included.

32 10 00 Bases, Ballasts, and Paving

• When estimating paving, keep in mind the project schedule. Also note that prices for asphalt and concrete are generally higher in the cold seasons. Lines for pavement markings, including tactile warning systems and fence lines, are included.

32 90 00 Planting

• The timing of planting and guarantee specifications often dictate the costs for establishing tree and shrub growth and a stand of grass or ground cover. Establish the work performance schedule to coincide with the local planting season. Maintenance and growth guarantees can add from 20%–100% to the total landscaping cost and can be contractually cumbersome. The cost to replace trees and shrubs can be as high as 5% of the total cost, depending on the planting zone, soil conditions, and time of year.

Reference Numbers

Reference numbers are shown in shaded boxes at the beginning of some major classifications. These numbers refer to related items in the Reference Section. The reference information may be an estimating procedure, an alternate pricing method, or technical information.

Note: Not all subdivisions listed here necessarily appear in this publication.

Division 32 - Exterior Improvements

32 01 Operation and Maintenance of Exterior Improvements

32 01 13 – Flexible Paving Surface Treatment

32 01 13.66 Fog Seal	Crew	Daily Output	Labor-Hours	Unit	Material	2014 Bare Costs Labor	Equipment	Total	Total Incl O&P
0010 **FOG SEAL**									
0012 Sealcoating, 2 coat coal tar pitch emulsion over 10,000 S.Y.	B-45	5000	.003	S.Y.	1.29	.08	.06	1.43	1.63
0030 1000 to 10,000 S.Y.	"	3000	.005		1.29	.13	.10	1.52	1.76
0100 Under 1000 S.Y.	B-1	1050	.023		1.29	.56		1.85	2.36
0300 Petroleum resistant, over 10,000 S.Y.	B-45	5000	.003		1.29	.08	.06	1.43	1.63
0320 1000 to 10,000 S.Y.	"	3000	.005		1.29	.13	.10	1.52	1.76
0400 Under 1000 S.Y.	B-1	1050	.023		1.29	.56		1.85	2.36

32 06 Schedules for Exterior Improvements

32 06 10 – Schedules for Bases, Ballasts, and Paving

32 06 10.10 Sidewalks, Driveways and Patios

	Crew	Daily Output	Labor-Hours	Unit	Material	2014 Bare Costs Labor	Equipment	Total	Total Incl O&P
0010 **SIDEWALKS, DRIVEWAYS AND PATIOS** No base									
0021 Asphaltic concrete, 2" thick	B-37	6480	.007	S.F.	.80	.19	.02	1.01	1.23
0101 2-1/2" thick	"	5950	.008	"	1.01	.21	.03	1.25	1.50
0300 Concrete, 3000 psi, CIP, 6 x 6 - W1.4 x W1.4 mesh,									
0310 broomed finish, no base, 4" thick	B-24	600	.040	S.F.	1.65	1.16		2.81	3.74
0350 5" thick		545	.044		2.20	1.27		3.47	4.53
0400 6" thick		510	.047		2.57	1.36		3.93	5.10
0450 For bank run gravel base, 4" thick, add	B-18	2500	.010		.51	.23	.02	.76	.98
0520 8" thick, add	"	1600	.015		1.03	.37	.03	1.43	1.78
1000 Crushed stone, 1" thick, white marble	2 Clab	1700	.009		.40	.22		.62	.82
1050 Bluestone	"	1700	.009		.22	.22		.44	.62
1700 Redwood, prefabricated, 4' x 4' sections	2 Carp	316	.051		4.77	1.63		6.40	8
1750 Redwood planks, 1" thick, on sleepers	"	240	.067		4.77	2.14		6.91	8.85
2250 Stone dust, 4" thick	B-62	900	.027	S.Y.	3.89	.71	.19	4.79	5.65

32 06 10.20 Steps

	Crew	Daily Output	Labor-Hours	Unit	Material	2014 Bare Costs Labor	Equipment	Total	Total Incl O&P
0010 **STEPS**									
0011 Incl. excav., borrow & concrete base as required									
0100 Brick steps	B-24	35	.686	LF Riser	15	19.85		34.85	49.50
0200 Railroad ties	2 Clab	25	.640		3.55	15.25		18.80	29.50
0300 Bluestone treads, 12" x 2" or 12" x 1-1/2"	B-24	30	.800		33	23		56	74.50
0600 Precast concrete, see Section 03 41 23.50									
4025 Steel edge strips, incl. stakes, 1/4" x 5"	B-1	390	.062	L.F.	3.90	1.51		5.41	6.80
4050 Edging, landscape timber or railroad ties, 6" x 8"	2 Carp	170	.094	"	3.03	3.02		6.05	8.45

32 11 Base Courses

32 11 23 – Aggregate Base Courses

32 11 23.23 Base Course Drainage Layers

	Crew	Daily Output	Labor-Hours	Unit	Material	2014 Bare Costs Labor	Equipment	Total	Total Incl O&P
0010 **BASE COURSE DRAINAGE LAYERS**									
0011 For roadways and large areas									
0051 3/4" stone compacted to 3" deep	B-36	36000	.001	S.F.	.31	.03	.04	.38	.44
0101 6" deep		35100	.001		.61	.03	.05	.69	.77
0201 9" deep		25875	.002		.89	.04	.06	.99	1.12
0305 12" deep		21150	.002		1.27	.05	.08	1.40	1.56
0306 Crushed 1-1/2" stone base, compacted to 4" deep		47000	.001		.05	.02	.03	.10	.13
0307 6" deep		35100	.001		.63	.03	.05	.71	.80
0308 8" deep		27000	.001		.84	.04	.06	.94	1.07
0309 12" deep		16200	.002		1.27	.07	.10	1.44	1.62
0350 Bank run gravel, spread and compacted									

32 11 Base Courses

32 11 23 - Aggregate Base Courses

32 11 23.23 Base Course Drainage Layers

	32 11 23.23 Base Course Drainage Layers	Crew	Daily Output	Labor-Hours	Unit	Material	2014 Bare Costs Labor	Equipment	Total	Total Incl O&P
0371	6" deep	B-32	54000	.001	S.F.	.47	.02	.04	.53	.60
0391	9" deep		39600	.001		.69	.03	.06	.78	.86
0401	12" deep	↓	32400	.001	↓	.95	.03	.07	1.05	1.17
6900	For small and irregular areas, add						50%	50%		

32 11 26 - Asphaltic Base Courses

32 11 26.19 Bituminous-Stabilized Base Courses

		Crew	Daily Output	Labor-Hours	Unit	Material	2014 Bare Costs Labor	Equipment	Total	Total Incl O&P
0010	**BITUMINOUS-STABILIZED BASE COURSES**									
0020	And large paved areas									
0700	Liquid application to gravel base, asphalt emulsion	B-45	6000	.003	Gal.	4.25	.07	.05	4.37	4.85
0800	Prime and seal, cut back asphalt		6000	.003	"	5	.07	.05	5.12	5.65
1000	Macadam penetration crushed stone, 2 gal. per S.Y., 4" thick		6000	.003	S.Y.	8.50	.07	.05	8.62	9.50
1100	6" thick, 3 gal. per S.Y.		4000	.004		12.75	.10	.08	12.93	14.30
1200	8" thick, 4 gal. per S.Y.	↓	3000	.005	↓	17	.13	.10	17.23	19.05
8900	For small and irregular areas, add						50%	50%		

32 12 Flexible Paving

32 12 16 - Asphalt Paving

32 12 16.14 Paving Asphaltic Concrete

		Crew	Daily Output	Labor-Hours	Unit	Material	2014 Bare Costs Labor	Equipment	Total	Total Incl O&P
0010	**PAVING ASPHALTIC CONCRETE**									
0020	6" stone base, 2" binder course, 1" topping	B-25C	9000	.005	S.F.	1.74	.15	.27	2.16	2.45
0025	2" binder course, 2" topping		9000	.005		2.16	.15	.27	2.58	2.90
0030	3" binder course, 2" topping		9000	.005		2.57	.15	.27	2.99	3.36
0035	4" binder course, 2" topping		9000	.005		2.98	.15	.27	3.40	3.81
0040	1.5" binder course, 1" topping		9000	.005		1.54	.15	.27	1.96	2.22
0042	3" binder course, 1" topping		9000	.005		2.16	.15	.27	2.58	2.90
0045	3" binder course, 3" topping		9000	.005		2.98	.15	.27	3.40	3.81
0050	4" binder course, 3" topping		9000	.005		3.39	.15	.27	3.81	4.26
0055	4" binder course, 4" topping		9000	.005		3.80	.15	.27	4.22	4.71
0300	Binder course, 1-1/2" thick		35000	.001		.62	.04	.07	.73	.82
0400	2" thick		25000	.002		.80	.05	.10	.95	1.08
0500	3" thick		15000	.003		1.24	.09	.16	1.49	1.69
0600	4" thick		10800	.004		1.62	.12	.22	1.96	2.23
0800	Sand finish course, 3/4" thick		41000	.001		.32	.03	.06	.41	.46
0900	1" thick	↓	34000	.001		.39	.04	.07	.50	.57
1000	Fill pot holes, hot mix, 2" thick	B-16	4200	.008		.84	.19	.16	1.19	1.42
1100	4" thick		3500	.009		1.23	.23	.20	1.66	1.95
1120	6" thick	↓	3100	.010		1.65	.26	.22	2.13	2.50
1140	Cold patch, 2" thick	B-51	3000	.016		.98	.39	.09	1.46	1.83
1160	4" thick		2700	.018		1.86	.44	.10	2.40	2.88
1180	6" thick	↓	1900	.025	↓	2.89	.62	.14	3.65	4.38

32 13 Rigid Paving

32 13 13 – Concrete Paving

32 13 13.23 Concrete Paving Surface Treatment	Crew	Daily Output	Labor-Hours	Unit	Material	2014 Bare Costs Labor	Equipment	Total	Total Incl O&P
0010 **CONCRETE PAVING SURFACE TREATMENT**									
0015 Including joints, finishing and curing									
0021 Fixed form, 12' pass, unreinforced, 6" thick	B-26	18000	.005	S.F.	3.08	.13	.19	3.40	3.82
0101 8" thick	"	13500	.007		4.15	.18	.25	4.58	5.15
0701 Finishing, broom finish small areas	2 Cefi	1215	.013	↓		.41		.41	.66

32 14 Unit Paving

32 14 13 – Precast Concrete Unit Paving

32 14 13.18 Precast Concrete Plantable Pavers

	Crew	Daily Output	Labor-Hours	Unit	Material	2014 Bare Costs Labor	Equipment	Total	Total Incl O&P
0010 **PRECAST CONCRETE PLANTABLE PAVERS** (50% grass)									
0300 3/4" crushed stone base for plantable pavers, 6 inch depth	B-62	1000	.024	S.Y.	5.50	.64	.17	6.31	7.30
0400 8 inch depth		900	.027		7.40	.71	.19	8.30	9.55
0500 10 inch depth		800	.030		9.20	.80	.22	10.22	11.70
0600 12 inch depth	↓	700	.034	↓	11.05	.91	.25	12.21	13.95
0700 Hydro seeding plantable pavers	B-81A	20	.800	M.S.F.	19.35	19.90	23.50	62.75	80.50
0800 Apply fertilizer and seed to plantable pavers	1 Clab	8	1	"	51.50	24		75.50	96.50

32 14 16 – Brick Unit Paving

32 14 16.10 Brick Paving

	Crew	Daily Output	Labor-Hours	Unit	Material	2014 Bare Costs Labor	Equipment	Total	Total Incl O&P
0010 **BRICK PAVING**									
0012 4" x 8" x 1-1/2", without joints (4.5 brick/S.F.)	D-1	110	.145	S.F.	2.21	4.20		6.41	9.45
0100 Grouted, 3/8" joint (3.9 brick/S.F.)		90	.178		2.15	5.15		7.30	10.90
0200 4" x 8" x 2-1/4", without joints (4.5 bricks/S.F.)		110	.145		2.48	4.20		6.68	9.75
0300 Grouted, 3/8" joint (3.9 brick/S.F.)	↓	90	.178		2.15	5.15		7.30	10.90
0500 Bedding, asphalt, 3/4" thick	B-25	5130	.017		.68	.46	.54	1.68	2.11
0540 Course washed sand bed, 1" thick	B-18	5000	.005		.29	.12	.01	.42	.53
0580 Mortar, 1" thick	D-1	300	.053		.63	1.54		2.17	3.27
0620 2" thick		200	.080		1.27	2.31		3.58	5.25
1500 Brick on 1" thick sand bed laid flat, 4.5 per S.F.		100	.160		3.12	4.62		7.74	11.15
2000 Brick pavers, laid on edge, 7.2 per S.F.	↓	70	.229	↓	3.83	6.60		10.43	15.20

32 14 23 – Asphalt Unit Paving

32 14 23.10 Asphalt Blocks

	Crew	Daily Output	Labor-Hours	Unit	Material	2014 Bare Costs Labor	Equipment	Total	Total Incl O&P
0010 **ASPHALT BLOCKS**									
0020 Rectangular, 6" x 12" x 1-1/4", w/bed & neopr. adhesive	D-1	135	.119	S.F.	9.20	3.43		12.63	15.80
0100 3" thick		130	.123		12.90	3.56		16.46	20
0300 Hexagonal tile, 8" wide, 1-1/4" thick		135	.119		9.20	3.43		12.63	15.80
0400 2" thick		130	.123		12.90	3.56		16.46	20
0500 Square, 8" x 8", 1-1/4" thick		135	.119		9.20	3.43		12.63	15.80
0600 2" thick	↓	130	.123	↓	12.90	3.56		16.46	20

32 14 40 – Stone Paving

32 14 40.10 Stone Pavers

	Crew	Daily Output	Labor-Hours	Unit	Material	2014 Bare Costs Labor	Equipment	Total	Total Incl O&P
0010 **STONE PAVERS**									
1100 Flagging, bluestone, irregular, 1" thick,	D-1	81	.198	S.F.	6.35	5.70		12.05	16.50
1150 Snapped random rectangular, 1" thick		92	.174		9.60	5.05		14.65	18.95
1200 1-1/2" thick		85	.188		11.55	5.45		17	22
1250 2" thick		83	.193		13.45	5.55		19	24
1300 Slate, natural cleft, irregular, 3/4" thick		92	.174		9.15	5.05		14.20	18.40
1310 1" thick		85	.188		10.65	5.45		16.10	21
1351 Random rectangular, gauged, 1/2" thick		105	.152		19.80	4.40		24.20	29.50
1400 Random rectangular, butt joint, gauged, 1/4" thick	↓	150	.107		21.50	3.08		24.58	28.50

32 14 Unit Paving

32 14 40 – Stone Paving

32 14 40.10 Stone Pavers

32 14 40.10 Stone Pavers	Crew	Daily Output	Labor-Hours	Unit	Material	2014 Bare Costs Labor	Equipment	Total	Total Incl O&P
1450	For sand rubbed finish, add				S.F.	9.20			9.20	10.10
1500	For interior setting, add								25%	25%
1550	Granite blocks, 3-1/2" x 3-1/2" x 3-1/2"	D-1	92	.174	S.F.	11.60	5.05		16.65	21

32 16 Curbs, Gutters, Sidewalks, and Driveways

32 16 13 – Curbs and Gutters

32 16 13.13 Cast-in-Place Concrete Curbs and Gutters

32 16 13.13 Cast-in-Place Concrete Curbs and Gutters	Crew	Daily Output	Labor-Hours	Unit	Material	2014 Bare Costs Labor	Equipment	Total	Total Incl O&P
0010	**CAST-IN-PLACE CONCRETE CURBS AND GUTTERS**									
0290	Forms only, no concrete									
0300	Concrete, wood forms, 6" x 18", straight	C-2	500	.096	L.F.	2.95	2.72		5.67	7.80
0400	6" x 18", radius	"	200	.240		3.06	6.80		9.86	14.80
0404	Concrete, wood forms, 6" x 18", straight & concrete	C-2A	500	.096		5.70	2.96		8.66	11.25
0406	6" x 18", radius	"	200	.240		5.85	7.40		13.25	18.75

32 16 13.23 Precast Concrete Curbs and Gutters

32 16 13.23 Precast Concrete Curbs and Gutters	Crew	Daily Output	Labor-Hours	Unit	Material	2014 Bare Costs Labor	Equipment	Total	Total Incl O&P
0010	**PRECAST CONCRETE CURBS AND GUTTERS**									
0550	Precast, 6" x 18", straight	B-29	700	.069	L.F.	9.90	1.78	1.26	12.94	15.25
0600	6" x 18", radius	"	325	.148	"	10.40	3.83	2.71	16.94	21

32 16 13.33 Asphalt Curbs

32 16 13.33 Asphalt Curbs	Crew	Daily Output	Labor-Hours	Unit	Material	2014 Bare Costs Labor	Equipment	Total	Total Incl O&P
0010	**ASPHALT CURBS**									
0012	Curbs, asphaltic, machine formed, 8" wide, 6" high, 40 L.F./ton	B-27	1000	.032	L.F.	1.74	.78	.29	2.81	3.55
0100	8" wide, 8" high, 30 L.F. per ton		900	.036		2.33	.86	.33	3.52	4.37
0150	Asphaltic berm, 12" W, 3"-6" H, 35 L.F./ton, before pavement		700	.046		.04	1.11	.42	1.57	2.37
0200	12" W, 1-1/2" to 4" H, 60 L.F. per ton, laid with pavement	B-2	1050	.038		.02	.92		.94	1.58

32 16 13.43 Stone Curbs

32 16 13.43 Stone Curbs	Crew	Daily Output	Labor-Hours	Unit	Material	2014 Bare Costs Labor	Equipment	Total	Total Incl O&P
0010	**STONE CURBS**									
1000	Granite, split face, straight, 5" x 16"	D-13	275	.175	L.F.	12.30	5.35	1.75	19.40	24.50
1100	6" x 18"	"	250	.192		16.15	5.90	1.93	23.98	29.50
1300	Radius curbing, 6" x 18", over 10' radius	B-29	260	.185		19.80	4.79	3.39	27.98	34
1400	Corners, 2' radius	"	80	.600	Ea.	66.50	15.55	11	93.05	111
1600	Edging, 4-1/2" x 12", straight	d-13	300	.160	L.F.	6.15	4.91	1.60	12.66	16.65
1800	Curb inlets, (guttermouth) straight	B-29	41	1.171	Ea.	148	30.50	21.50	200	237
2000	Indian granite (belgian block)									
2100	Jumbo, 10-1/2" x 7-1/2" x 4", grey	D-1	150	.107	L.F.	6.05	3.08		9.13	11.80
2150	Pink		150	.107		8.20	3.08		11.28	14.15
2200	Regular, 9" x 4-1/2" x 4-1/2", grey		160	.100		4.53	2.89		7.42	9.80
2250	Pink		160	.100		5.80	2.89		8.69	11.15
2300	Cubes, 4" x 4" x 4", grey		175	.091		3.30	2.64		5.94	8.05
2350	Pink		175	.091		3.58	2.64		6.22	8.35
2400	6" x 6" x 6", pink		155	.103		11.85	2.98		14.83	17.95
2500	Alternate pricing method for indian granite									
2550	Jumbo, 10-1/2" x 7-1/2" x 4" (30 lb.), grey				Ton	345			345	380
2600	Pink					475			475	525
2650	Regular, 9" x 4-1/2" x 4-1/2" (20 lb.), grey					320			320	350
2700	Pink					405			405	445
2750	Cubes, 4" x 4" x 4" (5 lb.), grey					400			400	440
2800	Pink					460			460	505
2850	6" x 6" x 6" (25 lb.), pink					460			460	505
2900	For pallets, add					22			22	24

32 31 Fences and Gates

32 31 13 – Chain Link Fences and Gates

32 31 13.15 Chain Link Fence

		Crew	Daily Output	Labor-Hours	Unit	Material	2014 Bare Costs Labor	Equipment	Total	Total Incl O&P
0010	**CHAIN LINK FENCE**									
0020	1-5/8" post 10' O.C., 1-3/8" top rail, 2" corner post galv. stl., 3' high	B-1	185	.130	L.F.	9.10	3.17		12.27	15.35
0050	4' high		170	.141		9.15	3.45		12.60	15.85
0100	6' high		115	.209		10.90	5.10		16	20.50
0150	Add for gate 3' wide, 1-3/8" frame 3' high		12	2	Ea.	82.50	49		131.50	174
0170	4' high		10	2.400		89.50	58.50		148	198
0190	6' high		10	2.400		112	58.50		170.50	222
0200	Add for gate 4' wide, 1-3/8" frame 3' high		9	2.667		87	65.50		152.50	206
0220	4' high		9	2.667		94.50	65.50		160	214
0240	6' high		8	3		120	73.50		193.50	255
0350	Aluminized steel, 9 ga. wire, 3' high		185	.130	L.F.	7.45	3.17		10.62	13.55
0380	4' high		170	.141		7.15	3.45		10.60	13.65
0400	6' high		115	.209		9.30	5.10		14.40	18.85
0450	Add for gate 3' wide, 1-3/8" frame 3' high		12	2	Ea.	120	49		169	214
0470	4' high		10	2.400		129	58.50		187.50	241
0490	6' high		10	2.400		166	58.50		224.50	281
0500	Add for gate 4' wide, 1-3/8" frame 3' high		10	2.400		126	58.50		184.50	238
0520	4' high		9	2.667		135	65.50		200.50	259
0540	6' high		8	3		176	73.50		249.50	315
0620	Vinyl covered 9 ga. wire, 3' high		185	.130	L.F.	7.40	3.17		10.57	13.50
0640	4' high		170	.141		7.25	3.45		10.70	13.80
0660	6' high		115	.209		9.50	5.10		14.60	19.05
0720	Add for gate 3' wide, 1-3/8" frame 3' high		12	2	Ea.	94	49		143	186
0740	4' high		10	2.400		99	58.50		157.50	208
0760	6' high		10	2.400		121	58.50		179.50	232
0780	Add for gate 4' wide, 1-3/8" frame 3' high		10	2.400		100	58.50		158.50	209
0800	4' high		9	2.667		103	65.50		168.50	223
0820	6' high		8	3		132	73.50		205.50	269
0860	Tennis courts, 11 ga. wire, 2 1/2" post 10' O.C., 1-5/8" top rail									
0900	2-1/2" corner post, 10' high	B-1	95	.253	L.F.	7.55	6.20		13.75	18.70
0920	12' high		80	.300	"	7.25	7.35		14.60	20.50
1000	Add for gate 3' wide, 1-5/8" frame 10' high		10	2.400	Ea.	222	58.50		280.50	345
1040	Aluminized, 11 ga. wire 10' high		95	.253	L.F.	8.65	6.20		14.85	19.90
1100	12' high		80	.300	"	9.25	7.35		16.60	22.50
1140	Add for gate 3' wide, 1-5/8" frame, 10' high		10	2.400	Ea.	129	58.50		187.50	241
1250	Vinyl covered 11 ga. wire, 10' high		95	.253	L.F.	7.25	6.20		13.45	18.40
1300	12' high		80	.300	"	8.70	7.35		16.05	22
1400	Add for gate 3' wide, 1-3/8" frame, 10' high		10	2.400	Ea.	168	58.50		226.50	284

32 31 23 – Plastic Fences and Gates

32 31 23.10 Fence, Vinyl

		Crew	Daily Output	Labor-Hours	Unit	Material	2014 Bare Costs Labor	Equipment	Total	Total Incl O&P
0010	**FENCE, VINYL**									
0011	White, steel reinforced, stainless steel fasteners									
0020	Picket, 4" x 4" posts @ 6' - 0" OC, 3' high	B-1	140	.171	L.F.	21	4.19		25.19	30
0030	4' high		130	.185		23.50	4.52		28.02	33
0040	5' high		120	.200		26	4.89		30.89	37
0100	Board (semi-privacy), 5" x 5" posts @ 7' - 6" OC, 5' high		130	.185		23	4.52		27.52	33
0120	6' high		125	.192		27	4.70		31.70	37.50
0200	Basketweave, 5" x 5" posts @ 7' - 6" OC, 5' high		160	.150		23.50	3.67		27.17	32
0220	6' high		150	.160		26.50	3.92		30.42	36
0300	Privacy, 5" x 5" posts @ 7' - 6" OC, 5' high		130	.185		23	4.52		27.52	33
0320	6' high		150	.160		27	3.92		30.92	36
0350	Gate, 5' high		9	2.667	Ea.	320	65.50		385.50	465

32 31 Fences and Gates

32 31 23 – Plastic Fences and Gates

32 31 23.10 Fence, Vinyl		Crew	Daily Output	Labor-Hours	Unit	Material	2014 Bare Costs Labor	Equipment	Total	Total Incl O&P
0360	6' high	B-1	9	2.667	Ea.	370	65.50		435.50	515
0400	For posts set in concrete, add		25	.960	↓	8.10	23.50		31.60	48.50
0500	Post and rail fence, 2 rail		150	.160	L.F.	5.40	3.92		9.32	12.55
0510	3 rail		150	.160		6.95	3.92		10.87	14.25
0515	4 rail	↓	150	.160	↓	9.05	3.92		12.97	16.55

32 31 26 – Wire Fences and Gates

32 31 26.10 Fences, Misc. Metal		Crew	Daily Output	Labor-Hours	Unit	Material	2014 Bare Costs Labor	Equipment	Total	Total Incl O&P
0010	**FENCES, MISC. METAL**									
0012	Chicken wire, posts @ 4', 1" mesh, 4' high	B-80C	410	.059	L.F.	3.61	1.43	.68	5.72	7.10
0100	2" mesh, 6' high		350	.069		3.80	1.68	.79	6.27	7.85
0200	Galv. steel, 12 ga., 2" x 4" mesh, posts 5' O.C., 3' high		300	.080		2.75	1.96	.93	5.64	7.35
0300	5' high		300	.080		3.35	1.96	.93	6.24	8
0400	14 ga., 1" x 2" mesh, 3' high		300	.080		3.40	1.96	.93	6.29	8.05
0500	5' high	↓	300	.080	↓	4.55	1.96	.93	7.44	9.30
1000	Kennel fencing, 1-1/2" mesh, 6' long, 3'-6" wide, 6'-2" high	2 Clab	4	4	Ea.	500	95		595	710
1050	12' long		4	4		715	95		810	945
1200	Top covers, 1-1/2" mesh, 6' long		15	1.067		135	25.50		160.50	192
1250	12' long	↓	12	1.333	↓	190	31.50		221.50	263

32 31 29 – Wood Fences and Gates

32 31 29.10 Fence, Wood		Crew	Daily Output	Labor-Hours	Unit	Material	2014 Bare Costs Labor	Equipment	Total	Total Incl O&P
0010	**FENCE, WOOD**									
0011	Basket weave, 3/8" x 4" boards, 2" x 4"									
0020	stringers on spreaders, 4" x 4" posts									
0050	No. 1 cedar, 6' high	B-80C	160	.150	L.F.	25.50	3.68	1.74	30.92	36
0070	Treated pine, 6' high		150	.160		34	3.92	1.85	39.77	46
0090	Vertical weave 6' high	↓	145	.166	↓	22.50	4.06	1.92	28.48	34
0200	Board fence, 1" x 4" boards, 2" x 4" rails, 4" x 4" post									
0220	Preservative treated, 2 rail, 3' high	B-80C	145	.166	L.F.	9.05	4.06	1.92	15.03	18.85
0240	4' high		135	.178		10.45	4.36	2.06	16.87	21
0260	3 rail, 5' high		130	.185		11.55	4.52	2.14	18.21	22.50
0300	6' high		125	.192		13.25	4.70	2.23	20.18	25
0320	No. 2 grade western cedar, 2 rail, 3' high		145	.166		9.80	4.06	1.92	15.78	19.70
0340	4' high		135	.178		10.80	4.36	2.06	17.22	21.50
0360	3 rail, 5' high		130	.185		12.25	4.52	2.14	18.91	23.50
0400	6' high		125	.192		13.15	4.70	2.23	20.08	25
0420	No. 1 grade cedar, 2 rail, 3' high		145	.166		11.85	4.06	1.92	17.83	22
0440	4' high		135	.178		13.80	4.36	2.06	20.22	24.50
0460	3 rail, 5' high		130	.185		16.95	4.52	2.14	23.61	28.50
0500	6' high	↓	125	.192	↓	18.45	4.70	2.23	25.38	31
0540	Shadow box, 1" x 6" board, 2" x 4" rail, 4" x 4"post									
0560	Pine, pressure treated, 3 rail, 6' high	B-80C	150	.160	L.F.	15.90	3.92	1.85	21.67	26
0600	Gate, 3'-6" wide		8	3	Ea.	85	73.50	35	193.50	255
0620	No. 1 cedar, 3 rail, 4' high		130	.185	L.F.	17.60	4.52	2.14	24.26	29.50
0640	6' high		125	.192		22.50	4.70	2.23	29.43	35
0860	Open rail fence, split rails, 2 rail 3' high, no. 1 cedar		160	.150		11.70	3.68	1.74	17.12	21
0870	No. 2 cedar		160	.150		10.90	3.68	1.74	16.32	20
0880	3 rail, 4' high, no. 1 cedar		150	.160		12.10	3.92	1.85	17.87	22
0890	No. 2 cedar		150	.160		8.70	3.92	1.85	14.47	18.15
0920	Rustic rails, 2 rail 3' high, no. 1 cedar		160	.150		9.35	3.68	1.74	14.77	18.35
0930	No. 2 cedar		160	.150		8.70	3.68	1.74	14.12	17.65
0940	3 rail, 4' high		150	.160		9	3.92	1.85	14.77	18.50
0950	No. 2 cedar	↓	150	.160	↓	7.30	3.92	1.85	13.07	16.60

635

32 31 29 – Wood Fences and Gates

32 31 29.10 Fence, Wood		Crew	Daily Output	Labor-Hours	Unit	Material	2014 Bare Costs Labor	Equipment	Total	Total Incl O&P
0960	Picket fence, gothic, pressure treated pine									
1000	2 rail, 3' high	B-80C	140	.171	L.F.	6.75	4.20	1.99	12.94	16.70
1020	3 rail, 4' high		130	.185	"	7.65	4.52	2.14	14.31	18.35
1040	Gate, 3'-6" wide		9	2.667	Ea.	60	65.50	31	156.50	210
1060	No. 2 cedar, 2 rail, 3' high		140	.171	L.F.	7.45	4.20	1.99	13.64	17.40
1100	3 rail, 4' high		130	.185	"	7.50	4.52	2.14	14.16	18.20
1120	Gate, 3'-6" wide		9	2.667	Ea.	65	65.50	31	161.50	216
1140	No. 1 cedar, 2 rail 3' high		140	.171	L.F.	12.45	4.20	1.99	18.64	23
1160	3 rail, 4' high		130	.185		16	4.52	2.14	22.66	27.50
1200	Rustic picket, molded pine, 2 rail, 3' high		140	.171		7.65	4.20	1.99	13.84	17.65
1220	No. 1 cedar, 2 rail, 3' high		140	.171		8.90	4.20	1.99	15.09	19.05
1240	Stockade fence, no. 1 cedar, 3-1/4" rails, 6' high		160	.150		11.95	3.68	1.74	17.37	21
1260	8' high		155	.155		16.50	3.79	1.79	22.08	26.50
1300	No. 2 cedar, treated wood rails, 6' high		160	.150	↓	12.30	3.68	1.74	17.72	21.50
1320	Gate, 3'-6" wide		8	3	Ea.	80	73.50	35	188.50	250
1360	Treated pine, treated rails, 6' high		160	.150	L.F.	12.80	3.68	1.74	18.22	22
1400	8' high	↓	150	.160	"	18.65	3.92	1.85	24.42	29

32 31 29.20 Fence, Wood Rail

32 31 29.20 Fence, Wood Rail		Crew	Daily Output	Labor-Hours	Unit	Material	2014 Bare Costs Labor	Equipment	Total	Total Incl O&P
0010	**FENCE, WOOD RAIL**									
0012	Picket, No. 2 cedar, Gothic, 2 rail, 3' high	B-1	160	.150	L.F.	7.55	3.67		11.22	14.50
0050	Gate, 3'-6" wide	B-80C	9	2.667	Ea.	76.50	65.50	31	173	228
0400	3 rail, 4' high		150	.160	L.F.	8.45	3.92	1.85	14.22	17.90
0500	Gate, 3'-6" wide		9	2.667	Ea.	94.50	65.50	31	191	248
1200	Stockade, No. 2 cedar, treated wood rails, 6' high		160	.150	L.F.	8.80	3.68	1.74	14.22	17.75
1250	Gate, 3' wide		9	2.667	Ea.	95	65.50	31	191.50	249
1300	No. 1 cedar, 3-1/4" cedar rails, 6' high		160	.150	L.F.	19.85	3.68	1.74	25.27	30
1500	Gate, 3' wide		9	2.667	Ea.	215	65.50	31	311.50	380
2700	Prefabricated redwood or cedar, 4' high		160	.150	L.F.	15.75	3.68	1.74	21.17	25.50
2800	6' high		150	.160	↓	23	3.92	1.85	28.77	34
3300	Board, shadow box, 1" x 6", treated pine, 6' high		160	.150		12.40	3.68	1.74	17.82	21.50
3400	No. 1 cedar, 6' high		150	.160		24.50	3.92	1.85	30.27	35.50
3900	Basket weave, No. 1 cedar, 6' high	↓	160	.150	↓	33.50	3.68	1.74	38.92	45
4200	Gate, 3'-6" wide	B-1	9	2.667	Ea.	160	65.50		225.50	286
5000	Fence rail, redwood, 2" x 4", merch. grade 8'	"	2400	.010	L.F.	2.39	.24		2.63	3.04

32 32 13 – Cast-in-Place Concrete Retaining Walls

32 32 13.10 Retaining Walls, Cast Concrete

32 32 13.10 Retaining Walls, Cast Concrete		Crew	Daily Output	Labor-Hours	Unit	Material	2014 Bare Costs Labor	Equipment	Total	Total Incl O&P
0010	**RETAINING WALLS, CAST CONCRETE**									
1800	Concrete gravity wall with vertical face including excavation & backfill									
1850	No reinforcing									
1900	6' high, level embankment	C-17C	36	2.306	L.F.	71.50	76	17.20	164.70	226
2000	33° slope embankment	"	32	2.594	"	84	85.50	19.35	188.85	258
2800	Reinforced concrete cantilever, incl. excavation, backfill & reinf.									
2900	6' high, 33° slope embankment	C-17C	35	2.371	L.F.	66	78	17.70	161.70	224

32 32 Retaining Walls

32 32 23 – Segmental Retaining Walls

32 32 23.13 Segmental Conc. Unit Masonry Retaining Walls	Crew	Daily Output	Labor-Hours	Unit	Material	2014 Bare Costs Labor	Equipment	Total	Total Incl O&P
0010 **SEGMENTAL CONC. UNIT MASONRY RETAINING WALLS**									
7100 Segmental Retaining Wall system, incl. pins, and void fill									
7120 base not included									
7140 Large unit, 8" high x 18" wide x 20" deep, 3 plane split	B-62	300	.080	S.F.	13.60	2.13	.58	16.31	19.15
7150 Straight split		300	.080		13.50	2.13	.58	16.21	19.05
7160 Medium, lt. wt., 8" high x 18" wide x 12" deep, 3 plane split		400	.060		10.45	1.60	.44	12.49	14.65
7170 Straight split		400	.060		9.85	1.60	.44	11.89	14
7180 Small unit, 4" x 18" x 10" deep, 3 plane split		400	.060		13.35	1.60	.44	15.39	17.80
7190 Straight split		400	.060		13	1.60	.44	15.04	17.45
7200 Cap unit, 3 plane split		300	.080		13.60	2.13	.58	16.31	19.15
7210 Cap unit, straight split		300	.080		13.60	2.13	.58	16.31	19.15
7250 Geo-grid soil reinforcement 4' x 50'	2 Clab	22500	.001		.70	.02		.72	.80
7255 Geo-grid soil reinforcement 6' x 150'	"	22500	.001		.56	.02		.58	.65
8000 For higher walls, add components as necessary									

32 32 26 – Metal Crib Retaining Walls

32 32 26.10 Metal Bin Retaining Walls

	Crew	Daily Output	Labor-Hours	Unit	Material	Labor	Equipment	Total	Total Incl O&P
0010 **METAL BIN RETAINING WALLS**									
0011 Aluminized steel bin, excavation									
0020 and backfill not included, 10' wide									
0100 4' high, 5.5' deep	B-13	650	.074	S.F.	27.50	1.92	1.15	30.57	34.50
0200 8' high, 5.5' deep		615	.078		31.50	2.02	1.21	34.73	39
0300 10' high, 7.7' deep		580	.083		34.50	2.15	1.29	37.94	43
0400 12' high, 7.7' deep		530	.091		37.50	2.35	1.41	41.26	46.50
0500 16' high, 7.7' deep		515	.093		39.50	2.42	1.45	43.37	49

32 32 29 – Timber Retaining Walls

32 32 29.10 Landscape Timber Retaining Walls

	Crew	Daily Output	Labor-Hours	Unit	Material	Labor	Equipment	Total	Total Incl O&P
0010 **LANDSCAPE TIMBER RETAINING WALLS**									
0100 Treated timbers, 6" x 6"	1 Clab	265	.030	L.F.	2	.72		2.72	3.41
0110 6" x 8"	"	200	.040	"	2.62	.95		3.57	4.48
0120 Drilling holes in timbers for fastening, 1/2"	1 Carp	450	.018	Inch		.57		.57	.96
0130 5/8"	"	450	.018	"		.57		.57	.96
0140 Reinforcing rods for fastening, 1/2"	1 Clab	312	.026	L.F.	.37	.61		.98	1.43
0150 5/8"	"	312	.026	"	.57	.61		1.18	1.66
0160 Reinforcing fabric	2 Clab	2500	.006	S.Y.	1.88	.15		2.03	2.33
0170 Gravel backfill		28	.571	C.Y.	19.90	13.60		33.50	45
0180 Perforated pipe, 4" diameter with silt sock		1200	.013	L.F.	1.29	.32		1.61	1.95
0190 Galvanized 60d common nails	1 Clab	625	.013	Ea.	.16	.30		.46	.69
0200 20d common nails	"	3800	.002	"	.04	.05		.09	.12

32 32 60 – Stone Retaining Walls

32 32 60.10 Retaining Walls, Stone

	Crew	Daily Output	Labor-Hours	Unit	Material	Labor	Equipment	Total	Total Incl O&P
0010 **RETAINING WALLS, STONE**									
0015 Including excavation, concrete footing and									
0020 stone 3' below grade. Price is exposed face area.									
0200 Decorative random stone, to 6' high, 1'-6" thick, dry set	D-1	35	.457	S.F.	30.50	13.20		43.70	55.50
0300 Mortar set		40	.400		33.50	11.55		45.05	56.50
0500 Cut stone, to 6' high, 1'-6" thick, dry set		35	.457		31.50	13.20		44.70	57
0600 Mortar set		40	.400		32.50	11.55		44.05	55.50
0800 Random stone, 6' to 10' high, 2' thick, dry set		45	.356		41	10.30		51.30	62
0900 Mortar set		50	.320		42	9.25		51.25	61.50
1100 Cut stone, 6' to 10' high, 2' thick, dry set		45	.356		40	10.30		50.30	61

32 32 Retaining Walls

32 32 60 – Stone Retaining Walls

32 32 60.10 Retaining Walls, Stone	Crew	Daily Output	Labor-Hours	Unit	Material	2014 Bare Costs Labor	2014 Bare Costs Equipment	Total	Total Incl O&P
1200	Mortar set	D-1	50	.320	S.F.	42	9.25		51.25	61.50

32 84 Planting Irrigation

32 84 23 – Underground Sprinklers

32 84 23.10 Sprinkler Irrigation System

		Crew	Daily Output	Labor-Hours	Unit	Material	Labor	Equipment	Total	Total Incl O&P
0010	**SPRINKLER IRRIGATION SYSTEM**									
0011	For lawns									
0800	Residential system, custom, 1" supply	B-20	2000	.012	S.F.	.26	.29		.55	.78
0900	1-1/2" supply	"	1800	.013	"	.49	.33		.82	1.09

32 91 Planting Preparation

32 91 13 – Soil Preparation

32 91 13.16 Mulching

		Crew	Daily Output	Labor-Hours	Unit	Material	Labor	Equipment	Total	Total Incl O&P
0010	**MULCHING**									
0100	Aged barks, 3" deep, hand spread	1 Clab	100	.080	S.Y.	3.38	1.90		5.28	6.90
0150	Skid steer loader	B-63	13.50	2.963	M.S.F.	375	70.50	12.90	458.40	550
0200	Hay, 1" deep, hand spread	1 Clab	475	.017	S.Y.	.48	.40		.88	1.20
0250	Power mulcher, small	B-64	180	.089	M.S.F.	53.50	2.21	2.39	58.10	65
0350	Large	B-65	530	.030	"	53.50	.75	1.12	55.37	61
0400	Humus peat, 1" deep, hand spread	1 Clab	700	.011	S.Y.	2.56	.27		2.83	3.28
0450	Push spreader	"	2500	.003	"	2.56	.08		2.64	2.95
0550	Tractor spreader	B-66	700	.011	M.S.F.	284	.37	.37	284.74	315
0600	Oat straw, 1" deep, hand spread	1 Clab	475	.017	S.Y.	.55	.40		.95	1.28
0650	Power mulcher, small	B-64	180	.089	M.S.F.	61	2.21	2.39	65.60	73.50
0700	Large	B-65	530	.030	"	61	.75	1.12	62.87	69.50
0750	Add for asphaltic emulsion	B-45	1770	.009	Gal.	5.75	.23	.17	6.15	6.90
0800	Peat moss, 1" deep, hand spread	1 Clab	900	.009	S.Y.	2.63	.21		2.84	3.25
0850	Push spreader	"	2500	.003	"	2.63	.08		2.71	3.02
0950	Tractor spreader	B-66	700	.011	M.S.F.	292	.37	.37	292.74	320
1000	Polyethylene film, 6 mil	2 Clab	2000	.008	S.Y.	.44	.19		.63	.80
1100	Redwood nuggets, 3" deep, hand spread	1 Clab	150	.053	"	2.77	1.27		4.04	5.20
1150	Skid steer loader	B-63	13.50	2.963	M.S.F.	310	70.50	12.90	393.40	475
1200	Stone mulch, hand spread, ceramic chips, economy	1 Clab	125	.064	S.Y.	6.85	1.52		8.37	10.10
1250	Deluxe	"	95	.084	"	10.50	2		12.50	14.90
1300	Granite chips	B-1	10	2.400	C.Y.	69.50	58.50		128	176
1400	Marble chips		10	2.400		152	58.50		210.50	266
1600	Pea gravel		28	.857		75.50	21		96.50	119
1700	Quartz		10	2.400		188	58.50		246.50	305
1800	Tar paper, 15 lb. felt	1 Clab	800	.010	S.Y.	.49	.24		.73	.93
1900	Wood chips, 2" deep, hand spread	"	220	.036	"	1.45	.87		2.32	3.06
1950	Skid steer loader	B-63	20.30	1.970	M.S.F.	161	47	8.60	216.60	265

32 91 13.26 Planting Beds

		Crew	Daily Output	Labor-Hours	Unit	Material	Labor	Equipment	Total	Total Incl O&P
0010	**PLANTING BEDS**									
0100	Backfill planting pit, by hand, on site topsoil	2 Clab	18	.889	C.Y.		21		21	35.50
0200	Prepared planting mix, by hand	"	24	.667			15.85		15.85	26.50
0300	Skid steer loader, on site topsoil	B-62	340	.071			1.88	.51	2.39	3.71
0400	Prepared planting mix	"	410	.059			1.56	.43	1.99	3.08
1000	Excavate planting pit, by hand, sandy soil	2 Clab	16	1			24		24	40
1100	Heavy soil or clay	"	8	2			47.50		47.50	80

32 91 Planting Preparation

32 91 13 - Soil Preparation

32 91 13.26 Planting Beds

		Crew	Daily Output	Labor-Hours	Unit	Material	Labor	Equipment	Total	Total Incl O&P
1200	1/2 C.Y. backhoe, sandy soil	B-11C	150	.107	C.Y.		3.07	2.44	5.51	7.80
1300	Heavy soil or clay	"	115	.139			4	3.18	7.18	10.20
2000	Mix planting soil, incl. loam, manure, peat, by hand	2 Clab	60	.267		43	6.35		49.35	58
2100	Skid steer loader	B-62	150	.160	↓	43	4.27	1.16	48.43	56
3000	Pile sod, skid steer loader	"	2800	.009	S.Y.		.23	.06	.29	.45
3100	By hand	2 Clab	400	.040			.95		.95	1.60
4000	Remove sod, F.E. loader	B-10S	2000	.004			.14	.19	.33	.43
4100	Sod cutter	B-12K	3200	.005			.15	.31	.46	.59
4200	By hand	2 Clab	240	.067	↓		1.59		1.59	2.67

32 91 19 - Landscape Grading

32 91 19.13 Topsoil Placement and Grading

		Crew	Daily Output	Labor-Hours	Unit	Material	Labor	Equipment	Total	Total Incl O&P
0010	**TOPSOIL PLACEMENT AND GRADING**									
0300	Fine grade, base course for paving, see Section 32 11 23.23									
0701	Furnish and place, truck dumped, unscreened, 4" deep	B-10S	12000	.001	S.F.	.41	.02	.03	.46	.52
0801	6" deep	"	7400	.001	"	.50	.04	.05	.59	.67
0900	Fine grading and seeding, incl. lime, fertilizer & seed,									
1001	With equipment	B-14	9000	.005	S.F.	.07	.14	.04	.25	.35

32 92 Turf and Grasses

32 92 19 - Seeding

32 92 19.13 Mechanical Seeding

		Crew	Daily Output	Labor-Hours	Unit	Material	Labor	Equipment	Total	Total Incl O&P
0010	**MECHANICAL SEEDING**									
0020	Mechanical seeding, 215 lb./acre	B-66	1.50	5.333	Acre	650	173	173	996	1,200
0100	44 lb./M.S.Y.	"	2500	.003	S.Y.	.18	.10	.10	.38	.48
0101	$2.00/lb., 44 lb./M.S.Y.	1 Clab	13950	.001	S.F.	.02	.01		.03	.04
0300	Fine grading and seeding incl. lime, fertilizer & seed,									
0310	with equipment	B-14	1000	.048	S.Y.	.44	1.23	.37	2.04	2.94
0400	Fertilizer hand push spreader, 35 lb. per M.S.F.	1 Clab	200	.040	M.S.F.	14.95	.95		15.90	18
0600	Limestone hand push spreader, 50 lb. per M.S.F.		180	.044		5.70	1.06		6.76	8.05
0800	Grass seed hand push spreader, 4.5 lb. per M.S.F.	↓	180	.044	↓	20	1.06		21.06	24
1000	Hydro or air seeding for large areas, incl. seed and fertilizer	B-81	8900	.002	S.Y.	.43	.05	.08	.56	.64
1100	With wood fiber mulch added	"	8900	.002	"	1.76	.05	.08	1.89	2.11
1300	Seed only, over 100 lb., field seed, minimum				Lb.	.75			.75	.83
1400	Maximum					4.30			4.30	4.73
1500	Lawn seed, minimum					1.25			1.25	1.38
1600	Maximum				↓	2.45			2.45	2.70
1800	Aerial operations, seeding only, field seed	B-58	50	.480	Acre	244	12.80	62	318.80	360
1900	Lawn seed		50	.480		405	12.80	62	479.80	535
2100	Seed and liquid fertilizer, field seed		50	.480		735	12.80	62	809.80	895
2200	Lawn seed	↓	50	.480	↓	895	12.80	62	969.80	1,075

32 92 23 - Sodding

32 92 23.10 Sodding Systems

		Crew	Daily Output	Labor-Hours	Unit	Material	Labor	Equipment	Total	Total Incl O&P
0010	**SODDING SYSTEMS**									
0020	Sodding, 1" deep, bluegrass sod, on level ground, over 8 M.S.F.	B-63	22	1.818	M.S.F.	250	43.50	7.95	301.45	355
0200	4 M.S.F.		17	2.353		265	56	10.25	331.25	395
0300	1000 S.F.		13.50	2.963		290	70.50	12.90	373.40	455
0500	Sloped ground, over 8 M.S.F.		6	6.667		250	159	29	438	575
0600	4 M.S.F.		5	8		265	190	35	490	650
0700	1000 S.F.		4	10		290	238	43.50	571.50	770
1000	Bent grass sod, on level ground, over 6 M.S.F.	↓	20	2		253	47.50	8.70	309.20	370

32 92 Turf and Grasses

32 92 23 - Sodding

32 92 23.10 Sodding Systems	Crew	Daily Output	Labor-Hours	Unit	Material	2014 Bare Costs Labor	2014 Bare Costs Equipment	Total	Total Incl O&P
1100	3 M.S.F.	B-63	18	2.222	M.S.F.	265	53	9.70	327.70	390
1200	Sodding 1000 S.F. or less		14	2.857		293	68	12.45	373.45	455
1500	Sloped ground, over 6 M.S.F.		15	2.667		253	63.50	11.65	328.15	400
1600	3 M.S.F.		13.50	2.963		265	70.50	12.90	348.40	425
1700	1000 S.F.		12	3.333		293	79.50	14.55	387.05	475

32 93 Plants

32 93 13 - Ground Covers

32 93 13.10 Ground Cover Plants

		Crew	Daily Output	Labor-Hours	Unit	Material	Labor	Equipment	Total	Total Incl O&P
0010	**GROUND COVER PLANTS**									
0012	Plants, pachysandra, in prepared beds	B-1	15	1.600	C	79.50	39		118.50	153
0200	Vinca minor, 1 yr., bare root, in prepared beds		12	2	"	64.50	49		113.50	154
0600	Stone chips, in 50 lb. bags, Georgia marble		520	.046	Bag	4.13	1.13		5.26	6.45
0700	Onyx gemstone		260	.092		16.50	2.26		18.76	22
0800	Quartz		260	.092		6.15	2.26		8.41	10.55
0900	Pea gravel, truckload lots		28	.857	Ton	24	21		45	61.50

32 93 33 - Shrubs

32 93 33.10 Shrubs and Trees

		Crew	Daily Output	Labor-Hours	Unit	Material	Labor	Equipment	Total	Total Incl O&P
0010	**SHRUBS AND TREES**									
0011	Evergreen, in prepared beds, B & B									
0100	Arborvitae pyramidal, 4'-5'	B-17	30	1.067	Ea.	110	28.50	26	164.50	197
0150	Globe, 12"-15"	B-1	96	.250		21.50	6.10		27.60	34
0300	Cedar, blue, 8'-10'	B-17	18	1.778		230	47.50	43.50	321	380
0500	Hemlock, Canadian, 2-1/2'-3'	B-1	36	.667		30.50	16.30		46.80	61
0550	Holly, Savannah, 8' - 10' H		9.68	2.479		258	60.50		318.50	385
0600	Juniper, andorra, 18"-24"		80	.300		36	7.35		43.35	52
0620	Wiltoni, 15"-18"		80	.300		28.50	7.35		35.85	44
0640	Skyrocket, 4-1/2'-5'	B-17	55	.582		117	15.50	14.25	146.75	171
0660	Blue pfitzer, 2'-2-1/2'	B-1	44	.545		42.50	13.35		55.85	69
0680	Ketleerie, 2-1/2'-3'		50	.480		51	11.75		62.75	76
0700	Pine, black, 2-1/2'-3'		50	.480		59.50	11.75		71.25	85.50
0720	Mugo, 18"-24"		60	.400		59	9.80		68.80	81.50
0740	White, 4'-5'	B-17	75	.427		51	11.40	10.45	72.85	86.50
0800	Spruce, blue, 18"-24"	B-1	60	.400		66.50	9.80		76.30	89.50
0840	Norway, 4'-5'	B-17	75	.427		82	11.40	10.45	103.85	121
0900	Yew, denisforma, 12"-15"	B-1	60	.400		36	9.80		45.80	56
1000	Capitata, 18"-24"		30	.800		32.50	19.60		52.10	69
1100	Hicksi, 2'-2-1/2'		30	.800		86.50	19.60		106.10	128

32 93 33.20 Shrubs

		Crew	Daily Output	Labor-Hours	Unit	Material	Labor	Equipment	Total	Total Incl O&P
0010	**SHRUBS**									
0011	Broadleaf Evergreen, planted in prepared beds									
0100	Andromeda, 15"-18", container	B-1	96	.250	Ea.	33	6.10		39.10	47
0200	Azalea, 15" - 18", container		96	.250		28.50	6.10		34.60	42
0300	Barberry, 9"-12", container		130	.185		17.55	4.52		22.07	27
0400	Boxwood, 15"-18", B&B		96	.250		42	6.10		48.10	56.50
0500	Euonymus, emerald gaiety, 12" to 15", container		115	.209		23	5.10		28.10	34
0600	Holly, 15"-18", B & B		96	.250		35.50	6.10		41.60	50
0900	Mount laurel, 18" - 24", B & B		80	.300		70	7.35		77.35	89.50
1000	Paxistema, 9 - 12" high		130	.185		22	4.52		26.52	31.50
1100	Rhododendron, 18"-24", container		48	.500		38	12.25		50.25	62.50

32 93 Plants

32 93 33 – Shrubs

32 93 33.20 Shrubs

		Crew	Daily Output	Labor-Hours	Unit	Material	2014 Bare Costs Labor	Equipment	Total	Total Incl O&P
1200	Rosemary, 1 gal. container	B-1	600	.040	Ea.	18	.98		18.98	21.50
2000	Deciduous, planted in prepared beds, amelanchier, 2'-3', B & B		57	.421		120	10.30		130.30	149
2100	Azalea, 15"-18", B & B		96	.250		28.50	6.10		34.60	42
2300	Bayberry, 2'-3', B & B		57	.421		24	10.30		34.30	43.50
2600	Cotoneaster, 15"-18", B & B		80	.300		27	7.35		34.35	42
2800	Dogwood, 3'-4', B & B	B-17	40	.800		31.50	21.50	19.55	72.55	91.50
2900	Euonymus, alatus compacta, 15" to 18", container	B-1	80	.300		25.50	7.35		32.85	40.50
3200	Forsythia, 2'-3', container	"	60	.400		18.70	9.80		28.50	37
3300	Hibiscus, 3'-4', B & B	B-17	75	.427		48	11.40	10.45	69.85	83
3400	Honeysuckle, 3'-4', B & B	B-1	60	.400		26	9.80		35.80	45
3500	Hydrangea, 2'-3', B & B	"	57	.421		29.50	10.30		39.80	50
3600	Lilac, 3'-4', B & B	B-17	40	.800		27.50	21.50	19.55	68.55	87
3900	Privet, bare root, 18"-24"	B-1	80	.300		14.25	7.35		21.60	28
4100	Quince, 2'-3', B & B	"	57	.421		28	10.30		38.30	48
4200	Russian olive, 3'-4', B & B	B-17	75	.427		26.50	11.40	10.45	48.35	59.50
4400	Spirea, 3'-4', B & B	B-1	70	.343		20	8.40		28.40	36
4500	Viburnum, 3'-4', B & B	B-17	40	.800		24	21.50	19.55	65.05	83.50

32 93 43 – Trees

32 93 43.20 Trees

			Crew	Daily Output	Labor-Hours	Unit	Material	2014 Bare Costs Labor	Equipment	Total	Total Incl O&P
0010	**TREES**										
0011	Deciduous, in prep. beds, balled & burlapped (B&B)										
0100	Ash, 2" caliper	G	B-17	8	4	Ea.	185	107	98	390	490
0200	Beech, 5'-6'	G		50	.640		185	17.10	15.65	217.75	250
0300	Birch, 6'-8', 3 stems	G		20	1.600		170	42.50	39	251.50	300
0500	Crabapple, 6'-8'	G		20	1.600		140	42.50	39	221.50	269
0600	Dogwood, 4'-5'	G		40	.800		130	21.50	19.55	171.05	200
0700	Eastern redbud 4'-5'	G		40	.800		148	21.50	19.55	189.05	219
0800	Elm, 8'-10'	G		20	1.600		260	42.50	39	341.50	400
0900	Ginkgo, 6'-7'	G		24	1.333		150	35.50	32.50	218	261
1000	Hawthorn, 8'-10', 1" caliper	G		20	1.600		163	42.50	39	244.50	294
1100	Honeylocust, 10'-12', 1-1/2" caliper	G		10	3.200		205	85.50	78	368.50	455
1300	Larch, 8'	G		32	1		125	26.50	24.50	176	210
1400	Linden, 8'-10', 1" caliper	G		20	1.600		143	42.50	39	224.50	272
1500	Magnolia, 4'-5'	G		20	1.600		100	42.50	39	181.50	225
1600	Maple, red, 8'-10', 1-1/2" caliper	G		10	3.200		200	85.50	78	363.50	450
1700	Mountain ash, 8'-10', 1" caliper	G		16	2		175	53.50	49	277.50	335
1800	Oak, 2-1/2"-3" caliper	G		6	5.333		320	142	130	592	730
2100	Planetree, 9'-11', 1-1/4" caliper	G		10	3.200		240	85.50	78	403.50	495
2200	Plum, 6'-8', 1" caliper	G		20	1.600		80	42.50	39	161.50	203
2300	Poplar, 9'-11', 1-1/4" caliper	G		10	3.200		145	85.50	78	308.50	390
2500	Sumac, 2'-3'	G		75	.427		45	11.40	10.45	66.85	80
2700	Tulip, 5'-6'	G		40	.800		48	21.50	19.55	89.05	110
2800	Willow, 6'-8', 1" caliper	G		20	1.600		95	42.50	39	176.50	220

32 94 Planting Accessories

32 94 13 – Landscape Edging

32 94 13.20 Edging	Crew	Daily Output	Labor-Hours	Unit	Material	2014 Bare Costs Labor	Equipment	Total	Total Incl O&P
0010 **EDGING**									
0050 Aluminum alloy, including stakes, 1/8" x 4", mill finish	B-1	390	.062	L.F.	2.26	1.51		3.77	5
0051 Black paint		390	.062		2.62	1.51		4.13	5.40
0052 Black anodized		390	.062		3.03	1.51		4.54	5.85
0100 Brick, set horizontally, 1-1/2 bricks per L.F.	D-1	370	.043		1.39	1.25		2.64	3.60
0150 Set vertically, 3 bricks per L.F.	"	135	.119		3.60	3.43		7.03	9.65
0200 Corrugated aluminum, roll, 4" wide	1 Carp	650	.012		1.95	.40		2.35	2.81
0250 6" wide	"	550	.015		2.44	.47		2.91	3.47
0600 Railroad ties, 6" x 8"	2 Carp	170	.094		3.03	3.02		6.05	8.45
0650 7" x 9"		136	.118		3.36	3.78		7.14	10.05
0750 Redwood 2" x 4"		330	.048		2.26	1.56		3.82	5.10
0800 Steel edge strips, incl. stakes, 1/4" x 5"	B-1	390	.062		3.90	1.51		5.41	6.80
0850 3/16" x 4"	"	390	.062		3.08	1.51		4.59	5.90

32 94 50 – Tree Guying

32 94 50.10 Tree Guying Systems	Crew	Daily Output	Labor-Hours	Unit	Material	2014 Bare Costs Labor	Equipment	Total	Total Incl O&P
0010 **TREE GUYING SYSTEMS**									
0015 Tree guying Including stakes, guy wire and wrap									
0100 Less than 3" caliper, 2 stakes	2 Clab	35	.457	Ea.	14.20	10.90		25.10	34
0200 3" to 4" caliper, 3 stakes	"	21	.762	"	19.20	18.15		37.35	51.50
1000 Including arrowhead anchor, cable, turnbuckles and wrap									
1100 Less than 3" caliper, 3" anchors	2 Clab	20	.800	Ea.	44.50	19.05		63.55	81
1200 3" to 6" caliper, 4" anchors		15	1.067		38	25.50		63.50	84.50
1300 6" caliper, 6" anchors		12	1.333		44.50	31.50		76	103
1400 8" caliper, 8" anchors		9	1.778		128	42.50		170.50	212

32 96 Transplanting

32 96 23 – Plant and Bulb Transplanting

32 96 23.23 Planting	Crew	Daily Output	Labor-Hours	Unit	Material	2014 Bare Costs Labor	Equipment	Total	Total Incl O&P
0010 **PLANTING**									
0012 Moving shrubs on site, 12" ball	B-62	28	.857	Ea.		23	6.20	29.20	45.50
0100 24" ball	"	22	1.091	"		29	7.90	36.90	57

32 96 23.43 Moving Trees

0010 **MOVING TREES**, On site									
0300 Moving trees on site, 36" ball	B-6	3.75	6.400	Ea.		171	97.50	268.50	395
0400 60" ball	"	1	24	"		640	365	1,005	1,475

Estimating Tips

33 10 00 Water Utilities
33 30 00 Sanitary Sewerage Utilities
33 40 00 Storm Drainage Utilities

- Never assume that the water, sewer, and drainage lines will go in at the early stages of the project. Consider the site access needs before dividing the site in half with open trenches, loose pipe, and machinery obstructions. Always inspect the site to establish that the site drawings are complete. Check off all existing utilities on your drawings as you locate them. Be especially careful with underground utilities because appurtenances are sometimes buried during regrading or repaving operations. If you find any discrepancies, mark up the site plan for further research. Differing site conditions can be very costly if discovered later in the project.

- See also Section 33 01 00 for restoration of pipe where removal/replacement may be undesirable. Use of new types of piping materials can reduce the overall project cost. Owners/design engineers should consider the installing contractor as a valuable source of current information on utility products and local conditions that could lead to significant cost savings.

Reference Numbers

Reference numbers are shown in shaded boxes at the beginning of some major classifications. These numbers refer to related items in the Reference Section. The reference information may be an estimating procedure, an alternate pricing method, or technical information.

Note: Not all subdivisions listed here necessarily appear in this publication.

Note: **Trade Service,** *in part, has been used as a reference source for some of the material prices used in Division 33.*

Division 33 - Utilities

33 05 Common Work Results for Utilities

33 05 16 – Utility Structures

33 05 16.13 Precast Concrete Utility Boxes

33 05 16.13 Precast Concrete Utility Boxes	Crew	Daily Output	Labor-Hours	Unit	Material	2014 Bare Costs Labor	Equipment	Total	Total Incl O&P
0010 **PRECAST CONCRETE UTILITY BOXES**, 6" thick									
0050 5' x 10' x 6' high, I.D.	B-13	2	24	Ea.	3,675	625	375	4,675	5,475
0350 Hand hole, precast concrete, 1-1/2" thick									
0400 1'-0" x 2'-0" x 1'-9", I.D., light duty	B-1	4	6	Ea.	410	147		557	695
0450 4'-6" x 3'-2" x 2'-0", O.D., heavy duty	B-6	3	8	"	1,475	213	122	1,810	2,100

33 05 23 – Trenchless Utility Installation

33 05 23.19 Microtunneling

33 05 23.19 Microtunneling	Crew	Daily Output	Labor-Hours	Unit	Material	2014 Bare Costs Labor	Equipment	Total	Total Incl O&P
0010 **MICROTUNNELING**									
0011 Not including excavation, backfill, shoring,									
0020 or dewatering, average 50'/day, slurry method									
0100 24" to 48" outside diameter, minimum				L.F.				875	965
0110 Adverse conditions, add				%				50%	50%
1000 Rent microtunneling machine, average monthly lease				Month				97,500	107,000
1010 Operating technician				Day				630	690
1100 Mobilization and demobilization, minimum				Job				41,200	45,900
1110 Maximum				"				445,500	490,500

33 11 Water Utility Distribution Piping

33 11 13 – Public Water Utility Distribution Piping

33 11 13.15 Water Supply, Ductile Iron Pipe

33 11 13.15 Water Supply, Ductile Iron Pipe	Crew	Daily Output	Labor-Hours	Unit	Material	2014 Bare Costs Labor	Equipment	Total	Total Incl O&P
0010 **WATER SUPPLY, DUCTILE IRON PIPE**									
0020 Not including excavation or backfill									
2000 Pipe, class 50 water piping, 18' lengths									
2020 Mechanical joint, 4" diameter	B-21A	200	.200	L.F.	15.60	6.10	2.41	24.11	30
2040 6" diameter		160	.250		17.75	7.65	3.01	28.41	35.50
3000 Tyton, push-on joint, 4" diameter		400	.100		17	3.05	1.20	21.25	25
3020 6" diameter		333.33	.120		17.85	3.66	1.44	22.95	27.50
8000 Fittings, mechanical joint									
8006 90° bend, 4" diameter	B-20A	16	2	Ea.	273	59		332	400
8020 6" diameter		12.80	2.500		405	74		479	570
8200 Wye or tee, 4" diameter		10.67	2.999		440	88.50		528.50	630
8220 6" diameter		8.53	3.751		670	111		781	920
8398 45° bends, 4" diameter		16	2		254	59		313	375
8400 6" diameter		12.80	2.500		365	74		439	530
8405 8" diameter		10.67	2.999		520	88.50		608.50	720
8450 Decreaser, 6" x 4" diameter		14.22	2.250		360	66.50		426.50	505
8460 8" x 6" diameter		11.64	2.749		525	81		606	715
8550 Piping, butterfly valves, cast iron									
8560 4" diameter	B-20	6	4	Ea.	715	98		813	955
8700 Joint restraint, ductile iron mechanical joints									
8710 4" diameter	B-20A	32	1	Ea.	36.50	29.50		66	89.50
8720 6" diameter		25.60	1.250		43.50	37		80.50	110
8730 8" diameter		21.33	1.500		64	44.50		108.50	144
8740 10" diameter		18.28	1.751		92	51.50		143.50	187
8750 12" diameter		16.84	1.900		131	56		187	239
8760 14" diameter		16	2		170	59		229	285
8770 16" diameter		11.64	2.749		227	81		308	385
8780 18" diameter		11.03	2.901		315	85.50		400.50	485
8785 20" diameter		9.14	3.501		385	103		488	595
8790 24" diameter		7.53	4.250		505	125		630	765

33 11 Water Utility Distribution Piping

33 11 13 – Public Water Utility Distribution Piping

33 11 13.15 Water Supply, Ductile Iron Pipe

	33 11 13.15 Water Supply, Ductile Iron Pipe	Crew	Daily Output	Labor-Hours	Unit	Material	2014 Bare Costs Labor	Equipment	Total	Total Incl O&P
9600	Steel sleeve with tap, 4" diameter	B-20	3	8	Ea.	430	196		626	805
9620	6" diameter	"	2	12	↓	470	294		764	1,025

33 11 13.25 Water Supply, Polyvinyl Chloride Pipe

	33 11 13.25 Water Supply, Polyvinyl Chloride Pipe	Crew	Daily Output	Labor-Hours	Unit	Material	2014 Bare Costs Labor	Equipment	Total	Total Incl O&P
0010	**WATER SUPPLY, POLYVINYL CHLORIDE PIPE**									
2100	PVC pipe, Class 150, 1-1/2" diameter	Q-1A	750	.013	L.F.	.43	.51		.94	1.31
2120	2" diameter		686	.015		.67	.56		1.23	1.66
2140	2-1/2" diameter	↓	500	.020	↓	1.28	.77		2.05	2.68
2160	3" diameter	B-20	430	.056	↓	1.38	1.37		2.75	3.82
8700	PVC pipe, joint restraint									
8710	4" diameter	B-20A	32	1	Ea.	46	29.50		75.50	99.50
8720	6" diameter		25.60	1.250		57	37		94	125
8730	8" diameter		21.33	1.500		79.50	44.50		124	161
8740	10" diameter		18.28	1.751		141	51.50		192.50	242
8750	12" diameter		16.84	1.900		148	56		204	257
8760	14" diameter		16	2		221	59		280	340
8770	16" diameter		11.64	2.749		274	81		355	435
8780	18" diameter		11.03	2.901		330	85.50		415.50	505
8785	20" diameter		9.14	3.501		400	103		503	610
8790	24" diameter	↓	7.53	4.250	↓	465	125		590	720

33 12 Water Utility Distribution Equipment

33 12 13 – Water Service Connections

33 12 13.15 Tapping, Crosses and Sleeves

	33 12 13.15 Tapping, Crosses and Sleeves	Crew	Daily Output	Labor-Hours	Unit	Material	2014 Bare Costs Labor	Equipment	Total	Total Incl O&P
0010	**TAPPING, CROSSES AND SLEEVES**									
4000	Drill and tap pressurized main (labor only)									
4100	6" main, 1" to 2" service	Q-1	3	5.333	Ea.		182		182	300
4150	8" main, 1" to 2" service	"	2.75	5.818	"		199		199	330
4500	Tap and insert gate valve									
4600	8" main, 4" branch	B-21	3.20	8.750	Ea.		227	44	271	430
4650	6" branch		2.70	10.370			269	52	321	505
4700	10" Main, 4" branch		2.70	10.370			269	52	321	505
4750	6" branch		2.35	11.915			310	59.50	369.50	585
4800	12" main, 6" branch	↓	2.35	11.915	↓		310	59.50	369.50	585

33 21 Water Supply Wells

33 21 13 – Public Water Supply Wells

33 21 13.10 Wells and Accessories

	33 21 13.10 Wells and Accessories	Crew	Daily Output	Labor-Hours	Unit	Material	2014 Bare Costs Labor	Equipment	Total	Total Incl O&P
0010	**WELLS & ACCESSORIES**									
0011	Domestic									
0100	Drilled, 4" to 6" diameter	B-23	120	.333	L.F.		8.05	24	32.05	40
1500	Pumps, installed in wells to 100' deep, 4" submersible									
1520	3/4 H.P.	Q-1	2.66	6.015	Ea.	590	206		796	990
1600	1 H.P.	"	2.29	6.987	"	680	239		919	1,150

33 31 Sanitary Utility Sewerage Piping

33 31 13 – Public Sanitary Utility Sewerage Piping

33 31 13.15 Sewage Collection, Concrete Pipe	Crew	Daily Output	Labor-Hours	Unit	Material	2014 Bare Costs Labor	Equipment	Total	Total Incl O&P
0010 **SEWAGE COLLECTION, CONCRETE PIPE**									
0020 See Section 33 41 13.60 for sewage/drainage collection, concrete pipe									

33 31 13.25 Sewage Collection, Polyvinyl Chloride Pipe	Crew	Daily Output	Labor-Hours	Unit	Material	Labor	Equipment	Total	Total Incl O&P
0010 **SEWAGE COLLECTION, POLYVINYL CHLORIDE PIPE**									
0020 Not including excavation or backfill									
2000 20' lengths, SDR 35, B&S, 4" diameter	B-20	375	.064	L.F.	1.46	1.57		3.03	4.24
2040 6" diameter		350	.069		3.29	1.68		4.97	6.45
2080 13' lengths , SDR 35, B&S, 8" diameter	↓	335	.072		6.95	1.75		8.70	10.55
2120 10" diameter	B-21	330	.085		11.40	2.20	.42	14.02	16.70
4000 Piping, DWV PVC, no exc./bkfill., 10' L, Sch 40, 4" diameter	B-20	375	.064		4.64	1.57		6.21	7.75
4010 6" diameter		350	.069		10.20	1.68		11.88	14
4020 8" diameter	↓	335	.072	↓	19.70	1.75		21.45	24.50

33 36 Utility Septic Tanks

33 36 13 – Utility Septic Tank and Effluent Wet Wells

33 36 13.13 Concrete Utility Septic Tank

	Crew	Daily Output	Labor-Hours	Unit	Material	Labor	Equipment	Total	Total Incl O&P
0010 **CONCRETE UTILITY SEPTIC TANK**									
0011 Not including excavation or piping									
0015 Septic tanks, precast, 1,000 gallon	B-21	8	3.500	Ea.	1,075	90.50	17.50	1,183	1,375
0060 1,500 gallon		7	4		1,500	104	20	1,624	1,850
0100 2,000 gallon	↓	5	5.600		1,975	145	28	2,148	2,425
1150 Leaching field chambers, 13' x 3'-7" x 1'-4", standard	B-13	16	3		480	78	46.50	604.50	710
1420 Leaching pit, precast concrete, 6', dia, 3' deep	B-21	4.70	5.957	↓	885	154	30	1,069	1,275

33 36 13.19 Polyethylene Utility Septic Tank

	Crew	Daily Output	Labor-Hours	Unit	Material	Labor	Equipment	Total	Total Incl O&P
0010 **POLYETHYLENE UTILITY SEPTIC TANK**									
0015 High density polyethylene, 1,000 gallon	B-21	8	3.500	Ea.	1,300	90.50	17.50	1,408	1,600
0020 1,250 gallon		8	3.500		1,400	90.50	17.50	1,508	1,725
0025 1,500 gallon	↓	7	4	↓	1,650	104	20	1,774	2,025

33 36 19 – Utility Septic Tank Effluent Filter

33 36 19.13 Utility Septic Tank Effluent Tube Filter

	Crew	Daily Output	Labor-Hours	Unit	Material	Labor	Equipment	Total	Total Incl O&P
0010 **UTILITY SEPTIC TANK EFFLUENT TUBE FILTER**									
3000 Effluent filter, 4" diameter	1 Skwk	8	1	Ea.	55.50	32.50		88	116
3020 6" diameter	"	7	1.143	"	230	37		267	315

33 36 33 – Utility Septic Tank Drainage Field

33 36 33.13 Utility Septic Tank Tile Drainage Field

	Crew	Daily Output	Labor-Hours	Unit	Material	Labor	Equipment	Total	Total Incl O&P
0010 **UTILITY SEPTIC TANK TILE DRAINAGE FIELD**									
0015 Distribution box, concrete, 5 outlets	2 Clab	20	.800	Ea.	78.50	19.05		97.55	118
0020 7 outlets		16	1		78.50	24		102.50	126
0025 9 outlets		8	2		475	47.50		522.50	605
0115 Distribution boxes, HDPE, 5 outlets		20	.800		64.50	19.05		83.55	103
0120 8 outlets	↓	10	1.600		68.50	38		106.50	140
0240 Distribution boxes, Outlet Flow Leveler	1 Clab	50	.160	↓	2.22	3.81		6.03	8.85

33 36 50 – Drainage Field Systems

33 36 50.10 Drainage Field Excavation and Fill

	Crew	Daily Output	Labor-Hours	Unit	Material	Labor	Equipment	Total	Total Incl O&P
0010 **DRAINAGE FIELD EXCAVATION AND FILL**									
2200 Septic tank & drainage field excavation with 3/4 c.y backhoe	B-12F	145	.110	C.Y.		3.23	4.57	7.80	10.40
2400 4' trench for disposal field, 3/4 C.Y. backhoe	"	335	.048	L.F.		1.40	1.98	3.38	4.50
2600 Gravel fill, run of bank	B-6	150	.160	C.Y.	19.90	4.27	2.44	26.61	32
2800 Crushed stone, 3/4"	"	150	.160	"	34.50	4.27	2.44	41.21	47.50

33 41 Storm Utility Drainage Piping

33 41 13 – Public Storm Utility Drainage Piping

33 41 13.60 Sewage/Drainage Collection, Concrete Pipe	Crew	Daily Output	Labor-Hours	Unit	Material	2014 Bare Costs Labor	Equipment	Total	Total Incl O&P
0010 **SEWAGE/DRAINAGE COLLECTION, CONCRETE PIPE**									
0020 Not including excavation or backfill									
1020 8" diameter	B-14	224	.214	L.F.	6.15	5.50	1.63	13.28	17.80
1030 10" diameter	"	216	.222	"	6.85	5.70	1.69	14.24	18.90
3780 Concrete slotted pipe, class 4 mortar joint									
3800 12" diameter	B-21	168	.167	L.F.	27	4.32	.83	32.15	37.50
3840 18" diameter	"	152	.184	"	31.50	4.77	.92	37.19	43.50
3900 Concrete slotted pipe, Class 4 O-ring joint									
3940 12" diameter	B-21	168	.167	L.F.	27	4.32	.83	32.15	37.50
3960 18" diameter	"	152	.184	"	31.50	4.77	.92	37.19	43.50

33 44 Storm Utility Water Drains

33 44 13 – Utility Area Drains

33 44 13.13 Catchbasins

	Crew	Daily Output	Labor-Hours	Unit	Material	2014 Bare Costs Labor	Equipment	Total	Total Incl O&P
0010 **CATCHBASINS**									
0011 Not including footing & excavation									
1600 Frames & grates, C.I., 24" square, 500 lb.	B-6	7.80	3.077	Ea.	340	82	47	469	565

33 46 Subdrainage

33 46 16 – Subdrainage Piping

33 46 16.25 Piping, Subdrainage, Corrugated Metal

	Crew	Daily Output	Labor-Hours	Unit	Material	2014 Bare Costs Labor	Equipment	Total	Total Incl O&P
0010 **PIPING, SUBDRAINAGE, CORRUGATED METAL**									
0021 Not including excavation and backfill									
2010 Aluminum, perforated									
2020 6" diameter, 18 ga.	B-20	380	.063	L.F.	6.55	1.55		8.10	9.80
2200 8" diameter, 16 ga.	"	370	.065		8.60	1.59		10.19	12.10
2220 10" diameter, 16 ga.	B-21	360	.078		10.75	2.02	.39	13.16	15.60
3000 Uncoated galvanized, perforated									
3020 6" diameter, 18 ga.	B-20	380	.063	L.F.	6.05	1.55		7.60	9.25
3200 8" diameter, 16 ga.	"	370	.065		8.35	1.59		9.94	11.80
3220 10" diameter, 16 ga.	B-21	360	.078		8.85	2.02	.39	11.26	13.50
3240 12" diameter, 16 ga.	"	285	.098		9.85	2.55	.49	12.89	15.60
4000 Steel, perforated, asphalt coated									
4020 6" diameter 18 ga.	B-20	380	.063	L.F.	6.55	1.55		8.10	9.80
4030 8" diameter 18 ga.	"	370	.065		8.60	1.59		10.19	12.10
4040 10" diameter 16 ga.	B-21	360	.078		10.10	2.02	.39	12.51	14.90
4050 12" diameter 16 ga.		285	.098		11.10	2.55	.49	14.14	17
4060 18" diameter 16 ga.		205	.137		17.15	3.54	.68	21.37	25.50

33 49 Storm Drainage Structures

33 49 13 – Storm Drainage Manholes, Frames, and Covers

33 49 13.10 Storm Drainage Manholes, Frames and Covers	Crew	Daily Output	Labor-Hours	Unit	Material	2014 Bare Costs Labor	Equipment	Total	Total Incl O&P
0010 **STORM DRAINAGE MANHOLES, FRAMES & COVERS**									
0020 Excludes footing, excavation, backfill (See line items for frame & cover)									
0050 Brick, 4' inside diameter, 4' deep	D-1	1	16	Ea.	510	460		970	1,325
1110 Precast, 4' I.D., 4' deep	B-22	4.10	7.317	"	775	194	51	1,020	1,225

33 51 Natural-Gas Distribution

33 51 13 – Natural-Gas Piping

33 51 13.10 Piping, Gas Service and Distribution, P.E.

		Crew	Daily Output	Labor-Hours	Unit	Material	2014 Bare Costs Labor	Equipment	Total	Total Incl O&P
0010	**PIPING, GAS SERVICE AND DISTRIBUTION, POLYETHYLENE**									
0020	Not including excavation or backfill									
1000	60 psi coils, compression coupling @ 100', 1/2" diameter, SDR 11	B-20A	608	.053	L.F.	.61	1.55		2.16	3.25
1010	1" diameter, SDR 11		544	.059		1.41	1.74		3.15	4.44
1040	1-1/4" diameter, SDR 11		544	.059		1.76	1.74		3.50	4.82
1100	2" diameter, SDR 11		488	.066		2.85	1.93		4.78	6.35
1160	3" diameter, SDR 11		408	.078		5.60	2.31		7.91	10
1500	60 PSI 40' joints with coupling, 3" diameter, SDR 11	B-21A	408	.098		5.55	2.99	1.18	9.72	12.35
1540	4" diameter, SDR 11		352	.114		12.15	3.47	1.37	16.99	20.50
1600	6" diameter, SDR 11		328	.122		33.50	3.72	1.47	38.69	45
1640	8" diameter, SDR 11		272	.147		51.50	4.49	1.77	57.76	66

33 51 13.20 Piping, Gas Service and Distribution, Steel

		Crew	Daily Output	Labor-Hours	Unit	Material	2014 Bare Costs Labor	Equipment	Total	Total Incl O&P
0010	**PIPING, GAS SERVICE & DISTRIBUTION, STEEL**									
0020	Not including excavation or backfill, tar coated and wrapped									
4000	Pipe schedule 40, plain end									
4040	1" diameter	Q-4	300	.107	L.F.	5.25	3.85	.18	9.28	12.35
4080	2" diameter	"	280	.114	"	8.25	4.13	.20	12.58	16.05

Estimating Tips

- When estimating costs for the installation of electrical power generation equipment, factors to review include access to the job site, access and setting at the installation site, required connections, uncrating pads, anchors, leveling, final assembly of the components, and temporary protection from physical damage, including from exposure to the environment.

- Be aware of the cost of equipment supports, concrete pads, and vibration isolators, and cross-reference to other trades' specifications. Also, review site and structural drawings for items that must be included in the estimates.

- It is important to include items that are not documented in the plans and specifications but must be priced. These items include, but are not limited to, testing, dust protection, roof penetration, core drilling concrete floors and walls, patching, cleanup, and final adjustments. Add a contingency or allowance for utility company fees for power hookups, if needed.

- The project size and scope of electrical power generation equipment will have a significant impact on cost. The intent of RSMeans cost data is to provide a benchmark cost so that owners, engineers, and electrical contractors will have a comfortable number with which to start a project. Additionally, there are many websites available to use for research and to obtain a vendor's quote to finalize costs.

Reference Numbers

Reference numbers are shown in shaded boxes at the beginning of some major classifications. These numbers refer to related items in the Reference Section. The reference information may be an estimating procedure, an alternate pricing method, or technical information.

Note: Not all subdivisions listed here necessarily appear in this publication.

Division 48 - Electrical Power Generation

48 15 Wind Energy Electrical Power Generation Equipment

48 15 13 – Wind Turbines

48 15 13.50 Wind Turbines and Components		Crew	Daily Output	Labor-Hours	Unit	Material	2014 Bare Costs Labor	Equipment	Total	Total Incl O&P
0010	**WIND TURBINES & COMPONENTS**									
0500	Complete system, grid connected									
1000	20 kW, 31' dia, incl. labor & material, min	G				System				49,900
1010	Maximum	G								55,000
1500	10 kW, 23' dia, incl. labor & material	G								74,000
2000	2.4 kW, 12' dia, incl. labor & material	G								18,000
2900	Component system									
3000	Turbine, 400 watt, 3' dia	G	1 Elec	3.41	2.346	Ea.	755	84		839	965
3100	600 watt, 3' dia	G		2.56	3.125		955	112		1,067	1,225
3200	1000 watt, 9' dia	G		2.05	3.902		3,825	140		3,965	4,450
3400	Mounting hardware									
3500	30' guyed tower kit	G	2 Clab	5.12	3.125	Ea.	455	74.50		529.50	625
3505	3' galvanized helical earth screw	G	1 Clab	8	1		53	24		77	98
3510	Attic mount kit	G	1 Rofc	2.56	3.125		133	84.50		217.50	300
3520	Roof mount kit	G	1 Clab	3.41	2.346		118	56		174	223
8900	Equipment									
9100	DC to AC inverter for, 48 V, 4,000 watt	G	1 Elec	2	4	Ea.	2,750	143		2,893	3,250

Reference Section

All the reference information is in one section, making it easy to find what you need to know ... and easy to use the book on a daily basis. This section is visually identified by a vertical gray bar on the page edges.

In this Reference Section, we've included Equipment Rental Costs, a listing of rental and operating costs; Crew Listings, a full listing of all crews, equipment, and their costs; Location Factors for adjusting costs to the region you are in; Reference Tables, where you will find explanations, estimating information and procedures, or technical data; an explanation of all the Abbreviations in the book; and sample Estimating Forms.

Table of Contents

Estimating Tips

- This section contains the average costs to rent and operate hundreds of pieces of construction equipment. This is useful information when estimating the time and material requirements of any particular operation in order to establish a unit or total cost. Equipment costs include not only rental, but also operating costs for equipment under normal use.

Rental Costs

- Equipment rental rates are obtained from industry sources throughout North America–contractors, suppliers, dealers, manufacturers, and distributors.
- Rental rates vary throughout the country, with larger cities generally having lower rates. Lease plans for new equipment are available for periods in excess of six months, with a percentage of payments applying toward purchase.
- Monthly rental rates vary from 2% to 5% of the purchase price of the equipment depending on the anticipated life of the equipment and its wearing parts.
- Weekly rental rates are about 1/3 the monthly rates, and daily rental rates are about 1/3 the weekly rate.
- Rental rates can also be treated as reimbursement costs for contractor-owned equipment. Owned equipment costs include depreciation, loan payments, interest, taxes, insurance, storage, and major repairs.

Operating Costs

- The operating costs include parts and labor for routine servicing, such as repair and replacement of pumps, filters and worn lines. Normal operating expendables, such as fuel, lubricants, tires and electricity (where applicable), are also included.
- Extraordinary operating expendables with highly variable wear patterns, such as diamond bits and blades, are excluded. These costs can be found as material costs in the Unit Price section.
- The hourly operating costs listed do not include the operator's wages.

Equipment Cost/Day

- Any power equipment required by a crew is shown in the Crew Listings with a daily cost.
- The daily cost of equipment needed by a crew is based on dividing the weekly rental rate by 5 (number of working days in the week), and then adding the hourly operating cost times 8 (the number of hours in a day). This "Equipment Cost/ Day" is shown in the far right column of the Equipment Rental pages.
- If equipment is needed for only one or two days, it is best to develop your own cost by including components for daily rent and hourly operating cost. This is important when the listed Crew for a task does not contain the equipment needed, such as a crane for lifting mechanical heating/cooling equipment up onto a roof.

- If the quantity of work is less than the crew's Daily Output shown for a Unit Price line item that includes a bare unit equipment cost, it is recommended to estimate one day's rental cost and operating cost for equipment shown in the Crew Listing for that line item.

Mobilization/ Demobilization

- The cost to move construction equipment from an equipment yard or rental company to the jobsite and back again is not included in equipment rental costs listed in the Reference section, nor in the bare equipment cost of any Unit Price line item, nor in any equipment costs shown in the Crew listings.
- Mobilization (to the site) and demobilization (from the site) costs can be found in the Unit Price section.
- If a piece of equipment is already at the jobsite, it is not appropriate to utilize mobil./ demob. costs again in an estimate.

01 54 33 | Equipment Rental

			UNIT	HOURLY OPER. COST	RENT PER DAY	RENT PER WEEK	RENT PER MONTH	EQUIPMENT COST/DAY	
10	0010	**CONCRETE EQUIPMENT RENTAL** without operators	R015433 -10						**10**
	0200	Bucket, concrete lightweight, 1/2 C.Y.	Ea.	.80	23	69	207	20.20	
	0300	1 C.Y.		.85	27	81	243	23	
	0400	1-1/2 C.Y.		1.10	36.50	110	330	30.80	
	0500	2 C.Y.		1.20	43.50	130	390	35.60	
	0580	8 C.Y.		5.95	252	755	2,275	198.60	
	0600	Cart, concrete, self-propelled, operator walking, 10 C.F.		3.40	55	165	495	60.20	
	0700	Operator riding, 18 C.F.		5.65	93.50	280	840	101.20	
	0800	Conveyer for concrete, portable, gas, 16" wide, 26' long		13.50	122	365	1,100	181	
	0900	46' long		13.90	147	440	1,325	199.20	
	1000	56' long		14.05	155	465	1,400	205.40	
	1100	Core drill, electric, 2-1/2 H.P., 1" to 8" bit diameter		1.50	57	171	515	46.20	
	1150	11 H.P., 8" to 18" cores		5.90	115	345	1,025	116.20	
	1200	Finisher, concrete floor, gas, riding trowel, 96" wide		14.05	142	425	1,275	197.40	
	1300	Gas, walk-behind, 3 blade, 36" trowel		2.35	20	60	180	30.80	
	1400	4 blade, 48" trowel		4.70	26.50	80	240	53.60	
	1500	Float, hand-operated (Bull float) 48" wide		.08	13.35	40	120	8.65	
	1570	Curb builder, 14 H.P., gas, single screw		14.65	250	750	2,250	267.20	
	1590	Double screw		15.30	287	860	2,575	294.40	
	1600	Floor grinder, concrete and terrazzo, electric, 22" path		2.19	134	402	1,200	97.90	
	1700	Edger, concrete, electric, 7" path		1.02	51.50	155	465	39.15	
	1750	Vacuum pick-up system for floor grinders, wet/dry		1.47	81.50	245	735	60.75	
	1800	Mixer, powered, mortar and concrete, gas, 6 C.F., 18 H.P.		9.20	117	350	1,050	143.60	
	1900	10 C.F., 25 H.P.		11.60	140	420	1,250	176.80	
	2000	16 C.F.		11.95	162	485	1,450	192.60	
	2100	Concrete, stationary, tilt drum, 2 C.Y.		6.80	228	685	2,050	191.40	
	2120	Pump, concrete, truck mounted 4" line 80' boom		24.55	855	2,570	7,700	710.40	
	2140	5" line, 110' boom		31.75	1,125	3,400	10,200	934	
	2160	Mud jack, 50 C.F. per hr.		7.35	127	380	1,150	134.80	
	2180	225 C.F. per hr.		9.65	145	435	1,300	164.20	
	2190	Shotcrete pump rig, 12 C.Y./hr.		15.10	220	660	1,975	252.80	
	2200	35 C.Y./hr.		17.80	237	710	2,125	284.40	
	2600	Saw, concrete, manual, gas, 18 H.P.		7.25	43.50	130	390	84	
	2650	Self-propelled, gas, 30 H.P.		14.40	100	300	900	175.20	
	2675	V-groove crack chaser, manual, gas, 6 H.P.		2.55	17.35	52	156	30.80	
	2700	Vibrators, concrete, electric, 60 cycle, 2 H.P.		.43	8.65	26	78	8.65	
	2800	3 H.P.		.61	11.65	35	105	11.90	
	2900	Gas engine, 5 H.P.		2.20	16	48	144	27.20	
	3000	8 H.P.		3.00	15	45	135	33	
	3050	Vibrating screed, gas engine, 8 H.P.		2.78	68.50	205	615	63.25	
	3120	Concrete transit mixer, 6 x 4, 250 H.P., 8 C.Y., rear discharge		62.50	565	1,690	5,075	838	
	3200	Front discharge		73.60	690	2,065	6,200	1,002	
	3300	6 x 6, 285 H.P., 12 C.Y., rear discharge		72.65	650	1,950	5,850	971.20	
	3400	Front discharge		75.95	695	2,085	6,250	1,025	
20	0010	**EARTHWORK EQUIPMENT RENTAL** without operators	R015433 -10						**20**
	0040	Aggregate spreader, push type 8' to 12' wide	Ea.	3.25	25.50	76	228	41.20	
	0045	Tailgate type, 8' wide		3.10	32.50	98	294	44.40	
	0055	Earth auger, truck-mounted, for fence & sign posts, utility poles		19.75	445	1,335	4,000	425	
	0060	For borings and monitoring wells		47.30	680	2,040	6,125	786.40	
	0070	Portable, trailer mounted		3.15	32.50	98	294	44.80	
	0075	Truck-mounted, for caissons, water wells		100.90	2,900	8,720	26,200	2,551	
	0080	Horizontal boring machine, 12" to 36" diameter, 45 H.P.		24.60	193	580	1,750	312.80	
	0090	12" to 48" diameter, 65 H.P.		34.85	335	1,005	3,025	479.80	
	0095	Auger, for fence posts, gas engine, hand held		.55	6	18	54	8	
	0100	Excavator, diesel hydraulic, crawler mounted, 1/2 C.Y. cap.		25.00	415	1,240	3,725	448	
	0120	5/8 C.Y. capacity		33.05	550	1,650	4,950	594.40	
	0140	3/4 C.Y. capacity		36.00	625	1,870	5,600	662	
	0150	1 C.Y. capacity		50.60	685	2,050	6,150	814.80	

01 54 33 | Equipment Rental

		UNIT	HOURLY OPER. COST	RENT PER DAY	RENT PER WEEK	RENT PER MONTH	EQUIPMENT COST/DAY	
20	0200	1-1/2 C.Y. capacity	Ea.	60.80	910	2,725	8,175	1,031	20
	0300	2 C.Y. capacity		68.50	1,050	3,135	9,400	1,175	
	0320	2-1/2 C.Y. capacity		104.75	1,325	3,995	12,000	1,637	
	0325	3-1/2 C.Y. capacity		147.35	2,100	6,315	18,900	2,442	
	0330	4-1/2 C.Y. capacity		176.65	2,725	8,150	24,500	3,043	
	0335	6 C.Y. capacity		224.40	2,875	8,640	25,900	3,523	
	0340	7 C.Y. capacity		226.60	2,975	8,915	26,700	3,596	
	0342	Excavator attachments, bucket thumbs		3.20	245	735	2,200	172.60	
	0345	Grapples		2.75	193	580	1,750	138	
	0347	Hydraulic hammer for boom mounting, 5000 ft lb.		14.30	425	1,280	3,850	370.40	
	0349	11,000 ft lb.		23.20	750	2,250	6,750	635.60	
	0350	Gradall type, truck mounted, 3 ton @ 15' radius, 5/8 C.Y.		43.45	890	2,670	8,000	881.60	
	0370	1 C.Y. capacity		47.65	1,050	3,120	9,350	1,005	
	0400	Backhoe-loader, 40 to 45 H.P., 5/8 C.Y. capacity		14.95	233	700	2,100	259.60	
	0450	45 H.P. to 60 H.P., 3/4 C.Y. capacity		23.90	290	870	2,600	365.20	
	0460	80 H.P., 1-1/4 C.Y. capacity		26.20	315	940	2,825	397.60	
	0470	112 H.P., 1-1/2 C.Y. capacity		41.65	645	1,935	5,800	720.20	
	0482	Backhoe-loader attachment, compactor, 20,000 lb.		5.75	142	425	1,275	131	
	0485	Hydraulic hammer, 750 ft lb.		3.25	96.50	290	870	84	
	0486	Hydraulic hammer, 1200 ft lb.		6.30	217	650	1,950	180.40	
	0500	Brush chipper, gas engine, 6" cutter head, 35 H.P.		11.95	107	320	960	159.60	
	0550	Diesel engine, 12" cutter head, 130 H.P.		28.20	285	855	2,575	396.60	
	0600	15" cutter head, 165 H.P.		33.90	330	985	2,950	468.20	
	0750	Bucket, clamshell, general purpose, 3/8 C.Y.		1.25	38.50	115	345	33	
	0800	1/2 C.Y.		1.35	45	135	405	37.80	
	0850	3/4 C.Y.		1.50	53.50	160	480	44	
	0900	1 C.Y.		1.55	58.50	175	525	47.40	
	0950	1-1/2 C.Y.		2.55	80	240	720	68.40	
	1000	2 C.Y.		2.65	88.50	265	795	74.20	
	1010	Bucket, dragline, medium duty, 1/2 C.Y.		.75	23.50	70	210	20	
	1020	3/4 C.Y.		.75	24.50	74	222	20.80	
	1030	1 C.Y.		.80	26	78	234	22	
	1040	1-1/2 C.Y.		1.20	40	120	360	33.60	
	1050	2 C.Y.		1.25	45	135	405	37	
	1070	3 C.Y.		1.95	61.50	185	555	52.60	
	1200	Compactor, manually guided 2-drum vibratory smooth roller, 7.5 H.P.		7.35	207	620	1,850	182.80	
	1250	Rammer/tamper, gas, 8"		2.70	46.50	140	420	49.60	
	1260	15"		3.00	53.50	160	480	56	
	1300	Vibratory plate, gas, 18" plate, 3000 lb. blow		2.65	24.50	73	219	35.80	
	1350	21" plate, 5000 lb. blow		3.30	32.50	98	294	46	
	1370	Curb builder/extruder, 14 H.P., gas, single screw		14.65	250	750	2,250	267.20	
	1390	Double screw		15.30	287	860	2,575	294.40	
	1500	Disc harrow attachment, for tractor		.43	72.50	217	650	46.85	
	1810	Feller buncher, shearing & accumulating trees, 100 H.P.		42.50	650	1,945	5,825	729	
	1860	Grader, self-propelled, 25,000 lb.		39.55	595	1,780	5,350	672.40	
	1910	30,000 lb.		43.25	600	1,805	5,425	707	
	1920	40,000 lb.		64.65	1,000	3,015	9,050	1,120	
	1930	55,000 lb.		84.65	1,600	4,800	14,400	1,637	
	1950	Hammer, pavement breaker, self-propelled, diesel, 1000 to 1250 lb.		30.25	355	1,060	3,175	454	
	2000	1300 to 1500 lb.		45.38	705	2,120	6,350	787.05	
	2050	Pile driving hammer, steam or air, 4150 ft lb. @ 225 bpm		10.35	475	1,425	4,275	367.80	
	2100	8750 ft lb. @ 145 bpm		12.35	660	1,980	5,950	494.80	
	2150	15,000 ft lb. @ 60 bpm		13.95	795	2,380	7,150	587.60	
	2200	24,450 ft lb. @ 111 bpm		14.95	880	2,640	7,925	647.60	
	2250	Leads, 60' high for pile driving hammers up to 20,000 ft lb.		3.30	80.50	242	725	74.80	
	2300	90' high for hammers over 20,000 ft lb.		4.95	141	424	1,275	124.40	
	2350	Diesel type hammer, 22,400 ft lb.		26.93	535	1,610	4,825	537.45	
	2400	41,300 ft lb.		36.30	585	1,760	5,275	642.40	

01 54 33 | Equipment Rental

		UNIT	HOURLY OPER. COST	RENT PER DAY	RENT PER WEEK	RENT PER MONTH	EQUIPMENT COST/DAY	
20	2450	141,000 ft lb.	Ea.	55.55	1,050	3,160	9,475	1,076	**20**
	2500	Vib. elec. hammer/extractor, 200 kW diesel generator, 34 H.P.		56.25	635	1,910	5,725	832	
	2550	80 H.P.		103.45	930	2,785	8,350	1,385	
	2600	150 H.P.		196.65	1,775	5,335	16,000	2,640	
	2800	Log chipper, up to 22" diameter, 600 H.P.		64.95	630	1,895	5,675	898.60	
	2850	Logger, for skidding & stacking logs, 150 H.P.		53.45	820	2,460	7,375	919.60	
	2860	Mulcher, diesel powered, trailer mounted		24.70	213	640	1,925	325.60	
	2900	Rake, spring tooth, with tractor		18.31	335	1,007	3,025	347.90	
	3000	Roller, vibratory, tandem, smooth drum, 20 H.P.		8.75	148	445	1,325	159	
	3050	35 H.P.		11.25	253	760	2,275	242	
	3100	Towed type vibratory compactor, smooth drum, 50 H.P.		26.25	335	1,010	3,025	412	
	3150	Sheepsfoot, 50 H.P.		27.60	370	1,115	3,350	443.80	
	3170	Landfill compactor, 220 H.P.		91.85	1,500	4,485	13,500	1,632	
	3200	Pneumatic tire roller, 80 H.P.		17.00	355	1,065	3,200	349	
	3250	120 H.P.		25.45	605	1,815	5,450	566.60	
	3300	Sheepsfoot vibratory roller, 240 H.P.		69.65	1,100	3,305	9,925	1,218	
	3320	340 H.P.		101.85	1,600	4,830	14,500	1,781	
	3350	Smooth drum vibratory roller, 75 H.P.		25.15	595	1,790	5,375	559.20	
	3400	125 H.P.		32.85	715	2,150	6,450	692.80	
	3410	Rotary mower, brush, 60", with tractor		22.65	305	915	2,750	364.20	
	3420	Rototiller, walk-behind, gas, 5 H.P.		2.23	66	198	595	57.45	
	3422	8 H.P.		3.30	91.50	275	825	81.40	
	3440	Scrapers, towed type, 7 C.Y. capacity		5.70	110	330	990	111.60	
	3450	10 C.Y. capacity		6.45	150	450	1,350	141.60	
	3500	15 C.Y. capacity		6.85	173	520	1,550	158.80	
	3525	Self-propelled, single engine, 14 C.Y. capacity		113.60	1,525	4,600	13,800	1,829	
	3550	Dual engine, 21 C.Y. capacity		174.50	2,000	6,015	18,000	2,599	
	3600	31 C.Y. capacity		232.10	2,850	8,545	25,600	3,566	
	3640	44 C.Y. capacity		287.55	3,650	10,960	32,900	4,492	
	3650	Elevating type, single engine, 11 C.Y. capacity		71.20	1,025	3,050	9,150	1,180	
	3700	22 C.Y. capacity		138.15	2,225	6,690	20,100	2,443	
	3710	Screening plant 110 H.P. w/5' x 10' screen		31.63	435	1,300	3,900	513.05	
	3720	5' x 16' screen		34.85	540	1,615	4,850	601.80	
	3850	Shovel, crawler-mounted, front-loading, 7 C.Y. capacity		246.75	2,900	8,700	26,100	3,714	
	3855	12 C.Y. capacity		354.50	3,950	11,840	35,500	5,204	
	3860	Shovel/backhoe bucket, 1/2 C.Y.		2.45	66.50	200	600	59.60	
	3870	3/4 C.Y.		2.50	73.50	220	660	64	
	3880	1 C.Y.		2.60	83.50	250	750	70.80	
	3890	1-1/2 C.Y.		2.75	96.50	290	870	80	
	3910	3 C.Y.		3.10	130	390	1,175	102.80	
	3950	Stump chipper, 18" deep, 30 H.P.		7.06	176	528	1,575	162.10	
	4110	Dozer, crawler, torque converter, diesel 80 H.P.		29.75	405	1,215	3,650	481	
	4150	105 H.P.		36.10	505	1,515	4,550	591.80	
	4200	140 H.P.		52.10	780	2,335	7,000	883.80	
	4260	200 H.P.		77.35	1,175	3,530	10,600	1,325	
	4310	300 H.P.		100.55	1,700	5,065	15,200	1,817	
	4360	410 H.P.		135.65	2,200	6,620	19,900	2,409	
	4370	500 H.P.		174.30	2,875	8,610	25,800	3,116	
	4380	700 H.P.		261.35	4,000	11,970	35,900	4,485	
	4400	Loader, crawler, torque conv., diesel, 1-1/2 C.Y., 80 H.P.		31.35	455	1,360	4,075	522.80	
	4450	1-1/2 to 1-3/4 C.Y., 95 H.P.		34.15	585	1,760	5,275	625.20	
	4510	1-3/4 to 2-1/4 C.Y., 130 H.P.		54.60	870	2,615	7,850	959.80	
	4530	2-1/2 to 3-1/4 C.Y., 190 H.P.		67.00	1,100	3,275	9,825	1,191	
	4560	3-1/2 to 5 C.Y., 275 H.P.		86.10	1,400	4,215	12,600	1,532	
	4610	Front end loader, 4WD, articulated frame, diesel, 1 to 1-1/4 C.Y., 70 H.P.		19.90	227	680	2,050	295.20	
	4620	1-1/2 to 1-3/4 C.Y., 95 H.P.		25.30	285	855	2,575	373.40	
	4650	1-3/4 to 2 C.Y., 130 H.P.		29.45	365	1,100	3,300	455.60	
	4710	2-1/2 to 3-1/2 C.Y., 145 H.P.		33.35	425	1,280	3,850	522.80	

01 54 33 | Equipment Rental

		UNIT	HOURLY OPER. COST	RENT PER DAY	RENT PER WEEK	RENT PER MONTH	EQUIPMENT COST/DAY	
20	4730	3 to 4-1/2 C.Y., 185 H.P.	Ea.	42.85	550	1,655	4,975	673.80	**20**
	4760	5-1/4 to 5-3/4 C.Y., 270 H.P.		67.80	845	2,535	7,600	1,049	
	4810	7 to 9 C.Y., 475 H.P.		116.25	1,775	5,295	15,900	1,989	
	4870	9 - 11 C.Y., 620 H.P.		155.75	2,425	7,285	21,900	2,703	
	4880	Skid steer loader, wheeled, 10 C.F., 30 H.P. gas		10.90	145	435	1,300	174.20	
	4890	1 C.Y., 78 H.P., diesel		20.35	243	730	2,200	308.80	
	4892	Skid-steer attachment, auger		.50	83.50	251	755	54.20	
	4893	Backhoe		.66	111	332	995	71.70	
	4894	Broom		.74	124	372	1,125	80.30	
	4895	Forks		.23	38.50	115	345	24.85	
	4896	Grapple		.56	92.50	278	835	60.10	
	4897	Concrete hammer		1.06	177	531	1,600	114.70	
	4898	Tree spade		1.03	172	515	1,550	111.25	
	4899	Trencher		.67	112	335	1,000	72.35	
	4900	Trencher, chain, boom type, gas, operator walking, 12 H.P.		5.40	46.50	140	420	71.20	
	4910	Operator riding, 40 H.P.		20.55	292	875	2,625	339.40	
	5000	Wheel type, diesel, 4' deep, 12" wide		87.50	845	2,530	7,600	1,206	
	5100	6' deep, 20" wide		93.25	1,925	5,760	17,300	1,898	
	5150	Chain type, diesel, 5' deep, 8" wide		38.85	560	1,685	5,050	647.80	
	5200	Diesel, 8' deep, 16" wide		156.45	3,550	10,620	31,900	3,376	
	5202	Rock trencher, wheel type, 6" wide x 18" deep		21.50	330	985	2,950	369	
	5206	Chain type, 18" wide x 7' deep		112.60	2,825	8,445	25,300	2,590	
	5210	Tree spade, self-propelled		14.00	267	800	2,400	272	
	5250	Truck, dump, 2-axle, 12 ton, 8 C.Y. payload, 220 H.P.		35.15	227	680	2,050	417.20	
	5300	Three axle dump, 16 ton, 12 C.Y. payload, 400 H.P.		62.40	320	965	2,900	692.20	
	5310	Four axle dump, 25 ton, 18 C.Y. payload, 450 H.P.		73.20	470	1,410	4,225	867.60	
	5350	Dump trailer only, rear dump, 16-1/2 C.Y.		5.40	138	415	1,250	126.20	
	5400	20 C.Y.		5.85	157	470	1,400	140.80	
	5450	Flatbed, single axle, 1-1/2 ton rating		28.65	68.50	205	615	270.20	
	5500	3 ton rating		34.25	98.50	295	885	333	
	5550	Off highway rear dump, 25 ton capacity		74.55	1,200	3,590	10,800	1,314	
	5600	35 ton capacity		83.10	1,350	4,025	12,100	1,470	
	5610	50 ton capacity		103.40	1,600	4,800	14,400	1,787	
	5620	65 ton capacity		106.30	1,575	4,735	14,200	1,797	
	5630	100 ton capacity		154.35	2,775	8,315	24,900	2,898	
	6000	Vibratory plow, 25 H.P., walking		9.25	60	180	540	110	
40	0010	**GENERAL EQUIPMENT RENTAL** without operators							**40**
	0150	Aerial lift, scissor type, to 15' high, 1000 lb. cap., electric	Ea.	3.10	51.50	155	465	55.80	
	0160	To 25' high, 2000 lb. capacity		3.55	66.50	200	600	68.40	
	0170	Telescoping boom to 40' high, 500 lb. capacity, diesel		17.00	315	945	2,825	325	
	0180	To 45' high, 500 lb. capacity		18.85	355	1,070	3,200	364.80	
	0190	To 60' high, 600 lb. capacity		21.25	475	1,430	4,300	456	
	0195	Air compressor, portable, 6.5 CFM, electric		.56	12.65	38	114	12.10	
	0196	Gasoline		.79	19	57	171	17.70	
	0200	Towed type, gas engine, 60 CFM		13.55	48.50	145	435	137.40	
	0300	160 CFM		15.80	51.50	155	465	157.40	
	0400	Diesel engine, rotary screw, 250 CFM		17.05	110	330	990	202.40	
	0500	365 CFM		23.10	133	400	1,200	264.80	
	0550	450 CFM		29.35	167	500	1,500	334.80	
	0600	600 CFM		51.70	232	695	2,075	552.60	
	0700	750 CFM		51.90	240	720	2,150	559.20	
	0800	For silenced models, small sizes, add to rent		3%	5%	5%	5%		
	0900	Large sizes, add to rent		5%	7%	7%	7%		
	0930	Air tools, breaker, pavement, 60 lb.	Ea.	.50	9.65	29	87	9.80	
	0940	80 lb.		.50	10.35	31	93	10.20	
	0950	Drills, hand (jackhammer) 65 lb.		.60	17.35	52	156	15.20	
	0960	Track or wagon, swing boom, 4" drifter		63.45	885	2,660	7,975	1,040	
	0970	5" drifter		75.50	1,075	3,255	9,775	1,255	

R015433 -10

01 54 33 | Equipment Rental

		UNIT	HOURLY OPER. COST	RENT PER DAY	RENT PER WEEK	RENT PER MONTH	EQUIPMENT COST/DAY	
40	0975	Track mounted quarry drill, 6" diameter drill	Ea.	129.75	1,600	4,830	14,500	2,004	40
	0980	Dust control per drill		.97	24	72	216	22.15	
	0990	Hammer, chipping, 12 lb.		.55	26	78	234	20	
	1000	Hose, air with couplings, 50' long, 3/4" diameter		.03	5	15	45	3.25	
	1100	1" diameter		.04	6.35	19	57	4.10	
	1200	1-1/2" diameter		.05	9	27	81	5.80	
	1300	2" diameter		.07	12	36	108	7.75	
	1400	2-1/2" diameter		.11	19	57	171	12.30	
	1410	3" diameter		.14	23	69	207	14.90	
	1450	Drill, steel, 7/8" x 2'		.05	8.65	26	78	5.60	
	1460	7/8" x 6'		.05	9	27	81	5.80	
	1520	Moil points		.02	3.33	10	30	2.15	
	1525	Pneumatic nailer w/accessories		.47	31	93	279	22.35	
	1530	Sheeting driver for 60 lb. breaker		.03	5.65	17	51	3.65	
	1540	For 90 lb. breaker		.11	7.35	22	66	5.30	
	1550	Spade, 25 lb.		.45	7	21	63	7.80	
	1560	Tamper, single, 35 lb.		.55	36.50	109	325	26.20	
	1570	Triple, 140 lb.		.82	54.50	164	490	39.35	
	1580	Wrenches, impact, air powered, up to 3/4" bolt		.40	12.65	38	114	10.80	
	1590	Up to 1-1/4" bolt		.50	23.50	70	210	18	
	1600	Barricades, barrels, reflectorized, 1 to 99 barrels		.03	4.60	13.80	41.50	3	
	1610	100 to 200 barrels		.02	3.53	10.60	32	2.30	
	1620	Barrels with flashers, 1 to 99 barrels		.03	5.25	15.80	47.50	3.40	
	1630	100 to 200 barrels		.03	4.20	12.60	38	2.75	
	1640	Barrels with steady burn type C lights		.04	7	21	63	4.50	
	1650	Illuminated board, trailer mounted, with generator		3.55	130	390	1,175	106.40	
	1670	Portable barricade, stock, with flashers, 1 to 6 units		.03	5.25	15.80	47.50	3.40	
	1680	25 to 50 units		.03	4.90	14.70	44	3.20	
	1685	Butt fusion machine, wheeled, 1.5 HP electric, 2" - 8" diameter pipe		2.62	167	500	1,500	120.95	
	1690	Tracked, 20 HP diesel, 4"-12" diameter pipe		11.10	490	1,465	4,400	381.80	
	1695	83 HP diesel, 8" - 24" diameter pipe		30.30	975	2,930	8,800	828.40	
	1700	Carts, brick, hand powered, 1000 lb. capacity		.44	72.50	218	655	47.10	
	1800	Gas engine, 1500 lb., 7-1/2' lift		4.10	115	345	1,025	101.80	
	1822	Dehumidifier, medium, 6 lb./hr., 150 CFM		.99	62	186	560	45.10	
	1824	Large, 18 lb./hr., 600 CFM		2.01	126	378	1,125	91.70	
	1830	Distributor, asphalt, trailer mounted, 2000 gal., 38 H.P. diesel		10.15	330	985	2,950	278.20	
	1840	3000 gal., 38 H.P. diesel		11.65	360	1,075	3,225	308.20	
	1850	Drill, rotary hammer, electric		1.00	26.50	80	240	24	
	1860	Carbide bit, 1-1/2" diameter, add to electric rotary hammer		.02	3.61	10.84	32.50	2.35	
	1865	Rotary, crawler, 250 H.P.		150.45	2,100	6,285	18,900	2,461	
	1870	Emulsion sprayer, 65 gal., 5 H.P. gas engine		2.90	98	294	880	82	
	1880	200 gal., 5 H.P. engine		7.85	163	490	1,475	160.80	
	1900	Floor auto-scrubbing machine, walk-behind, 28" path		4.52	293	880	2,650	212.15	
	1930	Floodlight, mercury vapor, or quartz, on tripod, 1000 watt		.41	19.35	58	174	14.90	
	1940	2000 watt		.78	39	117	350	29.65	
	1950	Floodlights, trailer mounted with generator, 1 - 300 watt light		3.65	71.50	215	645	72.20	
	1960	2 - 1000 watt lights		4.90	98.50	295	885	98.20	
	2000	4 - 300 watt lights		4.60	93.50	280	840	92.80	
	2005	Foam spray rig, incl. box trailer, compressor, generator, proportioner		36.53	490	1,465	4,400	585.25	
	2020	Forklift, straight mast, 12' lift, 5000 lb., 2 wheel drive, gas		25.35	203	610	1,825	324.80	
	2040	21' lift, 5000 lb., 4 wheel drive, diesel		21.15	242	725	2,175	314.20	
	2050	For rough terrain, 42' lift, 35' reach, 9000 lb., 110 H.P.		29.95	485	1,460	4,375	531.60	
	2060	For plant, 4 ton capacity, 80 H.P., 2 wheel drive, gas		15.50	93.50	280	840	180	
	2080	10 ton capacity, 120 H.P., 2 wheel drive, diesel		24.30	162	485	1,450	291.40	
	2100	Generator, electric, gas engine, 1.5 kW to 3 kW		3.95	11.35	34	102	38.40	
	2200	5 kW		5.10	15.35	46	138	50	
	2300	10 kW		9.65	36.50	110	330	99.20	
	2400	25 kW		11.00	86.50	260	780	140	

01 54 33 | Equipment Rental

		UNIT	HOURLY OPER. COST	RENT PER DAY	RENT PER WEEK	RENT PER MONTH	EQUIPMENT COST/DAY	
40	2500	Diesel engine, 20 kW	Ea.	12.55	68.50	205	615	141.40	40
	2600	50 kW		24.35	103	310	930	256.80	
	2700	100 kW		45.15	130	390	1,175	439.20	
	2800	250 kW		88.85	237	710	2,125	852.80	
	2850	Hammer, hydraulic, for mounting on boom, to 500 ft lb.		2.55	75	225	675	65.40	
	2860	1000 ft lb.		4.35	127	380	1,150	110.80	
	2900	Heaters, space, oil or electric, 50 MBH		1.93	7.65	23	69	20.05	
	3000	100 MBH		3.61	10.65	32	96	35.30	
	3100	300 MBH		10.58	38.50	115	345	107.65	
	3150	500 MBH		17.40	45	135	405	166.20	
	3200	Hose, water, suction with coupling, 20' long, 2" diameter		.02	3	9	27	1.95	
	3210	3" diameter		.03	4.33	13	39	2.85	
	3220	4" diameter		.03	5	15	45	3.25	
	3230	6" diameter		.11	17.65	53	159	11.50	
	3240	8" diameter		.20	33.50	100	300	21.60	
	3250	Discharge hose with coupling, 50' long, 2" diameter		.01	1.33	4	12	.90	
	3260	3" diameter		.01	2.33	7	21	1.50	
	3270	4" diameter		.02	3.67	11	33	2.35	
	3280	6" diameter		.06	9.35	28	84	6.10	
	3290	8" diameter		.20	33.50	100	300	21.60	
	3295	Insulation blower		.77	6	18	54	9.75	
	3300	Ladders, extension type, 16' to 36' long		.14	22.50	68	204	14.70	
	3400	40' to 60' long		.19	31	93	279	20.10	
	3405	Lance for cutting concrete		2.52	89	267	800	73.55	
	3407	Lawn mower, rotary, 22", 5 H.P.		2.10	59	177	530	52.20	
	3408	48" self propelled		2.92	75	225	675	68.35	
	3410	Level, electronic, automatic, with tripod and leveling rod		1.49	99	297	890	71.30	
	3430	Laser type, for pipe and sewer line and grade		.73	48.50	145	435	34.85	
	3440	Rotating beam for interior control		.97	64	192	575	46.15	
	3460	Builder's optical transit, with tripod and rod		.10	16.65	50	150	10.80	
	3500	Light towers, towable, with diesel generator, 2000 watt		4.60	93.50	280	840	92.80	
	3600	4000 watt		4.90	98.50	295	885	98.20	
	3700	Mixer, powered, plaster and mortar, 6 C.F., 7 H.P.		2.90	19	57	171	34.60	
	3800	10 C.F., 9 H.P.		3.05	30.50	91	273	42.60	
	3850	Nailer, pneumatic		.47	31	93	279	22.35	
	3900	Paint sprayers complete, 8 CFM		.94	62.50	187	560	44.90	
	4000	17 CFM		1.57	104	313	940	75.15	
	4020	Pavers, bituminous, rubber tires, 8' wide, 50 H.P., diesel		31.85	500	1,500	4,500	554.80	
	4030	10' wide, 150 H.P.		107.95	1,825	5,460	16,400	1,956	
	4050	Crawler, 8' wide, 100 H.P., diesel		90.45	1,825	5,500	16,500	1,824	
	4060	10' wide, 150 H.P.		115.10	2,250	6,715	20,100	2,264	
	4070	Concrete paver, 12' to 24' wide, 250 H.P.		102.05	1,525	4,600	13,800	1,736	
	4080	Placer-spreader-trimmer, 24' wide, 300 H.P.		147.05	2,475	7,405	22,200	2,657	
	4100	Pump, centrifugal gas pump, 1-1/2" diam., 65 GPM		3.95	50	150	450	61.60	
	4200	2" diameter, 130 GPM		5.30	55	165	495	75.40	
	4300	3" diameter, 250 GPM		5.60	56.50	170	510	78.80	
	4400	6" diameter, 1500 GPM		29.35	177	530	1,600	340.80	
	4500	Submersible electric pump, 1-1/4" diameter, 55 GPM		.38	16.65	50	150	13.05	
	4600	1-1/2" diameter, 83 GPM		.42	19	57	171	14.75	
	4700	2" diameter, 120 GPM		1.43	23.50	71	213	25.65	
	4800	3" diameter, 300 GPM		2.55	41.50	125	375	45.40	
	4900	4" diameter, 560 GPM		10.65	160	480	1,450	181.20	
	5000	6" diameter, 1590 GPM		15.75	215	645	1,925	255	
	5100	Diaphragm pump, gas, single, 1-1/2" diameter		1.18	50.50	152	455	39.85	
	5200	2" diameter		4.25	63.50	190	570	72	
	5300	3" diameter		4.25	63.50	190	570	72	
	5400	Double, 4" diameter		6.35	108	325	975	115.80	
	5450	Pressure washer 5 GPM, 3000 psi		4.80	51.50	155	465	69.40	

01 54 33 | Equipment Rental

		UNIT	HOURLY OPER. COST	RENT PER DAY	RENT PER WEEK	RENT PER MONTH	EQUIPMENT COST/DAY	
40	5460	7 GPM, 3000 psi	Ea.	6.25	60	180	540	86	**40**
	5500	Trash pump, self-priming, gas, 2″ diameter		4.50	21.50	64	192	48.80	
	5600	Diesel, 4″ diameter		9.30	90	270	810	128.40	
	5650	Diesel, 6″ diameter		25.55	150	450	1,350	294.40	
	5655	Grout Pump		26.80	260	780	2,350	370.40	
	5700	Salamanders, L.P. gas fired, 100,000 Btu		3.81	13.65	41	123	38.70	
	5705	50,000 Btu		2.39	10.35	31	93	25.30	
	5720	Sandblaster, portable, open top, 3 C.F. capacity		.55	26.50	80	240	20.40	
	5730	6 C.F. capacity		.95	40	120	360	31.60	
	5740	Accessories for above		.13	21.50	64	192	13.85	
	5750	Sander, floor		.71	17	51	153	15.90	
	5760	Edger		.57	18.35	55	165	15.55	
	5800	Saw, chain, gas engine, 18″ long		2.25	22	66	198	31.20	
	5900	Hydraulic powered, 36″ long		.75	65	195	585	45	
	5950	60″ long		.75	66.50	200	600	46	
	6000	Masonry, table mounted, 14″ diameter, 5 H.P.		1.31	56.50	170	510	44.50	
	6050	Portable cut-off, 8 H.P.		2.40	33.50	100	300	39.20	
	6100	Circular, hand held, electric, 7-1/4″ diameter		.22	4.67	14	42	4.55	
	6200	12″ diameter		.22	8	24	72	6.55	
	6250	Wall saw, w/hydraulic power, 10 H.P.		10.45	60	180	540	119.60	
	6275	Shot blaster, walk-behind, 20″ wide		4.80	293	880	2,650	214.40	
	6280	Sidewalk broom, walk-behind		2.32	70	210	630	60.55	
	6300	Steam cleaner, 100 gallons per hour		3.70	76.50	230	690	75.60	
	6310	200 gallons per hour		5.25	95	285	855	99	
	6340	Tar Kettle/Pot, 400 gallons		10.50	76.50	230	690	130	
	6350	Torch, cutting, acetylene-oxygen, 150′ hose, excludes gases		.30	15	45	135	11.40	
	6360	Hourly operating cost includes tips and gas		19.00				152	
	6410	Toilet, portable chemical		.12	20.50	62	186	13.35	
	6420	Recycle flush type		.15	24.50	74	222	16	
	6430	Toilet, fresh water flush, garden hose,		.18	29.50	89	267	19.25	
	6440	Hoisted, non-flush, for high rise		.15	24.50	73	219	15.80	
	6465	Tractor, farm with attachment		21.90	277	830	2,500	341.20	
	6500	Trailers, platform, flush deck, 2 axle, 25 ton capacity		5.45	117	350	1,050	113.60	
	6600	40 ton capacity		7.00	160	480	1,450	152	
	6700	3 axle, 50 ton capacity		7.55	177	530	1,600	166.40	
	6800	75 ton capacity		9.35	232	695	2,075	213.80	
	6810	Trailer mounted cable reel for high voltage line work		5.35	255	764	2,300	195.60	
	6820	Trailer mounted cable tensioning rig		10.64	505	1,520	4,550	389.10	
	6830	Cable pulling rig		71.33	2,825	8,510	25,500	2,273	
	6900	Water tank trailer, engine driven discharge, 5000 gallons		6.95	143	430	1,300	141.60	
	6925	10,000 gallons		9.50	198	595	1,775	195	
	6950	Water truck, off highway, 6000 gallons		89.80	775	2,330	7,000	1,184	
	7010	Tram car for high voltage line work, powered, 2 conductor		6.27	138	415	1,250	133.15	
	7020	Transit (builder's level) with tripod		.10	16.65	50	150	10.80	
	7030	Trench box, 3000 lb., 6′ x 8′		.56	93.50	280	840	60.50	
	7040	7200 lb., 6′ x 20′		.78	130	389	1,175	84.05	
	7050	8000 lb., 8′ x 16′		1.08	180	540	1,625	116.65	
	7060	9500 lb., 8′ x 20′		1.21	201	603	1,800	130.30	
	7065	11,000 lb., 8′ x 24′		1.27	211	633	1,900	136.75	
	7070	12,000 lb., 10′ x 20′		1.36	227	680	2,050	146.90	
	7100	Truck, pickup, 3/4 ton, 2 wheel drive		15.25	58.50	175	525	157	
	7200	4 wheel drive		15.55	73.50	220	660	168.40	
	7250	Crew carrier, 9 passenger		21.60	86.50	260	780	224.80	
	7290	Flat bed truck, 20,000 lb. GVW		22.30	125	375	1,125	253.40	
	7300	Tractor, 4 x 2, 220 H.P.		31.05	197	590	1,775	366.40	
	7410	330 H.P.		46.05	272	815	2,450	531.40	
	7500	6 x 4, 380 H.P.		52.85	315	950	2,850	612.80	
	7600	450 H.P.		64.05	385	1,150	3,450	742.40	

01 54 33 | Equipment Rental

			UNIT	HOURLY OPER. COST	RENT PER DAY	RENT PER WEEK	RENT PER MONTH	EQUIPMENT COST/DAY	
40	7610	Tractor, with A frame, boom and winch, 225 H.P.	Ea.	33.95	272	815	2,450	434.60	40
	7620	Vacuum truck, hazardous material, 2500 gallons		12.00	292	875	2,625	271	
	7625	5,000 gallons		14.27	410	1,230	3,700	360.15	
	7650	Vacuum, HEPA, 16 gallon, wet/dry		.83	18	54	162	17.45	
	7655	55 gallon, wet/dry		.77	27	81	243	22.35	
	7660	Water tank, portable		.16	26.50	80	240	17.30	
	7690	Sewer/catch basin vacuum, 14 C.Y., 1500 gallons		18.61	615	1,850	5,550	518.90	
	7700	Welder, electric, 200 amp		3.64	16.35	49	147	38.90	
	7800	300 amp		5.41	20	60	180	55.30	
	7900	Gas engine, 200 amp		13.90	23.50	70	210	125.20	
	8000	300 amp		15.90	24.50	74	222	142	
	8100	Wheelbarrow, any size		.08	13	39	117	8.45	
	8200	Wrecking ball, 4000 lb.	▼	2.30	68.50	205	615	59.40	
50	0010	**HIGHWAY EQUIPMENT RENTAL** without operators							50
	0050	Asphalt batch plant, portable drum mixer, 100 ton/hr.	Ea.	79.15	1,450	4,320	13,000	1,497	
	0060	200 ton/hr.		90.32	1,525	4,590	13,800	1,641	
	0070	300 ton/hr.		107.39	1,800	5,390	16,200	1,937	
	0100	Backhoe attachment, long stick, up to 185 H.P., 10.5' long		.35	23	69	207	16.60	
	0140	Up to 250 H.P., 12' long		.37	24.50	74	222	17.75	
	0180	Over 250 H.P., 15' long		.52	34.50	103	310	24.75	
	0200	Special dipper arm, up to 100 H.P., 32' long		1.06	70.50	211	635	50.70	
	0240	Over 100 H.P., 33' long		1.32	87.50	263	790	63.15	
	0280	Catch basin/sewer cleaning truck, 3 ton, 9 C.Y., 1000 gal.		46.25	390	1,170	3,500	604	
	0300	Concrete batch plant, portable, electric, 200 C.Y./hr.		22.08	510	1,525	4,575	481.65	
	0520	Grader/dozer attachment, ripper/scarifier, rear mounted, up to 135 H.P.		3.45	65	195	585	66.60	
	0540	Up to 180 H.P.		4.05	81.50	245	735	81.40	
	0580	Up to 250 H.P.		4.45	93.50	280	840	91.60	
	0700	Pvmt. removal bucket, for hyd. excavator, up to 90 H.P.		1.90	51.50	155	465	46.20	
	0740	Up to 200 H.P.		2.10	73.50	220	660	60.80	
	0780	Over 200 H.P.		2.25	85	255	765	69	
	0900	Aggregate spreader, self-propelled, 187 H.P.		53.75	685	2,055	6,175	841	
	1000	Chemical spreader, 3 C.Y.		3.40	43.50	130	390	53.20	
	1900	Hammermill, traveling, 250 H.P.		77.73	2,050	6,120	18,400	1,846	
	2000	Horizontal borer, 3" diameter, 13 H.P. gas driven		6.25	55	165	495	83	
	2150	Horizontal directional drill, 20,000 lb. thrust, 78 H.P. diesel		31.55	675	2,030	6,100	658.40	
	2160	30,000 lb. thrust, 115 H.P.		39.40	1,025	3,105	9,325	936.20	
	2170	50,000 lb. thrust, 170 H.P.		56.45	1,325	3,970	11,900	1,246	
	2190	Mud trailer for HDD, 1500 gallons, 175 H.P., gas		35.35	153	460	1,375	374.80	
	2200	Hydromulcher, diesel, 3000 gallon, for truck mounting		24.05	247	740	2,225	340.40	
	2300	Gas, 600 gallon		9.20	98.50	295	885	132.60	
	2400	Joint & crack cleaner, walk behind, 25 H.P.		4.35	50	150	450	64.80	
	2500	Filler, trailer mounted, 400 gallons, 20 H.P.		9.60	212	635	1,900	203.80	
	3000	Paint striper, self-propelled, 40 gallon, 22 H.P.		7.60	157	470	1,400	154.80	
	3100	120 gallon, 120 H.P.		24.80	400	1,195	3,575	437.40	
	3200	Post drivers, 6" I-Beam frame, for truck mounting		19.65	380	1,145	3,425	386.20	
	3400	Road sweeper, self-propelled, 8' wide, 90 H.P.		40.30	570	1,715	5,150	665.40	
	3450	Road sweeper, vacuum assisted, 4 C.Y., 220 gallons		77.55	625	1,870	5,600	994.40	
	4000	Road mixer, self-propelled, 130 H.P.		47.80	775	2,320	6,950	846.40	
	4100	310 H.P.		84.40	2,100	6,335	19,000	1,942	
	4220	Cold mix paver, incl. pug mill and bitumen tank, 165 H.P.		98.80	2,325	6,965	20,900	2,183	
	4240	Pavement brush, towed		3.20	93.50	280	840	81.60	
	4250	Paver, asphalt, wheel or crawler, 130 H.P., diesel		98.45	2,300	6,905	20,700	2,169	
	4300	Paver, road widener, gas 1' to 6', 67 H.P.		49.40	905	2,715	8,150	938.20	
	4400	Diesel, 2' to 14', 88 H.P.		63.70	1,050	3,170	9,500	1,144	
	4600	Slipform pavers, curb and gutter, 2 track, 75 H.P.		52.00	805	2,410	7,225	898	
	4700	4 track, 165 H.P.		41.65	730	2,185	6,550	770.20	
	4800	Median barrier, 215 H.P.	▼	54.00	890	2,670	8,000	966	

R015433 -10

01 54 33 | Equipment Rental

			UNIT	HOURLY OPER. COST	RENT PER DAY	RENT PER WEEK	RENT PER MONTH	EQUIPMENT COST/DAY	
50	4901	Trailer, low bed, 75 ton capacity	Ea.	10.10	232	695	2,075	219.80	50
	5000	Road planer, walk behind, 10" cutting width, 10 H.P.		4.00	33.50	100	300	52	
	5100	Self-propelled, 12" cutting width, 64 H.P.		11.45	113	340	1,025	159.60	
	5120	Traffic line remover, metal ball blaster, truck mounted, 115 H.P.		48.75	750	2,245	6,725	839	
	5140	Grinder, truck mounted, 115 H.P.		55.45	810	2,435	7,300	930.60	
	5160	Walk-behind, 11 H.P.		4.55	53.50	160	480	68.40	
	5200	Pavement profiler, 4' to 6' wide, 450 H.P.		258.10	3,350	10,045	30,100	4,074	
	5300	8' to 10' wide, 750 H.P.		405.10	4,400	13,180	39,500	5,877	
	5400	Roadway plate, steel, 1" x 8' x 20'		.08	13	39	117	8.45	
	5600	Stabilizer, self-propelled, 150 H.P.		50.10	610	1,835	5,500	767.80	
	5700	310 H.P.		100.25	1,700	5,125	15,400	1,827	
	5800	Striper, truck mounted, 120 gallon paint, 460 H.P.		71.05	485	1,460	4,375	860.40	
	5900	Thermal paint heating kettle, 115 gallons		5.95	25.50	77	231	63	
	6000	Tar kettle, 330 gallon, trailer mounted		8.70	58.50	175	525	104.60	
	7000	Tunnel locomotive, diesel, 8 to 12 ton		32.40	585	1,760	5,275	611.20	
	7005	Electric, 10 ton		26.55	670	2,010	6,025	614.40	
	7010	Muck cars, 1/2 C.Y. capacity		2.05	24.50	74	222	31.20	
	7020	1 C.Y. capacity		2.30	32.50	98	294	38	
	7030	2 C.Y. capacity		2.45	36.50	110	330	41.60	
	7040	Side dump, 2 C.Y. capacity		2.65	45	135	405	48.20	
	7050	3 C.Y. capacity		3.55	51.50	155	465	59.40	
	7060	5 C.Y. capacity		5.10	65	195	585	79.80	
	7100	Ventilating blower for tunnel, 7-1/2 H.P.		2.05	51.50	155	465	47.40	
	7110	10 H.P.		2.22	53.50	160	480	49.75	
	7120	20 H.P.		3.43	69.50	208	625	69.05	
	7140	40 H.P.		5.59	98.50	295	885	103.70	
	7160	60 H.P.		8.54	152	455	1,375	159.30	
	7175	75 H.P.		11.25	207	620	1,850	214	
	7180	200 H.P.		22.56	305	910	2,725	362.50	
	7800	Windrow loader, elevating		55.95	1,325	3,960	11,900	1,240	
60	0010	**LIFTING AND HOISTING EQUIPMENT RENTAL** without operators [R015433-10]							60
	0120	Aerial lift truck, 2 person, to 80'	Ea.	26.75	715	2,145	6,425	643	
	0140	Boom work platform, 40' snorkel [R015433-15]		16.10	277	830	2,500	294.80	
	0150	Crane, flatbed mounted, 3 ton capacity		16.55	193	580	1,750	248.40	
	0200	Crane, climbing, 106' jib, 6000 lb. capacity, 410 fpm [R312316-45]		37.76	1,625	4,860	14,600	1,274	
	0300	101' jib, 10,250 lb. capacity, 270 fpm		44.26	2,050	6,160	18,500	1,586	
	0500	Tower, static, 130' high, 106' jib, 6200 lb. capacity at 400 fpm		41.56	1,875	5,620	16,900	1,456	
	0600	Crawler mounted, lattice boom, 1/2 C.Y., 15 tons at 12' radius		37.52	640	1,920	5,750	684.15	
	0700	3/4 C.Y., 20 tons at 12' radius		50.03	800	2,400	7,200	880.25	
	0800	1 C.Y., 25 tons at 12' radius		66.70	1,075	3,195	9,575	1,173	
	0900	1-1/2 C.Y., 40 tons at 12' radius		66.70	1,075	3,225	9,675	1,179	
	1000	2 C.Y., 50 tons at 12' radius		70.70	1,250	3,765	11,300	1,319	
	1100	3 C.Y., 75 tons at 12' radius		75.65	1,475	4,435	13,300	1,492	
	1200	100 ton capacity, 60' boom		85.65	1,700	5,090	15,300	1,703	
	1300	165 ton capacity, 60' boom		109.15	2,000	5,980	17,900	2,069	
	1400	200 ton capacity, 70' boom		132.10	2,500	7,480	22,400	2,553	
	1500	350 ton capacity, 80' boom		184.60	3,725	11,210	33,600	3,719	
	1600	Truck mounted, lattice boom, 6 x 4, 20 tons at 10' radius		37.31	1,100	3,310	9,925	960.50	
	1700	25 tons at 10' radius		40.35	1,200	3,610	10,800	1,045	
	1800	8 x 4, 30 tons at 10' radius		43.85	1,275	3,840	11,500	1,119	
	1900	40 tons at 12' radius		46.92	1,325	4,010	12,000	1,177	
	2000	60 tons at 15' radius		53.24	1,425	4,240	12,700	1,274	
	2050	82 tons at 15' radius		60.06	1,525	4,540	13,600	1,388	
	2100	90 tons at 15' radius		67.57	1,650	4,940	14,800	1,529	
	2200	115 tons at 15' radius		76.34	1,850	5,520	16,600	1,715	
	2300	150 tons at 18' radius		84.40	1,950	5,815	17,400	1,838	
	2350	165 tons at 18' radius		90.25	2,050	6,160	18,500	1,954	
	2400	Truck mounted, hydraulic, 12 ton capacity		43.00	530	1,595	4,775	663	

01 54 33 | Equipment Rental

			UNIT	HOURLY OPER. COST	RENT PER DAY	RENT PER WEEK	RENT PER MONTH	EQUIPMENT COST/DAY	
60	2500	25 ton capacity	Ea.	45.35	640	1,915	5,750	745.80	60
	2550	33 ton capacity		45.90	655	1,960	5,875	759.20	
	2560	40 ton capacity		59.35	765	2,290	6,875	932.80	
	2600	55 ton capacity		77.50	860	2,585	7,750	1,137	
	2700	80 ton capacity		101.35	1,400	4,205	12,600	1,652	
	2720	100 ton capacity		94.95	1,450	4,325	13,000	1,625	
	2740	120 ton capacity		109.95	1,550	4,665	14,000	1,813	
	2760	150 ton capacity		128.55	2,050	6,135	18,400	2,255	
	2800	Self-propelled, 4 x 4, with telescoping boom, 5 ton		17.75	230	690	2,075	280	
	2900	12-1/2 ton capacity		32.65	365	1,100	3,300	481.20	
	3000	15 ton capacity		33.35	385	1,160	3,475	498.80	
	3050	20 ton capacity		36.30	450	1,350	4,050	560.40	
	3100	25 ton capacity		37.90	505	1,520	4,550	607.20	
	3150	40 ton capacity		46.50	570	1,705	5,125	713	
	3200	Derricks, guy, 20 ton capacity, 60' boom, 75' mast		27.18	395	1,190	3,575	455.45	
	3300	100' boom, 115' mast		42.63	685	2,050	6,150	751.05	
	3400	Stiffleg, 20 ton capacity, 70' boom, 37' mast		29.70	515	1,550	4,650	547.60	
	3500	100' boom, 47' mast		45.64	825	2,480	7,450	861.10	
	3550	Helicopter, small, lift to 1250 lb. maximum, w/pilot		100.87	3,200	9,610	28,800	2,729	
	3600	Hoists, chain type, overhead, manual, 3/4 ton		.10	.33	1	3	1	
	3900	10 ton		.75	6	18	54	9.60	
	4000	Hoist and tower, 5000 lb. cap., portable electric, 40' high		4.77	228	685	2,050	175.15	
	4100	For each added 10' section, add		.11	18	54	162	11.70	
	4200	Hoist and single tubular tower, 5000 lb. electric, 100' high		6.47	320	957	2,875	243.15	
	4300	For each added 6'-6" section, add		.19	31	93	279	20.10	
	4400	Hoist and double tubular tower, 5000 lb., 100' high		6.95	350	1,054	3,150	266.40	
	4500	For each added 6'-6" section, add		.21	34.50	103	310	22.30	
	4550	Hoist and tower, mast type, 6000 lb., 100' high		7.48	365	1,093	3,275	278.45	
	4570	For each added 10' section, add		.13	21.50	64	192	13.85	
	4600	Hoist and tower, personnel, electric, 2000 lb., 100' @ 125 fpm		15.90	970	2,910	8,725	709.20	
	4700	3000 lb., 100' @ 200 fpm		18.13	1,100	3,290	9,875	803.05	
	4800	3000 lb., 150' @ 300 fpm		20.13	1,225	3,690	11,100	899.05	
	4900	4000 lb., 100' @ 300 fpm		20.82	1,250	3,760	11,300	918.55	
	5000	6000 lb., 100' @ 275 fpm	▼	22.44	1,325	3,950	11,900	969.50	
	5100	For added heights up to 500', add	L.F.	.01	1.67	5	15	1.10	
	5200	Jacks, hydraulic, 20 ton	Ea.	.05	2	6	18	1.60	
	5500	100 ton		.40	11.65	35	105	10.20	
	6100	Jacks, hydraulic, climbing w/50' jackrods, control console, 30 ton cap.		1.97	131	394	1,175	94.55	
	6150	For each added 10' jackrod section, add		.05	3.33	10	30	2.40	
	6300	50 ton capacity		3.17	211	633	1,900	151.95	
	6350	For each added 10' jackrod section, add		.06	4	12	36	2.90	
	6500	125 ton capacity		8.30	555	1,660	4,975	398.40	
	6550	For each added 10' jackrod section, add		.57	37.50	113	340	27.15	
	6600	Cable jack, 10 ton capacity with 200' cable		1.65	110	329	985	79	
	6650	For each added 50' of cable, add	▼	.20	13	39	117	9.40	
70	0010	**WELLPOINT EQUIPMENT RENTAL** without operators							70
	0020	Based on 2 months rental							
	0100	Combination jetting & wellpoint pump, 60 H.P. diesel	Ea.	18.14	325	976	2,925	340.30	
	0200	High pressure gas jet pump, 200 H.P., 300 psi	"	43.54	278	834	2,500	515.10	
	0300	Discharge pipe, 8" diameter	L.F.	.01	.53	1.59	4.77	.40	
	0350	12" diameter		.01	.78	2.33	7	.55	
	0400	Header pipe, flows up to 150 GPM, 4" diameter		.01	.48	1.44	4.32	.35	
	0500	400 GPM, 6" diameter		.01	.56	1.69	5.05	.40	
	0600	800 GPM, 8" diameter		.01	.78	2.33	7	.55	
	0700	1500 GPM, 10" diameter		.01	.82	2.46	7.40	.55	
	0800	2500 GPM, 12" diameter		.02	1.55	4.65	13.95	1.10	
	0900	4500 GPM, 16" diameter	▼	.03	1.98	5.95	17.85	1.45	

Note in row 0010: R015433 -10

01 54 33 | Equipment Rental

			UNIT	HOURLY OPER. COST	RENT PER DAY	RENT PER WEEK	RENT PER MONTH	EQUIPMENT COST/DAY	
70	0950	For quick coupling aluminum and plastic pipe, add	L.F.	.03	2.05	6.16	18.50	1.45	70
	1100	Wellpoint, 25' long, with fittings & riser pipe, 1-1/2" or 2" diameter		.06	4.10	12.29	37	2.95	
	1200	Wellpoint pump, diesel powered, 4" suction, 20 H.P.		7.71	188	563	1,700	174.30	
	1300	6" suction, 30 H.P.		10.54	233	698	2,100	223.90	
	1400	8" suction, 40 H.P.		14.24	320	957	2,875	305.30	
	1500	10" suction, 75 H.P.		21.97	375	1,119	3,350	399.55	
	1600	12" suction, 100 H.P.		31.24	590	1,770	5,300	603.90	
	1700	12" suction, 175 H.P.		46.78	655	1,970	5,900	768.25	
80	0010	**MARINE EQUIPMENT RENTAL** without operators	R015433 -10						80
	0200	Barge, 400 Ton, 30' wide x 90' long	Ea.	17.50	1,075	3,205	9,625	781	
	0240	800 Ton, 45' wide x 90' long		21.20	1,300	3,900	11,700	949.60	
	2000	Tugboat, diesel, 100 H.P.		38.95	217	650	1,950	441.60	
	2040	250 H.P.		81.55	395	1,185	3,550	889.40	
	2080	380 H.P.		160.00	1,175	3,545	10,600	1,989	
	3000	Small work boat, gas, 16-foot, 50 H.P.		19.15	60	180	540	189.20	
	4000	Large, diesel, 48-foot, 200 H.P.		90.80	1,250	3,745	11,200	1,475	

Crew No.	Bare Costs		Incl. Subs O&P		Cost Per Labor-Hour	
Crew A-1	Hr.	Daily	Hr.	Daily	Bare Costs	Incl. O&P
1 Building Laborer	$23.80	$190.40	$40.05	$320.40	$23.80	$40.05
1 Concrete Saw, Gas Manual		84.00		92.40	10.50	11.55
8 L.H., Daily Totals		$274.40		$412.80	$34.30	$51.60
Crew A-1A	Hr.	Daily	Hr.	Daily	Bare Costs	Incl. O&P
1 Skilled Worker	$32.45	$259.60	$54.80	$438.40	$32.45	$54.80
1 Shot Blaster, 20"		214.40		235.84	26.80	29.48
8 L.H., Daily Totals		$474.00		$674.24	$59.25	$84.28
Crew A-1B	Hr.	Daily	Hr.	Daily	Bare Costs	Incl. O&P
1 Building Laborer	$23.80	$190.40	$40.05	$320.40	$23.80	$40.05
1 Concrete Saw		175.20		192.72	21.90	24.09
8 L.H., Daily Totals		$365.60		$513.12	$45.70	$64.14
Crew A-1C	Hr.	Daily	Hr.	Daily	Bare Costs	Incl. O&P
1 Building Laborer	$23.80	$190.40	$40.05	$320.40	$23.80	$40.05
1 Chain Saw, Gas, 18"		31.20		34.32	3.90	4.29
8 L.H., Daily Totals		$221.60		$354.72	$27.70	$44.34
Crew A-1D	Hr.	Daily	Hr.	Daily	Bare Costs	Incl. O&P
1 Building Laborer	$23.80	$190.40	$40.05	$320.40	$23.80	$40.05
1 Vibrating Plate, Gas, 18"		35.80		39.38	4.47	4.92
8 L.H., Daily Totals		$226.20		$359.78	$28.27	$44.97
Crew A-1E	Hr.	Daily	Hr.	Daily	Bare Costs	Incl. O&P
1 Building Laborer	$23.80	$190.40	$40.05	$320.40	$23.80	$40.05
1 Vibrating Plate, Gas, 21"		46.00		50.60	5.75	6.33
8 L.H., Daily Totals		$236.40		$371.00	$29.55	$46.38
Crew A-1F	Hr.	Daily	Hr.	Daily	Bare Costs	Incl. O&P
1 Building Laborer	$23.80	$190.40	$40.05	$320.40	$23.80	$40.05
1 Rammer/Tamper, Gas, 8"		49.60		54.56	6.20	6.82
8 L.H., Daily Totals		$240.00		$374.96	$30.00	$46.87
Crew A-1G	Hr.	Daily	Hr.	Daily	Bare Costs	Incl. O&P
1 Building Laborer	$23.80	$190.40	$40.05	$320.40	$23.80	$40.05
1 Rammer/Tamper, Gas, 15"		56.00		61.60	7.00	7.70
8 L.H., Daily Totals		$246.40		$382.00	$30.80	$47.75
Crew A-1H	Hr.	Daily	Hr.	Daily	Bare Costs	Incl. O&P
1 Building Laborer	$23.80	$190.40	$40.05	$320.40	$23.80	$40.05
1 Exterior Steam Cleaner		75.60		83.16	9.45	10.40
8 L.H., Daily Totals		$266.00		$403.56	$33.25	$50.45
Crew A-1J	Hr.	Daily	Hr.	Daily	Bare Costs	Incl. O&P
1 Building Laborer	$23.80	$190.40	$40.05	$320.40	$23.80	$40.05
1 Cultivator, Walk-Behind, 5 H.P.		57.45		63.20	7.18	7.90
8 L.H., Daily Totals		$247.85		$383.60	$30.98	$47.95
Crew A-1K	Hr.	Daily	Hr.	Daily	Bare Costs	Incl. O&P
1 Building Laborer	$23.80	$190.40	$40.05	$320.40	$23.80	$40.05
1 Cultivator, Walk-Behind, 8 H.P.		81.40		89.54	10.18	11.19
8 L.H., Daily Totals		$271.80		$409.94	$33.98	$51.24
Crew A-1M	Hr.	Daily	Hr.	Daily	Bare Costs	Incl. O&P
1 Building Laborer	$23.80	$190.40	$40.05	$320.40	$23.80	$40.05
1 Snow Blower, Walk-Behind		60.55		66.61	7.57	8.33
8 L.H., Daily Totals		$250.95		$387.01	$31.37	$48.38

Crew No.	Bare Costs		Incl. Subs O&P		Cost Per Labor-Hour	
Crew A-2	Hr.	Daily	Hr.	Daily	Bare Costs	Incl. O&P
2 Laborers	$23.80	$380.80	$40.05	$640.80	$24.50	$41.08
1 Truck Driver (light)	25.90	207.20	43.15	345.20		
1 Flatbed Truck, Gas, 1.5 Ton		270.20		297.22	11.26	12.38
24 L.H., Daily Totals		$858.20		$1283.22	$35.76	$53.47
Crew A-2A	Hr.	Daily	Hr.	Daily	Bare Costs	Incl. O&P
2 Laborers	$23.80	$380.80	$40.05	$640.80	$24.50	$41.08
1 Truck Driver (light)	25.90	207.20	43.15	345.20		
1 Flatbed Truck, Gas, 1.5 Ton		270.20		297.22		
1 Concrete Saw		175.20		192.72	18.56	20.41
24 L.H., Daily Totals		$1033.40		$1475.94	$43.06	$61.50
Crew A-2B	Hr.	Daily	Hr.	Daily	Bare Costs	Incl. O&P
1 Truck Driver (light)	$25.90	$207.20	$43.15	$345.20	$25.90	$43.15
1 Flatbed Truck, Gas, 1.5 Ton		270.20		297.22	33.77	37.15
8 L.H., Daily Totals		$477.40		$642.42	$59.67	$80.30
Crew A-3A	Hr.	Daily	Hr.	Daily	Bare Costs	Incl. O&P
1 Truck Driver (light)	$25.90	$207.20	$43.15	$345.20	$25.90	$43.15
1 Pickup Truck, 4 x 4, 3/4 Ton		168.40		185.24	21.05	23.16
8 L.H., Daily Totals		$375.60		$530.44	$46.95	$66.31
Crew A-3B	Hr.	Daily	Hr.	Daily	Bare Costs	Incl. O&P
1 Equip. Oper. (medium)	$33.75	$270.00	$55.90	$447.20	$30.20	$50.15
1 Truck Driver (heavy)	26.65	213.20	44.40	355.20		
1 Dump Truck, 12 C.Y., 400 H.P.		692.20		761.42		
1 F.E. Loader, W.M.,2.5 C.Y.		522.80		575.08	75.94	83.53
16 L.H., Daily Totals		$1698.20		$2138.90	$106.14	$133.68
Crew A-3C	Hr.	Daily	Hr.	Daily	Bare Costs	Incl. O&P
1 Equip. Oper. (light)	$32.45	$259.60	$53.75	$430.00	$32.45	$53.75
1 Loader, Skid Steer, 78 H.P.		308.80		339.68	38.60	42.46
8 L.H., Daily Totals		$568.40		$769.68	$71.05	$96.21
Crew A-3D	Hr.	Daily	Hr.	Daily	Bare Costs	Incl. O&P
1 Truck Driver (light)	$25.90	$207.20	$43.15	$345.20	$25.90	$43.15
1 Pickup Truck, 4 x 4, 3/4 Ton		168.40		185.24		
1 Flatbed Trailer, 25 Ton		113.60		124.96	35.25	38.77
8 L.H., Daily Totals		$489.20		$655.40	$61.15	$81.92
Crew A-3E	Hr.	Daily	Hr.	Daily	Bare Costs	Incl. O&P
1 Equip. Oper. (crane)	$34.65	$277.20	$57.40	$459.20	$30.65	$50.90
1 Truck Driver (heavy)	26.65	213.20	44.40	355.20		
1 Pickup Truck, 4 x 4, 3/4 Ton		168.40		185.24	10.53	11.58
16 L.H., Daily Totals		$658.80		$999.64	$41.17	$62.48
Crew A-3F	Hr.	Daily	Hr.	Daily	Bare Costs	Incl. O&P
1 Equip. Oper. (crane)	$34.65	$277.20	$57.40	$459.20	$30.65	$50.90
1 Truck Driver (heavy)	26.65	213.20	44.40	355.20		
1 Pickup Truck, 4 x 4, 3/4 Ton		168.40		185.24		
1 Truck Tractor, 6x4, 380 H.P.		612.80		674.08		
1 Lowbed Trailer, 75 Ton		219.80		241.78	62.56	68.82
16 L.H., Daily Totals		$1491.40		$1915.50	$93.21	$119.72

Crews

Crew No.	Bare Costs Hr.	Daily	Incl. Subs O&P Hr.	Daily	Cost Per Labor-Hour Bare Costs	Incl. O&P
Crew A-3G	**Hr.**	**Daily**	**Hr.**	**Daily**	**Bare Costs**	**Incl. O&P**
1 Equip. Oper. (crane)	$34.65	$277.20	$57.40	$459.20	$30.65	$50.90
1 Truck Driver (heavy)	26.65	213.20	44.40	355.20		
1 Pickup Truck, 4 x 4, 3/4 Ton		168.40		185.24		
1 Truck Tractor, 6x4, 450 H.P.		742.40		816.64		
1 Lowbed Trailer, 75 Ton		219.80		241.78	70.66	77.73
16 L.H., Daily Totals		$1621.00		$2058.06	$101.31	$128.63
Crew A-3H	**Hr.**	**Daily**	**Hr.**	**Daily**	**Bare Costs**	**Incl. O&P**
1 Equip. Oper. (crane)	$34.65	$277.20	$57.40	$459.20	$34.65	$57.40
1 Hyd. Crane, 12 Ton (Daily)		874.00		961.40	109.25	120.18
8 L.H., Daily Totals		$1151.20		$1420.60	$143.90	$177.57
Crew A-3I	**Hr.**	**Daily**	**Hr.**	**Daily**	**Bare Costs**	**Incl. O&P**
1 Equip. Oper. (crane)	$34.65	$277.20	$57.40	$459.20	$34.65	$57.40
1 Hyd. Crane, 25 Ton (Daily)		1003.00		1103.30	125.38	137.91
8 L.H., Daily Totals		$1280.20		$1562.50	$160.03	$195.31
Crew A-3J	**Hr.**	**Daily**	**Hr.**	**Daily**	**Bare Costs**	**Incl. O&P**
1 Equip. Oper. (crane)	$34.65	$277.20	$57.40	$459.20	$34.65	$57.40
1 Hyd. Crane, 40 Ton (Daily)		1240.00		1364.00	155.00	170.50
8 L.H., Daily Totals		$1517.20		$1823.20	$189.65	$227.90
Crew A-3K	**Hr.**	**Daily**	**Hr.**	**Daily**	**Bare Costs**	**Incl. O&P**
1 Equip. Oper. (crane)	$34.65	$277.20	$57.40	$459.20	$32.35	$53.58
1 Equip. Oper. (oiler)	30.05	240.40	49.75	398.00		
1 Hyd. Crane, 55 Ton (Daily)		1480.00		1628.00		
1 P/U Truck, 3/4 Ton (Daily)		182.00		200.20	103.88	114.26
16 L.H., Daily Totals		$2179.60		$2685.40	$136.22	$167.84
Crew A-3L	**Hr.**	**Daily**	**Hr.**	**Daily**	**Bare Costs**	**Incl. O&P**
1 Equip. Oper. (crane)	$34.65	$277.20	$57.40	$459.20	$32.35	$53.58
1 Equip. Oper. (oiler)	30.05	240.40	49.75	398.00		
1 Hyd. Crane, 80 Ton (Daily)		2211.00		2432.10		
1 P/U Truck, 3/4 Ton (Daily)		182.00		200.20	149.56	164.52
16 L.H., Daily Totals		$2910.60		$3489.50	$181.91	$218.09
Crew A-3M	**Hr.**	**Daily**	**Hr.**	**Daily**	**Bare Costs**	**Incl. O&P**
1 Equip. Oper. (crane)	$34.65	$277.20	$57.40	$459.20	$32.35	$53.58
1 Equip. Oper. (oiler)	30.05	240.40	49.75	398.00		
1 Hyd. Crane, 100 Ton (Daily)		2200.00		2420.00		
1 P/U Truck, 3/4 Ton (Daily)		182.00		200.20	148.88	163.76
16 L.H., Daily Totals		$2899.60		$3477.40	$181.22	$217.34
Crew A-3N	**Hr.**	**Daily**	**Hr.**	**Daily**	**Bare Costs**	**Incl. O&P**
1 Equip. Oper. (crane)	$34.65	$277.20	$57.40	$459.20	$34.65	$57.40
1 Tower Cane (monthly)		1100.00		1210.00	137.50	151.25
8 L.H., Daily Totals		$1377.20		$1669.20	$172.15	$208.65
Crew A-3P	**Hr.**	**Daily**	**Hr.**	**Daily**	**Bare Costs**	**Incl. O&P**
1 Equip. Oper. (light)	$32.45	$259.60	$53.75	$430.00	$32.45	$53.75
1 A.T. Forklift, 42' lift		531.60		584.76	66.45	73.09
8 L.H., Daily Totals		$791.20		$1014.76	$98.90	$126.85
Crew A-4	**Hr.**	**Daily**	**Hr.**	**Daily**	**Bare Costs**	**Incl. O&P**
2 Carpenters	$32.10	$513.60	$54.00	$864.00	$30.77	$51.40
1 Painter, Ordinary	28.10	224.80	46.20	369.60		
24 L.H., Daily Totals		$738.40		$1233.60	$30.77	$51.40

Crew No.	Bare Costs Hr.	Daily	Incl. Subs O&P Hr.	Daily	Cost Per Labor-Hour Bare Costs	Incl. O&P
Crew A-5	**Hr.**	**Daily**	**Hr.**	**Daily**	**Bare Costs**	**Incl. O&P**
2 Laborers	$23.80	$380.80	$40.05	$640.80	$24.03	$40.39
.25 Truck Driver (light)	25.90	51.80	43.15	86.30		
.25 Flatbed Truck, Gas, 1.5 Ton		67.55		74.31	3.75	4.13
18 L.H., Daily Totals		$500.15		$801.40	$27.79	$44.52
Crew A-6	**Hr.**	**Daily**	**Hr.**	**Daily**	**Bare Costs**	**Incl. O&P**
1 Instrument Man	$32.45	$259.60	$54.80	$438.40	$31.88	$53.40
1 Rodman/Chainman	31.30	250.40	52.00	416.00		
1 Level, Electronic		71.30		78.43	4.46	4.90
16 L.H., Daily Totals		$581.30		$932.83	$36.33	$58.30
Crew A-7	**Hr.**	**Daily**	**Hr.**	**Daily**	**Bare Costs**	**Incl. O&P**
1 Chief of Party	$39.55	$316.40	$66.35	$530.80	$34.43	$57.72
1 Instrument Man	32.45	259.60	54.80	438.40		
1 Rodman/Chainman	31.30	250.40	52.00	416.00		
1 Level, Electronic		71.30		78.43	2.97	3.27
24 L.H., Daily Totals		$897.70		$1463.63	$37.40	$60.98
Crew A-8	**Hr.**	**Daily**	**Hr.**	**Daily**	**Bare Costs**	**Incl. O&P**
1 Chief of Party	$39.55	$316.40	$66.35	$530.80	$33.65	$56.29
1 Instrument Man	32.45	259.60	54.80	438.40		
2 Rodmen/Chainmen	31.30	500.80	52.00	832.00		
1 Level, Electronic		71.30		78.43	2.23	2.45
32 L.H., Daily Totals		$1148.10		$1879.63	$35.88	$58.74
Crew A-9	**Hr.**	**Daily**	**Hr.**	**Daily**	**Bare Costs**	**Incl. O&P**
1 Asbestos Foreman	$34.25	$274.00	$58.10	$464.80	$33.81	$57.36
7 Asbestos Workers	33.75	1890.00	57.25	3206.00		
64 L.H., Daily Totals		$2164.00		$3670.80	$33.81	$57.36
Crew A-10A	**Hr.**	**Daily**	**Hr.**	**Daily**	**Bare Costs**	**Incl. O&P**
1 Asbestos Foreman	$34.25	$274.00	$58.10	$464.80	$33.92	$57.53
2 Asbestos Workers	33.75	540.00	57.25	916.00		
24 L.H., Daily Totals		$814.00		$1380.80	$33.92	$57.53
Crew A-10B	**Hr.**	**Daily**	**Hr.**	**Daily**	**Bare Costs**	**Incl. O&P**
1 Asbestos Foreman	$34.25	$274.00	$58.10	$464.80	$33.88	$57.46
3 Asbestos Workers	33.75	810.00	57.25	1374.00		
32 L.H., Daily Totals		$1084.00		$1838.80	$33.88	$57.46
Crew A-10C	**Hr.**	**Daily**	**Hr.**	**Daily**	**Bare Costs**	**Incl. O&P**
3 Asbestos Workers	$33.75	$810.00	$57.25	$1374.00	$33.75	$57.25
1 Flatbed Truck, Gas, 1.5 Ton		270.20		297.22	11.26	12.38
24 L.H., Daily Totals		$1080.20		$1671.22	$45.01	$69.63
Crew A-10D	**Hr.**	**Daily**	**Hr.**	**Daily**	**Bare Costs**	**Incl. O&P**
2 Asbestos Workers	$33.75	$540.00	$57.25	$916.00	$33.05	$55.41
1 Equip. Oper. (crane)	34.65	277.20	57.40	459.20		
1 Equip. Oper. (oiler)	30.05	240.40	49.75	398.00		
1 Hydraulic Crane, 33 Ton		759.20		835.12	23.73	26.10
32 L.H., Daily Totals		$1816.80		$2608.32	$56.77	$81.51
Crew A-11	**Hr.**	**Daily**	**Hr.**	**Daily**	**Bare Costs**	**Incl. O&P**
1 Asbestos Foreman	$34.25	$274.00	$58.10	$464.80	$33.81	$57.36
7 Asbestos Workers	33.75	1890.00	57.25	3206.00		
2 Chip. Hammers, 12 Lb., Elec.		40.00		44.00	0.63	0.69
64 L.H., Daily Totals		$2204.00		$3714.80	$34.44	$58.04

Crews

Crew A-12	Hr.	Daily	Hr.	Daily	Bare Costs	Incl. O&P
1 Asbestos Foreman	$34.25	$274.00	$58.10	$464.80	$33.81	$57.36
7 Asbestos Workers	33.75	1890.00	57.25	3206.00		
1 Trk-Mtd Vac, 14 CY, 1500 Gal.		518.90		570.79		
1 Flatbed Truck, 20,000 GVW		253.40		278.74	12.07	13.27
64 L.H., Daily Totals		$2936.30		$4520.33	$45.88	$70.63

Crew A-13	Hr.	Daily	Hr.	Daily	Bare Costs	Incl. O&P
1 Equip. Oper. (light)	$32.45	$259.60	$53.75	$430.00	$32.45	$53.75
1 Trk-Mtd Vac, 14 CY, 1500 Gal.		518.90		570.79		
1 Flatbed Truck, 20,000 GVW		253.40		278.74	96.54	106.19
8 L.H., Daily Totals		$1031.90		$1279.53	$128.99	$159.94

Crew B-1	Hr.	Daily	Hr.	Daily	Bare Costs	Incl. O&P
1 Labor Foreman (outside)	$25.80	$206.40	$43.40	$347.20	$24.47	$41.17
2 Laborers	23.80	380.80	40.05	640.80		
24 L.H., Daily Totals		$587.20		$988.00	$24.47	$41.17

Crew B-1A	Hr.	Daily	Hr.	Daily	Bare Costs	Incl. O&P
1 Labor Foreman (outside)	$25.80	$206.40	$43.40	$347.20	$24.47	$41.17
2 Laborers	23.80	380.80	40.05	640.80		
2 Cutting Torches		22.80		25.08		
2 Sets of Gases		304.00		334.40	13.62	14.98
24 L.H., Daily Totals		$914.00		$1347.48	$38.08	$56.15

Crew B-1B	Hr.	Daily	Hr.	Daily	Bare Costs	Incl. O&P
1 Labor Foreman (outside)	$25.80	$206.40	$43.40	$347.20	$27.01	$45.23
2 Laborers	23.80	380.80	40.05	640.80		
1 Equip. Oper. (crane)	34.65	277.20	57.40	459.20		
2 Cutting Torches		22.80		25.08		
2 Sets of Gases		304.00		334.40		
1 Hyd. Crane, 12 Ton		663.00		729.30	30.93	34.02
32 L.H., Daily Totals		$1854.20		$2535.98	$57.94	$79.25

Crew B-1C	Hr.	Daily	Hr.	Daily	Bare Costs	Incl. O&P
1 Labor Foreman (outside)	$25.80	$206.40	$43.40	$347.20	$24.47	$41.17
2 Laborers	23.80	380.80	40.05	640.80		
1 Aerial Lift Truck, 60' Boom		456.00		501.60	19.00	20.90
24 L.H., Daily Totals		$1043.20		$1489.60	$43.47	$62.07

Crew B-1D	Hr.	Daily	Hr.	Daily	Bare Costs	Incl. O&P
2 Laborers	$23.80	$380.80	$40.05	$640.80	$23.80	$40.05
1 Small Work Boat, Gas, 50 H.P.		189.20		208.12		
1 Pressure Washer, 7 GPM		86.00		94.60	17.20	18.92
16 L.H., Daily Totals		$656.00		$943.52	$41.00	$58.97

Crew B-1E	Hr.	Daily	Hr.	Daily	Bare Costs	Incl. O&P
1 Labor Foreman (outside)	$25.80	$206.40	$43.40	$347.20	$24.30	$40.89
3 Laborers	23.80	571.20	40.05	961.20		
1 Work Boat, Diesel, 200 H.P.		1475.00		1622.50		
2 Pressure Washer, 7 GPM		172.00		189.20	51.47	56.62
32 L.H., Daily Totals		$2424.60		$3120.10	$75.77	$97.50

Crew B-1F	Hr.	Daily	Hr.	Daily	Bare Costs	Incl. O&P
2 Skilled Workers	$32.45	$519.20	$54.80	$876.80	$29.57	$49.88
1 Laborer	23.80	190.40	40.05	320.40		
1 Small Work Boat, Gas, 50 H.P.		189.20		208.12		
1 Pressure Washer, 7 GPM		86.00		94.60	11.47	12.61
24 L.H., Daily Totals		$984.80		$1499.92	$41.03	$62.50

Crew B-1G	Hr.	Daily	Hr.	Daily	Bare Costs	Incl. O&P
2 Laborers	$23.80	$380.80	$40.05	$640.80	$23.80	$40.05
1 Small Work Boat, Gas, 50 H.P.		189.20		208.12	11.82	13.01
16 L.H., Daily Totals		$570.00		$848.92	$35.63	$53.06

Crew B-1H	Hr.	Daily	Hr.	Daily	Bare Costs	Incl. O&P
2 Skilled Workers	$32.45	$519.20	$54.80	$876.80	$29.57	$49.88
1 Laborer	23.80	190.40	40.05	320.40		
1 Small Work Boat, Gas, 50 H.P.		189.20		208.12	7.88	8.67
24 L.H., Daily Totals		$898.80		$1405.32	$37.45	$58.56

Crew B-1J	Hr.	Daily	Hr.	Daily	Bare Costs	Incl. O&P
1 Labor Foreman (inside)	$24.30	$194.40	$40.90	$327.20	$24.05	$40.48
1 Laborer	23.80	190.40	40.05	320.40		
16 L.H., Daily Totals		$384.80		$647.60	$24.05	$40.48

Crew B-1K	Hr.	Daily	Hr.	Daily	Bare Costs	Incl. O&P
1 Carpenter Foreman (inside)	$32.60	$260.80	$54.85	$438.80	$32.35	$54.42
1 Carpenter	32.10	256.80	54.00	432.00		
16 L.H., Daily Totals		$517.60		$870.80	$32.35	$54.42

Crew B-2	Hr.	Daily	Hr.	Daily	Bare Costs	Incl. O&P
1 Labor Foreman (outside)	$25.80	$206.40	$43.40	$347.20	$24.20	$40.72
4 Laborers	23.80	761.60	40.05	1281.60		
40 L.H., Daily Totals		$968.00		$1628.80	$24.20	$40.72

Crew B-2A	Hr.	Daily	Hr.	Daily	Bare Costs	Incl. O&P
1 Labor Foreman (outside)	$25.80	$206.40	$43.40	$347.20	$24.47	$41.17
2 Laborers	23.80	380.80	40.05	640.80		
1 Aerial Lift Truck, 60' Boom		456.00		501.60	19.00	20.90
24 L.H., Daily Totals		$1043.20		$1489.60	$43.47	$62.07

Crew B-3	Hr.	Daily	Hr.	Daily	Bare Costs	Incl. O&P
1 Labor Foreman (outside)	$25.80	$206.40	$43.40	$347.20	$26.74	$44.70
2 Laborers	23.80	380.80	40.05	640.80		
1 Equip. Oper. (medium)	33.75	270.00	55.90	447.20		
2 Truck Drivers (heavy)	26.65	426.40	44.40	710.40		
1 Crawler Loader, 3 C.Y.		1191.00		1310.10		
2 Dump Trucks, 12 C.Y., 400 H.P.		1384.40		1522.84	53.65	59.02
48 L.H., Daily Totals		$3859.00		$4978.54	$80.40	$103.72

Crew B-3A	Hr.	Daily	Hr.	Daily	Bare Costs	Incl. O&P
4 Laborers	$23.80	$761.60	$40.05	$1281.60	$25.79	$43.22
1 Equip. Oper. (medium)	33.75	270.00	55.90	447.20		
1 Hyd. Excavator, 1.5 C.Y.		1031.00		1134.10	25.77	28.35
40 L.H., Daily Totals		$2062.60		$2862.90	$51.56	$71.57

Crew B-3B	Hr.	Daily	Hr.	Daily	Bare Costs	Incl. O&P
2 Laborers	$23.80	$380.80	$40.05	$640.80	$27.00	$45.10
1 Equip. Oper. (medium)	33.75	270.00	55.90	447.20		
1 Truck Driver (heavy)	26.65	213.20	44.40	355.20		
1 Backhoe Loader, 80 H.P.		397.60		437.36		
1 Dump Truck, 12 C.Y., 400 H.P.		692.20		761.42	34.06	37.46
32 L.H., Daily Totals		$1953.80		$2641.98	$61.06	$82.56

Crew B-3C	Hr.	Daily	Hr.	Daily	Bare Costs	Incl. O&P
3 Laborers	$23.80	$571.20	$40.05	$961.20	$26.29	$44.01
1 Equip. Oper. (medium)	33.75	270.00	55.90	447.20		
1 Crawler Loader, 4 C.Y.		1532.00		1685.20	47.88	52.66
32 L.H., Daily Totals		$2373.20		$3093.60	$74.16	$96.67

667

Crew B-4

	Bare Costs		Incl. Subs O&P		Cost Per Labor-Hour	
Crew B-4	Hr.	Daily	Hr.	Daily	Bare Costs	Incl. O&P
1 Labor Foreman (outside)	$25.80	$206.40	$43.40	$347.20	$24.61	$41.33
4 Laborers	23.80	761.60	40.05	1281.60		
1 Truck Driver (heavy)	26.65	213.20	44.40	355.20		
1 Truck Tractor, 220 H.P.		366.40		403.04		
1 Flatbed Trailer, 40 Ton		152.00		167.20	10.80	11.88
48 L.H., Daily Totals		$1699.60		$2554.24	$35.41	$53.21

Crew B-5

Crew B-5	Hr.	Daily	Hr.	Daily	Bare Costs	Incl. O&P
1 Labor Foreman (outside)	$25.80	$206.40	$43.40	$347.20	$26.19	$43.89
3 Laborers	23.80	571.20	40.05	961.20		
1 Equip. Oper. (medium)	33.75	270.00	55.90	447.20		
1 Air Compressor, 250 cfm		202.40		222.64		
2 Breakers, Pavement, 60 lb.		19.60		21.56		
2 -50' Air Hoses, 1.5"		11.60		12.76		
1 Crawler Loader, 3 C.Y.		1191.00		1310.10	35.62	39.18
40 L.H., Daily Totals		$2472.20		$3322.66	$61.81	$83.07

Crew B-5A

Crew B-5A	Hr.	Daily	Hr.	Daily	Bare Costs	Incl. O&P
1 Labor Foreman (outside)	$25.80	$206.40	$43.40	$347.20	$26.82	$44.84
6 Laborers	23.80	1142.40	40.05	1922.40		
2 Equip. Oper. (medium)	33.75	540.00	55.90	894.40		
1 Equip. Oper. (light)	32.45	259.60	53.75	430.00		
2 Truck Drivers (heavy)	26.65	426.40	44.40	710.40		
1 Air Compressor, 365 cfm		264.80		291.28		
2 Breakers, Pavement, 60 lb.		19.60		21.56		
8 -50' Air Hoses, 1"		32.80		36.08		
2 Dump Trucks, 8 C.Y., 220 H.P.		834.40		917.84	12.00	13.20
96 L.H., Daily Totals		$3726.40		$5571.16	$38.82	$58.03

Crew B-5B

Crew B-5B	Hr.	Daily	Hr.	Daily	Bare Costs	Incl. O&P
1 Powderman	$32.45	$259.60	$54.80	$438.40	$29.98	$49.97
2 Equip. Oper. (medium)	33.75	540.00	55.90	894.40		
3 Truck Drivers (heavy)	26.65	639.60	44.40	1065.60		
1 F.E. Loader, W.M.,2.5 C.Y.		522.80		575.08		
3 Dump Trucks, 12 C.Y., 400 H.P.		2076.60		2284.26		
1 Air Compressor, 365 CFM		264.80		291.28	59.67	65.64
48 L.H., Daily Totals		$4303.40		$5549.02	$89.65	$115.60

Crew B-5C

Crew B-5C	Hr.	Daily	Hr.	Daily	Bare Costs	Incl. O&P
3 Laborers	$23.80	$571.20	$40.05	$961.20	$27.89	$46.50
1 Equip. Oper. (medium)	33.75	270.00	55.90	447.20		
2 Truck Drivers (heavy)	26.65	426.40	44.40	710.40		
1 Equip. Oper. (crane)	34.65	277.20	57.40	459.20		
1 Equip. Oper. (oiler)	30.05	240.40	49.75	398.00		
2 Dump Trucks, 12 C.Y., 400 H.P.		1384.40		1522.84		
1 Crawler Loader, 4 C.Y.		1532.00		1685.20		
1 S.P. Crane, 4x4, 25 Ton		607.20		667.92	55.06	60.56
64 L.H., Daily Totals		$5308.80		$6851.96	$82.95	$107.06

Crew B-5D

Crew B-5D	Hr.	Daily	Hr.	Daily	Bare Costs	Incl. O&P
1 Labor Foreman (outside)	$25.80	$206.40	$43.40	$347.20	$26.27	$43.98
3 Laborers	23.80	571.20	40.05	961.20		
1 Equip. Oper. (medium)	33.75	270.00	55.90	447.20		
1 Truck Driver (heavy)	26.65	213.20	44.40	355.20		
1 Air Compressor, 250 cfm		202.40		222.64		
2 Breakers, Pavement, 60 lb.		19.60		21.56		
2 -50' Air Hoses, 1.5"		11.60		12.76		
1 Crawler Loader, 3 C.Y.		1191.00		1310.10		
1 Dump Truck, 12 C.Y., 400 H.P.		692.20		761.42	44.10	48.51
48 L.H., Daily Totals		$3377.60		$4439.28	$70.37	$92.48

Crew B-6

	Bare Costs		Incl. Subs O&P		Cost Per Labor-Hour	
Crew B-6	Hr.	Daily	Hr.	Daily	Bare Costs	Incl. O&P
2 Laborers	$23.80	$380.80	$40.05	$640.80	$26.68	$44.62
1 Equip. Oper. (light)	32.45	259.60	53.75	430.00		
1 Backhoe Loader, 48 H.P.		365.20		401.72	15.22	16.74
24 L.H., Daily Totals		$1005.60		$1472.52	$41.90	$61.35

Crew B-6B

Crew B-6B	Hr.	Daily	Hr.	Daily	Bare Costs	Incl. O&P
2 Labor Foremen (outside)	$25.80	$412.80	$43.40	$694.40	$24.47	$41.17
4 Laborers	23.80	761.60	40.05	1281.60		
1 S.P. Crane, 4x4, 5 Ton		280.00		308.00		
1 Flatbed Truck, Gas, 1.5 Ton		270.00		297.22		
1 Butt Fusion Mach., 4"-12" diam.		381.80		419.98	19.42	21.36
48 L.H., Daily Totals		$2106.40		$3001.20	$43.88	$62.52

Crew B-6C

Crew B-6C	Hr.	Daily	Hr.	Daily	Bare Costs	Incl. O&P
2 Labor Foremen (outside)	$25.80	$412.80	$43.40	$694.40	$24.47	$41.17
4 Laborers	23.80	761.60	40.05	1281.60		
1 S.P. Crane, 4x4, 12 Ton		481.20		529.32		
1 Flatbed Truck, Gas, 3 Ton		333.00		366.30		
1 Butt Fusion Mach., 8"-24" diam.		828.40		911.24	34.22	37.64
48 L.H., Daily Totals		$2817.00		$3782.86	$58.69	$78.81

Crew B-7

Crew B-7	Hr.	Daily	Hr.	Daily	Bare Costs	Incl. O&P
1 Labor Foreman (outside)	$25.80	$206.40	$43.40	$347.20	$25.79	$43.25
4 Laborers	23.80	761.60	40.05	1281.60		
1 Equip. Oper. (medium)	33.75	270.00	55.90	447.20		
1 Brush Chipper, 12", 130 H.P.		396.60		436.26		
1 Crawler Loader, 3 C.Y.		1191.00		1310.10		
2 Chain Saws, Gas, 36" Long		90.00		99.00	34.95	38.45
48 L.H., Daily Totals		$2915.60		$3921.36	$60.74	$81.69

Crew B-7A

Crew B-7A	Hr.	Daily	Hr.	Daily	Bare Costs	Incl. O&P
2 Laborers	$23.80	$380.80	$40.05	$640.80	$26.68	$44.62
1 Equip. Oper. (light)	32.45	259.60	53.75	430.00		
1 Rake w/Tractor		347.90		382.69		
2 Chain Saw, Gas, 18"		62.40		68.64	17.10	18.81
24 L.H., Daily Totals		$1050.70		$1522.13	$43.78	$63.42

Crew B-7B

Crew B-7B	Hr.	Daily	Hr.	Daily	Bare Costs	Incl. O&P
1 Labor Foreman (outside)	$25.80	$206.40	$43.40	$347.20	$25.91	$43.41
4 Laborers	23.80	761.60	40.05	1281.60		
1 Equip. Oper. (medium)	33.75	270.00	55.90	447.20		
1 Truck Driver (heavy)	26.65	213.20	44.40	355.20		
1 Brush Chipper, 12", 130 H.P.		396.60		436.26		
1 Crawler Loader, 3 C.Y.		1191.00		1310.10		
2 Chain Saws, Gas, 36" Long		90.00		99.00		
1 Dump Truck, 8 C.Y., 220 H.P.		417.20		458.92	37.41	41.15
56 L.H., Daily Totals		$3546.00		$4735.48	$63.32	$84.56

Crew B-7C

Crew B-7C	Hr.	Daily	Hr.	Daily	Bare Costs	Incl. O&P
1 Labor Foreman (outside)	$25.80	$206.40	$43.40	$347.20	$25.91	$43.41
4 Laborers	23.80	761.60	40.05	1281.60		
1 Equip. Oper. (medium)	33.75	270.00	55.90	447.20		
1 Truck Driver (heavy)	26.65	213.20	44.40	355.20		
1 Brush Chipper, 12", 130 H.P.		396.60		436.26		
1 Crawler Loader, 3 C.Y.		1191.00		1310.10		
2 Chain Saws, Gas, 36" Long		90.00		99.00		
1 Dump Truck, 12 C.Y., 400 H.P.		692.20		761.42	42.32	46.55
56 L.H., Daily Totals		$3821.00		$5037.98	$68.23	$89.96

| Crew No. | Bare Costs | | Incl. Subs O&P | | Cost Per Labor-Hour | |

Crew B-8	Hr.	Daily	Hr.	Daily	Bare Costs	Incl. O&P
1 Labor Foreman (outside)	$25.80	$206.40	$43.40	$347.20	$27.74	$46.30
2 Laborers	23.80	380.80	40.05	640.80		
2 Equip. Oper. (medium)	33.75	540.00	55.90	894.40		
2 Truck Drivers (heavy)	26.65	426.40	44.40	710.40		
1 Hyd. Crane, 25 Ton		745.80		820.38		
1 Crawler Loader, 3 C.Y.		1191.00		1310.10		
2 Dump Trucks, 12 C.Y., 400 H.P.		1384.40		1522.84	59.31	65.24
56 L.H., Daily Totals		$4874.80		$6246.12	$87.05	$111.54

Crew B-9	Hr.	Daily	Hr.	Daily	Bare Costs	Incl. O&P
1 Labor Foreman (outside)	$25.80	$206.40	$43.40	$347.20	$24.20	$40.72
4 Laborers	23.80	761.60	40.05	1281.60		
1 Air Compressor, 250 cfm		202.40		222.64		
2 Breakers, Pavement, 60 lb.		19.60		21.56		
2 -50' Air Hoses, 1.5"		11.60		12.76	5.84	6.42
40 L.H., Daily Totals		$1201.60		$1885.76	$30.04	$47.14

Crew B-9A	Hr.	Daily	Hr.	Daily	Bare Costs	Incl. O&P
2 Laborers	$23.80	$380.80	$40.05	$640.80	$24.75	$41.50
1 Truck Driver (heavy)	26.65	213.20	44.40	355.20		
1 Water Tank Trailer, 5000 Gal.		141.60		155.76		
1 Truck Tractor, 220 H.P.		366.40		403.04		
2 -50' Discharge Hoses, 3"		3.00		3.30	21.29	23.42
24 L.H., Daily Totals		$1105.00		$1558.10	$46.04	$64.92

Crew B-9B	Hr.	Daily	Hr.	Daily	Bare Costs	Incl. O&P
2 Laborers	$23.80	$380.80	$40.05	$640.80	$24.75	$41.50
1 Truck Driver (heavy)	26.65	213.20	44.40	355.20		
2 -50' Discharge Hoses, 3"		3.00		3.30		
1 Water Tank Trailer, 5000 Gal.		141.60		155.76		
1 Truck Tractor, 220 H.P.		366.40		403.04		
1 Pressure Washer		69.40		76.34	24.18	26.60
24 L.H., Daily Totals		$1174.40		$1634.44	$48.93	$68.10

Crew B-9D	Hr.	Daily	Hr.	Daily	Bare Costs	Incl. O&P
1 Labor Foreman (outside)	$25.80	$206.40	$43.40	$347.20	$24.20	$40.72
4 Common Laborers	23.80	761.60	40.05	1281.60		
1 Air Compressor, 250 cfm		202.40		222.64		
2 -50' Air Hoses, 1.5"		11.60		12.76		
2 Air Powered Tampers		52.40		57.64	6.66	7.33
40 L.H., Daily Totals		$1234.40		$1921.84	$30.86	$48.05

Crew B-10	Hr.	Daily	Hr.	Daily	Bare Costs	Incl. O&P
1 Equip. Oper. (medium)	$33.75	$270.00	$55.90	$447.20	$33.75	$55.90
8 L.H., Daily Totals		$270.00		$447.20	$33.75	$55.90

Crew B-10A	Hr.	Daily	Hr.	Daily	Bare Costs	Incl. O&P
1 Equip. Oper. (medium)	$33.75	$270.00	$55.90	$447.20	$33.75	$55.90
1 Roller, 2-Drum, W.B., 7.5 H.P.		182.80		201.08	22.85	25.14
8 L.H., Daily Totals		$452.80		$648.28	$56.60	$81.03

Crew B-10B	Hr.	Daily	Hr.	Daily	Bare Costs	Incl. O&P
1 Equip. Oper. (medium)	$33.75	$270.00	$55.90	$447.20	$33.75	$55.90
1 Dozer, 200 H.P.		1325.00		1457.50	165.63	182.19
8 L.H., Daily Totals		$1595.00		$1904.70	$199.38	$238.09

Crew B-10C	Hr.	Daily	Hr.	Daily	Bare Costs	Incl. O&P
1 Equip. Oper. (medium)	$33.75	$270.00	$55.90	$447.20	$33.75	$55.90
1 Dozer, 200 H.P.		1325.00		1457.50		
1 Vibratory Roller, Towed, 23 Ton		412.00		453.20	217.13	238.84
8 L.H., Daily Totals		$2007.00		$2357.90	$250.88	$294.74

Crew B-10D	Hr.	Daily	Hr.	Daily	Bare Costs	Incl. O&P
1 Equip. Oper. (medium)	$33.75	$270.00	$55.90	$447.20	$33.75	$55.90
1 Dozer, 200 H.P.		1325.00		1457.50		
1 Sheepsft. Roller, Towed		443.80		488.18	221.10	243.21
8 L.H., Daily Totals		$2038.80		$2392.88	$254.85	$299.11

Crew B-10E	Hr.	Daily	Hr.	Daily	Bare Costs	Incl. O&P
1 Equip. Oper. (medium)	$33.75	$270.00	$55.90	$447.20	$33.75	$55.90
1 Tandem Roller, 5 Ton		159.00		174.90	19.88	21.86
8 L.H., Daily Totals		$429.00		$622.10	$53.63	$77.76

Crew B-10F	Hr.	Daily	Hr.	Daily	Bare Costs	Incl. O&P
1 Equip. Oper. (medium)	$33.75	$270.00	$55.90	$447.20	$33.75	$55.90
1 Tandem Roller, 10 Ton		242.00		266.20	30.25	33.27
8 L.H., Daily Totals		$512.00		$713.40	$64.00	$89.17

Crew B-10G	Hr.	Daily	Hr.	Daily	Bare Costs	Incl. O&P
1 Equip. Oper. (medium)	$33.75	$270.00	$55.90	$447.20	$33.75	$55.90
1 Sheepsfoot Roller, 240 H.P.		1218.00		1339.80	152.25	167.47
8 L.H., Daily Totals		$1488.00		$1787.00	$186.00	$223.38

Crew B-10H	Hr.	Daily	Hr.	Daily	Bare Costs	Incl. O&P
1 Equip. Oper. (medium)	$33.75	$270.00	$55.90	$447.20	$33.75	$55.90
1 Diaphragm Water Pump, 2"		72.00		79.20		
1 -20' Suction Hose, 2"		1.95		2.15		
2 -50' Discharge Hoses, 2"		1.80		1.98	9.47	10.42
8 L.H., Daily Totals		$345.75		$530.52	$43.22	$66.32

Crew B-10I	Hr.	Daily	Hr.	Daily	Bare Costs	Incl. O&P
1 Equip. Oper. (medium)	$33.75	$270.00	$55.90	$447.20	$33.75	$55.90
1 Diaphragm Water Pump, 4"		115.80		127.38		
1 -20' Suction Hose, 4"		3.25		3.58		
2 -50' Discharge Hoses, 4"		4.70		5.17	15.47	17.02
8 L.H., Daily Totals		$393.75		$583.33	$49.22	$72.92

Crew B-10J	Hr.	Daily	Hr.	Daily	Bare Costs	Incl. O&P
1 Equip. Oper. (medium)	$33.75	$270.00	$55.90	$447.20	$33.75	$55.90
1 Centrifugal Water Pump, 3"		78.80		86.68		
1 -20' Suction Hose, 3"		2.85		3.13		
2 -50' Discharge Hoses, 3"		3.00		3.30	10.58	11.64
8 L.H., Daily Totals		$354.65		$540.32	$44.33	$67.54

Crew B-10K	Hr.	Daily	Hr.	Daily	Bare Costs	Incl. O&P
1 Equip. Oper. (medium)	$33.75	$270.00	$55.90	$447.20	$33.75	$55.90
1 Centr. Water Pump, 6"		340.80		374.88		
1 -20' Suction Hose, 6"		11.50		12.65		
2 -50' Discharge Hoses, 6"		12.20		13.42	45.56	50.12
8 L.H., Daily Totals		$634.50		$848.15	$79.31	$106.02

Crew B-10L	Hr.	Daily	Hr.	Daily	Bare Costs	Incl. O&P
1 Equip. Oper. (medium)	$33.75	$270.00	$55.90	$447.20	$33.75	$55.90
1 Dozer, 80 H.P.		481.00		529.10	60.13	66.14
8 L.H., Daily Totals		$751.00		$976.30	$93.88	$122.04

Crew B-10M	Bare Costs Hr.	Daily	Incl. Subs O&P Hr.	Daily	Bare Costs	Incl. O&P
1 Equip. Oper. (medium)	$33.75	$270.00	$55.90	$447.20	$33.75	$55.90
1 Dozer, 300 H.P.		1817.00		1998.70	227.13	249.84
8 L.H., Daily Totals		$2087.00		$2445.90	$260.88	$305.74

Crew B-10N	Bare Costs Hr.	Daily	Incl. Subs O&P Hr.	Daily	Bare Costs	Incl. O&P
1 Equip. Oper. (medium)	$33.75	$270.00	$55.90	$447.20	$33.75	$55.90
1 F.E. Loader, T.M., 1.5 C.Y.		522.80		575.08	65.35	71.89
8 L.H., Daily Totals		$792.80		$1022.28	$99.10	$127.79

Crew B-10O	Bare Costs Hr.	Daily	Incl. Subs O&P Hr.	Daily	Bare Costs	Incl. O&P
1 Equip. Oper. (medium)	$33.75	$270.00	$55.90	$447.20	$33.75	$55.90
1 F.E. Loader, T.M., 2.25 C.Y.		959.80		1055.78	119.97	131.97
8 L.H., Daily Totals		$1229.80		$1502.98	$153.72	$187.87

Crew B-10P	Bare Costs Hr.	Daily	Incl. Subs O&P Hr.	Daily	Bare Costs	Incl. O&P
1 Equip. Oper. (medium)	$33.75	$270.00	$55.90	$447.20	$33.75	$55.90
1 Crawler Loader, 3 C.Y.		1191.00		1310.10	148.88	163.76
8 L.H., Daily Totals		$1461.00		$1757.30	$182.63	$219.66

Crew B-10Q	Bare Costs Hr.	Daily	Incl. Subs O&P Hr.	Daily	Bare Costs	Incl. O&P
1 Equip. Oper. (medium)	$33.75	$270.00	$55.90	$447.20	$33.75	$55.90
1 Crawler Loader, 4 C.Y.		1532.00		1685.20	191.50	210.65
8 L.H., Daily Totals		$1802.00		$2132.40	$225.25	$266.55

Crew B-10R	Bare Costs Hr.	Daily	Incl. Subs O&P Hr.	Daily	Bare Costs	Incl. O&P
1 Equip. Oper. (medium)	$33.75	$270.00	$55.90	$447.20	$33.75	$55.90
1 F.E. Loader, W.M., 1 C.Y.		295.20		324.72	36.90	40.59
8 L.H., Daily Totals		$565.20		$771.92	$70.65	$96.49

Crew B-10S	Bare Costs Hr.	Daily	Incl. Subs O&P Hr.	Daily	Bare Costs	Incl. O&P
1 Equip. Oper. (medium)	$33.75	$270.00	$55.90	$447.20	$33.75	$55.90
1 F.E. Loader, W.M., 1.5 C.Y.		373.40		410.74	46.67	51.34
8 L.H., Daily Totals		$643.40		$857.94	$80.42	$107.24

Crew B-10T	Bare Costs Hr.	Daily	Incl. Subs O&P Hr.	Daily	Bare Costs	Incl. O&P
1 Equip. Oper. (medium)	$33.75	$270.00	$55.90	$447.20	$33.75	$55.90
1 F.E. Loader, W.M., 2.5 C.Y.		522.80		575.08	65.35	71.89
8 L.H., Daily Totals		$792.80		$1022.28	$99.10	$127.79

Crew B-10U	Bare Costs Hr.	Daily	Incl. Subs O&P Hr.	Daily	Bare Costs	Incl. O&P
1 Equip. Oper. (medium)	$33.75	$270.00	$55.90	$447.20	$33.75	$55.90
1 F.E. Loader, W.M., 5.5 C.Y.		1049.00		1153.90	131.13	144.24
8 L.H., Daily Totals		$1319.00		$1601.10	$164.88	$200.14

Crew B-10V	Bare Costs Hr.	Daily	Incl. Subs O&P Hr.	Daily	Bare Costs	Incl. O&P
1 Equip. Oper. (medium)	$33.75	$270.00	$55.90	$447.20	$33.75	$55.90
1 Dozer, 700 H.P.		4485.00		4933.50	560.63	616.69
8 L.H., Daily Totals		$4755.00		$5380.70	$594.38	$672.59

Crew B-10W	Bare Costs Hr.	Daily	Incl. Subs O&P Hr.	Daily	Bare Costs	Incl. O&P
1 Equip. Oper. (medium)	$33.75	$270.00	$55.90	$447.20	$33.75	$55.90
1 Dozer, 105 H.P.		591.80		650.98	73.97	81.37
8 L.H., Daily Totals		$861.80		$1098.18	$107.72	$137.27

Crew B-10X	Bare Costs Hr.	Daily	Incl. Subs O&P Hr.	Daily	Bare Costs	Incl. O&P
1 Equip. Oper. (medium)	$33.75	$270.00	$55.90	$447.20	$33.75	$55.90
1 Dozer, 410 H.P.		2409.00		2649.90	301.13	331.24
8 L.H., Daily Totals		$2679.00		$3097.10	$334.88	$387.14

Crew B-10Y	Bare Costs Hr.	Daily	Incl. Subs O&P Hr.	Daily	Bare Costs	Incl. O&P
1 Equip. Oper. (medium)	$33.75	$270.00	$55.90	$447.20	$33.75	$55.90
1 Vibr. Roller, Towed, 12 Ton		559.20		615.12	69.90	76.89
8 L.H., Daily Totals		$829.20		$1062.32	$103.65	$132.79

Crew B-11A	Bare Costs Hr.	Daily	Incl. Subs O&P Hr.	Daily	Bare Costs	Incl. O&P
1 Equipment Oper. (med.)	$33.75	$270.00	$55.90	$447.20	$28.77	$47.98
1 Laborer	23.80	190.40	40.05	320.40		
1 Dozer, 200 H.P.		1325.00		1457.50	82.81	91.09
16 L.H., Daily Totals		$1785.40		$2225.10	$111.59	$139.07

Crew B-11B	Bare Costs Hr.	Daily	Incl. Subs O&P Hr.	Daily	Bare Costs	Incl. O&P
1 Equipment Oper. (light)	$32.45	$259.60	$53.75	$430.00	$28.13	$46.90
1 Laborer	23.80	190.40	40.05	320.40		
1 Air Powered Tamper		26.20		28.82		
1 Air Compressor, 365 cfm		264.80		291.28		
2 -50' Air Hoses, 1.5"		11.60		12.76	18.91	20.80
16 L.H., Daily Totals		$752.60		$1083.26	$47.04	$67.70

Crew B-11C	Bare Costs Hr.	Daily	Incl. Subs O&P Hr.	Daily	Bare Costs	Incl. O&P
1 Equipment Oper. (med.)	$33.75	$270.00	$55.90	$447.20	$28.77	$47.98
1 Laborer	23.80	190.40	40.05	320.40		
1 Backhoe Loader, 48 H.P.		365.20		401.72	22.82	25.11
16 L.H., Daily Totals		$825.60		$1169.32	$51.60	$73.08

Crew B-11K	Bare Costs Hr.	Daily	Incl. Subs O&P Hr.	Daily	Bare Costs	Incl. O&P
1 Equipment Oper. (med.)	$33.75	$270.00	$55.90	$447.20	$28.77	$47.98
1 Laborer	23.80	190.40	40.05	320.40		
1 Trencher, Chain Type, 8' D		3376.00		3713.60	211.00	232.10
16 L.H., Daily Totals		$3836.40		$4481.20	$239.78	$280.07

Crew B-11L	Bare Costs Hr.	Daily	Incl. Subs O&P Hr.	Daily	Bare Costs	Incl. O&P
1 Equipment Oper. (med.)	$33.75	$270.00	$55.90	$447.20	$28.77	$47.98
1 Laborer	23.80	190.40	40.05	320.40		
1 Grader, 30,000 Lbs.		707.00		777.70	44.19	48.61
16 L.H., Daily Totals		$1167.40		$1545.30	$72.96	$96.58

Crew B-11M	Bare Costs Hr.	Daily	Incl. Subs O&P Hr.	Daily	Bare Costs	Incl. O&P
1 Equipment Oper. (med.)	$33.75	$270.00	$55.90	$447.20	$28.77	$47.98
1 Laborer	23.80	190.40	40.05	320.40		
1 Backhoe Loader, 80 H.P.		397.60		437.36	24.85	27.34
16 L.H., Daily Totals		$858.00		$1204.96	$53.63	$75.31

Crew B-11W	Bare Costs Hr.	Daily	Incl. Subs O&P Hr.	Daily	Bare Costs	Incl. O&P
1 Equipment Operator (med.)	$33.75	$270.00	$55.90	$447.20	$27.00	$45.00
1 Common Laborer	23.80	190.40	40.05	320.40		
10 Truck Drivers (heavy)	26.65	2132.00	44.40	3552.00		
1 Dozer, 200 H.P.		1325.00		1457.50		
1 Vibratory Roller, Towed, 23 Ton		412.00		453.20		
10 Dump Trucks, 8 C.Y., 220 H.P.		4172.00		4589.20	61.55	67.71
96 L.H., Daily Totals		$8501.40		$10819.50	$88.56	$112.70

Crew B-11Y	Bare Costs Hr.	Daily	Incl. Subs O&P Hr.	Daily	Bare Costs	Incl. O&P
1 Labor Foreman (outside)	$25.80	$206.40	$43.40	$347.20	$27.34	$45.71
5 Common Laborers	23.80	952.00	40.05	1602.00		
3 Equipment Operators (med.)	33.75	810.00	55.90	1341.60		
1 Dozer, 80 H.P.		481.00		529.10		
2 Roller, 2-Drum, W.B., 7.5 H.P.		365.60		402.16		
4 Vibrating Plate, Gas, 21"		184.00		202.40	14.31	15.75
72 L.H., Daily Totals		$2999.00		$4424.46	$41.65	$61.45

Crew No.	Bare Costs		Incl. Subs O&P		Cost Per Labor-Hour	
Crew B-12A	Hr.	Daily	Hr.	Daily	Bare Costs	Incl. O&P
1 Equip. Oper. (crane)	$34.65	$277.20	$57.40	$459.20	$29.23	$48.73
1 Laborer	23.80	190.40	40.05	320.40		
1 Hyd. Excavator, 1 C.Y.		814.80		896.28	50.92	56.02
16 L.H., Daily Totals		$1282.40		$1675.88	$80.15	$104.74
Crew B-12B	Hr.	Daily	Hr.	Daily	Bare Costs	Incl. O&P
1 Equip. Oper. (crane)	$34.65	$277.20	$57.40	$459.20	$29.23	$48.73
1 Laborer	23.80	190.40	40.05	320.40		
1 Hyd. Excavator, 1.5 C.Y.		1031.00		1134.10	64.44	70.88
16 L.H., Daily Totals		$1498.60		$1913.70	$93.66	$119.61
Crew B-12C	Hr.	Daily	Hr.	Daily	Bare Costs	Incl. O&P
1 Equip. Oper. (crane)	$34.65	$277.20	$57.40	$459.20	$29.23	$48.73
1 Laborer	23.80	190.40	40.05	320.40		
1 Hyd. Excavator, 2 C.Y.		1175.00		1292.50	73.44	80.78
16 L.H., Daily Totals		$1642.60		$2072.10	$102.66	$129.51
Crew B-12D	Hr.	Daily	Hr.	Daily	Bare Costs	Incl. O&P
1 Equip. Oper. (crane)	$34.65	$277.20	$57.40	$459.20	$29.23	$48.73
1 Laborer	23.80	190.40	40.05	320.40		
1 Hyd. Excavator, 3.5 C.Y.		2442.00		2686.20	152.63	167.89
16 L.H., Daily Totals		$2909.60		$3465.80	$181.85	$216.61
Crew B-12E	Hr.	Daily	Hr.	Daily	Bare Costs	Incl. O&P
1 Equip. Oper. (crane)	$34.65	$277.20	$57.40	$459.20	$29.23	$48.73
1 Laborer	23.80	190.40	40.05	320.40		
1 Hyd. Excavator, .5 C.Y.		448.00		492.80	28.00	30.80
16 L.H., Daily Totals		$915.60		$1272.40	$57.23	$79.53
Crew B-12F	Hr.	Daily	Hr.	Daily	Bare Costs	Incl. O&P
1 Equip. Oper. (crane)	$34.65	$277.20	$57.40	$459.20	$29.23	$48.73
1 Laborer	23.80	190.40	40.05	320.40		
1 Hyd. Excavator, .75 C.Y.		662.00		728.20	41.38	45.51
16 L.H., Daily Totals		$1129.60		$1507.80	$70.60	$94.24
Crew B-12G	Hr.	Daily	Hr.	Daily	Bare Costs	Incl. O&P
1 Equip. Oper. (crane)	$34.65	$277.20	$57.40	$459.20	$29.23	$48.73
1 Laborer	23.80	190.40	40.05	320.40		
1 Crawler Crane, 15 Ton		684.15		752.57		
1 Clamshell Bucket, .5 C.Y.		37.80		41.58	45.12	49.63
16 L.H., Daily Totals		$1189.55		$1573.74	$74.35	$98.36
Crew B-12H	Hr.	Daily	Hr.	Daily	Bare Costs	Incl. O&P
1 Equip. Oper. (crane)	$34.65	$277.20	$57.40	$459.20	$29.23	$48.73
1 Laborer	23.80	190.40	40.05	320.40		
1 Crawler Crane, 25 Ton		1173.00		1290.30		
1 Clamshell Bucket, 1 C.Y.		47.40		52.14	76.28	83.90
16 L.H., Daily Totals		$1688.00		$2122.04	$105.50	$132.63
Crew B-12I	Hr.	Daily	Hr.	Daily	Bare Costs	Incl. O&P
1 Equip. Oper. (crane)	$34.65	$277.20	$57.40	$459.20	$29.23	$48.73
1 Laborer	23.80	190.40	40.05	320.40		
1 Crawler Crane, 20 Ton		880.25		968.27		
1 Dragline Bucket, .75 C.Y.		20.80		22.88	56.32	61.95
16 L.H., Daily Totals		$1368.65		$1770.76	$85.54	$110.67

Crew No.	Bare Costs		Incl. Subs O&P		Cost Per Labor-Hour	
Crew B-12J	Hr.	Daily	Hr.	Daily	Bare Costs	Incl. O&P
1 Equip. Oper. (crane)	$34.65	$277.20	$57.40	$459.20	$29.23	$48.73
1 Laborer	23.80	190.40	40.05	320.40		
1 Gradall, 5/8 C.Y.		881.60		969.76	55.10	60.61
16 L.H., Daily Totals		$1349.20		$1749.36	$84.33	$109.33
Crew B-12K	Hr.	Daily	Hr.	Daily	Bare Costs	Incl. O&P
1 Equip. Oper. (crane)	$34.65	$277.20	$57.40	$459.20	$29.23	$48.73
1 Laborer	23.80	190.40	40.05	320.40		
1 Gradall, 3 Ton, 1 C.Y.		1005.00		1105.50	62.81	69.09
16 L.H., Daily Totals		$1472.60		$1885.10	$92.04	$117.82
Crew B-12L	Hr.	Daily	Hr.	Daily	Bare Costs	Incl. O&P
1 Equip. Oper. (crane)	$34.65	$277.20	$57.40	$459.20	$29.23	$48.73
1 Laborer	23.80	190.40	40.05	320.40		
1 Crawler Crane, 15 Ton		684.15		752.57		
1 F.E. Attachment, .5 C.Y.		59.60		65.56	46.48	51.13
16 L.H., Daily Totals		$1211.35		$1597.72	$75.71	$99.86
Crew B-12M	Hr.	Daily	Hr.	Daily	Bare Costs	Incl. O&P
1 Equip. Oper. (crane)	$34.65	$277.20	$57.40	$459.20	$29.23	$48.73
1 Laborer	23.80	190.40	40.05	320.40		
1 Crawler Crane, 20 Ton		880.25		968.27		
1 F.E. Attachment, .75 C.Y.		64.00		70.40	59.02	64.92
16 L.H., Daily Totals		$1411.85		$1818.28	$88.24	$113.64
Crew B-12N	Hr.	Daily	Hr.	Daily	Bare Costs	Incl. O&P
1 Equip. Oper. (crane)	$34.65	$277.20	$57.40	$459.20	$29.23	$48.73
1 Laborer	23.80	190.40	40.05	320.40		
1 Crawler Crane, 25 Ton		1173.00		1290.30		
1 F.E. Attachment, 1 C.Y.		70.80		77.88	77.74	85.51
16 L.H., Daily Totals		$1711.40		$2147.78	$106.96	$134.24
Crew B-12O	Hr.	Daily	Hr.	Daily	Bare Costs	Incl. O&P
1 Equip. Oper. (crane)	$34.65	$277.20	$57.40	$459.20	$29.23	$48.73
1 Laborer	23.80	190.40	40.05	320.40		
1 Crawler Crane, 40 Ton		1179.00		1296.90		
1 F.E. Attachment, 1.5 C.Y.		80.00		88.00	78.69	86.56
16 L.H., Daily Totals		$1726.60		$2164.50	$107.91	$135.28
Crew B-12P	Hr.	Daily	Hr.	Daily	Bare Costs	Incl. O&P
1 Equip. Oper. (crane)	$34.65	$277.20	$57.40	$459.20	$29.23	$48.73
1 Laborer	23.80	190.40	40.05	320.40		
1 Crawler Crane, 40 Ton		1179.00		1296.90		
1 Dragline Bucket, 1.5 C.Y.		33.60		36.96	75.79	83.37
16 L.H., Daily Totals		$1680.20		$2113.46	$105.01	$132.09
Crew B-12Q	Hr.	Daily	Hr.	Daily	Bare Costs	Incl. O&P
1 Equip. Oper. (crane)	$34.65	$277.20	$57.40	$459.20	$29.23	$48.73
1 Laborer	23.80	190.40	40.05	320.40		
1 Hyd. Excavator, 5/8 C.Y.		594.40		653.84	37.15	40.87
16 L.H., Daily Totals		$1062.00		$1433.44	$66.38	$89.59
Crew B-12S	Hr.	Daily	Hr.	Daily	Bare Costs	Incl. O&P
1 Equip. Oper. (crane)	$34.65	$277.20	$57.40	$459.20	$29.23	$48.73
1 Laborer	23.80	190.40	40.05	320.40		
1 Hyd. Excavator, 2.5 C.Y.		1637.00		1800.70	102.31	112.54
16 L.H., Daily Totals		$2104.60		$2580.30	$131.54	$161.27

Crew No.	Bare Costs Hr.	Daily	Incl. Subs O&P Hr.	Daily	Bare Costs	Incl. O&P
Crew B-12T	Hr.	Daily	Hr.	Daily	Bare Costs	Incl. O&P
1 Equip. Oper. (crane)	$34.65	$277.20	$57.40	$459.20	$29.23	$48.73
1 Laborer	23.80	190.40	40.05	320.40		
1 Crawler Crane, 75 Ton		1492.00		1641.20		
1 F.E. Attachment, 3 C.Y.		102.80		113.08	99.67	109.64
16 L.H., Daily Totals		$2062.40		$2533.88	$128.90	$158.37

Crew B-12V	Hr.	Daily	Hr.	Daily	Bare Costs	Incl. O&P
1 Equip. Oper. (crane)	$34.65	$277.20	$57.40	$459.20	$29.23	$48.73
1 Laborer	23.80	190.40	40.05	320.40		
1 Crawler Crane, 75 Ton		1492.00		1641.20		
1 Dragline Bucket, 3 C.Y.		52.60		57.86	96.54	106.19
16 L.H., Daily Totals		$2012.20		$2478.66	$125.76	$154.92

Crew B-12Y	Hr.	Daily	Hr.	Daily	Bare Costs	Incl. O&P
1 Equip. Oper. (crane)	$34.65	$277.20	$57.40	$459.20	$27.42	$45.83
2 Laborers	23.80	380.80	40.05	640.80		
1 Hyd. Excavator, 3.5 C.Y.		2442.00		2686.20	101.75	111.93
24 L.H., Daily Totals		$3100.00		$3786.20	$129.17	$157.76

Crew B-12Z	Hr.	Daily	Hr.	Daily	Bare Costs	Incl. O&P
1 Equip. Oper. (crane)	$34.65	$277.20	$57.40	$459.20	$27.42	$45.83
2 Laborers	23.80	380.80	40.05	640.80		
1 Hyd. Excavator, 2.5 C.Y.		1637.00		1800.70	68.21	75.03
24 L.H., Daily Totals		$2295.00		$2900.70	$95.63	$120.86

Crew B-13	Hr.	Daily	Hr.	Daily	Bare Costs	Incl. O&P
1 Labor Foreman (outside)	$25.80	$206.40	$43.40	$347.20	$25.94	$43.50
4 Laborers	23.80	761.60	40.05	1281.60		
1 Equip. Oper. (crane)	34.65	277.20	57.40	459.20		
1 Hyd. Crane, 25 Ton		745.80		820.38	15.54	17.09
48 L.H., Daily Totals		$1991.00		$2908.38	$41.48	$60.59

Crew B-13A	Hr.	Daily	Hr.	Daily	Bare Costs	Incl. O&P
1 Labor Foreman (outside)	$25.80	$206.40	$43.40	$347.20	$27.74	$46.30
2 Laborers	23.80	380.80	40.05	640.80		
2 Equipment Operators (med.)	33.75	540.00	55.90	894.40		
2 Truck Drivers (heavy)	26.65	426.40	44.40	710.40		
1 Crawler Crane, 75 Ton		1492.00		1641.20		
1 Crawler Loader, 4 C.Y.		1532.00		1685.20		
2 Dump Trucks, 8 C.Y., 220 H.P.		834.40		917.84	68.90	75.79
56 L.H., Daily Totals		$5412.00		$6837.04	$96.64	$122.09

Crew B-13B	Hr.	Daily	Hr.	Daily	Bare Costs	Incl. O&P
1 Labor Foreman (outside)	$25.80	$206.40	$43.40	$347.20	$26.53	$44.39
4 Laborers	23.80	761.60	40.05	1281.60		
1 Equip. Oper. (crane)	34.65	277.20	57.40	459.20		
1 Equip. Oper. (oiler)	30.05	240.40	49.75	398.00		
1 Hyd. Crane, 55 Ton		1137.00		1250.70	20.30	22.33
56 L.H., Daily Totals		$2622.60		$3736.70	$46.83	$66.73

Crew B-13C	Hr.	Daily	Hr.	Daily	Bare Costs	Incl. O&P
1 Labor Foreman (outside)	$25.80	$206.40	$43.40	$347.20	$26.53	$44.39
4 Laborers	23.80	761.60	40.05	1281.60		
1 Equip. Oper. (crane)	34.65	277.20	57.40	459.20		
1 Equip. Oper. (oiler)	30.05	240.40	49.75	398.00		
1 Crawler Crane, 100 Ton		1703.00		1873.30	30.41	33.45
56 L.H., Daily Totals		$3188.60		$4359.30	$56.94	$77.84

Crew B-13D	Hr.	Daily	Hr.	Daily	Bare Costs	Incl. O&P
1 Laborer	$23.80	$190.40	$40.05	$320.40	$29.23	$48.73
1 Equip. Oper. (crane)	34.65	277.20	57.40	459.20		
1 Hyd. Excavator, 1 C.Y.		814.80		896.28		
1 Trench Box		84.05		92.45	56.18	61.80
16 L.H., Daily Totals		$1366.45		$1768.34	$85.40	$110.52

Crew B-13E	Hr.	Daily	Hr.	Daily	Bare Costs	Incl. O&P
1 Laborer	$23.80	$190.40	$40.05	$320.40	$29.23	$48.73
1 Equip. Oper. (crane)	34.65	277.20	57.40	459.20		
1 Hyd. Excavator, 1.5 C.Y.		1031.00		1134.10		
1 Trench Box		84.05		92.45	69.69	76.66
16 L.H., Daily Totals		$1582.65		$2006.16	$98.92	$125.38

Crew B-13F	Hr.	Daily	Hr.	Daily	Bare Costs	Incl. O&P
1 Laborer	$23.80	$190.40	$40.05	$320.40	$29.23	$48.73
1 Equip. Oper. (crane)	34.65	277.20	57.40	459.20		
1 Hyd. Excavator, 3.5 C.Y.		2442.00		2686.20		
1 Trench Box		84.05		92.45	157.88	173.67
16 L.H., Daily Totals		$2993.65		$3558.26	$187.10	$222.39

Crew B-13G	Hr.	Daily	Hr.	Daily	Bare Costs	Incl. O&P
1 Laborer	$23.80	$190.40	$40.05	$320.40	$29.23	$48.73
1 Equip. Oper. (crane)	34.65	277.20	57.40	459.20		
1 Hyd. Excavator, .75 C.Y.		662.00		728.20		
1 Trench Box		84.05		92.45	46.63	51.29
16 L.H., Daily Totals		$1213.65		$1600.26	$75.85	$100.02

Crew B-13H	Hr.	Daily	Hr.	Daily	Bare Costs	Incl. O&P
1 Laborer	$23.80	$190.40	$40.05	$320.40	$29.23	$48.73
1 Equip. Oper. (crane)	34.65	277.20	57.40	459.20		
1 Gradall, 5/8 C.Y.		881.60		969.76		
1 Trench Box		84.05		92.45	60.35	66.39
16 L.H., Daily Totals		$1433.25		$1841.82	$89.58	$115.11

Crew B-13I	Hr.	Daily	Hr.	Daily	Bare Costs	Incl. O&P
1 Laborer	$23.80	$190.40	$40.05	$320.40	$29.23	$48.73
1 Equip. Oper. (crane)	34.65	277.20	57.40	459.20		
1 Gradall, 3 Ton, 1 C.Y.		1005.00		1105.50		
1 Trench Box		84.05		92.45	68.07	74.87
16 L.H., Daily Totals		$1556.65		$1977.56	$97.29	$123.60

Crew B-13J	Hr.	Daily	Hr.	Daily	Bare Costs	Incl. O&P
1 Laborer	$23.80	$190.40	$40.05	$320.40	$29.23	$48.73
1 Equip. Oper. (crane)	34.65	277.20	57.40	459.20		
1 Hyd. Excavator, 2.5 C.Y.		1637.00		1800.70		
1 Trench Box		84.05		92.45	107.57	118.32
16 L.H., Daily Totals		$2188.65		$2672.76	$136.79	$167.05

Crew B-14	Hr.	Daily	Hr.	Daily	Bare Costs	Incl. O&P
1 Labor Foreman (outside)	$25.80	$206.40	$43.40	$347.20	$25.57	$42.89
4 Laborers	23.80	761.60	40.05	1281.60		
1 Equip. Oper. (light)	32.45	259.60	53.75	430.00		
1 Backhoe Loader, 48 H.P.		365.20		401.72	7.61	8.37
48 L.H., Daily Totals		$1592.80		$2460.52	$33.18	$51.26

Crew B-14A	Hr.	Daily	Hr.	Daily	Bare Costs	Incl. O&P
1 Equip. Oper. (crane)	$34.65	$277.20	$57.40	$459.20	$31.03	$51.62
.5 Laborer	23.80	95.20	40.05	160.20		
1 Hyd. Excavator, 4.5 C.Y.		3043.00		3347.30	253.58	278.94
12 L.H., Daily Totals		$3415.40		$3966.70	$284.62	$330.56

Crew No.	Bare Costs Hr.	Daily	Incl. Subs O&P Hr.	Daily	Cost Per Labor-Hour Bare Costs	Incl. O&P
Crew B-14B	Hr.	Daily	Hr.	Daily	Bare Costs	Incl. O&P
1 Equip. Oper. (crane)	$34.65	$277.20	$57.40	$459.20	$31.03	$51.62
.5 Laborer	23.80	95.20	40.05	160.20		
1 Hyd. Excavator, 6 C.Y.		3523.00		3875.30	293.58	322.94
12 L.H., Daily Totals		$3895.40		$4494.70	$324.62	$374.56
Crew B-14C	Hr.	Daily	Hr.	Daily	Bare Costs	Incl. O&P
1 Equip. Oper. (crane)	$34.65	$277.20	$57.40	$459.20	$31.03	$51.62
.5 Laborer	23.80	95.20	40.05	160.20		
1 Hyd. Excavator, 7 C.Y.		3596.00		3955.60	299.67	329.63
12 L.H., Daily Totals		$3968.40		$4575.00	$330.70	$381.25
Crew B-14F	Hr.	Daily	Hr.	Daily	Bare Costs	Incl. O&P
1 Equip. Oper. (crane)	$34.65	$277.20	$57.40	$459.20	$31.03	$51.62
.5 Laborer	23.80	95.20	40.05	160.20		
1 Hyd. Shovel, 7 C.Y.		3714.00		4085.40	309.50	340.45
12 L.H., Daily Totals		$4086.40		$4704.80	$340.53	$392.07
Crew B-14G	Hr.	Daily	Hr.	Daily	Bare Costs	Incl. O&P
1 Equip. Oper. (crane)	$34.65	$277.20	$57.40	$459.20	$31.03	$51.62
.5 Laborer	23.80	95.20	40.05	160.20		
1 Hyd. Shovel, 12 C.Y.		5204.00		5724.40	433.67	477.03
12 L.H., Daily Totals		$5576.40		$6343.80	$464.70	$528.65
Crew B-14J	Hr.	Daily	Hr.	Daily	Bare Costs	Incl. O&P
1 Equip. Oper. (medium)	$33.75	$270.00	$55.90	$447.20	$30.43	$50.62
.5 Laborer	23.80	95.20	40.05	160.20		
1 F.E. Loader, 8 C.Y.		1989.00		2187.90	165.75	182.32
12 L.H., Daily Totals		$2354.20		$2795.30	$196.18	$232.94
Crew B-14K	Hr.	Daily	Hr.	Daily	Bare Costs	Incl. O&P
1 Equip. Oper. (medium)	$33.75	$270.00	$55.90	$447.20	$30.43	$50.62
.5 Laborer	23.80	95.20	40.05	160.20		
1 F.E. Loader, 10 C.Y.		2703.00		2973.30	225.25	247.78
12 L.H., Daily Totals		$3068.20		$3580.70	$255.68	$298.39
Crew B-15	Hr.	Daily	Hr.	Daily	Bare Costs	Incl. O&P
1 Equipment Oper. (med.)	$33.75	$270.00	$55.90	$447.20	$28.27	$47.06
.5 Laborer	23.80	95.20	40.05	160.20		
2 Truck Drivers (heavy)	26.65	426.40	44.40	710.40		
2 Dump Trucks, 12 C.Y., 400 H.P.		1384.40		1522.84		
1 Dozer, 200 H.P.		1325.00		1457.50	96.76	106.44
28 L.H., Daily Totals		$3501.00		$4298.14	$125.04	$153.51
Crew B-16	Hr.	Daily	Hr.	Daily	Bare Costs	Incl. O&P
1 Labor Foreman (outside)	$25.80	$206.40	$43.40	$347.20	$25.01	$41.98
2 Laborers	23.80	380.80	40.05	640.80		
1 Truck Driver (heavy)	26.65	213.20	44.40	355.20		
1 Dump Truck, 12 C.Y., 400 H.P.		692.20		761.42	21.63	23.79
32 L.H., Daily Totals		$1492.60		$2104.62	$46.64	$65.77
Crew B-17	Hr.	Daily	Hr.	Daily	Bare Costs	Incl. O&P
2 Laborers	$23.80	$380.80	$40.05	$640.80	$26.68	$44.56
1 Equip. Oper. (light)	32.45	259.60	53.75	430.00		
1 Truck Driver (heavy)	26.65	213.20	44.40	355.20		
1 Backhoe Loader, 48 H.P.		365.20		401.72		
1 Dump Truck, 8 C.Y., 220 H.P.		417.20		458.92	24.45	26.90
32 L.H., Daily Totals		$1636.00		$2286.64	$51.13	$71.46

Crew No.	Bare Costs Hr.	Daily	Incl. Subs O&P Hr.	Daily	Cost Per Labor-Hour Bare Costs	Incl. O&P
Crew B-17A	Hr.	Daily	Hr.	Daily	Bare Costs	Incl. O&P
2 Labor Foremen (outside)	$25.80	$412.80	$43.40	$694.40	$26.13	$44.01
6 Laborers	23.80	1142.40	40.05	1922.40		
1 Skilled Worker Foreman (out)	34.45	275.60	58.20	465.60		
1 Skilled Worker	32.45	259.60	54.80	438.40		
80 L.H., Daily Totals		$2090.40		$3520.80	$26.13	$44.01
Crew B-17B	Hr.	Daily	Hr.	Daily	Bare Costs	Incl. O&P
2 Laborers	$23.80	$380.80	$40.05	$640.80	$26.68	$44.56
1 Equip. Oper. (light)	32.45	259.60	53.75	430.00		
1 Truck Driver (heavy)	26.65	213.20	44.40	355.20		
1 Backhoe Loader, 48 H.P.		365.20		401.72		
1 Dump Truck, 12 C.Y., 400 H.P.		692.20		761.42	33.04	36.35
32 L.H., Daily Totals		$1911.00		$2589.14	$59.72	$80.91
Crew B-18	Hr.	Daily	Hr.	Daily	Bare Costs	Incl. O&P
1 Labor Foreman (outside)	$25.80	$206.40	$43.40	$347.20	$24.47	$41.17
2 Laborers	23.80	380.80	40.05	640.80		
1 Vibrating Plate, Gas, 21"		46.00		50.60	1.92	2.11
24 L.H., Daily Totals		$633.20		$1038.60	$26.38	$43.27
Crew B-19	Hr.	Daily	Hr.	Daily	Bare Costs	Incl. O&P
1 Pile Driver Foreman (outside)	$33.10	$264.80	$57.15	$457.20	$30.85	$52.77
4 Pile Drivers	31.10	995.20	53.70	1718.40		
1 Equip. Oper. (crane)	34.65	277.20	57.40	459.20		
1 Building Laborer	23.80	190.40	40.05	320.40		
1 Crawler Crane, 40 Ton		1179.00		1296.90		
1 Lead, 90' High		124.40		136.84		
1 Hammer, Diesel, 22k ft-lb		537.45		591.20	32.87	36.16
56 L.H., Daily Totals		$3568.45		$4980.14	$63.72	$88.93
Crew B-19A	Hr.	Daily	Hr.	Daily	Bare Costs	Incl. O&P
1 Pile Driver Foreman (outside)	$33.10	$264.80	$57.15	$457.20	$30.85	$52.77
4 Pile Drivers	31.10	995.20	53.70	1718.40		
1 Equip. Oper. (crane)	34.65	277.20	57.40	459.20		
1 Common Laborer	23.80	190.40	40.05	320.40		
1 Crawler Crane, 75 Ton		1492.00		1641.20		
1 Lead, 90' high		124.40		136.84		
1 Hammer, Diesel, 41k ft-lb		642.40		706.64	40.34	44.37
56 L.H., Daily Totals		$3986.40		$5439.88	$71.19	$97.14
Crew B-19B	Hr.	Daily	Hr.	Daily	Bare Costs	Incl. O&P
1 Pile Driver Foreman (outside)	$33.10	$264.80	$57.15	$457.20	$30.85	$52.77
4 Pile Drivers	31.10	995.20	53.70	1718.40		
1 Equip. Oper. (crane)	34.65	277.20	57.40	459.20		
1 Common Laborer	23.80	190.40	40.05	320.40		
1 Crawler Crane, 40 Ton		1179.00		1296.90		
1 Lead, 90' High		124.40		136.84		
1 Hammer, Diesel, 22k ft-lb		537.45		591.20		
1 Barge, 400 Ton		781.00		859.10	46.82	51.50
56 L.H., Daily Totals		$4349.45		$5839.23	$77.67	$104.27
Crew B-19C	Hr.	Daily	Hr.	Daily	Bare Costs	Incl. O&P
1 Pile Driver Foreman (outside)	$33.10	$264.80	$57.15	$457.20	$30.85	$52.77
4 Pile Drivers	31.10	995.20	53.70	1718.40		
1 Equip. Oper. (crane)	34.65	277.20	57.40	459.20		
1 Common Laborer	23.80	190.40	40.05	320.40		
1 Crawler Crane, 75 Ton		1492.00		1641.20		
1 Lead, 90' High		124.40		136.84		
1 Hammer, Diesel, 41k ft-lb		642.40		706.64		
1 Barge, 400 Ton		781.00		859.10	54.28	59.71
56 L.H., Daily Totals		$4767.40		$6298.98	$85.13	$112.48

Crew B-20

Crew No.	Bare Costs Hr.	Daily	Incl. Subs O&P Hr.	Daily	Cost Per Labor-Hour Bare Costs	Incl. O&P
1 Labor Foreman (outside)	$25.80	$206.40	$43.40	$347.20	$24.47	$41.17
2 Laborers	23.80	380.80	40.05	640.80		
24 L.H., Daily Totals		$587.20		$988.00	$24.47	$41.17

Crew B-20A

Crew No.	Bare Costs Hr.	Daily	Incl. Subs O&P Hr.	Daily	Cost Per Labor-Hour Bare Costs	Incl. O&P
1 Labor Foreman (outside)	$25.80	$206.40	$43.40	$347.20	$29.50	$49.08
1 Laborer	23.80	190.40	40.05	320.40		
1 Plumber	38.00	304.00	62.70	501.60		
1 Plumber Apprentice	30.40	243.20	50.15	401.20		
32 L.H., Daily Totals		$944.00		$1570.40	$29.50	$49.08

Crew B-21

Crew No.	Bare Costs Hr.	Daily	Incl. Subs O&P Hr.	Daily	Cost Per Labor-Hour Bare Costs	Incl. O&P
1 Labor Foreman (outside)	$25.80	$206.40	$43.40	$347.20	$25.92	$43.49
2 Laborers	23.80	380.80	40.05	640.80		
.5 Equip. Oper. (crane)	34.65	138.60	57.40	229.60		
.5 S.P. Crane, 4x4, 5 Ton		140.00		154.00	5.00	5.50
28 L.H., Daily Totals		$865.80		$1371.60	$30.92	$48.99

Crew B-21A

Crew No.	Bare Costs Hr.	Daily	Incl. Subs O&P Hr.	Daily	Cost Per Labor-Hour Bare Costs	Incl. O&P
1 Labor Foreman (outside)	$25.80	$206.40	$43.40	$347.20	$30.53	$50.74
1 Laborer	23.80	190.40	40.05	320.40		
1 Plumber	38.00	304.00	62.70	501.60		
1 Plumber Apprentice	30.40	243.20	50.15	401.20		
1 Equip. Oper. (crane)	34.65	277.20	57.40	459.20		
1 S.P. Crane, 4x4, 12 Ton		481.20		529.32	12.03	13.23
40 L.H., Daily Totals		$1702.40		$2558.92	$42.56	$63.97

Crew B-21B

Crew No.	Bare Costs Hr.	Daily	Incl. Subs O&P Hr.	Daily	Cost Per Labor-Hour Bare Costs	Incl. O&P
1 Labor Foreman (outside)	$25.80	$206.40	$43.40	$347.20	$26.37	$44.19
3 Laborers	23.80	571.20	40.05	961.20		
1 Equip. Oper. (crane)	34.65	277.20	57.40	459.20		
1 Hyd. Crane, 12 Ton		663.00		729.30	16.57	18.23
40 L.H., Daily Totals		$1717.80		$2496.90	$42.95	$62.42

Crew B-21C

Crew No.	Bare Costs Hr.	Daily	Incl. Subs O&P Hr.	Daily	Cost Per Labor-Hour Bare Costs	Incl. O&P
1 Labor Foreman (outside)	$25.80	$206.40	$43.40	$347.20	$26.53	$44.39
4 Laborers	23.80	761.60	40.05	1281.60		
1 Equip. Oper. (crane)	34.65	277.20	57.40	459.20		
1 Equip. Oper. (oiler)	30.05	240.40	49.75	398.00		
2 Cutting Torches		22.80		25.08		
2 Sets of Gases		304.00		334.40		
1 Lattice Boom Crane, 90 Ton		1529.00		1681.90	33.14	36.45
56 L.H., Daily Totals		$3341.40		$4527.38	$59.67	$80.85

Crew B-22

Crew No.	Bare Costs Hr.	Daily	Incl. Subs O&P Hr.	Daily	Cost Per Labor-Hour Bare Costs	Incl. O&P
1 Labor Foreman (outside)	$25.80	$206.40	$43.40	$347.20	$26.50	$44.41
2 Laborers	23.80	380.80	40.05	640.80		
.75 Equip. Oper. (crane)	34.65	207.90	57.40	344.40		
.75 S.P. Crane, 4x4, 5 Ton		210.00		231.00	7.00	7.70
30 L.H., Daily Totals		$1005.10		$1563.40	$33.50	$52.11

Crew B-22A

Crew No.	Bare Costs Hr.	Daily	Incl. Subs O&P Hr.	Daily	Cost Per Labor-Hour Bare Costs	Incl. O&P
1 Labor Foreman (outside)	$25.80	$206.40	$43.40	$347.20	$28.10	$47.14
1 Skilled Worker	32.45	259.60	54.80	438.40		
2 Laborers	23.80	380.80	40.05	640.80		
1 Equipment Operator, Crane	34.65	277.20	57.40	459.20		
1 S.P. Crane, 4x4, 5 Ton		280.00		308.00		
1 Butt Fusion Mach., 4"-12" diam.		381.80		419.98	16.55	18.20
40 L.H., Daily Totals		$1785.80		$2613.58	$44.65	$65.34

Crew B-22B

Crew No.	Bare Costs Hr.	Daily	Incl. Subs O&P Hr.	Daily	Cost Per Labor-Hour Bare Costs	Incl. O&P
1 Labor Foreman (outside)	$25.80	$206.40	$43.40	$347.20	$28.10	$47.14
1 Skilled Worker	32.45	259.60	54.80	438.40		
2 Laborers	23.80	380.80	40.05	640.80		
1 Equip. Oper. (crane)	34.65	277.20	57.40	459.20		
1 S.P. Crane, 4x4, 5 Ton		280.00		308.00		
1 Butt Fusion Mach., 8"-24" diam.		828.40		911.24	27.71	30.48
40 L.H., Daily Totals		$2232.40		$3104.84	$55.81	$77.62

Crew B-22C

Crew No.	Bare Costs Hr.	Daily	Incl. Subs O&P Hr.	Daily	Cost Per Labor-Hour Bare Costs	Incl. O&P
1 Skilled Worker	$32.45	$259.60	$54.80	$438.40	$28.13	$47.42
1 Laborer	23.80	190.40	40.05	320.40		
1 Butt Fusion Mach., 2"-8" diam.		120.95		133.04	7.56	8.32
16 L.H., Daily Totals		$570.95		$891.85	$35.68	$55.74

Crew B-23

Crew No.	Bare Costs Hr.	Daily	Incl. Subs O&P Hr.	Daily	Cost Per Labor-Hour Bare Costs	Incl. O&P
1 Labor Foreman (outside)	$25.80	$206.40	$43.40	$347.20	$24.20	$40.72
4 Laborers	23.80	761.60	40.05	1281.60		
1 Drill Rig, Truck-Mounted		2551.00		2806.10		
1 Flatbed Truck, Gas, 3 Ton		333.00		366.30	72.10	79.31
40 L.H., Daily Totals		$3852.00		$4801.20	$96.30	$120.03

Crew B-23A

Crew No.	Bare Costs Hr.	Daily	Incl. Subs O&P Hr.	Daily	Cost Per Labor-Hour Bare Costs	Incl. O&P
1 Labor Foreman (outside)	$25.80	$206.40	$43.40	$347.20	$27.78	$46.45
1 Laborer	23.80	190.40	40.05	320.40		
1 Equip. Oper. (medium)	33.75	270.00	55.90	447.20		
1 Drill Rig, Truck-Mounted		2551.00		2806.10		
1 Pickup Truck, 3/4 Ton		157.00		172.70	112.83	124.12
24 L.H., Daily Totals		$3374.80		$4093.60	$140.62	$170.57

Crew B-23B

Crew No.	Bare Costs Hr.	Daily	Incl. Subs O&P Hr.	Daily	Cost Per Labor-Hour Bare Costs	Incl. O&P
1 Labor Foreman (outside)	$25.80	$206.40	$43.40	$347.20	$27.78	$46.45
1 Laborer	23.80	190.40	40.05	320.40		
1 Equip. Oper. (medium)	33.75	270.00	55.90	447.20		
1 Drill Rig, Truck-Mounted		2551.00		2806.10		
1 Pickup Truck, 3/4 Ton		157.00		172.70		
1 Centr. Water Pump, 6"		340.80		374.88	127.03	139.74
24 L.H., Daily Totals		$3715.60		$4468.48	$154.82	$186.19

Crew B-24

Crew No.	Bare Costs Hr.	Daily	Incl. Subs O&P Hr.	Daily	Cost Per Labor-Hour Bare Costs	Incl. O&P
1 Cement Finisher	$30.85	$246.80	$49.90	$399.20	$28.92	$47.98
1 Laborer	23.80	190.40	40.05	320.40		
1 Carpenter	32.10	256.80	54.00	432.00		
24 L.H., Daily Totals		$694.00		$1151.60	$28.92	$47.98

Crew B-25

Crew No.	Bare Costs Hr.	Daily	Incl. Subs O&P Hr.	Daily	Cost Per Labor-Hour Bare Costs	Incl. O&P
1 Labor Foreman (outside)	$25.80	$206.40	$43.40	$347.20	$26.70	$44.68
7 Laborers	23.80	1332.80	40.05	2242.80		
3 Equip. Oper. (medium)	33.75	810.00	55.90	1341.60		
1 Asphalt Paver, 130 H.P.		2169.00		2385.90		
1 Tandem Roller, 10 Ton		242.00		266.20		
1 Roller, Pneum. Whl., 12 Ton		349.00		383.90	31.36	34.50
88 L.H., Daily Totals		$5109.20		$6967.60	$58.06	$79.18

Crew B-25B

Crew No.	Bare Costs Hr.	Daily	Incl. Subs O&P Hr.	Daily	Cost Per Labor-Hour Bare Costs	Incl. O&P
1 Labor Foreman (outside)	$25.80	$206.40	$43.40	$347.20	$27.28	$45.61
7 Laborers	23.80	1332.80	40.05	2242.80		
4 Equip. Oper. (medium)	33.75	1080.00	55.90	1788.80		
1 Asphalt Paver, 130 H.P.		2169.00		2385.90		
2 Tandem Rollers, 10 Ton		484.00		532.40		
1 Roller, Pneum. Whl., 12 Ton		349.00		383.90	31.27	34.40
96 L.H., Daily Totals		$5621.20		$7681.00	$58.55	$80.01

Crew B-25C

Crew No.	Bare Costs Hr.	Daily	Incl. Subs O&P Hr.	Daily	Cost Per Labor-Hour Bare Costs	Incl. O&P
1 Labor Foreman (outside)	$25.80	$206.40	$43.40	$347.20	$27.45	$45.89
3 Laborers	23.80	571.20	40.05	961.20		
2 Equip. Oper. (medium)	33.75	540.00	55.90	894.40		
1 Asphalt Paver, 130 H.P.		2169.00		2385.90		
1 Tandem Roller, 10 Ton		242.00		266.20	50.23	55.25
48 L.H., Daily Totals		$3728.60		$4854.90	$77.68	$101.14

Crew B-25D

Crew No.	Bare Costs Hr.	Daily	Incl. Subs O&P Hr.	Daily	Cost Per Labor-Hour Bare Costs	Incl. O&P
1 Labor Foreman (outside)	$25.80	$206.40	$43.40	$347.20	$27.56	$46.06
3 Laborers	23.80	571.20	40.05	961.20		
2.125 Equip. Oper. (medium)	33.75	573.75	55.90	950.30		
.125 Truck Driver (heavy)	26.65	26.65	44.40	44.40		
.125 Truck Tractor, 6x4, 380 H.P.		76.60		84.26		
.125 Dist. Tanker, 3000 Gallon		38.52		42.38		
1 Asphalt Paver, 130 H.P.		2169.00		2385.90		
1 Tandem Roller, 10 Ton		242.00		266.20	50.52	55.57
50 L.H., Daily Totals		$3904.13		$5081.84	$78.08	$101.64

Crew B-25E

Crew No.	Bare Costs Hr.	Daily	Incl. Subs O&P Hr.	Daily	Cost Per Labor-Hour Bare Costs	Incl. O&P
1 Labor Foreman (outside)	$25.80	$206.40	$43.40	$347.20	$27.66	$46.22
3 Laborers	23.80	571.20	40.05	961.20		
2.250 Equip. Oper. (medium)	33.75	607.50	55.90	1006.20		
.25 Truck Driver (heavy)	26.65	53.30	44.40	88.80		
.25 Truck Tractor, 6x4, 380 H.P.		153.20		168.52		
.25 Dist. Tanker, 3000 Gallon		77.05		84.75		
1 Asphalt Paver, 130 H.P.		2169.00		2385.90		
1 Tandem Roller, 10 Ton		242.00		266.20	50.79	55.87
52 L.H., Daily Totals		$4079.65		$5308.77	$78.45	$102.09

Crew B-26

Crew No.	Bare Costs Hr.	Daily	Incl. Subs O&P Hr.	Daily	Cost Per Labor-Hour Bare Costs	Incl. O&P
1 Labor Foreman (outside)	$25.80	$206.40	$43.40	$347.20	$27.35	$45.77
6 Laborers	23.80	1142.40	40.05	1922.40		
2 Equip. Oper. (medium)	33.75	540.00	55.90	894.40		
1 Rodman (reinf.)	33.95	271.60	58.10	464.80		
1 Cement Finisher	30.85	246.80	49.90	399.20		
1 Grader, 30,000 Lbs.		707.00		777.70		
1 Paving Mach. & Equip.		2657.00		2922.70	38.23	42.05
88 L.H., Daily Totals		$5771.20		$7728.40	$65.58	$87.82

Crew B-26A

Crew No.	Bare Costs Hr.	Daily	Incl. Subs O&P Hr.	Daily	Cost Per Labor-Hour Bare Costs	Incl. O&P
1 Labor Foreman (outside)	$25.80	$206.40	$43.40	$347.20	$27.35	$45.77
6 Laborers	23.80	1142.40	40.05	1922.40		
2 Equip. Oper. (medium)	33.75	540.00	55.90	894.40		
1 Rodman (reinf.)	33.95	271.60	58.10	464.80		
1 Cement Finisher	30.85	246.80	49.90	399.20		
1 Grader, 30,000 Lbs.		707.00		777.70		
1 Paving Mach. & Equip.		2657.00		2922.70		
1 Concrete Saw		175.20		192.72	40.22	44.24
88 L.H., Daily Totals		$5946.40		$7921.12	$67.57	$90.01

Crew B-26B

Crew No.	Bare Costs Hr.	Daily	Incl. Subs O&P Hr.	Daily	Cost Per Labor-Hour Bare Costs	Incl. O&P
1 Labor Foreman (outside)	$25.80	$206.40	$43.40	$347.20	$27.89	$46.62
6 Laborers	23.80	1142.40	40.05	1922.40		
3 Equip. Oper. (medium)	33.75	810.00	55.90	1341.60		
1 Rodman (reinf.)	33.95	271.60	58.10	464.80		
1 Cement Finisher	30.85	246.80	49.90	399.20		
1 Grader, 30,000 Lbs.		707.00		777.70		
1 Paving Mach. & Equip.		2657.00		2922.70		
1 Concrete Pump, 110' Boom		934.00		1027.40	44.77	49.25
96 L.H., Daily Totals		$6975.20		$9203.00	$72.66	$95.86

Crew B-26C

Crew No.	Bare Costs Hr.	Daily	Incl. Subs O&P Hr.	Daily	Cost Per Labor-Hour Bare Costs	Incl. O&P
1 Labor Foreman (outside)	$25.80	$206.40	$43.40	$347.20	$26.72	$44.76
6 Laborers	23.80	1142.40	40.05	1922.40		
1 Equip. Oper. (medium)	33.75	270.00	55.90	447.20		
1 Rodman (reinf.)	33.95	271.60	58.10	464.80		
1 Cement Finisher	30.85	246.80	49.90	399.20		
1 Paving Mach. & Equip.		2657.00		2922.70		
1 Concrete Saw		175.20		192.72	35.40	38.94
80 L.H., Daily Totals		$4969.40		$6696.22	$62.12	$83.70

Crew B-27

Crew No.	Bare Costs Hr.	Daily	Incl. Subs O&P Hr.	Daily	Cost Per Labor-Hour Bare Costs	Incl. O&P
1 Labor Foreman (outside)	$25.80	$206.40	$43.40	$347.20	$24.30	$40.89
3 Laborers	23.80	571.20	40.05	961.20		
1 Berm Machine		294.40		323.84	9.20	10.12
32 L.H., Daily Totals		$1072.00		$1632.24	$33.50	$51.01

Crew B-28

Crew No.	Bare Costs Hr.	Daily	Incl. Subs O&P Hr.	Daily	Cost Per Labor-Hour Bare Costs	Incl. O&P
2 Carpenters	$32.10	$513.60	$54.00	$864.00	$29.33	$49.35
1 Laborer	23.80	190.40	40.05	320.40		
24 L.H., Daily Totals		$704.00		$1184.40	$29.33	$49.35

Crew B-29

Crew No.	Bare Costs Hr.	Daily	Incl. Subs O&P Hr.	Daily	Cost Per Labor-Hour Bare Costs	Incl. O&P
1 Labor Foreman (outside)	$25.80	$206.40	$43.40	$347.20	$25.94	$43.50
4 Laborers	23.80	761.60	40.05	1281.60		
1 Equip. Oper. (crane)	34.65	277.20	57.40	459.20		
1 Gradall, 5/8 C.Y.		881.60		969.76	18.37	20.20
48 L.H., Daily Totals		$2126.80		$3057.76	$44.31	$63.70

Crew B-30

Crew No.	Bare Costs Hr.	Daily	Incl. Subs O&P Hr.	Daily	Cost Per Labor-Hour Bare Costs	Incl. O&P
1 Equip. Oper. (medium)	$33.75	$270.00	$55.90	$447.20	$29.02	$48.23
2 Truck Drivers (heavy)	26.65	426.40	44.40	710.40		
1 Hyd. Excavator, 1.5 C.Y.		1031.00		1134.10		
2 Dump Trucks, 12 C.Y., 400 H.P.		1384.40		1522.84	100.64	110.71
24 L.H., Daily Totals		$3111.80		$3814.54	$129.66	$158.94

Crew B-31

Crew No.	Bare Costs Hr.	Daily	Incl. Subs O&P Hr.	Daily	Cost Per Labor-Hour Bare Costs	Incl. O&P
1 Labor Foreman (outside)	$25.80	$206.40	$43.40	$347.20	$24.20	$40.72
4 Laborers	23.80	761.60	40.05	1281.60		
1 Air Compressor, 250 cfm		202.40		222.64		
1 Sheeting Driver		5.30		5.83		
2 -50' Air Hoses, 1.5"		11.60		12.76	5.48	6.03
40 L.H., Daily Totals		$1187.30		$1870.03	$29.68	$46.75

Crew B-32

Crew No.	Bare Costs Hr.	Daily	Incl. Subs O&P Hr.	Daily	Cost Per Labor-Hour Bare Costs	Incl. O&P
1 Laborer	$23.80	$190.40	$40.05	$320.40	$31.26	$51.94
3 Equip. Oper. (medium)	33.75	810.00	55.90	1341.60		
1 Grader, 30,000 Lbs.		707.00		777.70		
1 Tandem Roller, 10 Ton		242.00		266.20		
1 Dozer, 200 H.P.		1325.00		1457.50	71.06	78.17
32 L.H., Daily Totals		$3274.40		$4163.40	$102.33	$130.11

Crew B-32A

Crew No.	Bare Costs Hr.	Daily	Incl. Subs O&P Hr.	Daily	Cost Per Labor-Hour Bare Costs	Incl. O&P
1 Laborer	$23.80	$190.40	$40.05	$320.40	$30.43	$50.62
2 Equip. Oper. (medium)	33.75	540.00	55.90	894.40		
1 Grader, 30,000 Lbs.		707.00		777.70		
1 Roller, Vibratory, 25 Ton		692.80		762.08	58.33	64.16
24 L.H., Daily Totals		$2130.20		$2754.58	$88.76	$114.77

Crew B-32B	Hr.	Daily	Hr.	Daily	Bare Costs	Incl. O&P
1 Laborer	$23.80	$190.40	$40.05	$320.40	$30.43	$50.62
2 Equip. Oper. (medium)	33.75	540.00	55.90	894.40		
1 Dozer, 200 H.P.		1325.00		1457.50		
1 Roller, Vibratory, 25 Ton		692.80		762.08	84.08	92.48
24 L.H., Daily Totals		$2748.20		$3434.38	$114.51	$143.10

Crew B-32C	Hr.	Daily	Hr.	Daily	Bare Costs	Incl. O&P
1 Labor Foreman (outside)	$25.80	$206.40	$43.40	$347.20	$29.11	$48.53
2 Laborers	23.80	380.80	40.05	640.80		
3 Equip. Oper. (medium)	33.75	810.00	55.90	1341.60		
1 Grader, 30,000 Lbs.		707.00		777.70		
1 Tandem Roller, 10 Ton		242.00		266.20		
1 Dozer, 200 H.P.		1325.00		1457.50	47.38	52.11
48 L.H., Daily Totals		$3671.20		$4831.00	$76.48	$100.65

Crew B-33A	Hr.	Daily	Hr.	Daily	Bare Costs	Incl. O&P
1 Equip. Oper. (medium)	$33.75	$270.00	$55.90	$447.20	$33.75	$55.90
.25 Equip. Oper. (medium)	33.75	67.50	55.90	111.80		
1 Scraper, Towed, 7 C.Y.		111.60		122.76		
1.250 Dozers, 300 H.P.		2271.25		2498.38	238.29	262.11
10 L.H., Daily Totals		$2720.35		$3180.14	$272.04	$318.01

Crew B-33B	Hr.	Daily	Hr.	Daily	Bare Costs	Incl. O&P
1 Equip. Oper. (medium)	$33.75	$270.00	$55.90	$447.20	$33.75	$55.90
.25 Equip. Oper. (medium)	33.75	67.50	55.90	111.80		
1 Scraper, Towed, 10 C.Y.		141.60		155.76		
1.250 Dozers, 300 H.P.		2271.25		2498.38	241.29	265.41
10 L.H., Daily Totals		$2750.35		$3213.14	$275.04	$321.31

Crew B-33C	Hr.	Daily	Hr.	Daily	Bare Costs	Incl. O&P
1 Equip. Oper. (medium)	$33.75	$270.00	$55.90	$447.20	$33.75	$55.90
.25 Equip. Oper. (medium)	33.75	67.50	55.90	111.80		
1 Scraper, Towed, 15 C.Y.		158.80		174.68		
1.250 Dozers, 300 H.P.		2271.25		2498.38	243.01	267.31
10 L.H., Daily Totals		$2767.55		$3232.05	$276.76	$323.21

Crew B-33D	Hr.	Daily	Hr.	Daily	Bare Costs	Incl. O&P
1 Equip. Oper. (medium)	$33.75	$270.00	$55.90	$447.20	$33.75	$55.90
.25 Equip. Oper. (medium)	33.75	67.50	55.90	111.80		
1 S.P. Scraper, 14 C.Y.		1829.00		2011.90		
.25 Dozer, 300 H.P.		454.25		499.68	228.32	251.16
10 L.H., Daily Totals		$2620.75		$3070.57	$262.07	$307.06

Crew B-33E	Hr.	Daily	Hr.	Daily	Bare Costs	Incl. O&P
1 Equip. Oper. (medium)	$33.75	$270.00	$55.90	$447.20	$33.75	$55.90
.25 Equip. Oper. (medium)	33.75	67.50	55.90	111.80		
1 S.P. Scraper, 21 C.Y.		2599.00		2858.90		
.25 Dozer, 300 H.P.		454.25		499.68	305.32	335.86
10 L.H., Daily Totals		$3390.75		$3917.57	$339.07	$391.76

Crew B-33F	Hr.	Daily	Hr.	Daily	Bare Costs	Incl. O&P
1 Equip. Oper. (medium)	$33.75	$270.00	$55.90	$447.20	$33.75	$55.90
.25 Equip. Oper. (medium)	33.75	67.50	55.90	111.80		
1 Elev. Scraper, 11 C.Y.		1180.00		1298.00		
.25 Dozer, 300 H.P.		454.25		499.68	163.43	179.77
10 L.H., Daily Totals		$1971.75		$2356.68	$197.18	$235.67

Crew B-33G	Hr.	Daily	Hr.	Daily	Bare Costs	Incl. O&P
1 Equip. Oper. (medium)	$33.75	$270.00	$55.90	$447.20	$33.75	$55.90
.25 Equip. Oper. (medium)	33.75	67.50	55.90	111.80		
1 Elev. Scraper, 22 C.Y.		2443.00		2687.30		
.25 Dozer, 300 H.P.		454.25		499.68	289.73	318.70
10 L.H., Daily Totals		$3234.75		$3745.97	$323.48	$374.60

Crew B-33K	Hr.	Daily	Hr.	Daily	Bare Costs	Incl. O&P
1 Equipment Operator (med.)	$33.75	$270.00	$55.90	$447.20	$30.91	$51.37
.25 Equipment Operator (med.)	33.75	67.50	55.90	111.80		
.5 Laborer	23.80	95.20	40.05	160.20		
1 S.P. Scraper, 31 C.Y.		3566.00		3922.60		
.25 Dozer, 410 H.P.		602.25		662.48	297.73	327.51
14 L.H., Daily Totals		$4600.95		$5304.27	$328.64	$378.88

Crew B-34A	Hr.	Daily	Hr.	Daily	Bare Costs	Incl. O&P
1 Truck Driver (heavy)	$26.65	$213.20	$44.40	$355.20	$26.65	$44.40
1 Dump Truck, 8 C.Y., 220 H.P.		417.20		458.92	52.15	57.37
8 L.H., Daily Totals		$630.40		$814.12	$78.80	$101.77

Crew B-34B	Hr.	Daily	Hr.	Daily	Bare Costs	Incl. O&P
1 Truck Driver (heavy)	$26.65	$213.20	$44.40	$355.20	$26.65	$44.40
1 Dump Truck, 12 C.Y., 400 H.P.		692.20		761.42	86.53	95.18
8 L.H., Daily Totals		$905.40		$1116.62	$113.18	$139.58

Crew B-34C	Hr.	Daily	Hr.	Daily	Bare Costs	Incl. O&P
1 Truck Driver (heavy)	$26.65	$213.20	$44.40	$355.20	$26.65	$44.40
1 Truck Tractor, 6x4, 380 H.P.		612.80		674.08		
1 Dump Trailer, 16.5 C.Y.		126.20		138.82	92.38	101.61
8 L.H., Daily Totals		$952.20		$1168.10	$119.03	$146.01

Crew B-34D	Hr.	Daily	Hr.	Daily	Bare Costs	Incl. O&P
1 Truck Driver (heavy)	$26.65	$213.20	$44.40	$355.20	$26.65	$44.40
1 Truck Tractor, 6x4, 380 H.P.		612.80		674.08		
1 Dump Trailer, 20 C.Y.		140.80		154.88	94.20	103.62
8 L.H., Daily Totals		$966.80		$1184.16	$120.85	$148.02

Crew B-34E	Hr.	Daily	Hr.	Daily	Bare Costs	Incl. O&P
1 Truck Driver (heavy)	$26.65	$213.20	$44.40	$355.20	$26.65	$44.40
1 Dump Truck, Off Hwy., 25 Ton		1314.00		1445.40	164.25	180.68
8 L.H., Daily Totals		$1527.20		$1800.60	$190.90	$225.07

Crew B-34F	Hr.	Daily	Hr.	Daily	Bare Costs	Incl. O&P
1 Truck Driver (heavy)	$26.65	$213.20	$44.40	$355.20	$26.65	$44.40
1 Dump Truck, Off Hwy., 35 Ton		1470.00		1617.00	183.75	202.13
8 L.H., Daily Totals		$1683.20		$1972.20	$210.40	$246.53

Crew B-34G	Hr.	Daily	Hr.	Daily	Bare Costs	Incl. O&P
1 Truck Driver (heavy)	$26.65	$213.20	$44.40	$355.20	$26.65	$44.40
1 Dump Truck, Off Hwy., 50 Ton		1787.00		1965.70	223.38	245.71
8 L.H., Daily Totals		$2000.20		$2320.90	$250.03	$290.11

Crew B-34H	Hr.	Daily	Hr.	Daily	Bare Costs	Incl. O&P
1 Truck Driver (heavy)	$26.65	$213.20	$44.40	$355.20	$26.65	$44.40
1 Dump Truck, Off Hwy., 65 Ton		1797.00		1976.70	224.63	247.09
8 L.H., Daily Totals		$2010.20		$2331.90	$251.28	$291.49

Crews

Crew B-34I

Crew No.	Hr.	Daily	Hr.	Daily	Bare Costs	Incl. O&P
1 Truck Driver (heavy)	$26.65	$213.20	$44.40	$355.20	$26.65	$44.40
1 Dump Truck, 18 C.Y., 450 H.P.		867.60		954.36	108.45	119.30
8 L.H., Daily Totals		$1080.80		$1309.56	$135.10	$163.69

Crew B-34J

Crew No.	Hr.	Daily	Hr.	Daily	Bare Costs	Incl. O&P
1 Truck Driver (heavy)	$26.65	$213.20	$44.40	$355.20	$26.65	$44.40
1 Dump Truck, Off Hwy., 100 Ton		2898.00		3187.80	362.25	398.48
8 L.H., Daily Totals		$3111.20		$3543.00	$388.90	$442.88

Crew B-34K

Crew No.	Hr.	Daily	Hr.	Daily	Bare Costs	Incl. O&P
1 Truck Driver (heavy)	$26.65	$213.20	$44.40	$355.20	$26.65	$44.40
1 Truck Tractor, 6x4, 450 H.P.		742.40		816.64		
1 Lowbed Trailer, 75 Ton		219.80		241.78	120.28	132.30
8 L.H., Daily Totals		$1175.40		$1413.62	$146.93	$176.70

Crew B-34L

Crew No.	Hr.	Daily	Hr.	Daily	Bare Costs	Incl. O&P
1 Equip. Oper. (light)	$32.45	$259.60	$53.75	$430.00	$32.45	$53.75
1 Flatbed Truck, Gas, 1.5 Ton		270.20		297.22	33.77	37.15
8 L.H., Daily Totals		$529.80		$727.22	$66.22	$90.90

Crew B-34M

Crew No.	Hr.	Daily	Hr.	Daily	Bare Costs	Incl. O&P
1 Equip. Oper. (light)	$32.45	$259.60	$53.75	$430.00	$32.45	$53.75
1 Flatbed Truck, Gas, 3 Ton		333.00		366.30	41.63	45.79
8 L.H., Daily Totals		$592.60		$796.30	$74.08	$99.54

Crew B-34N

Crew No.	Hr.	Daily	Hr.	Daily	Bare Costs	Incl. O&P
1 Truck Driver (heavy)	$26.65	$213.20	$44.40	$355.20	$26.65	$44.40
1 Dump Truck, 8 C.Y., 220 H.P.		417.20		458.92		
1 Flatbed Trailer, 40 Ton		152.00		167.20	71.15	78.27
8 L.H., Daily Totals		$782.40		$981.32	$97.80	$122.67

Crew B-34P

Crew No.	Hr.	Daily	Hr.	Daily	Bare Costs	Incl. O&P
1 Pipe Fitter	$38.60	$308.80	$63.70	$509.60	$32.75	$54.25
1 Truck Driver (light)	25.90	207.20	43.15	345.20		
1 Equip. Oper. (medium)	33.75	270.00	55.90	447.20		
1 Flatbed Truck, Gas, 3 Ton		333.00		366.30		
1 Backhoe Loader, 48 H.P.		365.20		401.72	29.09	32.00
24 L.H., Daily Totals		$1484.20		$2070.02	$61.84	$86.25

Crew B-34Q

Crew No.	Hr.	Daily	Hr.	Daily	Bare Costs	Incl. O&P
1 Pipe Fitter	$38.60	$308.80	$63.70	$509.60	$33.05	$54.75
1 Truck Driver (light)	25.90	207.20	43.15	345.20		
1 Equip. Oper. (crane)	34.65	277.20	57.40	459.20		
1 Flatbed Trailer, 25 Ton		113.60		124.96		
1 Dump Truck, 8 C.Y., 220 H.P.		417.20		458.92		
1 Hyd. Crane, 25 Ton		745.80		820.38	53.19	58.51
24 L.H., Daily Totals		$2069.80		$2718.26	$86.24	$113.26

Crew B-34R

Crew No.	Hr.	Daily	Hr.	Daily	Bare Costs	Incl. O&P
1 Pipe Fitter	$38.60	$308.80	$63.70	$509.60	$33.05	$54.75
1 Truck Driver (light)	25.90	207.20	43.15	345.20		
1 Equip. Oper. (crane)	34.65	277.20	57.40	459.20		
1 Flatbed Trailer, 25 Ton		113.60		124.96		
1 Dump Truck, 8 C.Y., 220 H.P.		417.20		458.92		
1 Hyd. Crane, 25 Ton		745.80		820.38		
1 Hyd. Excavator, 1 C.Y.		814.80		896.28	87.14	95.86
24 L.H., Daily Totals		$2884.60		$3614.54	$120.19	$150.61

Crew B-34S

Crew No.	Hr.	Daily	Hr.	Daily	Bare Costs	Incl. O&P
2 Pipe Fitters	$38.60	$617.60	$63.70	$1019.20	$34.63	$57.30
1 Truck Driver (heavy)	26.65	213.20	44.40	355.20		
1 Equip. Oper. (crane)	34.65	277.20	57.40	459.20		
1 Flatbed Trailer, 40 Ton		152.00		167.20		
1 Truck Tractor, 6x4, 380 H.P.		612.80		674.08		
1 Hyd. Crane, 80 Ton		1652.00		1817.20		
1 Hyd. Excavator, 2 C.Y.		1175.00		1292.50	112.24	123.47
32 L.H., Daily Totals		$4699.80		$5784.58	$146.87	$180.77

Crew B-34T

Crew No.	Hr.	Daily	Hr.	Daily	Bare Costs	Incl. O&P
2 Pipe Fitters	$38.60	$617.60	$63.70	$1019.20	$34.63	$57.30
1 Truck Driver (heavy)	26.65	213.20	44.40	355.20		
1 Equip. Oper. (crane)	34.65	277.20	57.40	459.20		
1 Flatbed Trailer, 40 Ton		152.00		167.20		
1 Truck Tractor, 6x4, 380 H.P.		612.80		674.08		
1 Hyd. Crane, 80 Ton		1652.00		1817.20	75.53	83.08
32 L.H., Daily Totals		$3524.80		$4492.08	$110.15	$140.38

Crew B-35

Crew No.	Hr.	Daily	Hr.	Daily	Bare Costs	Incl. O&P
1 Labor Foreman (outside)	$25.80	$206.40	$43.40	$347.20	$30.94	$51.67
1 Skilled Worker	32.45	259.60	54.80	438.40		
1 Welder (plumber)	38.00	304.00	62.70	501.60		
1 Laborer	23.80	190.40	40.05	320.40		
1 Equip. Oper. (crane)	34.65	277.20	57.40	459.20		
1 Welder, Electric, 300 amp		55.30		60.83		
1 Hyd. Excavator, .75 C.Y.		662.00		728.20	17.93	19.73
40 L.H., Daily Totals		$1954.90		$2855.83	$48.87	$71.40

Crew B-35A

Crew No.	Hr.	Daily	Hr.	Daily	Bare Costs	Incl. O&P
1 Labor Foreman (outside)	$25.80	$206.40	$43.40	$347.20	$29.79	$49.74
2 Laborers	23.80	380.80	40.05	640.80		
1 Skilled Worker	32.45	259.60	54.80	438.40		
1 Welder (plumber)	38.00	304.00	62.70	501.60		
1 Equip. Oper. (crane)	34.65	277.20	57.40	459.20		
1 Equip. Oper. (oiler)	30.05	240.40	49.75	398.00		
1 Welder, Gas Engine, 300 amp		142.00		156.20		
1 Crawler Crane, 75 Ton		1492.00		1641.20	29.18	32.10
56 L.H., Daily Totals		$3302.40		$4582.60	$58.97	$81.83

Crew B-36

Crew No.	Hr.	Daily	Hr.	Daily	Bare Costs	Incl. O&P
1 Labor Foreman (outside)	$25.80	$206.40	$43.40	$347.20	$28.18	$47.06
2 Laborers	23.80	380.80	40.05	640.80		
2 Equip. Oper. (medium)	33.75	540.00	55.90	894.40		
1 Dozer, 200 H.P.		1325.00		1457.50		
1 Aggregate Spreader		41.20		45.32		
1 Tandem Roller, 10 Ton		242.00		266.20	40.20	44.23
40 L.H., Daily Totals		$2735.40		$3651.42	$68.39	$91.29

Crew B-36A

Crew No.	Hr.	Daily	Hr.	Daily	Bare Costs	Incl. O&P
1 Labor Foreman (outside)	$25.80	$206.40	$43.40	$347.20	$29.77	$49.59
2 Laborers	23.80	380.80	40.05	640.80		
4 Equip. Oper. (medium)	33.75	1080.00	55.90	1788.80		
1 Dozer, 200 H.P.		1325.00		1457.50		
1 Aggregate Spreader		41.20		45.32		
1 Tandem Roller, 10 Ton		242.00		266.20		
1 Roller, Pneum. Whl., 12 Ton		349.00		383.90	34.95	38.45
56 L.H., Daily Totals		$3624.40		$4929.72	$64.72	$88.03

Crew No.	Bare Costs		Incl. Subs O&P		Cost Per Labor-Hour	

Crew B-36B

Crew B-36B	Hr.	Daily	Hr.	Daily	Bare Costs	Incl. O&P
1 Labor Foreman (outside)	$25.80	$206.40	$43.40	$347.20	$29.38	$48.94
2 Laborers	23.80	380.80	40.05	640.80		
4 Equip. Oper. (medium)	33.75	1080.00	55.90	1788.80		
1 Truck Driver (heavy)	26.65	213.20	44.40	355.20		
1 Grader, 30,000 Lbs.		707.00		777.70		
1 F.E. Loader, Crl. 1.5 C.Y.		625.20		687.72		
1 Dozer, 300 H.P.		1817.00		1998.70		
1 Roller, Vibratory, 25 Ton		692.80		762.08		
1 Truck Tractor, 6x4, 450 H.P.		742.40		816.64		
1 Water Tank Trailer, 5000 Gal.		141.60		155.76	73.84	81.23
64 L.H., Daily Totals		$6606.40		$8330.60	$103.23	$130.17

Crew B-36C	Hr.	Daily	Hr.	Daily	Bare Costs	Incl. O&P
1 Labor Foreman (outside)	$25.80	$206.40	$43.40	$347.20	$30.74	$51.10
3 Equip. Oper. (medium)	33.75	810.00	55.90	1341.60		
1 Truck Driver (heavy)	26.65	213.20	44.40	355.20		
1 Grader, 30,000 Lbs.		707.00		777.70		
1 Dozer, 300 H.P.		1817.00		1998.70		
1 Roller, Vibratory, 25 Ton		692.80		762.08		
1 Truck Tractor, 6x4, 450 H.P.		742.40		816.64		
1 Water Tank Trailer, 5000 Gal.		141.60		155.76	102.52	112.77
40 L.H., Daily Totals		$5330.40		$6554.88	$133.26	$163.87

Crew B-36E	Hr.	Daily	Hr.	Daily	Bare Costs	Incl. O&P
1 Labor Foreman (outside)	$25.80	$206.40	$43.40	$347.20	$31.24	$51.90
4 Equip. Oper. (medium)	33.75	1080.00	55.90	1788.80		
1 Truck Driver (heavy)	26.65	213.20	44.40	355.20		
1 Grader, 30,000 Lbs.		707.00		777.70		
1 Dozer, 300 H.P.		1817.00		1998.70		
1 Roller, Vibratory, 25 Ton		692.80		762.08		
1 Truck Tractor, 6x4, 380 H.P.		612.80		674.08		
1 Dist. Tanker, 3000 Gallon		308.20		339.02	86.20	94.82
48 L.H., Daily Totals		$5637.40		$7042.78	$117.45	$146.72

Crew B-37	Hr.	Daily	Hr.	Daily	Bare Costs	Incl. O&P
1 Labor Foreman (outside)	$25.80	$206.40	$43.40	$347.20	$25.57	$42.89
4 Laborers	23.80	761.60	40.05	1281.60		
1 Equip. Oper. (light)	32.45	259.60	53.75	430.00		
1 Tandem Roller, 5 Ton		159.00		174.90	3.31	3.64
48 L.H., Daily Totals		$1386.60		$2233.70	$28.89	$46.54

Crew B-37A	Hr.	Daily	Hr.	Daily	Bare Costs	Incl. O&P
2 Laborers	$23.80	$380.80	$40.05	$640.80	$24.50	$41.08
1 Truck Driver (light)	25.90	207.20	43.15	345.20		
1 Flatbed Truck, Gas, 1.5 Ton		270.20		297.22		
1 Tar Kettle, T.M.		104.60		115.06	15.62	17.18
24 L.H., Daily Totals		$962.80		$1398.28	$40.12	$58.26

Crew B-37B	Hr.	Daily	Hr.	Daily	Bare Costs	Incl. O&P
3 Laborers	$23.80	$571.20	$40.05	$961.20	$24.32	$40.83
1 Truck Driver (light)	25.90	207.20	43.15	345.20		
1 Flatbed Truck, Gas, 1.5 Ton		270.20		297.22		
1 Tar Kettle, T.M.		104.60		115.06	11.71	12.88
32 L.H., Daily Totals		$1153.20		$1718.68	$36.04	$53.71

Crew B-37C	Hr.	Daily	Hr.	Daily	Bare Costs	Incl. O&P
2 Laborers	$23.80	$380.80	$40.05	$640.80	$24.85	$41.60
2 Truck Drivers (light)	25.90	414.40	43.15	690.40		
2 Flatbed Trucks, Gas, 1.5 Ton		540.40		594.44		
1 Tar Kettle, T.M.		104.60		115.06	20.16	22.17
32 L.H., Daily Totals		$1440.20		$2040.70	$45.01	$63.77

Crew No.	Bare Costs		Incl. Subs O&P		Cost Per Labor-Hour	

Crew B-37D	Hr.	Daily	Hr.	Daily	Bare Costs	Incl. O&P
1 Laborer	$23.80	$190.40	$40.05	$320.40	$24.85	$41.60
1 Truck Driver (light)	25.90	207.20	43.15	345.20		
1 Pickup Truck, 3/4 Ton		157.00		172.70	9.81	10.79
16 L.H., Daily Totals		$554.60		$838.30	$34.66	$52.39

Crew B-37E	Hr.	Daily	Hr.	Daily	Bare Costs	Incl. O&P
3 Laborers	$23.80	$571.20	$40.05	$961.20	$27.06	$45.16
1 Equip. Oper. (light)	32.45	259.60	53.75	430.00		
1 Equip. Oper. (medium)	33.75	270.00	55.90	447.20		
2 Truck Drivers (light)	25.90	414.40	43.15	690.40		
4 Barrels w/ Flasher		13.60		14.96		
1 Concrete Saw		175.20		192.72		
1 Rotary Hammer Drill		24.00		26.40		
1 Hammer Drill Bit		2.35		2.59		
1 Loader, Skid Steer, 30 H.P.		174.20		191.62		
1 Conc. Hammer Attach.		114.70		126.17		
1 Vibrating Plate, Gas, 18"		35.80		39.38		
2 Flatbed Trucks, Gas, 1.5 Ton		540.40		594.44	19.29	21.22
56 L.H., Daily Totals		$2595.45		$3717.07	$46.35	$66.38

Crew B-37F	Hr.	Daily	Hr.	Daily	Bare Costs	Incl. O&P
3 Laborers	$23.80	$571.20	$40.05	$961.20	$24.32	$40.83
1 Truck Driver (light)	25.90	207.20	43.15	345.20		
4 Barrels w/ Flasher		13.60		14.96		
1 Concrete Mixer, 10 C.F.		176.80		194.48		
1 Air Compressor, 60 cfm		137.40		151.14		
1 -50' Air Hose, 3/4"		3.25		3.58		
1 Spade (Chipper)		7.80		8.58		
1 Flatbed Truck, Gas, 1.5 Ton		270.20		297.22	19.03	20.94
32 L.H., Daily Totals		$1387.45		$1976.36	$43.36	$61.76

Crew B-37G	Hr.	Daily	Hr.	Daily	Bare Costs	Incl. O&P
1 Labor Foreman (outside)	$25.80	$206.40	$43.40	$347.20	$25.57	$42.89
4 Laborers	23.80	761.60	40.05	1281.60		
1 Equip. Oper. (light)	32.45	259.60	53.75	430.00		
1 Berm Machine		294.40		323.84		
1 Tandem Roller, 5 Ton		159.00		174.90	9.45	10.39
48 L.H., Daily Totals		$1681.00		$2557.54	$35.02	$53.28

Crew B-37H	Hr.	Daily	Hr.	Daily	Bare Costs	Incl. O&P
1 Labor Foreman (outside)	$25.80	$206.40	$43.40	$347.20	$25.57	$42.89
4 Laborers	23.80	761.60	40.05	1281.60		
1 Equip. Oper. (light)	32.45	259.60	53.75	430.00		
1 Tandem Roller, 5 Ton		159.00		174.90		
1 Flatbed Trucks, Gas, 1.5 Ton		270.20		297.22		
1 Tar Kettle, T.M.		104.60		115.06	11.12	12.23
48 L.H., Daily Totals		$1761.40		$2645.98	$36.70	$55.12

Crew B-37I

Crew No.	Bare Costs		Incl. Subs O&P		Cost Per Labor-Hour	
Crew B-37I	Hr.	Daily	Hr.	Daily	Bare Costs	Incl. O&P
3 Laborers	$23.80	$571.20	$40.05	$961.20	$27.06	$45.16
1 Equip. Oper. (light)	32.45	259.60	53.75	430.00		
1 Equip. Oper. (medium)	33.75	270.00	55.90	447.20		
2 Truck Drivers (light)	25.90	414.40	43.15	690.40		
4 Barrels w/ Flasher		13.60		14.96		
1 Concrete Saw		175.20		192.72		
1 Rotary Hammer Drill		24.00		26.40		
1 Hammer Drill Bit		2.35		2.59		
1 Air Compressor, 60 cfm		137.40		151.14		
1 -50' Air Hose, 3/4"		3.25		3.58		
1 Spade (Chipper)		7.80		8.58		
1 Loader, Skid Steer, 30 H.P.		174.20		191.62		
1 Conc. Hammer Attach.		114.70		126.17		
1 Concrete Mixer, 10 C.F.		176.80		194.48		
1 Vibrating Plate, Gas, 18"		35.80		39.38		
2 Flatbed Trucks, Gas, 1.5 Ton		540.40		594.44	25.10	27.61
56 L.H., Daily Totals		$2920.70		$4074.85	$52.16	$72.77

Crew B-37J	Hr.	Daily	Hr.	Daily	Bare Costs	Incl. O&P
1 Labor Foreman (outside)	$25.80	$206.40	$43.40	$347.20	$25.57	$42.89
4 Laborers	23.80	761.60	40.05	1281.60		
1 Equip. Oper. (light)	32.45	259.60	53.75	430.00		
1 Air Compressor, 60 cfm		137.40		151.14		
1 -50' Air Hose, 3/4"		3.25		3.58		
2 Concrete Mixer, 10 C.F.		353.60		388.96		
2 Flatbed Trucks, Gas, 1.5 Ton		540.40		594.44		
1 Shot Blaster, 20"		214.40		235.84	26.02	28.62
48 L.H., Daily Totals		$2476.65		$3432.76	$51.60	$71.52

Crew B-37K	Hr.	Daily	Hr.	Daily	Bare Costs	Incl. O&P
1 Labor Foreman (outside)	$25.80	$206.40	$43.40	$347.20	$25.57	$42.89
4 Laborers	23.80	761.60	40.05	1281.60		
1 Equip. Oper. (light)	32.45	259.60	53.75	430.00		
1 Air Compressor, 60 cfm		137.40		151.14		
1 -50' Air Hose, 3/4"		3.25		3.58		
2 Flatbed Trucks, Gas, 1.5 Ton		540.40		594.44		
1 Shot Blaster, 20"		214.40		235.84	18.66	20.52
48 L.H., Daily Totals		$2123.05		$3043.80	$44.23	$63.41

Crew B-38	Hr.	Daily	Hr.	Daily	Bare Costs	Incl. O&P
2 Laborers	$23.80	$380.80	$40.05	$640.80	$26.68	$44.62
1 Equip. Oper. (light)	32.45	259.60	53.75	430.00		
1 Backhoe Loader, 48 H.P.		365.20		401.72		
1 Hyd. Hammer, (1200 lb.)		180.40		198.44	22.73	25.01
24 L.H., Daily Totals		$1186.00		$1670.96	$49.42	$69.62

Crew B-39	Hr.	Daily	Hr.	Daily	Bare Costs	Incl. O&P
1 Labor Foreman (outside)	$25.80	$206.40	$43.40	$347.20	$24.13	$40.61
5 Laborers	23.80	952.00	40.05	1602.00		
1 Air Compressor, 250 cfm		202.40		222.64		
2 Breakers, Pavement, 60 lb.		19.60		21.56		
2 -50' Air Hoses, 1.5"		11.60		12.76	4.87	5.35
48 L.H., Daily Totals		$1392.00		$2206.16	$29.00	$45.96

Crew B-40	Hr.	Daily	Hr.	Daily	Bare Costs	Incl. O&P
1 Pile Driver Foreman (outside)	$33.10	$264.80	$57.15	$457.20	$30.85	$52.77
4 Pile Drivers	31.10	995.20	53.70	1718.40		
1 Building Laborer	23.80	190.40	40.05	320.40		
1 Equip. Oper. (crane)	34.65	277.20	57.40	459.20		
1 Crawler Crane, 40 Ton		1179.00		1296.90		
1 Vibratory Hammer & Gen.		2640.00		2904.00	68.20	75.02
56 L.H., Daily Totals		$5546.60		$7156.10	$99.05	$127.79

Crew B-40B	Hr.	Daily	Hr.	Daily	Bare Costs	Incl. O&P
1 Labor Foreman (outside)	$25.80	$206.40	$43.40	$347.20	$26.98	$45.12
3 Laborers	23.80	571.20	40.05	961.20		
1 Equip. Oper. (crane)	34.65	277.20	57.40	459.20		
1 Equip. Oper. (oiler)	30.05	240.40	49.75	398.00		
1 Lattice Boom Crane, 40 Ton		1177.00		1294.70	24.52	26.97
48 L.H., Daily Totals		$2472.20		$3460.30	$51.50	$72.09

Crew B-41	Hr.	Daily	Hr.	Daily	Bare Costs	Incl. O&P
1 Labor Foreman (outside)	$25.80	$206.40	$43.40	$347.20	$24.94	$41.89
4 Laborers	23.80	761.60	40.05	1281.60		
.25 Equip. Oper. (crane)	34.65	69.30	57.40	114.80		
.25 Equip. Oper. (oiler)	30.05	60.10	49.75	99.50		
.25 Crawler Crane, 40 Ton		294.75		324.23	6.70	7.37
44 L.H., Daily Totals		$1392.15		$2167.32	$31.64	$49.26

Crew B-42	Hr.	Daily	Hr.	Daily	Bare Costs	Incl. O&P
1 Labor Foreman (outside)	$25.80	$206.40	$43.40	$347.20	$27.66	$46.24
4 Laborers	23.80	761.60	40.05	1281.60		
1 Equip. Oper. (crane)	34.65	277.20	57.40	459.20		
1 Welder	38.00	304.00	62.70	501.60		
1 Hyd. Crane, 25 Ton		745.80		820.38		
1 Welder, Gas Engine, 300 amp		142.00		156.20		
1 Horz. Boring Csg. Mch.		479.80		527.78	24.42	26.86
56 L.H., Daily Totals		$2916.80		$4093.96	$52.09	$73.11

Crew B-43	Hr.	Daily	Hr.	Daily	Bare Costs	Incl. O&P
1 Labor Foreman (outside)	$25.80	$206.40	$43.40	$347.20	$24.20	$40.72
4 Laborers	23.80	761.60	40.05	1281.60		
1 Drill Rig, Truck-Mounted		2551.00		2806.10	63.77	70.15
40 L.H., Daily Totals		$3519.00		$4434.90	$87.97	$110.87

Crew B-44	Hr.	Daily	Hr.	Daily	Bare Costs	Incl. O&P
1 Pile Driver Foreman (outside)	$33.10	$264.80	$57.15	$457.20	$29.97	$51.18
4 Pile Drivers	31.10	995.20	53.70	1718.40		
1 Equip. Oper. (crane)	34.65	277.20	57.40	459.20		
2 Laborers	23.80	380.80	40.05	640.80		
1 Crawler Crane, 40 Ton		1179.00		1296.90		
1 Lead, 60' High		74.80		82.28		
1 Hammer, Diesel, 15K ft.-lbs.		587.60		646.36	28.77	31.65
64 L.H., Daily Totals		$3759.40		$5301.14	$58.74	$82.83

Crew B-45	Hr.	Daily	Hr.	Daily	Bare Costs	Incl. O&P
1 Building Laborer	$23.80	$190.40	$40.05	$320.40	$25.23	$42.23
1 Truck Driver (heavy)	26.65	213.20	44.40	355.20		
1 Dist. Tanker, 3000 Gallon		308.20		339.02	19.26	21.19
16 L.H., Daily Totals		$711.80		$1014.62	$44.49	$63.41

Crew B-46	Hr.	Daily	Hr.	Daily	Bare Costs	Incl. O&P
1 Pile Driver Foreman (outside)	$33.10	$264.80	$57.15	$457.20	$27.78	$47.45
2 Pile Drivers	31.10	497.60	53.70	859.20		
3 Laborers	23.80	571.20	40.05	961.20		
1 Chain Saw, Gas, 36" Long		45.00		49.50	0.94	1.03
48 L.H., Daily Totals		$1378.60		$2327.10	$28.72	$48.48

Crew B-47	Hr.	Daily	Hr.	Daily	Bare Costs	Incl. O&P
1 Blast Foreman (outside)	$25.80	$206.40	$43.40	$347.20	$24.80	$41.73
1 Driller	23.80	190.40	40.05	320.40		
1 Air Track Drill, 4"		1040.00		1144.00		
1 Air Compressor, 600 cfm		552.60		607.86		
2 -50' Air Hoses, 3"		29.80		32.78	101.40	111.54
16 L.H., Daily Totals		$2019.20		$2452.24	$126.20	$153.26

Crew No.	Bare Costs		Incl. Subs O&P		Cost Per Labor-Hour	
Crew B-47A	Hr.	Daily	Hr.	Daily	Bare Costs	Incl. O&P
1 Drilling Foreman (outside)	$25.80	$206.40	$43.40	$347.20	$30.17	$50.18
1 Equip. Oper. (heavy)	34.65	277.20	57.40	459.20		
1 Equip. Oper. (oiler)	30.05	240.40	49.75	398.00		
1 Air Track Drill, 5"		1255.00		1380.50	52.29	57.52
24 L.H., Daily Totals		$1979.00		$2584.90	$82.46	$107.70
Crew B-47C	Hr.	Daily	Hr.	Daily	Bare Costs	Incl. O&P
1 Laborer	$23.80	$190.40	$40.05	$320.40	$28.13	$46.90
1 Equip. Oper. (light)	32.45	259.60	53.75	430.00		
1 Air Compressor, 750 cfm		559.20		615.12		
2 -50' Air Hoses, 3"		29.80		32.78		
1 Air Track Drill, 4"		1040.00		1144.00	101.81	111.99
16 L.H., Daily Totals		$2079.00		$2542.30	$129.94	$158.89
Crew B-47E	Hr.	Daily	Hr.	Daily	Bare Costs	Incl. O&P
1 Labor Foreman (outside)	$25.80	$206.40	$43.40	$347.20	$24.30	$40.89
3 Laborers	23.80	571.20	40.05	961.20		
1 Flatbed Truck, Gas, 3 Ton		333.00		366.30	10.41	11.45
32 L.H., Daily Totals		$1110.60		$1674.70	$34.71	$52.33
Crew B-47G	Hr.	Daily	Hr.	Daily	Bare Costs	Incl. O&P
1 Labor Foreman (outside)	$25.80	$206.40	$43.40	$347.20	$24.47	$41.17
2 Laborers	23.80	380.80	40.05	640.80		
1 Air Track Drill, 4"		1040.00		1144.00		
1 Air Compressor, 600 cfm		552.60		607.86		
2 -50' Air Hoses, 3"		29.80		32.78		
1 Gunite Pump Rig		370.40		407.44	83.03	91.34
24 L.H., Daily Totals		$2580.00		$3180.08	$107.50	$132.50
Crew B-47H	Hr.	Daily	Hr.	Daily	Bare Costs	Incl. O&P
1 Skilled Worker Foreman (out)	$34.45	$275.60	$58.20	$465.60	$32.95	$55.65
3 Skilled Workers	32.45	778.80	54.80	1315.20		
1 Flatbed Truck, Gas, 3 Ton		333.00		366.30	10.41	11.45
32 L.H., Daily Totals		$1387.40		$2147.10	$43.36	$67.10
Crew B-48	Hr.	Daily	Hr.	Daily	Bare Costs	Incl. O&P
1 Labor Foreman (outside)	$25.80	$206.40	$43.40	$347.20	$25.94	$43.50
4 Laborers	23.80	761.60	40.05	1281.60		
1 Equip. Oper. (crane)	34.65	277.20	57.40	459.20		
1 Centr. Water Pump, 6"		340.80		374.88		
1 -20' Suction Hose, 6"		11.50		12.65		
1 -50' Discharge Hose, 6"		6.10		6.71		
1 Drill Rig, Truck-Mounted		2551.00		2806.10	60.61	66.67
48 L.H., Daily Totals		$4154.60		$5288.34	$86.55	$110.17
Crew B-49	Hr.	Daily	Hr.	Daily	Bare Costs	Incl. O&P
1 Labor Foreman (outside)	$25.80	$206.40	$43.40	$347.20	$26.85	$45.38
5 Laborers	23.80	952.00	40.05	1602.00		
1 Equip. Oper. (crane)	34.65	277.20	57.40	459.20		
2 Pile Drivers	31.10	497.60	53.70	859.20		
1 Hyd. Crane, 25 Ton		745.80		820.38		
1 Centr. Water Pump, 6"		340.80		374.88		
1 -20' Suction Hose, 6"		11.50		12.65		
1 -50' Discharge Hose, 6"		6.10		6.71		
1 Drill Rig, Truck-Mounted		2551.00		2806.10	50.77	55.84
72 L.H., Daily Totals		$5588.40		$7288.32	$77.62	$101.23

Crew No.	Bare Costs		Incl. Subs O&P		Cost Per Labor-Hour	
Crew B-50	Hr.	Daily	Hr.	Daily	Bare Costs	Incl. O&P
1 Pile Driver Foreman (outside)	$33.10	$264.80	$57.15	$457.20	$28.72	$49.00
6 Pile Drivers	31.10	1492.80	53.70	2577.60		
1 Equip. Oper. (crane)	34.65	277.20	57.40	459.20		
5 Laborers	23.80	952.00	40.05	1602.00		
1 Crawler Crane, 40 Ton		1179.00		1296.90		
1 Lead, 60' High		74.80		82.28		
1 Hammer, Diesel, 15K ft.-lbs.		587.60		646.36		
1 Air Compressor, 600 cfm		552.60		607.86		
2 -50' Air Hoses, 3"		29.80		32.78		
1 Chain Saw, Gas, 36" Long		45.00		49.50	23.74	26.11
104 L.H., Daily Totals		$5455.60		$7811.68	$52.46	$75.11
Crew B-51	Hr.	Daily	Hr.	Daily	Bare Costs	Incl. O&P
1 Labor Foreman (outside)	$25.80	$206.40	$43.40	$347.20	$24.48	$41.13
4 Laborers	23.80	761.60	40.05	1281.60		
1 Truck Driver (light)	25.90	207.20	43.15	345.20		
1 Flatbed Truck, Gas, 1.5 Ton		270.20		297.22	5.63	6.19
48 L.H., Daily Totals		$1445.40		$2271.22	$30.11	$47.32
Crew B-52	Hr.	Daily	Hr.	Daily	Bare Costs	Incl. O&P
1 Labor Foreman (outside)	$25.80	$206.40	$43.40	$347.20	$26.71	$44.94
1 Carpenter	32.10	256.80	54.00	432.00		
4 Laborers	23.80	761.60	40.05	1281.60		
.5 Rodman (reinf.)	33.95	135.80	58.10	232.40		
.5 Equip. Oper. (medium)	33.75	135.00	55.90	223.60		
.5 Crawler Loader, 3 C.Y.		595.50		655.05	10.63	11.70
56 L.H., Daily Totals		$2091.10		$3171.85	$37.34	$56.64
Crew B-53	Hr.	Daily	Hr.	Daily	Bare Costs	Incl. O&P
1 Building Laborer	$23.80	$190.40	$40.05	$320.40	$23.80	$40.05
1 Trencher, Chain, 12 H.P.		71.20		78.32	8.90	9.79
8 L.H., Daily Totals		$261.60		$398.72	$32.70	$49.84
Crew B-54	Hr.	Daily	Hr.	Daily	Bare Costs	Incl. O&P
1 Equip. Oper. (light)	$32.45	$259.60	$53.75	$430.00	$32.45	$53.75
1 Trencher, Chain, 40 H.P.		339.40		373.34	42.42	46.67
8 L.H., Daily Totals		$599.00		$803.34	$74.88	$100.42
Crew B-54A	Hr.	Daily	Hr.	Daily	Bare Costs	Incl. O&P
.17 Labor Foreman (outside)	$25.80	$35.09	$43.40	$59.02	$32.59	$54.08
1 Equipment Operator (med.)	33.75	270.00	55.90	447.20		
1 Wheel Trencher, 67 H.P.		1206.00		1326.60	128.85	141.73
9.36 L.H., Daily Totals		$1511.09		$1832.82	$161.44	$195.81
Crew B-54B	Hr.	Daily	Hr.	Daily	Bare Costs	Incl. O&P
.25 Labor Foreman (outside)	$25.80	$51.60	$43.40	$86.80	$32.16	$53.40
1 Equipment Operator (med.)	33.75	270.00	55.90	447.20		
1 Wheel Trencher, 150 H.P.		1898.00		2087.80	189.80	208.78
10 L.H., Daily Totals		$2219.60		$2621.80	$221.96	$262.18
Crew B-54D	Hr.	Daily	Hr.	Daily	Bare Costs	Incl. O&P
1 Laborer	$23.80	$190.40	$40.05	$320.40	$28.77	$47.98
1 Equipment Operator (med.)	33.75	270.00	55.90	447.20		
1 Rock Trencher, 6" Width		369.00		405.90	23.06	25.37
16 L.H., Daily Totals		$829.40		$1173.50	$51.84	$73.34

Crew B-54E

Crew B-54E	Bare Costs Hr.	Daily	Incl. Subs O&P Hr.	Daily	Cost Per Labor-Hour Bare Costs	Incl. O&P
1 Laborer	$23.80	$190.40	$40.05	$320.40	$28.77	$47.98
1 Equipment Operator (med.)	33.75	270.00	55.90	447.20		
1 Rock Trencher, 18" Width		2590.00		2849.00	161.88	178.06
16 L.H., Daily Totals		$3050.40		$3616.60	$190.65	$226.04

Crew B-55

Crew B-55	Bare Costs Hr.	Daily	Incl. Subs O&P Hr.	Daily	Cost Per Labor-Hour Bare Costs	Incl. O&P
1 Laborer	$23.80	$190.40	$40.05	$320.40	$24.85	$41.60
1 Truck Driver (light)	25.90	207.20	43.15	345.20		
1 Truck-Mounted Earth Auger		786.40		865.04		
1 Flatbed Truck, Gas, 3 Ton		333.00		366.30	69.96	76.96
16 L.H., Daily Totals		$1517.00		$1896.94	$94.81	$118.56

Crew B-56

Crew B-56	Bare Costs Hr.	Daily	Incl. Subs O&P Hr.	Daily	Cost Per Labor-Hour Bare Costs	Incl. O&P
2 Laborers	$23.80	$380.80	$40.05	$640.80	$23.80	$40.05
1 Air Track Drill, 4"		1040.00		1144.00		
1 Air Compressor, 600 cfm		552.60		607.86		
1 -50' Air Hose, 3"		14.90		16.39	100.47	110.52
16 L.H., Daily Totals		$1988.30		$2409.05	$124.27	$150.57

Crew B-57

Crew B-57	Bare Costs Hr.	Daily	Incl. Subs O&P Hr.	Daily	Cost Per Labor-Hour Bare Costs	Incl. O&P
1 Labor Foreman (outside)	$25.80	$206.40	$43.40	$347.20	$26.37	$44.19
3 Laborers	23.80	571.20	40.05	961.20		
1 Equip. Oper. (crane)	34.65	277.20	57.40	459.20		
1 Barge, 400 Ton		781.00		859.10		
1 Crawler Crane, 25 Ton		1173.00		1290.30		
1 Clamshell Bucket, 1 C.Y.		47.40		52.14		
1 Centr. Water Pump, 6"		340.80		374.88		
1 -20' Suction Hose, 6"		11.50		12.65		
20 -50' Discharge Hoses, 6"		122.00		134.20	61.89	68.08
40 L.H., Daily Totals		$3530.50		$4490.87	$88.26	$112.27

Crew B-58

Crew B-58	Bare Costs Hr.	Daily	Incl. Subs O&P Hr.	Daily	Cost Per Labor-Hour Bare Costs	Incl. O&P
2 Laborers	$23.80	$380.80	$40.05	$640.80	$26.68	$44.62
1 Equip. Oper. (light)	32.45	259.60	53.75	430.00		
1 Backhoe Loader, 48 H.P.		365.20		401.72		
1 Small Helicopter, w/ Pilot		2729.00		3001.90	128.93	141.82
24 L.H., Daily Totals		$3734.60		$4474.42	$155.61	$186.43

Crew B-59

Crew B-59	Bare Costs Hr.	Daily	Incl. Subs O&P Hr.	Daily	Cost Per Labor-Hour Bare Costs	Incl. O&P
1 Truck Driver (heavy)	$26.65	$213.20	$44.40	$355.20	$26.65	$44.40
1 Truck Tractor, 220 H.P.		366.40		403.04		
1 Water Tank Trailer, 5000 Gal.		141.60		155.76	63.50	69.85
8 L.H., Daily Totals		$721.20		$914.00	$90.15	$114.25

Crew B-60

Crew B-60	Bare Costs Hr.	Daily	Incl. Subs O&P Hr.	Daily	Cost Per Labor-Hour Bare Costs	Incl. O&P
1 Labor Foreman (outside)	$25.80	$206.40	$43.40	$347.20	$27.38	$45.78
3 Laborers	23.80	571.20	40.05	961.20		
1 Equip. Oper. (crane)	34.65	277.20	57.40	459.20		
1 Equip. Oper. (light)	32.45	259.60	53.75	430.00		
1 Crawler Crane, 40 Ton		1179.00		1296.90		
1 Lead, 60' High		74.80		82.28		
1 Hammer, Diesel, 15K ft.-lbs.		587.60		646.36		
1 Backhoe Loader, 48 H.P.		365.20		401.72	45.97	50.57
48 L.H., Daily Totals		$3521.00		$4624.86	$73.35	$96.35

Crew B-61

Crew B-61	Bare Costs Hr.	Daily	Incl. Subs O&P Hr.	Daily	Cost Per Labor-Hour Bare Costs	Incl. O&P
1 Labor Foreman (outside)	$25.80	$206.40	$43.40	$347.20	$24.20	$40.72
4 Laborers	23.80	761.60	40.05	1281.60		
1 Cement Mixer, 2 C.Y.		191.40		210.54		
1 Air Compressor, 160 cfm		157.40		173.14	8.72	9.59
40 L.H., Daily Totals		$1316.80		$2012.48	$32.92	$50.31

Crew B-62

Crew B-62	Bare Costs Hr.	Daily	Incl. Subs O&P Hr.	Daily	Cost Per Labor-Hour Bare Costs	Incl. O&P
2 Laborers	$23.80	$380.80	$40.05	$640.80	$26.68	$44.62
1 Equip. Oper. (light)	32.45	259.60	53.75	430.00		
1 Loader, Skid Steer, 30 H.P.		174.20		191.62	7.26	7.98
24 L.H., Daily Totals		$814.60		$1262.42	$33.94	$52.60

Crew B-63

Crew B-63	Bare Costs Hr.	Daily	Incl. Subs O&P Hr.	Daily	Cost Per Labor-Hour Bare Costs	Incl. O&P
5 Laborers	$23.80	$952.00	$40.05	$1602.00	$23.80	$40.05
1 Loader, Skid Steer, 30 H.P.		174.20		191.62	4.36	4.79
40 L.H., Daily Totals		$1126.20		$1793.62	$28.16	$44.84

Crew B-63B

Crew B-63B	Bare Costs Hr.	Daily	Incl. Subs O&P Hr.	Daily	Cost Per Labor-Hour Bare Costs	Incl. O&P
1 Labor Foreman (inside)	$24.30	$194.40	$40.90	$327.20	$26.09	$43.69
2 Laborers	23.80	380.80	40.05	640.80		
1 Equip. Oper. (light)	32.45	259.60	53.75	430.00		
1 Loader, Skid Steer, 78 H.P.		308.80		339.68	9.65	10.62
32 L.H., Daily Totals		$1143.60		$1737.68	$35.74	$54.30

Crew B-64

Crew B-64	Bare Costs Hr.	Daily	Incl. Subs O&P Hr.	Daily	Cost Per Labor-Hour Bare Costs	Incl. O&P
1 Laborer	$23.80	$190.40	$40.05	$320.40	$24.85	$41.60
1 Truck Driver (light)	25.90	207.20	43.15	345.20		
1 Power Mulcher (small)		159.60		175.56		
1 Flatbed Truck, Gas, 1.5 Ton		270.20		297.22	26.86	29.55
16 L.H., Daily Totals		$827.40		$1138.38	$51.71	$71.15

Crew B-65

Crew B-65	Bare Costs Hr.	Daily	Incl. Subs O&P Hr.	Daily	Cost Per Labor-Hour Bare Costs	Incl. O&P
1 Laborer	$23.80	$190.40	$40.05	$320.40	$24.85	$41.60
1 Truck Driver (light)	25.90	207.20	43.15	345.20		
1 Power Mulcher (Large)		325.60		358.16		
1 Flatbed Truck, Gas, 1.5 Ton		270.20		297.22	37.24	40.96
16 L.H., Daily Totals		$993.40		$1320.98	$62.09	$82.56

Crew B-66

Crew B-66	Bare Costs Hr.	Daily	Incl. Subs O&P Hr.	Daily	Cost Per Labor-Hour Bare Costs	Incl. O&P
1 Equip. Oper. (light)	$32.45	$259.60	$53.75	$430.00	$32.45	$53.75
1 Loader-Backhoe, 40 H.P.		259.60		285.56	32.45	35.70
8 L.H., Daily Totals		$519.20		$715.56	$64.90	$89.44

Crew B-67

Crew B-67	Bare Costs Hr.	Daily	Incl. Subs O&P Hr.	Daily	Cost Per Labor-Hour Bare Costs	Incl. O&P
1 Millwright	$33.65	$269.20	$54.30	$434.40	$33.05	$54.02
1 Equip. Oper. (light)	32.45	259.60	53.75	430.00		
1 Forklift, R/T, 4,000 Lb.		314.20		345.62	19.64	21.60
16 L.H., Daily Totals		$843.00		$1210.02	$52.69	$75.63

Crew B-67B

Crew B-67B	Bare Costs Hr.	Daily	Incl. Subs O&P Hr.	Daily	Cost Per Labor-Hour Bare Costs	Incl. O&P
1 Millwright Foreman (inside)	$34.15	$273.20	$55.10	$440.80	$33.90	$54.70
1 Millwright	33.65	269.20	54.30	434.40		
16 L.H., Daily Totals		$542.40		$875.20	$33.90	$54.70

Crew B-68

Crew B-68	Bare Costs Hr.	Daily	Incl. Subs O&P Hr.	Daily	Cost Per Labor-Hour Bare Costs	Incl. O&P
2 Millwrights	$33.65	$538.40	$54.30	$868.80	$33.25	$54.12
1 Equip. Oper. (light)	32.45	259.60	53.75	430.00		
1 Forklift, R/T, 4,000 Lb.		314.20		345.62	13.09	14.40
24 L.H., Daily Totals		$1112.20		$1644.42	$46.34	$68.52

Crew B-68A

Crew B-68A	Bare Costs Hr.	Daily	Incl. Subs O&P Hr.	Daily	Cost Per Labor-Hour Bare Costs	Incl. O&P
1 Millwright Foreman (inside)	$34.15	$273.20	$55.10	$440.80	$33.82	$54.57
2 Millwrights	33.65	538.40	54.30	868.80		
1 Forklift, 8,000 Lb.		180.00		198.00	7.50	8.25
24 L.H., Daily Totals		$991.60		$1507.60	$41.32	$62.82

Crew No.	Bare Costs		Incl. Subs O&P		Cost Per Labor-Hour	
Crew B-68B	Hr.	Daily	Hr.	Daily	Bare Costs	Incl. O&P
1 Millwright Foreman (inside)	$34.15	$273.20	$55.10	$440.80	$35.56	$58.01
2 Millwrights	33.65	538.40	54.30	868.80		
2 Electricians	35.75	572.00	58.50	936.00		
2 Plumbers	38.00	608.00	62.70	1003.20		
1 Forklift, 5,000 Lb.		324.80		357.28	5.80	6.38
56 L.H., Daily Totals		$2316.40		$3606.08	$41.36	$64.39
Crew B-68C	Hr.	Daily	Hr.	Daily	Bare Costs	Incl. O&P
1 Millwright Foreman (inside)	$34.15	$273.20	$55.10	$440.80	$35.39	$57.65
1 Millwright	33.65	269.20	54.30	434.40		
1 Electrician	35.75	286.00	58.50	468.00		
1 Plumber	38.00	304.00	62.70	501.60		
1 Forklift, 5,000 Lb.		324.80		357.28	10.15	11.16
32 L.H., Daily Totals		$1457.20		$2202.08	$45.54	$68.81
Crew B-68D	Hr.	Daily	Hr.	Daily	Bare Costs	Incl. O&P
1 Labor Foreman (inside)	$24.30	$194.40	$40.90	$327.20	$26.85	$44.90
1 Laborer	23.80	190.40	40.05	320.40		
1 Equip. Oper. (light)	32.45	259.60	53.75	430.00		
1 Forklift, 5,000 Lb.		324.80		357.28	13.53	14.89
24 L.H., Daily Totals		$969.20		$1434.88	$40.38	$59.79
Crew B-68E	Hr.	Daily	Hr.	Daily	Bare Costs	Incl. O&P
1 Struc. Steel Foreman (inside)	$34.75	$278.00	$66.20	$529.60	$34.35	$65.44
3 Struc. Steel Workers	34.25	822.00	65.25	1566.00		
1 Welder	34.25	274.00	65.25	522.00		
1 Forklift, 8,000 Lb.		180.00		198.00	4.50	4.95
40 L.H., Daily Totals		$1554.00		$2815.60	$38.85	$70.39
Crew B-68F	Hr.	Daily	Hr.	Daily	Bare Costs	Incl. O&P
1 Skilled Worker Foreman (out)	$34.45	$275.60	$58.20	$465.60	$33.12	$55.93
2 Skilled Workers	32.45	519.20	54.80	876.80		
1 Forklift, 5,000 Lb.		324.80		357.28	13.53	14.89
24 L.H., Daily Totals		$1119.60		$1699.68	$46.65	$70.82
Crew B-69	Hr.	Daily	Hr.	Daily	Bare Costs	Incl. O&P
1 Labor Foreman (outside)	$25.80	$206.40	$43.40	$347.20	$26.98	$45.12
3 Laborers	23.80	571.20	40.05	961.20		
1 Equip. Oper. (crane)	34.65	277.20	57.40	459.20		
1 Equip. Oper. (oiler)	30.05	240.40	49.75	398.00		
1 Hyd. Crane, 80 Ton		1652.00		1817.20	34.42	37.86
48 L.H., Daily Totals		$2947.20		$3982.80	$61.40	$82.97
Crew B-69A	Hr.	Daily	Hr.	Daily	Bare Costs	Incl. O&P
1 Labor Foreman (outside)	$25.80	$206.40	$43.40	$347.20	$26.97	$44.89
3 Laborers	23.80	571.20	40.05	961.20		
1 Equip. Oper. (medium)	33.75	270.00	55.90	447.20		
1 Concrete Finisher	30.85	246.80	49.90	399.20		
1 Curb/Gutter Paver, 2-Track		898.00		987.80	18.71	20.58
48 L.H., Daily Totals		$2192.40		$3142.60	$45.67	$65.47
Crew B-69B	Hr.	Daily	Hr.	Daily	Bare Costs	Incl. O&P
1 Labor Foreman (outside)	$25.80	$206.40	$43.40	$347.20	$26.97	$44.89
3 Laborers	23.80	571.20	40.05	961.20		
1 Equip. Oper. (medium)	33.75	270.00	55.90	447.20		
1 Cement Finisher	30.85	246.80	49.90	399.20		
1 Curb/Gutter Paver, 4-Track		770.20		847.22	16.05	17.65
48 L.H., Daily Totals		$2064.60		$3002.02	$43.01	$62.54

Crew No.	Bare Costs		Incl. Subs O&P		Cost Per Labor-Hour	
Crew B-70	Hr.	Daily	Hr.	Daily	Bare Costs	Incl. O&P
1 Labor Foreman (outside)	$25.80	$206.40	$43.40	$347.20	$28.35	$47.32
3 Laborers	23.80	571.20	40.05	961.20		
3 Equip. Oper. (medium)	33.75	810.00	55.90	1341.60		
1 Grader, 30,000 Lbs.		707.00		777.70		
1 Ripper, Beam & 1 Shank		81.40		89.54		
1 Road Sweeper, S.P., 8' wide		665.40		731.94		
1 F.E. Loader, W.M., 1.5 C.Y.		373.40		410.74	32.63	35.89
56 L.H., Daily Totals		$3414.80		$4659.92	$60.98	$83.21
Crew B-71	Hr.	Daily	Hr.	Daily	Bare Costs	Incl. O&P
1 Labor Foreman (outside)	$25.80	$206.40	$43.40	$347.20	$28.35	$47.32
3 Laborers	23.80	571.20	40.05	961.20		
3 Equip. Oper. (medium)	33.75	810.00	55.90	1341.60		
1 Pvmt. Profiler, 750 H.P.		5877.00		6464.70		
1 Road Sweeper, S.P., 8' wide		665.40		731.94		
1 F.E. Loader, W.M., 1.5 C.Y.		373.40		410.74	123.50	135.85
56 L.H., Daily Totals		$8503.40		$10257.38	$151.85	$183.17
Crew B-72	Hr.	Daily	Hr.	Daily	Bare Costs	Incl. O&P
1 Labor Foreman (outside)	$25.80	$206.40	$43.40	$347.20	$29.02	$48.39
3 Laborers	23.80	571.20	40.05	961.20		
4 Equip. Oper. (medium)	33.75	1080.00	55.90	1788.80		
1 Pvmt. Profiler, 750 H.P.		5877.00		6464.70		
1 Hammermill, 250 H.P.		1846.00		2030.60		
1 Windrow Loader		1240.00		1364.00		
1 Mix Paver 165 H.P.		2183.00		2401.30		
1 Roller, Pneum. Whl., 12 Ton		349.00		383.90	179.61	197.57
64 L.H., Daily Totals		$13352.60		$15741.70	$208.63	$245.96
Crew B-73	Hr.	Daily	Hr.	Daily	Bare Costs	Incl. O&P
1 Labor Foreman (outside)	$25.80	$206.40	$43.40	$347.20	$30.27	$50.38
2 Laborers	23.80	380.80	40.05	640.80		
5 Equip. Oper. (medium)	33.75	1350.00	55.90	2236.00		
1 Road Mixer, 310 H.P.		1942.00		2136.20		
1 Tandem Roller, 10 Ton		242.00		266.20		
1 Hammermill, 250 H.P.		1846.00		2030.60		
1 Grader, 30,000 Lbs.		707.00		777.70		
.5 F.E. Loader, W.M., 1.5 C.Y.		186.70		205.37		
.5 Truck Tractor, 220 H.P.		183.20		201.52		
.5 Water Tank Trailer, 5000 Gal.		70.80		77.88	80.90	88.99
64 L.H., Daily Totals		$7114.90		$8919.47	$111.17	$139.37
Crew B-74	Hr.	Daily	Hr.	Daily	Bare Costs	Incl. O&P
1 Labor Foreman (outside)	$25.80	$206.40	$43.40	$347.20	$29.74	$49.48
1 Laborer	23.80	190.40	40.05	320.40		
4 Equip. Oper. (medium)	33.75	1080.00	55.90	1788.80		
2 Truck Drivers (heavy)	26.65	426.40	44.40	710.40		
1 Grader, 30,000 Lbs.		707.00		777.70		
1 Ripper, Beam & 1 Shank		81.40		89.54		
2 Stabilizers, 310 H.P.		3654.00		4019.40		
1 Flatbed Truck, Gas, 3 Ton		333.00		366.30		
1 Chem. Spreader, Towed		53.20		58.52		
1 Roller, Vibratory, 25 Ton		692.80		762.08		
1 Water Tank Trailer, 5000 Gal.		141.60		155.76		
1 Truck Tractor, 220 H.P.		366.40		403.04	94.21	103.63
64 L.H., Daily Totals		$7932.60		$9799.14	$123.95	$153.11

Crew No.	Bare Costs		Incl. Subs O&P		Cost Per Labor-Hour	

Crew B-75

Crew B-75	Hr.	Daily	Hr.	Daily	Bare Costs	Incl. O&P
1 Labor Foreman (outside)	$25.80	$206.40	$43.40	$347.20	$30.18	$50.21
1 Laborer	23.80	190.40	40.05	320.40		
4 Equip. Oper. (medium)	33.75	1080.00	55.90	1788.80		
1 Truck Driver (heavy)	26.65	213.20	44.40	355.20		
1 Grader, 30,000 Lbs.		707.00		777.70		
1 Ripper, Beam & 1 Shank		81.40		89.54		
2 Stabilizers, 310 H.P.		3654.00		4019.40		
1 Dist. Tanker, 3000 Gallon		308.20		339.02		
1 Truck Tractor, 6x4, 380 H.P.		612.80		674.08		
1 Roller, Vibratory, 25 Ton		692.80		762.08	108.15	118.96
56 L.H., Daily Totals		$7746.20		$9473.42	$138.32	$169.17

Crew B-76	Hr.	Daily	Hr.	Daily	Bare Costs	Incl. O&P
1 Dock Builder Foreman (outside)	$33.10	$264.80	$57.15	$457.20	$31.99	$54.47
5 Dock Builders	31.10	1244.00	53.70	2148.00		
2 Equip. Oper. (crane)	34.65	554.40	57.40	918.40		
1 Equip. Oper. (oiler)	30.05	240.40	49.75	398.00		
1 Crawler Crane, 50 Ton		1319.00		1450.90		
1 Barge, 400 Ton		781.00		859.10		
1 Hammer, Diesel, 15K ft.-lbs.		587.60		646.36		
1 Lead, 60' High		74.80		82.28		
1 Air Compressor, 600 cfm		552.60		607.86		
2 -50' Air Hoses, 3"		29.80		32.78	46.46	51.10
72 L.H., Daily Totals		$5648.40		$7600.88	$78.45	$105.57

Crew B-76A	Hr.	Daily	Hr.	Daily	Bare Costs	Incl. O&P
1 Labor Foreman (outside)	$25.80	$206.40	$43.40	$347.20	$26.19	$43.85
5 Laborers	23.80	952.00	40.05	1602.00		
1 Equip. Oper. (crane)	34.65	277.20	57.40	459.20		
1 Equip. Oper. (oiler)	30.05	240.40	49.75	398.00		
1 Crawler Crane, 50 Ton		1319.00		1450.90		
1 Barge, 400 Ton		781.00		859.10	32.81	36.09
64 L.H., Daily Totals		$3776.00		$5116.40	$59.00	$79.94

Crew B-77	Hr.	Daily	Hr.	Daily	Bare Costs	Incl. O&P
1 Labor Foreman (outside)	$25.80	$206.40	$43.40	$347.20	$24.62	$41.34
3 Laborers	23.80	571.20	40.05	961.20		
1 Truck Driver (light)	25.90	207.20	43.15	345.20		
1 Crack Cleaner, 25 H.P.		64.80		71.28		
1 Crack Filler, Trailer Mtd.		203.80		224.18		
1 Flatbed Truck, Gas, 3 Ton		333.00		366.30	15.04	16.54
40 L.H., Daily Totals		$1586.40		$2315.36	$39.66	$57.88

Crew B-78	Hr.	Daily	Hr.	Daily	Bare Costs	Incl. O&P
1 Labor Foreman (outside)	$25.80	$206.40	$43.40	$347.20	$24.20	$40.72
4 Laborers	23.80	761.60	40.05	1281.60		
1 Paint Striper, S.P., 40 Gallon		154.80		170.28		
1 Flatbed Truck, Gas, 3 Ton		333.00		366.30		
1 Pickup Truck, 3/4 Ton		157.00		172.70	16.12	17.73
40 L.H., Daily Totals		$1612.80		$2338.08	$40.32	$58.45

Crew B-78B	Hr.	Daily	Hr.	Daily	Bare Costs	Incl. O&P
2 Laborers	$23.80	$380.80	$40.05	$640.80	$24.76	$41.57
.25 Equip. Oper. (light)	32.45	64.90	53.75	107.50		
1 Pickup Truck, 3/4 Ton		157.00		172.70		
1 Line Rem.,11 H.P.,Walk Behind		68.40		75.24		
.25 Road Sweeper, S.P., 8' wide		166.35		182.99	21.76	23.94
18 L.H., Daily Totals		$837.45		$1179.22	$46.52	$65.51

Crew B-78C	Hr.	Daily	Hr.	Daily	Bare Costs	Incl. O&P
1 Labor Foreman (outside)	$25.80	$206.40	$43.40	$347.20	$24.48	$41.13
4 Laborers	23.80	761.60	40.05	1281.60		
1 Truck Driver (light)	25.90	207.20	43.15	345.20		
1 Paint Striper, T.M., 120 Gal.		860.40		946.44		
1 Flatbed Truck, Gas, 3 Ton		333.00		366.30		
1 Pickup Truck, 3/4 Ton		157.00		172.70	28.13	30.95
48 L.H., Daily Totals		$2525.60		$3459.44	$52.62	$72.07

Crew B-78D	Hr.	Daily	Hr.	Daily	Bare Costs	Incl. O&P
2 Labor Foremen (outside)	$25.80	$412.80	$43.40	$694.40	$24.41	$41.03
7 Laborers	23.80	1332.80	40.05	2242.80		
1 Truck Driver (light)	25.90	207.20	43.15	345.20		
1 Paint Striper, T.M., 120 Gal.		860.40		946.44		
1 Flatbed Truck, Gas, 3 Ton		333.00		366.30		
3 Pickup Trucks, 3/4 Ton		471.00		518.10		
1 Air Compressor, 60 cfm		137.40		151.14		
1 -50' Air Hose, 3/4"		3.25		3.58		
1 Breakers, Pavement, 60 lb.		9.80		10.78	22.69	24.95
80 L.H., Daily Totals		$3767.65		$5278.73	$47.10	$65.98

Crew B-78E	Hr.	Daily	Hr.	Daily	Bare Costs	Incl. O&P
2 Labor Foremen (outside)	$25.80	$412.80	$43.40	$694.40	$24.31	$40.87
9 Laborers	23.80	1713.60	40.05	2883.60		
1 Truck Driver (light)	25.90	207.20	43.15	345.20		
1 Paint Striper, T.M., 120 Gal.		860.40		946.44		
1 Flatbed Truck, Gas, 3 Ton		333.00		366.30		
4 Pickup Trucks, 3/4 Ton		628.00		690.80		
2 Air Compressor, 60 cfm		274.80		302.28		
2 -50' Air Hose, 3/4"		6.50		7.15		
2 Breakers, Pavement, 60 lb.		19.60		21.56	22.11	24.32
96 L.H., Daily Totals		$4455.90		$6257.73	$46.42	$65.18

Crew B-78F	Hr.	Daily	Hr.	Daily	Bare Costs	Incl. O&P
2 Labor Foremen (outside)	$25.80	$412.80	$43.40	$694.40	$24.24	$40.75
11 Laborers	23.80	2094.40	40.05	3524.40		
1 Truck Driver (light)	25.90	207.20	43.15	345.20		
1 Paint Striper, T.M., 120 Gal.		860.40		946.44		
1 Flatbed Truck, Gas, 3 Ton		333.00		366.30		
7 Pickup Trucks, 3/4 Ton		1099.00		1208.90		
3 Air Compressor, 60 cfm		412.20		453.42		
3 -50' Air Hose, 3/4"		9.75		10.73		
3 Breakers, Pavement, 60 lb.		29.40		32.34	24.50	26.95
112 L.H., Daily Totals		$5458.15		$7582.13	$48.73	$67.70

Crew B-79	Hr.	Daily	Hr.	Daily	Bare Costs	Incl. O&P
1 Labor Foreman (outside)	$25.80	$206.40	$43.40	$347.20	$24.62	$41.34
3 Laborers	23.80	571.20	40.05	961.20		
1 Truck Driver (light)	25.90	207.20	43.15	345.20		
1 Paint Striper, T.M., 120 Gal.		860.40		946.44		
1 Heating Kettle, 115 Gallon		63.00		69.30		
1 Flatbed Truck, Gas, 3 Ton		333.00		366.30		
2 Pickup Trucks, 3/4 Ton		314.00		345.40	39.26	43.19
40 L.H., Daily Totals		$2555.20		$3381.04	$63.88	$84.53

Crew B-79B	Hr.	Daily	Hr.	Daily	Bare Costs	Incl. O&P
1 Laborer	$23.80	$190.40	$40.05	$320.40	$23.80	$40.05
1 Set of Gases		152.00		167.20	19.00	20.90
8 L.H., Daily Totals		$342.40		$487.60	$42.80	$60.95

Crew No.	Bare Costs		Incl. Subs O&P		Cost Per Labor-Hour	
Crew B-79C	Hr.	Daily	Hr.	Daily	Bare Costs	Incl. O&P
1 Labor Foreman (outside)	$25.80	$206.40	$43.40	$347.20	$24.39	$40.97
5 Laborers	23.80	952.00	40.05	1602.00		
1 Truck Driver (light)	25.90	207.20	43.15	345.20		
1 Paint Striper, T.M., 120 Gal.		860.40		946.44		
1 Heating Kettle, 115 Gallon		63.00		69.30		
1 Flatbed Truck, Gas, 3 Ton		333.00		366.30		
3 Pickup Trucks, 3/4 Ton		471.00		518.10		
1 Air Compressor, 60 cfm		137.40		151.14		
1 -50' Air Hose, 3/4"		3.25		3.58		
1 Breakers, Pavement, 60 lb.		9.80		10.78	33.53	36.89
56 L.H., Daily Totals		$3243.45		$4360.03	$57.92	$77.86
Crew B-79D	Hr.	Daily	Hr.	Daily	Bare Costs	Incl. O&P
2 Labor Foremen (outside)	$25.80	$412.80	$43.40	$694.40	$24.56	$41.27
5 Laborers	23.80	952.00	40.05	1602.00		
1 Truck Driver (light)	25.90	207.20	43.15	345.20		
1 Paint Striper, T.M., 120 Gal.		860.40		946.44		
1 Heating Kettle, 115 Gallon		63.00		69.30		
1 Flatbed Truck, Gas, 3 Ton		333.00		366.30		
4 Pickup Trucks, 3/4 Ton		628.00		690.80		
1 Air Compressor, 60 cfm		137.40		151.14		
1 -50' Air Hose, 3/4"		3.25		3.58		
1 Breakers, Pavement, 60 lb.		9.80		10.78	31.79	34.97
64 L.H., Daily Totals		$3606.85		$4879.94	$56.36	$76.25
Crew B-79E	Hr.	Daily	Hr.	Daily	Bare Costs	Incl. O&P
2 Labor Foremen (outside)	$25.80	$412.80	$43.40	$694.40	$24.41	$41.03
7 Laborers	23.80	1332.80	40.05	2242.80		
1 Truck Driver (light)	25.90	207.20	43.15	345.20		
1 Paint Striper, T.M., 120 Gal.		860.40		946.44		
1 Heating Kettle, 115 Gallon		63.00		69.30		
1 Flatbed Truck, Gas, 3 Ton		333.00		366.30		
5 Pickup Trucks, 3/4 Ton		785.00		863.50		
2 Air Compressors, 60 cfm		274.80		302.28		
2 -50' Air Hoses, 3/4"		6.50		7.15		
2 Breakers, Pavement, 60 lb.		19.60		21.56	29.28	32.21
80 L.H., Daily Totals		$4295.10		$5858.93	$53.69	$73.24
Crew B-80	Hr.	Daily	Hr.	Daily	Bare Costs	Incl. O&P
1 Labor Foreman (outside)	$25.80	$206.40	$43.40	$347.20	$24.47	$41.17
2 Laborers	23.80	380.80	40.05	640.80		
1 Flatbed Truck, Gas, 3 Ton		333.00		366.30		
1 Earth Auger, Truck-Mtd.		425.00		467.50	31.58	34.74
24 L.H., Daily Totals		$1345.20		$1821.80	$56.05	$75.91
Crew B-80A	Hr.	Daily	Hr.	Daily	Bare Costs	Incl. O&P
3 Laborers	$23.80	$571.20	$40.05	$961.20	$23.80	$40.05
1 Flatbed Truck, Gas, 3 Ton		333.00		366.30	13.88	15.26
24 L.H., Daily Totals		$904.20		$1327.50	$37.67	$55.31
Crew B-80B	Hr.	Daily	Hr.	Daily	Bare Costs	Incl. O&P
3 Laborers	$23.80	$571.20	$40.05	$961.20	$25.96	$43.48
1 Equip. Oper. (light)	32.45	259.60	53.75	430.00		
1 Crane, Flatbed Mounted, 3 Ton		248.40		273.24	7.76	8.54
32 L.H., Daily Totals		$1079.20		$1664.44	$33.73	$52.01

Crew No.	Bare Costs		Incl. Subs O&P		Cost Per Labor-Hour	
Crew B-80C	Hr.	Daily	Hr.	Daily	Bare Costs	Incl. O&P
2 Laborers	$23.80	$380.80	$40.05	$640.80	$24.50	$41.08
1 Truck Driver (light)	25.90	207.20	43.15	345.20		
1 Flatbed Truck, Gas, 1.5 Ton		270.20		297.22		
1 Manual Fence Post Auger, Gas		8.00		8.80	11.59	12.75
24 L.H., Daily Totals		$866.20		$1292.02	$36.09	$53.83
Crew B-81	Hr.	Daily	Hr.	Daily	Bare Costs	Incl. O&P
1 Laborer	$23.80	$190.40	$40.05	$320.40	$25.23	$42.23
1 Truck Driver (heavy)	26.65	213.20	44.40	355.20		
1 Hydromulcher, T.M., 3000 Gal.		340.40		374.44		
1 Truck Tractor, 220 H.P.		366.40		403.04	44.17	48.59
16 L.H., Daily Totals		$1110.40		$1453.08	$69.40	$90.82
Crew B-81A	Hr.	Daily	Hr.	Daily	Bare Costs	Incl. O&P
1 Laborer	$23.80	$190.40	$40.05	$320.40	$24.85	$41.60
1 Truck Driver (light)	25.90	207.20	43.15	345.20		
1 Hydromulcher, T.M., 600 Gal.		132.60		145.86		
1 Flatbed Truck, Gas, 3 Ton		333.00		366.30	29.10	32.01
16 L.H., Daily Totals		$863.20		$1177.76	$53.95	$73.61
Crew B-82	Hr.	Daily	Hr.	Daily	Bare Costs	Incl. O&P
1 Laborer	$23.80	$190.40	$40.05	$320.40	$28.13	$46.90
1 Equip. Oper. (light)	32.45	259.60	53.75	430.00		
1 Horiz. Borer, 6 H.P.		83.00		91.30	5.19	5.71
16 L.H., Daily Totals		$533.00		$841.70	$33.31	$52.61
Crew B-82A	Hr.	Daily	Hr.	Daily	Bare Costs	Incl. O&P
1 Laborer	$23.80	$190.40	$40.05	$320.40	$28.13	$46.90
1 Equip. Oper. (light)	32.45	259.60	53.75	430.00		
1 Flatbed Truck, Gas, 3 Ton		333.00		366.30		
1 Flatbed Trailer, 25 Ton		113.60		124.96		
1 Horiz. Dir. Drill, 20k lb. Thrust		658.40		724.24	69.06	75.97
16 L.H., Daily Totals		$1555.00		$1965.90	$97.19	$122.87
Crew B-82B	Hr.	Daily	Hr.	Daily	Bare Costs	Incl. O&P
2 Laborers	$23.80	$380.80	$40.05	$640.80	$26.68	$44.62
1 Equip. Oper. (light)	32.45	259.60	53.75	430.00		
1 Flatbed Truck, Gas, 3 Ton		333.00		366.30		
1 Flatbed Trailer, 25 Ton		113.60		124.96		
1 Horiz. Dir. Drill, 30k lb. Thrust		936.20		1029.82	57.62	63.38
24 L.H., Daily Totals		$2023.20		$2591.88	$84.30	$108.00
Crew B-82C	Hr.	Daily	Hr.	Daily	Bare Costs	Incl. O&P
2 Laborers	$23.80	$380.80	$40.05	$640.80	$26.68	$44.62
1 Equip. Oper. (light)	32.45	259.60	53.75	430.00		
1 Flatbed Truck, Gas, 3 Ton		333.00		366.30		
1 Flatbed Trailer, 25 Ton		113.60		124.96		
1 Horiz. Dir. Drill, 50k lb. Thrust		1246.00		1370.60	70.53	77.58
24 L.H., Daily Totals		$2333.00		$2932.66	$97.21	$122.19
Crew B-82D	Hr.	Daily	Hr.	Daily	Bare Costs	Incl. O&P
1 Equip. Oper. (light)	$32.45	$259.60	$53.75	$430.00	$32.45	$53.75
1 Mud Trailer for HDD, 1500 Gal.		374.80		412.28	46.85	51.53
8 L.H., Daily Totals		$634.40		$842.28	$79.30	$105.29
Crew B-83	Hr.	Daily	Hr.	Daily	Bare Costs	Incl. O&P
1 Tugboat Captain	$33.75	$270.00	$55.90	$447.20	$28.77	$47.98
1 Tugboat Hand	23.80	190.40	40.05	320.40		
1 Tugboat, 250 H.P.		889.40		978.34	55.59	61.15
16 L.H., Daily Totals		$1349.80		$1745.94	$84.36	$109.12

Crew No.	Bare Costs		Incl. Subs O&P		Cost Per Labor-Hour	
Crew B-84	Hr.	Daily	Hr.	Daily	Bare Costs	Incl. O&P
1 Equip. Oper. (medium)	$33.75	$270.00	$55.90	$447.20	$33.75	$55.90
1 Rotary Mower/Tractor		364.20		400.62	45.52	50.08
8 L.H., Daily Totals		$634.20		$847.82	$79.28	$105.98
Crew B-85	Hr.	Daily	Hr.	Daily	Bare Costs	Incl. O&P
3 Laborers	$23.80	$571.20	$40.05	$961.20	$26.36	$44.09
1 Equip. Oper. (medium)	33.75	270.00	55.90	447.20		
1 Truck Driver (heavy)	26.65	213.20	44.40	355.20		
1 Aerial Lift Truck, 80'		643.00		707.30		
1 Brush Chipper, 12", 130 H.P.		396.60		436.26		
1 Pruning Saw, Rotary		6.55		7.21	26.15	28.77
40 L.H., Daily Totals		$2100.55		$2914.36	$52.51	$72.86
Crew B-86	Hr.	Daily	Hr.	Daily	Bare Costs	Incl. O&P
1 Equip. Oper. (medium)	$33.75	$270.00	$55.90	$447.20	$33.75	$55.90
1 Stump Chipper, S.P.		162.10		178.31	20.26	22.29
8 L.H., Daily Totals		$432.10		$625.51	$54.01	$78.19
Crew B-86A	Hr.	Daily	Hr.	Daily	Bare Costs	Incl. O&P
1 Equip. Oper. (medium)	$33.75	$270.00	$55.90	$447.20	$33.75	$55.90
1 Grader, 30,000 Lbs.		707.00		777.70	88.38	97.21
8 L.H., Daily Totals		$977.00		$1224.90	$122.13	$153.11
Crew B-86B	Hr.	Daily	Hr.	Daily	Bare Costs	Incl. O&P
1 Equip. Oper. (medium)	$33.75	$270.00	$55.90	$447.20	$33.75	$55.90
1 Dozer, 200 H.P.		1325.00		1457.50	165.63	182.19
8 L.H., Daily Totals		$1595.00		$1904.70	$199.38	$238.09
Crew B-87	Hr.	Daily	Hr.	Daily	Bare Costs	Incl. O&P
1 Laborer	$23.80	$190.40	$40.05	$320.40	$31.76	$52.73
4 Equip. Oper. (medium)	33.75	1080.00	55.90	1788.80		
2 Feller Bunchers, 100 H.P.		1458.00		1603.80		
1 Log Chipper, 22" Tree		898.60		988.46		
1 Dozer, 105 H.P.		591.80		650.98		
1 Chain Saw, Gas, 36" Long		45.00		49.50	74.83	82.32
40 L.H., Daily Totals		$4263.80		$5401.94	$106.60	$135.05
Crew B-88	Hr.	Daily	Hr.	Daily	Bare Costs	Incl. O&P
1 Laborer	$23.80	$190.40	$40.05	$320.40	$32.33	$53.64
6 Equip. Oper. (medium)	33.75	1620.00	55.90	2683.20		
2 Feller Bunchers, 100 H.P.		1458.00		1603.80		
1 Log Chipper, 22" Tree		898.60		988.46		
2 Log Skidders, 50 H.P.		1839.20		2023.12		
1 Dozer, 105 H.P.		591.80		650.98		
1 Chain Saw, Gas, 36" Long		45.00		49.50	86.30	94.93
56 L.H., Daily Totals		$6643.00		$8319.46	$118.63	$148.56
Crew B-89	Hr.	Daily	Hr.	Daily	Bare Costs	Incl. O&P
1 Skilled Worker	$32.45	$259.60	$54.80	$438.40	$28.13	$47.42
1 Building Laborer	23.80	190.40	40.05	320.40		
1 Flatbed Truck, Gas, 3 Ton		333.00		366.30		
1 Concrete Saw		175.20		192.72		
1 Water Tank, 65 Gal.		17.30		19.03	32.84	36.13
16 L.H., Daily Totals		$975.50		$1336.85	$60.97	$83.55
Crew B-89A	Hr.	Daily	Hr.	Daily	Bare Costs	Incl. O&P
1 Skilled Worker	$32.45	$259.60	$54.80	$438.40	$28.13	$47.42
1 Laborer	23.80	190.40	40.05	320.40		
1 Core Drill (Large)		116.20		127.82	7.26	7.99
16 L.H., Daily Totals		$566.20		$886.62	$35.39	$55.41

Crew No.	Bare Costs		Incl. Subs O&P		Cost Per Labor-Hour	
Crew B-89B	Hr.	Daily	Hr.	Daily	Bare Costs	Incl. O&P
1 Equip. Oper. (light)	$32.45	$259.60	$53.75	$430.00	$29.18	$48.45
1 Truck Driver (light)	25.90	207.20	43.15	345.20		
1 Wall Saw, Hydraulic, 10 H.P.		119.60		131.56		
1 Generator, Diesel, 100 kW		439.20		483.12		
1 Water Tank, 65 Gal.		17.30		19.03		
1 Flatbed Truck, Gas, 3 Ton		333.00		366.30	56.82	62.50
16 L.H., Daily Totals		$1375.90		$1775.21	$85.99	$110.95
Crew B-90	Hr.	Daily	Hr.	Daily	Bare Costs	Incl. O&P
1 Labor Foreman (outside)	$25.80	$206.40	$43.40	$347.20	$26.93	$44.98
3 Laborers	23.80	571.20	40.05	961.20		
2 Equip. Oper. (light)	32.45	519.20	53.75	860.00		
2 Truck Drivers (heavy)	26.65	426.40	44.40	710.40		
1 Road Mixer, 310 H.P.		1942.00		2136.20		
1 Dist. Truck, 2000 Gal.		278.20		306.02	34.69	38.16
64 L.H., Daily Totals		$3943.40		$5321.02	$61.62	$83.14
Crew B-90A	Hr.	Daily	Hr.	Daily	Bare Costs	Incl. O&P
1 Labor Foreman (outside)	$25.80	$206.40	$43.40	$347.20	$29.77	$49.59
2 Laborers	23.80	380.80	40.05	640.80		
4 Equip. Oper. (medium)	33.75	1080.00	55.90	1788.80		
2 Graders, 30,000 Lbs.		1414.00		1555.40		
1 Tandem Roller, 10 Ton		242.00		266.20		
1 Roller, Pneum. Whl., 12 Ton		349.00		383.90	35.80	39.38
56 L.H., Daily Totals		$3672.20		$4982.30	$65.58	$88.97
Crew B-90B	Hr.	Daily	Hr.	Daily	Bare Costs	Incl. O&P
1 Labor Foreman (outside)	$25.80	$206.40	$43.40	$347.20	$29.11	$48.53
2 Laborers	23.80	380.80	40.05	640.80		
3 Equip. Oper. (medium)	33.75	810.00	55.90	1341.60		
1 Roller, Pneum. Whl., 12 Ton		349.00		383.90		
1 Road Mixer, 310 H.P.		1942.00		2136.20	47.73	52.50
48 L.H., Daily Totals		$3688.20		$4849.70	$76.84	$101.04
Crew B-90C	Hr.	Daily	Hr.	Daily	Bare Costs	Incl. O&P
1 Labor Foreman (outside)	$25.80	$206.40	$43.40	$347.20	$27.47	$45.86
4 Laborers	23.80	761.60	40.05	1281.60		
3 Equip. Oper. (medium)	33.75	810.00	55.90	1341.60		
3 Truck Drivers (heavy)	26.65	639.60	44.40	1065.60		
3 Road Mixers, 310 H.P.		5826.00		6408.60	66.20	72.83
88 L.H., Daily Totals		$8243.60		$10444.60	$93.68	$118.69
Crew B-90D	Hr.	Daily	Hr.	Daily	Bare Costs	Incl. O&P
1 Labor Foreman (outside)	$25.80	$206.40	$43.40	$347.20	$26.91	$44.97
6 Laborers	23.80	1142.40	40.05	1922.40		
3 Equip. Oper. (medium)	33.75	810.00	55.90	1341.60		
3 Truck Drivers (heavy)	26.65	639.60	44.40	1065.60		
3 Road Mixers, 310 H.P.		5826.00		6408.60	56.02	61.62
104 L.H., Daily Totals		$8624.40		$11085.40	$82.93	$106.59
Crew B-90E	Hr.	Daily	Hr.	Daily	Bare Costs	Incl. O&P
1 Labor Foreman (outside)	$25.80	$206.40	$43.40	$347.20	$27.66	$46.19
4 Laborers	23.80	761.60	40.05	1281.60		
3 Equip. Oper. (medium)	33.75	810.00	55.90	1341.60		
1 Truck Driver (heavy)	26.65	213.20	44.40	355.20		
1 Road Mixers, 310 H.P.		1942.00		2136.20	26.97	29.67
72 L.H., Daily Totals		$3933.20		$5461.80	$54.63	$75.86

Crew B-91

Crew No.	Bare Costs Hr.	Daily	Incl. Subs O&P Hr.	Daily	Cost Per Labor-Hour Bare Costs	Incl. O&P
1 Labor Foreman (outside)	$25.80	$206.40	$43.40	$347.20	$29.38	$48.94
2 Laborers	23.80	380.80	40.05	640.80		
4 Equip. Oper. (medium)	33.75	1080.00	55.90	1788.80		
1 Truck Driver (heavy)	26.65	213.20	44.40	355.20		
1 Dist. Tanker, 3000 Gallon		308.20		339.02		
1 Truck Tractor, 6x4, 380 H.P.		612.80		674.08		
1 Aggreg. Spreader, S.P.		841.00		925.10		
1 Roller, Pneum. Whl., 12 Ton		349.00		383.90		
1 Tandem Roller, 10 Ton		242.00		266.20	36.77	40.44
64 L.H., Daily Totals		$4233.40		$5720.30	$66.15	$89.38

Crew B-91B

Crew No.	Bare Costs Hr.	Daily	Incl. Subs O&P Hr.	Daily	Cost Per Labor-Hour Bare Costs	Incl. O&P
1 Laborer	$23.80	$190.40	$40.05	$320.40	$28.77	$47.98
1 Equipment Oper. (med.)	33.75	270.00	55.90	447.20		
1 Road Sweeper, Vac. Assist.		994.40		1093.84	62.15	68.36
16 L.H., Daily Totals		$1454.80		$1861.44	$90.92	$116.34

Crew B-91C

Crew No.	Bare Costs Hr.	Daily	Incl. Subs O&P Hr.	Daily	Cost Per Labor-Hour Bare Costs	Incl. O&P
1 Laborer	$23.80	$190.40	$40.05	$320.40	$24.85	$41.60
1 Truck Driver (light)	25.90	207.20	43.15	345.20		
1 Catch Basin Cleaning Truck		604.00		664.40	37.75	41.52
16 L.H., Daily Totals		$1001.60		$1330.00	$62.60	$83.13

Crew B-91D

Crew No.	Bare Costs Hr.	Daily	Incl. Subs O&P Hr.	Daily	Cost Per Labor-Hour Bare Costs	Incl. O&P
1 Labor Foreman (outside)	$25.80	$206.40	$43.40	$347.20	$28.22	$47.07
5 Laborers	23.80	952.00	40.05	1602.00		
5 Equip. Oper. (medium)	33.75	1350.00	55.90	2236.00		
2 Truck Drivers (heavy)	26.65	426.40	44.40	710.40		
1 Aggreg. Spreader, S.P.		841.00		925.10		
2 Truck Tractor, 6x4, 380 H.P.		1225.60		1348.16		
2 Dist. Tanker, 3000 Gallon		616.40		678.04		
2 Pavement Brush, Towed		163.20		179.52		
2 Roller, Pneum. Whl., 12 Ton		698.00		767.80	34.08	37.49
104 L.H., Daily Totals		$6479.00		$8794.22	$62.30	$84.56

Crew B-92

Crew No.	Bare Costs Hr.	Daily	Incl. Subs O&P Hr.	Daily	Cost Per Labor-Hour Bare Costs	Incl. O&P
1 Labor Foreman (outside)	$25.80	$206.40	$43.40	$347.20	$24.30	$40.89
3 Laborers	23.80	571.20	40.05	961.20		
1 Crack Cleaner, 25 H.P.		64.80		71.28		
1 Air Compressor, 60 cfm		137.40		151.14		
1 Tar Kettle, T.M.		104.60		115.06		
1 Flatbed Truck, Gas, 3 Ton		333.00		366.30	19.99	21.99
32 L.H., Daily Totals		$1417.40		$2012.18	$44.29	$62.88

Crew B-93

Crew No.	Bare Costs Hr.	Daily	Incl. Subs O&P Hr.	Daily	Cost Per Labor-Hour Bare Costs	Incl. O&P
1 Equip. Oper. (medium)	$33.75	$270.00	$55.90	$447.20	$33.75	$55.90
1 Feller Buncher, 100 H.P.		729.00		801.90	91.13	100.24
8 L.H., Daily Totals		$999.00		$1249.10	$124.88	$156.14

Crew B-94A

Crew No.	Bare Costs Hr.	Daily	Incl. Subs O&P Hr.	Daily	Cost Per Labor-Hour Bare Costs	Incl. O&P
1 Laborer	$23.80	$190.40	$40.05	$320.40	$23.80	$40.05
1 Diaphragm Water Pump, 2"		72.00		79.20		
1 -20' Suction Hose, 2"		1.95		2.15		
2 -50' Discharge Hoses, 2"		1.80		1.98	9.47	10.42
8 L.H., Daily Totals		$266.15		$403.73	$33.27	$50.47

Crew B-94B

Crew No.	Bare Costs Hr.	Daily	Incl. Subs O&P Hr.	Daily	Cost Per Labor-Hour Bare Costs	Incl. O&P
1 Laborer	$23.80	$190.40	$40.05	$320.40	$23.80	$40.05
1 Diaphragm Water Pump, 4"		115.80		127.38		
1 -20' Suction Hose, 4"		3.25		3.58		
2 -50' Discharge Hoses, 4"		4.70		5.17	15.47	17.02
8 L.H., Daily Totals		$314.15		$456.52	$39.27	$57.07

Crew B-94C

Crew No.	Bare Costs Hr.	Daily	Incl. Subs O&P Hr.	Daily	Cost Per Labor-Hour Bare Costs	Incl. O&P
1 Laborer	$23.80	$190.40	$40.05	$320.40	$23.80	$40.05
1 Centrifugal Water Pump, 3"		78.80		86.68		
1 -20' Suction Hose, 3"		2.85		3.13		
2 -50' Discharge Hoses, 3"		3.00		3.30	10.58	11.64
8 L.H., Daily Totals		$275.05		$413.51	$34.38	$51.69

Crew B-94D

Crew No.	Bare Costs Hr.	Daily	Incl. Subs O&P Hr.	Daily	Cost Per Labor-Hour Bare Costs	Incl. O&P
1 Laborer	$23.80	$190.40	$40.05	$320.40	$23.80	$40.05
1 Centr. Water Pump, 6"		340.80		374.88		
1 -20' Suction Hose, 6"		11.50		12.65		
2 -50' Discharge Hoses, 6"		12.20		13.42	45.56	50.12
8 L.H., Daily Totals		$554.90		$721.35	$69.36	$90.17

Crew C-1

Crew No.	Bare Costs Hr.	Daily	Incl. Subs O&P Hr.	Daily	Cost Per Labor-Hour Bare Costs	Incl. O&P
2 Carpenters	$32.10	$513.60	$54.00	$864.00	$27.96	$47.09
1 Carpenter Helper	23.85	190.80	40.30	322.40		
1 Laborer	23.80	190.40	40.05	320.40		
32 L.H., Daily Totals		$894.80		$1506.80	$27.96	$47.09

Crew C-2

Crew No.	Bare Costs Hr.	Daily	Incl. Subs O&P Hr.	Daily	Cost Per Labor-Hour Bare Costs	Incl. O&P
1 Carpenter Foreman (outside)	$34.10	$272.80	$57.40	$459.20	$28.30	$47.67
2 Carpenters	32.10	513.60	54.00	864.00		
2 Carpenter Helpers	23.85	381.60	40.30	644.80		
1 Laborer	23.80	190.40	40.05	320.40		
48 L.H., Daily Totals		$1358.40		$2288.40	$28.30	$47.67

Crew C-2A

Crew No.	Bare Costs Hr.	Daily	Incl. Subs O&P Hr.	Daily	Cost Per Labor-Hour Bare Costs	Incl. O&P
1 Carpenter Foreman (outside)	$34.10	$272.80	$57.40	$459.20	$30.84	$51.56
3 Carpenters	32.10	770.40	54.00	1296.00		
1 Cement Finisher	30.85	246.80	49.90	399.20		
1 Laborer	23.80	190.40	40.05	320.40		
48 L.H., Daily Totals		$1480.40		$2474.80	$30.84	$51.56

Crew C-3

Crew No.	Bare Costs Hr.	Daily	Incl. Subs O&P Hr.	Daily	Cost Per Labor-Hour Bare Costs	Incl. O&P
1 Rodman Foreman (outside)	$35.95	$287.60	$61.50	$492.00	$30.21	$51.21
3 Rodmen (reinf.)	33.95	814.80	58.10	1394.40		
1 Equip. Oper. (light)	32.45	259.60	53.75	430.00		
3 Laborers	23.80	571.20	40.05	961.20		
3 Stressing Equipment		30.60		33.66		
.5 Grouting Equipment		82.10		90.31	1.76	1.94
64 L.H., Daily Totals		$2045.90		$3401.57	$31.97	$53.15

Crew C-4

Crew No.	Bare Costs Hr.	Daily	Incl. Subs O&P Hr.	Daily	Cost Per Labor-Hour Bare Costs	Incl. O&P
1 Rodman Foreman (outside)	$35.95	$287.60	$61.50	$492.00	$31.91	$54.44
2 Rodmen (reinf.)	33.95	543.20	58.10	929.60		
1 Building Laborer	23.80	190.40	40.05	320.40		
3 Stressing Equipment		30.60		33.66	0.96	1.05
32 L.H., Daily Totals		$1051.80		$1775.66	$32.87	$55.49

Crew C-4A

Crew No.	Bare Costs Hr.	Daily	Incl. Subs O&P Hr.	Daily	Cost Per Labor-Hour Bare Costs	Incl. O&P
2 Rodmen (reinf.)	$33.95	$543.20	$58.10	$929.60	$33.95	$58.10
4 Stressing Equipment		40.80		44.88	2.55	2.81
16 L.H., Daily Totals		$584.00		$974.48	$36.50	$60.91

Crew No.	Bare Costs		Incl. Subs O&P		Cost Per Labor-Hour	

Crew C-5

Crew C-5	Hr.	Daily	Hr.	Daily	Bare Costs	Incl. O&P
1 Rodman Foreman (outside)	$35.95	$287.60	$61.50	$492.00	$31.02	$52.53
2 Rodmen (reinf.)	33.95	543.20	58.10	929.60		
1 Equip. Oper. (crane)	34.65	277.20	57.40	459.20		
2 Building Laborers	23.80	380.80	40.05	640.80		
1 Hyd. Crane, 25 Ton		745.80		820.38	15.54	17.09
48 L.H., Daily Totals		$2234.60		$3341.98	$46.55	$69.62

Crew C-6

Crew C-6	Hr.	Daily	Hr.	Daily	Bare Costs	Incl. O&P
1 Labor Foreman (outside)	$25.80	$206.40	$43.40	$347.20	$25.31	$42.25
4 Laborers	23.80	761.60	40.05	1281.60		
1 Cement Finisher	30.85	246.80	49.90	399.20		
2 Gas Engine Vibrators		66.00		72.60	1.38	1.51
48 L.H., Daily Totals		$1280.80		$2100.60	$26.68	$43.76

Crew C-7

Crew C-7	Hr.	Daily	Hr.	Daily	Bare Costs	Incl. O&P
1 Labor Foreman (outside)	$25.80	$206.40	$43.40	$347.20	$26.61	$44.36
5 Laborers	23.80	952.00	40.05	1602.00		
1 Cement Finisher	30.85	246.80	49.90	399.20		
1 Equip. Oper. (medium)	33.75	270.00	55.90	447.20		
1 Equip. Oper. (oiler)	30.05	240.40	49.75	398.00		
2 Gas Engine Vibrators		66.00		72.60		
1 Concrete Bucket, 1 C.Y.		23.00		25.30		
1 Hyd. Crane, 55 Ton		1137.00		1250.70	17.03	18.73
72 L.H., Daily Totals		$3141.60		$4542.20	$43.63	$63.09

Crew C-8

Crew C-8	Hr.	Daily	Hr.	Daily	Bare Costs	Incl. O&P
1 Labor Foreman (outside)	$25.80	$206.40	$43.40	$347.20	$27.52	$45.61
3 Laborers	23.80	571.20	40.05	961.20		
2 Cement Finishers	30.85	493.60	49.90	798.40		
1 Equip. Oper. (medium)	33.75	270.00	55.90	447.20		
1 Concrete Pump (Small)		710.40		781.44	12.69	13.95
56 L.H., Daily Totals		$2251.60		$3335.44	$40.21	$59.56

Crew C-8A

Crew C-8A	Hr.	Daily	Hr.	Daily	Bare Costs	Incl. O&P
1 Labor Foreman (outside)	$25.80	$206.40	$43.40	$347.20	$26.48	$43.89
3 Laborers	23.80	571.20	40.05	961.20		
2 Cement Finishers	30.85	493.60	49.90	798.40		
48 L.H., Daily Totals		$1271.20		$2106.80	$26.48	$43.89

Crew C-8B

Crew C-8B	Hr.	Daily	Hr.	Daily	Bare Costs	Incl. O&P
1 Labor Foreman (outside)	$25.80	$206.40	$43.40	$347.20	$26.19	$43.89
3 Laborers	23.80	571.20	40.05	961.20		
1 Equip. Oper. (medium)	33.75	270.00	55.90	447.20		
1 Vibrating Power Screed		63.25		69.58		
1 Roller, Vibratory, 25 Ton		692.80		762.08		
1 Dozer, 200 H.P.		1325.00		1457.50	52.03	57.23
40 L.H., Daily Totals		$3128.65		$4044.76	$78.22	$101.12

Crew C-8C

Crew C-8C	Hr.	Daily	Hr.	Daily	Bare Costs	Incl. O&P
1 Labor Foreman (outside)	$25.80	$206.40	$43.40	$347.20	$26.97	$44.89
3 Laborers	23.80	571.20	40.05	961.20		
1 Cement Finisher	30.85	246.80	49.90	399.20		
1 Equip. Oper. (medium)	33.75	270.00	55.90	447.20		
1 Shotcrete Rig, 12 C.Y./hr		252.80		278.08		
1 Air Compressor, 160 cfm		157.40		173.14		
4 -50' Air Hoses, 1"		16.40		18.04		
4 -50' Air Hoses, 2"		31.00		34.10	9.53	10.49
48 L.H., Daily Totals		$1752.00		$2658.16	$36.50	$55.38

Crew C-8D

Crew C-8D	Hr.	Daily	Hr.	Daily	Bare Costs	Incl. O&P
1 Labor Foreman (outside)	$25.80	$206.40	$43.40	$347.20	$28.23	$46.77
1 Laborer	23.80	190.40	40.05	320.40		
1 Cement Finisher	30.85	246.80	49.90	399.20		
1 Equipment Oper. (light)	32.45	259.60	53.75	430.00		
1 Air Compressor, 250 cfm		202.40		222.64		
2 -50' Air Hoses, 1"		8.20		9.02	6.58	7.24
32 L.H., Daily Totals		$1113.80		$1728.46	$34.81	$54.01

Crew C-8E

Crew C-8E	Hr.	Daily	Hr.	Daily	Bare Costs	Incl. O&P
1 Labor Foreman (outside)	$25.80	$206.40	$43.40	$347.20	$26.75	$44.53
3 Laborers	23.80	571.20	40.05	961.20		
1 Cement Finisher	30.85	246.80	49.90	399.20		
1 Equipment Oper. (light)	32.45	259.60	53.75	430.00		
1 Shotcrete Rig, 35 C.Y./hr		284.40		312.84		
1 Air Compressor, 250 cfm		202.40		222.64		
4 -50' Air Hoses, 1"		16.40		18.04		
4 -50' Air Hoses, 2"		31.00		34.10	11.13	12.24
48 L.H., Daily Totals		$1818.20		$2725.22	$37.88	$56.78

Crew C-10

Crew C-10	Hr.	Daily	Hr.	Daily	Bare Costs	Incl. O&P
1 Laborer	$23.80	$190.40	$40.05	$320.40	$28.50	$46.62
2 Cement Finishers	30.85	493.60	49.90	798.40		
24 L.H., Daily Totals		$684.00		$1118.80	$28.50	$46.62

Crew C-10B

Crew C-10B	Hr.	Daily	Hr.	Daily	Bare Costs	Incl. O&P
3 Laborers	$23.80	$571.20	$40.05	$961.20	$26.62	$43.99
2 Cement Finishers	30.85	493.60	49.90	798.40		
1 Concrete Mixer, 10 C.F.		176.80		194.48		
2 Trowels, 48" Walk-Behind		107.20		117.92	7.10	7.81
40 L.H., Daily Totals		$1348.80		$2072.00	$33.72	$51.80

Crew C-10C

Crew C-10C	Hr.	Daily	Hr.	Daily	Bare Costs	Incl. O&P
1 Laborer	$23.80	$190.40	$40.05	$320.40	$28.50	$46.62
2 Cement Finishers	30.85	493.60	49.90	798.40		
1 Trowel, 48" Walk-Behind		53.60		58.96	2.23	2.46
24 L.H., Daily Totals		$737.60		$1177.76	$30.73	$49.07

Crew C-10D

Crew C-10D	Hr.	Daily	Hr.	Daily	Bare Costs	Incl. O&P
1 Laborer	$23.80	$190.40	$40.05	$320.40	$28.50	$46.62
2 Cement Finishers	30.85	493.60	49.90	798.40		
1 Vibrating Power Screed		63.25		69.58		
1 Trowel, 48" Walk-Behind		53.60		58.96	4.87	5.36
24 L.H., Daily Totals		$800.85		$1247.34	$33.37	$51.97

Crew C-10E

Crew C-10E	Hr.	Daily	Hr.	Daily	Bare Costs	Incl. O&P
1 Laborer	$23.80	$190.40	$40.05	$320.40	$28.50	$46.62
2 Cement Finishers	30.85	493.60	49.90	798.40		
1 Vibrating Power Screed		63.25		69.58		
1 Cement Trowel, 96" Ride-On		197.40		217.14	10.86	11.95
24 L.H., Daily Totals		$944.65		$1405.52	$39.36	$58.56

Crew C-10F

Crew C-10F	Hr.	Daily	Hr.	Daily	Bare Costs	Incl. O&P
1 Laborer	$23.80	$190.40	$40.05	$320.40	$28.50	$46.62
2 Cement Finishers	30.85	493.60	49.90	798.40		
1 Aerial Lift Truck, 60' Boom		456.00		501.60	19.00	20.90
24 L.H., Daily Totals		$1140.00		$1620.40	$47.50	$67.52

Crews

Crew No.	Bare Costs		Incl. Subs O&P		Cost Per Labor-Hour	
Crew C-11	Hr.	Daily	Hr.	Daily	Bare Costs	Incl. O&P
1 Skilled Worker Foreman	$34.45	$275.60	$58.20	$465.60	$33.05	$55.66
5 Skilled Workers	32.45	1298.00	54.80	2192.00		
1 Equip. Oper. (crane)	34.65	277.20	57.40	459.20		
1 Lattice Boom Crane, 150 Ton		1838.00		2021.80	32.82	36.10
56 L.H., Daily Totals		$3688.80		$5138.60	$65.87	$91.76

Crew C-12	Hr.	Daily	Hr.	Daily	Bare Costs	Incl. O&P
1 Carpenter Foreman (outside)	$34.10	$272.80	$57.40	$459.20	$31.48	$52.81
3 Carpenters	32.10	770.40	54.00	1296.00		
1 Laborer	23.80	190.40	40.05	320.40		
1 Equip. Oper. (crane)	34.65	277.20	57.40	459.20		
1 Hyd. Crane, 12 Ton		663.00		729.30	13.81	15.19
48 L.H., Daily Totals		$2173.80		$3264.10	$45.29	$68.00

Crew C-13	Hr.	Daily	Hr.	Daily	Bare Costs	Incl. O&P
2 Struc. Steel Workers	$34.25	$548.00	$65.25	$1044.00	$33.53	$61.50
1 Carpenter	32.10	256.80	54.00	432.00		
1 Welder, Gas Engine, 300 amp		142.00		156.20	5.92	6.51
24 L.H., Daily Totals		$946.80		$1632.20	$39.45	$68.01

Crew C-14	Hr.	Daily	Hr.	Daily	Bare Costs	Incl. O&P
1 Carpenter Foreman (outside)	$34.10	$272.80	$57.40	$459.20	$28.54	$47.89
3 Carpenters	32.10	770.40	54.00	1296.00		
2 Carpenter Helpers	23.85	381.60	40.30	644.80		
4 Laborers	23.80	761.60	40.05	1281.60		
2 Rodmen (reinf.)	33.95	543.20	58.10	929.60		
2 Rodman Helpers	23.85	381.60	40.30	644.80		
2 Cement Finishers	30.85	493.60	49.90	798.40		
1 Equip. Oper. (crane)	34.65	277.20	57.40	459.20		
1 Hyd. Crane, 80 Ton		1652.00		1817.20	12.15	13.36
136 L.H., Daily Totals		$5534.00		$8330.80	$40.69	$61.26

Crew C-14A	Hr.	Daily	Hr.	Daily	Bare Costs	Incl. O&P
1 Carpenter Foreman (outside)	$34.10	$272.80	$57.40	$459.20	$31.83	$53.59
16 Carpenters	32.10	4108.80	54.00	6912.00		
4 Rodmen (reinf.)	33.95	1086.40	58.10	1859.20		
2 Laborers	23.80	380.80	40.05	640.80		
1 Cement Finisher	30.85	246.80	49.90	399.20		
1 Equip. Oper. (medium)	33.75	270.00	55.90	447.20		
1 Gas Engine Vibrator		33.00		36.30		
1 Concrete Pump (Small)		710.40		781.44	3.72	4.09
200 L.H., Daily Totals		$7109.00		$11535.34	$35.55	$57.68

Crew C-14B	Hr.	Daily	Hr.	Daily	Bare Costs	Incl. O&P
1 Carpenter Foreman (outside)	$34.10	$272.80	$57.40	$459.20	$31.79	$53.45
16 Carpenters	32.10	4108.80	54.00	6912.00		
4 Rodmen (reinf.)	33.95	1086.40	58.10	1859.20		
2 Laborers	23.80	380.80	40.05	640.80		
2 Cement Finishers	30.85	493.60	49.90	798.40		
1 Equip. Oper. (medium)	33.75	270.00	55.90	447.20		
1 Gas Engine Vibrator		33.00		36.30		
1 Concrete Pump (Small)		710.40		781.44	3.57	3.93
208 L.H., Daily Totals		$7355.80		$11934.54	$35.36	$57.38

Crew C-14C	Hr.	Daily	Hr.	Daily	Bare Costs	Incl. O&P
1 Carpenter Foreman (outside)	$34.10	$272.80	$57.40	$459.20	$30.05	$50.55
6 Carpenters	32.10	1540.80	54.00	2592.00		
2 Rodmen (reinf.)	33.95	543.20	58.10	929.60		
4 Laborers	23.80	761.60	40.05	1281.60		
1 Cement Finisher	30.85	246.80	49.90	399.20		
1 Gas Engine Vibrator		33.00		36.30	0.29	0.32
112 L.H., Daily Totals		$3398.20		$5697.90	$30.34	$50.87

Crew C-14D	Hr.	Daily	Hr.	Daily	Bare Costs	Incl. O&P
1 Carpenter Foreman (outside)	$34.10	$272.80	$57.40	$459.20	$31.68	$53.26
18 Carpenters	32.10	4622.40	54.00	7776.00		
2 Rodmen (reinf.)	33.95	543.20	58.10	929.60		
2 Laborers	23.80	380.80	40.05	640.80		
1 Cement Finisher	30.85	246.80	49.90	399.20		
1 Equip. Oper. (medium)	33.75	270.00	55.90	447.20		
1 Gas Engine Vibrator		33.00		36.30		
1 Concrete Pump (Small)		710.40		781.44	3.72	4.09
200 L.H., Daily Totals		$7079.40		$11469.74	$35.40	$57.35

Crew C-14E	Hr.	Daily	Hr.	Daily	Bare Costs	Incl. O&P
1 Carpenter Foreman (outside)	$34.10	$272.80	$57.40	$459.20	$30.58	$51.62
2 Carpenters	32.10	513.60	54.00	864.00		
4 Rodmen (reinf.)	33.95	1086.40	58.10	1859.20		
3 Laborers	23.80	571.20	40.05	961.20		
1 Cement Finisher	30.85	246.80	49.90	399.20		
1 Gas Engine Vibrator		33.00		36.30	0.38	0.41
88 L.H., Daily Totals		$2723.80		$4579.10	$30.95	$52.04

Crew C-14F	Hr.	Daily	Hr.	Daily	Bare Costs	Incl. O&P
1 Labor Foreman (outside)	$25.80	$206.40	$43.40	$347.20	$28.72	$46.99
2 Laborers	23.80	380.80	40.05	640.80		
6 Cement Finishers	30.85	1480.80	49.90	2395.20		
1 Gas Engine Vibrator		33.00		36.30	0.46	0.50
72 L.H., Daily Totals		$2101.00		$3419.50	$29.18	$47.49

Crew C-14G	Hr.	Daily	Hr.	Daily	Bare Costs	Incl. O&P
1 Labor Foreman (outside)	$25.80	$206.40	$43.40	$347.20	$28.11	$46.16
2 Laborers	23.80	380.80	40.05	640.80		
4 Cement Finishers	30.85	987.20	49.90	1596.80		
1 Gas Engine Vibrator		33.00		36.30	0.59	0.65
56 L.H., Daily Totals		$1607.40		$2621.10	$28.70	$46.81

Crew C-14H	Hr.	Daily	Hr.	Daily	Bare Costs	Incl. O&P
1 Carpenter Foreman (outside)	$34.10	$272.80	$57.40	$459.20	$31.15	$52.24
2 Carpenters	32.10	513.60	54.00	864.00		
1 Rodman (reinf.)	33.95	271.60	58.10	464.80		
1 Laborer	23.80	190.40	40.05	320.40		
1 Cement Finisher	30.85	246.80	49.90	399.20		
1 Gas Engine Vibrator		33.00		36.30	0.69	0.76
48 L.H., Daily Totals		$1528.20		$2543.90	$31.84	$53.00

Crew C-14L	Hr.	Daily	Hr.	Daily	Bare Costs	Incl. O&P
1 Carpenter Foreman (outside)	$34.10	$272.80	$57.40	$459.20	$29.40	$49.29
6 Carpenters	32.10	1540.80	54.00	2592.00		
4 Laborers	23.80	761.60	40.05	1281.60		
1 Cement Finisher	30.85	246.80	49.90	399.20		
1 Gas Engine Vibrator		33.00		36.30	0.34	0.38
96 L.H., Daily Totals		$2855.00		$4768.30	$29.74	$49.67

Crew No.	Bare Costs		Incl. Subs O&P		Cost Per Labor-Hour	

Crew C-14M	Hr.	Daily	Hr.	Daily	Bare Costs	Incl. O&P
1 Carpenter Foreman (outside)	$34.10	$272.80	$57.40	$459.20	$30.56	$51.17
2 Carpenters	32.10	513.60	54.00	864.00		
1 Rodman (reinf.)	33.95	271.60	58.10	464.80		
2 Laborers	23.80	380.80	40.05	640.80		
1 Cement Finisher	30.85	246.80	49.90	399.20		
1 Equip. Oper. (medium)	33.75	270.00	55.90	447.20		
1 Gas Engine Vibrator		33.00		36.30		
1 Concrete Pump (Small)		710.40		781.44	11.62	12.78
64 L.H., Daily Totals		$2699.00		$4092.94	$42.17	$63.95

Crew C-15	Hr.	Daily	Hr.	Daily	Bare Costs	Incl. O&P
1 Carpenter Foreman (outside)	$34.10	$272.80	$57.40	$459.20	$29.48	$49.27
2 Carpenters	32.10	513.60	54.00	864.00		
3 Laborers	23.80	571.20	40.05	961.20		
2 Cement Finishers	30.85	493.60	49.90	798.40		
1 Rodman (reinf.)	33.95	271.60	58.10	464.80		
72 L.H., Daily Totals		$2122.80		$3547.60	$29.48	$49.27

Crew C-16	Hr.	Daily	Hr.	Daily	Bare Costs	Incl. O&P
1 Labor Foreman (outside)	$25.80	$206.40	$43.40	$347.20	$27.52	$45.61
3 Laborers	23.80	571.20	40.05	961.20		
2 Cement Finishers	30.85	493.60	49.90	798.40		
1 Equip. Oper. (medium)	33.75	270.00	55.90	447.20		
1 Gunite Pump Rig		370.40		407.44		
2 -50' Air Hoses, 3/4"		6.50		7.15		
2 -50' Air Hoses, 2"		15.50		17.05	7.01	7.71
56 L.H., Daily Totals		$1933.60		$2985.64	$34.53	$53.31

Crew C-16A	Hr.	Daily	Hr.	Daily	Bare Costs	Incl. O&P
1 Laborer	$23.80	$190.40	$40.05	$320.40	$29.81	$48.94
2 Cement Finishers	30.85	493.60	49.90	798.40		
1 Equip. Oper. (medium)	33.75	270.00	55.90	447.20		
1 Gunite Pump Rig		370.40		407.44		
2 -50' Air Hoses, 3/4"		6.50		7.15		
2 -50' Air Hoses, 2"		15.50		17.05		
1 Aerial Lift Truck, 60' Boom		456.00		501.60	26.51	29.16
32 L.H., Daily Totals		$1802.40		$2499.24	$56.33	$78.10

Crew C-17	Hr.	Daily	Hr.	Daily	Bare Costs	Incl. O&P
2 Skilled Worker Foremen (out)	$34.45	$551.20	$58.20	$931.20	$32.85	$55.48
8 Skilled Workers	32.45	2076.80	54.80	3507.20		
80 L.H., Daily Totals		$2628.00		$4438.40	$32.85	$55.48

Crew C-17A	Hr.	Daily	Hr.	Daily	Bare Costs	Incl. O&P
2 Skilled Worker Foremen (out)	$34.45	$551.20	$58.20	$931.20	$32.87	$55.50
8 Skilled Workers	32.45	2076.80	54.80	3507.20		
.125 Equip. Oper. (crane)	34.65	34.65	57.40	57.40		
.125 Hyd. Crane, 80 Ton		206.50		227.15	2.55	2.80
81 L.H., Daily Totals		$2869.15		$4722.95	$35.42	$58.31

Crew C-17B	Hr.	Daily	Hr.	Daily	Bare Costs	Incl. O&P
2 Skilled Worker Foremen (out)	$34.45	$551.20	$58.20	$931.20	$32.89	$55.53
8 Skilled Workers	32.45	2076.80	54.80	3507.20		
.25 Equip. Oper. (crane)	34.65	69.30	57.40	114.80		
.25 Hyd. Crane, 80 Ton		413.00		454.30		
.25 Trowel, 48" Walk-Behind		13.40		14.74	5.20	5.72
82 L.H., Daily Totals		$3123.70		$5022.24	$38.09	$61.25

Crew C-17C	Hr.	Daily	Hr.	Daily	Bare Costs	Incl. O&P
2 Skilled Worker Foremen (out)	$34.45	$551.20	$58.20	$931.20	$32.92	$55.55
8 Skilled Workers	32.45	2076.80	54.80	3507.20		
.375 Equip. Oper. (crane)	34.65	103.95	57.40	172.20		
.375 Hyd. Crane, 80 Ton		619.50		681.45	7.46	8.21
83 L.H., Daily Totals		$3351.45		$5292.05	$40.38	$63.76

Crew C-17D	Hr.	Daily	Hr.	Daily	Bare Costs	Incl. O&P
2 Skilled Worker Foremen (out)	$34.45	$551.20	$58.20	$931.20	$32.94	$55.57
8 Skilled Workers	32.45	2076.80	54.80	3507.20		
.5 Equip. Oper. (crane)	34.65	138.60	57.40	229.60		
.5 Hyd. Crane, 80 Ton		826.00		908.60	9.83	10.82
84 L.H., Daily Totals		$3592.60		$5576.60	$42.77	$66.39

Crew C-17E	Hr.	Daily	Hr.	Daily	Bare Costs	Incl. O&P
2 Skilled Worker Foremen (out)	$34.45	$551.20	$58.20	$931.20	$32.85	$55.48
8 Skilled Workers	32.45	2076.80	54.80	3507.20		
1 Hyd. Jack with Rods		94.55		104.01	1.18	1.30
80 L.H., Daily Totals		$2722.55		$4542.40	$34.03	$56.78

Crew C-18	Hr.	Daily	Hr.	Daily	Bare Costs	Incl. O&P
.125 Labor Foreman (outside)	$25.80	$25.80	$43.40	$43.40	$24.02	$40.42
1 Laborer	23.80	190.40	40.05	320.40		
1 Concrete Cart, 10 C.F.		60.20		66.22	6.69	7.36
9 L.H., Daily Totals		$276.40		$430.02	$30.71	$47.78

Crew C-19	Hr.	Daily	Hr.	Daily	Bare Costs	Incl. O&P
.125 Labor Foreman (outside)	$25.80	$25.80	$43.40	$43.40	$24.02	$40.42
1 Laborer	23.80	190.40	40.05	320.40		
1 Concrete Cart, 18 C.F.		101.20		111.32	11.24	12.37
9 L.H., Daily Totals		$317.40		$475.12	$35.27	$52.79

Crew C-20	Hr.	Daily	Hr.	Daily	Bare Costs	Incl. O&P
1 Labor Foreman (outside)	$25.80	$206.40	$43.40	$347.20	$26.18	$43.68
5 Laborers	23.80	952.00	40.05	1602.00		
1 Cement Finisher	30.85	246.80	49.90	399.20		
1 Equip. Oper. (medium)	33.75	270.00	55.90	447.20		
2 Gas Engine Vibrators		66.00		72.60		
1 Concrete Pump (Small)		710.40		781.44	12.13	13.34
64 L.H., Daily Totals		$2451.60		$3649.64	$38.31	$57.03

Crew C-21	Hr.	Daily	Hr.	Daily	Bare Costs	Incl. O&P
1 Labor Foreman (outside)	$25.80	$206.40	$43.40	$347.20	$26.18	$43.68
5 Laborers	23.80	952.00	40.05	1602.00		
1 Cement Finisher	30.85	246.80	49.90	399.20		
1 Equip. Oper. (medium)	33.75	270.00	55.90	447.20		
2 Gas Engine Vibrators		66.00		72.60		
1 Concrete Conveyer		205.40		225.94	4.24	4.66
64 L.H., Daily Totals		$1946.60		$3094.14	$30.42	$48.35

Crew C-22	Hr.	Daily	Hr.	Daily	Bare Costs	Incl. O&P
1 Rodman Foreman (outside)	$35.95	$287.60	$61.50	$492.00	$34.25	$58.53
4 Rodmen (reinf.)	33.95	1086.40	58.10	1859.20		
.125 Equip. Oper. (crane)	34.65	34.65	57.40	57.40		
.125 Equip. Oper. (oiler)	30.05	30.05	49.75	49.75		
.125 Hyd. Crane, 25 Ton		93.22		102.55	2.22	2.44
42 L.H., Daily Totals		$1531.93		$2560.90	$36.47	$60.97

Crews

Crew C-23

Crew C-23	Hr.	Daily	Hr.	Daily	Bare Costs	Incl. O&P
2 Skilled Worker Foremen (out)	$34.45	$551.20	$58.20	$931.20	$32.83	$55.23
6 Skilled Workers	32.45	1557.60	54.80	2630.40		
1 Equip. Oper. (crane)	34.65	277.20	57.40	459.20		
1 Equip. Oper. (oiler)	30.05	240.40	49.75	398.00		
1 Lattice Boom Crane, 90 Ton		1529.00		1681.90	19.11	21.02
80 L.H., Daily Totals		$4155.40		$6100.70	$51.94	$76.26

Crew C-24

Crew C-24	Hr.	Daily	Hr.	Daily	Bare Costs	Incl. O&P
2 Skilled Worker Foremen (out)	$34.45	$551.20	$58.20	$931.20	$32.83	$55.23
6 Skilled Workers	32.45	1557.60	54.80	2630.40		
1 Equip. Oper. (crane)	34.65	277.20	57.40	459.20		
1 Equip. Oper. (oiler)	30.05	240.40	49.75	398.00		
1 Lattice Boom Crane, 150 Ton		1838.00		2021.80	22.98	25.27
80 L.H., Daily Totals		$4464.40		$6440.60	$55.81	$80.51

Crew C-25

Crew C-25	Hr.	Daily	Hr.	Daily	Bare Costs	Incl. O&P
2 Rodmen (reinf.)	$33.95	$543.20	$58.10	$929.60	$27.02	$47.55
2 Rodmen Helpers	20.10	321.60	37.00	592.00		
32 L.H., Daily Totals		$864.80		$1521.60	$27.02	$47.55

Crew C-27

Crew C-27	Hr.	Daily	Hr.	Daily	Bare Costs	Incl. O&P
2 Cement Finishers	$30.85	$493.60	$49.90	$798.40	$30.85	$49.90
1 Concrete Saw		175.20		192.72	10.95	12.05
16 L.H., Daily Totals		$668.80		$991.12	$41.80	$61.95

Crew C-28

Crew C-28	Hr.	Daily	Hr.	Daily	Bare Costs	Incl. O&P
1 Cement Finisher	$30.85	$246.80	$49.90	$399.20	$30.85	$49.90
1 Portable Air Compressor, Gas		17.70		19.47	2.21	2.43
8 L.H., Daily Totals		$264.50		$418.67	$33.06	$52.33

Crew C-29

Crew C-29	Hr.	Daily	Hr.	Daily	Bare Costs	Incl. O&P
1 Laborer	$23.80	$190.40	$40.05	$320.40	$23.80	$40.05
1 Pressure Washer		69.40		76.34	8.68	9.54
8 L.H., Daily Totals		$259.80		$396.74	$32.48	$49.59

Crew C-30

Crew C-30	Hr.	Daily	Hr.	Daily	Bare Costs	Incl. O&P
1 Laborer	$23.80	$190.40	$40.05	$320.40	$23.80	$40.05
1 Concrete Mixer, 10 C.F.		176.80		194.48	22.10	24.31
8 L.H., Daily Totals		$367.20		$514.88	$45.90	$64.36

Crew C-31

Crew C-31	Hr.	Daily	Hr.	Daily	Bare Costs	Incl. O&P
1 Cement Finisher	$30.85	$246.80	$49.90	$399.20	$30.85	$49.90
1 Grout Pump		370.40		407.44	46.30	50.93
8 L.H., Daily Totals		$617.20		$806.64	$77.15	$100.83

Crew C-32

Crew C-32	Hr.	Daily	Hr.	Daily	Bare Costs	Incl. O&P
1 Cement Finisher	$30.85	$246.80	$49.90	$399.20	$27.32	$44.98
1 Laborer	23.80	190.40	40.05	320.40		
1 Crack Chaser Saw, Gas, 6 H.P.		30.80		33.88		
1 Vacuum Pick-Up System		60.75		66.83	5.72	6.29
16 L.H., Daily Totals		$528.75		$820.30	$33.05	$51.27

Crew D-1

Crew D-1	Hr.	Daily	Hr.	Daily	Bare Costs	Incl. O&P
1 Bricklayer	$31.90	$255.20	$53.10	$424.80	$28.90	$48.10
1 Bricklayer Helper	25.90	207.20	43.10	344.80		
16 L.H., Daily Totals		$462.40		$769.60	$28.90	$48.10

Crew D-2

Crew D-2	Hr.	Daily	Hr.	Daily	Bare Costs	Incl. O&P
3 Bricklayers	$31.90	$765.60	$53.10	$1274.40	$29.50	$49.10
2 Bricklayers Helpers	25.90	414.40	43.10	689.60		
40 L.H., Daily Totals		$1180.00		$1964.00	$29.50	$49.10

Crew D-3

Crew D-3	Hr.	Daily	Hr.	Daily	Bare Costs	Incl. O&P
3 Bricklayers	$31.90	$765.60	$53.10	$1274.40	$29.62	$49.33
2 Bricklayer Helpers	25.90	414.40	43.10	689.60		
.25 Carpenter	32.10	64.20	54.00	108.00		
42 L.H., Daily Totals		$1244.20		$2072.00	$29.62	$49.33

Crew D-4

Crew D-4	Hr.	Daily	Hr.	Daily	Bare Costs	Incl. O&P
1 Bricklayer	$31.90	$255.20	$53.10	$424.80	$26.68	$44.49
3 Bricklayer Helpers	25.90	621.60	43.10	1034.40		
1 Building Laborer	23.80	190.40	40.05	320.40		
1 Grout Pump, 50 C.F./hr.		134.80		148.28	3.37	3.71
40 L.H., Daily Totals		$1202.00		$1927.88	$30.05	$48.20

Crew D-5

Crew D-5	Hr.	Daily	Hr.	Daily	Bare Costs	Incl. O&P
1 Block Mason Helper	$25.90	$207.20	$43.10	$344.80	$25.90	$43.10
8 L.H., Daily Totals		$207.20		$344.80	$25.90	$43.10

Crew D-6

Crew D-6	Hr.	Daily	Hr.	Daily	Bare Costs	Incl. O&P
3 Bricklayers	$31.90	$765.60	$53.10	$1274.40	$28.90	$48.10
3 Bricklayer Helpers	25.90	621.60	43.10	1034.40		
48 L.H., Daily Totals		$1387.20		$2308.80	$28.90	$48.10

Crew D-7

Crew D-7	Hr.	Daily	Hr.	Daily	Bare Costs	Incl. O&P
1 Tile Layer	$29.35	$234.80	$47.35	$378.80	$26.32	$42.48
1 Tile Layer Helper	23.30	186.40	37.60	300.80		
16 L.H., Daily Totals		$421.20		$679.60	$26.32	$42.48

Crew D-8

Crew D-8	Hr.	Daily	Hr.	Daily	Bare Costs	Incl. O&P
3 Bricklayers	$31.90	$765.60	$53.10	$1274.40	$29.50	$49.10
2 Bricklayer Helpers	25.90	414.40	43.10	689.60		
40 L.H., Daily Totals		$1180.00		$1964.00	$29.50	$49.10

Crew D-9

Crew D-9	Hr.	Daily	Hr.	Daily	Bare Costs	Incl. O&P
3 Bricklayers	$31.90	$765.60	$53.10	$1274.40	$28.90	$48.10
3 Bricklayer Helpers	25.90	621.60	43.10	1034.40		
48 L.H., Daily Totals		$1387.20		$2308.80	$28.90	$48.10

Crew D-10

Crew D-10	Hr.	Daily	Hr.	Daily	Bare Costs	Incl. O&P
1 Bricklayer Foreman (outside)	$33.90	$271.20	$56.40	$451.20	$31.59	$52.50
1 Bricklayer	31.90	255.20	53.10	424.80		
1 Bricklayer Helper	25.90	207.20	43.10	344.80		
1 Equip. Oper. (crane)	34.65	277.20	57.40	459.20		
1 S.P. Crane, 4x4, 12 Ton		481.20		529.32	15.04	16.54
32 L.H., Daily Totals		$1492.00		$2209.32	$46.63	$69.04

Crew D-11

Crew D-11	Hr.	Daily	Hr.	Daily	Bare Costs	Incl. O&P
2 Bricklayers	$31.90	$510.40	$53.10	$849.60	$29.90	$49.77
1 Bricklayer Helper	25.90	207.20	43.10	344.80		
24 L.H., Daily Totals		$717.60		$1194.40	$29.90	$49.77

Crew D-12

Crew D-12	Hr.	Daily	Hr.	Daily	Bare Costs	Incl. O&P
2 Bricklayers	$31.90	$510.40	$53.10	$849.60	$28.90	$48.10
2 Bricklayer Helpers	25.90	414.40	43.10	689.60		
32 L.H., Daily Totals		$924.80		$1539.20	$28.90	$48.10

Crews

Crew No.	Bare Costs Hr.	Bare Costs Daily	Incl. Subs O&P Hr.	Incl. Subs O&P Daily	Cost Per Labor-Hour Bare Costs	Cost Per Labor-Hour Incl. O&P
Crew D-13	Hr.	Daily	Hr.	Daily	Bare Costs	Incl. O&P
1 Bricklayer Foreman (outside)	$33.90	$271.20	$56.40	$451.20	$30.69	$51.03
2 Bricklayers	31.90	510.40	53.10	849.60		
2 Bricklayer Helpers	25.90	414.40	43.10	689.60		
1 Equip. Oper. (crane)	34.65	277.20	57.40	459.20		
1 S.P. Crane, 4x4, 12 Ton		481.20		529.32	10.03	11.03
48 L.H., Daily Totals		$1954.40		$2978.92	$40.72	$62.06
Crew E-1	Hr.	Daily	Hr.	Daily	Bare Costs	Incl. O&P
2 Struc. Steel Workers	$34.25	$548.00	$65.25	$1044.00	$34.25	$65.25
1 Welder, Gas Engine, 300 amp		142.00		156.20	8.88	9.76
16 L.H., Daily Totals		$690.00		$1200.20	$43.13	$75.01
Crew E-2	Hr.	Daily	Hr.	Daily	Bare Costs	Incl. O&P
1 Struc. Steel Foreman (outside)	$36.25	$290.00	$69.05	$552.40	$34.65	$64.58
4 Struc. Steel Workers	34.25	1096.00	65.25	2088.00		
1 Equip. Oper. (crane)	34.65	277.20	57.40	459.20		
1 Lattice Boom Crane, 90 Ton		1529.00		1681.90	31.85	35.04
48 L.H., Daily Totals		$3192.20		$4781.50	$66.50	$99.61
Crew E-3	Hr.	Daily	Hr.	Daily	Bare Costs	Incl. O&P
1 Struc. Steel Foreman (outside)	$36.25	$290.00	$69.05	$552.40	$34.92	$66.52
2 Struc. Steel Workers	34.25	548.00	65.25	1044.00		
1 Welder, Gas Engine, 300 amp		142.00		156.20	5.92	6.51
24 L.H., Daily Totals		$980.00		$1752.60	$40.83	$73.03
Crew E-3A	Hr.	Daily	Hr.	Daily	Bare Costs	Incl. O&P
1 Struc. Steel Foreman (outside)	$36.25	$290.00	$69.05	$552.40	$34.92	$66.52
2 Struc. Steel Workers	34.25	548.00	65.25	1044.00		
1 Welder, Gas Engine, 300 amp		142.00		156.20		
1 Aerial Lift Truck, 40' Boom		325.00		357.50	19.46	21.40
24 L.H., Daily Totals		$1305.00		$2110.10	$54.38	$87.92
Crew E-4	Hr.	Daily	Hr.	Daily	Bare Costs	Incl. O&P
1 Struc. Steel Foreman (outside)	$36.25	$290.00	$69.05	$552.40	$34.75	$66.20
3 Struc. Steel Workers	34.25	822.00	65.25	1566.00		
1 Welder, Gas Engine, 300 amp		142.00		156.20	4.44	4.88
32 L.H., Daily Totals		$1254.00		$2274.60	$39.19	$71.08
Crew E-5	Hr.	Daily	Hr.	Daily	Bare Costs	Incl. O&P
1 Struc. Steel Foreman (outside)	$36.25	$290.00	$69.05	$552.40	$34.52	$64.80
7 Struc. Steel Workers	34.25	1918.00	65.25	3654.00		
1 Equip. Oper. (crane)	34.65	277.20	57.40	459.20		
1 Lattice Boom Crane, 90 Ton		1529.00		1681.90		
1 Welder, Gas Engine, 300 amp		142.00		156.20	23.21	25.53
72 L.H., Daily Totals		$4156.20		$6503.70	$57.73	$90.33
Crew E-6	Hr.	Daily	Hr.	Daily	Bare Costs	Incl. O&P
1 Struc. Steel Foreman (outside)	$36.25	$290.00	$69.05	$552.40	$34.29	$64.21
12 Struc. Steel Workers	34.25	3288.00	65.25	6264.00		
1 Equip. Oper. (crane)	34.65	277.20	57.40	459.20		
1 Equip. Oper. (light)	32.45	259.60	53.75	430.00		
1 Lattice Boom Crane, 90 Ton		1529.00		1681.90		
1 Welder, Gas Engine, 300 amp		142.00		156.20		
1 Air Compressor, 160 cfm		157.40		173.14		
2 Impact Wrenches		36.00		39.60	15.54	17.09
120 L.H., Daily Totals		$5979.20		$9756.44	$49.83	$81.30

Crew No.	Bare Costs Hr.	Bare Costs Daily	Incl. Subs O&P Hr.	Incl. Subs O&P Daily	Cost Per Labor-Hour Bare Costs	Cost Per Labor-Hour Incl. O&P
Crew E-7	Hr.	Daily	Hr.	Daily	Bare Costs	Incl. O&P
1 Struc. Steel Foreman (outside)	$36.25	$290.00	$69.05	$552.40	$34.52	$64.80
7 Struc. Steel Workers	34.25	1918.00	65.25	3654.00		
1 Equip. Oper. (crane)	34.65	277.20	57.40	459.20		
1 Lattice Boom Crane, 90 Ton		1529.00		1681.90		
2 Welder, Gas Engine, 300 amp		284.00		312.40	25.18	27.70
72 L.H., Daily Totals		$4298.20		$6659.90	$59.70	$92.50
Crew E-8	Hr.	Daily	Hr.	Daily	Bare Costs	Incl. O&P
1 Struc. Steel Foreman (outside)	$36.25	$290.00	$69.05	$552.40	$34.47	$64.88
9 Struc. Steel Workers	34.25	2466.00	65.25	4698.00		
1 Equip. Oper. (crane)	34.65	277.20	57.40	459.20		
1 Lattice Boom Crane, 90 Ton		1529.00		1681.90		
4 Welder, Gas Engine, 300 amp		568.00		624.80	23.83	26.21
88 L.H., Daily Totals		$5130.20		$8016.30	$58.30	$91.09
Crew E-9	Hr.	Daily	Hr.	Daily	Bare Costs	Incl. O&P
2 Struc. Steel Foremen (outside)	$36.25	$580.00	$69.05	$1104.80	$34.27	$63.78
5 Struc. Steel Workers	34.25	1370.00	65.25	2610.00		
1 Welder Foreman (outside)	36.25	290.00	69.05	552.40		
5 Welders	34.25	1370.00	65.25	2610.00		
1 Equip. Oper. (crane)	34.65	277.20	57.40	459.20		
1 Equip. Oper. (oiler)	30.05	240.40	49.75	398.00		
1 Equip. Oper. (light)	32.45	259.60	53.75	430.00		
1 Lattice Boom Crane, 90 Ton		1529.00		1681.90		
5 Welder, Gas Engine, 300 amp		710.00		781.00	17.49	19.24
128 L.H., Daily Totals		$6626.20		$10627.30	$51.77	$83.03
Crew E-10	Hr.	Daily	Hr.	Daily	Bare Costs	Incl. O&P
1 Struc. Steel Foreman (outside)	$36.25	$290.00	$69.05	$552.40	$34.92	$66.52
2 Struc. Steel Workers	34.25	548.00	65.25	1044.00		
1 Welder, Gas Engine, 300 amp		142.00		156.20		
1 Flatbed Truck, Gas, 3 Ton		333.00		366.30	19.79	21.77
24 L.H., Daily Totals		$1313.00		$2118.90	$54.71	$88.29
Crew E-11	Hr.	Daily	Hr.	Daily	Bare Costs	Incl. O&P
2 Painters, Struc. Steel	$28.75	$460.00	$55.90	$894.40	$28.44	$51.40
1 Building Laborer	23.80	190.40	40.05	320.40		
1 Equip. Oper. (light)	32.45	259.60	53.75	430.00		
1 Air Compressor, 250 cfm		202.40		222.64		
1 Sandblaster, Portable, 3 C.F.		20.40		22.44		
1 Set Sand Blasting Accessories		13.85		15.23	7.40	8.13
32 L.H., Daily Totals		$1146.65		$1905.12	$35.83	$59.53
Crew E-11A	Hr.	Daily	Hr.	Daily	Bare Costs	Incl. O&P
2 Painters, Struc. Steel	$28.75	$460.00	$55.90	$894.40	$28.44	$51.40
1 Building Laborer	23.80	190.40	40.05	320.40		
1 Equip. Oper. (light)	32.45	259.60	53.75	430.00		
1 Air Compressor, 250 cfm		202.40		222.64		
1 Sandblaster, Portable, 3 C.F.		20.40		22.44		
1 Set Sand Blasting Accessories		13.85		15.23		
1 Aerial Lift Truck, 60' Boom		456.00		501.60	21.65	23.81
32 L.H., Daily Totals		$1602.65		$2406.72	$50.08	$75.21
Crew E-11B	Hr.	Daily	Hr.	Daily	Bare Costs	Incl. O&P
2 Painters, Struc. Steel	$28.75	$460.00	$55.90	$894.40	$27.10	$50.62
1 Building Laborer	23.80	190.40	40.05	320.40		
2 Paint Sprayer, 8 C.F.M.		89.80		98.78		
1 Aerial Lift Truck, 60' Boom		456.00		501.60	22.74	25.02
24 L.H., Daily Totals		$1196.20		$1815.18	$49.84	$75.63

691

Crew No.	Bare Costs Hr.	Daily	Incl. Subs O&P Hr.	Daily	Cost Per Labor-Hour Bare Costs	Incl. O&P
Crew E-12	Hr.	Daily	Hr.	Daily	Bare Costs	Incl. O&P
1 Welder Foreman (outside)	$36.25	$290.00	$69.05	$552.40	$34.35	$61.40
1 Equip. Oper. (light)	32.45	259.60	53.75	430.00		
1 Welder, Gas Engine, 300 amp		142.00		156.20	8.88	9.76
16 L.H., Daily Totals		$691.60		$1138.60	$43.23	$71.16

Crew E-13	Hr.	Daily	Hr.	Daily	Bare Costs	Incl. O&P
1 Welder Foreman (outside)	$36.25	$290.00	$69.05	$552.40	$34.98	$63.95
.5 Equip. Oper. (light)	32.45	129.80	53.75	215.00		
1 Welder, Gas Engine, 300 amp		142.00		156.20	11.83	13.02
12 L.H., Daily Totals		$561.80		$923.60	$46.82	$76.97

Crew E-14	Hr.	Daily	Hr.	Daily	Bare Costs	Incl. O&P
1 Struc. Steel Worker	$34.25	$274.00	$65.25	$522.00	$34.25	$65.25
1 Welder, Gas Engine, 300 amp		142.00		156.20	17.75	19.52
8 L.H., Daily Totals		$416.00		$678.20	$52.00	$84.78

Crew E-16	Hr.	Daily	Hr.	Daily	Bare Costs	Incl. O&P
1 Welder Foreman (outside)	$36.25	$290.00	$69.05	$552.40	$35.25	$67.15
1 Welder	34.25	274.00	65.25	522.00		
1 Welder, Gas Engine, 300 amp		142.00		156.20	8.88	9.76
16 L.H., Daily Totals		$706.00		$1230.60	$44.13	$76.91

Crew E-17	Hr.	Daily	Hr.	Daily	Bare Costs	Incl. O&P
1 Struc. Steel Foreman (outside)	$36.25	$290.00	$69.05	$552.40	$35.25	$67.15
1 Structural Steel Worker	34.25	274.00	65.25	522.00		
16 L.H., Daily Totals		$564.00		$1074.40	$35.25	$67.15

Crew E-18	Hr.	Daily	Hr.	Daily	Bare Costs	Incl. O&P
1 Struc. Steel Foreman (outside)	$36.25	$290.00	$69.05	$552.40	$34.55	$64.14
3 Structural Steel Workers	34.25	822.00	65.25	1566.00		
1 Equipment Operator (med.)	33.75	270.00	55.90	447.20		
1 Lattice Boom Crane, 20 Ton		960.50		1056.55	24.01	26.41
40 L.H., Daily Totals		$2342.50		$3622.15	$58.56	$90.55

Crew E-19	Hr.	Daily	Hr.	Daily	Bare Costs	Incl. O&P
1 Struc. Steel Foreman (outside)	$36.25	$290.00	$69.05	$552.40	$34.32	$62.68
1 Structural Steel Worker	34.25	274.00	65.25	522.00		
1 Equip. Oper. (light)	32.45	259.60	53.75	430.00		
1 Lattice Boom Crane, 20 Ton		960.50		1056.55	40.02	44.02
24 L.H., Daily Totals		$1784.10		$2560.95	$74.34	$106.71

Crew E-20	Hr.	Daily	Hr.	Daily	Bare Costs	Incl. O&P
1 Struc. Steel Foreman (outside)	$36.25	$290.00	$69.05	$552.40	$34.02	$62.81
5 Structural Steel Workers	34.25	1370.00	65.25	2610.00		
1 Equip. Oper. (crane)	34.65	277.20	57.40	459.20		
1 Equip. Oper. (oiler)	30.05	240.40	49.75	398.00		
1 Lattice Boom Crane, 40 Ton		1177.00		1294.70	18.39	20.23
64 L.H., Daily Totals		$3354.60		$5314.30	$52.42	$83.04

Crew E-22	Hr.	Daily	Hr.	Daily	Bare Costs	Incl. O&P
1 Skilled Worker Foreman (out)	$34.45	$275.60	$58.20	$465.60	$33.12	$55.93
2 Skilled Workers	32.45	519.20	54.80	876.80		
24 L.H., Daily Totals		$794.80		$1342.40	$33.12	$55.93

Crew E-24	Hr.	Daily	Hr.	Daily	Bare Costs	Incl. O&P
3 Structural Steel Workers	$34.25	$822.00	$65.25	$1566.00	$34.13	$62.91
1 Equipment Operator (med.)	33.75	270.00	55.90	447.20		
1 Hyd. Crane, 25 Ton		745.80		820.38	23.31	25.64
32 L.H., Daily Totals		$1837.80		$2833.58	$57.43	$88.55

Crew No.	Bare Costs Hr.	Daily	Incl. Subs O&P Hr.	Daily	Cost Per Labor-Hour Bare Costs	Incl. O&P
Crew E-25	Hr.	Daily	Hr.	Daily	Bare Costs	Incl. O&P
1 Welder	$34.25	$274.00	$65.25	$522.00	$34.25	$65.25
1 Cutting Torch		11.40		12.54	1.43	1.57
8 L.H., Daily Totals		$285.40		$534.54	$35.67	$66.82

Crew F-3	Hr.	Daily	Hr.	Daily	Bare Costs	Incl. O&P
2 Carpenters	$32.10	$513.60	$54.00	$864.00	$29.31	$49.20
2 Carpenter Helpers	23.85	381.60	40.30	644.80		
1 Equip. Oper. (crane)	34.65	277.20	57.40	459.20		
1 Hyd. Crane, 12 Ton		663.00		729.30	16.57	18.23
40 L.H., Daily Totals		$1835.40		$2697.30	$45.88	$67.43

Crew F-4	Hr.	Daily	Hr.	Daily	Bare Costs	Incl. O&P
2 Carpenters	$32.10	$513.60	$54.00	$864.00	$29.31	$49.20
2 Carpenter Helpers	23.85	381.60	40.30	644.80		
1 Equip. Oper. (crane)	34.65	277.20	57.40	459.20		
1 Hyd. Crane, 55 Ton		1137.00		1250.70	28.43	31.27
40 L.H., Daily Totals		$2309.40		$3218.70	$57.73	$80.47

Crew F-5	Hr.	Daily	Hr.	Daily	Bare Costs	Incl. O&P
2 Carpenters	$32.10	$513.60	$54.00	$864.00	$27.98	$47.15
2 Carpenter Helpers	23.85	381.60	40.30	644.80		
32 L.H., Daily Totals		$895.20		$1508.80	$27.98	$47.15

Crew F-6	Hr.	Daily	Hr.	Daily	Bare Costs	Incl. O&P
2 Carpenters	$32.10	$513.60	$54.00	$864.00	$29.29	$49.10
2 Building Laborers	23.80	380.80	40.05	640.80		
1 Equip. Oper. (crane)	34.65	277.20	57.40	459.20		
1 Hyd. Crane, 12 Ton		663.00		729.30	16.57	18.23
40 L.H., Daily Totals		$1834.60		$2693.30	$45.87	$67.33

Crew F-7	Hr.	Daily	Hr.	Daily	Bare Costs	Incl. O&P
2 Carpenters	$32.10	$513.60	$54.00	$864.00	$27.95	$47.02
2 Building Laborers	23.80	380.80	40.05	640.80		
32 L.H., Daily Totals		$894.40		$1504.80	$27.95	$47.02

Crew G-1	Hr.	Daily	Hr.	Daily	Bare Costs	Incl. O&P
1 Roofer Foreman (outside)	$29.00	$232.00	$53.40	$427.20	$25.31	$46.63
4 Roofers Composition	27.00	864.00	49.75	1592.00		
2 Roofer Helpers	20.10	321.60	37.00	592.00		
1 Application Equipment		199.20		219.12		
1 Tar Kettle/Pot		130.00		143.00		
1 Crew Truck		224.80		247.28	9.89	10.88
56 L.H., Daily Totals		$1971.60		$3220.60	$35.21	$57.51

Crew G-2	Hr.	Daily	Hr.	Daily	Bare Costs	Incl. O&P
1 Plasterer	$29.35	$234.80	$48.30	$386.40	$26.40	$43.73
1 Plasterer Helper	26.05	208.40	42.85	342.80		
1 Building Laborer	23.80	190.40	40.05	320.40		
1 Grout Pump, 50 C.F./hr.		134.80		148.28	5.62	6.18
24 L.H., Daily Totals		$768.40		$1197.88	$32.02	$49.91

Crew G-2A	Hr.	Daily	Hr.	Daily	Bare Costs	Incl. O&P
1 Roofer Composition	$27.00	$216.00	$49.75	$398.00	$23.63	$42.27
1 Roofer Helper	20.10	160.80	37.00	296.00		
1 Building Laborer	23.80	190.40	40.05	320.40		
1 Foam Spray Rig, Trailer-Mtd.		585.25		643.77		
1 Pickup Truck, 3/4 Ton		157.00		172.70	30.93	34.02
24 L.H., Daily Totals		$1309.45		$1830.88	$54.56	$76.29

Crew No.	Bare Costs		Incl. Subs O&P		Cost Per Labor-Hour	
Crew G-3	Hr.	Daily	Hr.	Daily	Bare Costs	Incl. O&P
2 Sheet Metal Workers	$36.10	$577.60	$60.20	$963.20	$29.95	$50.13
2 Building Laborers	23.80	380.80	40.05	640.80		
32 L.H., Daily Totals		$958.40		$1604.00	$29.95	$50.13
Crew G-4	Hr.	Daily	Hr.	Daily	Bare Costs	Incl. O&P
1 Labor Foreman (outside)	$25.80	$206.40	$43.40	$347.20	$24.47	$41.17
2 Building Laborers	23.80	380.80	40.05	640.80		
1 Flatbed Truck, Gas, 1.5 Ton		270.20		297.22		
1 Air Compressor, 160 cfm		157.40		173.14	17.82	19.60
24 L.H., Daily Totals		$1014.80		$1458.36	$42.28	$60.77
Crew G-5	Hr.	Daily	Hr.	Daily	Bare Costs	Incl. O&P
1 Roofer Foreman (outside)	$29.00	$232.00	$53.40	$427.20	$24.64	$45.38
2 Roofers Composition	27.00	432.00	49.75	796.00		
2 Roofer Helpers	20.10	321.60	37.00	592.00		
1 Application Equipment		199.20		219.12	4.98	5.48
40 L.H., Daily Totals		$1184.80		$2034.32	$29.62	$50.86
Crew G-6A	Hr.	Daily	Hr.	Daily	Bare Costs	Incl. O&P
2 Roofers Composition	$27.00	$432.00	$49.75	$796.00	$27.00	$49.75
1 Small Compressor, Electric		12.10		13.31		
2 Pneumatic Nailers		44.70		49.17	3.55	3.90
16 L.H., Daily Totals		$488.80		$858.48	$30.55	$53.66
Crew G-7	Hr.	Daily	Hr.	Daily	Bare Costs	Incl. O&P
1 Carpenter	$32.10	$256.80	$54.00	$432.00	$32.10	$54.00
1 Small Compressor, Electric		12.10		13.31		
1 Pneumatic Nailer		22.35		24.59	4.31	4.74
8 L.H., Daily Totals		$291.25		$469.89	$36.41	$58.74
Crew H-1	Hr.	Daily	Hr.	Daily	Bare Costs	Incl. O&P
2 Glaziers	$31.30	$500.80	$52.00	$832.00	$32.77	$58.63
2 Struc. Steel Workers	34.25	548.00	65.25	1044.00		
32 L.H., Daily Totals		$1048.80		$1876.00	$32.77	$58.63
Crew H-2	Hr.	Daily	Hr.	Daily	Bare Costs	Incl. O&P
2 Glaziers	$31.30	$500.80	$52.00	$832.00	$28.80	$48.02
1 Building Laborer	23.80	190.40	40.05	320.40		
24 L.H., Daily Totals		$691.20		$1152.40	$28.80	$48.02
Crew H-3	Hr.	Daily	Hr.	Daily	Bare Costs	Incl. O&P
1 Glazier	$31.30	$250.40	$52.00	$416.00	$27.57	$46.15
1 Helper	23.85	190.80	40.30	322.40		
16 L.H., Daily Totals		$441.20		$738.40	$27.57	$46.15
Crew H-4	Hr.	Daily	Hr.	Daily	Bare Costs	Incl. O&P
1 Carpenter	$32.10	$256.80	$54.00	$432.00	$29.53	$49.42
1 Carpenter Helper	23.85	190.80	40.30	322.40		
.5 Electrician	35.75	143.00	58.50	234.00		
20 L.H., Daily Totals		$590.60		$988.40	$29.53	$49.42
Crew J-1	Hr.	Daily	Hr.	Daily	Bare Costs	Incl. O&P
3 Plasterers	$29.35	$704.40	$48.30	$1159.20	$28.03	$46.12
2 Plasterer Helpers	26.05	416.80	42.85	685.60		
1 Mixing Machine, 6 C.F.		143.60		157.96	3.59	3.95
40 L.H., Daily Totals		$1264.80		$2002.76	$31.62	$50.07

Crew No.	Bare Costs		Incl. Subs O&P		Cost Per Labor-Hour	
Crew J-2	Hr.	Daily	Hr.	Daily	Bare Costs	Incl. O&P
3 Plasterers	$29.35	$704.40	$48.30	$1159.20	$28.09	$46.05
2 Plasterer Helpers	26.05	416.80	42.85	685.60		
1 Lather	28.40	227.20	45.70	365.60		
1 Mixing Machine, 6 C.F.		143.60		157.96	2.99	3.29
48 L.H., Daily Totals		$1492.00		$2368.36	$31.08	$49.34
Crew J-3	Hr.	Daily	Hr.	Daily	Bare Costs	Incl. O&P
1 Terrazzo Worker	$29.15	$233.20	$47.05	$376.40	$26.75	$43.17
1 Terrazzo Helper	24.35	194.80	39.30	314.40		
1 Floor Grinder, 22" Path		97.90		107.69		
1 Terrazzo Mixer		192.60		211.86	18.16	19.97
16 L.H., Daily Totals		$718.50		$1010.35	$44.91	$63.15
Crew J-4	Hr.	Daily	Hr.	Daily	Bare Costs	Incl. O&P
2 Cement Finishers	$30.85	$493.60	$49.90	$798.40	$28.50	$46.62
1 Laborer	23.80	190.40	40.05	320.40		
1 Floor Grinder, 22" Path		97.90		107.69		
1 Floor Edger, 7" Path		39.15		43.06		
1 Vacuum Pick-Up System		60.75		66.83	8.24	9.07
24 L.H., Daily Totals		$881.80		$1336.38	$36.74	$55.68
Crew J-4A	Hr.	Daily	Hr.	Daily	Bare Costs	Incl. O&P
2 Cement Finishers	$30.85	$493.60	$49.90	$798.40	$27.32	$44.98
2 Laborers	23.80	380.80	40.05	640.80		
1 Floor Grinder, 22" Path		97.90		107.69		
1 Floor Edger, 7" Path		39.15		43.06		
1 Vacuum Pick-Up System		60.75		66.83		
1 Floor Auto Scrubber		212.15		233.37	12.81	14.09
32 L.H., Daily Totals		$1284.35		$1890.15	$40.14	$59.07
Crew J-4B	Hr.	Daily	Hr.	Daily	Bare Costs	Incl. O&P
1 Laborer	$23.80	$190.40	$40.05	$320.40	$23.80	$40.05
1 Floor Auto Scrubber		212.15		233.37	26.52	29.17
8 L.H., Daily Totals		$402.55		$553.76	$50.32	$69.22
Crew J-6	Hr.	Daily	Hr.	Daily	Bare Costs	Incl. O&P
2 Painters	$28.10	$449.60	$46.20	$739.20	$28.11	$46.55
1 Building Laborer	23.80	190.40	40.05	320.40		
1 Equip. Oper. (light)	32.45	259.60	53.75	430.00		
1 Air Compressor, 250 cfm		202.40		222.64		
1 Sandblaster, Portable, 3 C.F.		20.40		22.44		
1 Set Sand Blasting Accessories		13.85		15.23	7.40	8.13
32 L.H., Daily Totals		$1136.25		$1749.92	$35.51	$54.68
Crew J-7	Hr.	Daily	Hr.	Daily	Bare Costs	Incl. O&P
2 Painters	$28.10	$449.60	$46.20	$739.20	$28.10	$46.20
1 Floor Belt Sander		15.90		17.49		
1 Floor Sanding Edger		15.55		17.11	1.97	2.16
16 L.H., Daily Totals		$481.05		$773.79	$30.07	$48.36
Crew K-1	Hr.	Daily	Hr.	Daily	Bare Costs	Incl. O&P
1 Carpenter	$32.10	$256.80	$54.00	$432.00	$29.00	$48.58
1 Truck Driver (light)	25.90	207.20	43.15	345.20		
1 Flatbed Truck, Gas, 3 Ton		333.00		366.30	20.81	22.89
16 L.H., Daily Totals		$797.00		$1143.50	$49.81	$71.47

Crew K-2

Crew No.	Bare Costs Hr.	Bare Costs Daily	Incl. Subs O&P Hr.	Incl. Subs O&P Daily	Cost Per Labor-Hour Bare Costs	Cost Per Labor-Hour Incl. O&P
1 Struc. Steel Foreman (outside)	$36.25	$290.00	$69.05	$552.40	$32.13	$59.15
1 Struc. Steel Worker	34.25	274.00	65.25	522.00		
1 Truck Driver (light)	25.90	207.20	43.15	345.20		
1 Flatbed Truck, Gas, 3 Ton		333.00		366.30	13.88	15.26
24 L.H., Daily Totals		$1104.20		$1785.90	$46.01	$74.41

Crew L-1

Crew No.	Hr.	Daily	Hr.	Daily	Bare Costs	Incl. O&P
.25 Electrician	$35.75	$71.50	$58.50	$117.00	$37.55	$61.86
1 Plumber	38.00	304.00	62.70	501.60		
10 L.H., Daily Totals		$375.50		$618.60	$37.55	$61.86

Crew L-2

Crew No.	Hr.	Daily	Hr.	Daily	Bare Costs	Incl. O&P
1 Carpenter	$32.10	$256.80	$54.00	$432.00	$27.98	$47.15
1 Carpenter Helper	23.85	190.80	40.30	322.40		
16 L.H., Daily Totals		$447.60		$754.40	$27.98	$47.15

Crew L-3

Crew No.	Hr.	Daily	Hr.	Daily	Bare Costs	Incl. O&P
1 Carpenter	$32.10	$256.80	$54.00	$432.00	$32.83	$54.90
.25 Electrician	35.75	71.50	58.50	117.00		
10 L.H., Daily Totals		$328.30		$549.00	$32.83	$54.90

Crew L-3A

Crew No.	Hr.	Daily	Hr.	Daily	Bare Costs	Incl. O&P
1 Carpenter Foreman (outside)	$34.10	$272.80	$57.40	$459.20	$34.77	$58.33
.5 Sheet Metal Worker	36.10	144.40	60.20	240.80		
12 L.H., Daily Totals		$417.20		$700.00	$34.77	$58.33

Crew L-4

Crew No.	Hr.	Daily	Hr.	Daily	Bare Costs	Incl. O&P
1 Skilled Worker	$32.45	$259.60	$54.80	$438.40	$28.15	$47.55
1 Helper	23.85	190.80	40.30	322.40		
16 L.H., Daily Totals		$450.40		$760.80	$28.15	$47.55

Crew L-5

Crew No.	Hr.	Daily	Hr.	Daily	Bare Costs	Incl. O&P
1 Struc. Steel Foreman (outside)	$36.25	$290.00	$69.05	$552.40	$34.59	$64.67
5 Struc. Steel Workers	34.25	1370.00	65.25	2610.00		
1 Equip. Oper. (crane)	34.65	277.20	57.40	459.20		
1 Hyd. Crane, 25 Ton		745.80		820.38	13.32	14.65
56 L.H., Daily Totals		$2683.00		$4441.98	$47.91	$79.32

Crew L-5A

Crew No.	Hr.	Daily	Hr.	Daily	Bare Costs	Incl. O&P
1 Struc. Steel Foreman (outside)	$36.25	$290.00	$69.05	$552.40	$34.85	$64.24
2 Structural Steel Workers	34.25	548.00	65.25	1044.00		
1 Equip. Oper. (crane)	34.65	277.20	57.40	459.20		
1 S.P. Crane, 4x4, 25 Ton		607.20		667.92	18.98	20.87
32 L.H., Daily Totals		$1722.40		$2723.52	$53.83	$85.11

Crew L-5B

Crew No.	Hr.	Daily	Hr.	Daily	Bare Costs	Incl. O&P
1 Struc. Steel Foreman (outside)	$36.25	$290.00	$69.05	$552.40	$34.66	$60.16
2 Structural Steel Workers	34.25	548.00	65.25	1044.00		
2 Electricians	35.75	572.00	58.50	936.00		
2 Steamfitters/Pipefitters	38.60	617.60	63.70	1019.20		
1 Equip. Oper. (crane)	34.65	277.20	57.40	459.20		
1 Common Laborer	23.80	190.40	40.05	320.40		
1 Hyd. Crane, 80 Ton		1652.00		1817.20	22.94	25.24
72 L.H., Daily Totals		$4147.20		$6148.40	$57.60	$85.39

Crew L-6

Crew No.	Hr.	Daily	Hr.	Daily	Bare Costs	Incl. O&P
1 Plumber	$38.00	$304.00	$62.70	$501.60	$37.25	$61.30
.5 Electrician	35.75	143.00	58.50	234.00		
12 L.H., Daily Totals		$447.00		$735.60	$37.25	$61.30

Crew L-7

Crew No.	Hr.	Daily	Hr.	Daily	Bare Costs	Incl. O&P
1 Carpenter	$32.10	$256.80	$54.00	$432.00	$27.30	$45.92
2 Carpenter Helpers	23.85	381.60	40.30	644.80		
.25 Electrician	35.75	71.50	58.50	117.00		
26 L.H., Daily Totals		$709.90		$1193.80	$27.30	$45.92

Crew L-8

Crew No.	Hr.	Daily	Hr.	Daily	Bare Costs	Incl. O&P
1 Carpenter	$32.10	$256.80	$54.00	$432.00	$29.98	$50.26
1 Carpenter Helper	23.85	190.80	40.30	322.40		
.5 Plumber	38.00	152.00	62.70	250.80		
20 L.H., Daily Totals		$599.60		$1005.20	$29.98	$50.26

Crew L-9

Crew No.	Hr.	Daily	Hr.	Daily	Bare Costs	Incl. O&P
1 Skilled Worker Foreman	$34.45	$275.60	$58.20	$465.60	$29.44	$49.52
1 Skilled Worker	32.45	259.60	54.80	438.40		
2 Helpers	23.85	381.60	40.30	644.80		
.5 Electrician	35.75	143.00	58.50	234.00		
36 L.H., Daily Totals		$1059.80		$1782.80	$29.44	$49.52

Crew L-10

Crew No.	Hr.	Daily	Hr.	Daily	Bare Costs	Incl. O&P
1 Struc. Steel Foreman (outside)	$36.25	$290.00	$69.05	$552.40	$35.05	$63.90
1 Structural Steel Worker	34.25	274.00	65.25	522.00		
1 Equip. Oper. (crane)	34.65	277.20	57.40	459.20		
1 Hyd. Crane, 12 Ton		663.00		729.30	27.63	30.39
24 L.H., Daily Totals		$1504.20		$2262.90	$62.67	$94.29

Crew L-11

Crew No.	Hr.	Daily	Hr.	Daily	Bare Costs	Incl. O&P
2 Wreckers	$24.55	$392.80	$44.70	$715.20	$29.05	$50.14
1 Equip. Oper. (crane)	34.65	277.20	57.40	459.20		
1 Equip. Oper. (light)	32.45	259.60	53.75	430.00		
1 Hyd. Excavator, 2.5 C.Y.		1637.00		1800.70		
1 Loader, Skid Steer, 78 H.P.		308.80		339.68	60.81	66.89
32 L.H., Daily Totals		$2875.40		$3744.78	$89.86	$117.02

Crew M-1

Crew No.	Hr.	Daily	Hr.	Daily	Bare Costs	Incl. O&P
3 Elevator Constructors	$49.70	$1192.80	$81.30	$1951.20	$47.21	$77.24
1 Elevator Apprentice	39.75	318.00	65.05	520.40		
5 Hand Tools		48.00		52.80	1.50	1.65
32 L.H., Daily Totals		$1558.80		$2524.40	$48.71	$78.89

Crew M-3

Crew No.	Hr.	Daily	Hr.	Daily	Bare Costs	Incl. O&P
1 Electrician Foreman (outside)	$37.75	$302.00	$61.80	$494.40	$37.51	$61.69
1 Common Laborer	23.80	190.40	40.05	320.40		
.25 Equipment Operator (med.)	33.75	67.50	55.90	111.80		
1 Elevator Constructor	49.70	397.60	81.30	650.40		
1 Elevator Apprentice	39.75	318.00	65.05	520.40		
.25 S.P. Crane, 4x4, 20 Ton		140.10		154.11	4.12	4.53
34 L.H., Daily Totals		$1415.60		$2251.51	$41.64	$66.22

Crew M-4

Crew No.	Hr.	Daily	Hr.	Daily	Bare Costs	Incl. O&P
1 Electrician Foreman (outside)	$37.75	$302.00	$61.80	$494.40	$37.15	$61.11
1 Common Laborer	23.80	190.40	40.05	320.40		
.25 Equipment Operator, Crane	34.65	69.30	57.40	114.80		
.25 Equip. Oper. (oiler)	30.05	60.10	49.75	99.50		
1 Elevator Constructor	49.70	397.60	81.30	650.40		
1 Elevator Apprentice	39.75	318.00	65.05	520.40		
.25 S.P. Crane, 4x4, 40 Ton		178.25		196.07	4.95	5.45
36 L.H., Daily Totals		$1515.65		$2395.97	$42.10	$66.55

Crew No.	Bare Costs		Incl. Subs O&P		Cost Per Labor-Hour	
Crew Q-1	Hr.	Daily	Hr.	Daily	Bare Costs	Incl. O&P
1 Plumber	$38.00	$304.00	$62.70	$501.60	$34.20	$56.42
1 Plumber Apprentice	30.40	243.20	50.15	401.20		
16 L.H., Daily Totals		$547.20		$902.80	$34.20	$56.42
Crew Q-1A	Hr.	Daily	Hr.	Daily	Bare Costs	Incl. O&P
.25 Plumber Foreman (outside)	$40.00	$80.00	$66.00	$132.00	$38.40	$63.36
1 Plumber	38.00	304.00	62.70	501.60		
10 L.H., Daily Totals		$384.00		$633.60	$38.40	$63.36
Crew Q-1C	Hr.	Daily	Hr.	Daily	Bare Costs	Incl. O&P
1 Plumber	$38.00	$304.00	$62.70	$501.60	$34.05	$56.25
1 Plumber Apprentice	30.40	243.20	50.15	401.20		
1 Equip. Oper. (medium)	33.75	270.00	55.90	447.20		
1 Trencher, Chain Type, 8' D		3376.00		3713.60	140.67	154.73
24 L.H., Daily Totals		$4193.20		$5063.60	$174.72	$210.98
Crew Q-2	Hr.	Daily	Hr.	Daily	Bare Costs	Incl. O&P
1 Plumber	$38.00	$304.00	$62.70	$501.60	$32.93	$54.33
2 Plumber Apprentices	30.40	486.40	50.15	802.40		
24 L.H., Daily Totals		$790.40		$1304.00	$32.93	$54.33
Crew Q-3	Hr.	Daily	Hr.	Daily	Bare Costs	Incl. O&P
2 Plumbers	$38.00	$608.00	$62.70	$1003.20	$34.20	$56.42
2 Plumber Apprentices	30.40	486.40	50.15	802.40		
32 L.H., Daily Totals		$1094.40		$1805.60	$34.20	$56.42
Crew Q-4	Hr.	Daily	Hr.	Daily	Bare Costs	Incl. O&P
2 Plumbers	$38.00	$608.00	$62.70	$1003.20	$36.10	$59.56
1 Welder (plumber)	38.00	304.00	62.70	501.60		
1 Plumber Apprentice	30.40	243.20	50.15	401.20		
1 Welder, Electric, 300 amp		55.30		60.83	1.73	1.90
32 L.H., Daily Totals		$1210.50		$1966.83	$37.83	$61.46
Crew Q-5	Hr.	Daily	Hr.	Daily	Bare Costs	Incl. O&P
1 Steamfitter	$38.60	$308.80	$63.70	$509.60	$34.75	$57.35
1 Steamfitter Apprentice	30.90	247.20	51.00	408.00		
16 L.H., Daily Totals		$556.00		$917.60	$34.75	$57.35
Crew Q-6	Hr.	Daily	Hr.	Daily	Bare Costs	Incl. O&P
1 Steamfitter	$38.60	$308.80	$63.70	$509.60	$33.47	$55.23
2 Steamfitter Apprentices	30.90	494.40	51.00	816.00		
24 L.H., Daily Totals		$803.20		$1325.60	$33.47	$55.23
Crew Q-7	Hr.	Daily	Hr.	Daily	Bare Costs	Incl. O&P
2 Steamfitters	$38.60	$617.60	$63.70	$1019.20	$34.75	$57.35
2 Steamfitter Apprentices	30.90	494.40	51.00	816.00		
32 L.H., Daily Totals		$1112.00		$1835.20	$34.75	$57.35
Crew Q-8	Hr.	Daily	Hr.	Daily	Bare Costs	Incl. O&P
2 Steamfitters	$38.60	$617.60	$63.70	$1019.20	$36.67	$60.52
1 Welder (steamfitter)	38.60	308.80	63.70	509.60		
1 Steamfitter Apprentice	30.90	247.20	51.00	408.00		
1 Welder, Electric, 300 amp		55.30		60.83	1.73	1.90
32 L.H., Daily Totals		$1228.90		$1997.63	$38.40	$62.43
Crew Q-9	Hr.	Daily	Hr.	Daily	Bare Costs	Incl. O&P
1 Sheet Metal Worker	$36.10	$288.80	$60.20	$481.60	$32.50	$54.20
1 Sheet Metal Apprentice	28.90	231.20	48.20	385.60		
16 L.H., Daily Totals		$520.00		$867.20	$32.50	$54.20

Crew No.	Bare Costs		Incl. Subs O&P		Cost Per Labor-Hour	
Crew Q-10	Hr.	Daily	Hr.	Daily	Bare Costs	Incl. O&P
2 Sheet Metal Workers	$36.10	$577.60	$60.20	$963.20	$33.70	$56.20
1 Sheet Metal Apprentice	28.90	231.20	48.20	385.60		
24 L.H., Daily Totals		$808.80		$1348.80	$33.70	$56.20
Crew Q-11	Hr.	Daily	Hr.	Daily	Bare Costs	Incl. O&P
2 Sheet Metal Workers	$36.10	$577.60	$60.20	$963.20	$32.50	$54.20
2 Sheet Metal Apprentices	28.90	462.40	48.20	771.20		
32 L.H., Daily Totals		$1040.00		$1734.40	$32.50	$54.20
Crew Q-12	Hr.	Daily	Hr.	Daily	Bare Costs	Incl. O&P
1 Sprinkler Installer	$36.55	$292.40	$60.35	$482.80	$32.90	$54.33
1 Sprinkler Apprentice	29.25	234.00	48.30	386.40		
16 L.H., Daily Totals		$526.40		$869.20	$32.90	$54.33
Crew Q-13	Hr.	Daily	Hr.	Daily	Bare Costs	Incl. O&P
2 Sprinkler Installers	$36.55	$584.80	$60.35	$965.60	$32.90	$54.33
2 Sprinkler Apprentices	29.25	468.00	48.30	772.80		
32 L.H., Daily Totals		$1052.80		$1738.40	$32.90	$54.33
Crew Q-14	Hr.	Daily	Hr.	Daily	Bare Costs	Incl. O&P
1 Asbestos Worker	$33.75	$270.00	$57.25	$458.00	$30.38	$51.52
1 Asbestos Apprentice	27.00	216.00	45.80	366.40		
16 L.H., Daily Totals		$486.00		$824.40	$30.38	$51.52
Crew Q-15	Hr.	Daily	Hr.	Daily	Bare Costs	Incl. O&P
1 Plumber	$38.00	$304.00	$62.70	$501.60	$34.20	$56.42
1 Plumber Apprentice	30.40	243.20	50.15	401.20		
1 Welder, Electric, 300 amp		55.30		60.83	3.46	3.80
16 L.H., Daily Totals		$602.50		$963.63	$37.66	$60.23
Crew Q-16	Hr.	Daily	Hr.	Daily	Bare Costs	Incl. O&P
2 Plumbers	$38.00	$608.00	$62.70	$1003.20	$35.47	$58.52
1 Plumber Apprentice	30.40	243.20	50.15	401.20		
1 Welder, Electric, 300 amp		55.30		60.83	2.30	2.53
24 L.H., Daily Totals		$906.50		$1465.23	$37.77	$61.05
Crew Q-17	Hr.	Daily	Hr.	Daily	Bare Costs	Incl. O&P
1 Steamfitter	$38.60	$308.80	$63.70	$509.60	$34.75	$57.35
1 Steamfitter Apprentice	30.90	247.20	51.00	408.00		
1 Welder, Electric, 300 amp		55.30		60.83	3.46	3.80
16 L.H., Daily Totals		$611.30		$978.43	$38.21	$61.15
Crew Q-17A	Hr.	Daily	Hr.	Daily	Bare Costs	Incl. O&P
1 Steamfitter	$38.60	$308.80	$63.70	$509.60	$34.72	$57.37
1 Steamfitter Apprentice	30.90	247.20	51.00	408.00		
1 Equip. Oper. (crane)	34.65	277.20	57.40	459.20		
1 Hyd. Crane, 12 Ton		663.00		729.30		
1 Welder, Electric, 300 amp		55.30		60.83	29.93	32.92
24 L.H., Daily Totals		$1551.50		$2166.93	$64.65	$90.29
Crew Q-18	Hr.	Daily	Hr.	Daily	Bare Costs	Incl. O&P
2 Steamfitters	$38.60	$617.60	$63.70	$1019.20	$36.03	$59.47
1 Steamfitter Apprentice	30.90	247.20	51.00	408.00		
1 Welder, Electric, 300 amp		55.30		60.83	2.30	2.53
24 L.H., Daily Totals		$920.10		$1488.03	$38.34	$62.00

Crew Q-19

Crew No.	Bare Costs Hr.	Bare Costs Daily	Incl. Subs O&P Hr.	Incl. Subs O&P Daily	Cost Per Labor-Hour Bare Costs	Cost Per Labor-Hour Incl. O&P
1 Steamfitter	$38.60	$308.80	$63.70	$509.60	$35.08	$57.73
1 Steamfitter Apprentice	30.90	247.20	51.00	408.00		
1 Electrician	35.75	286.00	58.50	468.00		
24 L.H., Daily Totals		$842.00		$1385.60	$35.08	$57.73

Crew Q-20

Crew No.	Bare Costs Hr.	Bare Costs Daily	Incl. Subs O&P Hr.	Incl. Subs O&P Daily	Cost Per Labor-Hour Bare Costs	Cost Per Labor-Hour Incl. O&P
1 Sheet Metal Worker	$36.10	$288.80	$60.20	$481.60	$33.15	$55.06
1 Sheet Metal Apprentice	28.90	231.20	48.20	385.60		
.5 Electrician	35.75	143.00	58.50	234.00		
20 L.H., Daily Totals		$663.00		$1101.20	$33.15	$55.06

Crew Q-21

Crew No.	Bare Costs Hr.	Bare Costs Daily	Incl. Subs O&P Hr.	Incl. Subs O&P Daily	Cost Per Labor-Hour Bare Costs	Cost Per Labor-Hour Incl. O&P
2 Steamfitters	$38.60	$617.60	$63.70	$1019.20	$35.96	$59.23
1 Steamfitter Apprentice	30.90	247.20	51.00	408.00		
1 Electrician	35.75	286.00	58.50	468.00		
32 L.H., Daily Totals		$1150.80		$1895.20	$35.96	$59.23

Crew Q-22

Crew No.	Bare Costs Hr.	Bare Costs Daily	Incl. Subs O&P Hr.	Incl. Subs O&P Daily	Cost Per Labor-Hour Bare Costs	Cost Per Labor-Hour Incl. O&P
1 Plumber	$38.00	$304.00	$62.70	$501.60	$34.20	$56.42
1 Plumber Apprentice	30.40	243.20	50.15	401.20		
1 Hyd. Crane, 12 Ton		663.00		729.30	41.44	45.58
16 L.H., Daily Totals		$1210.20		$1632.10	$75.64	$102.01

Crew Q-22A

Crew No.	Bare Costs Hr.	Bare Costs Daily	Incl. Subs O&P Hr.	Incl. Subs O&P Daily	Cost Per Labor-Hour Bare Costs	Cost Per Labor-Hour Incl. O&P
1 Plumber	$38.00	$304.00	$62.70	$501.60	$31.71	$52.58
1 Plumber Apprentice	30.40	243.20	50.15	401.20		
1 Laborer	23.80	190.40	40.05	320.40		
1 Equip. Oper. (crane)	34.65	277.20	57.40	459.20		
1 Hyd. Crane, 12 Ton		663.00		729.30	20.72	22.79
32 L.H., Daily Totals		$1677.80		$2411.70	$52.43	$75.37

Crew Q-23

Crew No.	Bare Costs Hr.	Bare Costs Daily	Incl. Subs O&P Hr.	Incl. Subs O&P Daily	Cost Per Labor-Hour Bare Costs	Cost Per Labor-Hour Incl. O&P
1 Plumber Foreman (outside)	$40.00	$320.00	$66.00	$528.00	$37.25	$61.53
1 Plumber	38.00	304.00	62.70	501.60		
1 Equip. Oper. (medium)	33.75	270.00	55.90	447.20		
1 Lattice Boom Crane, 20 Ton		960.50		1056.55	40.02	44.02
24 L.H., Daily Totals		$1854.50		$2533.35	$77.27	$105.56

Crew R-1

Crew No.	Bare Costs Hr.	Bare Costs Daily	Incl. Subs O&P Hr.	Incl. Subs O&P Daily	Cost Per Labor-Hour Bare Costs	Cost Per Labor-Hour Incl. O&P
1 Electrician Foreman	$36.25	$290.00	$59.35	$474.80	$31.87	$52.58
3 Electricians	35.75	858.00	58.50	1404.00		
2 Helpers	23.85	381.60	40.30	644.80		
48 L.H., Daily Totals		$1529.60		$2523.60	$31.87	$52.58

Crew R-1A

Crew No.	Bare Costs Hr.	Bare Costs Daily	Incl. Subs O&P Hr.	Incl. Subs O&P Daily	Cost Per Labor-Hour Bare Costs	Cost Per Labor-Hour Incl. O&P
1 Electrician	$35.75	$286.00	$58.50	$468.00	$29.80	$49.40
1 Helper	23.85	190.80	40.30	322.40		
16 L.H., Daily Totals		$476.80		$790.40	$29.80	$49.40

Crew R-2

Crew No.	Bare Costs Hr.	Bare Costs Daily	Incl. Subs O&P Hr.	Incl. Subs O&P Daily	Cost Per Labor-Hour Bare Costs	Cost Per Labor-Hour Incl. O&P
1 Electrician Foreman	$36.25	$290.00	$59.35	$474.80	$32.26	$53.26
3 Electricians	35.75	858.00	58.50	1404.00		
2 Helpers	23.85	381.60	40.30	644.80		
1 Equip. Oper. (crane)	34.65	277.20	57.40	459.20		
1 S.P. Crane, 4x4, 5 Ton		280.00		308.00	5.00	5.50
56 L.H., Daily Totals		$2086.80		$3290.80	$37.26	$58.76

Crew R-3

Crew No.	Bare Costs Hr.	Bare Costs Daily	Incl. Subs O&P Hr.	Incl. Subs O&P Daily	Cost Per Labor-Hour Bare Costs	Cost Per Labor-Hour Incl. O&P
1 Electrician Foreman	$36.25	$290.00	$59.35	$474.80	$35.73	$58.62
1 Electrician	35.75	286.00	58.50	468.00		
.5 Equip. Oper. (crane)	34.65	138.60	57.40	229.60		
.5 S.P. Crane, 4x4, 5 Ton		140.00		154.00	7.00	7.70
20 L.H., Daily Totals		$854.60		$1326.40	$42.73	$66.32

Crew R-4

Crew No.	Bare Costs Hr.	Bare Costs Daily	Incl. Subs O&P Hr.	Incl. Subs O&P Daily	Cost Per Labor-Hour Bare Costs	Cost Per Labor-Hour Incl. O&P
1 Struc. Steel Foreman (outside)	$36.25	$290.00	$69.05	$552.40	$34.95	$64.66
3 Struc. Steel Workers	34.25	822.00	65.25	1566.00		
1 Electrician	35.75	286.00	58.50	468.00		
1 Welder, Gas Engine, 300 amp		142.00		156.20	3.55	3.90
40 L.H., Daily Totals		$1540.00		$2742.60	$38.50	$68.56

Crew R-5

Crew No.	Bare Costs Hr.	Bare Costs Daily	Incl. Subs O&P Hr.	Incl. Subs O&P Daily	Cost Per Labor-Hour Bare Costs	Cost Per Labor-Hour Incl. O&P
1 Electrician Foreman	$36.25	$290.00	$59.35	$474.80	$31.47	$51.96
4 Electrician Linemen	35.75	1144.00	58.50	1872.00		
2 Electrician Operators	35.75	572.00	58.50	936.00		
4 Electrician Groundmen	23.85	763.20	40.30	1289.60		
1 Crew Truck		224.80		247.28		
1 Flatbed Truck, 20,000 GVW		253.40		278.74		
1 Pickup Truck, 3/4 Ton		157.00		172.70		
.2 Hyd. Crane, 55 Ton		227.40		250.14		
.2 Hyd. Crane, 12 Ton		132.60		145.86		
.2 Earth Auger, Truck-Mtd.		85.00		93.50		
1 Tractor w/Winch		434.60		478.06	17.21	18.93
88 L.H., Daily Totals		$4284.00		$6238.68	$48.68	$70.89

Crew R-6

Crew No.	Bare Costs Hr.	Bare Costs Daily	Incl. Subs O&P Hr.	Incl. Subs O&P Daily	Cost Per Labor-Hour Bare Costs	Cost Per Labor-Hour Incl. O&P
1 Electrician Foreman	$36.25	$290.00	$59.35	$474.80	$31.47	$51.96
4 Electrician Linemen	35.75	1144.00	58.50	1872.00		
2 Electrician Operators	35.75	572.00	58.50	936.00		
4 Electrician Groundmen	23.85	763.20	40.30	1289.60		
1 Crew Truck		224.80		247.28		
1 Flatbed Truck, 20,000 GVW		253.40		278.74		
1 Pickup Truck, 3/4 Ton		157.00		172.70		
.2 Hyd. Crane, 55 Ton		227.40		250.14		
.2 Hyd. Crane, 12 Ton		132.60		145.86		
.2 Earth Auger, Truck-Mtd.		85.00		93.50		
1 Tractor w/Winch		434.60		478.06		
3 Cable Trailers		586.80		645.48		
.5 Tensioning Rig		194.55		214.01		
.5 Cable Pulling Rig		1136.50		1250.15	39.01	42.91
88 L.H., Daily Totals		$6201.85		$8348.32	$70.48	$94.87

Crew R-7

Crew No.	Bare Costs Hr.	Bare Costs Daily	Incl. Subs O&P Hr.	Incl. Subs O&P Daily	Cost Per Labor-Hour Bare Costs	Cost Per Labor-Hour Incl. O&P
1 Electrician Foreman	$36.25	$290.00	$59.35	$474.80	$25.92	$43.48
5 Electrician Groundmen	23.85	954.00	40.30	1612.00		
1 Crew Truck		224.80		247.28	4.68	5.15
48 L.H., Daily Totals		$1468.80		$2334.08	$30.60	$48.63

Crew R-8

Crew No.	Bare Costs Hr.	Bare Costs Daily	Incl. Subs O&P Hr.	Incl. Subs O&P Daily	Cost Per Labor-Hour Bare Costs	Cost Per Labor-Hour Incl. O&P
1 Electrician Foreman	$36.25	$290.00	$59.35	$474.80	$31.87	$52.58
3 Electrician Linemen	35.75	858.00	58.50	1404.00		
2 Electrician Groundmen	23.85	381.60	40.30	644.80		
1 Pickup Truck, 3/4 Ton		157.00		172.70		
1 Crew Truck		224.80		247.28	7.95	8.75
48 L.H., Daily Totals		$1911.40		$2943.58	$39.82	$61.32

Crew No.	Bare Costs		Incl. Subs O&P		Cost Per Labor-Hour	
Crew R-9	Hr.	Daily	Hr.	Daily	Bare Costs	Incl. O&P
1 Electrician Foreman	$36.25	$290.00	$59.35	$474.80	$29.86	$49.51
1 Electrician Lineman	35.75	286.00	58.50	468.00		
2 Electrician Operators	35.75	572.00	58.50	936.00		
4 Electrician Groundmen	23.85	763.20	40.30	1289.60		
1 Pickup Truck, 3/4 Ton		157.00		172.70		
1 Crew Truck		224.80		247.28	5.97	6.56
64 L.H., Daily Totals		$2293.00		$3588.38	$35.83	$56.07
Crew R-10	Hr.	Daily	Hr.	Daily	Bare Costs	Incl. O&P
1 Electrician Foreman	$36.25	$290.00	$59.35	$474.80	$33.85	$55.61
4 Electrician Linemen	35.75	1144.00	58.50	1872.00		
1 Electrician Groundman	23.85	190.80	40.30	322.40		
1 Crew Truck		224.80		247.28		
3 Tram Cars		399.45		439.39	13.01	14.31
48 L.H., Daily Totals		$2249.05		$3355.88	$46.86	$69.91
Crew R-11	Hr.	Daily	Hr.	Daily	Bare Costs	Incl. O&P
1 Electrician Foreman	$36.25	$290.00	$59.35	$474.80	$33.96	$55.83
4 Electricians	35.75	1144.00	58.50	1872.00		
1 Equip. Oper. (crane)	34.65	277.20	57.40	459.20		
1 Common Laborer	23.80	190.40	40.05	320.40		
1 Crew Truck		224.80		247.28		
1 Hyd. Crane, 12 Ton		663.00		729.30	15.85	17.44
56 L.H., Daily Totals		$2789.40		$4102.98	$49.81	$73.27
Crew R-12	Hr.	Daily	Hr.	Daily	Bare Costs	Incl. O&P
1 Carpenter Foreman (inside)	$32.60	$260.80	$54.85	$438.80	$29.47	$50.20
4 Carpenters	32.10	1027.20	54.00	1728.00		
4 Common Laborers	23.80	761.60	40.05	1281.60		
1 Equip. Oper. (medium)	33.75	270.00	55.90	447.20		
1 Steel Worker	34.25	274.00	65.25	522.00		
1 Dozer, 200 H.P.		1325.00		1457.50		
1 Pickup Truck, 3/4 Ton		157.00		172.70	16.84	18.52
88 L.H., Daily Totals		$4075.60		$6047.80	$46.31	$68.72
Crew R-15	Hr.	Daily	Hr.	Daily	Bare Costs	Incl. O&P
1 Electrician Foreman	$36.25	$290.00	$59.35	$474.80	$35.28	$57.85
4 Electricians	35.75	1144.00	58.50	1872.00		
1 Equipment Oper. (light)	32.45	259.60	53.75	430.00		
1 Aerial Lift Truck, 40' Boom		325.00		357.50	6.77	7.45
48 L.H., Daily Totals		$2018.60		$3134.30	$42.05	$65.30
Crew R-15A	Hr.	Daily	Hr.	Daily	Bare Costs	Incl. O&P
1 Electrician Foreman	$36.25	$290.00	$59.35	$474.80	$31.30	$51.70
2 Electricians	35.75	572.00	58.50	936.00		
2 Common Laborers	23.80	380.80	40.05	640.80		
1 Equip. Oper. (light)	32.45	259.60	53.75	430.00		
1 Aerial Lift Truck, 40' Boom		325.00		357.50	6.77	7.45
48 L.H., Daily Totals		$1827.40		$2839.10	$38.07	$59.15
Crew R-18	Hr.	Daily	Hr.	Daily	Bare Costs	Incl. O&P
.25 Electrician Foreman	$36.25	$72.50	$59.35	$118.70	$28.47	$47.37
1 Electrician	35.75	286.00	58.50	468.00		
2 Helpers	23.85	381.60	40.30	644.80		
26 L.H., Daily Totals		$740.10		$1231.50	$28.47	$47.37
Crew R-19	Hr.	Daily	Hr.	Daily	Bare Costs	Incl. O&P
.5 Electrician Foreman	$36.25	$145.00	$59.35	$237.40	$35.85	$58.67
2 Electricians	35.75	572.00	58.50	936.00		
20 L.H., Daily Totals		$717.00		$1173.40	$35.85	$58.67

Crew No.	Bare Costs		Incl. Subs O&P		Cost Per Labor-Hour	
Crew R-21	Hr.	Daily	Hr.	Daily	Bare Costs	Incl. O&P
1 Electrician Foreman	$36.25	$290.00	$59.35	$474.80	$35.82	$58.64
3 Electricians	35.75	858.00	58.50	1404.00		
.1 Equip. Oper. (medium)	33.75	27.00	55.90	44.72		
.1 S.P. Crane, 4x4, 25 Ton		60.72		66.79	1.85	2.04
32.8 L.H., Daily Totals		$1235.72		$1990.31	$37.67	$60.68
Crew R-22	Hr.	Daily	Hr.	Daily	Bare Costs	Incl. O&P
.66 Electrician Foreman	$36.25	$191.40	$59.35	$313.37	$30.71	$50.81
2 Electricians	35.75	572.00	58.50	936.00		
2 Helpers	23.85	381.60	40.30	644.80		
37.28 L.H., Daily Totals		$1145.00		$1894.17	$30.71	$50.81
Crew R-30	Hr.	Daily	Hr.	Daily	Bare Costs	Incl. O&P
.25 Electrician Foreman (outside)	$37.75	$75.50	$61.80	$123.60	$28.55	$47.40
1 Electrician	35.75	286.00	58.50	468.00		
2 Laborers, (Semi-Skilled)	23.80	380.80	40.05	640.80		
26 L.H., Daily Totals		$742.30		$1232.40	$28.55	$47.40

697

Location Factors

Costs shown in *RSMeans Residential Cost Data* are based on national averages for materials and installation. To adjust these costs to a specific location, simply multiply the base cost by the factor for that city. The data is arranged alphabetically by state and postal zip code numbers. For a city not listed, use the factor for a nearby city with similar economic characteristics.

STATE	CITY	Residential
ALABAMA		
350-352	Birmingham	.86
354	Tuscaloosa	.78
355	Jasper	.72
356	Decatur	.76
357-358	Huntsville	.85
359	Gadsden	.75
360-361	Montgomery	.76
362	Anniston	.76
363	Dothan	.74
364	Evergreen	.72
365-366	Mobile	.81
367	Selma	.72
368	Phenix City	.73
369	Butler	.72
ALASKA		
995-996	Anchorage	1.22
997	Fairbanks	1.24
998	Juneau	1.22
999	Ketchikan	1.26
ARIZONA		
850,853	Phoenix	.86
851,852	Mesa/Tempe	.85
855	Globe	.82
856-857	Tucson	.84
859	Show Low	.86
860	Flagstaff	.86
863	Prescott	.81
864	Kingman	.83
865	Chambers	.83
ARKANSAS		
716	Pine Bluff	.78
717	Camden	.69
718	Texarkana	.73
719	Hot Springs	.69
720-722	Little Rock	.80
723	West Memphis	.77
724	Jonesboro	.75
725	Batesville	.72
726	Harrison	.73
727	Fayetteville	.69
728	Russellville	.75
729	Fort Smith	.80
CALIFORNIA		
900-902	Los Angeles	1.09
903-905	Inglewood	1.06
906-908	Long Beach	1.05
910-912	Pasadena	1.04
913-916	Van Nuys	1.07
917-918	Alhambra	1.08
919-921	San Diego	1.03
922	Palm Springs	1.04
923-924	San Bernardino	1.05
925	Riverside	1.07
926-927	Santa Ana	1.05
928	Anaheim	1.06
930	Oxnard	1.08
931	Santa Barbara	1.07
932-933	Bakersfield	1.06
934	San Luis Obispo	1.07
935	Mojave	1.05
936-938	Fresno	1.10
939	Salinas	1.13
940-941	San Francisco	1.24
942,956-958	Sacramento	1.11
943	Palo Alto	1.18
944	San Mateo	1.22
945	Vallejo	1.16
946	Oakland	1.21
947	Berkeley	1.23
948	Richmond	1.23
949	San Rafael	1.22
950	Santa Cruz	1.15
951	San Jose	1.21
952	Stockton	1.11
953	Modesto	1.10

STATE	CITY	Residential
CALIFORNIA (CONT'D)		
954	Santa Rosa	1.19
955	Eureka	1.11
959	Marysville	1.11
960	Redding	1.11
961	Susanville	1.11
COLORADO		
800-802	Denver	.89
803	Boulder	.91
804	Golden	.87
805	Fort Collins	.88
806	Greeley	.85
807	Fort Morgan	.89
808-809	Colorado Springs	.86
810	Pueblo	.88
811	Alamosa	.84
812	Salida	.87
813	Durango	.88
814	Montrose	.86
815	Grand Junction	.91
816	Glenwood Springs	.88
CONNECTICUT		
060	New Britain	1.11
061	Hartford	1.10
062	Willimantic	1.11
063	New London	1.10
064	Meriden	1.10
065	New Haven	1.11
066	Bridgeport	1.11
067	Waterbury	1.11
068	Norwalk	1.12
069	Stamford	1.12
D.C.		
200-205	Washington	.94
DELAWARE		
197	Newark	1.02
198	Wilmington	1.02
199	Dover	1.01
FLORIDA		
320,322	Jacksonville	.82
321	Daytona Beach	.87
323	Tallahassee	.78
324	Panama City	.77
325	Pensacola	.81
326,344	Gainesville	.80
327-328,347	Orlando	.87
329	Melbourne	.87
330-332,340	Miami	.86
333	Fort Lauderdale	.86
334,349	West Palm Beach	.86
335-336,346	Tampa	.90
337	St. Petersburg	.80
338	Lakeland	.87
339,341	Fort Myers	.86
342	Sarasota	.89
GEORGIA		
300-303,399	Atlanta	.87
304	Statesboro	.73
305	Gainesville	.77
306	Athens	.76
307	Dalton	.75
308-309	Augusta	.81
310-312	Macon	.79
313-314	Savannah	.80
315	Waycross	.79
316	Valdosta	.74
317,398	Albany	.77
318-319	Columbus	.80
HAWAII		
967	Hilo	1.18
968	Honolulu	1.22

Location Factors

STATE	CITY	Residential
STATES & POSS.		
969	Guam	.93
IDAHO		
832	Pocatello	.87
833	Twin Falls	.81
834	Idaho Falls	.85
835	Lewiston	.99
836-837	Boise	.88
838	Coeur d'Alene	.97
ILLINOIS		
600-603	North Suburban	1.19
604	Joliet	1.22
605	South Suburban	1.19
606-608	Chicago	1.22
609	Kankakee	1.13
610-611	Rockford	1.11
612	Rock Island	.98
613	La Salle	1.12
614	Galesburg	1.04
615-616	Peoria	1.07
617	Bloomington	1.04
618-619	Champaign	1.05
620-622	East St. Louis	1.04
623	Quincy	1.03
624	Effingham	1.05
625	Decatur	1.05
626-627	Springfield	1.05
628	Centralia	1.04
629	Carbondale	1.02
INDIANA		
460	Anderson	.91
461-462	Indianapolis	.93
463-464	Gary	1.06
465-466	South Bend	.91
467-468	Fort Wayne	.90
469	Kokomo	.92
470	Lawrenceburg	.88
471	New Albany	.88
472	Columbus	.92
473	Muncie	.92
474	Bloomington	.94
475	Washington	.91
476-477	Evansville	.91
478	Terre Haute	.90
479	Lafayette	.93
IOWA		
500-503,509	Des Moines	.91
504	Mason City	.77
505	Fort Dodge	.75
506-507	Waterloo	.82
508	Creston	.84
510-511	Sioux City	.87
512	Sibley	.74
513	Spencer	.76
514	Carroll	.80
515	Council Bluffs	.86
516	Shenandoah	.81
520	Dubuque	.86
521	Decorah	.78
522-524	Cedar Rapids	.93
525	Ottumwa	.86
526	Burlington	.88
527-528	Davenport	.97
KANSAS		
660-662	Kansas City	.98
664-666	Topeka	.78
667	Fort Scott	.89
668	Emporia	.83
669	Belleville	.81
670-672	Wichita	.79
673	Independence	.89
674	Salina	.80
675	Hutchinson	.79
676	Hays	.82
677	Colby	.83
678	Dodge City	.81
679	Liberal	.80
KENTUCKY		
400-402	Louisville	.92
403-405	Lexington	.90

STATE	CITY	Residential
KENTUCKY (CONT'D)		
406	Frankfort	.89
407-409	Corbin	.83
410	Covington	.94
411-412	Ashland	.95
413-414	Campton	.88
415-416	Pikeville	.92
417-418	Hazard	.87
420	Paducah	.89
421-422	Bowling Green	.90
423	Owensboro	.91
424	Henderson	.92
425-426	Somerset	.85
427	Elizabethtown	.88
LOUISIANA		
700-701	New Orleans	.86
703	Thibodaux	.82
704	Hammond	.75
705	Lafayette	.83
706	Lake Charles	.83
707-708	Baton Rouge	.82
710-711	Shreveport	.78
712	Monroe	.74
713-714	Alexandria	.76
MAINE		
039	Kittery	.92
040-041	Portland	.97
042	Lewiston	.97
043	Augusta	.93
044	Bangor	.96
045	Bath	.92
046	Machias	.96
047	Houlton	.97
048	Rockland	.96
049	Waterville	.91
MARYLAND		
206	Waldorf	.90
207-208	College Park	.88
209	Silver Spring	.90
210-212	Baltimore	.90
214	Annapolis	.89
215	Cumberland	.88
216	Easton	.83
217	Hagerstown	.87
218	Salisbury	.82
219	Elkton	.89
MASSACHUSETTS		
010-011	Springfield	1.07
012	Pittsfield	1.07
013	Greenfield	1.05
014	Fitchburg	1.13
015-016	Worcester	1.14
017	Framingham	1.16
018	Lowell	1.16
019	Lawrence	1.17
020-022, 024	Boston	1.21
023	Brockton	1.16
025	Buzzards Bay	1.14
026	Hyannis	1.13
027	New Bedford	1.16
MICHIGAN		
480,483	Royal Oak	1.02
481	Ann Arbor	1.03
482	Detroit	1.05
484-485	Flint	.96
486	Saginaw	.93
487	Bay City	.93
488-489	Lansing	.94
490	Battle Creek	.93
491	Kalamazoo	.92
492	Jackson	.94
493,495	Grand Rapids	.91
494	Muskegon	.90
496	Traverse City	.86
497	Gaylord	.89
498-499	Iron mountain	.91
MINNESOTA		
550-551	Saint Paul	1.11
553-555	Minneapolis	1.13
556-558	Duluth	1.06

Location Factors

STATE	CITY	Residential
MINNESOTA (CONT'd)		
559	Rochester	1.04
560	Mankato	1.00
561	Windom	.93
562	Willmar	.97
563	St. Cloud	1.05
564	Brainerd	.96
565	Detroit Lakes	.95
566	Bemidji	.94
567	Thief River Falls	.94
MISSISSIPPI		
386	Clarksdale	.74
387	Greenville	.81
388	Tupelo	.76
389	Greenwood	.78
390-392	Jackson	.82
393	Meridian	.81
394	Laurel	.77
395	Biloxi	.80
396	Mccomb	.75
397	Columbus	.76
MISSOURI		
630-631	St. Louis	1.03
633	Bowling Green	.96
634	Hannibal	.93
635	Kirksville	.90
636	Flat River	.96
637	Cape Girardeau	.89
638	Sikeston	.88
639	Poplar Bluff	.87
640-641	Kansas City	1.05
644-645	St. Joseph	.98
646	Chillicothe	.97
647	Harrisonville	.99
648	Joplin	.90
650-651	Jefferson City	.93
652	Columbia	.92
653	Sedalia	.92
654-655	Rolla	.97
656-658	Springfield	.89
MONTANA		
590-591	Billings	.90
592	Wolf Point	.87
593	Miles City	.88
594	Great Falls	.91
595	Havre	.84
596	Helena	.88
597	Butte	.88
598	Missoula	.88
599	Kalispell	.87
NEBRASKA		
680-681	Omaha	.90
683-685	Lincoln	.87
686	Columbus	.87
687	Norfolk	.89
688	Grand Island	.88
689	Hastings	.90
690	Mccook	.83
691	North Platte	.89
692	Valentine	.84
693	Alliance	.84
NEVADA		
889-891	Las Vegas	1.03
893	Ely	1.02
894-895	Reno	.95
897	Carson City	.96
898	Elko	.93
NEW HAMPSHIRE		
030	Nashua	.98
031	Manchester	.98
032-033	Concord	.97
034	Keene	.88
035	Littleton	.92
036	Charleston	.86
037	Claremont	.87
038	Portsmouth	.97

STATE	CITY	Residential
NEW JERSEY		
070-071	Newark	1.14
072	Elizabeth	1.16
073	Jersey City	1.13
074-075	Paterson	1.14
076	Hackensack	1.13
077	Long Branch	1.13
078	Dover	1.13
079	Summit	1.14
080,083	Vineland	1.11
081	Camden	1.12
082,084	Atlantic City	1.15
085-086	Trenton	1.13
087	Point Pleasant	1.10
088-089	New Brunswick	1.15
NEW MEXICO		
870-872	Albuquerque	.83
873	Gallup	.83
874	Farmington	.83
875	Santa Fe	.85
877	Las Vegas	.83
878	Socorro	.83
879	Truth/Consequences	.82
880	Las Cruces	.81
881	Clovis	.83
882	Roswell	.83
883	Carrizozo	.83
884	Tucumcari	.83
NEW YORK		
100-102	New York	1.34
103	Staten Island	1.28
104	Bronx	1.30
105	Mount Vernon	1.12
106	White Plains	1.15
107	Yonkers	1.16
108	New Rochelle	1.16
109	Suffern	1.13
110	Queens	1.30
111	Long Island City	1.33
112	Brooklyn	1.34
113	Flushing	1.32
114	Jamaica	1.31
115,117,118	Hicksville	1.20
116	Far Rockaway	1.31
119	Riverhead	1.21
120-122	Albany	.98
123	Schenectady	.99
124	Kingston	1.05
125-126	Poughkeepsie	1.16
127	Monticello	1.05
128	Glens Falls	.91
129	Plattsburgh	.95
130-132	Syracuse	.98
133-135	Utica	.94
136	Watertown	.92
137-139	Binghamton	.97
140-142	Buffalo	1.06
143	Niagara Falls	1.02
144-146	Rochester	.99
147	Jamestown	.90
148-149	Elmira	.92
NORTH CAROLINA		
270,272-274	Greensboro	.85
271	Winston-Salem	.86
275-276	Raleigh	.86
277	Durham	.85
278	Rocky Mount	.81
279	Elizabeth City	.80
280	Gastonia	.85
281-282	Charlotte	.86
283	Fayetteville	.89
284	Wilmington	.86
285	Kinston	.81
286	Hickory	.80
287-288	Asheville	.83
289	Murphy	.82
NORTH DAKOTA		
580-581	Fargo	.79
582	Grand Forks	.73
583	Devils Lake	.77
584	Jamestown	.71
585	Bismarck	.78

Location Factors

STATE	CITY	Residential
NORTH DAKOTA (CONT'D)		
586	Dickinson	.75
587	Minot	.82
588	Williston	.75
OHIO		
430-432	Columbus	.95
433	Marion	.90
434-436	Toledo	.98
437-438	Zanesville	.90
439	Steubenville	.95
440	Lorain	.96
441	Cleveland	1.00
442-443	Akron	.98
444-445	Youngstown	.95
446-447	Canton	.93
448-449	Mansfield	.91
450	Hamilton	.92
451-452	Cincinnati	.92
453-454	Dayton	.92
455	Springfield	.93
456	Chillicothe	.96
457	Athens	.90
458	Lima	.91
OKLAHOMA		
730-731	Oklahoma City	.82
734	Ardmore	.78
735	Lawton	.80
736	Clinton	.80
737	Enid	.76
738	Woodward	.79
739	Guymon	.79
740-741	Tulsa	.78
743	Miami	.85
744	Muskogee	.74
745	Mcalester	.75
746	Ponca City	.78
747	Durant	.77
748	Shawnee	.76
749	Poteau	.76
OREGON		
970-972	Portland	.99
973	Salem	.98
974	Eugene	.99
975	Medford	.97
976	Klamath Falls	.97
977	Bend	1.00
978	Pendleton	.98
979	Vale	.96
PENNSYLVANIA		
150-152	Pittsburgh	1.01
153	Washington	.96
154	Uniontown	.95
155	Bedford	.91
156	Greensburg	.97
157	Indiana	.94
158	Dubois	.92
159	Johnstown	.92
160	Butler	.94
161	New Castle	.93
162	Kittanning	.94
163	Oil City	.91
164-165	Erie	.94
166	Altoona	.88
167	Bradford	.91
168	State College	.91
169	Wellsboro	.92
170-171	Harrisburg	.97
172	Chambersburg	.90
173-174	York	.93
175-176	Lancaster	.92
177	Williamsport	.85
178	Sunbury	.94
179	Pottsville	.94
180	Lehigh Valley	1.02
181	Allentown	1.04
182	Hazleton	.93
183	Stroudsburg	.92
184-185	Scranton	.98
186-187	Wilkes-Barre	.95
188	Montrose	.92
189	Doylestown	1.06

STATE	CITY	Residential
PENNSYLVANIA (CONT'D)		
190-191	Philadelphia	1.16
193	Westchester	1.10
194	Norristown	1.10
195-196	Reading	.98
PUERTO RICO		
009	San Juan	.75
RHODE ISLAND		
028	Newport	1.09
029	Providence	1.10
SOUTH CAROLINA		
290-292	Columbia	.86
293	Spartanburg	.86
294	Charleston	.94
295	Florence	.82
296	Greenville	.85
297	Rock Hill	.80
298	Aiken	.97
299	Beaufort	.79
SOUTH DAKOTA		
570-571	Sioux Falls	.76
572	Watertown	.73
573	Mitchell	.74
574	Aberdeen	.75
575	Pierre	.77
576	Mobridge	.73
577	Rapid City	.78
TENNESSEE		
370-372	Nashville	.85
373-374	Chattanooga	.83
375,380-381	Memphis	.84
376	Johnson City	.72
377-379	Knoxville	.75
382	Mckenzie	.73
383	Jackson	.77
384	Columbia	.78
385	Cookeville	.71
TEXAS		
750	Mckinney	.72
751	Waxahackie	.78
752-753	Dallas	.84
754	Greenville	.70
755	Texarkana	.73
756	Longview	.68
757	Tyler	.74
758	Palestine	.75
759	Lufkin	.78
760-761	Fort Worth	.83
762	Denton	.75
763	Wichita Falls	.78
764	Eastland	.75
765	Temple	.77
766-767	Waco	.78
768	Brownwood	.72
769	San Angelo	.73
770-772	Houston	.85
773	Huntsville	.77
774	Wharton	.72
775	Galveston	.83
776-777	Beaumont	.81
778	Bryan	.74
779	Victoria	.71
780	Laredo	.75
781-782	San Antonio	.80
783-784	Corpus Christi	.79
785	Mc Allen	.76
786-787	Austin	.78
788	Del Rio	.73
789	Giddings	.78
790-791	Amarillo	.79
792	Childress	.80
793-794	Lubbock	.80
795-796	Abilene	.76
797	Midland	.80
798-799,885	El Paso	.74
UTAH		
840-841	Salt Lake City	.80
842,844	Ogden	.79
843	Logan	.79

STATE	CITY	Residential
UTAH (CONT'D)		
845	Price	.77
846-847	Provo	.79
VERMONT		
050	White River Jct.	.90
051	Bellows Falls	.97
052	Bennington	1.01
053	Brattleboro	.96
054	Burlington	.95
056	Montpelier	.94
057	Rutland	.94
058	St. Johnsbury	.91
059	Guildhall	.91
VIRGINIA		
220-221	Fairfax	1.02
222	Arlington	1.04
223	Alexandria	1.06
224-225	Fredericksburg	1.02
226	Winchester	1.01
227	Culpeper	1.02
228	Harrisonburg	.87
229	Charlottesville	.90
230-232	Richmond	.96
233-235	Norfolk	.98
236	Newport News	.97
237	Portsmouth	.91
238	Petersburg	.94
239	Farmville	.85
240-241	Roanoke	.96
242	Bristol	.84
243	Pulaski	.84
244	Staunton	.87
245	Lynchburg	.93
246	Grundy	.81
WASHINGTON		
980-981,987	Seattle	1.02
982	Everett	1.04
983-984	Tacoma	1.01
985	Olympia	.99
986	Vancouver	.97
988	Wenatchee	.94
989	Yakima	.98
990-992	Spokane	.97
993	Richland	.97
994	Clarkston	.92
WEST VIRGINIA		
247-248	Bluefield	.94
249	Lewisburg	.93
250-253	Charleston	.97
254	Martinsburg	.89
255-257	Huntington	.98
258-259	Beckley	.93
260	Wheeling	.95
261	Parkersburg	.93
262	Buckhannon	.94
263-264	Clarksburg	.94
265	Morgantown	.94
266	Gassaway	.94
267	Romney	.93
268	Petersburg	.94
WISCONSIN		
530,532	Milwaukee	1.08
531	Kenosha	1.03
534	Racine	1.02
535	Beloit	1.01
537	Madison	.99
538	Lancaster	.97
539	Portage	.97
540	New Richmond	.99
541-543	Green Bay	1.02
544	Wausau	.96
545	Rhinelander	.96
546	La Crosse	.96
547	Eau Claire	.99
548	Superior	.97
549	Oshkosh	.96
WYOMING		
820	Cheyenne	.80
821	Yellowstone Nat. Pk.	.80
822	Wheatland	.77

STATE	CITY	Residential
WYOMING (CONT'D)		
823	Rawlins	.81
824	Worland	.80
825	Riverton	.80
826	Casper	.75
827	Newcastle	.81
828	Sheridan	.80
829-831	Rock Springs	.84
CANADIAN FACTORS (reflect Canadian currency)		
ALBERTA		
	Calgary	1.13
	Edmonton	1.12
	Fort McMurray	1.14
	Lethbridge	1.12
	Lloydminster	1.07
	Medicine Hat	1.07
	Red Deer	1.07
BRITISH COLUMBIA		
	Kamloops	1.05
	Prince George	1.05
	Vancouver	1.07
	Victoria	1.05
MANITOBA		
	Brandon	1.06
	Portage la Prairie	1.02
	Winnipeg	1.00
NEW BRUNSWICK		
	Bathurst	.95
	Dalhousie	.95
	Fredericton	1.00
	Moncton	.96
	Newcastle	.95
	St. John	1.03
NEWFOUNDLAND		
	Corner Brook	.99
	St Johns	1.04
NORTHWEST TERRITORIES		
	Yellowknife	1.09
NOVA SCOTIA		
	Bridgewater	.98
	Dartmouth	1.00
	Halifax	1.01
	New Glasgow	1.00
	Sydney	.99
	Truro	.97
	Yarmouth	1.00
ONTARIO		
	Barrie	1.14
	Brantford	1.15
	Cornwall	1.14
	Hamilton	1.12
	Kingston	1.14
	Kitchener	1.07
	London	1.10
	North Bay	1.15
	Oshawa	1.13
	Ottawa	1.11
	Owen Sound	1.13
	Peterborough	1.12
	Sarnia	1.15
	Sault Ste Marie	1.07
	St. Catharines	1.09
	Sudbury	1.06
	Thunder Bay	1.11
	Timmins	1.11
	Toronto	1.13
	Windsor	1.10
PRINCE EDWARD ISLAND		
	Charlottetown	.92
	Summerside	.94
QUEBEC		
	Cap-de-la-Madeleine	1.13
	Charlesbourg	1.13
	Chicoutimi	1.15
	Gatineau	1.13
	Granby	1.13

Location Factors

STATE	CITY	Residential
QUEBEC (CONT'D)		
	Hull	1.13
	Joliette	1.13
	Laval	1.13
	Montreal	1.14
	Quebec	1.13
	Rimouski	1.15
	Rouyn-Noranda	1.13
	Saint Hyacinthe	1.13
	Sherbrooke	1.13
	Sorel	1.13
	St Jerome	1.13
	Trois Rivieres	1.17
SASKATCHEWAN		
	Moose Jaw	.95
	Prince Albert	.93
	Regina	1.07
	Saskatoon	1.05
YUKON		
	Whitehorse	.98

R011105-05   Tips for Accurate Estimating

1. Use pre-printed or columnar forms for orderly sequence of dimensions and locations and for recording telephone quotations.

2. Use only the front side of each paper or form except for certain pre-printed summary forms.

3. Be consistent in listing dimensions: For example, length x width x height. This helps in rechecking to ensure that, the total length of partitions is appropriate for the building area.

4. Use printed (rather than measured) dimensions where given.

5. Add up multiple printed dimensions for a single entry where possible.

6. Measure all other dimensions carefully.

7. Use each set of dimensions to calculate multiple related quantities.

8. Convert foot and inch measurements to decimal feet when listing. Memorize decimal equivalents to .01 parts of a foot (1/8" equals approximately .01').

9. Do not "round off" quantities until the final summary.

10. Mark drawings with different colors as items are taken off.

11. Keep similar items together, different items separate.

12. Identify location and drawing numbers to aid in future checking for completeness.

13. Measure or list everything on the drawings or mentioned in the specifications.

14. It may be necessary to list items not called for to make the job complete.

15. Be alert for: Notes on plans such as N.T.S. (not to scale); changes in scale throughout the drawings; reduced size drawings; discrepancies between the specifications and the drawings.

16. Develop a consistent pattern of performing an estimate. For example:
    a. Start the quantity takeoff at the lower floor and move to the next higher floor.
    b. Proceed from the main section of the building to the wings.
    c. Proceed from south to north or vice versa, clockwise or counterclockwise.
    d. Take off floor plan quantities first, elevations next, then detail drawings.

17. List all gross dimensions that can be either used again for different quantities, or used as a rough check of other quantities for verification (exterior perimeter, gross floor area, individual floor areas, etc.).

18. Utilize design symmetry or repetition (repetitive floors, repetitive wings, symmetrical design around a center line, similar room layouts, etc.). Note: Extreme caution is needed here so as not to omit or duplicate an area.

19. Do not convert units until the final total is obtained. For instance, when estimating concrete work, keep all units to the nearest cubic foot, then summarize and convert to cubic yards.

20. When figuring alternatives, it is best to total all items involved in the basic system, then total all items involved in the alternates. Therefore you work with positive numbers in all cases. When adds and deducts are used, it is often confusing whether to add or subtract a portion of an item; especially on a complicated or involved alternate.

R011105-50 Metric Conversion Factors

Description: This table is primarily for converting customary U.S. units in the left hand column to SI metric units in the right hand column. In addition, conversion factors for some commonly encountered Canadian and non-SI metric units are included.

	If You Know		Multiply By		To Find
Length	Inches	x	25.4[a]	=	Millimeters
	Feet	x	0.3048[a]	=	Meters
	Yards	x	0.9144[a]	=	Meters
	Miles (statute)	x	1.609	=	Kilometers
Area	Square inches	x	645.2	=	Square millimeters
	Square feet	x	0.0929	=	Square meters
	Square yards	x	0.8361	=	Square meters
Volume (Capacity)	Cubic inches	x	16,387	=	Cubic millimeters
	Cubic feet	x	0.02832	=	Cubic meters
	Cubic yards	x	0.7646	=	Cubic meters
	Gallons (U.S. liquids)[b]	x	0.003785	=	Cubic meters[c]
	Gallons (Canadian liquid)[b]	x	0.004546	=	Cubic meters[c]
	Ounces (U.S. liquid)[b]	x	29.57	=	Milliliters[c, d]
	Quarts (U.S. liquid)[b]	x	0.9464	=	Liters[c, d]
	Gallons (U.S. liquid)[b]	x	3.785	=	Liters[c, d]
Force	Kilograms force[d]	x	9.807	=	Newtons
	Pounds force	x	4.448	=	Newtons
	Pounds force	x	0.4536	=	Kilograms force[d]
	Kips	x	4448	=	Newtons
	Kips	x	453.6	=	Kilograms force[d]
Pressure, Stress, Strength (Force per unit area)	Kilograms force per square centimeter[d]	x	0.09807	=	Megapascals *
	Pounds force per square inch (psi)	x	0.006895	=	Megapascals
	Kips per square inch	x	6.895	=	Megapascals
	Pounds force per square inch (psi)	x	0.07031	=	Kilograms force per square centimeter[d]
	Pounds force per square foot	x	47.88	=	Pascals
	Pounds force per square foot	x	4.882	=	Kilograms force per square meter[d]
Bending Moment Or Torque	Inch-pounds force	x	0.01152	=	Meter-kilograms force[d]
	Inch-pounds force	x	0.1130	=	Newton-meters
	Foot-pounds force	x	0.1383	=	Meter-kilograms force[d]
	Foot-pounds force	x	1.356	=	Newton-meters
	Meter-kilograms force[d]	x	9.807	=	Newton-meters
Mass	Ounces (avoirdupois)	x	28.35	=	Grams
	Pounds (avoirdupois)	x	0.4536	=	Kilograms
	Tons (metric)	x	1000	=	Kilograms
	Tons, short (2000 pounds)	x	907.2	=	Kilograms
	Tons, short (2000 pounds)	x	0.9072	=	Megagrams[e]
Mass per Unit Volume	Pounds mass per cubic foot	x	16.02	=	Kilograms per cubic meter
	Pounds mass per cubic yard	x	0.5933	=	Kilograms per cubic meter
	Pounds mass per gallon (U.S. liquid)[b]	x	119.8	=	Kilograms per cubic meter
	Pounds mass per gallon (Canadian liquid)[b]	x	99.78	=	Kilograms per cubic meter
Temperature	Degrees Fahrenheit	(F-32)/1.8		=	Degrees Celsius
	Degrees Fahrenheit	(F+459.67)/1.8		=	Degrees Kelvin
	Degrees Celsius	C+273.15		=	Degrees Kelvin

[a]The factor given is exact
[b]One U.S. gallon = 0.8327 Canadian gallon
[c]1 liter = 1000 milliliters = 1000 cubic centimeters
 1 cubic decimeter = 0.001 cubic meter
[d]Metric but not SI unit
[e]Called "tonne" in England and "metric ton" in other metric countries

R011105-60   Weights and Measures

Measures of Length
1 Mile = 1760 Yards = 5280 Feet
1 Yard = 3 Feet = 36 inches
1 Foot = 12 Inches
1 Mil = 0.001 Inch
1 Fathom = 2 Yards = 6 Feet
1 Rod = 5.5 Yards = 16.5 Feet
1 Hand = 4 Inches
1 Span = 9 Inches
1 Micro-inch = One Millionth Inch or 0.000001 Inch
1 Micron = One Millionth Meter + 0.00003937 Inch

Surveyor's Measure
1 Mile = 8 Furlongs = 80 Chains
1 Furlong = 10 Chains = 220 Yards
1 Chain = 4 Rods = 22 Yards = 66 Feet = 100 Links
1 Link = 7.92 Inches

Square Measure
1 Square Mile = 640 Acres = 6400 Square Chains
1 Acre = 10 Square Chains = 4840 Square Yards = 43,560 Sq. Ft.
1 Square Chain = 16 Square Rods = 484 Square Yards = 4356 Sq. Ft.
1 Square Rod = 30.25 Square Yards = 272.25 Square Feet = 625 Square Lines
1 Square Yard = 9 Square Feet
1 Square Foot = 144 Square Inches
An Acre equals a Square 208.7 Feet per Side

Cubic Measure
1 Cubic Yard = 27 Cubic Feet
1 Cubic Foot = 1728 Cubic Inches
1 Cord of Wood = 4 x 4 x 8 Feet = 128 Cubic Feet
1 Perch of Masonry = 16½ x 1½ x 1 Foot = 24.75 Cubic Feet

Avoirdupois or Commercial Weight
1 Gross or Long Ton = 2240 Pounds
1 Net or Short ton = 2000 Pounds
1 Pound = 16 Ounces = 7000 Grains
1 Ounce = 16 Drachms = 437.5 Grains
1 Stone = 14 Pounds

Shipping Measure
For Measuring Internal Capacity of a Vessel:
   1 Register Ton = 100 Cubic Feet

For Measurement of Cargo:
   Approximately 40 Cubic Feet of Merchandise is considered a Shipping Ton, unless that bulk would weigh more than 2000 Pounds, in which case Freight Charge may be based upon weight.

40 Cubic Feet = 32.143 U.S. Bushels = 31.16 Imp. Bushels

Liquid Measure
1 Imperial Gallon = 1.2009 U.S. Gallon = 277.42 Cu. In.
1 Cubic Foot = 7.48 U.S. Gallons

R011110-10   Architectural Fees

Tabulated below are typical percentage fees by project size, for good professional architectural service. Fees may vary from those listed depending upon degree of design difficulty and economic conditions in any particular area.

Rates can be interpolated horizontally and vertically. Various portions of the same project requiring different rates should be adjusted proportionally. For alterations, add 50% to the fee for the first $500,000 of project cost and add 25% to the fee for project cost over $500,000.

Architectural fees tabulated below include Structural, Mechanical and Electrical Engineering Fees. They do not include the fees for special consultants such as kitchen planning, security, acoustical, interior design, etc.

Civil Engineering fees are included in the Architectural fee for project sites requiring minimal design such as city sites. However, separate Civil Engineering fees must be added when utility connections require design, drainage calculations are needed, stepped foundations are required, or provisions are required to protect adjacent wetlands.

Building Types	Total Project Size in Thousands of Dollars						
	100	250	500	1,000	5,000	10,000	50,000
Factories, garages, warehouses, repetitive housing	9.0%	8.0%	7.0%	6.2%	5.3%	4.9%	4.5%
Apartments, banks, schools, libraries, offices, municipal buildings	12.2	12.3	9.2	8.0	7.0	6.6	6.2
Churches, hospitals, homes, laboratories, museums, research	15.0	13.6	12.7	11.9	9.5	8.8	8.0
Memorials, monumental work, decorative furnishings	—	16.0	14.5	13.1	10.0	9.0	8.3

R012909-80   Sales Tax by State

State sales tax on materials is tabulated below (5 states have no sales tax). Many states allow local jurisdictions, such as a county or city, to levy additional sales tax.

Some projects may be sales tax exempt, particularly those constructed with public funds.

State	Tax (%)	State	Tax (%)	State	Tax (%)	State	Tax (%)
Alabama	4	Illinois	6.25	Montana	0	Rhode Island	7
Alaska	0	Indiana	7	Nebraska	5.5	South Carolina	6
Arizona	5.6	Iowa	6	Nevada	6.85	South Dakota	4
Arkansas	6	Kansas	6.3	New Hampshire	0	Tennessee	7
California	7.25	Kentucky	6	New Jersey	7	Texas	6.25
Colorado	2.9	Louisiana	4	New Mexico	5.13	Utah	5.95
Connecticut	6.35	Maine	5	New York	4	Vermont	6
Delaware	0	Maryland	6	North Carolina	4.75	Virginia	5
District of Columbia	6	Massachusetts	6.25	North Dakota	5	Washington	6.5
Florida	6	Michigan	6	Ohio	5.5	West Virginia	6
Georgia	4	Minnesota	6.88	Oklahoma	4.5	Wisconsin	5
Hawaii	4	Mississippi	7	Oregon	0	Wyoming	4
Idaho	6	Missouri	4.23	Pennsylvania	6	Average	5.06%

Sales Tax by Province (Canada)

GST - a value-added tax, which the government imposes on most goods and services provided in or imported into Canada. PST - a retail sales tax, which three of the provinces impose on the price of most goods and some services. QST - a value-added tax, similar to the federal GST, which Quebec imposes. HST - Five provinces have combined their retail sales tax with the federal GST into one harmonized tax.

Province	PST (%)	QST (%)	GST(%)	HST(%)
Alberta	0	0	5	0
British Columbia	7	0	5	0
Manitoba	7	0	5	0
New Brunswick	0	0	0	13
Newfoundland	0	0	0	13
Northwest Territories	0	0	5	0
Nova Scotia	0	0	0	15
Ontario	0	0	0	13
Prince Edward Island	0	0	5	14
Quebec	0	9.975	5	0
Saskatchewan	5	0	5	0
Yukon	0	0	5	0

R012909-85   Unemployment Taxes and Social Security Taxes

State unemployment tax rates vary not only from state to state, but also with the experience rating of the contractor. The federal unemployment tax rate is 6.0% of the first $7,000 of wages. This is reduced by a credit of up to 5.4% for timely payment to the state. The minimum federal unemployment tax is 0.6% after all credits.

Social security (FICA) for 2014 is estimated at time of publication to be 7.65% of wages up to $115,800.

R013113-40   Builder's Risk Insurance

Builder's Risk Insurance is insurance on a building during construction. Premiums are paid by the owner or the contractor. Blasting, collapse and underground insurance would raise total insurance costs above those listed. Floater policy for materials delivered to the job runs $.75 to $1.25 per $100 value. Contractor equipment insurance runs $.50 to $1.50 per $100 value. Insurance for miscellaneous tools to $1,500 value runs from $3.00 to $7.50 per $100 value.

Tabulated below are New England Builder's Risk insurance rates in dollars per $100 value for $1,000 deductible. For $25,000 deductible, rates can be reduced 13% to 34%. On contracts over $1,000,000, rates may be lower than those tabulated. Policies are written annually for the total completed value in place. For "all risk" insurance (excluding flood, earthquake and certain other perils) add $.025 to total rates below.

Coverage	Frame Construction (Class 1)		Brick Construction (Class 4)		Fire Resistive (Class 6)	
	Range	Average	Range	Average	Range	Average
Fire Insurance	$.350 to $ .850	$.600	$.158 to $.189	$.174	$.052 to $.080	$.070
Extended Coverage	.115 to .200	.158	.080 to .105	.101	.081 to .105	.100
Vandalism	.012 to .016	.014	.008 to .011	.011	.008 to .011	.010
Total Annual Rate	$.477 to $1.066	$.772	$.246 to $.305	$.286	$.141 to $.196	$.180

R013113-50   General Contractor's Overhead

There are two distinct types of overhead on a construction project: Project Overhead and Main Office Overhead. Project Overhead includes those costs at a construction site not directly associated with the installation of construction materials. Examples of Project Overhead costs include the following:

1. Superintendent
2. Construction office and storage trailers
3. Temporary sanitary facilities
4. Temporary utilities
5. Security fencing
6. Photographs
7. Clean up
8. Performance and payment bonds

The above Project Overhead items are also referred to as General Requirements and therefore are estimated in Division 1. Division 1 is the first division listed in the CSI MasterFormat but it is usually the last division estimated. The sum of the costs in Divisions 1 through 49 is referred to as the sum of the direct costs.

All construction projects also include indirect costs. The primary components of indirect costs are the contractor's Main Office Overhead and profit. The amount of the Main Office Overhead expense varies depending on the the following:

1. Owner's compensation
2. Project managers and estimator's wages
3. Clerical support wages
4. Office rent and utilities
5. Corporate legal and accounting costs
6. Advertising
7. Automobile expenses
8. Association dues
9. Travel and entertainment expenses

These costs are usually calculated as a percentage of annual sales volume. This percentage can range from 35% for a small contractor doing less than $500,000 to 5% for a large contractor with sales in excess of $100 million.

R013113-60   Workers' Compensation Insurance Rates by Trade

The table below tabulates the national averages for workers' compensation insurance rates by trade and type of building. The average "Insurance Rate" is multiplied by the "% of Building Cost" for each trade. This produces the "Workers' Compensation" cost by % of total labor cost, to be added for each trade by building type to determine the weighted average workers' compensation rate for the building types analyzed.

Trade	Insurance Rate (% Labor Cost) Range		Average	% of Building Cost Office Bldgs.	Schools & Apts.	Mfg.	Workers' Compensation Office Bldgs.	Schools & Apts.	Mfg.
Excavation, Grading, etc.	3.9 % to	18.7%	9.7%	4.8%	4.9%	4.5%	0.47%	0.48%	0.44%
Piles & Foundations	5.8 to	37	14.7	7.1	5.2	8.7	1.04	0.76	1.28
Concrete	4.6 to	38.6	13.1	5.0	14.8	3.7	0.66	1.94	0.48
Masonry	5.1 to	35	13.5	6.9	7.5	1.9	0.93	1.01	0.26
Structural Steel	5.8 to	108.2	34.6	10.7	3.9	17.6	3.70	1.35	6.09
Miscellaneous & Ornamental Metals	5.3 to	31.2	12.0	2.8	4.0	3.6	0.34	0.48	0.43
Carpentry & Millwork	5.5 to	34.9	15.4	3.7	4.0	0.5	0.57	0.62	0.08
Metal or Composition Siding	5.8 to	68.3	18.2	2.3	0.3	4.3	0.42	0.05	0.78
Roofing	5.8 to	93.3	31.3	2.3	2.6	3.1	0.72	0.81	0.97
Doors & Hardware	4.2 to	34.8	11.1	0.9	1.4	0.4	0.10	0.16	0.04
Sash & Glazing	5.3 to	36.8	13.1	3.5	4.0	1.0	0.46	0.52	0.13
Lath & Plaster	3.7 to	35	11.6	3.3	6.9	0.8	0.38	0.80	0.09
Tile, Marble & Floors	3.3 to	27.1	8.5	2.6	3.0	0.5	0.22	0.26	0.04
Acoustical Ceilings	3.4 to	36.7	8.1	2.4	0.2	0.3	0.19	0.02	0.02
Painting	5 to	33	11.5	1.5	1.6	1.6	0.17	0.18	0.18
Interior Partitions	5.5 to	34.9	15.4	3.9	4.3	4.4	0.60	0.66	0.68
Miscellaneous Items	2.5 to	150	14.4	5.2	3.7	9.7	0.75	0.53	1.40
Elevators	1.6 to	14.4	5.7	2.1	1.1	2.2	0.12	0.06	0.13
Sprinklers	3.2 to	18.3	7.2	0.5	—	2.0	0.04	—	0.14
Plumbing	2.6 to	17.5	7.1	4.9	7.2	5.2	0.35	0.51	0.37
Heat., Vent., Air Conditioning	4 to	18.8	8.8	13.5	11.0	12.9	1.19	0.97	1.14
Electrical	2.8 to	13.2	5.8	10.1	8.4	11.1	0.59	0.49	0.64
Total	1.6 % to	150%	—	100.0%	100.0%	100.0%	14.01%	12.66%	15.81%
			Overall Weighted Average 14.16%						

Workers' Compensation Insurance Rates by States

The table below lists the weighted average workers' compensation base rate for each state with a factor comparing this with the national average of 14%.

State	Weighted Average	Factor	State	Weighted Average	Factor	State	Weighted Average	Factor
Alabama	20.3%	145	Kentucky	14.9%	106	North Dakota	9.6%	69
Alaska	14.3	102	Louisiana	19.3	138	Ohio	8.6	61
Arizona	13.1	94	Maine	12.7	91	Oklahoma	12.9	92
Arkansas	8.6	61	Maryland	14.6	104	Oregon	12.3	88
California	26.8	191	Massachusetts	12.0	86	Pennsylvania	18.1	129
Colorado	7.5	54	Michigan	16.9	121	Rhode Island	12.6	90
Connecticut	24.6	176	Minnesota	23.5	168	South Carolina	19.6	140
Delaware	12.4	89	Mississippi	13.8	99	South Dakota	15.5	111
District of Columbia	11.5	82	Missouri	15.4	110	Tennessee	12.5	89
Florida	11.1	79	Montana	8.9	64	Texas	9.5	68
Georgia	29.2	209	Nebraska	18.3	131	Utah	9.1	65
Hawaii	8.4	60	Nevada	9.0	64	Vermont	13.6	97
Idaho	10.7	76	New Hampshire	20.8	149	Virginia	9.9	71
Illinois	28.1	201	New Jersey	15.0	107	Washington	10.9	78
Indiana	5.7	41	New Mexico	15.0	107	West Virginia	8.3	59
Iowa	15.1	108	New York	17.9	128	Wisconsin	13.6	97
Kansas	8.7	62	North Carolina	17.4	124	Wyoming	6.3	45
			Weighted Average for U.S. is 14.2% of payroll = 100%					

Rates in the following table are the base or manual costs per $100 of payroll for workers' compensation in each state. Rates are usually applied to straight time wages only and not to premium time wages and bonuses.

The weighted average skilled worker rate for 35 trades is 14%. For bidding purposes, apply the full value of workers' compensation directly to total labor costs, or if labor is 38%, materials 42% and overhead and profit 20% of total cost, carry 38/80 x 14% =6.6% of cost (before overhead and profit) into overhead. Rates vary not only from state to state but also with the experience rating of the contractor.

Rates are the most current available at the time of publication.

R013113-60 Workers' Compensation Insurance Rates by Trade and State (cont.)

State	Carpentry — 3 stories or less 5651	Carpentry — interior cab. work 5437	Carpentry — general 5403	Concrete Work — NOC 5213	Concrete Work — flat (flr., sdwk.) 5221	Electrical Wiring — inside 5190	Excavation — earth NOC 6217	Excavation — rock 6217	Glaziers 5462	Insulation Work 5479	Lathing 5443	Masonry 5022	Painting & Decorating 5474	Pile Driving 6003	Plastering 5480	Plumbing 5183
AL	34.03	17.01	24.59	13.79	10.37	8.87	16.42	16.42	19.75	19.84	9.24	23.79	15.91	18.57	15.88	8.73
AK	17.14	9.44	11.58	10.41	9.44	5.63	8.23	8.23	32.03	14.36	11.73	10.86	10.79	21.68	11.31	6.20
AZ	21.40	9.27	20.28	10.31	6.93	6.08	7.07	7.07	10.80	14.99	5.47	13.01	12.78	10.80	8.64	6.84
AR	12.80	4.77	9.18	6.63	5.16	4.03	6.82	6.82	8.14	7.67	3.99	8.30	7.08	8.10	13.00	4.55
CA	34.87	34.83	34.86	16.55	16.55	13.24	18.65	18.65	24.16	16.48	17.83	25.13	23.59	23.18	35.04	17.48
CO	8.95	4.93	6.07	6.68	4.75	2.92	5.49	5.49	6.00	7.27	3.95	8.29	6.56	6.51	5.69	4.16
CT	30.95	18.48	31.07	26.49	14.43	7.89	16.02	16.02	20.24	20.60	9.92	31.53	18.60	20.17	18.75	11.28
DE	12.46	12.46	9.93	10.07	8.80	4.53	7.70	7.70	10.90	9.93	6.60	11.53	13.39	15.03	10.90	6.60
DC	8.92	7.25	6.94	12.65	7.38	4.69	8.02	8.02	9.61	6.63	9.83	9.32	5.82	17.36	8.00	7.80
FL	11.32	8.62	11.92	12.51	6.20	6.17	7.30	7.30	10.56	10.45	5.53	10.92	10.23	17.84	9.68	5.63
GA	68.34	20.32	28.40	21.36	15.09	12.05	17.32	17.32	19.39	18.80	11.94	35.11	33.04	26.44	19.65	12.76
HI	8.51	6.92	12.69	7.05	4.02	4.47	5.40	5.40	8.22	5.20	6.26	7.01	6.19	7.32	8.33	5.31
ID	14.63	6.84	12.43	11.48	5.28	4.43	7.25	7.25	8.81	9.06	4.46	10.55	9.38	7.65	8.43	5.10
IL	33.34	21.75	28.57	38.59	16.83	10.03	14.53	14.53	25.55	21.41	14.32	28.94	18.57	24.53	32.84	12.51
IN	8.36	4.21	6.98	4.56	4.15	2.83	3.92	3.92	5.29	6.15	3.85	5.14	4.97	7.23	3.71	2.56
IA	15.46	11.35	19.21	14.85	11.16	5.20	11.01	11.01	15.76	9.89	6.48	14.30	10.13	11.38	21.73	7.80
KS	14.92	7.39	9.74	8.07	5.70	4.46	5.55	5.55	7.54	8.17	4.09	8.38	7.75	7.56	6.20	5.23
KY	18.75	13.00	20.00	8.50	6.50	6.00	14.00	14.00	22.12	11.15	7.60	7.50	9.00	16.03	12.93	5.00
LA	31.05	16.86	25.02	13.35	12.37	7.85	14.11	14.11	19.19	15.06	7.99	17.31	17.64	18.85	14.84	7.10
ME	12.24	8.87	16.18	16.43	8.70	4.74	12.34	12.34	14.82	12.79	5.09	10.88	12.44	9.00	9.99	5.90
MD	11.40	15.89	15.00	19.22	6.00	5.23	8.11	8.11	13.77	12.42	6.15	10.11	6.40	15.19	9.17	6.65
MA	8.68	5.23	9.61	18.85	6.24	2.84	4.35	4.35	9.58	7.78	5.27	10.55	5.09	12.92	4.68	3.50
MI	18.41	10.45	18.41	18.27	12.58	5.82	13.28	13.28	11.67	10.92	10.45	18.82	13.49	37.00	10.88	7.18
MN	20.27	20.82	34.13	11.58	13.15	5.83	11.00	11.00	36.85	18.37	11.55	15.59	17.55	27.58	11.58	8.09
MS	22.76	9.99	13.34	9.60	6.67	6.18	9.49	9.49	14.94	10.15	5.94	13.12	11.01	13.14	10.43	8.17
MO	19.66	11.10	12.81	12.38	10.34	6.15	9.96	9.96	9.47	11.55	7.44	15.13	11.42	13.38	12.15	9.00
MT	9.67	6.59	10.80	6.22	5.67	3.71	7.41	7.41	7.50	8.67	4.15	7.62	8.22	7.95	6.80	4.79
NE	21.80	13.15	21.48	18.23	11.20	8.03	17.38	17.38	12.05	21.53	8.35	18.73	13.00	13.93	13.68	8.73
NV	10.41	6.82	12.39	10.83	5.26	4.33	8.75	8.75	6.55	7.55	3.41	6.63	7.10	8.43	6.21	6.76
NH	24.24	11.06	19.63	28.40	16.47	5.63	12.61	12.61	14.12	12.63	7.30	16.19	20.93	18.53	11.20	9.49
NJ	18.69	13.18	18.69	15.51	11.69	5.13	10.83	10.83	11.21	12.63	15.13	18.71	11.28	15.79	15.13	6.96
NM	25.01	9.56	18.92	11.73	9.43	6.05	7.22	7.22	10.95	10.56	6.11	15.74	12.91	12.66	14.20	6.70
NY	12.54	10.74	19.18	23.71	17.15	7.85	12.16	12.16	18.72	10.88	12.86	21.24	14.99	20.13	10.02	10.83
NC	30.12	9.54	15.76	16.11	9.31	10.56	15.41	15.41	14.28	13.03	8.11	13.05	14.08	16.61	14.12	10.73
ND	9.54	4.31	9.54	5.43	5.43	3.75	4.13	4.13	10.50	10.50	9.93	6.52	6.00	10.59	9.93	6.11
OH	7.73	4.31	5.52	4.67	4.92	3.43	4.79	4.79	8.83	11.38	36.65	6.93	8.15	6.99	7.80	3.52
OK	18.82	10.32	12.49	13.50	7.66	6.82	9.48	9.48	11.79	11.31	5.13	14.63	10.66	11.24	14.01	6.82
OR	22.30	8.52	11.92	10.51	10.42	5.35	9.08	9.08	12.64	10.88	6.09	14.37	11.81	11.44	10.81	6.35
PA	19.22	19.22	15.60	19.54	13.58	7.39	11.11	11.11	14.34	15.60	14.34	16.04	17.13	19.44	14.34	9.19
RI	9.84	11.55	13.75	12.56	9.68	4.58	8.16	8.16	10.61	12.48	5.17	10.07	8.82	19.30	8.69	6.75
SC	29.32	13.80	17.10	12.84	8.21	9.82	12.01	12.01	12.92	14.13	9.57	15.39	16.10	15.67	14.47	9.40
SD	20.86	17.96	20.35	16.10	10.49	5.08	9.75	9.75	10.84	14.71	6.95	14.65	11.22	12.63	10.35	10.02
TN	22.71	10.14	11.54	10.75	7.08	5.49	10.05	10.05	11.07	10.34	6.60	11.69	8.27	12.08	11.04	5.17
TX	10.12	7.33	10.12	8.08	5.99	5.98	7.60	7.60	8.25	9.27	4.15	8.69	7.28	10.26	7.28	5.27
UT	14.72	6.59	7.50	7.34	6.57	3.56	6.79	6.79	7.45	7.15	6.41	8.96	7.73	6.72	5.56	4.17
VT	15.69	10.21	13.77	13.60	11.57	4.37	11.83	11.83	12.40	15.34	5.79	11.92	8.78	10.43	9.35	7.38
VA	12.38	8.14	8.89	10.51	5.76	4.50	7.40	7.40	8.02	7.27	5.45	7.98	8.93	8.31	6.69	5.07
WA	9.18	9.18	9.18	8.55	8.55	3.18	6.68	6.68	13.99	6.79	9.18	13.26	12.26	21.68	10.43	4.33
WV	14.85	5.54	8.34	7.68	4.51	3.53	6.46	6.46	6.74	6.29	4.33	8.39	6.03	8.09	6.54	3.52
WI	12.52	13.14	17.06	11.98	7.59	5.08	7.84	7.84	13.88	11.22	4.00	13.69	12.43	28.24	10.16	5.95
WY	5.82	5.82	5.82	5.82	5.82	5.82	5.82	5.82	5.82	5.82	5.82	5.82	5.82	5.82	5.82	5.82
AVG.	18.19	11.07	15.38	13.15	8.92	5.83	9.69	9.69	13.15	11.67	8.12	13.49	11.54	14.65	11.55	7.08

Reference Tables

R013113-60 Workers' Compensation Insurance Rates by Trade and State (cont.)

State	Roofing 5551	Sheet Metal Work (HVAC) 5538	Steel Erection — door & sash 5102	Steel Erection — inter., ornam. 5102	Steel Erection — structure 5040	Steel Erection — NOC 5057	Tile Work — (interior ceramic) 5348	Waterproofing 9014	Wrecking 5701	Boiler- making 3726	Mill- wrights 3724	Structural Painters 5037	Elevator Constructor 5160	Truck Drivers 7219	Sprinkler Installer 5188
AL	54.71	10.34	12.52	12.52	40.75	21.56	12.35	9.27	40.75	11.93	12.83	55.64	10.09	23.31	8.40
AK	25.49	8.05	7.82	7.82	29.28	26.40	5.33	5.77	29.28	8.56	8.24	31.37	4.06	11.75	5.13
AZ	29.22	10.31	13.61	13.61	26.91	12.89	4.50	6.21	26.91	9.07	7.41	59.76	5.09	8.01	5.48
AR	16.03	4.74	8.34	8.34	15.40	11.28	6.69	2.58	15.40	4.94	5.76	25.69	2.73	10.96	5.72
CA	71.13	18.78	18.41	18.41	35.28	19.69	14.59	23.59	19.69	8.98	13.58	35.28	5.07	27.13	18.32
CO	15.60	4.16	5.36	5.36	23.64	10.59	4.10	3.23	18.40	4.37	3.87	22.88	2.78	7.22	3.85
CT	58.74	12.93	21.24	21.24	65.13	29.83	15.63	6.43	65.13	19.44	14.12	66.07	11.07	22.67	10.49
DE	26.71	5.55	13.16	13.16	23.27	13.16	8.00	11.53	23.27	6.17	6.19	23.27	6.19	11.13	6.60
DC	17.05	6.45	23.33	23.33	26.02	7.91	6.08	4.38	26.02	15.31	7.62	35.16	9.65	14.34	4.00
FL	18.17	7.69	9.91	9.91	23.04	12.59	5.63	5.26	23.04	9.07	6.05	39.44	3.54	9.24	6.41
GA	93.33	16.61	22.17	22.17	60.89	25.88	13.50	11.64	60.89	19.54	14.79	72.60	7.53	19.39	15.17
HI	17.24	4.93	7.60	7.60	21.77	6.88	6.52	5.40	21.77	4.82	7.71	24.83	2.28	10.54	3.49
ID	24.73	7.46	12.31	12.31	25.42	10.44	6.15	4.84	25.42	5.30	5.61	29.98	3.26	9.46	4.65
IL	47.55	15.21	31.16	31.16	84.68	19.36	27.09	7.88	84.68	23.23	15.10	101.23	14.42	19.73	16.65
IN	11.57	4.32	5.32	5.32	11.59	4.80	3.26	2.77	11.59	3.85	3.70	13.20	1.58	5.75	3.20
IA	28.01	8.53	9.15	9.15	52.79	14.30	9.38	6.15	25.61	14.19	8.59	87.69	6.14	13.60	7.75
KS	16.26	5.64	6.71	6.71	18.97	11.93	5.23	4.63	11.96	6.01	7.60	26.96	3.22	7.88	5.30
KY	34.00	12.00	11.72	11.72	36.00	11.02	16.73	3.50	36.00	12.15	8.35	150.00	9.56	10.00	10.32
LA	43.53	14.84	20.14	20.14	44.26	12.79	9.99	7.91	44.20	15.48	10.94	55.57	6.11	23.25	11.22
ME	22.72	6.77	8.92	8.92	37.18	12.21	5.76	4.64	37.18	8.08	6.58	54.29	4.39	8.15	6.70
MD	29.05	11.90	11.92	11.92	59.02	17.92	6.49	5.84	32.91	14.58	9.95	43.60	4.46	16.02	11.88
MA	30.99	5.72	6.89	6.89	54.08	33.00	5.81	2.48	23.75	15.42	5.98	23.51	4.21	8.28	4.13
MI	41.18	9.83	12.28	12.28	37.00	11.27	11.73	6.46	37.00	9.41	8.67	11.27	5.13	9.09	8.21
MN	67.71	17.30	9.82	9.82	108.16	7.70	14.69	7.95	7.70	10.92	12.24	36.60	6.41	11.39	7.62
MS	31.61	7.46	15.08	15.08	38.45	7.53	8.45	5.85	38.45	7.77	9.97	38.74	4.78	52.03	7.53
MO	36.73	8.64	12.33	12.33	47.55	24.29	10.41	5.92	47.55	14.45	9.66	60.85	6.20	12.44	8.43
MT	29.42	4.80	6.98	6.98	18.72	5.89	5.47	4.64	5.89	5.03	5.91	28.63	3.01	6.06	3.67
NE	35.08	12.88	14.80	14.80	59.03	14.13	8.68	6.73	67.83	16.33	11.35	66.18	7.13	15.98	10.30
NV	16.59	7.34	7.06	7.06	19.32	12.20	4.42	4.23	12.20	4.79	6.15	28.67	4.30	10.30	5.47
NH	36.82	8.93	14.28	14.28	95.03	28.57	12.35	7.17	95.03	8.91	9.04	54.18	6.29	36.82	10.68
NJ	40.10	7.22	12.87	12.87	17.25	13.36	9.55	6.63	16.86	4.18	9.20	23.37	7.00	15.75	5.89
NM	35.07	9.63	11.79	11.79	45.52	16.76	7.73	7.53	45.52	8.00	8.00	42.38	8.41	14.60	7.75
NY	35.96	13.56	19.25	19.25	35.26	19.08	10.35	7.49	18.10	21.41	10.22	42.40	12.20	14.37	6.45
NC	35.39	11.87	14.43	14.43	45.05	22.54	7.62	6.10	45.05	18.41	9.71	78.32	8.90	17.84	10.60
ND	17.63	6.11	10.59	10.59	10.90	10.59	10.50	17.63	8.18	3.33	10.50	10.59	3.33	8.79	6.11
OH	14.89	4.00	6.58	6.58	11.33	5.84	4.85	4.58	5.84	2.76	4.52	24.79	2.13	10.02	3.68
OK	22.44	9.62	10.98	10.98	29.21	15.15	6.69	6.41	32.94	9.25	6.21	52.38	3.88	11.26	6.40
OR	27.22	6.85	7.08	7.08	22.04	13.44	9.10	6.73	22.04	9.10	9.28	11.81	3.70	14.41	6.02
PA	38.35	8.92	19.10	19.10	30.01	19.10	11.69	16.04	30.01	7.95	8.85	30.01	8.85	16.69	9.19
RI	23.59	8.48	7.37	7.37	35.11	24.46	5.33	4.98	22.15	11.33	6.32	39.60	4.85	10.13	5.85
SC	46.45	10.88	15.24	15.24	31.33	24.73	7.98	5.42	31.33	11.24	10.59	66.07	8.64	15.07	10.12
SD	34.39	7.29	14.74	14.74	33.52	23.05	6.19	5.30	33.52	22.67	11.38	66.74	6.69	10.62	8.14
TN	29.78	8.13	13.42	13.42	16.07	18.88	7.46	4.09	16.07	8.10	7.46	40.34	4.92	10.23	6.10
TX	16.22	11.69	7.60	7.60	22.99	9.48	4.68	5.57	7.13	4.30	5.95	7.34	3.34	12.75	5.27
UT	23.93	5.78	5.71	5.71	24.61	11.81	5.75	4.31	20.14	5.91	4.77	21.36	3.71	7.05	4.16
VT	27.01	7.30	12.01	12.01	34.39	18.99	7.01	7.90	34.39	8.67	7.28	48.29	6.07	13.40	6.27
VA	25.97	5.47	7.46	7.46	29.39	10.80	5.76	3.30	29.39	4.92	7.38	27.90	5.39	9.03	5.30
WA	21.14	4.47	8.09	8.09	8.09	8.09	7.86	21.14	8.09	2.77	6.15	12.26	2.46	8.52	4.70
WV	19.62	5.62	7.13	7.13	19.39	9.55	4.86	3.11	20.70	5.62	6.64	35.86	4.23	8.93	3.76
WI	28.04	9.43	12.08	12.08	20.72	16.12	13.78	5.07	20.72	9.68	8.34	24.08	4.11	10.15	4.64
WY	5.82	5.82	5.82	5.82	5.82	5.82	5.82	5.82	5.82	5.82	5.82	5.82	5.82	5.82	5.82
AVG.	31.29	8.79	11.95	11.95	34.64	15.21	8.54	6.86	29.21	9.87	8.39	41.47	5.67	13.67	7.24

R013113-60 Workers' Compensation (cont.) (Canada in Canadian dollars)

Province		Alberta	British Columbia	Manitoba	Ontario	New Brunswick	Newfndld. & Labrador	Northwest Territories	Nova Scotia	Prince Edward Island	Quebec	Saskatchewan	Yukon
Carpentry—3 stories or less	Rate	5.71	3.27	3.98	4.55	3.17	7.81	4.99	6.85	6.42	12.03	3.43	6.63
	Code	42143	721028	40102	723	238130	4226	4-41	4226	403	80110	B1226	202
Carpentry—interior cab. work	Rate	1.89	2.80	3.98	4.55	3.17	4.07	4.99	5.87	3.94	12.03	3.43	6.63
	Code	42133	721021	40102	723	238350	4279	4-41	4274	402	80110	B1127	202
CARPENTRY—general	Rate	5.71	3.27	3.98	4.55	3.17	4.07	4.99	6.85	6.42	12.03	3.43	6.63
	Code	42143	721028	40102	723	238130	4299	4-41	4226	403	80110	B1202	202
CONCRETE WORK—NOC	Rate	3.88	3.57	6.50	18.31	3.17	7.81	4.99	5.75	3.94	1.92	2.99	6.63
	Code	42104	721010	40110	748	238110	4224	4-41	4224	402	80100	B1314	203
CONCRETE WORK—flat (flr. sidewalk)	Rate	3.88	3.57	6.50	18.31	3.17	7.81	4.99	5.75	3.94	11.92	2.99	6.63
	Code	42104	721010	40110	748	238110	4224	4-41	4224	402	80100	B1314	203
ELECTRICAL Wiring—inside	Rate	1.56	1.18	1.65	3.69	1.28	2.29	2.44	1.97	3.94	5.04	1.83	3.89
	Code	42124	721019	40203	704	238210	4261	4-46	4261	402	80170	B1105	206
EXCAVATION—earth NOC	Rate	1.86	3.79	4.00	5.29	3.17	2.93	3.88	3.89	3.94	6.40	2.19	3.89
	Code	40604	721031	40706	711	238190	4214	4-43	4214	402	80030	R1106	207
EXCAVATION—rock	Rate	1.86	3.79	4.00	5.29	3.17	2.93	3.88	3.89	3.94	6.40	2.19	3.89
	Code	40604	721031	40706	711	238190	4214	4-43	4214	402	80030	R1106	207
GLAZIERS	Rate	2.23	3.79	3.98	10.25	3.17	5.10	4.99	5.22	3.94	15.02	2.99	3.89
	Code	42121	715020	40109	751	238150	4233	4-41	4233	402	80150	B1304	212
INSULATION WORK	Rate	1.62	9.87	3.98	10.25	3.17	5.10	4.99	5.22	3.94	12.03	3.43	6.63
	Code	42184	721029	40102	751	238310	4234	4-41	4234	402	80110	B1207	202
LATHING	Rate	4.20	7.84	3.98	4.55	3.17	4.07	4.99	5.87	3.94	12.03	2.99	6.63
	Code	42135	721042	40102	723	238390	4279	4-41	4271	402	80110	B1316	202
MASONRY	Rate	3.88	3.30	3.98	12.70	3.17	5.10	4.99	5.22	3.94	11.92	2.99	6.63
	Code	42102	721037	40102	741	238140	4231	4-41	4231	402	80100	B1318	202
PAINTING & DECORATING	Rate	3.16	3.62	3.11	7.51	3.17	4.07	4.99	5.87	3.94	12.03	3.43	6.63
	Code	42111	721041	40105	719	238320	4275	4-41	4275	402	80110	B1201	202
PILE DRIVING	Rate	3.88	3.42	4.00	7.03	3.17	2.93	3.88	5.75	6.42	6.40	2.99	6.63
	Code	42159	722004	40706	732	238190	4129	4-43	4221	403	80030	B1310	202
PLASTERING	Rate	4.20	7.84	4.45	7.51	3.17	4.07	4.99	5.87	3.94	12.03	3.43	6.63
	Code	42135	721042	40108	719	238390	4271	4-41	4271	402	80110	B1221	202
PLUMBING	Rate	1.56	2.55	2.78	4.16	1.28	2.47	2.44	2.81	3.94	5.89	1.83	3.89
	Code	42122	721043	40204	707	238220	4241	4-46	4241	401	80160	B1101	214
ROOFING	Rate	4.71	5.42	7.22	14.80	3.17	7.81	4.99	9.43	3.94	18.52	2.99	6.63
	Code	42118	721036	40403	728	238160	4236	4-41	4236	402	80130	B1320	202
SHEET METAL WORK (HVAC)	Rate	1.56	2.55	7.22	4.16	1.28	2.47	2.44	2.81	3.94	5.89	1.83	3.89
	Code	42117	721043	40402	707	238220	4244	4-46	4244	401	80160	B1107	208
STEEL ERECTION—door & sash	Rate	1.62	10.62	6.82	18.31	3.17	7.81	4.99	5.22	3.94	16.70	2.99	6.63
	Code	42106	722005	40502	748	238120	4227	-37	4227	402	80080	B1322	202
STEEL ERECTION—inter., ornam.	Rate	1.62	10.62	6.82	18.31	3.17	7.81	4.99	5.22	3.94	16.70	2.99	6.63
	Code	42106	722005	40502	748	238120	4227	4-41	4227	402	80080	B1322	202
STEEL ERECTION—structure	Rate	1.62	10.62	6.82	18.31	3.17	7.81	4.99	5.22	3.94	16.70	2.99	6.63
	Code	42106	722005	40502	748	238120	4227	4-41	4227	402	80080	B1322	202
STEEL ERECTION—NOC	Rate	1.62	10.62	6.82	18.31	3.17	7.81	4.99	5.22	3.94	16.70	2.99	6.63
	Code	42106	722005	40502	748	238120	4227	4-41	4227	402	80080	B1322	202
TILE WORK—inter. (ceramic)	Rate	3.02	3.65	1.86	7.51	3.17	4.07	4.99	5.87	3.94	12.03	2.99	6.63
	Code	42113	721054	40103	719	238340	4276	4-41	4276	402	80110	B1301	202
WATERPROOFING	Rate	3.16	3.62	3.98	4.55	3.17	4.07	4.99	5.22	3.94	18.52	3.13	6.63
	Code	42139	721016	40102	723	238190	4299	4-41	4239	402	80130	B1217	202
WRECKING	Rate	1.86	5.64	6.90	18.31	3.17	2.93	3.88	3.89	3.94	12.03	2.19	6.63
	Code	40604	721005	40106	748	238190	4211	4-43	4211	402	80110	R1125	202

R015423-10   Steel Tubular Scaffolding

On new construction, tubular scaffolding is efficient up to 60' high or five stories. Above this it is usually better to use a hung scaffolding if construction permits. Swing scaffolding operations may interfere with tenants. In this case, the tubular is more practical at all heights.

In repairing or cleaning the front of an existing building the cost of tubular scaffolding per S.F. of building front increases as the height increases above the first tier. The first tier cost is relatively high due to leveling and alignment.

The minimum efficient crew for erecting and dismantling is three workers. They can set up and remove 18 frame sections per day up to 5 stories high. For 6 to 12 stories high, a crew of four is most efficient. Use two or more on top and two on the bottom for handing up or hoisting. They can

also set up and remove 18 frame sections per day. At 7' horizontal spacing, this will run about 800 S.F. per day of erecting and dismantling. Time for placing and removing planks must be added to the above. A crew of three can place and remove 72 planks per day up to 5 stories. For over 5 stories, a crew of four can place and remove 80 planks per day.

The table below shows the number of pieces required to erect tubular steel scaffolding for 1000 S.F. of building frontage. This area is made up of a scaffolding system that is 12 frames (11 bays) long by 2 frames high.

For jobs under twenty-five frames, add 50% to rental cost. Rental rates will be lower for jobs over three months duration. Large quantities for long periods can reduce rental rates by 20%.

Description of Component	Number of Pieces for 1000 S.F. of Building Front	Unit
5' Wide Standard Frame, 6'-4" High	24	Ea.
Leveling Jack & Plate	24	
Cross Brace	44	
Side Arm Bracket, 21"	12	
Guardrail Post	12	
Guardrail, 7' section	22	
Stairway Section	2	
Stairway Starter Bar	1	
Stairway Inside Handrail	2	
Stairway Outside Handrail	2	
Walk-Thru Frame Guardrail	2	

Scaffolding is often used as falsework over 15' high during construction of cast-in-place concrete beams and slabs. Two foot wide scaffolding is generally used for heavy beam construction. The span between frames depends upon the load to be carried with a maximum span of 5'.

Heavy duty shoring frames with a capacity of 10,000#/leg can be spaced up to 10' O.C. depending upon form support design and loading.

Scaffolding used as horizontal shoring requires less than half the material required with conventional shoring.

On new construction, erection is done by carpenters.

Rolling towers supporting horizontal shores can reduce labor and speed the job. For maintenance work, catwalks with spans up to 70' can be supported by the rolling towers.

R015423-20   Pump Staging

Pump staging is generally not available for rent. The table below shows the number of pieces required to erect pump staging for 2400 S.F. of building frontage. This area is made up of a pump jack system that is 3 poles (2 bays) wide by 2 poles high.

Item	Number of Pieces for 2400 S.F. of Building Front	Unit
Aluminum pole section, 24' long	6	Ea.
Aluminum splice joint, 6' long	3	
Aluminum foldable brace	3	
Aluminum pump jack	3	
Aluminum support for workbench/back safety rail	3	
Aluminum scaffold plank/workbench, 14" wide x 24' long	4	
Safety net, 22' long	2	
Aluminum plank end safety rail	2	

The cost in place for this 2400 S.F. will depend on how many uses are realized during the life of the equipment.

R024119-10   Demolition Defined

Whole Building Demolition - Demolition of the whole building with no concern for any particular building element, component, or material type being demolished. This type of demolition is accomplished with large pieces of construction equipment that break up the structure, load it into trucks and haul it to a disposal site, but disposal or dump fees are not included. Demolition of below-grade foundation elements, such as footings, foundation walls, grade beams, slabs on grade, etc., is not included. Certain mechanical equipment containing flammable liquids or ozone-depleting refrigerants, electric lighting elements, communication equipment components, and other building elements may contain hazardous waste, and must be removed, either selectively or carefully, as hazardous waste before the building can be demolished.

Foundation Demolition - Demolition of below-grade foundation footings, foundation walls, grade beams, and slabs on grade. This type of demolition is accomplished by hand or pneumatic hand tools, and does not include saw cutting, or handling, loading, hauling, or disposal of the debris.

Gutting - Removal of building interior finishes and electrical/mechanical systems down to the load-bearing and sub-floor elements of the rough building frame, with no concern for any particular building element, component, or material type being demolished. This type of demolition is accomplished by hand or pneumatic hand tools, and includes loading into trucks, but not hauling, disposal or dump fees, scaffolding, or shoring. Certain mechanical equipment containing flammable liquids or ozone-depleting refrigerants, electric lighting elements, communication equipment components, and other building elements may contain hazardous waste, and must be removed, either selectively or carefully, as hazardous waste, before the building is gutted.

Selective Demolition - Demolition of a selected building element, component, or finish, with some concern for surrounding or adjacent elements, components, or finishes (see the first Subdivision (s) at the beginning of appropriate Divisions). This type of demolition is accomplished by hand or pneumatic hand tools, and does not include handling, loading, storing, hauling, or disposal of the debris, scaffolding, or shoring. "Gutting" methods may be used in order to save time, but damage that is caused to surrounding or adjacent elements, components, or finishes may have to be repaired at a later time.

Careful Removal - Removal of a piece of service equipment, building element or component, or material type, with great concern for both the removed item and surrounding or adjacent elements, components or finishes. The purpose of careful removal may be to protect the removed item for later re-use, preserve a higher salvage value of the removed item, or replace an item while taking care to protect surrounding or adjacent elements, components, connections, or finishes from cosmetic and/or structural damage. An approximation of the time required to perform this type of removal is 1/3 to 1/2 the time it would take to install a new item of like kind. This type of removal is accomplished by hand or pneumatic hand tools, and does not include loading, hauling, or storing the removed item, scaffolding, shoring, or lifting equipment.

Cutout Demolition - Demolition of a small quantity of floor, wall, roof, or other assembly, with concern for the appearance and structural integrity of the surrounding materials. This type of demolition is accomplished by hand or pneumatic hand tools, and does not include saw cutting, handling, loading, hauling, or disposal of debris, scaffolding, or shoring.

Rubbish Handling - Work activities that involve handling, loading or hauling of debris. Generally, the cost of rubbish handling must be added to the cost of all types of demolition, with the exception of whole building demolition.

Minor Site Demolition - Demolition of site elements outside the footprint of a building. This type of demolition is accomplished by hand or pneumatic hand tools, or with larger pieces of construction equipment, and may include loading a removed item onto a truck (check the Crew for equipment used). It does not include saw cutting, hauling or disposal of debris, and, sometimes, handling or loading.

R024119-20   Dumpsters

Dumpster rental costs on construction sites are presented in two ways.

The cost per week rental includes the delivery of the dumpster; its pulling or emptying once per week, and its final removal. The assumption is made that the dumpster contractor could choose to empty a dumpster by simply bringing in an empty unit and removing the full one. These costs also include the disposal of the materials in the dumpster.

The Alternate Pricing can be used when actual planned conditions are not approximated by the weekly numbers. For example, these lines can be used when a dumpster is needed for 4 weeks and will need to be emptied 2 or 3 times per week. Conversely the Alternate Pricing lines can be used when a dumpster will be rented for several weeks or months but needs to be emptied only a few times over this period.

R040130-10 Cleaning Face Brick

On smooth brick a person can clean 70 S.F. an hour; on rough brick 50 S.F. per hour. Use one gallon muriatic acid to 20 gallons of water for 1000

S.F. Do not use acid solution until wall is at least seven days old, but a mild soap solution may be used after two days.

Time has been allowed for clean-up in brick prices.

R040513-10 Cement Mortar (material only)

Type N - 1:1:6 mix by volume. Use everywhere above grade except as noted below. - 1:3 mix using conventional masonry cement which saves handling two separate bagged materials.

Type M - 1:1/4:3 mix by volume, or 1 part cement, 1/4 (10% by wt.) lime, 3 parts sand. Use for heavy loads and where earthquakes or hurricanes may occur. Also for reinforced brick, sewers, manholes and everywhere below grade.

Mix Proportions by Volume and Compressive Strength of Mortar

Where Used	Allowable Proportions by Volume					Compressive Strength @ 28 days
	Mortar Type	Portland Cement	Masonry Cement	Hydrated Lime	Masonry Sand	
Plain Masonry	M	1	1	—	6	
		1	—	1/4	3	2500 psi
	S	1/2	1	—	4	
		1	—	1/4 to 1/2	4	1800 psi
	N	—	1	—	3	
		1	—	1/2 to 1-1/4	6	750 psi
	O	—	1	—	3	
		1	—	1-1/4 to 2-1/2	9	350 psi
	K	1	—	2-1/2 to 4	12	75 psi
Reinforced Masonry	PM	1	1	—	6	2500 psi
	PL	1	—	1/4 to 1/2	4	2500 psi

Note: The total aggregate should be between 2.25 to 3 times the sum of the cement and lime used.

The labor cost to mix the mortar is included in the productivity and labor cost of unit price lines in unit cost sections for brickwork, blockwork and stonework.

The material cost of mixed mortar is included in the material cost of those same unit price lines and includes the cost of renting and operating a 10 C.F. mixer at the rate of 200 C.F. per day.

There are two types of mortar color used. One type is the inert additive type with about 100 lbs. per M brick as the typical quantity required. These colors are also available in smaller-batch-sized bags (1 lb. to 15 lb.) which can be placed directly into the mixer without measuring. The other type is premixed and replaces the masonry cement. Dark green color has the highest cost.

R040519-50 Masonry Reinforcing

Horizontal joint reinforcing helps prevent wall cracks where wall movement may occur and in many locations is required by code. Horizontal joint reinforcing is generally not considered to be structural reinforcing and an unreinforced wall may still contain joint reinforcing.

Reinforcing strips come in 10′ and 12′ lengths and in truss and ladder shapes, with and without drips. Field labor runs between 2.7 to 5.3 hours per 1000 L.F. for wall thicknesses up to 12″.

The wire meets ASTM A82 for cold drawn steel wire and the typical size is 9 ga. sides and ties with 3/16″ diameter also available. Typical finish is mill galvanized with zinc coating at .10 oz. per S.F. Class I (.40 oz. per S.F.) and Class III (.80 oz per S.F.) are also available, as is hot dipped galvanizing at 1.50 oz. per S.F.

R042110-10   Economy in Bricklaying

Have adequate supervision. Be sure bricklayers are always supplied with materials so there is no waiting. Place best bricklayers at corners and openings.

Use only screened sand for mortar. Otherwise, labor time will be wasted picking out pebbles. Use seamless metal tubs for mortar as they do not leak or catch the trowel. Locate stack and mortar for easy wheeling.

Have brick delivered for stacking. This makes for faster handling, reduces chipping and breakage, and requires less storage space. Many dealers will deliver select common in 2' x 3' x 4' pallets or face brick packaged. This affords quick handling with a crane or forklift and easy tonging in units of ten, which reduces waste.

Use wider bricks for one wythe wall construction. Keep scaffolding away from wall to allow mortar to fall clear and not stain wall.

On large jobs develop specialized crews for each type of masonry unit.

Consider designing for prefabricated panel construction on high rise projects.

Avoid excessive corners or openings. Each opening adds about 50% to labor cost for area of opening.

Bolting stone panels and using window frames as stops reduces labor costs and speeds up erection.

R042110-20   Common and Face Brick

Common building brick manufactured according to ASTM C62 and facing brick manufactured according to ASTM C216 are the two standard bricks available for general building use.

Building brick is made in three grades; SW, where high resistance to damage caused by cyclic freezing is required; MW, where moderate resistance to cyclic freezing is needed; and NW, where little resistance to cyclic freezing is needed. Facing brick is made in only the two grades SW and MW. Additionally, facing brick is available in three types; FBS, for general use; FBX, for general use where a higher degree of precision and lower permissible variation in size than FBS is needed; and FBA, for general use to produce characteristic architectural effects resulting from non-uniformity in size and texture of the units.

In figuring the material cost of brickwork, an allowance of 25% mortar waste and 3% brick breakage was included. If bricks are delivered palletized

with 280 to 300 per pallet, or packaged, allow only 1-1/2% for breakage. Packaged or palletized delivery is practical when a job is big enough to have a crane or other equipment available to handle a package of brick. This is so on all industrial work but not always true on small commercial buildings.

The use of buff and gray face is increasing, and there is a continuing trend to the Norman, Roman, Jumbo and SCR brick.

Common red clay brick for backup is not used that often. Concrete block is the most usual backup material with occasional use of sand lime or cement brick. Building brick is commonly used in solid walls for strength and as a fire stop.

Brick panels built on the ground and then crane erected to the upper floors have proven to be economical. This allows the work to be done under cover and without scaffolding.

R042110-50   Brick, Block & Mortar Quantities

Type Brick	Nominal Size (incl. mortar) L H W	Modular Coursing	Number of Brick per S.F.	C.F. of Mortar per M Bricks, Waste Included 3/8" Joint	1/2" Joint	Bond Type	Description	Factor
Standard	8 x 2-2/3 x 4	3C=8"	6.75	10.3	12.9	Common	full header every fifth course	+20%
Economy	8 x 4 x 4	1C=4"	4.50	11.4	14.6		full header every sixth course	+16.7%
Engineer	8 x 3-1/5 x 4	5C=16"	5.63	10.6	13.6	English	full header every second course	+50%
Fire	9 x 2-1/2 x 4-1/2	2C=5"	6.40	550 # Fireclay	—	Flemish	alternate headers every course	+33.3%
Jumbo	12 x 4 x 6 or 8	1C=4"	3.00	23.8	30.8		every sixth course	+5.6%
Norman	12 x 2-2/3 x 4	3C=8"	4.50	14.0	17.9	Header = W x H exposed		+100%
Norwegian	12 x 3-1/5 x 4	5C=16"	3.75	14.6	18.6	Rowlock = H x W exposed		+100%
Roman	12 x 2 x 4	2C=4"	6.00	13.4	17.0	Rowlock stretcher = L x W exposed		+33.3%
SCR	12 x 2-2/3 x 6	3C=8"	4.50	21.8	28.0	Soldier = H x L exposed		—
Utility	12 x 4 x 4	1C=4"	3.00	15.4	19.6	Sailor = W x L exposed		-33.3%

Header line above: **Running Bond** — Number of Brick per S.F. of Wall - Single Wythe with 3/8" Joints | C.F. of Mortar per M Bricks, Waste Included | **For Other Bonds Standard Size Add to S.F. Quantities in Table to Left**

Concrete Blocks Nominal Size	Approximate Weight per S.F. Standard	Lightweight	Blocks per 100 S.F.	Mortar per M block, waste included Partitions	Back up
2" x 8" x 16"	20 PSF	15 PSF	113	27 C.F.	36 C.F.
4"	30	20		41	51
6"	42	30		56	66
8"	55	38		72	82
10"	70	47		87	97
12"	85	55		102	112

Masonry — R0422 Concrete Unit Masonry

R042210-20   Concrete Block

The material cost of special block such as corner, jamb and head block can be figured at the same price as ordinary block of same size. Labor on specials is about the same as equal-sized regular block.

Bond beam and 16" high lintel blocks are more expensive than regular units of equal size. Lintel blocks are 8" long and either 8" or 16" high.

Use of motorized mortar spreader box will speed construction of continuous walls.

Hollow non-load-bearing units are made according to ASTM C129 and hollow load-bearing units according to ASTM C90.

Metals — R0531 Steel Decking

R053100-10   Decking Descriptions

General - All Deck Products

Steel deck is made by cold forming structural grade sheet steel into a repeating pattern of parallel ribs. The strength and stiffness of the panels are the result of the ribs and the material properties of the steel. Deck lengths can be varied to suit job conditions, but because of shipping considerations, are usually less than 40 feet. Standard deck width varies with the product used but full sheets are usually 12", 18", 24", 30", or 36". Deck is typically furnished in a standard width with the ends cut square. Any cutting for width, such as at openings or for angular fit, is done at the job site.

Deck is typically attached to the building frame with arc puddle welds, self-drilling screws, or powder or pneumatically driven pins. Sheet to sheet fastening is done with screws, button punching (crimping), or welds.

Composite Floor Deck

After installation and adequate fastening, floor deck serves several purposes. It (a) acts as a working platform, (b) stabilizes the frame, (c) serves as a concrete form for the slab, and (d) reinforces the slab to carry the design loads applied during the life of the building. Composite decks are distinguished by the presence of shear connector devices as part of the deck. These devices are designed to mechanically lock the concrete and deck together so that the concrete and the deck work together to carry subsequent floor loads. These shear connector devices can be rolled-in embossments, lugs, holes, or wires welded to the panels. The deck profile can also be used to interlock concrete and steel.

Composite deck finishes are either galvanized (zinc coated) or phosphatized/painted. Galvanized deck has a zinc coating on both the top and bottom surfaces. The phosphatized/painted deck has a bare (phosphatized) top surface that will come into contact with the concrete. This bare top surface can be expected to develop rust before the concrete is placed. The bottom side of the deck has a primer coat of paint.

Composite floor deck is normally installed so the panel ends do not overlap on the supporting beams. Shear lugs or panel profile shape often prevent a tight metal to metal fit if the panel ends overlap; the air gap caused by overlapping will prevent proper fusion with the structural steel supports when the panel end laps are shear stud welded.

Adequate end bearing of the deck must be obtained as shown on the drawings. If bearing is actually less in the field than shown on the drawings, further investigation is required.

Roof Deck

Roof deck is not designed to act compositely with other materials. Roof deck acts alone in transferring horizontal and vertical loads into the building frame. Roof deck rib openings are usually narrower than floor deck rib openings. This provides adequate support of rigid thermal insulation board.

Roof deck is typically installed to endlap approximately 2" over supports. However, it can be butted (or lapped more than 2") to solve field fit problems. Since designers frequently use the installed deck system as part of the horizontal bracing system (the deck as a diaphragm), any fastening substitution or change should be approved by the designer. Continuous perimeter support of the deck is necessary to limit edge deflection in the finished roof and may be required for diaphragm shear transfer.

Standard roof deck finishes are galvanized or primer painted. The standard factory applied paint for roof deck is a primer paint and is not intended to weather for extended periods of time. Field painting or touching up of abrasions and deterioration of the primer coat or other protective finishes is the responsibility of the contractor.

Cellular Deck

Cellular deck is made by attaching a bottom steel sheet to a roof deck or composite floor deck panel. Cellular deck can be used in the same manner as floor deck. Electrical, telephone, and data wires are easily run through the chase created between the deck panel and the bottom sheet.

When used as part of the electrical distribution system, the cellular deck must be installed so that the ribs line up and create a smooth cell transition at abutting ends. The joint that occurs at butting cell ends must be taped or otherwise sealed to prevent wet concrete from seeping into the cell. Cell interiors must be free of welding burrs, or other sharp intrusions, to prevent damage to wires.

When used as a roof deck, the bottom flat plate is usually left exposed to view. Care must be maintained during erection to keep good alignment and prevent damage.

Cellular deck is sometimes used with the flat plate on the top side to provide a flat working surface. Installation of the deck for this purpose requires special methods for attachment to the frame because the flat plate, now on the top, can prevent direct access to the deck material that is bearing on the structural steel. It may be advisable to treat the flat top surface to prevent slipping.

Cellular deck is always furnished galvanized or painted over galvanized.

Form Deck

Form deck can be any floor or roof deck product used as a concrete form. Connections to the frame are by the same methods used to anchor floor and roof deck. Welding washers are recommended when welding deck that is less than 20 gauge thickness.

Form deck is furnished galvanized, prime painted, or uncoated. Galvanized deck must be used for those roof deck systems where form deck is used to carry a lightweight insulating concrete fill.

Wood, Plastics & Comp. | R0611 Wood Framing

R061110-30 Lumber Product Material Prices

The price of forest products fluctuates widely from location to location and from season to season depending upon economic conditions. The bare material prices in the unit cost sections of the book show the National Average material prices in effect Jan. 1 of this book year. It must be noted that lumber prices in general may change significantly during the year.

Availability of certain items depends upon geographic location and must be checked prior to firm-price bidding.

Wood, Plastics & Comp. | R0616 Sheathing

R061636-20 Plywood

There are two types of plywood used in construction: interior, which is moisture-resistant but not waterproofed, and exterior, which is waterproofed.

The grade of the exterior surface of the plywood sheets is designated by the first letter: A, for smooth surface with patches allowed; B, for solid surface with patches and plugs allowed; C, which may be surface plugged or may have knot holes up to 1″ wide; and D, which is used only for interior type plywood and may have knot holes up to 2-1/2″ wide. "Structural Grade" is specifically designed for engineered applications such as box beams. All CC & DD grades have roof and floor spans marked on them.

Underlayment-grade plywood runs from 1/4″ to 1-1/4″ thick. Thicknesses 5/8″ and over have optional tongue and groove joints which eliminate the need for blocking the edges. Underlayment 19/32″ and over may be referred to as Sturd-i-Floor.

The price of plywood can fluctuate widely due to geographic and economic conditions.

Typical uses for various plywood grades are as follows:

AA-AD Interior — cupboards, shelving, paneling, furniture

BB Plyform — concrete form plywood

CDX — wall and roof sheathing

Structural — box beams, girders, stressed skin panels

AA-AC Exterior — fences, signs, siding, soffits, etc.

Underlayment — base for resilient floor coverings

Overlaid HDO — high density for concrete forms & highway signs

Overlaid MDO — medium density for painting, siding, soffits & signs

303 Siding — exterior siding, textured, striated, embossed, etc.

Thermal & Moist. Protec. | R0731 Shingles & Shakes

R073126-20 Roof Slate

16″, 18″ and 20″ are standard lengths, and slate usually comes in random widths. For standard 3/16″ thickness use 1-1/2″ copper nails. Allow for 3% breakage.

Thermal & Moist. Protec. | R0752 Modified Bituminous Membrane Roofing

R075213-30 Modified Bitumen Roofing

The cost of modified bitumen roofing is highly dependent on the type of installation that is planned. Installation is based on the type of modifier used in the bitumen. The two most popular modifiers are atactic polypropylene (APP) and styrene butadiene styrene (SBS). The modifiers are added to heated bitumen during the manufacturing process to change its characteristics. A polyethylene, polyester or fiberglass reinforcing sheet is then sandwiched between layers of this bitumen. When completed, the result is a pre-assembled, built-up roof that has increased elasticity and weatherablility. Some manufacturers include a surfacing material such as ceramic or mineral granules, metal particles or sand.

The preferred method of adhering SBS-modified bitumen roofing to the substrate is with hot-mopped asphalt (much the same as built-up roofing). This installation method requires a tar kettle/pot to heat the asphalt, as well as the labor, tools and equipment necessary to distribute and spread the hot asphalt.

The alternative method for applying APP and SBS modified bitumen is as follows. A skilled installer uses a torch to melt a small pool of bitumen off the membrane. This pool must form across the entire roll for proper adhesion. The installer must unroll the roofing at a pace slow enough to melt the bitumen, but fast enough to prevent damage to the rest of the membrane.

Modified bitumen roofing provides the advantages of both built-up and single-ply roofing. Labor costs are reduced over those of built-up roofing because only a single ply is necessary. The elasticity of single-ply roofing is attained with the reinforcing sheet and polymer modifiers. Modifieds have some self-healing characteristics and because of their multi-layer construction, they offer the reliability and safety of built-up roofing.

Openings   R0813 Metal Doors

R081313-20   Steel Door Selection Guide

Standard steel doors are classified into four levels, as recommended by the Steel Door Institute in the chart below. Each of the four levels offers a range of construction models and designs, to meet architectural requirements for preference and appearance, including full flush, seamless, and stile & rail. Recommended minimum gauge requirements are also included.

For complete standard steel door construction specifications and available sizes, refer to the Steel Door Institute Technical Data Series, ANSI A250.8-98 (SDI-100), and ANSI A250.4-94 Test Procedure and Acceptance Criteria for Physical Endurance of Steel Door and Hardware Reinforcements.

Level		Model	Construction	For Full Flush or Seamless		
				Min. Gauge	Thickness (in)	Thickness (mm)
I	Standard Duty	1	Full Flush	20	0.032	0.8
		2	Seamless			
II	Heavy Duty	1	Full Flush	18	0.042	1.0
		2	Seamless			
III	Extra Heavy Duty	1	Full Flush	16	0.053	1.3
		2	Seamless			
		3	*Stile & Rail			
IV	Maximum Duty	1	Full Flush	14	0.067	1.6
		2	Seamless			

*Stiles & rails are 16 gauge; flush panels, when specified, are 18 gauge.

Openings   R0852 Wood Windows

R085216-10   Window Estimates

To ensure a complete window estimate, be sure to include the material and labor costs for each window, as well as the material and labor costs for an interior wood trim set.

Openings   R0853 Plastic Windows

R085313-20   Replacement Windows

Replacement windows are typically measured per United Inch.

United Inches are calculated by rounding the width and height of the window opening up to the nearest inch, then adding the two figures.

The labor cost for replacement windows includes removal of sash, existing sash balance or weights, parting bead where necessary and installation of new window.

Debris hauling and dump fees are not included.

R087110-10   Hardware Finishes

This table describes hardware finishes used throughout the industry. It also shows the base metal and the respective symbols in the three predominate systems of identification. Many of these are used in pricing descriptions in Division Eight.

US″	BMHA*	CDN^	Base	Description
US P	600	CP	Steel	Primed for Painting
US 1B	601	C1B	Steel	Bright Black Japanned
US 2C	602	C2C	Steel	Zinc Plated
US 2G	603	C2G	Steel	Zinc Plated
US 3	605	C3	Brass	Bright Brass, Clear Coated
US 4	606	C4	Brass	Satin Brass, Clear Coated
US 5	609	C5	Brass	Satin Brass, Blackened, Satin Relieved, Clear Coated
US 7	610	C7	Brass	Satin Brass, Blackened, Bright Relived, Clear Coated
US 9	611	C9	Bronze	Bright Bronze, Clear Coated
US 10	612	C10	Bronze	Satin Bronze, Clear Coated
US 10A	641	C10A	Steel	Antiqued Bronze, Oiled and Lacquered
US 10B	613	C10B	Bronze	Antiqued Bronze, Oiled
US 11	616	C11	Bronze	Satin Bronze, Blackened, Satin Relieved, Clear Coated
US 14	618	C14	Brass/Bronze	Bright Nickel Plated, Clear Coated
US 15	619	C15	Brass/Bronze	Satin Nickel, Clear Coated
US 15A	620	C15A	Brass/Bronze	Satin Nickel Plated, Blackened, Satin Relieved, Clear Coated
US 17A	621	C17A	Brass/Bronze	Nickel Plated, Blackened, Relieved, Clear Coated
US 19	622	C19	Brass/Bronze	Flat Black Coated
US 20	623	C20	Brass/Bronze	Statuary Bronze, Light
US 20A	624	C20A	Brass/Bronze	Statuary Bronze, Dark
US 26	625	C26	Brass/Bronze	Bright Chromium
US 26D	626	C26D	Brass/Bronze	Satin Chromium
US 20	627	C27	Aluminum	Satin Aluminum Clear
US 28	628	C28	Aluminum	Anodized Dull Aluminum
US 32	629	C32	Stainless Steel	Bright Stainless Steel
US 32D	630	C32D	Stainless Steel	Stainless Steel
US 3	632	C3	Steel	Bright Brass Plated, Clear Coated
US 4	633	C4	Steel	Satin Brass, Clear Coated
US 7	636	C7	Steel	Satin Brass Plated, Blackened, Bright Relieved, Clear Coated
US 9	637	C9	Steel	Bright Bronze Plated, Clear Coated
US 5	638	C5	Steel	Satin Brass Plated, Blackened, Bright Relieved, Clear Coated
US 10	639	C10	Steel	Satin Bronze Plated, Clear Coated
US 10B	640	C10B	Steel	Antique Bronze, Oiled
US 10A	641	C10A	Steel	Antiqued Bronze, Oiled and Lacquered
US 11	643	C11	Steel	Satin Bronze Plated, Blackened, Bright Relieved, Clear Coated
US 14	645	C14	Steel	Bright Nickel Plated, Clear Coated
US 15	646	C15	Steel	Satin Nickel Plated, Clear Coated
US 15A	647	C15A	Steel	Nickel Plated, Blackened, Bright Relieved, Clear Coated
US 17A	648	C17A	Steel	Nickel Plated, Blackened, Relieved, Clear Coated
US 20	649	C20	Steel	Statuary Bronze, Light
US 20A	650	C20A	Steel	Statuary Bronze, Dark
US 26	651	C26	Steel	Bright Chromium Plated
US 26D	652	C26D	Steel	Satin Chromium Plated

* - BMHA Builders Hardware Manufacturing Association
″ - US Equivalent
^ - Canadian Equivalent
Japanning is imitating Asian lacquer work

R087120-10 Hinges

All closer equipped doors should have ball bearing hinges. Lead lined or extremely heavy doors require special strength hinges. Usually 1-1/2 pair of hinges are used per door up to 7'-6" high openings. Table below shows typical hinge requirements.

Use Frequency	Type Hinge Required	Type of Opening	Type of Structure
High	Heavy weight	Entrances	Banks, Office buildings, Schools, Stores & Theaters
	ball bearing	Toilet Rooms	Office buildings and Schools
Average	Standard	Entrances	Dwellings
	weight	Corridors	Office buildings and Schools
	ball bearing	Toilet Rooms	Stores
Low	Plain bearing	Interior	Dwellings

Door Thickness	Weight of Doors in Pounds per Square Foot				
	White Pine	Oak	Hollow Core	Solid Core	Hollow Metal
1-3/8"	3psf	6psf	1-1/2psf	3-1/2 — 4psf	6-1/2psf
1-3/4"	3-1/2	7	2-1/2	4-1/2 — 5-1/4	6-1/2
2-1/4"	4-1/2	9	—	5-1/2 — 6-3/4	6-1/2

R092000-50 Lath, Plaster and Gypsum Board

Gypsum board lath is available in 3/8″ thick x 16″ wide x 4′ long sheets as a base material for multi-layer plaster applications. It is also available as a base for either multi-layer or veneer plaster applications in 1/2″ and 5/8″ thick–4′ wide x 8′, 10′ or 12′ long sheets. Fasteners are screws or blued ring shank nails for wood framing and screws for metal framing.

Metal lath is available in diamond mesh pattern with flat or self-furring profiles. Paper backing is available for applications where excessive plaster waste needs to be avoided. A slotted mesh ribbed lath should be used in areas where the span between structural supports is greater than normal. Most metal lath comes in 27″ x 96″ sheets. Diamond mesh weighs 1.75, 2.5 or 3.4 pounds per square yard, slotted mesh lath weighs 2.75 or 3.4 pounds per square yard. Metal lath can be nailed, screwed or tied in place.

Many **accessories** are available. Corner beads, flat reinforcing strips, casing beads, control and expansion joints, furring brackets and channels are some examples. Note that accessories are not included in plaster or stucco line items.

Plaster is defined as a material or combination of materials that when mixed with a suitable amount of water, forms a plastic mass or paste. When applied to a surface, the paste adheres to it and subsequently hardens, preserving in a rigid state the form or texture imposed during the period of elasticity.

Gypsum plaster is made from ground calcined gypsum. It is mixed with aggregates and water for use as a base coat plaster.

Vermiculite plaster is a fire-retardant plaster covering used on steel beams, concrete slabs and other heavy construction materials. Vermiculite is a group name for certain clay minerals, hydrous silicates or aluminum, magnesium and iron that have been expanded by heat.

Perlite plaster is a plaster using perlite as an aggregate instead of sand. Perlite is a volcanic glass that has been expanded by heat.

Gauging plaster is a mix of gypsum plaster and lime putty that when applied produces a quick drying finish coat.

Veneer plaster is a one or two component gypsum plaster used as a thin finish coat over special gypsum board.

Keenes cement is a white cementitious material manufactured from gypsum that has been burned at a high temperature and ground to a fine powder. Alum is added to accelerate the set. The resulting plaster is hard and strong and accepts and maintains a high polish, hence it is used as a finishing plaster.

Stucco is a Portland cement based plaster used primarily as an exterior finish.

Plaster is used on both interior and exterior surfaces. Generally it is applied in multiple-coat systems. A three-coat system uses the terms scratch, brown and finish to identify each coat. A two-coat system uses base and finish to describe each coat. Each type of plaster and application system has attributes that are chosen by the designer to best fit the intended use.

Gypsum Plaster Quantities for 100 S.Y.	2 Coat, 5/8″ Thick		3 Coat, 3/4″ Thick		
	Base	Finish	Scratch	Brown	Finish
	1:3 Mix	2:1 Mix	1:2 Mix	1:3 Mix	2:1 Mix
Gypsum plaster	1,300 lb.		1,350 lb.	650 lb.	
Sand	1.75 C.Y.		1.85 C.Y.	1.35 C.Y.	
Finish hydrated lime		340 lb.			340 lb.
Gauging plaster		170 lb.			170 lb.

Vermiculite or Perlite Plaster Quantities for 100 S.Y.	2 Coat, 5/8″ Thick		3 Coat, 3/4″ Thick		
	Base	Finish	Scratch	Brown	Finish
Gypsum plaster	1,250 lb.		1,450 lb.	800 lb.	
Vermiculite or perlite	7.8 bags		8.0 bags	3.3 bags	
Finish hydrated lime		340 lb.			340 lb.
Gauging plaster		170 lb.			170 lb.

Stucco–Three-Coat System Quantities for 100 S.Y.	On Wood Frame	On Masonry
Portland cement	29 bags	21 bags
Sand	2.6 C.Y.	2.0 C.Y.
Hydrated lime	180 lb.	120 lb.

R092910-10 Levels of Gypsum Drywall Finish

In the past, contract documents often used phrases such as "industry standard" and "workmanlike finish" to specify the expected quality of gypsum board wall and ceiling installations. The vagueness of these descriptions led to unacceptable work and disputes.

In order to resolve this problem, four major trade associations concerned with the manufacture, erection, finish and decoration of gypsum board wall and ceiling systems have developed an industry-wide *Recommended Levels of Gypsum Board Finish.*

The finish of gypsum board walls and ceilings for specific final decoration is dependent on a number of factors. A primary consideration is the location of the surface and the degree of decorative treatment desired. Painted and unpainted surfaces in warehouses and other areas where appearance is normally not critical may simply require the taping of wallboard joints and 'spotting' of fastener heads. Blemish-free, smooth, monolithic surfaces often intended for painted and decorated walls and ceilings in habitated structures, ranging from single-family dwellings through monumental buildings, require additional finishing prior to the application of the final decoration.

Other factors to be considered in determining the level of finish of the gypsum board surface are (1) the type of angle of surface illumination (both natural and artificial lighting), and (2) the paint and method of application or the type and finish of wallcovering specified as the final decoration. Critical lighting conditions, gloss paints, and thin wall coverings require a higher level of gypsum board finish than do heavily textured surfaces which are subsequently painted or surfaces which are to be decorated with heavy grade wall coverings.

The following descriptions were developed jointly by the Association of the Wall and Ceiling Industries-International (AWCI), Ceiling & Interior Systems Construction Association (CISCA), Gypsum Association (GA), and Painting and Decorating Contractors of America (PDCA) as a guide.

Level 0: Used in temporary construction or wherever the final decoration has not been determined. Unfinished. No taping, finishing or corner beads are required. Also could be used where non-predecorated panels will be used in demountable-type partitions that are to be painted as a final finish. .

Level 1: Frequently used in plenum areas above ceilings, in attics, in areas where the assembly would generally be concealed, or in building service corridors and other areas not normally open to public view. Some degree of sound and smoke control is provided; in some geographic areas, this level is referred to as "fire-taping," although this level of finish does not typically meet fire-resistant assembly requirements. Where a fire resistance rating is required for the gypsum board assembly, details of construction should be in accordance with reports of fire tests of assemblies that have met the requirements of the fire rating acceptable.

All joints and interior angles shall have tape embedded in joint compound. Accessories are optional at specifier discretion in corridors and other areas with pedestrian traffic. Tape and fastener heads need not be covered with joint compound. Surface shall be free of excess joint compound. Tool marks and ridges are acceptable.

Level 2: It may be specified for standard gypsum board surfaces in garages, warehouse storage, or other similar areas where surface appearance is not of primary importance.

All joints and interior angles shall have tape embedded in joint compound and shall be immediately wiped with a joint knife or trowel, leaving a thin coating of joint compound over all joints and interior angles. Fastener heads and accessories shall be covered with a coat of joint compound. Surface shall be free of excess joint compound. Tool marks and ridges are acceptable.

Level 3: Typically used in areas that are to receive heavy texture (spray or hand applied) finishes before final painting, or where commercial-grade (heavy duty) wall coverings are to be applied as the final decoration. This level of finish should not be used where smooth painted surfaces or where lighter weight wall coverings are specified. The prepared surface shall be coated with a drywall primer prior to the application of final finishes.

All joints and interior angles shall have tape embedded in joint compound and shall be immediately wiped with a joint knife or trowel, leaving a thin coating of joint compound over all joints and interior angles. One additional coat of joint compound shall be applied over all joints and interior angles. Fastener heads and accessories shall be covered with two separate coats of joint compound. All joint compounds shall be smooth and free of tool marks and ridges. The prepared surface shall be covered with a drywall primer prior to the application of the final decoration.

Level 4: This level should be used where residential grade (light duty) wall coverings, flat paints, or light textures are to be applied. The prepared surface shall be coated with a drywall primer prior to the application of final finishes. Release agents for wall coverings are specifically formulated to minimize damage if coverings are subsequently removed.

The weight, texture, and sheen level of the wall covering material selected should be taken into consideration when specifying wall coverings over this level of drywall treatment. Joints and fasteners must be sufficiently concealed if the wall covering material is lightweight, contains limited pattern, has a glossy finish, or has any combination of these features. In critical lighting areas, flat paints applied over light textures tend to reduce joint photographing. Gloss, semi-gloss, and enamel paints are not recommended over this level of finish.

All joints and interior angles shall have tape embedded in joint compound and shall be immediately wiped with a joint knife or trowel, leaving a thin coating of joint compound over all joints and interior angles. In addition, two separate coats of joint compound shall be applied over all flat joints and one separate coat of joint compound applied over interior angles. Fastener heads and accessories shall be covered with three separate coats of joint compound. All joint compounds shall be smooth and free of tool marks and ridges. The prepared surface shall be covered with a drywall primer like Sheetrock first coat prior to the application of the final decoration.

Level 5: The highest quality finish is the most effective method to provide a uniform surface and minimize the possibility of joint photographing and of fasteners showing through the final decoration. This level of finish is required where gloss, semi-gloss, or enamel is specified; when flat joints are specified over an untextured surface; or where critical lighting conditions occur. The prepared surface shall be coated with a drywall primer prior to the application of final decoration.

All joints and interior angles shall have tape embedded in joint compound and be immediately wiped with a joint knife or trowel, leaving a thin coating of joint compound over all joints and interior angles. Two separate coats of joint compound shall be applied over all flat joints and one separate coat of joint compound applied over interior angles. Fastener heads and accessories shall be covered with three separate coats of joint compound.

A thin skim coat of joint compound shall be trowel applied to the entire surface. Excess compound is immediately troweled off, leaving a film or skim coating of compound completely covering the paper. As an alternative to a skim coat, a material manufactured especially for this purpose may be applied such as Sheetrock Tuff-Hide primer surfacer. The surface must be smooth and free of tool marks and ridges. The prepared surface shall be covered with a drywall primer prior to the application of the final decoration.

R097223-10   Wall Covering

The table below lists the quantities required for 100 S.F. of wall covering.

Description	Medium-Priced Paper	Expensive Paper
Paper	1.6 dbl. rolls	1.6 dbl. rolls
Wall sizing	0.25 gallon	0.25 gallon
Vinyl wall paste	0.6 gallon	0.6 gallon
Apply sizing	0.3 hour	0.3 hour
Apply paper	1.2 hours	1.5 hours

Most wallpapers now come in double rolls only.
To remove old paper, allow 1.3 hours per 100 S.F.

R099100-10   Painting Estimating Techniques

Proper estimating methodology is needed to obtain an accurate painting estimate. There is no known reliable shortcut or square foot method. The following steps should be followed:

- List all surfaces to be painted, with an accurate quantity (area) of each. Items having similar surface condition, finish, application method and accessibility may be grouped together.

- List all the tasks required for each surface to be painted, including surface preparation, masking, and protection of adjacent surfaces. Surface preparation may include minor repairs, washing, sanding and puttying.

- Select the proper Means line for each task. Review and consider all adjustments to labor and materials for type of paint and location of work. Apply the height adjustment carefully. For instance, when applying the adjustment for work over 8' high to a wall that is 12' high, apply the adjustment only to the area between 8' and 12' high, and not to the entire wall.

When applying more than one percent (%) adjustment, apply each to the base cost of the data, rather than applying one percentage adjustment on top of the other.

When estimating the cost of painting walls and ceilings remember to add the brushwork for all cut-ins at inside corners and around windows and doors as a LF measure. One linear foot of cut-in with brush equals one square foot of painting.

All items for spray painting include the labor for roll-back.

Deduct for openings greater than 100 SF, or openings that extend from floor to ceiling and are greater than 5' wide. Do not deduct small openings.

The cost of brushes, rollers, ladders and spray equipment are considered to be part of a painting contractor's overhead, and should not be added to the estimate. The cost of rented equipment such as scaffolding and swing staging should be added to the estimate.

R099100-20   Painting

Item	Coat	One Gallon Covers			In 8 Hours a Laborer Covers			Labor-Hours per 100 S.F.		
		Brush	Roller	Spray	Brush	Roller	Spray	Brush	Roller	Spray
Paint wood siding	prime	250 S.F.	225 S.F.	290 S.F.	1150 S.F.	1300 S.F.	2275 S.F.	.695	.615	.351
	others	270	250	290	1300	1625	2600	.615	.492	.307
Paint exterior trim	prime	400	—	—	650	—	—	1.230	—	—
	1st	475	—	—	800	—	—	1.000	—	—
	2nd	520	—	—	975	—	—	.820	—	—
Paint shingle siding	prime	270	255	300	650	975	1950	1.230	.820	.410
	others	360	340	380	800	1150	2275	1.000	.695	.351
Stain shingle siding	1st	180	170	200	750	1125	2250	1.068	.711	.355
	2nd	270	250	290	900	1325	2600	.888	.603	.307
Paint brick masonry	prime	180	135	160	750	800	1800	1.066	1.000	.444
	1st	270	225	290	815	975	2275	.981	.820	.351
	2nd	340	305	360	815	1150	2925	.981	.695	.273
Paint interior plaster or drywall	prime	400	380	495	1150	2000	3250	.695	.400	.246
	others	450	425	495	1300	2300	4000	.615	.347	.200
Paint interior doors and windows	prime	400	—	—	650	—	—	1.230	—	—
	1st	425	—	—	800	—	—	1.000	—	—
	2nd	450	—	—	975	—	—	.820	—	—

R131113-20   Swimming Pools

Pool prices given per square foot of surface area include pool structure, filter and chlorination equipment, pumps, related piping, ladders/steps, maintenance kit, skimmer and vacuum system. Decks and electrical service to equipment are not included.

Residential in-ground pool construction can be divided into two categories: vinyl lined and gunite. Vinyl lined pool walls are constructed of different materials including wood, concrete, plastic or metal. The bottom is often graded with sand over which the vinyl liner is installed. Vermiculite or soil cement bottoms may be substituted for an added cost.

Gunite pool construction is used both in residential and municipal installations. These structures are steel reinforced for strength and finished with a white cement limestone plaster.

Municipal pools will have a higher cost because plumbing codes require more expensive materials, chlorination equipment and higher filtration rates.

Municipal pools greater than 1,800 S.F. require gutter systems to control waves. This gutter may be formed into the concrete wall. Often a vinyl/stainless steel gutter or gutter/wall system is specified, which will raise the pool cost.

Competition pools usually require tile bottoms and sides with contrasting lane striping, which will also raise the pool cost.

Plumbing   R2211 Facility Water Distribution

R221113-50 Pipe Material Considerations

1. Malleable fittings should be used for gas service.
2. Malleable fittings are used where there are stresses/strains due to expansion and vibration.
3. Cast fittings may be broken as an aid to disassembling of heating lines frozen by long use, temperature and minerals.
4. Cast iron pipe is extensively used for underground and submerged service.
5. Type M (light wall) copper tubing is available in hard temper only and is used for nonpressure and less severe applications than K and L.

6. Type L (medium wall) copper tubing, available hard or soft for interior service.
7. Type K (heavy wall) copper tubing, available in hard or soft temper for use where conditions are severe. For underground and interior service.
8. Hard drawn tubing requires fewer hangers or supports but should not be bent. Silver brazed fittings are recommended, however soft solder is normally used.
9. Type DMV (very light wall) copper tubing designed for drainage, waste and vent plus other non-critical pressure services.

Domestic/Imported Pipe and Fittings Cost

The prices shown in this publication for steel/cast iron pipe and steel, cast iron, malleable iron fittings are based on domestic production sold at the normal trade discounts. The above listed items of foreign manufacture may be available at prices of 1/3 to 1/2 those shown. Some imported items after minor machining or finishing operations are being sold as domestic to further complicate the system.

Caution: Most pipe prices in this book also include a coupling and pipe hangers which for the larger sizes can add significantly to the per foot cost and should be taken into account when comparing "book cost" with quoted supplier's cost.

Plumbing   R2240 Plumbing Fixtures

R224000-40 Plumbing Fixture Installation Time

Item	Rough-In	Set	Total Hours	Item	Rough-In	Set	Total Hours
Bathtub	5	5	10	Shower head only	2	1	3
Bathtub and shower, cast iron	6	6	12	Shower drain	3	1	4
Fire hose reel and cabinet	4	2	6	Shower stall, slate		15	15
Floor drain to 4 inch diameter	3	1	4	Slop sink	5	3	8
Grease trap, single, cast iron	5	3	8	Test 6 fixtures			14
Kitchen gas range		4	4	Urinal, wall	6	2	8
Kitchen sink, single	4	4	8	Urinal, pedestal or floor	6	4	10
Kitchen sink, double	6	6	12	Water closet and tank	4	3	7
Laundry tubs	4	2	6	Water closet and tank, wall hung	5	3	8
Lavatory wall hung	5	3	8	Water heater, 45 gals. gas, automatic	5	2	7
Lavatory pedestal	5	3	8	Water heaters, 65 gals. gas, automatic	5	2	7
Shower and stall	6	4	10	Water heaters, electric, plumbing only	4	2	6

Fixture prices in front of book are based on the cost per fixture set in place. The rough-in cost, which must be added for each fixture, includes carrier, if required, some supply, waste and vent pipe connecting fittings and stops. The lengths of rough-in pipe are nominal runs which would connect to the larger runs and stacks. The supply runs and DWV runs and stacks must be accounted for in separate entries. In the eastern half of the United States it is common for the plumber to carry these to a point 5' outside the building.

Exterior Improvements   R3292 Turf & Grasses

R329219-50 Seeding

The type of grass is determined by light, shade and moisture content of soil plus intended use. Fertilizer should be disked 4" before seeding. For steep slopes disk five tons of mulch and lay two tons of hay or straw on surface per acre after seeding. Surface mulch can be staked, lightly disked or tar emulsion sprayed. Material for mulch can be wood chips, peat moss, partially rotted hay or straw, wood fibers and sprayed emulsions. Hemp seed blankets with fertilizer are also available. For spring seeding, watering is necessary. Late fall seeding may have to be reseeded in the spring. Hydraulic seeding, power mulching, and aerial seeding can be used on large areas.

R331113-80   Piping Designations

There are several systems currently in use to describe pipe and fittings. The following paragraphs will help to identify and clarify classifications of piping systems used for water distribution.

Piping may be classified by schedule. Piping schedules include 5S, 10S, 10, 20, 30, Standard, 40, 60, Extra Strong, 80, 100, 120, 140, 160 and Double Extra Strong. These schedules are dependent upon the pipe wall thickness. The wall thickness of a particular schedule may vary with pipe size.

Ductile iron pipe for water distribution is classified by Pressure Classes such as Class 150, 200, 250, 300 and 350. These classes are actually the rated water working pressure of the pipe in pounds per square inch (psi). The pipe in these pressure classes is designed to withstand the rated water working pressure plus a surge allowance of 100 psi.

The American Water Works Association (AWWA) provides standards for various types of **plastic pipe.** C-900 is the specification for polyvinyl chloride (PVC) piping used for water distribution in sizes ranging from 4″ through 12″. C-901 is the specification for polyethylene (PE) pressure pipe, tubing and fittings used for water distribution in sizes ranging from 1/2″ through 3″. C-905 is the specification for PVC piping sizes 14″ and greater.

PVC pressure-rated pipe is identified using the standard dimensional ratio (SDR) method. This method is defined by the American Society for Testing and Materials (ASTM) Standard D 2241. This pipe is available in SDR numbers 64, 41, 32.5, 26, 21, 17, and 13.5. Pipe with an SDR of 64 will have the thinnest wall while pipe with an SDR of 13.5 will have the thickest wall. When the pressure rating (PR) of a pipe is given in psi, it is based on a line supplying water at 73 degrees F.

The National Sanitation Foundation (NSF) seal of approval is applied to products that can be used with potable water. These products have been tested to ANSI/NSF Standard 14.

Valves and strainers are classified by American National Standards Institute (ANSI) Classes. These Classes are 125, 150, 200, 250, 300, 400, 600, 900, 1500 and 2500. Within each class there is an operating pressure range dependent upon temperature. Design parameters should be compared to the appropriate material dependent, pressure-temperature rating chart for accurate valve selection.

Abbreviation	Meaning
A	Area Square Feet; Ampere
AAFES	Army and Air Force Exchange Service
ABS	Acrylonitrile Butadiene Stryrene; Asbestos Bonded Steel
A.C., AC	Alternating Current; Air-Conditioning; Asbestos Cement; Plywood Grade A & C
ACI	American Concrete Institute
ACR	Air Conditioning Refrigeration
ADA	Americans with Disabilities Act
AD	Plywood, Grade A & D
Addit.	Additional
Adj.	Adjustable
af	Audio-frequency
AFUE	Annual Fuel Utilization Efficiency
AGA	American Gas Association
Agg.	Aggregate
A.H., Ah	Ampere Hours
A hr.	Ampere-hour
A.H.U., AHU	Air Handling Unit
A.I.A.	American Institute of Architects
AIC	Ampere Interrupting Capacity
Allow.	Allowance
alt., alt	Alternate
Alum.	Aluminum
a.m.	Ante Meridiem
Amp.	Ampere
Anod.	Anodized
ANSI	American National Standards Institute
APA	American Plywood Association
Approx.	Approximate
Apt.	Apartment
Asb.	Asbestos
A.S.B.C.	American Standard Building Code
Asbe.	Asbestos Worker
ASCE.	American Society of Civil Engineers
A.S.H.R.A.E.	American Society of Heating, Refrig. & AC Engineers
ASME	American Society of Mechanical Engineers
ASTM	American Society for Testing and Materials
Attchmt.	Attachment
Avg., Ave.	Average
AWG	American Wire Gauge
AWWA	American Water Works Assoc.
Bbl.	Barrel
B&B, BB	Grade B and Better; Balled & Burlapped
B&S	Bell and Spigot
B.&W.	Black and White
b.c.c.	Body-centered Cubic
B.C.Y.	Bank Cubic Yards
BE	Bevel End
B.F.	Board Feet
Bg. cem.	Bag of Cement
BHP	Boiler Horsepower; Brake Horsepower
B.I.	Black Iron
bidir.	bidirectional
Bit., Bitum.	Bituminous
Bit., Conc.	Bituminous Concrete
Bk.	Backed
Bkrs.	Breakers
Bldg., bldg	Building
Blk.	Block
Bm.	Beam
Boil.	Boilermaker
bpm	Blows per Minute
BR	Bedroom
Brg.	Bearing
Brhe.	Bricklayer Helper
Bric.	Bricklayer
Brk., brk	Brick
brkt	Bracket
Brng.	Bearing
Brs.	Brass
Brz.	Bronze
Bsn.	Basin
Btr.	Better
Btu	British Thermal Unit
BTUH	BTU per Hour
Bu.	bushels
BUR	Built-up Roofing
BX	Interlocked Armored Cable
°C	degree centegrade
c	Conductivity, Copper Sweat
C	Hundred; Centigrade
C/C	Center to Center, Cedar on Cedar
C-C	Center to Center
Cab	Cabinet
Cair.	Air Tool Laborer
Cal.	caliper
Calc	Calculated
Cap.	Capacity
Carp.	Carpenter
C.B.	Circuit Breaker
C.C.A.	Chromate Copper Arsenate
C.C.F.	Hundred Cubic Feet
cd	Candela
cd/sf	Candela per Square Foot
CD	Grade of Plywood Face & Back
CDX	Plywood, Grade C & D, exterior glue
Cefi.	Cement Finisher
Cem.	Cement
CF	Hundred Feet
C.F.	Cubic Feet
CFM	Cubic Feet per Minute
CFRP	Carbon Fiber Reinforced Plastic
c.g.	Center of Gravity
CHW	Chilled Water; Commercial Hot Water
C.I., CI	Cast Iron
C.I.P., CIP	Cast in Place
Circ.	Circuit
C.L.	Carload Lot
CL	Chain Link
Clab.	Common Laborer
Clam	Common maintenance laborer
C.L.F.	Hundred Linear Feet
CLF	Current Limiting Fuse
CLP	Cross Linked Polyethylene
cm	Centimeter
CMP	Corr. Metal Pipe
CMU	Concrete Masonry Unit
CN	Change Notice
Col.	Column
CO_2	Carbon Dioxide
Comb.	Combination
comm.	Commercial, Communication
Compr.	Compressor
Conc.	Concrete
Cont., cont	Continuous; Continued, Container
Corr.	Corrugated
Cos	Cosine
Cot	Cotangent
Cov.	Cover
C/P	Cedar on Paneling
CPA	Control Point Adjustment
Cplg.	Coupling
CPM	Critical Path Method
CPVC	Chlorinated Polyvinyl Chloride
C.Pr.	Hundred Pair
CRC	Cold Rolled Channel
Creos.	Creosote
Crpt.	Carpet & Linoleum Layer
CRT	Cathode-ray Tube
CS	Carbon Steel, Constant Shear Bar Joist
Csc	Cosecant
C.S.F.	Hundred Square Feet
CSI	Construction Specifications Institute
CT	Current Transformer
CTS	Copper Tube Size
Cu	Copper, Cubic
Cu. Ft.	Cubic Foot
cw	Continuous Wave
C.W.	Cool White; Cold Water
Cwt.	100 Pounds
C.W.X.	Cool White Deluxe
C.Y.	Cubic Yard (27 cubic feet)
C.Y./Hr.	Cubic Yard per Hour
Cyl.	Cylinder
d	Penny (nail size)
D	Deep; Depth; Discharge
Dis., Disch.	Discharge
Db	Decibel
Dbl.	Double
DC	Direct Current
DDC	Direct Digital Control
Demob.	Demobilization
d.f.t.	Dry Film Thickness
d.f.u.	Drainage Fixture Units
D.H.	Double Hung
DHW	Domestic Hot Water
DI	Ductile Iron
Diag.	Diagonal
Diam., Dia	Diameter
Distrib.	Distribution
Div.	Division
Dk.	Deck
D.L.	Dead Load; Diesel
DLH	Deep Long Span Bar Joist
dlx	Deluxe
Do.	Ditto
DOP	Dioctyl Phthalate Penetration Test (Air Filters)
Dp., dp	Depth
D.P.S.T.	Double Pole, Single Throw
Dr.	Drive
DR	Dimension Ratio
Drink.	Drinking
D.S.	Double Strength
D.S.A.	Double Strength A Grade
D.S.B.	Double Strength B Grade
Dty.	Duty
DWV	Drain Waste Vent
DX	Deluxe White, Direct Expansion
dyn	Dyne
e	Eccentricity
E	Equipment Only; East; emissivity
Ea.	Each
EB	Encased Burial
Econ.	Economy
E.C.Y	Embankment Cubic Yards
EDP	Electronic Data Processing
EIFS	Exterior Insulation Finish System
E.D.R.	Equiv. Direct Radiation
Eq.	Equation
EL	elevation
Elec.	Electrician; Electrical
Elev.	Elevator; Elevating
EMT	Electrical Metallic Conduit; Thin Wall Conduit
Eng.	Engine, Engineered
EPDM	Ethylene Propylene Diene Monomer
EPS	Expanded Polystyrene
Eqhv.	Equip. Oper., Heavy
Eqlt.	Equip. Oper., Light
Eqmd.	Equip. Oper., Medium
Eqmm.	Equip. Oper., Master Mechanic
Eqol.	Equip. Oper., Oilers
Equip.	Equipment
ERW	Electric Resistance Welded

E.S.	Energy Saver	H	High Henry
Est.	Estimated	HC	High Capacity
esu	Electrostatic Units	H.D., HD	Heavy Duty; High Density
E.W.	Each Way	H.D.O.	High Density Overlaid
EWT	Entering Water Temperature	HDPE	High density polyethelene plastic
Excav.	Excavation	Hdr.	Header
excl	Excluding	Hdwe.	Hardware
Exp., exp	Expansion, Exposure	H.I.D., HID	High Intensity Discharge
Ext., ext	Exterior; Extension	Help.	Helper Average
Extru.	Extrusion	HEPA	High Efficiency Particulate Air Filter
f.	Fiber stress	Hg	Mercury
F	Fahrenheit; Female; Fill	HIC	High Interrupting Capacity
Fab., fab	Fabricated; fabric	HM	Hollow Metal
FBGS	Fiberglass	HMWPE	high molecular weight polyethylene
F.C.	Footcandles	HO	High Output
f.c.c.	Face-centered Cubic	Horiz.	Horizontal
f'c.	Compressive Stress in Concrete; Extreme Compressive Stress	H.P., HP	Horsepower; High Pressure
F.E.	Front End	H.P.F.	High Power Factor
FEP	Fluorinated Ethylene Propylene (Teflon)	Hr.	Hour
F.G.	Flat Grain	Hrs./Day	Hours per Day
F.H.A.	Federal Housing Administration	HSC	High Short Circuit
Fig.	Figure	Ht.	Height
Fin.	Finished	Htg.	Heating
FIPS	Female Iron Pipe Size	Htrs.	Heaters
Fixt.	Fixture	HVAC	Heating, Ventilation & Air-Conditioning
FJP	Finger jointed and primed	Hvy.	Heavy
Fl. Oz.	Fluid Ounces	HW	Hot Water
Flr.	Floor	Hyd.; Hydr.	Hydraulic
FM	Frequency Modulation; Factory Mutual	Hz	Hertz (cycles)
Fmg.	Framing	I.	Moment of Inertia
FM/UL	Factory Mutual/Underwriters Labs	IBC	International Building Code
Fdn.	Foundation	I.C.	Interrupting Capacity
FNPT	Female National Pipe Thread	ID	Inside Diameter
Fori.	Foreman, Inside	I.D.	Inside Dimension; Identification
Foro.	Foreman, Outside	I.F.	Inside Frosted
Fount.	Fountain	I.M.C.	Intermediate Metal Conduit
fpm	Feet per Minute	In.	Inch
FPT	Female Pipe Thread	Incan.	Incandescent
Fr	Frame	Incl.	Included; Including
F.R.	Fire Rating	Int.	Interior
FRK	Foil Reinforced Kraft	Inst.	Installation
FSK	Foil/scrim/kraft	Insul., insul	Insulation/Insulated
FRP	Fiberglass Reinforced Plastic	I.P.	Iron Pipe
FS	Forged Steel	I.P.S., IPS	Iron Pipe Size
FSC	Cast Body; Cast Switch Box	IPT	Iron Pipe Threaded
Ft., ft	Foot; Feet	I.W.	Indirect Waste
Ftng.	Fitting	J	Joule
Ftg.	Footing	J.I.C.	Joint Industrial Council
Ft lb.	Foot Pound	K	Thousand; Thousand Pounds; Heavy Wall Copper Tubing, Kelvin
Furn.	Furniture	K.A.H.	Thousand Amp. Hours
FVNR	Full Voltage Non-Reversing	kcmil	Thousand Circular Mils
FVR	Full Voltage Reversing	KD	Knock Down
FXM	Female by Male	K.D.A.T.	Kiln Dried After Treatment
Fy.	Minimum Yield Stress of Steel	kg	Kilogram
g	Gram	kG	Kilogauss
G	Gauss	kgf	Kilogram Force
Ga.	Gauge	kHz	Kilohertz
Gal., gal.	Gallon	Kip	1000 Pounds
gpm, GPM	Gallon per Minute	KJ	Kiljoule
Galv., galv	Galvanized	K.L.	Effective Length Factor
GC/MS	Gas Chromatograph/Mass Spectrometer	K.L.F.	Kips per Linear Foot
Gen.	General	Km	Kilometer
GFI	Ground Fault Interrupter	KO	Knock Out
GFRC	Glass Fiber Reinforced Concrete	K.S.F.	Kips per Square Foot
Glaz.	Glazier	K.S.I.	Kips per Square Inch
GPD	Gallons per Day	kV	Kilovolt
gpf	Gallon per flush	kVA	Kilovolt Ampere
GPH	Gallons per Hour	kVAR	Kilovar (Reactance)
GPM	Gallons per Minute	KW	Kilowatt
GR	Grade	KWh	Kilowatt-hour
Gran.	Granular	L	Labor Only; Length; Long; Medium Wall Copper Tubing
Grnd.	Ground	Lab.	Labor
GVW	Gross Vehicle Weight	lat	Latitude
GWB	Gypsum wall board		

Lath.	Lather
Lav.	Lavatory
lb.; #	Pound
L.B., LB	Load Bearing; L Conduit Body
L. & E.	Labor & Equipment
lb./hr.	Pounds per Hour
lb./L.F.	Pounds per Linear Foot
lbf/sq.in.	Pound-force per Square Inch
L.C.L.	Less than Carload Lot
L.C.Y.	Loose Cubic Yard
Ld.	Load
LE	Lead Equivalent
LED	Light Emitting Diode
L.F.	Linear Foot
L.F. Nose	Linear Foot of Stair Nosing
L.F. Rsr	Linear Foot of Stair Riser
Lg.	Long; Length; Large
L & H	Light and Heat
LH	Long Span Bar Joist
L.H.	Labor Hours
L.L., LL	Live Load
L.L.D.	Lamp Lumen Depreciation
lm	Lumen
lm/sf	Lumen per Square Foot
lm/W	Lumen per Watt
LOA	Length Over All
log	Logarithm
L-O-L	Lateralolet
long.	longitude
L.P., LP	Liquefied Petroleum; Low Pressure
L.P.F.	Low Power Factor
LR	Long Radius
L.S.	Lump Sum
Lt.	Light
Lt. Ga.	Light Gauge
L.T.L.	Less than Truckload Lot
Lt. Wt.	Lightweight
L.V.	Low Voltage
M	Thousand; Material; Male; Light Wall Copper Tubing
M^2CA	Meters Squared Contact Area
m/hr.; M.H.	Man-hour
mA	Milliampere
Mach.	Machine
Mag. Str.	Magnetic Starter
Maint.	Maintenance
Marb.	Marble Setter
Mat; Mat'l.	Material
Max.	Maximum
MBF	Thousand Board Feet
MBH	Thousand BTU's per hr.
MC	Metal Clad Cable
MCC	Motor Control Center
M.C.F.	Thousand Cubic Feet
MCFM	Thousand Cubic Feet per Minute
M.C.M.	Thousand Circular Mils
MCP	Motor Circuit Protector
MD	Medium Duty
MDF	Medium-density fibreboard
M.D.O.	Medium Density Overlaid
Med.	Medium
MF	Thousand Feet
M.F.B.M.	Thousand Feet Board Measure
Mfg.	Manufacturing
Mfrs.	Manufacturers
mg	Milligram
MGD	Million Gallons per Day
MGPH	Thousand Gallons per Hour
MH, M.H.	Manhole; Metal Halide; Man-Hour
MHz	Megahertz
Mi.	Mile
MI	Malleable Iron; Mineral Insulated
MIPS	Male Iron Pipe Size
mj	Mechanical Joint
m	Meter
mm	Millimeter
Mill.	Millwright
Min., min.	Minimum, minute

Abbreviations

Misc.	Miscellaneous	PDCA	Painting and Decorating Contractors of America	SC	Screw Cover
ml	Milliliter, Mainline			SCFM	Standard Cubic Feet per Minute
M.L.F.	Thousand Linear Feet	P.E., PE	Professional Engineer; Porcelain Enamel; Polyethylene; Plain End	Scaf.	Scaffold
Mo.	Month			Sch., Sched.	Schedule
Mobil.	Mobilization			S.C.R.	Modular Brick
Mog.	Mogul Base	P.E.C.I.	Porcelain Enamel on Cast Iron	S.D.	Sound Deadening
MPH	Miles per Hour	Perf.	Perforated	SDR	Standard Dimension Ratio
MPT	Male Pipe Thread	PEX	Cross linked polyethylene	S.E.	Surfaced Edge
MRGWB	Moisture Resistant Gypsum Wallboard	Ph.	Phase	Sel, SEU	Select
		P.I.	Pressure Injected	SER, SEU	Service Entrance Cable
MRT	Mile Round Trip	Pile.	Pile Driver	S.F.	Square Foot
ms	Millisecond	Pkg.	Package	S.F.C.A.	Square Foot Contact Area
M.S.F.	Thousand Square Feet	Pl.	Plate	S.F. Flr.	Square Foot of Floor
Mstz.	Mosaic & Terrazzo Worker	Plah.	Plasterer Helper	S.F.G.	Square Foot of Ground
M.S.Y.	Thousand Square Yards	Plas.	Plasterer	S.F. Hor.	Square Foot Horizontal
Mtd., mtd, mtd	Mounted	plf	Pounds Per Linear Foot	SFR	Square Feet of Radiation
Mthe.	Mosaic & Terrazzo Helper	Pluh.	Plumbers Helper	S.F. Shlf.	Square Foot of Shelf
Mtng.	Mounting	Plum.	Plumber	S4S	Surface 4 Sides
Mult.	Multi; Multiply	Ply.	Plywood	Shee.	Sheet Metal Worker
M.V.A.	Million Volt Amperes	p.m.	Post Meridiem	Sin.	Sine
M.V.A.R.	Million Volt Amperes Reactance	Pntd.	Painted	Skwk.	Skilled Worker
MV	Megavolt	Pord.	Painter, Ordinary	SL	Saran Lined
MW	Megawatt	pp	Pages	S.L.	Slimline
MXM	Male by Male	PP, PPL	Polypropylene	Sldr.	Solder
MYD	Thousand Yards	P.P.M.	Parts per Million	SLH	Super Long Span Bar Joist
N	Natural; North	Pr.	Pair	S.N.	Solid Neutral
nA	Nanoampere	P.E.S.B.	Pre-engineered Steel Building	SO	Stranded with oil resistant inside insulation
NA	Not Available; Not Applicable	Prefab.	Prefabricated		
N.B.C.	National Building Code	Prefin.	Prefinished	S-O-L	Socketolet
NC	Normally Closed	Prop.	Propelled	sp	Standpipe
NEMA	National Electrical Manufacturers Assoc.	PSF, psf	Pounds per Square Foot	S.P.	Static Pressure; Single Pole; Self-Propelled
		PSI, psi	Pounds per Square Inch		
NEHB	Bolted Circuit Breaker to 600V.	PSIG	Pounds per Square Inch Gauge	Spri.	Sprinkler Installer
NFPA	National Fire Protection Association	PSP	Plastic Sewer Pipe	spwg	Static Pressure Water Gauge
NLB	Non-Load-Bearing	Pspr.	Painter, Spray	S.P.D.T.	Single Pole, Double Throw
NM	Non-Metallic Cable	Psst.	Painter, Structural Steel	SPF	Spruce Pine Fir; Sprayed Polyurethane Foam
nm	Nanometer	P.T.	Potential Transformer		
No.	Number	P. & T.	Pressure & Temperature	S.P.S.T.	Single Pole, Single Throw
NO	Normally Open	Ptd.	Painted	SPT	Standard Pipe Thread
N.O.C.	Not Otherwise Classified	Ptns.	Partitions	Sq.	Square; 100 Square Feet
Nose.	Nosing	Pu	Ultimate Load	Sq. Hd.	Square Head
NPT	National Pipe Thread	PVC	Polyvinyl Chloride	Sq. In.	Square Inch
NQOD	Combination Plug-on/Bolt on Circuit Breaker to 240V.	Pvmt.	Pavement	S.S.	Single Strength; Stainless Steel
		PRV	Pressure Relief Valve	S.S.B.	Single Strength B Grade
N.R.C., NRC	Noise Reduction Coefficient/ Nuclear Regulator Commission	Pwr.	Power	sst, ss	Stainless Steel
		Q	Quantity Heat Flow	Sswk.	Structural Steel Worker
N.R.S.	Non Rising Stem	Qt.	Quart	Sswl.	Structural Steel Welder
ns	Nanosecond	Quan., Qty.	Quantity	St.; Stl.	Steel
nW	Nanowatt	Q.C.	Quick Coupling	STC	Sound Transmission Coefficient
OB	Opposing Blade	r	Radius of Gyration	Std.	Standard
OC	On Center	R	Resistance	Stg.	Staging
OD	Outside Diameter	R.C.P.	Reinforced Concrete Pipe	STK	Select Tight Knot
O.D.	Outside Dimension	Rect.	Rectangle	STP	Standard Temperature & Pressure
ODS	Overhead Distribution System	recpt.	receptacle	Stpi.	Steamfitter, Pipefitter
O.G.	Ogee	Reg.	Regular	Str.	Strength; Starter; Straight
O.H.	Overhead	Reinf.	Reinforced	Strd.	Stranded
O&P	Overhead and Profit	Req'd.	Required	Struct.	Structural
Oper.	Operator	Res.	Resistant	Sty.	Story
Opng.	Opening	Resi.	Residential	Subj.	Subject
Orna.	Ornamental	RF	Radio Frequency	Subs.	Subcontractors
OSB	Oriented Strand Board	RFID	Radio-frequency identification	Surf.	Surface
OS&Y	Outside Screw and Yoke	Rgh.	Rough	Sw.	Switch
OSHA	Occupational Safety and Health Act	RGS	Rigid Galvanized Steel	Swbd.	Switchboard
		RHW	Rubber, Heat & Water Resistant; Residential Hot Water	S.Y.	Square Yard
Ovhd.	Overhead			Syn.	Synthetic
OWG	Oil, Water or Gas	rms	Root Mean Square	S.Y.P.	Southern Yellow Pine
Oz.	Ounce	Rnd.	Round	Sys.	System
P.	Pole; Applied Load; Projection	Rodm.	Rodman	t.	Thickness
p.	Page	Rofc.	Roofer, Composition	T	Temperature; Ton
Pape.	Paperhanger	Rofp.	Roofer, Precast	Tan	Tangent
P.A.P.R.	Powered Air Purifying Respirator	Rohe.	Roofer Helpers (Composition)	T.C.	Terra Cotta
PAR	Parabolic Reflector	Rots.	Roofer, Tile & Slate	T & C	Threaded and Coupled
P.B., PB	Push Button	R.O.W.	Right of Way	T.D.	Temperature Difference
Pc., Pcs.	Piece, Pieces	RPM	Revolutions per Minute	Tdd	Telecommunications Device for the Deaf
P.C.	Portland Cement; Power Connector	R.S.	Rapid Start		
P.C.F.	Pounds per Cubic Foot	Rsr	Riser	T.E.M.	Transmission Electron Microscopy
PCM	Phase Contrast Microscopy	RT	Round Trip	temp	Temperature, Tempered, Temporary
		S.	Suction; Single Entrance; South	TFFN	Nylon Jacketed Wire
		SBS	Styrene Butadiere Styrene		

Abbreviations

TFE	Tetrafluoroethylene (Teflon)	U.L., UL	Underwriters Laboratory	w/	With
T. & G.	Tongue & Groove;	Uld.	unloading	W.C., WC	Water Column; Water Closet
	Tar & Gravel	Unfin.	Unfinished	W.F.	Wide Flange
Th., Thk.	Thick	UPS	Uninterruptible Power Supply	W.G.	Water Gauge
Thn.	Thin	URD	Underground Residential	Wldg.	Welding
Thrded	Threaded		Distribution	W. Mile	Wire Mile
Tilf.	Tile Layer, Floor	US	United States	W-O-L	Weldolet
Tilh.	Tile Layer, Helper	USGBC	U.S. Green Building Council	W.R.	Water Resistant
THHN	Nylon Jacketed Wire	USP	United States Primed	Wrck.	Wrecker
THW.	Insulated Strand Wire	UTMCD	Uniform Traffic Manual For Control	W.S.P.	Water, Steam, Petroleum
THWN	Nylon Jacketed Wire		Devices	WT., Wt.	Weight
T.L., TL	Truckload	UTP	Unshielded Twisted Pair	WWF	Welded Wire Fabric
T.M.	Track Mounted	V	Volt	XFER	Transfer
Tot.	Total	VA	Volt Amperes	XFMR	Transformer
T-O-L	Threadolet	V.C.T.	Vinyl Composition Tile	XHD	Extra Heavy Duty
tmpd	Tempered	VAV	Variable Air Volume	XHHW,	Cross-Linked Polyethylene Wire
TPO	Thermoplastic Polyolefin	VC	Veneer Core	XLPE	Insulation
T.S.	Trigger Start	VDC	Volts Direct Current	XLP	Cross-linked Polyethylene
Tr.	Trade	Vent.	Ventilation	Xport	Transport
Transf.	Transformer	Vert.	Vertical	Y	Wye
Trhv.	Truck Driver, Heavy	V.F.	Vinyl Faced	yd	Yard
Trlr	Trailer	V.G.	Vertical Grain	yr	Year
Trlt.	Truck Driver, Light	VHF	Very High Frequency	Δ	Delta
TTY	Teletypewriter	VHO	Very High Output	%	Percent
TV	Television	Vib.	Vibrating	~	Approximately
T.W.	Thermoplastic Water Resistant	VLF	Vertical Linear Foot	Ø	Phase; diameter
	Wire	VOC	Volitile Organic Compound	@	At
UCI	Uniform Construction Index	Vol.	Volume	#	Pound; Number
UF	Underground Feeder	VRP	Vinyl Reinforced Polyester	<	Less Than
UGND	Underground Feeder	W	Wire; Watt; Wide; West	>	Greater Than
UHF	Ultra High Frequency			Z	zone
U.I.	United Inch				

RESIDENTIAL COST ESTIMATE

OWNER'S NAME: _____   APPRAISER: _____

RESIDENCE ADDRESS: _____   PROJECT: _____

CITY, STATE, ZIP CODE: _____   DATE: _____

CLASS OF CONSTRUCTION	RESIDENCE TYPE	CONFIGURATION	EXTERIOR WALL SYSTEM
☐ ECONOMY	☐ 1 STORY	☐ DETACHED	☐ WOOD SIDING—WOOD FRAME
☐ AVERAGE	☐ 1-1/2 STORY	☐ TOWN/ROW HOUSE	☐ BRICK VENEER—WOOD FRAME
☐ CUSTOM	☐ 2 STORY	☐ SEMI-DETACHED	☐ STUCCO ON WOOD FRAME
☐ LUXURY	☐ 2-1/2 STORY		☐ PAINTED CONCRETE BLOCK
	☐ 3 STORY	OCCUPANCY	☐ SOLID MASONRY (AVERAGE & CUSTOM)
	☐ BI-LEVEL	☐ ONE STORY	☐ STONE VENEER—WOOD FRAME
	☐ TRI-LEVEL	☐ TWO FAMILY	☐ SOLID BRICK (LUXURY)
		☐ THREE FAMILY	☐ SOLID STONE (LUXURY)
		☐ OTHER _____	

*LIVING AREA (Main Building)

First Level	_____	S.F.
Second Level	_____	S.F.
Third Level	_____	S.F.
Total	_____	S.F.

*LIVING AREA (Wing or Ell) (   )

First Level	_____	S.F.
Second Level	_____	S.F.
Third Level	_____	S.F.
Total	_____	S.F.

*LIVING AREA (Wing or Ell) (   )

First Level	_____	S.F.
Second Level	_____	S.F.
Third Level	_____	S.F.
Total	_____	S.F.

*Basement Area is not part of living area.

MAIN BUILDING	COSTS PER S.F. LIVING AREA
Cost per Square Foot of Living Area, from Page _____	$
Basement Addition: _____ % Finished, _____ % Unfinished	+
Roof Cover Adjustment: _____ Type, Page _____ (Add or Deduct)	( )
Central Air Conditioning: ☐ Separate Ducts ☐ Heating Ducts, Page _____	+
Heating System Adjustment: _____ Type, Page _____ (Add or Deduct)	( )
Main Building: Adjusted Cost per S.F. of Living Area	$

MAIN BUILDING TOTAL COST $ _____ /S.F.   x   _____ S.F.   x   _____   = $ _____

Cost per S.F. Living Area   Living Area   Town/Row House Multiplier (Use 1 for Detached)   TOTAL COST

WING OR ELL ( ) _____ STORY	COSTS PER S.F. LIVING AREA
Cost per Square Foot of Living Area, from Page _____	$
Basement Addition: _____ % Finished, _____ % Unfinished	+
Roof Cover Adjustment: _____ Type, Page _____ (Add or Deduct)	( )
Central Air Conditioning: ☐ Separate Ducts ☐ Heating Ducts, Page _____	+
Heating System Adjustment: _____ Type, Page _____ (Add or Deduct)	( )
Wing or Ell ( ): Adjusted Cost per S.F. of Living Area	$

WING OR ELL (   ) TOTAL COST $ _____ /S.F.   x   _____ S.F.   = $ _____

Cost per S.F. Living Area   Living Area   TOTAL COST

WING OR ELL ( ) _____ STORY	COSTS PER S.F. LIVING AREA
Cost per Square Foot of Living Area, from Page _____	$
Basement Addition: _____ % Finished, _____ % Unfinished	+
Roof Cover Adjustment: _____ Type, Page _____ (Add or Deduct)	( )
Central Air Conditioning: ☐ Separate Ducts ☐ Heating Ducts, Page _____	+
Heating System Adjustment: _____ Type, Page _____ (Add or Deduct)	( )
Wing or Ell ( ): Adjusted Cost per S.F. of Living Area	$

WING OR ELL (   ) TOTAL COST $ _____ /S.F.   x   _____ S.F.   = $ _____

Cost per S.F. Living Area   Living Area   TOTAL COST

TOTAL THIS PAGE   [_____]

**RESIDENTIAL
COST ESTIMATE**

Total Page 1			$
	QUANTITY	UNIT COST	
Additional Bathrooms: _____ Full, _____ Half			
Finished Attic: _____ Ft. x _____ Ft.	S.F.		+
Breezeway: ☐ Open ☐ Enclosed _____ Ft. x _____ Ft.	S.F.		+
Covered Porch: ☐ Open ☐ Enclosed _____ Ft. x _____ Ft.	S.F.		+
Fireplace: ☐ Interior Chimney ☐ Exterior Chimney ☐ No. of Flues ☐ Additional Fireplaces			+
Appliances:			+
Kitchen Cabinets Adjustment: (+/−)			
☐ Garage ☐ Carport: _____ Car(s) Description _____ (+/−)			
Miscellaneous:			+

ADJUSTED TOTAL BUILDING COST $ _____

REPLACEMENT COST	
ADJUSTED TOTAL BUILDING COST	$ _____
Site Improvements	
(A) Paving & Sidewalks	$ _____
(B) Landscaping	$ _____
(C) Fences	$ _____
(D) Swimming Pool	$ _____
(E) Miscellaneous	$ _____
TOTAL	$ _____
Location Factor	x _____
Location Replacement Cost	$ _____
Depreciation	−$ _____
LOCAL DEPRECIATED COST	$ _____

INSURANCE COST	
ADJUSTED TOTAL BUILDING COST	$ _____
Insurance Exclusions	
(A) Footings, Site Work, Underground Piping	−$ _____
(B) Architects' Fees	−$ _____
Total Building Cost Less Exclusion	$ _____
Location Factor	x _____
LOCAL INSURABLE REPLACEMENT COST	$ _____

SKETCH AND ADDITIONAL CALCULATIONS

Index

Index

Index

X

Y

Z

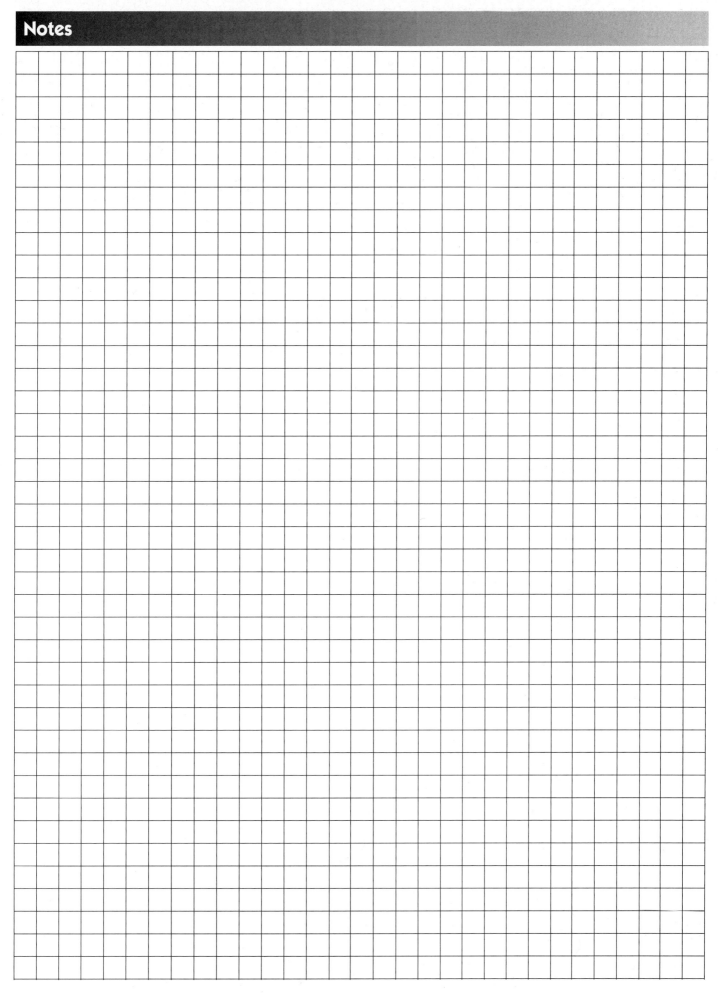

Division Notes

	CREW	DAILY OUTPUT	LABOR-HOURS	UNIT	BARE COSTS				TOTAL INCL O&P
					MAT.	LABOR	EQUIP.	TOTAL	

Division Notes

	CREW	DAILY OUTPUT	LABOR-HOURS	UNIT	BARE COSTS				TOTAL INCL O&P
					MAT.	LABOR	EQUIP.	TOTAL	

Division Notes

	CREW	DAILY OUTPUT	LABOR-HOURS	UNIT	BARE COSTS				TOTAL INCL O&P
					MAT.	LABOR	EQUIP.	TOTAL	

Division Notes

	CREW	DAILY OUTPUT	LABOR-HOURS	UNIT	BARE COSTS				TOTAL INCL O&P
					MAT.	LABOR	EQUIP.	TOTAL	

Table of Contents
Annual Cost Guides
Seminars
New Titles
Reference Books
Order Form

Reed Construction Data/RSMeans—
a tradition of excellence in construction cost information and services since 1942

For more information visit the RSMeans website at **www.rsmeans.com**

Unit prices according to the latest MasterFormat!

Book Selection Guide

The following table provides definitive information on the content of each cost data publication. The number of lines of data provided in each unit price or assemblies division, as well as the number of reference tables and crews, is listed for each book. The presence of other elements such as equipment rental costs, historical cost indexes, city cost indexes, square foot models, or cross-referenced indexes is also indicated. You can use the table to help select the RSMeans book that has the quantity and type of information you most need in your work.

Unit Cost Divisions	Building Construction	Mechanical	Electrical	Commercial Renovation	Square Foot	Site Work Landsc.	Green Building	Interior	Concrete Masonry	Open Shop	Heavy Construction	Light Commercial	Facilities Construction	Plumbing	Residential
1	582	395	411	508		521	196	319	463	581	511	244	1054	411	180
2	789	279	85	741		1005	180	399	222	788	746	481	1233	289	257
3	1689	347	231	1087		1477	995	329	2040	1688	1685	479	1787	317	385
4	963	21	0	932		729	179	620	1159	931	621	521	1176	0	435
5	1873	158	155	1068		811	1779	1073	716	1873	1034	954	1874	204	723
6	2404	18	18	2062		110	560	1523	278	2400	126	2085	2076	22	2612
7	1531	215	128	1569		584	747	516	509	1528	26	1282	1633	227	1018
8	2107	81	45	2530		268	1140	1768	112	2093	0	2109	2842	0	1511
9	1929	72	26	1726		313	449	2014	387	1870	15	1644	2179	54	1430
10	1006	17	10	623		215	27	818	158	1006	29	511	1098	235	224
11	1026	208	165	489		126	54	878	28	1010	0	230	1046	169	110
12	557	0	2	327		248	151	1669	12	545	19	364	1718	23	317
13	729	117	114	246		347	128	253	66	728	253	82	756	71	80
14	277	36	0	224		0	0	261	0	277	0	12	297	16	6
21	90	0	16	37		0	0	250	0	87	0	68	427	432	220
22	1159	7329	156	1170		1578	1099	849	20	1123	1687	861	7171	9082	712
23	1182	6901	586	886		160	898	741	38	1106	111	759	5013	1830	434
26	1379	499	10134	1039		816	661	1142	55	1351	562	1305	10083	444	621
27	72	0	298	34		13	0	60	0	72	39	52	280	0	4
28	97	58	137	72		0	21	79	0	100	0	41	152	44	26
31	1498	735	610	803		3206	289	7	1208	1443	3285	600	1560	660	611
32	782	54	8	859		4396	352	362	286	753	1824	407	1660	166	455
33	509	1020	542	209		2036	41	0	231	508	2024	120	1585	1211	118
34	109	0	47	4		192	0	0	31	64	195	0	130	0	0
35	18	0	0	0		327	0	0	0	18	442	0	83	0	0
41	60	0	0	32		0	0	22	0	60	30	0	67	14	0
44	75	83	0	0		0	0	0	0	0	0	0	75	75	0
46	23	16	0	0		274	151	0	0	23	264	0	33	33	0
48	12	0	27	0		0	27	0	0	12	19	12	12	0	12
Totals	24527	18659	13951	19277		19752	10124	15952	8019	24038	15547	15223	49100	16029	12501

Assem Div	Building Construction	Mechanical	Electrical	Commercial Renovation	Square Foot	Site Work Landscape	Assemblies	Green Building	Interior	Concrete Masonry	Heavy Construction	Light Commercial	Facilities Construction	Plumbing	Asm Div	Residential
A		15	0	188	150	577	598	0	0	536	571	154	24	0	1	368
B		0	0	848	2498	0	5658	56	329	1975	368	2089	174	0	2	211
C		0	0	647	872	0	1251	0	1576	146	0	762	249	0	3	588
D		1067	943	712	1856	72	2532	330	822	0	0	1342	1106	1081	4	851
E		0	0	86	260	0	300	0	5	0	0	257	5	0	5	392
F		0	0	0	114	0	114	0	0	0	0	114	3	0	6	357
G		522	442	318	262	3740	663	0	0	534	1558	199	288	758	7	307
															8	760
															9	80
															10	0
															11	0
															12	0
Totals		1604	1385	2799	6012	4389	11116	386	2732	3191	2497	4917	1849	1839		3914

Reference Section	Building Construction Costs	Mechanical	Electrical	Commercial Renovation	Square Foot	Site Work Landscape	Assem.	Green Building	Interior	Concrete Masonry	Open Shop	Heavy Construction	Light Commercial	Facilities Construction	Plumbing	Resi.
Reference Tables	yes	yes	yes	yes	no	yes	yes	yes	yes	yes	yes	yes	yes	yes	yes	yes
Models					111			25					50			28
Crews	561	561	561	540		561		558	561	561	538	561	538	540	561	538
Equipment Rental Costs	yes	yes	yes	yes		yes		yes	yes	yes	yes	yes	yes	yes	yes	yes
Historical Cost Indexes	yes	yes	yes	yes	yes	yes	yes	yes	yes	yes	yes	yes	yes	yes	yes	no
City Cost Indexes	yes	yes	yes	yes	yes	yes	yes	yes	yes	yes	yes	yes	yes	yes	yes	yes

760

RSMeans Electrical Cost Data 2014

Pricing information for every part of electrical cost planning. More than 13,000 unit and systems costs with design tables; clear specifications and drawings; engineering guides; illustrated estimating procedures; complete labor-hour and materials costs for better scheduling and procurement; and the latest electrical products and construction methods.

- A variety of special electrical systems, including cathodic protection
- Costs for maintenance, demolition, HVAC/mechanical, specialties, equipment, and more

$196.95 | Available Oct. 2013 | Catalog no. 60034

RSMeans Assemblies Cost Data 2014

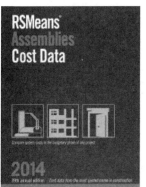

RSMeans Assemblies Cost Data takes the guesswork out of preliminary or conceptual estimates. Now you don't have to try to calculate the assembled cost by working up individual component costs. We've done all the work for you.

Presents detailed illustrations, descriptions, specifications, and costs for every conceivable building assembly—over 350 types in all—arranged in the easy-to-use UNIFORMAT II system. Each illustrated "assembled" cost includes a complete grouping of materials and associated installation costs, including the installing contractor's overhead and profit.

$315.95 | Available Sept. 2013 | Catalog no. 60064

RSMeans Residential Cost Data 2014

Contains square foot costs for 28 basic home models with the look of today, plus hundreds of custom additions and modifications you can quote right off the page. Includes costs for more than 700 residential systems. Complete with blank estimating forms, sample estimates, and step-by-step instructions.

Contains line items for cultured stone and brick, PVC trim lumber, and TPO roofing.

$139.95 | Available Oct. 2013 | Catalog no. 60174

RSMeans Electrical Change Order Cost Data 2014

RSMeans Electrical Change Order Cost Data provides you with electrical unit prices exclusively for pricing change orders—based on the recent, direct experience of contractors and suppliers. Analyze and check your own change order estimates against the experience others have had doing the same work. It also covers productivity analysis and change order cost justifications. With useful information for calculating the effects of change orders and dealing with their administration.

$187.95 | Available Dec. 2013 | Catalog no. 60234

RSMeans Open Shop Building Construction Cost Data 2014

The latest costs for accurate budgeting and estimating of new commercial and residential construction . . . renovation work . . . change orders . . . cost engineering.

RSMeans Open Shop "BCCD" will assist you to:

- Develop benchmark prices for change orders
- Plug gaps in preliminary estimates and budgets
- Estimate complex projects
- Substantiate invoices on contracts
- Price ADA-related renovations

$165.95 | Available Dec. 2013 | Catalog no. 60154

RSMeans Site Work & Landscape Cost Data 2014

Includes unit and assemblies costs for earthwork, sewerage, piped utilities, site improvements, drainage, paving, trees and shrubs, street openings/repairs, underground tanks, and more. Contains 78 types of assemblies costs for accurate conceptual estimates.

Includes:

- Estimating for infrastructure improvements
- Environmentally-oriented construction
- ADA-mandated handicapped access
- Hazardous waste line items

$187.95 | Available Dec. 2013 | Catalog no. 60284

RSMeans Facilities Maintenance & Repair Cost Data 2014

RSMeans Facilities Maintenance & Repair Cost Data gives you a complete system to manage and plan your facility repair and maintenance costs and budget efficiently. Guidelines for auditing a facility and developing an annual maintenance plan. Budgeting is included, along with reference tables on cost and management, and information on frequency and productivity of maintenance operations.

The only nationally recognized source of maintenance and repair costs. Developed in cooperation with the Civil Engineering Research Laboratory (CERL) of the Army Corps of Engineers.

$434.95 | Available Nov. 2013 | Catalog no. 60304

RSMeans Concrete & Masonry Cost Data 2014

Provides you with cost facts for virtually all concrete/masonry estimating needs, from complicated formwork to various sizes and face finishes of brick and block—all in great detail. The comprehensive Unit Price Section contains more than 8,000 selected entries. Also contains an Assemblies [Cost] Section, and a detailed Reference Section that supplements the cost data.

$177.95 | Available Dec. 2013 | Catalog no. 60114

RSMeans Construction Cost Indexes 2014

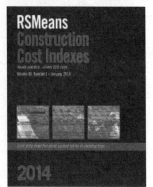

What materials and labor costs will change unexpectedly this year? By how much?

- Breakdowns for 318 major cities
- National averages for 30 key cities
- Expanded five major city indexes
- Historical construction cost indexes

$362.00 per year (subscription) | Catalog no. 50144
$93.50 individual quarters | Catalog no. 60144 A,B,C,D

RSMeans Light Commercial Cost Data 2014

Specifically addresses the light commercial market, which is a specialized niche in the construction industry. Aids you, the owner/designer/contractor, in preparing all types of estimates—from budgets to detailed bids. Includes new advances in methods and materials.

Assemblies Section allows you to evaluate alternatives in the early stages of design/planning.

More than 15,000 unit costs ensure that you have the prices you need . . . when you need them.

$144.95 | Available Nov. 2013 | Catalog no. 60184

RSMeans Labor Rates for the Construction Industry 2014

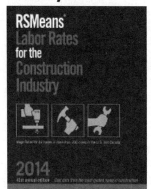

Complete information for estimating labor costs, making comparisons, and negotiating wage rates by trade for more than 300 U.S. and Canadian cities. With 46 construction trades listed by local union number in each city, and historical wage rates included for comparison. Each city chart lists the county and is alphabetically arranged with handy visual flip tabs for quick reference.

$424.95 | Available Dec. 2013 | Catalog no. 60124

RSMeans Interior Cost Data 2014

Provides you with prices and guidance needed to make accurate interior work estimates. Contains costs on materials, equipment, hardware, custom installations, furnishings, and labor costs . . . for new and remodel commercial and industrial interior construction, including updated information on office furnishings, and reference information.

$196.95 | Available Nov. 2013 | Catalog no. 60094

RSMeans Heavy Construction Cost Data 2014

A comprehensive guide to heavy construction costs. Includes costs for highly specialized projects such as tunnels, dams, highways, airports, and waterways. Information on labor rates, equipment, and materials costs is included. Features unit price costs, systems costs, and numerous reference tables for costs and design.

$192.95 | Available Dec. 2013 | Catalog no. 60164

RSMeans Plumbing Cost Data 2014

Comprehensive unit prices and assemblies for plumbing, irrigation systems, commercial and residential fire protection, point-of-use water heaters, and the latest approved materials. This publication and its companion, *RSMeans Mechanical Cost Data*, provide full-range cost estimating coverage for all the mechanical trades.

Now contains updated costs for potable water and radiant heat systems and high efficiency fixtures.

$194.95 | Available Oct. 2013 | Catalog no. 60214

2014 RSMeans Seminar Schedule

Note: call for exact dates and details.

Location	Dates	Location	Dates
Seattle, WA	January and August	Jacksonville FL	September
Dallas/Ft. Worth, TX	January	Dallas, TX	September
Austin, TX	February	Charleston, SC	October
Anchorage, AK	March and September	Houston, TX	October
Las Vegas, NV	March and October	Atlanta, GA	November
Washington, DC	April and September	Baltimore, MD	November
Phoenix, AZ	April	Orlando, FL	November
Kansas City, MO	April	San Diego, CA	December
Toronto	May	San Antonio, TX	December
Denver, CO	May	Raleigh, NC	December
San Francisco, CA	June		
Bethesda, MD	June		
Columbus, GA	June		
El Segundo, CA	August		

1-800-334-3509, Press 1

Professional Development

For more information visit the RSMeans website at **www.rsmeans.com**

eLearning Training Sessions

Learn how to use *RSMeans Online™* or *RSMeans CostWorks®* CD from the convenience of your home or office. Our eLearning training sessions let you join a training conference call and share the instructors' desktops, so you can view the presentation and step-by-step instructions on your own computer screen. The live webinars are held from 9 a.m. to 4 p.m. eastern standard time, with a one-hour break for lunch.

For these sessions, you must have a computer with high speed Internet access and a compatible Web browser. Learn more at www.rsmeansonline.com or call for a schedule: 1-800-334-3509 and press 1. Webinars are generally held on selected Wednesdays each month.

RSMeans Online™
$299 per person

RSMeans CostWorks® CD
$299 per person

Professional Development

For more information visit the RSMeans website at **www.rsmeans.com**

RSMeans Online™ Training

Construction estimating is vital to the decision-making process at each state of every project. RSMeansOnline works the way you do. It's systematic, flexible and intuitive. In this one day class you will see how you can estimate any phase of any project faster and better.

Some of what you'll learn:
- Customizing RSMeansOnline
- Making the most of RSMeans "Circle Reference" numbers
- How to integrate your cost data
- Generate reports, exporting estimates to MS Excel, sharing, collaborating and more

Also available: RSMeans Online™ training webinar

Facilities Construction Estimating

In this *two-day* course, professionals working in facilities management can get help with their daily challenges to establish budgets for all phases of a project.

Some of what you'll learn:
- Determining the full scope of a project
- Identifying the scope of risks and opportunities
- Creative solutions to estimating issues
- Organizing estimates for presentation and discussion
- Special techniques for repair/remodel and maintenance projects
- Negotiating project change orders

Who should attend: facility managers, engineers, contractors, facility tradespeople, planners, and project managers.

Scheduling with Microsoft Project

Two days of hands-on training gives you a look at the basics to putting it all together with MS Project to create a complete project schedule. Learn to work better and faster, manage changes and updates, enhance tracking, generate actionable reports, and boost control of your time and budget.

Some of what you'll learn:
- Defining task/activity relationships: link tasks, establish predecessor/successor relationships and create logs
- Baseline scheduling: the essential what/when
- Using MS Project to determine the critical path
- Integrate RSMeans data with MS Project
- The dollar-loaded schedule: enhance the reliability of this "must-know" technique for scheduling public projects.

Who should attend: contractors' project-management teams, architects and engineers, project owners and their representatives, and those interested in improving their project planning and scheduling and management skills.

Maintenance & Repair Estimating for Facilities

This *two-day* course teaches attendees how to plan, budget, and estimate the cost of ongoing and preventive maintenance and repair for existing buildings and grounds.

Some of what you'll learn:
- The most financially favorable maintenance, repair, and replacement scheduling and estimating
- Auditing and value engineering facilities
- Preventive planning and facilities upgrading
- Determining both in-house and contract-out service costs
- Annual, asset-protecting M&R plan

Who should attend: facility managers, maintenance supervisors, buildings and grounds superintendents, plant managers, planners, estimators, and others involved in facilities planning and budgeting.

Practical Project Management for Construction Professionals

In this *two-day* course, acquire the essential knowledge and develop the skills to effectively and efficiently execute the day-to-day responsibilities of the construction project manager.

Covers:
- General conditions of the construction contract
- Contract modifications: change orders and construction change directives
- Negotiations with subcontractors and vendors
- Effective writing: notification and communications
- Dispute resolution: claims and liens

Who should attend: architects, engineers, owner's representatives, project managers.

Mechanical & Electrical Estimating

This *two-day* course teaches attendees how to prepare more accurate and complete mechanical/electrical estimates, avoiding the pitfalls of omission and double-counting, while understanding the composition and rationale within the RSMeans mechanical/electrical database.

Some of what you'll learn:
- The unique way mechanical and electrical systems are interrelated
- M&E estimates—conceptual, planning, budgeting, and bidding stages
- Order of magnitude, square foot, assemblies, and unit price estimating
- Comparative cost analysis of equipment and design alternatives

Who should attend: architects, engineers, facilities managers, mechanical and electrical contractors, and others who need a highly reliable method for developing, understanding, and evaluating mechanical and electrical contracts.

Unit Price Estimating

This interactive *two-day* seminar teaches attendees how to interpret project information and process it into final, detailed estimates with the greatest accuracy level.

The most important credential an estimator can take to the job is the ability to visualize construction and estimate accurately.

Some of what you'll learn:

- Interpreting the design in terms of cost
- The most detailed, time-tested methodology for accurate pricing
- Key cost drivers—material, labor, equipment, staging, and subcontracts
- Understanding direct and indirect costs for accurate job cost accounting and change order management

Who should attend: corporate and government estimators and purchasers, architects, engineers, and others who need to produce accurate project estimates.

RSMeans CostWorks® CD Training

This one-day course helps users become more familiar with the functionality of *RSMeans CostWorks* program. Each menu, icon, screen, and function found in the program is explained in depth. Time is devoted to hands-on estimating exercises.

Some of what you'll learn:

- Searching the database using all navigation methods
- Exporting RSMeans data to your preferred spreadsheet format
- Viewing crews, assembly components, and much more
- Automatically regionalizing the database

This training session requires you to bring a laptop computer to class.

When you register for this course you will receive an outline for your laptop requirements.

Also offering web training for CostWorks CD!

Facilities Est. Using RSMeans CostWorks® CD

Combines hands-on skill building with best estimating practices and real-life problems. Brings you up-to-date with key concepts, and provides tips, pointers, and guidelines to save time and avoid cost oversights and errors.

Some of what you'll learn:

- Estimating process concepts
- Customizing and adapting RSMeans cost data
- Establishing scope of work to account for all known variables
- Budget estimating: when, why, and how
- Site visits: what to look for—what you can't afford to overlook
- How to estimate repair and remodeling variables

This training session requires you to bring a laptop computer to class.

Who should attend: facility managers, architects, engineers, contractors, facility tradespeople, planners, project managers and anyone involved with JOC, SABRE, or IDIQ.

Conceptual Estimating Using RSMeans CostWorks® CD

This *two day* class uses the leading industry data and a powerful software package to develop highly accurate conceptual estimates for your construction projects. All attendees must bring a laptop computer loaded with the current year *Square Foot Model Costs* and the *Assemblies Cost Data* CostWorks titles.

Some of what you'll learn:

- Introduction to conceptual estimating
- Types of conceptual estimates
- Helpful hints
- Order of magnitude estimating
- Square foot estimating
- Assemblies estimating

Who should attend: architects, engineers, contractors, construction estimators, owner's representatives, and anyone looking for an electronic method for performing square foot estimating.

Assessing Scope of Work for Facility Construction Estimating

This *two-day* practical training program addresses the vital importance of understanding the SCOPE of projects in order to produce accurate cost estimates for facility repair and remodeling.

Some of what you'll learn:

- Discussions of site visits, plans/specs, record drawings of facilities, and site-specific lists
- Review of CSI divisions, including means, methods, materials, and the challenges of scoping each topic
- Exercises in SCOPE identification and SCOPE writing for accurate estimating of projects
- Hands-on exercises that require SCOPE, take-off, and pricing

Who should attend: corporate and government estimators, planners, facility managers, and others who need to produce accurate project estimates.

Unit Price Est. Using RSMeans CostWorks® CD

Step-by-step instruction and practice problems to identify and track key cost drivers—material, labor, equipment, staging, and subcontractors—for each specific task. Learn the most detailed, time-tested methodology for accurately "pricing" these variables, their impact on each other and on total cost.

Some of what you'll learn:

- Unit price cost estimating
- Order of magnitude, square foot, and assemblies estimating
- Quantity takeoff
- Direct and indirect construction costs
- Development of contractor's bill rates
- How to use *RSMeans Building Construction Cost Data*

This training session requires you to bring a laptop computer to class.

Who should attend: architects, engineers, corporate and government estimators, facility managers, and government procurement staff.

Professional Development

For more information visit the RSMeans website at **www.rsmeans.com**

Registration Information

Register early . . . Save up to $100! Register 30 days before the start date of a seminar and save $100 off your total fee. *Note: This discount can be applied only once per order. It cannot be applied to team discount registrations or any other special offer.*

How to register Register by phone today! The RSMeans toll-free number for making reservations is **1-800-334-3509, Press 1.**

Two day seminar registration fee - $935. One-day *RSMeans CostWorks*® training registration fee - $375. To register by mail, complete the registration form and return, with your full fee, to: RSMeans Seminars, 700 Longwater Drive, Norwell, MA 02061.

Government pricing All federal government employees save off the regular seminar price. Other promotional discounts cannot be combined with the government discount.

Team discount program for two to four seminar registrations. Call for pricing: 1-800-334-3509, Press 1

Multiple course discounts When signing up for two or more courses, call for pricing.

Refund policy Cancellations will be accepted up to ten business days prior to the seminar start. There are no refunds for cancellations received later than ten working days prior to the first day of the seminar. A $150 processing fee will be applied for all cancellations. Written notice of cancellation is required. Substitutions can be made at any time before the session starts. **No-shows are subject to the full seminar fee.**

AACE approved courses Many seminars described and offered here have been approved for 14 hours (1.4 recertification credits) of credit by the AACE International Certification Board toward meeting the continuing education requirements for recertification as a Certified Cost Engineer/Certified Cost Consultant.

AIA Continuing Education We are registered with the AIA Continuing Education System (AIA/CES) and are committed to developing quality learning activities in accordance with the CES criteria. Many seminars meet the AIA/CES criteria for Quality Level 2. AIA members may receive (14) learning units (LUs) for each two-day RSMeans course.

Daily course schedule The first day of each seminar session begins at 8:30 a.m. and ends at 4:30 p.m. The second day begins at 8:00 a.m. and ends at 4:00 p.m. Participants are urged to bring a hand-held calculator, since many actual problems will be worked out in each session.

Continental breakfast Your registration includes the cost of a continental breakfast, and a morning and afternoon refreshment break. These informal segments allow you to discuss topics of mutual interest with other seminar attendees. (You are free to make your own lunch and dinner arrangements.)

Hotel/transportation arrangements RSMeans arranges to hold a block of rooms at most host hotels. To take advantage of special group rates when making your reservation, be sure to mention that you are attending the RSMeans seminar. You are, of course, free to stay at the lodging place of your choice. (**Hotel reservations and transportation arrangements should be made directly by seminar attendees.**)

Important Class sizes are limited, so please register as soon as possible.

Note: Pricing subject to change.

Registration Form   ADDS-1000

Call 1-800-334-3509, Press 1 to register or FAX this form 1-800-632-6732. Visit our website: www.rsmeans.com

Please register the following people for the RSMeans construction seminars as shown here. We understand that we must make our own hotel reservations if overnight stays are necessary.

☐ Full payment of $_____ enclosed.

☐ Bill me.

Please print name of registrant(s).

(To appear on certificate of completion)

_____

_____

_____

_____

P.O. #: _____
GOVERNMENT AGENCIES MUST SUPPLY PURCHASE ORDER NUMBER OR TRAINING FORM.

Firm name_____

Address_____

City/State/Zip_____

Telephone no._____ Fax no._____

E-mail address_____

Charge registration(s) to: ☐ MasterCard ☐ VISA ☐ American Express

Account no._____ Exp. date_____

Cardholder's signature_____

Seminar name_____

Seminar City_____

Please mail check to: RSMeans Seminars, 700 Longwater Drive, Norwell, MA 02061 USA

For more information visit the RSMeans website at **www.rsmeans.com**

Solar Energy: Technologies & Project Delivery for Buildings

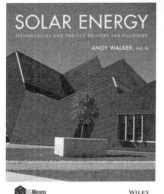

by Andy Walker

An authoritative reference on the design of solar energy systems in building projects, with applications, operating principles, and simple tools for the construction, engineering, and design professionals, the book simplifies the solar design and engineering process and provides sample documentation for the complete design of a solar energy system for buildings.

$85.00 | 320 pages, hardover | Catalog no. 67365

Project Scheduling & Management for Construction, 4th Edition

by David R. Pierce

First published in 1988 by RSMeans, the new edition of *Project Scheduling and Management for Construction* has been substantially revised for both professionals and students enrolled in construction management and civil engineering programs. While retaining its emphasis on developing practical, professional-level scheduling skills, the new edition is a relatable, real world case study.

$95.00 | 272 pages, softcover | Catalog no. 67367

Estimating Building Costs, 2nd Edition
For the Residential & Light Commercial Construction Professional

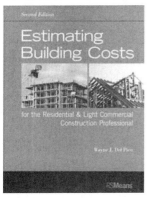

by Wayne J. Del Pico

This book guides readers through the entire estimating process, explaining in detail how to put together a reliable estimate that can be used not only for budgeting, but also for developing a schedule, managing a project, dealing with contingencies, and ultimately making a profit.

Completely revised and updated to reflect the CSI MasterFormat 2010 system, this practical guide describes estimating techniques for each building system and how to apply them according to the latest industry standards.

$75.00 | 398 pages, softcover | Catalog no. 67343A

Project Control: Integrating Cost & Schedule in Construction

by Wayne J. Del Pico

Written by a seasoned professional in the field, *Project Control: Integrating Cost and Schedule in Construction* fills a void in the area of project control as applied in the construction industry today. It demonstrates how productivity models for an individual project are created, monitored, and controlled, and how corrective actions are implemented as deviations from the baseline occur.

$95.00 | 240 pages, softcover | Catalog no. 67366

How to Estimate with Means Data & CostWorks, 4th Edition

by RSMeans and Saleh A. Mubarak, Ph.D.

This step-by-step guide takes you through all the major construction items with extensive coverage of site work, concrete and masonry, wood and metal framing, doors and windows, and other divisions. The only construction cost estimating handbook that uses the most popular source of construction data, RSMeans, this indispensible guide features access to the instructional version of CostWorks in electronic form, enabling you to practice techniques to solve real-world estimating problems.

$75.00 | 292 pages, softcover | Includes CostWorks CD
Catalog no. 67324C

RSMeans Cost Data, Student Edition

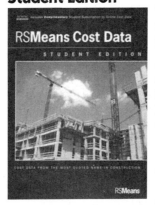

This book provides a thorough introduction to cost estimating in a self-contained print and online package. With clear explanations and a hands-on, example-driven approach, it is the ideal reference for students and new professionals.

Features include:

- Commercial and residential construction cost data in print and online formats
- Complete how-to guidance on the essentials of cost estimating
- A supplemental website with plans, problem sets, and a full sample estimate

$99.00 | 512 pages, softcover | Catalog no. 67363

For more information visit the RSMeans website at **www.rsmeans.com**

Value Engineering: Practical Applications

For Design, Construction, Maintenance & Operations

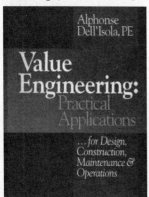

by Alphonse Dell'Isola, PE

A tool for immediate application—for engineers, architects, facility managers, owners, and contractors. Includes making the case for VE—the management briefing; integrating VE into planning, budgeting, and design; conducting life cycle costing; using VE methodology in design review and consultant selection; case studies; VE workbook; and a life cycle costing program on disk.

$85.00 | Over 450 pages, illustrated, softcover | Catalog no. 67319A

Risk Management for Design & Construction

Introduces risk as a central pillar of project management and shows how a project manager can prepare to deal with uncertainty. Experts in the field use clear, straightforward terminology to demystify the concepts of project uncertainty and risk. Includes:

- Integrated cost and schedule risk analysis
- An introduction to a ready-to-use system of analyzing a project's risks and tools to proactively manage risks
- A methodology that was developed and used by the Washington State Department of Transportation

- Case studies and examples on the proper application of principles
- Information about combining value analysis with risk analysis

$125.00 | Over 250 pages, softcover | Catalog no. 67359

How Your House Works, 2nd Edition

by Charlie Wing

Knowledge of your home's systems helps you control repair and construction costs and makes sure the correct elements are being installed or replaced. This book uncovers the mysteries behind just about every major appliance and building element in your house. See-through, cross-section drawings in full color show you exactly how these things should be put together and how they function, including what to check if they don't work. It just might save you having to call in a professional.

$22.95 | 192 pages, softcover | Catalog no. 67351A

Complete Book of Framing, 2nd Edition

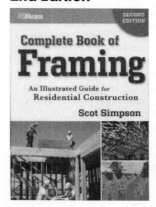

by Scot Simpson

This updated, easy-to-learn guide to rough carpentry and framing is written by an expert with more than thirty years of framing experience. Starting with the basics, this book begins with types of lumber, nails, and what tools are needed, followed by detailed, fully illustrated steps for framing each building element. Framer-Friendly Tips throughout the book show how to get a task done right—and more easily.

$29.95 | 352 pages, softcover | Catalog no. 67353A

Green Home Improvement

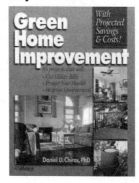

by Daniel D. Chiras, PhD

With energy costs rising and environmental awareness increasing, people are looking to make their homes greener. This book, with 65 projects and actual costs and projected savings help homeowners prioritize their green improvements.

Projects range from simple water savers that cost only a few dollars, to bigger-ticket items such as HVAC systems. With color photos and cost estimates, each project compares options and describes the work involved, the benefits, and the savings.

$34.95 | 320 pages, illustrated, softcover | Catalog no. 67355

Life Cycle Costing for Facilities

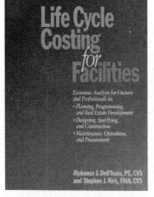

by Alphonse Dell'Isola and Dr. Steven Kirk

Guidance for achieving higher quality design and construction projects at lower costs! Cost-cutting efforts often sacrifice quality to yield the cheapest product. Life cycle costing enables building designers and owners to achieve both. The authors of this book show how LCC can work for a variety of projects — from roads to HVAC upgrades to different types of buildings.

$99.95 | 396 pages, hardcover | Catalog no. 67341

Builder's Essentials: Plan Reading & Material Takeoff

For Residential and Light Commercial Construction

by Wayne J. DelPico

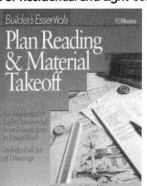

A valuable tool for understanding plans and specs, and accurately calculating material quantities. Step-by-step instructions and takeoff procedures based on a full set of working drawings.

$45.00 | Over 420 pages, softcover | Catalog no. 67307

Concrete Repair & Maintenance Illustrated

by Peter Emmons

Hundreds of illustrations show users how to analyze, repair, clean, and maintain concrete structures for optimal performance and cost effectiveness. From parking garages to roads and bridges to structural concrete, this comprehensive book describes the causes, effects, and remedies for concrete wear and failure. Invaluable for planning jobs, selecting materials, and training employees, this book is a must-have for concrete specialists, general contractors, facility managers, civil and structural engineers, and architects.

$75.00 | 300 pages, illustrated, softcover | Catalog no. 67146

Electrical Estimating Methods, 3rd Edition

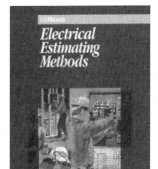

Expanded edition includes sample estimates and cost information in keeping with the latest version of the CSI MasterFormat and UNIFORMAT II. Complete coverage of fiber optic and uninterruptible power supply electrical systems, broken down by components, and explained in detail. Includes a new chapter on computerized estimating methods. A practical companion to *RSMeans Electrical Cost Data.*

$75.00 | Over 325 pages, hardcover | Catalog no. 67230B

Means Unit Price Estimating Methods, 4th Edition

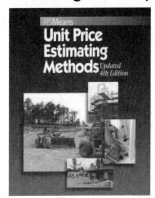

Includes cost data and estimating examples, updated to reflect changes to the CSI numbering system and new features of RSMeans cost data. It describes the most productive, universally accepted ways to estimate, and uses checklists and forms to illustrate shortcuts and timesavers. A model estimate demonstrates procedures. A new chapter explores computer estimating alternatives.

$75.00 | Over 350 pages, illustrated, softcover | Catalog no. 67303B

Square Foot & UNIFORMAT Assemblies Estimating Methods, 3rd Edition

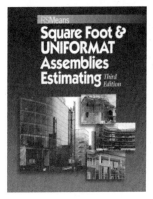

Develop realistic square foot and assemblies costs for budgeting and construction funding. The new edition features updated guidance on square foot and assemblies estimating using UNIFORMAT II. An essential reference for anyone who performs conceptual estimates.

$75.00 | Over 300 pages, illustrated, softcover | Catalog no. 67145B

Residential & Light Commercial Construction Standards, 3rd Edition

Updated by RSMeans and contributing authors

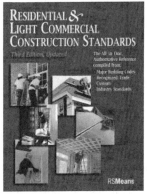

This book provides authoritative requirements and recommendations compiled from leading professional associations, industry publications, and building code organizations. This all-in-one reference helps establish a standard for workmanship, quickly resolve disputes, and avoid defect claims. Updated third edition includes new coverage of green building, seismic, hurricane, and mold-resistant construction.

$65.00 | Over 550 pages, illustrated, softcover | Catalog no. 67322B

Construction Business Management

by Nick Ganaway

Only 43% of construction firms stay in business after four years. Make sure your company thrives with valuable guidance from a pro with 25 years of success as a commercial contractor. Find out what it takes to build all aspects of a business that is profitable, enjoyable, and enduring. With a bonus chapter on retail construction.

$55.00 | 200 pages, softcover | Catalog no. 67352

The Practice of Cost Segregation Analysis

by Bruce A. Desrosiers and Wayne J. DelPico

This expert guide walks you through the practice of cost segregation analysis, which enables property owners to defer taxes and benefit from "accelerated cost recovery" through depreciation deductions on assets that are properly identified and classified.

With a glossary of terms, sample cost segregation estimates for various building types, key information resources, and updates via a dedicated website, this book is a critical resource for anyone involved in cost segregation analysis.

$105.00 | Over 225 pages | Catalog no. 67345

Green Building: Project Planning & Cost Estimating, 3rd Edition

Since the widely read first edition of this book, green building has gone from a growing trend to a major force in design and construction.

This new edition has been updated with the latest in green building technologies, design concepts, standards, and costs. Full-color with all new case studies—plus a new chapter on commercial real estate.

$110.00 | Over 450 pages, softcover | Catalog no. 67338B

Project Scheduling & Management for Construction, 3rd Edition

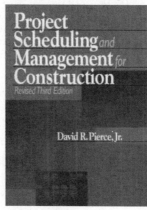

by David R. Pierce, Jr.

A comprehensive yet easy-to-follow guide to construction project scheduling and control—from vital project management principles through the latest scheduling, tracking, and controlling techniques. The author is a leading authority on scheduling, with years of field and teaching experience at leading academic institutions. Spend a few hours with this book and come away with a solid understanding of this essential management topic.

$64.95 | Over 300 pages, illustrated, hardcover | Catalog no. 67247B

Preventive Maintenance for Multi-Family Housing

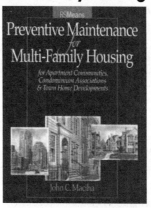

by John C. Maciha

Prepared by one of the nation's leading experts on multi-family housing.

This complete PM system for apartment and condominium communities features expert guidance, checklists for buildings and grounds maintenance tasks and their frequencies, a reusable wall chart to track maintenance, and a dedicated website featuring customizable electronic forms. A must-have for anyone involved with multi-family housing maintenance and upkeep.

$95.00 | 225 pages | Catalog no. 67346

Job Order Contracting: Expediting Construction Project Delivery

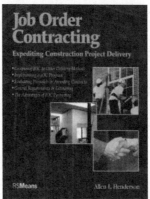

by Allen L. Henderson

Expert guidance to help you implement JOC—fast becoming the preferred project delivery method for repair and renovation, minor new construction, and maintenance projects in the public sector and in many states and municipalities. The author, a leading JOC expert and practitioner, shows how to:

- Establish a JOC program
- Evaluate proposals & award contracts
- Handle general requirements and estimating
- Partner for maximum benefits

$89.95 | 192 pages, illustrated, hardcover | Catalog no. 67348

Reference Books

For more information visit the RSMeans website at **www.rsmeans.com**

Construction Supervision

This brand new title inspires supervisory excellence with proven tactics and techniques applied by thousands of construction supervisors over the past decade. Recognizing the unique and critical role the supervisor plays in project success, the book's leadership guidelines carve out a practical blueprint for motivating work performance and increasing productivity through effective communication.

Features:

• A unique focus on field supervision and crew management

• Coverage of supervision from the foreman to the superintendent level

• An overview of technical skills whose mastery will build confidence and success for the supervisor

• A detailed view of "soft" management and communication skills

$95.00 | Over 450 pages, softcover | Catalog no. 67358

The Homeowner's Guide to Mold

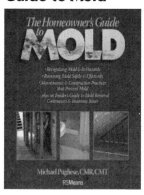

By Michael Pugliese

Expert guidance to protect your health and your home.

Mold, whether caused by leaks, humidity or flooding, is a real health and financial issue—for homeowners and contractors.

This full-color book explains:

• Construction and maintenance practices to prevent mold

• How to inspect for and remove mold

• Mold remediation procedures and costs

• What to do after a flood

• How to deal with insurance companies

$21.95 | 144 pages, softcover | Catalog no. 67344

Landscape Estimating Methods, 5th Edition

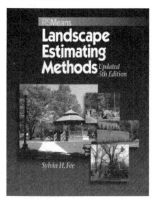

Answers questions about preparing competitive landscape construction estimates, with up-to-date cost estimates and the new MasterFormat classification system. Expanded and revised to address the latest materials and methods, including new coverage on approaches to green building. Includes:

• Step-by-step explanation of the estimating process

• Sample forms and worksheets that save time and prevent errors

$75.00 | Over 350 pages, softcover | Catalog no. 67295C

Building & Renovating Schools

This all-inclusive guide covers every step of the school construction process—from initial planning, needs assessment, and design, right through moving into the new facility. A must-have resource for anyone concerned with new school construction or renovation. With square foot cost models for elementary, middle, and high school facilities, and real-life case studies of recently completed school projects.

The contributors to this book—architects, construction project managers, contractors, and estimators who specialize in school construction—provide start-to-finish, expert guidance on the process.

$99.95 | Over 425 pages, hardcover | Catalog no. 67342

Universal Design Ideas for Style, Comfort & Safety

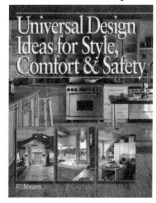

by RSMeans and Lexicon Consulting, Inc.

Incorporating universal design when building or remodeling helps people of any age and physical ability more fully and safely enjoy their living spaces. This book shows how universal design can be artfully blended into the most attractive homes. It discusses specialized products like adjustable countertops and chair lifts, as well as simple ways to enhance a home's safety and comfort. With color photos and expert guidance, every area of the home is covered. Includes budget estimates that give an idea how much projects will cost.

$21.95 | 160 pages, illustrated, softcover | Catalog no. 67354

Plumbing Estimating Methods, 3rd Edition

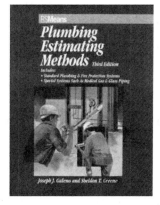

by Joseph J. Galeno and Sheldon T. Greene

Updated and revised! This practical guide walks you through a plumbing estimate, from basic materials and installation methods through change order analysis. *Plumbing Estimating Methods* covers residential, commercial, industrial, and medical systems, and features sample takeoff and estimate forms and detailed illustrations of systems and components.

$65.00 | 330+ pages, softcover | Catalog no. 67283B

Reference Books

For more information visit the RSMeans website at **www.rsmeans.com**

Understanding & Negotiating Construction Contracts

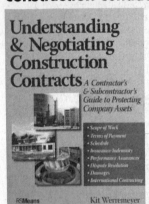

by Kit Werremeyer

Take advantage of the author's 30 years' experience in small-to-large (including international) construction projects. Learn how to identify, understand, and evaluate high risk terms and conditions typically found in all construction contracts—then negotiate to lower or eliminate the risk, improve terms of payment, and reduce exposure to claims and disputes. The author avoids "legalese" and gives real-life examples from actual projects.

$80.00 | 300 pages, softcover | Catalog no. 67350

The Gypsum Construction Handbook

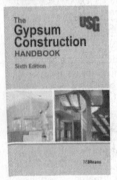

by USG

An invaluable reference of construction procedures for gypsum drywall, cement board, veneer plaster, and conventional plaster. This new edition includes the newest product developments, installation methods, fire- and sound-rated construction information, illustrated framing-to-finish application instructions, estimating and planning information, and more. Great for architects and engineers; contractors, builders, and dealers; apprentices and training programs; building inspectors and code officials; and anyone interested in gypsum construction. Features information on tools and safety practices, a glossary of construction terms, and a list of important agencies and associations. Also available in Spanish.

$40.00 | Over 575 pages, illustrated, softcover | Catalog no. 67357A

Mechanical Estimating Methods, 4th Edition

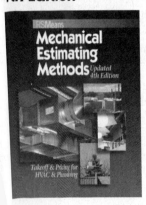

Completely updated, this guide assists you in making a review of plans, specs, and bid packages, with suggestions for takeoff procedures, listings, substitutions, and pre-bid scheduling for all components of HVAC. Includes suggestions for budgeting labor and equipment usage. Compares materials and construction methods to allow you to select the best option.

$70.00 per copy | Over 350 pages, illustrated, softcover | Catalog no. 67294B

Means Illustrated Construction Dictionary

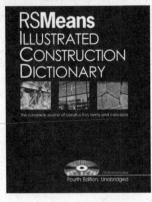

Unabridged 4th Edition, with CD-ROM

Long regarded as the industry's finest, *Means Illustrated Construction Dictionary* is now even better. With nearly 20,000 terms and more than 1,400 illustrations and photos, it is the clear choice for the most comprehensive and current information. The companion CD-ROM that comes with this new edition adds extra features such as: larger graphics and expanded definitions.

$99.95 | Over 790 pages, illust., hardcover | Catalog no. 67292B

RSMeans Estimating Handbook, 3rd Edition

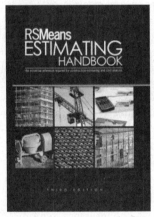

Widely used in the industry for tasks ranging from routine estimates to special cost analysis projects, this handbook has been completely updated and reorganized with new and expanded technical information.

RSMeans Estimating Handbook will help construction professionals:

- Evaluate architectural plans and specifications
- Prepare accurate quantity takeoffs
- Compare design alternatives and costs
- Perform value engineering
- Double-check estimates and quotes
- Estimate change orders

$110.00 | Over 900 pages, hardcover | Catalog No. 67276B

2014 Order Form

For more information visit the RSMeans website at **www.rsmeans.com**

Qty.	Book no.	COST ESTIMATING BOOKS	Unit Price	Total
	60064	Assemblies Cost Data 2014	$315.95	
	60014	Building Construction Cost Data 2014	194.95	
	60044	Commercial Renovaion Cost Data 2014	156.95	
	60114	Concrete & Masonry Cost Data 2014	177.95	
	50144	Construction Cost Indexes 2014 (subscription)	362.00	
	60144A	Construction Cost Index–January 2014	93.50	
	60144B	Construction Cost Index–April 2014	93.50	
	60144C	Construction Cost Index–July 2014	93.50	
	60144D	Construction Cost Index–October 2014	93.50	
	60344	Contr. Pricing Guide: Resid. R & R Costs 2014	39.95	
	60234	Electrical Change Order Cost Data 2014	187.95	
	60034	Electrical Cost Data 2014	196.95	
	60204	Facilities Construction Cost Data 2014	496.95	
	60304	Facilities Maintenance & Repair Cost Data 2014	434.95	
	60554	Green Building Cost Data 2014	160.95	
	60164	Heavy Construction Cost Data 2014	192.95	
	60094	Interior Cost Data 2014	196.95	
	60124	Labor Rates for the Const. Industry 2014	424.95	
	60184	Light Commercial Cost Data 2014	144.95	
	60024	Mechanical Cost Data 2014	191.95	
	60154	Open Shop Building Const. Cost Data 2014	165.95	
	60214	Plumbing Cost Data 2014	194.95	
	60174	Residential Cost Data 2014	139.95	
	60284	Site Work & Landscape Cost Data 2014	187.95	
	60054	Square Foot Costs 2014	205.95	
	62013	Yardsticks for Costing (2013)	185.95	
	62014	Yardsticks for Costing (2014)	189.95	
		REFERENCE BOOKS		
	67329	Bldrs Essentials: Best Bus. Practices for Bldrs	40.00	
	67307	Bldrs Essentials: Plan Reading & Takeoff	35.95	
	67342	Building & Renovating Schools	99.95	
	67261A	The Building Prof. Guide to Contract Documents	75.00	
	67339	Building Security: Strategies & Costs	95.00	
	67353A	Complete Book of Framing, 2nd Ed.	29.95	
	67146	Concrete Repair & Maintenance Illustrated	75.00	
	67352	Construction Business Management	55.00	
	67364	Construction Law	110.00	
	67358	Construction Supervision	95.00	
	67363	Cost Data Student Edition	99.00	
	67314	Cost Planning & Est. for Facil. Maint.	95.00	
	67230B	Electrical Estimating Methods, 3rd Ed.	75.00	
	67343A	Est. Bldg. Costs for Resi. & Lt. Comm., 2nd Ed.	75.00	
	67276B	Estimating Handbook, 3rd Ed.	110.00	
	67318	Facilities Operations & Engineering Reference	115.00	
	67301	Facilities Planning & Relocation	89.95	
	67338B	Green Building: Proj. Planning & Cost Est., 3rd Ed.	110.00	
	67355	Green Home Improvement	34.95	
	67357A	The Gypsum Construction Handbook	40.00	
	67148	Heavy Construction Handbook	110.00	
	67308E	Home Improvement Costs–Int. Projects, 9th Ed.	24.95	
	67309E	Home Improvement Costs–Ext. Projects, 9th Ed.	24.95	

Qty.	Book no.	REFERENCE BOOKS (Cont.)	Unit Price	Total
	67344	Homeowner's Guide to Mold	21.95	
	67324C	How to Est.w/Means Data & CostWorks, 4th Ed.	75.00	
	67351A	How Your House Works, 2nd Ed.	22.95	
	67282A	Illustrated Const. Dictionary, Condensed, 2nd Ed.	65.00	
	67292B	Illustrated Const. Dictionary, w/CD-ROM, 4th Ed.	99.95	
	67362	Illustrated Const. Dictionary, Student Ed.	55.00	
	67348	Job Order Contracting	89.95	
	67295C	Landscape Estimating Methods, 5th Ed.	75.00	
	67341	Life Cycle Costing for Facilities	99.95	
	67294B	Mechanical Estimating Methods, 4th Ed.	70.00	
	67283B	Plumbing Estimating Methods, 3rd Ed.	65.00	
	67345	Practice of Cost Segregation Analysis	105.00	
	67366	Project Control: Integrating Cost & Sched.	95.00	
	67346	Preventive Maint. for Multi-Family Housing	95.00	
	67367	Project Scheduling & Manag. for Constr., 4th Ed.	95.00	
	67322B	Resi. & Light Commercial Const. Stds., 3rd Ed.	65.00	
	67359	Risk Management for Design & Construction	125.00	
	67365	Solar Energy: Technology & Project Delivery	85.00	
	67145B	Sq. Ft. & Assem. Estimating Methods, 3rd Ed.	75.00	
	67321	Total Productive Facilities Management	85.00	
	67350	Understanding and Negotiating Const. Contracts	80.00	
	67303B	Unit Price Estimating Methods, 4th Ed.	75.00	
	67354	Universal Design	21.95	
	67319A	Value Engineering: Practical Applications	85.00	

MA residents add 6.25% state sales tax _____

Shipping & Handling** _____

Total (U.S. Funds)* _____

Prices are subject to change and are for U.S. delivery only. *Canadian customers may call for current prices. **Shipping & handling charges: Add 7% of total order for check and credit card payments. Add 9% of total order for invoiced orders.

Send order to: ADDV-1000

Name (please print) _____

Company _____

☐ Company

☐ Home Address _____

_____

City/State/Zip _____

Phone # _____ P.O. # _____

(Must accompany all orders being billed)

Mail to: RSMeans, 700 Longwater Drive, Norwell, MA 02061

RSMeans Project Cost Report

By filling out this report, your project data will contribute to the database that supports the RSMeans® Project Cost Square Foot Data. When you fill out this form, RSMeans will provide a $50 discount off one of the RSMeans products advertised in the preceding pages. Please complete the form including all items where you have cost data, and all the items marked (☑).

$50.00 Discount per product for each report you submit

Project Description (NEW construction only, please)

☑ Building Use (Office School . . .) _____

☑ Address (City, State) _____

_____

☑ Total Building Area (SF) _____

☑ Ground Floor (SF) _____

☑ Frame (Wood, Steel . . .) _____

☑ Exterior Wall (Brick, Tilt-up . . .) _____

☑ Basement: (check one)   ☐ Full   ☐ Partial   ☐ None

☑ Number of Stories _____

☑ Floor-to-Floor Height _____

☑ Volume (C.F.) _____

% Air Conditioned _____ Tons _____

Total Project Cost $ _____

Owner _____

Architect _____

General Contractor _____

☑ Bid Date _____

☑ Typical Bay Size _____

☑ Occupant Capacity _____

☑ Labor Force: _____ % Union _____ % Non-Union

☑ Project Description (Circle one number in each line.)

   1. Economy   2. Average   3. Custom   4. Luxury

   1. Square   2. Rectangular   3. Irregular   4. Very Irregular

Comments _____

_____

A	☑	General Conditions	$		K	☑	Specialties	$
B	☑	Site Work	$		L	☑	Equipment	$
C	☑	Concrete	$		M	☑	Furnishings	$
D	☑	Masonry	$		N	☑	SpecialConstruction	$
E	☑	Metals	$		P	☑	ConveyingSystems	$
F	☑	Wood & Plastics	$		Q	☑	Mechanical	$
G	☑	Thermal &Moisture Protection	$		QP		Plumbing	$
GR		Roofing & Flashing	$		QB		HVAC	$
H	☑	Doors and Windows	$		R	☑	Electrical	$
J	☑	Finishes	$		S	☑	Mech./Elec. Combined	$
JP		Painting & Wall Covering	$					

Please specify the RSMeans product you wish to receive.
Complete the address information.

Product Name _____

Product Number _____

Your Name _____

Title _____

Company _____

  ☐ Company

  ☐ Home   Street Address _____

City, State, Zip _____

Email Address _____

Return by mail or fax 888-492-6770.

Method of Payment:

Credit Card # _____

Expiration Date _____

Check _____

Purchase Order _____

Phone Number _____
(if you would prefer a sales call)

RSMeans
a division of Reed Construction Data
Square Foot Costs Department
700 Longwater Drive
Norwell, MA 02061
www.RSMeans.com